McGRAW-HILL PUBLICATIONS IN THE
ZOOLOGICAL SCIENCES

A. FRANKLIN SHULL, Consulting Editor

THE INVERTEBRATES:

Protozoa through Ctenophora

McGRAW-HILL PUBLICATIONS
IN THE BIOLOGICAL SCIENCES

Consulting Editors
Robert L. Sinsheimer, Colin S. Pittindrigh,
Theodore H. Bullock, Sydney Brenner

Series in Cell Biology
Gray, Handbook of Basic Microtechnique

Series in Developmental Biology
Patten, Foundations of Embryology
Weichert, Anatomy of the Chordates

Series in Organism Biology
Mazia and Tyler, General Physiology of Cell
Specialization

Series in Physiology
Leopold, Plant Growth and Development

Series in Population Biology
Ehrlich and Holm, The Process of Evolution

Series in Systematic Biology
Hyman, The Invertebrates: Protozoa through
Ctenophora (vol. I)
————, The Invertebrates: Platyhelminthes
and Rhynchocoela (vol. II)
————, The Invertebrates: Acanthocephala,
Aschelminthes, and Entoprocta (vol. III)
————, The Invertebrates: Echinodermata
(vol. IV)
————, The Invertebrates: Smaller Coelomate
Groups (vol. V)
Mayr, Linsley, and Usinger, Methods and Prin-
ciples of Systematic Zoology

THE INVERTEBRATES:

Protozoa through Ctenophora

BY

LIBBIE HENRIETTA HYMAN

American Museum of Natural History
New York

McGRAW-HILL BOOK COMPANY

NEW YORK AND LONDON

1940

PREFACE

This book is the outcome of a desire of many years' standing to further the teaching and the knowledge of invertebrate zoology. Since the publication of Lankester's *Treatise on Zoology* (never finished) almost forty years ago, no advanced text in English on invertebrate zoology has been available. My original idea was to write a comprehensive laboratory manual with textual comments, but I was dissuaded from this by the advice of zoological colleagues who were of the opinion that there was greater need of a text. Whether this advice was sound still remains to be seen, but I am sure that neither they nor I had any conception of the magnitude of the task upon which I started. It soon became evident to me that I could not write the sort of account of invertebrates which I had in mind within the confines of a single volume. Gradually the conception of the work grew until a three-volume treatise was planned: one volume devoted to the noncoelomate invertebrates, a second volume for the coelomate forms except arthropods, and a third volume for the arthropods. However, after six years of intensive labor I was still unable to complete the first volume, and it was by then evident that such a volume would be too bulky for convenience. Consequently, it was decided to publish it in two parts, of which this is the first. It includes the lowest invertebrates through the radiate forms; the second part, on which considerable work has been done, will be devoted to the acoelomate and pseudocoelomate bilateral animals. The plan of the remainder of the work remains unaltered, *i.e.*, the third part will treat the coelomate invertebrates except arthropods, and the arthropods will occupy the final volume. However, it will probably prove necessary to split the third part between the enterocoelous and schizocoelous groups.

The intent of this treatise, then, is to furnish a reasonably complete and modern account of the morphology, physiology, embryology, and biology of the invertebrates. Classification, phylogeny, and palaeontology are given but brief consideration. It is obviously impossible for any one person to have a comprehensive first-hand knowledge of the entire range of invertebrates, and consequently a work of this kind is essentially a compilation from the literature. As such it necessarily lacks the authority and authenticity of the specialist's information. I can only say that every effort has been made toward accuracy and completeness. All information has been obtained from original sources, but the two great German treatises—Kükenthal-Krumbach's *Handbuch der*

Zoologie and Bronn's *Klassen und Ordnungen des Tierreichs*—have proved invaluable in assisting me to orient myself in the mazes of the subject. References to all sources of the material in the text and to all articles which are specifically mentioned in the text will be found in the bibliographies at the end of each chapter. In these bibliographies, the titles of articles have been shortened in many cases in the interests of economy.

The viewpoint of this treatise is strictly zoological, and hence, no particular emphasis has been placed upon parasitic forms, nor has it been deemed within the province of the work to discuss symptoms and treatments of parasitic infections. The "type" method of presentation has been eschewed since one of the major purposes of this treatise is to give an extensive account of the range of morphological variation to be found within each group. When a subject is simplified by emphasizing or limiting the discussion to a type plan or type form, some degree of falsification inevitably results, and the student is left with a very narrow, and often erroneous, conception of the subject. It is, of course, much easier to describe a single animal form than to present a comprehensive account of the group as a whole to which the animal belongs.

I have made an earnest effort to bring order and clarity into the confusion of zoological terminology; to define each term precisely and to adhere to that definition; and to eliminate homonyms. I do not, however, believe that a uniform zoological terminology is feasible because of the fundamental differences in structural plan that exist between the various phyla. I have not hesitated to drop established terms when they appeared to me inept or confusing and have boldly coined new terms when these seemed to be badly needed. Among the innovations of the terminology is the limitation of such words as ectoderm, entoderm, and stomodaeum to embryological stages. I realize that many zoologists will not like this change, but it seemed to me high time to end a state of affairs in which the same epithelium is called ectoderm in coelenterates, epidermis in annelids, and hypodermis in insects.

Concepts and ideas current in zoological teaching have been critically scrutinized in the light of the available facts and have been passed or rejected according to the weight of the evidence. In regard to a number of matters, the facts were found to be otherwise than usually supposed and usually presented in elementary textbooks. Indeed, it has been my experience that elementary texts of zoology often contain many erroneous or doubtful statements about even the most common and best known invertebrates.

Whenever possible, the illustrations have been made directly from living or prepared material; and for this purpose several summers have been spent at various marine stations. Other illustrations have been redrawn from original sources and an effort has been made to avoid the stock illustrations repeated in a succession of zoological texts. All sources of copied figures are given in the bibliographies, and to facilitate finding them, the year of publication has been added to the author's name in the figure legends. It seemed to me that an advanced treatise of this sort should be profusely illustrated, and hence the number of illustrations is unusually large; it has therefore been necessary to reduce their size as much as consistent with clarity and to adopt a simple economical method of labeling. I realize that larger figures with labels printed in full on the figures are easier to follow, but they would have required a vast amount of space which it was impossible to provide. The fact that I executed the majority of the drawings myself is in large part responsible for the slow progress of the work. I am all too painfully aware of the technical imperfections of the figures, but I believe they illustrate sufficiently well the points intended. A considerable number of the drawings in the first half of the book were done by Mr. Walter Kessler.

Grateful acknowledgment is made to Drs. D. H. Wenrich, R. P. Hall, and M. Halpern for lending slides of parasitic Protozoa; to Dr. M. W. de Laubenfels and the late H. V. Wilson for lending slides of sponges; to Dr. M. W. de Laubenfels for a careful and conscientious reading of the chapter on sponges; to A. E. Galigher, Inc., Berkeley, Calif., for lending several slides; to the University of Chicago Press for permission to copy several copyrighted figures; to the librarians of the magnificent library of the American Museum of Natural History for their unfailing courtesy and helpfulness; and to Dr. G. K. Noble for permitting me to occupy a space in his Laboratory of Experimental Biology during the making of a part of this volume.

Whether I shall proceed with this treatise will depend upon the reception accorded the present volume. I ask charity for its imperfections in view of the labor involved.

LIBBIE HENRIETTA HYMAN.

NEW YORK,
January, 1940.

CONTENTS

CONTENTS

CHAPTER VI

CHAPTER VII

CHAPTER VIII

THE INVERTEBRATES:
Protozoa through Ctenophora

CHAPTER I

PROTOPLASM, THE CELL, AND THE ORGANISM

I. PROTOPLASM

The contents of this chapter are intended to serve merely as a brief review of essential facts and concepts that are presumed to be already known to the student but may need to be recalled and further presented with a somewhat broader viewpoint than may be customary in elementary courses.

Life is known to us only as definite formed organized individuals, or *organisms*, i.e., plants and animals. It is usually said that organisms are composed of living matter, or *protoplasm*, but protoplasm is unique matter in that it occurs only as formed organized beings, and any consideration of it apart from the organism is more or less misleading. The properties of protoplasm are usually listed as physical, chemical, and biological.

Physically, protoplasm is a fluid of changeable degree of consistency (viscosity), containing visible structures, particles, and droplets of various shapes and sizes and bestrewed with particles invisible with the ordinary microscope but evidenced as points of light in the ultramicroscope. Such a fluid containing ultramicroscopic particles, larger than molecules, in suspension, is called a *colloidal solution;* and protoplasm is of the type known as an *emulsoid* colloidal solution in which the suspended particles are swollen with water. An important property of emulsoid colloids is that they may alter from a fluid, watery condition, known as a *sol*, to a semisolid state, called a *gel*, or vice versa. Gelatin, before and after it has "set," illustrates the extensive changes of viscosity of which emulsoid colloids are capable. *Solation* and *gelation*, probably accomplished by increased dispersion, or aggregation, respectively, of the colloidal particles, are important processes in protoplasmic activity. The dispersed particles present further an enormous expanse of surface that exhibits all the properties of free surfaces in general, being the seat of adsorption, of chemical reactions, electrical charges, etc. The colloidal state is also peculiarly adapted for permitting changes in the quantity and distribu-

1

tion, imbibition and discharge, of water in the protoplasm, and it greatly affects the chemical reactions occurring in protoplasm and enables a number of reactions to occur simultaneously without intermingling. The remarkable ability of protoplasm to control the passage of materials through its surface probably results in part from the physical construction of that surface.

The microscopically visible structure of protoplasm has been the subject of numerous studies and controversies. The essential components of protoplasm have been in turn considered to be *granules, fibrils, networks,* and *alveoli.* The *spumoid* or *alveolar* theory, developed by Bütschli, and widely accepted, even today, states that protoplasm is composed of spheres, the *alveoli,* filled with a clear fluid, the *hyaloplasm* or *enchylema,* and suspended in a continuous *interalveolar substance.* Crowding of the alveoli causes the interalveolar substance to look like a network and produces the illusion of a reticular structure. These theories all express partial truths despite the fact that many of the older studies were made on fixed, i.e., coagulated, protoplasm, for living protoplasm does undoubtedly contain visible granules, fibrils, and alveoli, either temporarily or permanently. But these visible structures probably represent merely different arrangements of the colloidal particles and none of them can be regarded as the seat of life. The vital properties are apparently vested in the colloidal *ground substance,* itself microscopically structureless, in which visible structure and substances arise by chemical and physical change. Experiments show further that this ground substance possesses an *organization,* i.e., a spatial pattern of materials or processes or both, which to the present time has not been explained on physical or chemical grounds.

Chemically, protoplasm consists of the same elements that occur in the nonliving world, but these may form combinations which do not exist in nature except in living organisms, although many of them can be prepared in the laboratory, and which are therefore termed *organic.* The organic constituents of protoplasm fall into three large classes—*proteins, carbohydrates,* and *lipins*—for a detailed consideration of which works on physiological chemistry should be consulted. They are composed of oxygen, hydrogen, and carbon in definite proportions and arrangements, and in addition proteins always contain nitrogen and often phosphorus and sulphur. Active protoplasm contains 70 to 96 per cent of water and 4 to 30 per cent of solid material composed chiefly of the organic compounds just mentioned and a small quantity of common salts. Most abundant of the latter are sodium, potassium, calcium, and magnesium as chlorides, carbonates, phosphates, and sulphates. Other elements present in small to minute quantities are iron, copper, zinc, manganese, iodine, silicon, and a few others. The salts of protoplasm are thought to exist partly in true solution in the water and partly in combination with the organic materials.

This brief survey of the physical and chemical nature of protoplasm could be expanded into volumes, but such compendia of facts have so far brought us little nearer the comprehension of those properties of protoplasm which collectively constitute life and which are termed *biological*. The usual list of these properties is here altered to the following: *irritability, motility, metabolism, growth, reproduction, modifiability*, the *psychical property*, and *organization*.

Irritability is the power of *response*, that is, of undergoing some change when external or internal conditions change. Here is included *conductivity* or the transmission of change.

Motility or the power of movement, often called *contractility*, is of three sorts in animals: *amoeboid*, seen as protoplasmic flow; *ciliary*, in which progression results from the beating of hair-like projections; and *contractile*, involving the shortening of fibrillar structures.

Metabolism is a general term embracing all the predominantly chemical processes of organisms. These metabolic processes on which the maintenance of life depends result in the formation of protoplasm or other substances and in the release of energy. The principal metabolic processes of animals are *digestion, assimilation, oxidation, secretion*, and *excretion*. Digestion is the splitting of organic foods into simpler, absorbable substances. Assimilation is the building up or synthesis of the products of digestion into a variety of substances, including protoplasm. Oxidation or *aerobic*, better, *oxybiotic, respiration* is the burning of organic substances with the aid of free oxygen for the release of heat or other forms of energy. Energy-releasing reactions and transformations performed by organisms without the aid of free oxygen are called *anaerobic*, or better, *anoxybiotic, respiration* and are chemically of the same nature as oxidations. Secretion is the extraction and concentration, followed or not by recombination, of materials from the surrounding medium to serve the body functions. Excretion, very similar to secretion, is the active concentration of nongaseous waste by-products of the metabolic reactions preparatory to their elimination to the exterior. Most of this chemical work is performed with the aid of enzymes, remarkable bodies secreted by protoplasm and serving primarily to accelerate greatly chemical reactions which otherwise would occur so slowly as to be useless to the organism.

Growth is increase in volume chiefly through the production of new protoplasm from food. Changes in water content are also commonly involved.

Reproduction is the origination of new organisms from preexisting ones and is so far as known the only mode of origin of organisms. It is of two general sorts: *asexual,* in which the reproductive process does not involve the fusion of two cells; and *sexual,* where such fusion is the necessary starting point of the new organism. Here may be included *development* or *embryology,* the orderly sequence of changes from the fertilized egg to the young animal.

Modifiability, possibly only another manifestation of irritability, is used here to express the ability of organisms to change their responses and structure. Even in the simplest animals there exists between a stimulus and a response the possibility of an unpredictable modification of behavior, in contrast to the fixity of response in the inorganic world. Under this head may also be included *adaptation* or the correspondence between the structure and activities of organisms and their environment and mode of life. While every organism must be adapted in order to live at all, more exact adaptation has presumably arisen through change in organisms. Here, too, we may list *variation,* or small fluctuations in organization, and *evolution,* that continuous progression through the ages in structural complexity and skill of functional performance.

The *psychic property,* called by some authors *consciousness,* is difficult to define without recourse to objectionable terms. It expresses that which is known in human beings as mind and which biologists believe is traceable through the animal kingdom down to the simplest forms where it probably merges with irritability and modifiability.

Organization is inseparable from protoplasm, and the phenomena of life spring from this organization. Nothing is known of its nature but it is presumed to consist of a spatial arrangement or pattern of materials or processes or both. It expresses itself visibly as *differentiation* or the formation of specific structures and parts related to particular functions. These parts commonly exhibit *polarity* and *symmetry,* i.e., they are arranged in geometrical patterns. Under organization may be included *correlation* or *integration,* the harmonious unified functioning of the parts of an organism, and *regulation* or *regeneration,* i.e., the return to a stable organization when the original one has been disturbed.

A living organism is recognizable by the foregoing biological properties. Attempts to define life other than as the sum total of these properties have proved unsatisfactory.

II. THE CELL

Organisms may consist of an undivided mass of protoplasm but usually on microscopic examination are seen to be divided by partitions into minute portions called *cells.* This fact of the cellular construction of organisms was first emphasized in 1839 by two investigators named Schleiden and Schwann. Organisms are said to consist of one cell or of many cells, to be *unicellular* or *multicellular,* respectively, but it would be preferable to describe them as *acellular* and *cellular*, and this terminology will be here employed.

So far as known, even the simplest cells or acellular organisms always contain a special differentiated material, the *chromatin*, scattered throughout the protoplasm in a few cases but in the vast majority located along with other materials in one or more formed bodies, the *nuclei*. A cell is commonly defined as a mass of protoplasm containing a nucleus but would be better described as *one nucleated division of an organism*. The term protoplasm was first applied to the cell contents by Purkinje in 1840 for embryonic animal material and by von Mohl in 1846 for the substance of plant cells. The term in present usage generally signifies the entire cell contents or entire substance of acellular organisms including the nucleus. The protoplasm outside the nucleus is designated the *cytoplasm* or *cytosome* but protoplasm and cytoplasm are often used synonymously by biologists.

Although cells and acellular organisms usually contain a single nucleus, protoplasmic masses and organisms containing many nuclei and not divided up into cells are not uncommon and are probably widespread in embryonic materials (Fig. 1*A*). Such a multinucleate mass is called a *syncytium* when part of a cellular organism, and a *plasmodium* when an independent amoeboid organism. As interchange between nucleus and cytosome is essential to life and as each nucleus can interact with only a limited amount of cytoplasm, larger undivided protoplasmic masses are necessarily multinucleate. Some believe that in a given material under given conditions there exists a definite ratio of nuclear to cytoplasmic mass, the *karyoplasmic ratio* of R. Hertwig. Protoplasmic connections in the form of delicate strands called *cell bridges* or *plasmodesma* between cells apparently definitely bounded are not uncommon, especially in plants.

Acellular organisms and the various types of cells found in cellular organisms all exhibit much the same fundamental construction, and this fact permits the somewhat idealized description of a typical cell given in books. Here we shall simply list the sorts of structures most widely occurring in cells and acellular animals.

1. The Cell Parts.—The visible or morphological structures of cells have been divided by Meyer into three classes: *protoplasmic* or active living parts; *alloplasmic* or less active living parts, as cilia, flagella, and fibrils; and *ergastic* or nonliving materials. It seems inadvisable to attempt to distinguish different grades of living parts but the conception of ergastic substances, also called *inclusions, paraplasm,* and *metaplasm,* is useful. The cell parts will here be considered as of two sorts: the *organoids* or formed morphological elements, and the *ergastic* substances, lifeless deposits.

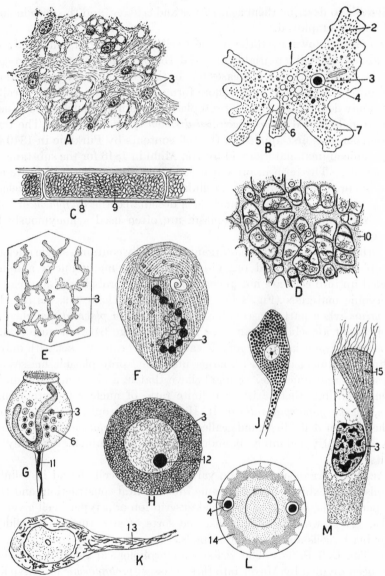

Fig. 1.—Various organoids and types of nuclei.   *A.* A syncytium; the parenchyma of a planarian consisting of a fibrous network containing scattered nuclei, drawn from a fixed preparation.   *B.* An acellular organism, *Amoeba vespertilio*, from life.   *C.* Cells of an algal filament, from life, showing the thick cell walls, and the interior filled with oval chloroplasts.   *D.* Cartilage from the radula of a snail, showing intercellular substance. (*After Schaffer*, 1913.)   *E–G.* Unusual shapes of nuclei.   *E*, branched nucleus of a cell of the spinning gland of the silkworm larva, from slide stained by Feulgen's method (*courtesy Dr. Hope Hibbard*); *F*, moniliform nucleus of *Stentor*, stained whole mount; *G*, band nucleus of *Vorticella*, live specimen stained with methyl green, also an example of a massive nucleus. *H.* Egg cell of a flatworm, from a section, showing a typical vesicular nucleus with a conspicuous plasmosome.   *J.* Gland cell secreting adhesive material, showing secretory

a. The Plasma Membrane and the Cell Wall.—The surface of the cytosome is differentiated as the *plasma membrane*, also called *ectoplast* (Fig. 1*B*). It is not a separable membrane but is the altered surface of the cytoplasm that is formed whenever cytoplasm is exposed to the surrounding medium and that loses its properties upon death. It is probably a protein gel containing lipins and calcium. The ectoplast possesses the remarkable property of *selective permeability*, regulating the passage of materials in and out of the cell, permitting some to pass, excluding or retaining others. Functional alterations of permeability occur and may be of great importance in cell activities.

Some cells, often termed *naked* cells, are bounded simply by the ectoplast (Fig. 1*B*), but generally an additional layer, called the *cell wall*, is present external to the ectoplast. This varies from the very thick cell walls of plant cells (Fig. 1*C*) composed of cellulose and other carbohydrates, to the thinner, less obvious walls of animal cells, seldom containing carbohydrates but usually nitrogenous. Generally in cellular animals, the cell wall is merely a thin partition but in some cases is increased to form a large mass of material, called *intercellular substance*, in which the cells lie imbedded (Fig. 1*D*). Although opinions differ, the cell wall and the intercellular substances are probably lifeless, ergastic products.

b. The Nucleus.—The nucleus is usually spherical or ellipsoidal, but ribbon, branched, and other shapes occur (Fig. 1*E–G*). It may consist of several nearly separate pieces and is then called a *polymorph* nucleus. As to construction there are three kinds of nuclei: *vesicular, massive,* and *scattered*. The great majority of nuclei are vesicular, that is, contain solid stainable material embedded in a clear transparent *nuclear sap* (Fig. 1*H*). The solid material usually takes the form of a network but in the nuclei of many Protozoa occurs as a solid central body, the *endosome* (Fig. 1*B, L*), surrounded by a zone of nuclear sap. Massive nuclei appear to consist of solid, nearly homogeneous material without nuclear sap. In scattered nuclei, the essential nuclear material, the chromatin, is not contained in a definite nucleus but is scattered through the cytosome as small granules called *chromidia* (Fig. 1*L*). Cells usually possess a single nucleus, but the occurrence of two to many nuclei is common in Protozoa.

The ordinary vesicular nucleus is enclosed in a definite *nuclear membrane*, having properties similar to those of the ectoplast. The nuclear

granules; from the posterior end of a flatworm, section. *K.* Mitochondria, osmic acid impregnation, nerve cell of the snail *Planorbis.* (*After Kolatchev,* 1916.) *L. Arcella,* stained, showing the so-called chromidial net and the two vesicular nuclei, each with a central endosome. (*After Hegner,* 1920.) *M.* Ciliated epithelial cell of the hepatic duct of a snail, showing anchoring fibrils of the cilia. (*After Heidenhain,* 1899.) 1, ectoplast; 2, crystal; 3, nucleus; 4, endosome; 5, vacuole; 6, food body; 7, microsomes; 8, cell wall; 9, chloroplasts; 10, intercellular substance; 11, myoneme of stalk of *Vorticella;* 12, plasmosome; 13, mitochondria; 14, chromidial net; 15, tonofibrils of cilia.

contents consist of a clear, apparently homogeneous *nuclear sap* or *karyolymph*, of variable consistency, and the nuclear network embedded therein. The structure of the nuclear network or *reticulum* is uncertain. It is usually held that it is made of a lightly staining net of *achromatin* or *linin* on which are strung granules or droplets of deeply staining *chromatin*, but it is possible that both materials are simply different chemical phases of chromatin, a lightly staining *oxychromatin* and a deeply staining *basichromatin*. Chromatin is the important constituent of the nucleus and differs from other cell proteins in its high phosphorus content. Besides the structures already enumerated, nuclei nearly always contain one or more small spherical bodies, the *nucleoli*, which are of two sorts: true nucleoli or *plasmosomes* (Figs. 1*H*, 2*C*), and chromatin nuclei or *karyosomes*. The former, of unknown function, stain like cytoplasm and are devoid of chromatin. The karyosomes consist of chromatin and are simply larger masses of this substance.

The function of the nucleus has been investigated by comparing the activities of nucleated and nonnucleated parts of acellular organisms. Such observations show that nonnucleated parts may live for a time and display some protoplasmic activities but are unable to assimilate food or grow or construct formed elements, that is, they have lost the ability to perform synthetic or constructive metabolism which may then be considered the chief function of the nucleus in ordinary cell life.

c. Mitochondria or Chondriosomes.—These organoids, widely distributed in plant and animal cells, occur as granules, rods, or filaments in the cytosome (Fig. 1*K*). They can be seen in living cells and made conspicuous in fixed cells after certain methods of preparation. They have been shown by Bensley and Hoen to consist of fatty substances and proteins. Their function is uncertain, but they appear to take part in the formation of other organoids and of secretions. The total mitochondrial content of a cell is termed the *chondriome*.

d. Chromidia.—This term should be reserved for chromatin granules scattered in the cytosome (Fig. 1*L*). They are stated to occur in some bacteria, algae, and Protozoa and may take the place of a nucleus or coexist with an ordinary nucleus from which they are supposed to originate. Their occurrence in animal cells may be gravely doubted as the supposed chromidial granules and networks are probably mitochondria.

e. Secretory Granules.—In cells with secretory functions, the secretion usually first appears as granules which subsequently discharge to the exterior. In many cases, these granules are preliminary stages in enzyme manufacture and then are called *zymogen* granules (Fig. 1*J*).

f. Microsomes.—Besides the foregoing types of granules and a variety of ergastic granules, to be mentioned later, cytoplasm usually exhibits a fine granulation, which seems to be an integral part of its construction (Fig. 1*B*). The nature and function of these cytoplasmic granules, or *microsomes*, are quite unknown.

g. Fibrillar Organoids.—Various sorts of fibrils are common elements of cells and serve supporting, contractile, and conductile functions. The numerous fibrils that anchor cilia and flagella are probably examples of supporting fibrils or *tonofibrils* (Fig. 1*M*). Fibrils that seem to be essential to the contractile process are usually present in contractile cells and are known as *myonemes* (Fig. 1*G*) or *myophan striations* in protozoan cells, and as *myofibrils* in muscle cells. Conductile protoplasm is commonly provided with fibrillar elements, the *neurofibrils* (Fig. 2*A*).

h. Plastids.—Plastids are bodies of various shapes and sizes, characteristic of plant cells, limited among animal cells to those with plant-like metabolism. Colorless plastids are called *leucoplasts;* but plastids are generally colored and are then named *chromoplasts.* The most common chromoplast is the *chloroplast* (Figs. 1*C*, 2*E*), which contains the green coloring matter of plants, *chlorophyll.* Plastids in general are centers of chemical activity, virtual manufacturing depots for various products. They reproduce by division and may possibly arise directly from protoplasm.

i. Vacuoles.—Vacuoles (Fig. 1*B*), much more common in plant than in animal cells, are cavities filled with a watery fluid and enclosed in a membrane that is probably similar in composition and properties to the ectoplast. Protozoan cells frequently possess a special sort of vacuole, the *contractile vacuole*, which discharges its contents by rhythmic contractions.

j. Golgi Apparatus.—This is a material, probably of a fatty nature, that, after the application of osmic acid or silver salts to cells, appears as a network or as isolated rods, granules, and spheres (Fig. 2*D*). It was discovered in 1898 by a cytologist named Golgi. Its structure and function are much debated owing to the highly artificial treatment required to render it visible. Some consider it identical with a system of canals, the *trophospongium*, which has been found permeating the cytosome of some cells; others consider it homologous with the system of vacuoles, or *vacuome*, of plant cells. Much evidence now indicates that the apparatus is concerned in secretion.

k. The Cytocentrum, Microcentrum, or Central Apparatus.—This structure consists of one, two, or several small granules, or rods, the *centrioles*, encircled by a sphere of altered cytoplasm (Fig. 2*B*). This sphere may be a definite round body, the *centrosome*,[1] but more commonly comprises a zone of hyaline or granular cytoplasm, variously known as the *sphere, centrosphere, attraction sphere, archoplasm*, etc. From or near

[1] This restricted usage of the word centrosome is taken from E. B. Wilson, *The Cell in Development and Heredity.*

the centriole, rays may radiate into the cytoplasm, forming the *aster*.   The cytocentrum is concerned with the division of cells and hence usually

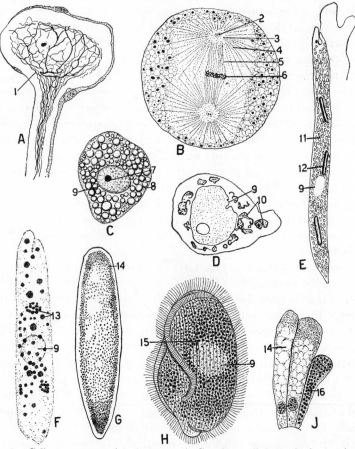

Fig. 2.—Cell structures and inclusions.   *A.* Ganglion cell from the brain of a leech, showing neurofibrils.   (*After Cajal*, 1903.)   *B.* Amphiastral mitotic figure, metaphase of the first cleavage of the egg of the echiuroid *Thalassema*.   (*After Griffin*, 1899.)   *C.* Egg of a polyclad flatworm, section, showing yolk spherules.   *D.* Golgi apparatus, nerve cell of the snail *Planorbis*.   (*After Kolatchev*, 1916.)   *E.* A species of *Euglena*, from life, showing chloroplasts and three paramylum bodies.   *F. Euglena gracilis*, stained to show volutin grains.   (*After Baker*, 1933.)   *G. Paramecium*, from life, after Sudan III staining, showing the numerous fat droplets.   *H. Nyctotherus*, a parasitic ciliate from the cloaca of the frog, stained to show glycogen particles.   (*After Barfurth*, 1885.)   *J.* Digestive epithelium of a fresh-water planarian, section, showing two phagocytic cells whose vacuoles are filled with fat in life and a club cell containing reserve protein spherules.   1, neurofibrils; 2, centrioles; 3, centrosphere; 4, aster; 5, spindle; 6, equatorial plate of chromosomes; 7, plasmosome; 8, yolk spheres; 9, nucleus; 10, Golgi network; 11, chloroplasts; 12, paramylum body; 13, volutin grains; 14, fat spheres; 15, glycogen; 16, protein spherules.

appears only when division is imminent; but it may persist in cells between divisions and is a permanent organoid of some cells that never divide. Its role in such cases is obscure.

1. Ergastic Substances, Inclusions, Metaplasm, Paraplasm.—These various names are applied to the inactive or lifeless materials that exist in cells as granules, spheres, or droplets and commonly represent stored or reserve food. Carbohydrates occur widely in plant cells as starch grains but in animals are stored as *paramylum* (Fig. 2*E*), a special kind of starch, or as *glycogen* (Fig. 2*H*). *Fats* and *oils* (Fig. 2*G, J*) are present in cells as droplets of various sizes, and other more complicated lipins may also occur. Egg cells contain spherules or droplets known as *yolk* or *deutoplasm* composed of proteins and lipins (Fig. 2*C*). Stored *protein* granules (Fig. 2*J*) are not very common in animals. *Volutin* grains, consisting of phosphorized proteins, occur in the cells of many lower forms and apparently constitute preliminary stages in chromatin formation (Fig. 2*F*). Pigment granules cause most animal colors and occur in various cells or in special cells termed *pigment cells* or *chromatophores*. Inorganic or organic crystals of varied chemical composition are not uncommon, especially in plant cells. Secretory granules, cell walls, and intercellular substances are often classed as ergastic materials.

2. Polarity.—Besides these morphological elements, cells possess an invisible organization that experiment shows is not vested in the organoids but resides in the ground substance. It expresses itself as *polarity* and *symmetry*, which may be defined as an arrangement of function and structure with respect to imaginary axes and planes. Examples of functional polarity are seen in the one-way conduction of nervous paths, the formation of secretory granules always in one end of gland cells, etc. Corresponding to such polarization of function there is nearly always a polarized arrangement of organoids and ergastic substances. Theories of cell polarity are of two sorts, morphological and physiological. The former seeks the cause of polarity in a polarized arrangement of invisible materials or an orientation of molecules in the ground substance. The second theory regards polarity as consisting in a graded difference in rate of metabolic reactions at different levels of the cell (metabolic gradient theory of Child) and as originating through the action of external factors upon the cell.

3. Cell Theory.—In the decades that followed the discovery of cells, emphasis was laid on the cellular construction of organisms and on the individuality, independence, and properties of cells. The organism was regarded, not as a functioning whole, but as a mosaic of multitudes of elementary units, the cells, and its properties merely as the sum of the properties of these units, a view termed the *cell theory*. A typical statement of the cell theory is that of Virchow (1858): "Every animal appears as a sum of vital units, each of which bears in itself the complete characteristics of life."[1] Such a statement is inadmissible today. An animal

---

[1] Quoted by Wilson at the head of the opening chapter of *The Cell in Development and Heredity.*

is not a sum of vital units but a functional whole. The complete characteristics of life are manifested by organisms, not by cells, which are to be regarded merely as structural parts of an organism. Organisms are composed of cells presumably because the cellular construction possesses certain advantages: morphologically, it permits of greater differentiation with increased efficiency of performance; physiologically, by breaking up the protoplasm into small units, it creates an immense amount of surface and greatly facilitates the interchange of food materials and respiratory gases and the elimination of metabolic wastes. Furthermore, the support of cell walls and intercellular substances permits increase in size.

4. Cell Division.—Cells come into being only by the division of preexisting cells. The important process in the division of cells is the nuclear behavior. The nucleus divides either by the *direct amitotic* method or the *indirect mitotic* method.

a. Direct Division or Amitosis.—In direct division the nucleus simply constricts at the middle and draws apart into two halves. This process, originally supposed to be the regular mode of nuclear division, is now recognized as rather infrequent. It occurs in some Protozoa (Fig. 3A), in certain gland cells, and in embryonic tissue. Although one group of observers considers amitosis to characterize rapidly growing and rapidly metabolizing regions, the dominant opinion at present regards it as evidence of degeneration and senility. In many cases where the nucleus has been observed to divide amitotically, no cytoplasmic division ensues and consequently the process is not truly one of cell multiplication. Recently, however, it has again been maintained that a highly modified mitosis, resembling amitosis, occurs during rapid growth as in developing embryos (Stough).

b. Indirect Division or Mitosis.—This is the regular mode of division of almost all cells. The nuclear division is a complex process and is called *karyokinesis;* the cytoplasmic division is named *cytokinesis.* For the complete details of mitosis the larger works on cytology should be consulted, as only a brief review can be given here.

Mitosis begins by the condensation of the chromatin of the nuclear reticulum into threads of chromatin that subsequently shorten and thicken and are known as *chromosomes.* Very early there appears in each chromosome a lengthwise split. Meantime the nuclear membrane has dissolved and disappeared so that the chromosomes lie free in the cytoplasm. They are definite in number and form in each species and vary from short ovals to slender filaments, often bent at some point. The chromosomes constitute the *chromatic figure.*

Meantime there has been forming in the cytoplasm the *achromatic* figure, which in animal cells is usually of the *amphiastral* type (Fig. 2B). This is initiated by the cytocentrum, which if not already present puts in an appearance as mitosis begins and if not already double very soon divides in two. Astral rays, if not previously present, form and the two cytocentra, each consisting of centrioles, sphere, and aster, draw apart until they come to lie at the opposite ends of the group of chromosomes. As the cytocentra move apart there is seen (in fixed preparations only) between them a fibrillar structure, named from its shape the *spindle*, which usually consists of *central* fibers running from one cytocentrum to

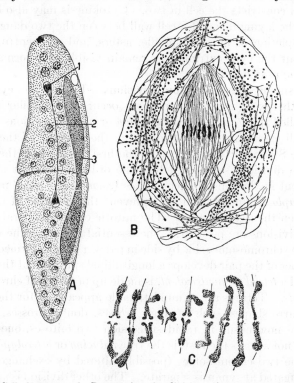

Fig. 3.—Cell division. *A. Paramecium* in division, the macronucleus dividing by amitosis, the micronucleus by mitosis, stained slide. (*Courtesy Miss Dolores Brockett.*) 1, micronucleus; 2, desmose; 3, macronucleus. *B.* Anastral figure in meiosis, pollen mother cell of the larch. (*After Devisé*, 1922.) *C.* Enlarged view of tetrads, spermatocyte of the polychaete annelid *Tomopteris.* (*After the Schreiners*, 1916.)

the other, and of peripheral *half fibers* attached at one point to the chromosomes. The spindle and astral fibers apparently do not exist as such in life but may be fluid channels in the cytoplasm. Cytocentra, asters, and spindle constitute the achromatic figure; achromatic and chromatic figures together constitute the *mitotic* or *karyokinetic* figure, which in the case described is of the amphiastral type. In some forms, and commonly in plant cells, cytocentra and asters are absent, and such a karyokinetic figure is termed *anastral* (Fig. 3*B*).

The chromosomes arrange themselves across the center of the spindle as the *equatorial plate* and separate into two halves along the longitudinal split already present, and each half moves towards the nearest cytocentrum. Arrived at the cytocentrum the group of chromosomes transforms into the reticulum of an ordinary "resting" nucleus, and a new nuclear membrane appears. Meantime the cytosome undergoes division, usually, in the amphiastral type, by the formation of a furrow which deepens and constricts the cell in two. Cytokinesis may also be accomplished by the laying down of a cell wall between the two daughter cells. At the completion of mitosis, spindle, asters, and cytocentrum usually disappear but the cytocentrum may remain visible in a dormant condition until the next mitosis.

c. Meiosis or the Reduction Divisions.—In the life cycle of all animals with sexual reproduction there occur two peculiar successive divisions called the *reduction* or *maturation* or *meiotic* divisions (Fig. 3*B*). In nearly all cases they take place during the ripening of the sex cells, but in some Sporozoa they happen in the first divisions of the fertilized egg. These divisions serve to reduce the ordinary number of chromosomes present in the cells of each species (*somatic* or *diploid* number) to one half (*haploid* number) and thus prevent the doubling of the diploid number when the sex cells fuse. The mitotic events preparatory to the reduction divisions are peculiar. The essential feature is the close association of the chromosomes side by side in pairs, a process termed *synapsis*. Each member of the pair develops a longitudinal split so that the resulting body, called a *tetrad* or *quadrivalent*, is made up of four half chromosomes, or *chromatids*. Tetrads are of unmistakable appearance for they usually assume bizarre shapes, such as rings, crosses, double crosses, etc. (Fig. 3*C*). There now ensue in rapid succession two mitoses, one of which, usually but not always the first, is the true *reducing* or *heterotypic* division, in which the two chromosomes (possibly altered by exchange of parts) which conjugated at synapsis separate. The other division is an ordinary one along the longitudinal split that developed in tetrad formation. The cells resulting from the reduction divisions possess the haploid number of chromosomes.

III. THE ORGANISM

1. Theories of the Organism.—As already emphasized, life manifests itself only as organized beings, which exhibit definite size, form, and spatial arrangement of parts, are structurally differentiated in relation to their mode of life, and in most cases pass through a remarkable process of development. Explanations of these properties since the beginning of modern zoology in the eighteenth century tend to follow a few recurrent lines of thought. As remarked by Woodger in *Biological Principles*, these explanations are usually stated as antitheses, such as form and function, preformation and epigenesis, mechanism and vitalism, etc.

Since anatomical knowledge developed earlier than physiological or embryological information, the question of the cause of adult form soon received attention. Two schools of thought arose that in one form or another still persist. The one school, headed by the great comparative anatomist Cuvier (1769–1832), maintained that form is determined or caused by function, i.e., mode of life, that correlation of anatomical parts for the harmonious functioning of the whole is the essential feature of animal form, and that several types or plans of form exist. The view that structure has arisen for the purpose of accomplishing certain functions in correlation with a specific environment or mode of life is designated *teleology* or purposiveness in nature. The opposite school, under the leadership of G. St. Hilaire (1772–1844), insisted that form is primary and precedes function and that all animal form can be reduced to one ideal morphological type or pattern. This explanation, that the forms of animals are simply variations from an ideal, preexisting plan, classifies philosophically as *transcendentalism*. The submergence of transcendentalism, through Cuvier's decisive proof that the facts of adult anatomy do not support the one-plan theory, was only temporary, however, and transcendentalism underwent a strong revival following the enunciation of the evolution principle by Darwin in 1859. This revival was due chiefly to Ernest Haeckel (1834–1919) whose ideas and those of the many great morphologists of the last half of the nineteenth century are essentially transcendental with their search for homologous parts, primitive types, generalized forms, transitional species, archetypes, etc.; their insistence on anatomy as the sole criterion; and their disregard of function. The old search for the ideal ground plan is revived in Haeckel's gastraea theory (page 250) with its attempted derivation of all the Metazoa from the gastrula. The dominance of such ideas in present-day zoological teaching is obvious, but the question involved, namely the role of function in the production of form, cannot be said to have received any answer. Probably the majority of zoologists today hold that variations of form arise through hereditary processes, that animals seek environments and situations to which such chance-inherited structural deviations fit them, and that therefore there is no direct causal relationship between environmental factors and adaptive structures. Others, however, find this explanation inadequate and believe with Cuvier that the wonderful adaptations seen in organisms somehow result from the interaction of the organism with its environment through function.

Quite analogous to the dispute over the nature of adult form was that regarding embryonic development. Here also two opposed ideas arose— *preformation* and *epigenesis*. The former, reaching its climax with

Bonnet (1720–1793), maintained that the adult is represented in miniature in the egg (or sperm) and that development consists merely in the unfolding[1] of that already present.   The opposed doctrine of epigenesis declared that the egg and early embryo are actually as formless as they appear and that the adult develops from them by a real process of structural elaboration.   Evidence presented by C. F. Wolff (1733–1794) and K. E. von Baer (1792–1876) from the study of developing embryos led to the general acceptance of the epigenetic viewpoint.   However, toward the end of the nineteenth century, research on the development of portions of eggs and embryos revealed an underlying organization of the egg that is definitely related to the form and localization of parts of the future animal.   Furthermore, since the eggs of two different species develop under identical external conditions into two different animals, it follows that some intrinsic difference, which may be called their organization, exists between two such eggs.   Thus a certain amount of preformation must be assumed as operating in development.   At the same time, the epigenetic viewpoint has been greatly strengthened by the line of research called by its founder, W. Roux, *Entwicklungsmechanik*, which may be freely translated as *causal morphology*, or the study of form-determining factors during development.   This work, constituting one of the most active branches of present zoological research, has demonstrated the importance of interactions of parts and spatial relationships during development.   Thus modern embryology holds that development is both preformative in a broad sense and epigenetic.

Despite the great mass of evidence pointing to the epigenetic nature of much of the developmental process, there still remains in modern biology a strong school of thought that is in its essential nature rigidly preformistic.   One refers here to what Delage called the *particulate* or *micromeristic* theories of development.   Such theories assert that the body cells contain a multitude of particles, capable of assimilation, growth, and reproduction, that these particles represent all the body characters, and that they operate during development to cause the appearance of the typical morphology of the species.   Particulate theory has prevailed in biology since the Greeks and at present takes the form of the widely accepted *chromosome-gene* theory, according to which all the body characters are vested in particles, the *genes*, located in the chromosomes of the nuclei.   All particulate theories are intellectually unsatisfactory since the very matters for which explanation is sought are attributed without explanation to imaginary particles.   A tremendous mass of evidence certainly relates the chromosomes to at least some body characters but it is impossible that the genes alone can be responsible

[1] Preformation was hence also termed *evolution*, i.e., an unfolding, the original meaning of the word evolution.

for morphological differentiation, since all body cells contain the same set of genes.   The role of the genes in morphogenesis remains a total mystery, and in addition the gene theory is difficult to reconcile with the facts of experimental embryology, which show that the fate of a part can be profoundly altered by altering surrounding conditions.

All recent particulate theories in biology derive in fact from that biological theory called the *mechanistic* or *physicochemical* explanation of life, and this in turn developed from the materialistic physics and chemistry of the nineteenth century, according to which the universe consists ultimately of particles of matter moving through space.   This conclusion was reached through the analysis of matter into molecules and atoms, and, naturally, when the same analytic mode of thought was applied to biology, similar particulate conceptions resulted.   The mechanistic or physico-chemical theory of life means the belief that all vital phenomena can be fully explained in terms of physics and chemistry and will be completely known to us as soon as physical and chemical knowledge has progressed sufficiently.   The organism as a whole (when not altogether neglected) is conceived as a machine operating entirely in accordance with physical and chemical laws.   Following the example of the physical sciences, biologists studied organisms by applying physical and chemical methods to their parts and so successful have been these procedures in accumulating information that the physicochemical theory has come to be almost universally accepted and forms the working basis for practically all biological research today.   Physicochemical investigation has achieved an illusory success by neglecting such matters as correlation, organization, adaptation, evolution, and psychic properties or by inventing special particulate theories for them.

The chief objection to mechanism lies in the analytical procedure followed.   The organism is studied by selecting from it certain parts which are then subjected to intensive investigation.   The information thus obtained is very fragmentary; the synthesis of physicochemical facts about the parts of organisms cannot reconstruct for us the living being.   The analytical method of investigation disregards and destroys organization and organization is life.   Further, as remarked by J. S. Haldane, when only physical and chemical methods are employed, only physical and chemical facts are forthcoming.   The whole is not to be understood by an analysis of its parts any more than an architectural masterpiece can be comprehended by chemical and physical analysis of the stones of which it is built.   The conception of the organism as a physicochemical machine encounters the insuperable difficulties of explaining a machine which runs itself, repairs itself, alters itself to meet the exigencies of surrounding conditions, and reproduces itself; and what is still worse, attains its final form by developing from a simple beginning through an orderly sequence of forms and evolves through time into a succession of machines of ever-increasing complexity of construction. Finally, as pointed out by several writers, the mechanistic theory of life was based on nineteenth century materialistic physics that has now been largely modified.

A small number of biologists, dissatisfied with the physicochemical theory, have proposed other ways of regarding organisms.   They fall into two camps, the *vitalists* and the *organicists*.   *Vitalism* or *animism*, of which the chief exponent today is Hans Driesch, is the belief that the properties of organisms cannot be explained except by postulating some mysterious force or agency (*entelechy*) that controls form and development and directs[1] activities.   This theory cannot be disproved but is not acceptable to most biologists and further renders experimentation futile. The organismal viewpoint, advocated by Ritter, Woodger, J. S. Haldane, E. S. Russell and others, maintains that biology should study entire living organisms, not merely the physics and chemistry of their isolated parts; and that as physical and chemical facts and laws pertain to the inorganic world so also there may be biological facts and laws pertaining to organisms, which will be concealed from us as long as biological research continues to be limited by physicochemical procedure.   The organism is a functional unity, all of whose parts cooperate for the good of the whole and for the maintenance of the whole in a changeable environment, and its properties are to be understood only from this viewpoint.   Growth, form, response, reproduction, development, adaptation, heredity, and evolution are manifestations of the whole and are hardly to be understood by analyzing the organism into elements, whether these be physical, chemical, or morphological.

2. Animal Form.—Morphology reveals that animals fall into a number of groups, each with its own characteristic anatomical construction, and that these groups or *phyla*, when considered from the standpoint of general symmetry, combine into a few types, as long ago remarked by Cuvier.   Current zoological ideas on symmetry derive chiefly from Haeckel.   By symmetry is meant an arrangement of parts into geometrical designs, although the idealistic patterns of geometry are never fully realized in nature.   Animals classify as follows with regard to symmetry.

a. Asymmetrical or Anaxial.—The body lacks definite form or geometrical arrangement of parts and cannot be divided by planes into like portions.   Most sponges and some Protozoa.

---

[1] This definition is what most biologists understand by vitalism.   There are other conceptions called vitalism by some (cf. Lovejoy, 1911).   Vitalism defined as organic autotomy or the doctrine of logical discontinuity between the inorganic and the organic—the doctrine that if you knew all the motions and configurations of the particles of a living body, you could not predict what the actions of that living body would be—appears to the author to be indistinguishable from organicism.

b. Spherical or Homaxial Apolar Symmetry (Fig. 4*A*).—The body has the form of a sphere with parts arranged concentrically around or radiating from a central point. Through the central point an infinite number of planes can be passed that divide the body into like halves. All axes through the central point are *apolar,* i.e., their ends are alike. Some Protozoa (Heliozoa, Radiolaria).

c. Radial or Monaxial Heteropolar Symmetry (Fig. 4*B*).—The body has the general form of a short or tall cylinder with one main longitudinal axis around and along which the parts are arranged. This main axis

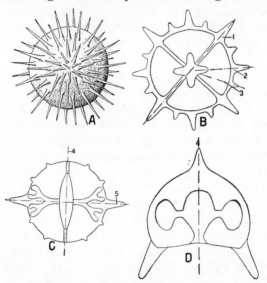

Fig. 4.—Diagrams of symmetry. *A.* Spherical symmetry. *B.* Radial symmetry of the tetramerous type; the halves produced by section along any two diameters at right angles to each other are identical. *C.* Biradial symmetry; the halves produced by section along the sagittal and transverse diameters are not identical. *D.* Bilateral symmetry, with differentiation of dorsal and ventral surfaces. 1, perradius; 2, interradius; 3, adradius; 4, sagittal axis; 5, transverse axis.

is *heteropolar,* i.e., its two ends are unlike, one being the *mouth, oral,* or *anterior* end, the other the *anal* or *aboral* or *posterior* end. It is named the *longitudinal* or *anteroposterior* or *oral-aboral* axis. Any plane passing through the longitudinal axis divides the body into like halves. In very few radially symmetrical animals are all possible radii from a central point to the periphery in any one cross section alike, but usually organs or special parts are located along a limited number of symmetrically arranged *perradii* and the regions between such radii are termed *interradii.* One perradius with half of the interradius to either side of it has been termed a *paramere.* Echinoderms and most coelenterates.

d. Biradial Symmetry or Dissymmetry (Fig. 4*C*).—The remaining two types of symmetry are *triaxial,* i.e., they have three axes of symmetry, *longitudinal, sagittal,* and *transverse.* In the biradial type, one particular diameter, termed the *sagittal axis,* is different from the others. The diameter at right angles to the sagittal axis is termed the *transverse axis* and may be different from or the same as the others. Both sagittal and transverse axes are apolar, since there is no differentiation into dorsal and ventral surfaces. There are two planes of symmetry, one through the longitudinal and sagittal axes, the other through the longitudinal and transverse axes. The biradial type seems to have been derived from the radial type primarily by the elongation of the mouth and associated parts, thus creating a sagittal axis. Ctenophores and most Anthozoa.

e. Bilateral Symmetry (Fig. 4D).—This type has three axes of symmetry like the preceding, but the sagittal axis is heteropolar, running between the dorsal and ventral surfaces, which are markedly differentiated. The transverse axis is apolar, as in the biradial type. There is but one plane of symmetry, the *median longitudinal* or *sagittal* plane passing through the longitudinal and sagittal axes and dividing the animal into symmetrical right and left halves. All remaining animals.

f. Asymmetrical Modifications of Bilateral Symmetry.—These are of common occurrence and include the spiral coiling of part of the body, the diminution or displacement or disappearance of organs of one side as a result of compression, the displacement of parts through the habit of lying or being fastened on one side, the formation of locking mechanisms, as in the shells of bivalves, and one-sided alterations of appendages for protective, sexual, or other purposes, as in the claws of the lobster.

Some other features of animal form may be listed here.

g. Antimeres.—Symmetrically corresponding parts, anatomically identical, as right and left limbs or the arms of a starfish, are called *antimeres.*

h. Metamerism.—The serial repetition of antimeres along the longitudinal axis is called *metamerism* or *segmentation,* and each part, consisting of right and left antimeres, is called a *segment* or *metamere.* Segmentation necessarily occurs only in bilaterally symmetrical animals. Segmentation is *homonomous* when all of the segments are approximately alike and *heteronomous* when they differ considerably among themselves. The heteronomous condition always appears first at the anterior end and progresses posteriorly.

i. Cephalization.—Cephalization is the differentiation of the anterior or oral end into a definite head and is always accompanied by concentration of nervous tissue in the head. Heteronomous segmentation is an expression of cephalization.

j. Polarity.—It will be observed that polarity or differentiation along an axis is a necessary accompaniment of all types of symmetry except the spherical. The chief feature of polarity is the specialization of one end of the axis as an anterior or oral end. Polarity and symmetry are obviously properties of the organism as a whole. Although cell polarity can conceivably spring from the orientation of internal particles, this explanation can hardly apply to the polarity of cellular organisms for this would then be the sum of the polarities of the cells, an impossibility, as the cells in a complex organism are oriented in all possible directions. It would seem to follow that organismal polarity must be dynamic in nature, i.e., must consist in activity, not in structure.

Bibliography

Agar, W. E.   1936.   Whitehead's philosophy of organism.   Quart. Rev. Biol. 11. **Baker, C. L.**   1933.   Studies on the cytoplasmic components of Euglena.   Arch. Protistk. 80.   **Barfurth, D.**   1885.   Vergleichen histochemische Untersuchungen über das Glycogen.   Arch. Mikro. Anat. 25.   **Bayliss, W. M.**   1924.   Principles of general physiology.   **Bensley, R. R., and N. L. Hoen.**   1934.   The preparation and properties of mitochondria.   Anat. Rec. 60.   **Bertananffy, L.**   1933.   Modern theories of development.   **Bütschli, O.**   1894.   Investigations on microscopic foams and on protoplasm.   **Cajal, Ramon y.**   1903.   Un sencillo metodo de coloracion del reticulo protoplasmico, etc.   Trabajos del Lab. Invest. Biol. Univ. Madrid 2.   **Child, C. M.**   1924.   The problem of pattern in organisms.   Amer. Nat. 58.   1928.   The physiological gradients.   Protoplasma. 5.   **Conklin, E. G.**   1917.   Mitosis and amitosis.   Biol. Bul. 33.   **Cowdry, E. V.** (ed.)   1924.   General cytology.   **Crow, W. B.**   1928.   Symmetry in organisms.   Amer. Nat. 62.   **Darlington, C. D.**   1931. Meiosis.   Biol. Rev., Cambridge Phil. Soc. 6.   **Devisé, R.**   1922.   La figure achromatique, etc.   La Cellule 32.   **Driesch, H.**   1929.   The science and philosophy of the organism.   **Eldridge, S.**   1925.   The organization of life.   **Griffin, B. B.**   1899. Studies on the maturation, etc.   Jour. Morph. 15.   **Haldane, J. S.**   1923.   Mechanism, life, and personality.   1935.   The philosophy of a biologist.   **Hegner, R. W.** 1920.   The relation between nuclear number, etc.   Jour. Expt. Zool. 30.   **Heidenhain, M.**   1899.   Beiträge zur Aufklärung, etc.   Anat. Anz. 16.   1911.   Plasma und Zelle.   **Hertwig, R.**   1903.   Über Korrelation von Zell- und Kerngrösse.   Biol. Zentbl. 23.   **Jennings, H. S.**   1911.   Vitalism and experimental investigation. Science 33.   **Johnstone, J.**   1914.   The philosophy of biology.   1932.   The essentials of biology.   **Kolatchev, A.**   1916.   Recherches cytologiques, etc.   Arch. Russ. Anat. Hist. Embry. 1.   **Lovejoy, A. O.**   1911.   The meaning of vitalism.   Science 33.   **Macklin, C. C.**   1916.   Binucleate cells in tissue cultures.   Carn. Instit. Wash., Pub. 224.   **Meyer, A.**   1920.   Morphologische und physiologische Analyse der Zelle der Pflanzen und Tiere.   **Needham, J.**   1928.   Organicism in biology.   Jour. Phil. Studies 3.   1929.   The sceptical biologist.   **Rhumbler, L.**   1914.   Das Protoplasma als physikalisches System.   Ergeb. Physiol. 14.   **Ritter, W. E.**   1919.   The unity of the organism.   2 vols.   **Russell, E. S.**   1916.   Form and function.   1930.   The interpretation of development and heredity.   **Russell, L. J., L. S. Stebbing, and A. E. Heath.**   1928.   Materialism in the light of modern scientific thought.   Aristot. Soc. Proc., Sup. 8.   **Schaffer, J.**   1913.   Über die feineren Bau, etc.   Zschr. Wiss. Zool. 105.   **Schreiner, A., and K. E. Schreiner.**   1916.   Die Reifung der männlichen Geschlechtszellen, etc.   Arch. Biol. 22.   **Seifriz, W.**   1929.   The structure of protoplasm.   Biol. Rev., Cambridge Phil. Soc. 4.   1936.   Protoplasm.   **Sharp, L. W.** 1933.   An introduction to cytology.   **Whitehead, A. N.**   1929.   Process and Reality. **Wilson, E. B.**   1925.   The cell in development and heredity.   3d ed.   **Woodger, J. H.** 1929.   Biological principles.   1930.   The concept of organism and the relation between embryology and genetics.   Quart. Rev. Biol. 5.

Cowdry, Sharp, and Wilson give extensive bibliographies on cell organoids, mitosis, etc.

CHAPTER II

CLASSIFICATION

I. GENERAL REMARKS ON CLASSIFICATION

When animals are studied anatomically, it is found that they can be arranged into some sort of plan, based on similarities and dissimilarities of structure. The branch of zoology that devotes itself to working out such arrangements is called *classification* or *taxonomy* or *systematics*. Since the enunciation of the evolution principle in 1859 it is conceded that all animals are related to each other by descent, and consequently any scheme of classification aims to give the genealogical relationships of the group of animals under consideration. Because of the incompleteness of the evidence, this ideal of classification is never reached in actual practice. Classification is based chiefly on the anatomy of adults and on embryological history. Geographical distribution is often of assistance and extinct animals, preserved in the rocks as *fossils*, are often invaluable in bridging the gaps between present-day forms. The uses or functions of parts and the habits and behavior of animals are considered of no importance as criteria of relationship.

The scheme of classification begins with the conception of the *species*, which may be defined as an assemblage of animals which are essentially alike in all the details of their anatomy (except as regards sex differences) and which interbreed freely with each other, as, for example, lions. Species that resemble each other rather closely, as lions, tigers, leopards, etc., are grouped together as a *genus* (plural, *genera*). Each species is then named by a combination of the generic and specific name, as *Felis leo*, the lion, and *Felis tigris*, the tiger, and this combination is known as the *scientific name*. This method of designating an animal by two Latinized names is called the *binomial system of nomenclature*. It was devised in the middle of the eighteenth century by a Swedish naturalist named Linnaeus (also given as Linné), who became interested in classification and published a manual in which all plants and animals known at that time were named and arranged in a scheme of classification. All subsequent taxonomy dates from the tenth edition of Linnaeus's work, *Systema Naturae*, published in 1758. The binomial system not only provides a distinct name for each kind of animal (this could also be accomplished by a *uninomial* system, giving each species one name) but it serves to indicate relationships as closely related species receive the same generic name.

Scientific names are always constructed in Latin or Latinized form. The first letter of the generic name is always capitalized, that of the specific name not, unless derived from a proper name, in which case an initial capital letter may be employed, although this is not compulsory. For very exact purposes, the scientific name is followed without intervening punctuation by the full or abbreviated name of the zoologist who first described the species and gave it its specific name, as *Felis leo* Linnaeus or *Felis leo* L. To ensure still further against mistakes, the year in which the species received its name is appended, set off by a comma or parentheses, as *Felis leo* L. (1758). In case the species is later transferred to a different genus from that in which it was originally placed, parentheses are put around the original describer, as *Planesticus migratoria* (L.), the robin redbreast.

Among the members of a species there are often minor variations that are called *varieties* when sufficiently distinct. Varieties are most noticeable among domestic animals. Distinct varieties inhabiting definite geographical areas are usually designated as *subspecies* and receive a third name which follows the specific name. Thus, the robin redbreast of the western United States presents slight but constant differences from the eastern form. Hence it is considered a subspecies and has been named *Planesticus migratoria propinqua* Ridgway.

The species included in a genus often vary in degree of resemblance and may fall into natural groups. For convenience a genus, especially one with a large number of species, may be subdivided into these groups of species, which are called *subgenera* and receive subgeneric names, one of which must always be the same as that of the genus itself. The subgeneric name when used must be placed in parentheses between the generic and specific name, as *Lymnaea* (*Lymnaea*) *stagnalis*, the common pond snail. This illustrates the only correct use of parentheses in a scientific name. When a generic name has been changed it is not correct to place the old generic name in parentheses after the new one but it is becoming customary to do this with the intervention of an equal sign as *Eimeria* (= *Coccidium*) although such usage has not been as yet officially recognized.

Genera bearing a certain degree of resemblance are united into a *family;* families with characters in common constitute an *order;* orders displaying important similarities are placed in a *class;* and classes having the same general anatomical construction form a *phylum.* Species, genus, family, order, class, phylum are then the chief taxonomic divisions; but many other divisions are commonly employed, usually formed by prefixing these names with "sub" for a lower division, "super" for a higher one, as subclass, superfamily, etc.

Taxonomic names of family and lower divisions are governed by definite set rules. Those regarding subspecies, species, subgenera, and genera have already been indicated. Family names must end in *idae* and must be derived from the name of the genus that has been fixed as typical. This genus is then known as the *type genus.* Subfamily names must end in *inae* and must also be derived from the stem of the name of their principal genus. Thus the generic name of cattle is *Bos;* the family is called *Bovidae* and the subfamily containing the most cattle-like members of the family is named *Bovinae.* No particular rules govern taxonomic names higher than family. They generally terminate in *a.* The priority principle does not apply to these names, i.e., the name first given to a class, order, etc., need not necessarily be retained although it is usually customary to keep such names as long as the same groups continue to be included under them and are recognized as constituting natural assemblages. When grounds are shown for changing the groups included under a phylum, class, or order, it may be desirable to alter the names of such divisions.

Changes in generic and specific names are made in accordance with a set of international rules (see below) and as such should be accepted with the assurance of eventual stability. The correct specific name of an animal is that which was first given to it with a published indication, definition, or description; but this rule of priority, simple enough in itself, is often difficult of application because many descriptions are inadequate and the animal concerned cannot be recognized. Again, many old descriptions are published in obscure places or are otherwise overlooked and consequently already named species are often redescribed later under new specific names. When such mistakes are discovered, it is necessary to drop the later specific name, even when it has been long in use, and to revert to the original name. A specific name once validly published cannot be altered unless it is shown that the same species had previously been described under some other specific name, or unless in rearranging genera forms happening to have the same specific name fall into the same genus, or unless the particular combination of generic and specific name had been used before, even if for an entirely different animal. A generic name is altered if it can be shown that it had been used before for some other genus of animals or that the species in question were previously described under some other generic name or fit better under an already existing genus or require the creation of a new genus. Many of the older genera were too inclusive, and, as knowledge of animals increases, it becomes desirable to split such genera up into a number of genera that can be accurately defined and that represent more natural assemblages. Thus originally almost any tapeworm was called *Taenia* whereas it is now recognized that most of these tapeworms must be distributed among a number of different genera. In such cases the original generic name is retained only for the species to which it was first applied and related species. When a generic name is altered, the specific name is retained, as already noted, together with its author. In case a taxonomic description is so indefinite that it cannot be determined with certainty what animal was meant, the name becomes a *nomen nudum* or blank name, which is dropped and cannot be used again.

The chief difficulties of taxonomy are the impossibility of erecting strict definitions for any given species, genus, etc.; of deciding when any given specimens differ sufficiently to warrant placing them in different species; or of deciding just how much species must differ from each other to constitute different genera; or what characters are the most important in making taxonomic distinctions. All such matters are questions of personal opinion on the part of taxonomists, and no rules can be formulated to cover them.

The number of known species of animals is so great (about one million) and the recognition of the differences between species depends so much upon special knowledge that in general only expert taxonomists can identify species with certainty. Special keys, manuals, and monographs can usually be employed only after considerable study of the anatomy of the groups treated, and many groups of animals have never been monographed. The most ambitious work on animal taxonomy is the German publication, *Das Tierreich* (*The Animal Kingdom*), which attempts to describe all known species of animals in the world. Begun in 1896, the work at present comprises about 70 large volumes, but these cover only a small part of the animal kingdom. R. Hesse, in charge of the undertaking, reported in 1929 that at the present rate of publication, 750 years would be required to complete the task of describing the species of animals now known, leaving out of consideration the new species that would be discovered in the interim. These facts may give the student some idea of the magnitude of the task of classifying and naming animals.

As already indicated, the application of names to animals is governed by a set of rules, the International Rules of Zoological Nomenclature. Debatable and uncertain points and motions to suspend the rules in a given case are considered and decided by an international commission on zoological nomenclature, which meets at intervals. The following are the more important of the international rules, briefly stated.

Art. 1. The generic name of an animal can be the same as that of a plant, but in general this is to be avoided.

Art. 2. The name of a species must be binomial, of a subspecies trinomial.

Art. 3. Scientific names must consist of Latin or Latinized words.

Art. 4. The name of a family is formed by adding *idae*, and of a subfamily by adding *inae* to the stem of the name of the type genus.

Art. 8. A generic name must consist of a single word, written with a capital initial letter and used as a nominative singular.

Art. 9. When a genus is divided into subgenera, the name of the typical subgenus must be the same as that of the genus.

Art. 10. When the subgeneric name is used, it must be placed in parentheses between the generic and specific names.

Art. 13. Specific names are written with a small initial letter, but when they are derived from the name of a person, they may be written with a capital initial letter; as *Equus Burchelli*, or *Equus burchelli*, Burchell's zebra.

Art. 14. Specific names are adjectives agreeing grammatically with the generic name; or nouns in the nominative or genitive cases.

Art. 17. The subspecific name, when used, must follow immediately after the specific name without the interposition of any mark of punctuation.

Art. 19. The original spelling of a name is to be preserved unless an error is evident.

Art. 20. In forming names from languages in which the Latin alphabet is used the exact original spelling including diacritic marks must be retained, as Mülleria.

Art. 21. The author of a scientific name is that person who first publishes the name in connection with an indication, a definition, or a description.

Art. 22. If desired to cite the author's name, this follows the scientific name without any intervening mark of punctuation; other information following the author's name is to be separated from it by a comma or parentheses.

Art. 23. When a species is transferred to another than the original genus, the name of the author of the specific name is retained but is placed in parentheses.

Art. 25. The valid name of a genus or species is that name by which it was first designated on the conditions that this name was published and accompanied by an indication or definition or description and that the author applied the rules of binomial nomenclature.

Art. 26. The year 1758, being the year of publication of the 10th ed. of Linnaeus' *Systema Naturae*, is the starting point for the application of the law of priority given in Art. 25.

Art. 27. The law of priority applies to descriptions including only a part of the animal, or a stage in the life history.

Art. 28. Type species are to be designated for genera according to certain specified rules.

Art. 32. A generic or specific name once published cannot be rejected because of inappropriateness.

Art. 33. A name cannot be rejected because generic and specific or specific and subspecific names are identical.

Art. 34. A generic name is to be rejected if it has previously been used for some other genus of animals.

Art. 35. A specific name is to be rejected if it has previously been used for some other species of the genus.

II. THE PRINCIPAL DIVISIONS OF THE ANIMAL KINGDOM

When animals are studied anatomically, most of them are found to fall into a limited number of natural groups, called *phyla*, each presenting a well-marked and easily recognizable assemblage of morphological characters. These several larger and more important phyla such as the sponges, coelenterates, echinoderms, annelids, mollusks, arthropods, and others are recognized as valid by all zoologists. Each such phylum comprises a group of obviously related forms, sharply marked off from all other phyla, and not easily derived from any other. But a number of smaller groups of animals exist that do not exactly fit into any of the larger phyla and yet do not possess outstanding characteristics. The disposition of these smaller groups remains a constant difficulty to the zoologist, who must either append them to one of the large phyla or regard them as independent phyla. Because of this and other difficulties zoologists have never come to any unanimity of opinion as to the number of phyla into which the animal kingdom should be divided. The general schemes of classification given in different texts and treatises are often at variance in large matters and practically never agree in detail. The classification within any group is constructed by those zoologists who have studied intensively the group in question and therefore represents their personal opinion as to the relationships of its members. As such relationships cannot be determined with finality and as our knowledge of invertebrate anatomy and embryology is still very faulty, there is room for much difference of opinion in any taxonomic scheme.

From the foregoing remarks the student will understand that he cannot expect to learn any "correct" final classificatory arrangement, for there is no such thing. What he will find in any text simply represents the best opinion of some zoologist. This opinion necessarily changes as knowledge of anatomy, embryology, distribution, and paleontology increases. The classification adopted in this book has been taken from a variety of sources and attempts to reflect the opinion of specialists in each group while preserving a conservative attitude. Wherever any difference of opinion exists as to the name or spelling of the larger units of classification, that name has been selected which is not necessarily the oldest but the one employed by that zoologist who first understood with reasonable adequacy the limitations and characteristics of a group. Such a zoologist may have utilized an old name that he redefined in more exact terms, or he may have invented a new one.

To understand some of the names and groupings used in modern schemes of classification a brief historical survey is necessary. Linnaeus in 1758 divided the animal kingdom into the classes Mammalia, Aves, Amphibia, Pisces, Insecta, and Vermes, thereby indiscriminately throwing all the invertebrates except insects into the group of Vermes or worms. This class he subdivided into the orders Intestina, Mollusca, Testacea, Lithophyta, and Zoophyta, none of which corresponds to any natural group except that Testacea were mostly bivalve mollusks, and Lithophyta, calcareous coelenterates. The Intestina included a variety of worms, the Mollusca was a heterogeneous assemblage from many groups (not mollusks) and the Zoophyta were mostly coelenterates. The unsatisfactory nature of Linnaeus's Vermes was early recognized, and various minor attempts at improvement soon appeared. At the beginning of the nineteenth century, Cuvier and Lamarck clearly grasped the distinction between vertebrates and invertebrates. Lamarck (1809) divided the invertebrates into Mollusca, Cirripedia, Annelida, Crustacea, Arachnida, Insecta, Vermes, Radiata, Polypes, and Infusoria; and later, (1815) added the groups Tunicata and Conchifera (ostracods, brachiopods, some mollusks). Lamarck understood the first six groups and Tunicata in practically the modern sense but was less fortunate in the others. By Infusoria he meant rotifers and some Protozoans; under Polypes he placed most polypoid coelenterates, sponges, and some Protozoans; under Radiata, the remaining coelenterates, ctenophores, and echinoderms, although earlier he had regarded echinoderms as a separate class; under Vermes, flukes, tapeworms, roundworms, Acanthocephala, and a few oligochaetes. In Cuvier's system (1816) the invertebrates were divided into Mollusca, including brachiopods and barnacles; Articulata, under which name annelids and arthropods were united; and Radiata or Zoophyta, comprising the rest of the invertebrates, many of which of course are not radiate. The Radiata were subdivided into Echinodermes; Intestinaux or Entozoa, divided into Intestinaux cavitaires (roundworms, nemertines), and Intestinaux parenchymatoux (flatworms, Acanthocephala); Acalephes (medusae, siphonophores, ctenophores); Polypes, (polypoid coelenterates plus Bryozoa); and Infusoires (protozoans and rotifers). These systems of Lamarck and Cuvier laid the foundations for all future work on classification. The great phyla Vertebrata, Mollusca, Annelida, and Arthropoda with its subdivisions were established and Cuvier's union of the annelids and arthropods under the name Articulata has continued to find favor with many zoologists. The subdivisions of Cuvier's Radiata or Zoophyta already indicate in a broad way the lower invertebrate groups but because of Cuvier's authoritative position there was little improvement in the classification of the Radiata for many years and in 1829 Cuvier reiterated his scheme practically unchanged. There was a tendency to split off the parasitic worms under the names Entozoa, Helmintha, Helminthica, etc. The term Radiata or Zoophyta then came gradually to be restricted to the truly radial animals, the coelenterates and echinoderms, in accordance with Lamarck's usage, and it was not until 1848 that Leuckart recognized the fundamental differences between the two radial groups and separated them as the phyla Coelenterata and Echinodermata, creating the former name. The separation of the Protozoa from the rotifers was achieved in 1838 by Ehrenberg. About 1840 the name Vermes was revived, not in Linnaeus's sense, nor entirely in Lamarck's usage, but as a term including all the bilateral, worm-like animals. Of several systems developed along this line that of Leuckart (1848) is the most noteworthy. Leuckart recognized the phyla Protozoa, Coelenterata (including sponges), Echinodermata, Vermes (including the Turbellaria, trematodes, cestodes, Acanthocephala, nematodes, rotifers, Bryozoa, and annelids), Arthropoda, Mollusca (including Tunicata), and Vertebrata. The chief fault of this system consists in a lack of understanding of relationships within the Vermes; thus leeches were allied to trematodes, and nematodes were considered to be annelids. These defects were remedied by Carl Vogt, who in 1851 divided the Vermes into Annelida, Rotatoria, Platyelmia, and Nematelmia, thus establishing the groups of flat and roundworms; Vogt also correctly assigned the leeches to the annelids. Some slight improvements originated with Gegenbaur (1859), who altered Vogt's names to Platyhelminthes and Nemathelminthes.

The embryological researches of Kowalewski (1871) demonstrated the affinity of the tunicates with the vertebrates, with which they were then united under the name Chordonia. Haeckel (1874) emphasized the distinction between the acellular animals, the Protozoa, and the cellular animals, which he believed to derive from the gastrula and for which he invented the name Metazoa. These attempts to found the classification of animals on an embryological basis led to the system of Hatschek (1888) from which all present German systems are derived. Hatschek's arrangement was:

I. Protozoa
II. Metazoa
    A. Protaxonia or Coelenterata. (Gastrular axis preserved as oral-aboral axis; blastophore becomes the mouth.)
        Type I. Spongiaria, the sponges.
        Type II. Cnidaria, coelenterates plus Mesozoa.
        Type III. Ctenophora, ctenophores.
    B. Heteraxonia or Bilateria. (Gastrular axis does not persist as adult axis.)
        Type IV. Zygoneura. (Bilateria derivable from the trochophore.)
          a. Subtype Autoscolecida or Protonephridozoa. (Bilateria with protonephridia.)
            Branch Scolecida
              Platodes
              Rotifera
              Endoprocta (Bryozoa in part)
              Nematodes
              Acanthocephali
              Nemertini
          b. Subtype Aposcolecida or Metanephridozoa. (Bilateria with metanephridia.)
            Branch Articulata
              Annelida, including sipunculids and chaetognaths
              Onychophora
              Arthropoda
            Branch Tentaculata
              Phoronida
              Bryozoa ectoprocta
              Brachiopoda
            Branch Mollusca

Type V. Ambulacralia
    Branch Echinodermata
    Branch Enteropneusta
Type VI. Chordonia, includes Tunicata, Amphioxus, and vertebrates.

The concepts underlying these assemblages are more fully explained in Chap. IX. The name Scolecida (Greek, *scolios*, a worm) for worms with protonephridia, originated with Huxley (1864). Ambulacralia comes from Metschnikoff (1881), who established on embryological grounds the affinity of the Enteropneusta with the echinoderms. The name Zygoneura (Greek, *zygon*, yoke, and *neuron*, nerve, referring to the double ventral nerve cord) is Hatschek's, and Tentaculata and Chordonia were here first used by Hatschek in the sense defined, although Tentaculata had been previously invented by Lankester for crinoids and Chordonia originated with Haeckel (1874) as a name for the hypothetical ancestors of the notochord groups.

In the last quarter of the nineteenth century there was a tendency to drop the group Vermes as well as other phyletic groupings and to divide the animal kingdom into a number of independent phyla. This usage was and is particularly followed by English and American zoologists. The chief advance at this time was the recognition of the peculiarities of the sponges, which were separated by Sollas (1884) into a branch Parazoa contrasted with the remainder of the Metazoa, later termed Eumetazoa. Up to this time the sponges had been grouped with the coelenterata and ctenophores, all three being often termed Radiata. With the removal of the sponges the old name Radiata becomes restricted to the coelenterates and ctenophores, in which sense it is still widely used and will be so employed in this book. The rest of the Eumetazoa thereupon become known as Bilateria or the bilateral animals, a designation going back to Hatschek (1888).

The twentieth century has witnessed renewed attempts to combine the phyla under a few large headings. Lankester (1900) created the group Enterocoela for those Eumetazoa in which the digestive cavity is the only internal space (i.e., the present Radiata) and Coelomocoela for the bilateral animals. The trouble with this arrangement is that in some Bilateria there is no coelom at all and in others the body space is not a true coelom. The proposals of a group of German workers (Goette, 1902; K. C. Schneider, 1902; Grobben, 1908; and Hatschek, 1911) have proved more acceptable and may attain wide adoption. The principal feature of this work is the division of the Bilateria into two main lines of ascent: one termed Protostomia (Grobben) or Zygoneura, later Ecterocoelia (Hatschek) or Bilateralia hypogastrica (Goette); the other called Deuterostomia (Grobben) or Enterocoelia (Hatschek) or Bilateralia pleurogastrica (Goette) or Plerocoelia (Schneider). Of these various names, Protostomia and Deuterostomia have been most widely used. In the Protostomia the blastopore becomes the mouth, embryonic development is of the determinate type, and the mesoderm originates from certain embryonic cells or masses. Among the Deuterostomia, the mouth is a new formation, cleavage is indeterminate, and the mesoderm and coelom originate as pouches of the gut wall (enterocoelous method). These matters are discussed further in Chap. IX. The Deuterostomia include the phyla Echinodermata, Chaetognatha, Branchiotremata, and Chordata. All other Bilateria belong to the Protostomia. The Protostomia are derivable from a larval type, termed the trochophore (see Chap. IX), or its simpler forerunner, the protrochula; the Deuterostomia are referable to the dipleurula larva. This idea has been carried so far that in 1910 Claus-Grobben in their *Lehrbuch der Zoologie* divided the Bilateria into two phyla, Protostomia and Deuterostomia, and reduced what are usually considered phyla to the level of subphyla or classes.

Along with these ideas there has been a restoration of the phylum Vermes, which is subdivided on either the presence or absence of an anus (whence such names as Aprocta, Euprocta, Neoprocta, and other terms founded on the Greek *proctos*, anus), or on the nature and presence of a body cavity (whence Schizocoelia, Pseudocoelia, Coelomata, etc., founded on *koilos*, a cavity), or on the occurrence of segmentation (Greek, *meros*, a part), as in Bütschli's scheme (1910), which has met with much favor. Bütschli divides the worms into the Amera, without segmentation (equivalent to the Scolecida); the Polymera or Annelida, the segmented worms; and the Oligomera, animals with two or three coelomic divisions (Phoronida, Bryozoa, Brachiopoda, Chaetognatha, Branchiotremata). This plan is followed in the most extensive modern treatise on zoology, Kükenthal-Krumbach's *Handbuch der Zoologie*, where we find the following scheme of classification:

Subkingdom Protozoa-Phylum Protozoa
Subkingdom Metazoa
  Subdivision Parazoa-Phylum Porifera
  Subdivision Eumetazoa
    Radiata
      Phylum Coelenterata
      Phylum Ctenophora
      Phylum Mesozoa or Planuloidea
    Bilateria
    Phylum Vermes
      Subphylum Amera
        Cladus Plathelminthes, including Nemertinea
        Cladus Nemathelminthes
          Class Rotatoria
          Class Gastrotricha
          Class Kinorhyncha

       Class Nematodes
       Class Nematomorpha
       Class Acanthocephala
       Cladus Kamptozoa (= Bryozoa entoprocta).
     Subphylum Polymera = Annelida
     Subphylum Oligomera
       Cladus Tentaculata (= Phoronida, Bryozoa ectoprocta)
       Cladus Brachiopoda
       Cladus Chaetognatha
       Cladus Branchiotremata
   Phylum Echinodermata
   Phylum Mollusca
   Phylum Arthropoda
   Phylum Chordata

The author believes that groupings based upon theoretical considerations such as Protostomia and Deuterostomia should not be regarded as taxonomic divisions but rather as convenient terms for purposes of discussion. It is further maintained that the retention of the phylum Vermes, which can only be defined in general and mostly negative terms (i.e., as worm-like animals without skeleton or jointed appendages) and which unites animals of remote and indeterminable relationship while separating groups admittedly closely allied, such as annelids and arthropods, and echinoderms and Branchiotremata, is futile and confusing. A phylum should consist of closely allied animals distinguishable from any other phylum by well-defined positive characteristics, some of which do not exist in other phyla or not in that particular combination. Any group of animals, however small, having such distinct characters, should be regarded as a separate phylum until evidence shall be forthcoming showing its relationship to some other phylum. The classification of animals should be based primarily on anatomical and embryological facts, and a number of important characters, not any one arbitrarily chosen feature, should be taken simultaneously into consideration. Some important characters are: general grade of construction, type of symmetry, presence and kinds of body space, absence or presence of an anus, presence of segmentation, possession of appendages, presence and nature of excretory, respiratory, and endoskeletal systems. On this basis we classify the animal kingdom as follows, into 22 phyla.

I. Subkingdom Protozoa: acellular animals.   **Phylum Protozoa**
II. Subkingdom Metazoa: cellular animals, composed of cells, which may lose their boundaries in the adult state.
   Branch *A*. Mesozoa. Cellular animals having the structure of a stereoblastula composed of a surface layer of somatic cells and interior reproductive cells.   **Phylum Mesozoa**

Branch *B*. Parazoa. Animals of the cellular grade of construction with incipient tissue formation, interior cells of several different kinds, without organ systems, digestive tract, or mouth; porous with one to many internal cavities lined by choanocytes.

Phylum **Porifera,** the sponges

Branch *C*. Eumetazoa. Animals of the tissue or organ-system grade of construction, with mouth and digestive tract (except when lost by parasitic degeneration), interior cells reproductive only in part, not porous, without body spaces lined by choanocytes.

Grade I. Radiata. Eumetazoa with primary radial symmetry, of the tissue grade of construction with incipient organ systems, incipient mesoderm mesenchymal in nature and mostly of ectodermal origin, digestive cavity the sole body space, no anus.

A. Symmetry radial, biradial, or radio-bilateral, mouth usually encircled by tentacles armed with nematocysts, no rows of ciliated plates.

Phylum **Cnidaria,** the coelenterates

B. Symmetry biradial, tentacles when present not encircling the mouth, no nematocysts, eight radial rows of ciliated swimming plates.

Phylum **Ctenophora,** the comb jellies

Grade II. Bilateria. Eumetazoa with bilateral symmetry or secondary radial symmetry, of the organ-system grade of construction, mostly with a well-developed mesoderm of entodermal origin, mostly with body spaces other than the digestive cavity, anus generally present.

A. Acoelomate animals, region between digestive tract and body wall filled with mesenchyme, excretory system of protonephridia with flame bulbs, unsegmented or, if segmented, youngest segments nearest the head.

1. Anus absent. Phylum **Platyhelminthes,** the flatworms

2. Anus present; eversible proboscis in hollow sheath above the digestive tract. Phylum **Nemertinea,** the nemertine worms

B. Pseudocoelomate animals, space present between digestive tract and body wall but this space is a pseudocoel (remnant of the blastocoel) and not a coelom, anus present, with or without protonephridia, flame bulbs present or not.

1. Intestine looped, bringing anus near mouth, mouth and anus encircled by a circlet of ciliated tentacles. Phylum **Entoprocta**

2. Intestine more or less straight, anus posterior, no anterior ciliated projections except in a few rotifers. Phylum **Aschelminthes** (includes the Classes Rotifera, Gastrotricha, Kinorhyncha, Nematoda, Nematomorpha, and Acanthocephala)

C. Coelomate animals, with a true coelom and usually well-developed entomesoderm, excretory organs are protonephridia with solenocytes or metanephridia with or without nephrostomes, anus present

1. With a circular or crescentic or double spirally coiled ridge, the lophophore, bearing ciliated tentacles; intestine looped, bringing mouth near anus, coelom various.

   a. Colonial with gelatinous, chitinous, or calcareous encasements; no nephridia or circulatory system.

   Phylum **Bryozoa** (Ectoprocta) or **Polyzoa,** the moss animals

   b. Solitary with one pair of metanephridia, and closed circulatory system.

   a′. Worm-like.   Phylum **Phoronida**

   b′. With a bivalve shell.

   Phylum **Brachiopoda,** the lamp shells

2. Without a lophophore; coelom a schizocoel.

   a. Unsegmented.

   a′. Visceral mass covered by a body fold, the mantle, which secretes a calcareous shell of one or more pieces, coelom usually reduced.   Phylum **Mollusca,** the mollusks

   b′. Without a mantle, naked, worm-like, coelom spacious.

   a″. With an eversible proboscis,

   a‴. Anus dorsal.   Phylum **Sipunculoidea**

   b‴. Anus posterior, terminal.

   Phylum **Priapuloidea**

   b″. No eversible proboscis, mouth ventral.

   Phylum **Echiuroidea**

   b. Segmented.

   a′. Without jointed appendages.

   Phylum **Annelida,** the segmented worms

   b′. With segmented appendages.

   Phylum **Arthropoda,** the arthropods

3. Without a lophophore, coelom an enterocoel.

   a. With secondary, usually pentamerous, radial symmetry, with a water vascular system.   Phylum **Echinodermata,** the echinoderms

   b. Bilateral symmetry retained throughout life.

   a′. Without gill slits or endoskeleton.

   Phylum **Chaetognatha,** the arrow worms

   b′. With gill slits or endoskeleton or both.

   a″. Without typical notochord in adult or embryonic stage.   Phylum **Hemichordata** or **Branchiotremata**

   b″. Embryo with notochord, adults with gill slits or vertebral column or both.   Phylum **Chordata**

It is not expected that the foregoing scheme will meet the approval of all zoologists, but the author believes it represents a considerable improvement on the standard arrangements found in many tests.

Probably many zoologists will object to the position here accorded the Mesozoa. In the absence, however, of any knowledge of the sexual stages of the dicyemids (which presumably exist) it seems best to judge them on the basis of their structural grade, which is unlike that of any other Metazoa and does not justify their inclusion in any other phylum or grouping of phyla. The position of sponges as a separate branch of Metazoa is well recognized. The division of the remaining Metazoa into radiate and bilateral grades appears to the author sound and preferable to the conception of diploblastic and triploblastic grades, which is here abandoned for reasons explained in later chapters. Among the Bilateria, three grades of structure are recognized, following Schimkevitch (1891), namely, the *acoelomate, pseudocoelomate,* and *eucoelomate* types. Such a division stands firmly on a realistic anatomical basis and eschews all theoretical vaporizings such as the alleged degradation of flatworms from annelids, the coelomic nature of the gonad cavities, and similar ideas.

The separation of the nemertines from the flatworms will probably be generally conceded. The absolute necessity of detaching the entoprocts from the typical bryozoans has not been generally recognized but must be admitted by anyone who studies their structure critically. They belong among the groups of animals in which a false coelom or pseudocoel separates the intestine from the body wall; the body wall consists of cuticle and epithelium and lacks the muscle layers and peritoneal lining characteristic of true coelomate animals. The digestive tract also is purely epithelial, devoid of muscle layers and visceral peritoneum. These pseudocoelomate forms are here arranged into two phyla, the Entoprocta and the Aschelminthes. Other names have been suggested as a phylum term for the entoproct bryozoans, as Calyssozoa by A. H. Clark (1921), and Kamptozoa by Cori in Kükenthal-Krumbach's *Handbuch der Zoologie.* However, there seems no objection to raising the original name Entoprocta to the rank of a phylum; the name originated with Nitsche (1870) and was already used as a phylum name by Hatschek (1888) (see above).

The Entoprocta are set off from the remaining pseudocoelomate groups by their possession of a crown of ciliated tentacles encircling the oral and anal openings. The other pseudocoelomate forms are here united under the name Aschelminthes, proposed by Grobben in 1908. This phylum comprises the classes Rotifera, Gastrotricha, Kinorhyncha (Echinoderida), Nematoda, Nematomorpha (Gordiacea), and Acanthocephala. The alternative would be to raise each of these groups to the rank of a phylum and this procedure has been followed in some recent texts. There is no special objection to such an arrangement, but study of these groups has convinced the author that they are interrelated, with the possible exception of the Acanthocephala, whose position remains uncertain.   The arrangement found in Parker and Haswell's *Textbook of Zoology* and copied widely, in which the nematodes, gordiaceans, acanthocephalans, and echinoderids are united under the name Nemathelminthes, and the rotifers and gastrotrichs under the name Trochelminthes is inadmissible, because the gastrotrichs are no more closely related to the rotifers than they are to the nematodes.   The inclusion of chaetognaths in this mixture is wholly out of the question since the chaetognaths are coelomate animals allied to the groups which culminate in the vertebrates.

The acoelomate and pseudocoelomate Bilateria are characterized by the presence of a nephridial system of the *protonephridial* type.   This means that the terminal fine twigs of the excretory system are closed by an apparatus commonly called a flame cell.   As this apparatus is not infrequently multicellular or even formed of only a part of a cell, the expression flame cell is a misnomer and is here replaced by the name *terminal flame bulb*.   Flame bulbs occur in the Platyhelminthes, Nemertinea, Rotifera, the fresh-water Gastrotricha, the Kinorhyncha, the Acanthocephala, and the Entoprocta.

The remaining Bilateria have a true coelom that arises embryologically by two general methods, the *schizocoelous* and the *enterocoelous*. In the former, the coelom originates as a space in the mesoderm; in the latter it forms as pouches from the embryonic gut.   The schizocoelous forms appear to be related to the acoelomate and pseudocoelomate groups and constitute with them the Protostomia; whereas the enterocoelous Bilateria, constituting the Deuterostomia, occupy a somewhat isolated position.

Among the coelomate animals, the groups Bryozoa (ectoprocts only), Phoronida, and Brachiopoda have given constant difficulty.   Their possession of a lophophore sets them apart from the other Eucoelomata. In many texts, these three groups are united under the name Molluscoidea or better Tentaculata; or the Brachiopoda are separated as a phylum and only the ectoprocts and phoronids retained under the name Tentaculata. It seems best here to regard all three as separate phyla.   They are usually placed among the schizocoelous Eucoelomata although in fact the coelom of brachiopods arises by the enterocoelous method.

The groups Sipunculoidea, Priapuloidea, and Echiuroidea also remain of uncertain status.   The alternative to considering them separate phyla is to append them to the Annelida.

Following the precedent of several German authorities, the Hemichordata are removed from the Chordata and placed among the enterocoelous invertebrates.   With this change it would be desirable to revert to the name Chordonia for the remaining groups of chordates

(Cephalochordata, Tunicata, and Vertebrata), as used by Hatschek (page 30).

The nephridial system of the coelomate invertebrates is of the *metanephridial* type, i.e., the nephridial tubules begin as coelomic openings. Protonephridia occur only in some polychaetes and these differ from those of noncoelomate Bilateria in that the tubule ends are closed by solenocytes. Solenocytes are very elongated cells having a flagellum as the current-producing mechanism instead of the ciliary tuft found in the flame bulbs. It is an inexplicable fact that solenocytes also occur in Amphioxus.

The arrangement of the animal phyla here proposed may for convenient reference then be tabulated as follows, using for the subdivisions of the Bilateria, Schimkevitch's terms (1891), Acoelomata, Pseudocoelomata, and Eucoelomata, and subdividing the last by means of T. H. Huxley's names (1875) Schizocoela and Enterocoela.

    I. Subkingdom Protozoa
         Phylum **Protozoa**
   II. Subkingdom Metazoa
        Branch *A*. Mesozoa
         Phylum **Mesozoa**
        Branch *B*. Parazoa
         Phylum **Porifera** or **Spongiaria**
        Branch *C*. Eumetazoa
         Grade I. Radiata
           Phylum **Cnidaria** or **Coelenterata**
           Phylum **Ctenophora**
         Grade II. Bilateria
          A. Acoelomata
             Phylum **Platyhelminthes**
             Phylum **Rhynchocoela** or **Nemertinea**
          B. Pseudocoelomata
             Phylum **Aschelminthes**
             Phylum **Entoprocta**
          C. Eucoelomata
            1. Schizocoela
              Phylum **Bryozoa** or **Polyzoa**
              Phylum **Phoronida**
              Phylum **Brachiopoda**
              Phylum **Mollusca**
              Phylum **Sipunculoidea**
              Phylum **Priapuloidea**
              Phylum **Echiuroidea**

Phylum **Annelida**
Phylum **Arthropoda**
2. Enterocoela
Phylum **Chaetognatha**
Phylum **Echinodermata**
Phylum **Hemichordata**
Phylum **Chordata**

The order of treatment of the phyla in a text may either follow current phylogenetic ideas or be based on grade of structure. When the

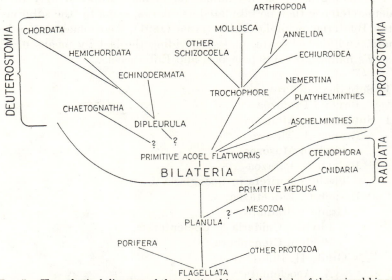

Fig. 5.—Hypothetical diagram of the relationships of the phyla of the animal kingdom. The radiate phyla are considered a side line, not in the direct ancestry of the Bilateria, which are postulated to come from a primitive flatworm by way of a stereogastrula type of ancestor. Above the ancestral flatworm, the phyla are arranged in two main lines of ascent (diphyletic theory), the groups with determinate cleavage and mesoderm originating from definite cells or bands (Protostomia) and the groups with indeterminate cleavage and mesoderm and coelom arising as entodermal sacs (Deuterostomia). (*Original, embodying some suggestions from Prof. W. K. Fisher.*)

first plan is adopted, the Protostomia, culminating in the mollusks and the arthropods, are treated first and then the Deuterostomia, terminating in the vertebrates. This method has the disadvantage that animals of relatively low grade of organization follow highly advanced groups. Furthermore, in an invertebrate text, in which the Chordata are not treated, the work would terminate with minor groups. For these reasons we prefer to arrange the phyla in the general order of their structural complexity. This plan meets with the difficulty of estimating the relative structural rank of the various phyla. Although some groups of animals are obviously "higher," i.e., structurally more complex, than others, many groups are difficult to evaluate, for they may rank high in some organ systems, low in others. If animals had evolved in a straight line, they could be arranged in a linear series of increasing complexity of structure, and each group would be higher than the preceding one. But all the evidence indicates that groups evolve by branching from preceding groups so that the animal kingdom must be graphed not as a line but as a branching tree. As a result, many branches are about on the same level, although anatomically different, and cannot be serially arranged. Thus no one would doubt that a lobster is higher, more complicated morphologically, than an earthworm, but who can decide the relative rank of a lobster and an octopus? One can only regard them as high members of their own particular branches of the evolutionary tree.

In this work we shall attempt to arrange the phyla in general according to their grade of construction while at the same time avoiding the separation of allied phyla. On this basis the bilateral groups will be treated in the following order: acoelomate phyla, pseudocoelomate phyla, enterocoelous phyla (omitting Chordata, which is not considered at all), and schizocoelous phyla.

The accompanying diagram (Fig. 5) attempts to depict the relationships of the animal phyla in accordance with the foregoing remarks and with the discussion to be presented in later chapters. Such a diagram like all phylogenetic schemes is not to be taken literally but to be regarded merely as suggestive.

Bibliography

History of Classification

Allmann, G. J. 1856. Monograph of the fresh-water Polyzoa. Ray Soc. **Bateson, W.** 1885. Development of Balanoglossus and the affinities of the Enteropneusta. Roy. Soc. London, Proc. 38, Quart. Jour. Micros. Sci. 25. **Clark, A. H.** 1921. A new classification of animals. Inst. Oceanogr. Monaco, Bul. 400. **Claus, C.** 1868. Grundzüge der Zoologie. **Claus-Grobben.** 1910. Lehrbuch der Zoologie, 2d ed. **Cohn, F.** 1853. Beiträge zur Entwicklungsgeschichte der Infusorien. Ztschr. Wiss. Zool. 4. **Cuvier, G.** 1816. Le règne animal distribué d'après son organisation. 1829. 2d ed. **De Blainville, M.** 1816. Prodrome d'une nouvelle distribution systématique du règne animal. Jour. Phys. Chem. Hist. Natur. 83. 1828. Articles Vers, Zoophytes in Dictionnaire des Sciences Naturelles 57, 60. **Dujardin, F.** 1841. Histoire naturelle des Zoophytes. 1845. Histoire naturelle des Helminthes ou Vers Intestinaux. 1851. Sur un petit animal marin, l'Echinodère. Ann. Sci. Nat. ser. 3, vol. 15. **Dutrochet, R.** 1812. Recherches sur les Rotifères. Ann. Museum Hist. Nat. Paris, 19, 20. **Ehlers, E.** 1864. Die Borstenwürmer. **Ehrenberg, C. G.** 1835. Über die Akalephen des rothen Meeres. Abhandl. König. Akad. Wiss. Berlin. 1838. Die Infusorienthierchen als volkommene Organismen. **Gegenbaur, C.** 1859. Grundzüge der vergleichenden Anatomie. 1870. 2d ed. **Goldfuss, G. A.** 1817. Ueber die Klassification der Zoophyten. 1820. Handbuch der Zoologie. **Grobben, K.** 1908. Die systematische Einteilung des Tierreiches. Verhandl. König. Zool. Bot. Gesell. Wien. 58. **Haeckel, E.** 1874. Die Gastraea-Theorie. Jenaische Ztschr. Naturw. 8. 1874. Anthropogenie oder Entwicklungsgeschichte des Menschen. **Hatschek, B.** 1888. Lehrbuch der Zoologie. 1911. Das neue zoologisches System. **Hesse, R.** 1929. Die Stufenleiter der Organisationshöhe der Tiere. Sitz. Preuss. Akad. Wiss. Berlin. Bericht über "Das Tierreich." Sitz. Preuss. Akad. Wiss. Berlin. **Hincks, T.** 1880. History of British marine Polyzoa. **Huxley, T. H.** 1853. Morphology of the cephalous Mollusca. Roy. Soc. London, Phil. Trans., 143. 1864. Lectures on the elements of comparative anatomy. 1875. The classification of animals. Quart. Jour. Micros. Sci. 15. **Heider, C.** 1885. Metamorphose der Oscarella. Arbeit. Zool. Inst. Univ., Wien. **International Rules of Zoological Nomenclature.** Proc. 10th Internatl. Congr. Zool. Budapest, part 2. **Lamarck, J. B. P. A.** 1802. Recherches sur les corps vivants. 1809. Philosophie Zoologique. 1815–1816. Histoire naturelle des animaux sans vertèbres. **Lankester, E. R.** 1877. Tabular view of the phyla of the animal kingdom. Quart. Jour. Micros. Sci. 17. 1900. The Enterocoela and the Coelomocoela. Treatise on zoology, part II. **Leuckart, R.** 1848. Über die Morphologie und die Verwandtschaftsverhältnisse der wirbellosen Tiere. **Linnaeus, C.** 1758. Systema naturae, 10th ed. **Metschnikoff, E.** 1865. Ueber einige wenig bekannte nieder Thierformen (Gastrotricha). Ztschr. Wiss. Zool. 15. 1881. Über die systematische Stellung von Balanoglossus. Zool. Anz. 4. **Milne-Edwards, H.** 1837. Éléments de Zoologie. **Müller, O. F.** 1773. Vermium terrestrium et fluviatilium seu Animalium Infusorium, etc. **Nitsche, H.** 1870. Beiträge zur Kenntnis der Bryozoen. Ztschr. Wiss. Zool. 20. **Perty, M.** 1852. Zur Kenntnis kleinster Lebensform. **Poche, F.** 1911. Klassen und höheren Gruppen des Tierreichs. Arch. Naturgesch. 77, Sup. 1. **Quatrefages, A.** 1847. Mémoire sur l'echiure. Ann. Sci. Nat. ser. 3, vol. 7. **Rudolphi, K. A.** 1819. Entozoorum Synopsis. **Savigny, M. J. C. L.** 1809. Système des Annelides. 1816. Mémoires sur les animaux sans vertèbres. **Schimkewitsch, W.** 1891. Versuch einer Klassification des Tierreiches. Biol. Zentbl. 11. **Schneider, A.** 1864. Über die Muskeln der Würmer und ihre Bedeutung für das System. Arch. Anat. Physiol. Wiss. Med. 1866. Monographie der Nematoden. **Schneider, K. S.** 1912. Zur Theorie des Systems. Festschr. 60th Geburtstag J. W. Spengel, Zool. Jahrb. Sup. 15, vol. 3. **Siebold, Th. von.** 1845. Lehrbuch der vergleichenden Anatomie der wirbellosen Thiere. **Sollas, W.** 1884. Development of Halisarca. Quar. Jour. Micros. Sci. 24. **Vogt, C.** 1851. Zoologische Briefe, Vol. I.

GENERAL WORKS AND ARTICLES ON INVERTEBRATES

Arndt, W. 1922. Lipoide und Lipoid Stoffwechsel der Evertebraten. Verh. Deut. Zool. Gesell. **Bethe, A.** 1903. Allgemeine Anatomie und Physiologie des Nervensystems. **Bethe, Bergmann, Embden, and Ellinger.** (eds.) 1925–1932. Handbuch der normalen und pathologischen Physiologie. 27 vols. **Block, R. J.,** and **D. Bolling.** 1939. The amino acid composition of keratins. Jour. Biol. Chem. 127. **Bock, F.,** and **F. Wetter.** 1938. Über die bei einiger Avertebraten vorkommenden antirachitischen Provitamine. Ztschr. Physiol. Chem. 256. **Bock, S.** (ed.). 1923. Further zoological results of the Swedish Antarctic Expedition 1901–1903. **Brand, T.** 1934. Das Leben ohne Sauerstoff bei wirbellosen Tieren. Ergeb. Biol. 10. **Brandt, K.,** and **Apstein, C.** (eds.). 1901. Nordisches Plankton. **Brauer, A.** (ed.). 1909. Die Süsswasser Fauna Deutschlands. **Brohmer, P., P. Ehrmann, and**

G. Ulmer (eds.). 1928. Die Tierwelt Mitteleuropas. **Bronn, H. G.** (ed.). 1880—
Klassen und Ordnungen des Tierreichs. **Buddenbrocks, W.** 1928. Grundriss der
vergleichenden Physiologie. **Bütschli, O.** 1910–1931. Vorlesungen über ver-
gleichende Anatomie. **The Cambridge Natural History.** 1895–1909. Vols. I–VI.
Caroyon, G., and **J. Gautrelet.** 1938. Présence de la choline chez les invertébrés.
Soc. Biol. [Paris], Compt. Rend. 127. **Chun, C.** (ed.). 1902– . Wissenschaftliche
Ergebnisse der deutsch. Tiefsee Expedition auf dem "Valdivia" 1898–99. **Clarke,
F. W.,** and **W. H. Wheeler.** 1922. Inorganic constituents of marine invertebrates.
U. S. Geol. Survey, Prof. Paper 124. **Coe, W. R.,** and **W. E. Allen.** 1937. Growth
of sedentary marine organisms on experimental blocks and plates. Bul. Scripps Inst.
Oceanogr. Tech. Ser. 4. **Dahl, F.** (ed.). 1925— Das Tierwelt Deutschlands und der
angrenzenden Meersteile. **Danish Ingolf Expedition.** 1899– . **Delage, Y.,** et **E.
Herouard.** 1896–1903. Traité de zoologie concrète. **Dawydoff, C.** 1928. Traité
d'embryologie comparée des invertébrés. **Delaunay, H.** 1931. L'excrétion azotée
des invertébrés. Biol. Rev. Cambridge Phil. Soc. 6. 1934. Le métabolisme de
l'ammoniaque d'après les recherches relatives aux invertébrés. Ann. Physiol.
Physicochem. Biol. 10. **Drygalski, E.** von. (ed.). 1908–1931. Deutsche Südpolar
Expedition, 1901–1903. Zool. vols. 9–20. **Duggar, B. M.** (ed.). 1936. Biological
effects of radiation. **Erhardt, A.** 1932. Die Verwandtschaftsbestimmungen
mittels der Immunitätsreaktionen in der Zoologie. Ergeb. Fortschr. Zool. 7. **Faune
de France.** 1921. **Florkin, M.,** and **H. F. Blum.** 1934. Sur la teneur en protéins
du sang et du liquide coelomique des invertébrés. Arch. Internatl. Physiol. 38.
Fortuyn, A. B. D. 1920. Vergleichende Anatomie des Nervensystems. I. Teil. Die
Leitungsbahnen in Nervensystem der wirbellosen Tiere. **Fosse, R.** 1913. Presence
de l'urée chez les invertébrés et dans leurs produits d'excrétion. Acad. Sci. Compt.
Rend. 157. **Fraenkel, G.** 1931. Die Mechanik der Orientierung der Tiere im
Raum. **Fürth, O.** von. 1903. Vergleichende chemische Physiologie der niederen
Tiere. **Great Barrier Reef Expedition,** 1928–1929. Scientific Rpts. 1930— **Grimpe,
G.,** and **E. Wagler** (eds.). 1925– . Die Tierwelt der Nord- und Ostsee. **Hand-
wörterbuch der Naturwissenschaften.** 2d ed. 1930. **Hanström, B.** 1925. Augen
und Sehzentren von Turbellarien, Anneliden, und Arthropoden. Kungl. Svenska
Vetensk. Handl. 4. 1938. Some points on the phylogeny of nerve cells and of the
central nervous system of invertebrates. Jour. Compar. Neurol. 46. 1928. Ver-
gleichende Anatomie des Nervensystems der wirbellosen Tiere. 1937. Inkretorische
Organe und Hormonenfunktionen bei den Wirbellosen. Ergeb. Biol. 14. **Harvey,
E. N.** 1920. Nature of Animal Light. **Haughton, I.** 1934. Amoebocytes and
allied cells in invertebrates. Roy. Micros. Soc. Jour. 54. **Heidermanns, C.** 1938.
Der Exkretstoffwechsel der wirbellosen Tiere. Naturwissenschaften 17, 18. **Heil-
brunn, L. V.** 1937. Outline of general physiology. **Hesse, R.** (transl. and ed. by
W. C. Allee and **K. P. Schmidt**). 1937. Ecological animal geography. **Huxley, J.,**
and **J. R. De Beer.** 1934. The elements of experimental embryology. **Jordan, H.**
1921. Die Leberfrage bei der wirbellosen Tiere. Zool. Jahrb. Sup. 15. 1926.
Physiologie des Nervenmuskelsystems bei den niederen Wirbellosen. Verhandl.
Deut. Zool. Gesell. 31. 1929. Allgemeine vergleichende Physiologie der Tiere.
Kappers, C. U. A. 1929. The evolution of the nervous system in invertebrate,
vertebrate, and man. **Koller, G.** 1929. Die innere Sekretion bei wirbellosen
Tieren. Biol. Rev., Cambridge Phil. Soc. 4. 1938. Hormone bei wirbellosen
Tieren. Problem der Biologie I. **Kollmann, M.** 1908. Recherches sur les leuco-
cytes et le tissue lymphoide des invertébrés. Ann. Sci. Nat., ser. 9, vol. 8. **Korschelt,
E.** 1927–1931. Regeneration und Transplantation. und **Heider, K.** 1890–1910.
Lehrbuch der vergleichenden Entwicklungsgeschichte der wirbellosen Tiere. (part

transl. into English as a textbook of comparative invertebrate embryology). **1936.** Vergleichende Entwicklungsgeschichte der Tiere. 2 vols. **Krüger, P.** 1929. Über die Verdauungsfermente der Wirbellosen. Sitzb. Preuss. Akad. Wissensch. Berlin. physik. math. Kl. **Kuhn, A.** 1919. Die Orientierung der Tiere im Raum. 1921. Morphologie der Tiere in Bildern. **Kükenthal, W.** und **Krumbach, T.** (eds.). 1923— Handbuch der Zoologie. **Kunike, G.** 1925. Nachweis und Verbreitung organischer Skeletsubstanzen bei Tieren. Ztschr. Vergleich. Physiol. 2. **Lang, A.** 1912— Handbuch der Morphologie der wirbellosen Tiere. 2–3d ed. (never completed). **Lankester, E. Ray** (ed.). 1900–1909. A treatise on zoology (never completed). **Lönnberg, E.** 1931. Vorkommen carotinoider Stoffe bei marinen Evertebraten. Arkiv Zool. 22 A. 1934. Presence of carotinoids in the "liver" organs of invertebrates. Arkiv Zool. 28 A. **MacBride, E. W.** 1914. Textbook of embryology. I. Invertebrata. **Martin, C. H.** 1914. Occurrence of nematocysts and similar structures in the various groups of the animal kingdom. Biol. Zentbl. 34. **Meisenheimer, J.** 1910. Die Exkretionsorgane der wirbellosen Tiere. Ergeb. Zool. 2. **Mitchell, P. H.** 1938. A textbook of general physiology. **Morgan, T. H.** 1927. Experimental embryology. **Murray, J., and H. Hjort.** 1910. Scientific Results of the "Michael Sars" North Atlantic Deep Sea Expedition 1910. **Myers, R. G.** 1920. Chemical study of the blood of several invertebrate animals. Jour. Biol. Chem. 41, 42. **Needham, J.** 1931. Chemical embryology. 3 vols. **Nordenskjöld, O.** (ed.) 1908–1920. Wissenschaftliche Ergebnisse der Schwedischen Südpolar Expedition. 1901–1903. **Nowikoff, M.** 1912. Das Knorpelgewebe von Wirbellosen. Ztschr. Wiss. Zool. 103. **Ohuye, T.** 1937. Coelomic corpuscles in the body fluid of some invertebrates. Tohoku Imp. Univ., Science Rpts., ser. 4, Biology, 11, 12, 13. **Oppenheimer, Carl.** 1925– . Handbuch der Biochemie des Menschen und der Tiere. 2d ed. **Plate, L.** 1922. Allgemeine Zoologie und Abstammungslehre (incomplete). **Pratje, A.** 1923. Das Leuchten der Organismen. Ergeb. Physiol. 21, pt. 1. **Przibram, H.** 1925. Transplantation and regeneration, their bearing on developmental mechanics. Brit. Jour. Expt. Biol. 3. **Przylicki, S. J.** 1922. L'excrétion ammoniacale chez les invertébrés. Arch. Internatl. Physiol. 20, 27. **Redfield, A. C.** 1934. The haemocyanins. Biol. Rev., Cambridge Phil. Soc. 9. **Roche, J.** 1936. Essai sur le biochemie générale et comparée des pigments respiratoires. **Rogers, C. G.** 1927. Textbook of comparative physiology. **Römer, F., and F. Schaudinn.** 1900. Fauna Arctica. **Schaffer, J.** 1901–1911. Über den feineren Bau und die Entwicklung des Knorpelgewebes. Ztschr. Wiss. Zool. 70, 80, 97. **Schindewolf, O. H.** (ed.). 1938. Handbuch der Paläozoologie. **Schleip, W.** 1929. Die Determination der Primitiventwicklung. **Schmidt, J.** (ed.). 1912. Danish oceanographical expeditions 1908–1910 to the Mediterranean and adjacent seas. **Schneider, K. C.** 1902. Lehrbuch der vergleichenden Histologie der Tiere. **Scholles, W.** 1933. Mineralregulation wasserlebenden Evertebraten. Zeitsch. Vergleich. Physiol. 19. **Schulze, P.** (ed.). 1912. Biologie der Tiere Deutschlands. **Sulina, A.** 1914. Harnsäurestoffwechsels niederer Tiere. Ztschr. Biol. 63. **Tabulae Biologicae.** 1925. **Das Tierreich.** 1897– . **Ten Cate, J.** 1931. Physiologie der Gangliensysteme der Wirbellosen. Ergeb. Physiol. 33. **Thomson, C. W., and J. Murray.** 1880–1889. Report on the scientific results of the voyage of H.M.S. Challenger during the years 1873–1876, Zoology. Vol. I–XXXII. **Tressler, D. K.** 1923. Marine products of commerce. **Truszkowski, R., and S. Chajkinanna.** 1935. Nitrogen metabolism of certain invertebrates. Biochem. Jour. 29. **Twenhofel, W. H., and R. R. Shrock.** 1935. Invertebrate Palaeontology. **Varga, L.** 1933. Wandelung und heutiger Stand der Pütter'schen Theorie. Arch. Hydrobiol. Planktonkunde 26. **Vonk, H. J.** 1937. Specificity and collaboration of digestive enzymes in Metazoa. Biol. Rev.,

Cambridge Phil. Soc. 12. **Ward, H.,** and **G. C. Whipple** (eds.). 1917. Fresh water biology. **Weber, M.,** and **L. F. de Beaufort.** (eds.). 1902– . Siboge Expédite aux Indes Néerlandaises orientales, 1899–1900. **Welsh, P.** 1935. Limnology. **Wester, D. H.** 1910. Verbreitung und Lokalization des Chitins im Tierreich. Zool. Jahrb., Abt. System. 28. **Winterstein, H.** (ed.). 1910–1915. Handbuch der vergleichenden Physiologie. **Woods, Henry.** 1926. Paleontology. **Yonge, C. M.** 1928. Feeding mechanisms in the invertebrates. Biol. Rev., Cambridge Phil. Soc. 3. 1937. Evolution and adaptation in the digestive system of Metazoa. Biol. Rev., Cambridge Phil. Soc. 12. 1938. Recent work on the digestion of cellulose and chitin by invertebrates. Sci. Prog. 32. **Zittel, K. A.** 1924. Grundzüge der Palaeontologie. I. Invertebrata.

CHAPTER III

THE ACELLULAR ANIMALS—PHYLUM PROTOZOA

I. CHARACTERS OF THE PHYLUM

1. Introduction.—The study of the invertebrates begins with the Protozoa, animals that are usually defined as consisting of a single cell. This point of view, inherited from the heyday of the dominance of the cell theory in the conception of organisms, which were regarded as aggregations of cells, is not only without advantage but conveys an erroneous impression. The Protozoa are not loose cells moving about but complete organisms that may be of more complicated construction than the simplest Metazoa. We therefore prefer to refer to the Protozoa as *acellular*, rather than as unicellular, animals, that is, as animals whose body substance is not partitioned into cells.

The Protozoa were naturally not seen until after the invention of the microscope (date uncertain, possibly as early as 1590). Many different sorts were observed and described by Leeuwenhoek in 1676 from standing rain water, etc. They and other microscopic animals were called simply animalcules until Ledermüller (1760–63) suggested the name Infusoria because of the occurrence of such forms in infusions. O. F. Müller (1773) included under the name Animalcula Infusoria protozoans, nematodes, rotifers, and bryozoans. An improvement was made by Lamarck (1809) who embraced under the name Infusoria protozoans and rotifers, and Cuvier's Infusoires, a subdivision of Radiata, had the same significance. The higher organization of the rotifers was recognized by Dutrochet in 1812, but it was not until after Ehrenberg's work in 1838 that the rotifers were separated from protozoans although Ehrenberg himself regarded both groups as classes of Infusoria. Ehrenberg called the protozoans Polygastrica under the belief that the food vacuoles were a series of stomachs and maintained that they are complex animals. This idea was successfully combated in the 1840's, first by Dujardin (1841), who recognized the lowly nature of the shelled Protozoa, previously considered mollusks, and created for them the term Rhizopoda.

The name Protozoa (Greek, *protos*, first, *zoon*, animal) comes from Goldfuss (1818), who, however, used this name simply for the lower groups of Cuvier's Zoophyta, including protozoans, sponges, coelenterates, rotifers, and bryozoans. Goldfuss did at least recognize several grades of structure in Cuvier's assemblage. The morphology of the Protozoa could not of course be understood until the discovery of cells in 1839. It was von Siebold (1845) who, recognizing the unicellular nature of the Protozoa, first used and defined the name Protozoa in the present sense. Accepting Dujardin's work, von Siebold divided the Protozoa into the two classes Infusoria and Rhizopoda, the former including both ciliates and flagellates. The ciliated forms were separated off as Ciliata by Perty in 1852 and the flagellated ones as Flagellata by Cohn in 1853. Finally the class Sporozoa was erected by Leuckart in 1879 for the spore-forming parasitic members.

The phylum is consequently to be termed Protozoa after von Siebold. The name Infusoria should clearly be abandoned and should not be used as synonymous with

44

Ciliata. No grounds are apparent for the rejection of Cohn's Flagellata in favor of the later name Mastigophora (Diesing, 1866).

2. Definition.—The Protozoa are acellular animals without tissues or organs, existing singly or in colonies of a few to many individuals; such colonies differ from a metazoan in that their components are all alike except when engaged in reproductive activities.[1]

3. Other Characters.—The Protozoa, being acellular, necessarily lack tissues and organs, since these are defined as aggregations of differentiated cells. Although in some Protozoa all the functions of food catching, locomotion, and perception, transmission, and response to stimuli are performed directly by relatively undifferentiated protoplasm, in other cases a remarkable degree of functional differentiation is attained. Such differentiations in an acellular organism are called *organelles*, *organoids*, or *organites*. The organelles of Protozoa take the form of cilia and flagella for locomotion and food capture, various other food-catching devices, contractile fibrils for a variety of movements, surface differentiations and skeletal secretions for protection and to confer shape and rigidity, organelles of attachment in parasitic forms, a water-regulating mechanism (contractile vacuole), sensory structures such as photoreceptors and sensory bristles, and conductile fibrils for coordination. Respiratory differentiations are absent and the presence of an excretory mechanism is debatable. In general the organelles of Protozoa resemble the cell differentiations of multicellular animals. Reproduction is sexual or asexual. Asexual reproduction occurs by *fission, budding,* or *multiple division*. Sexual reproduction is widespread, and all degrees of difference between the two fusing sex cells are found. Many forms have complicated life histories, with alternation of sexual and asexual generations and some degree of embryonic development. The Protozoa are of small to minute size, usually microscopic. They are naked or provided with simple to elaborate encasements, shells, and skeletons. They occur throughout the earth in fresh and salt waters and damp places and as external and internal parasites of every group of animals. Each protozoan is to be regarded not as equivalent to a cell of a more complex animal but as a complete organism with the same properties and characteristics as cellular animals. Some of the colonial Protozoa are practically multicellular individuals.

The phylum is usually divided into four classes: Flagellata, Rhizopoda, Ciliata, and Sporozoa, although the last is admittedly somewhat heterogeneous. Whereas the Rhizopoda were formerly considered the most primitive Protozoa, their derivation from the Flagellata is now

---

[1] Exception, *Proterospongia* (see p. 107). Some degree of differentiation also exists among the individuals forming the colonies of some of the Volvocales (p. 105).

universally accepted, and the latter are consequently placed at the bottom of the animal kingdom.

II. CLASSIFICATION OF THE PHYLUM[1]

Subphylum I. Plasmodroma. Locomotor organelles either pseudopodia or flagella; with one or more like nuclei; sexual reproduction by the complete fusion of gametes; often with complicated life cycles.

Class I. Flagellata or Mastigophora, the flagellates. With one to many flagella as locomotor organelles throughout life or intermittently or in young stages.

Order 1. Chrysomonadina. Small, simple, often amoeboid forms with one or two flagella, one to several yellow or brown chromoplasts; gullet lacking; endogenous cyst formation.

Order 2. Cryptomonadina. Small, not amoeboid, with two flagella, usually with gullet, colorless or with chromoplasts.

Order 3. Dinoflagellata. With two, rarely one, flagella, one transverse, the other trailing, generally borne in grooves.

Suborder 1. Adinida. Two flagella, grooves absent, usually with a cellulose covering.

Suborder 2. Dinifera. With transverse and longitudinal grooves and flagella; naked or with an armor of cellulose plates.

Suborder 3. Cystoflagellata. Gelatinous globular or medusa-shaped forms with only the longitudinal groove and flagellum.

Order 4. Chloromonadina. With two flagella and numerous chloroplasts; no stigma; reserve product fat.

Order 5. Euglenoidina or Euglenida. Larger forms with gullet, stigma, one or two flagella, sometimes more; colorless or with green or brown chromoplasts; reserve product carbohydrates.

Order 6. Phytomonadina or Volvocales. Small, usually green, with stigma and one to eight, usually two, flagella; no mouth or gullet; single or forming flat or spherical swimming colonies.

Order 7. Protomonadina. Colorless, often amoeboid, with one to three flagella, without cuticle, mouth, or gullet; with parabasal body.

Order 8. Polymastigina. With two to six, generally four, flagella, one often trailing or forming the border of an undulating membrane; with parabasal body and axostyle; or with two to many duplications of a structural unit consisting of flagella, nucleus, parabasal body, and axostyle filament; mostly intestinal parasites.

Order 9. Hypermastigina. With numerous flagella and many parabasal bodies; intestinal parasites of termites and cockroaches.

Order 10. Rhizomastigina or Pantostomatida. Colorless, permanently amoeboid, with one flagellum.

Class II. Rhizopoda or Sarcodina, the rhizopods. Pseudopodia serve for locomotion and food catching; asexual reproduction usually by binary fission; mostly free living.

Order 1. Amoebozoa or Lobosa, the amoeboid rhizopods   Pseudopods relatively short, changing, not stiff or ray-like or anastomosing.

---

[1] The classification follows chiefly Doflein-Reichenow *Lehrbuch der Protozoenkunde.* The Protozoa are exceedingly difficult to classify because of the many transitional types and forms of uncertain relationship. It is impossible to erect exclusive definitions, and consequently the definitions center about typical members.

Suborder 1. Gymnamoebaea or Amoebina or Nuda, the naked Lobosa. Body naked or enclosed in a thin membrane; pseudopods arising at any point.

Suborder 2. Thecamoebaea or Testacea, the shelled Lobosa. Enclosed in a shell with one aperture through which alone the pseudopods protrude.

Order 2. Foraminifera. Pseudopods slender, often anastomosing; enclosed in a simple or chambered shell with one opening or pierced with numerous pores for the pseudopodia.

Order 3. Heliozoa, the sun animalcules. Spherical with stiff radiating pseudopods.

Order 4. Radiolaria. Protoplasm divided into inner and outer parts by a spherical porous membrane; pseudopods ray-like, stiff or streaming; usually with a skeleton.

Class III. Sporozoa. Internal parasites without contractile vacuoles; asexual reproduction mostly by multiple fission; transmitted by encysted or naked young produced by multiple fission of the zygote.

SUBCLASS I. TELOSPORIDIA. Zygote sporulating into naked or encysted young without polar capsules; usually with both schizogony and sporogony.

Order 1. Gregarinida, the gregarines. Zygote producing one walled spore containing eight sporozoites; with or without schizogony; usually extracellular when mature.

Order 2. Coccidia, the coccidians. Intracellular parasites, chiefly of epithelial cells; with alternation of schizogony and sporogony; zygote immotile producing one to many walled spores containing sporozoites.

Order 3. Haemosporidia. Parasitic in blood cells or blood system of vertebrates; with alternation of schizogony and sporogony; zygote motile, sporulating into naked sporozoites.

SUBCLASS II. CNIDOSPORIDIA. Amoeboid, spores with one or more polar capsules, hatching into amoeboid young.

Order 1. Myxosporidia. Spores with two valves and one, two, or four polar capsules; mostly in fish.

Order 2. Actinomyxidia. Spores three-rayed, with three valves and three polar capsules; parasitic in annelids.

Order 3. Microsporidia. Spore simple with one reduced polar capsule; intracellular in arthropods and fish.

SUBCLASS III. SARCOSPORIDIA. Amoeboid parasites in the muscles or connective tissue of higher vertebrates, forming large cysts filled with spores; spores naked without polar capsules.

Order 1. Sarcosporidia. Cyst wall wholly or partly of parasitic origin, spores crescentic.

Order 2. Globidia. Cyst wall of host origin, cysts found only in the intestinal submucosa; spores fusiform.

SUBCLASS IV. HAPLOSPORIDIA. Spores oval, without polar capsules, opening by a lid.

Subphylum II. Ciliophora. Locomotor organelles in the form of cilia throughout life or in young stages.

Class IV. Ciliata, the ciliates. Cilia present throughout life; life cycles simple.

SUBCLASS I. PROTOCILIATA. Mouthless, two to many like nuclei, without conjugation, intestinal parasites of amphibians.

SUBCLASS II. EUCILIATA. Free or parasitic, mouth usually present, nuclei usually of two different kinds, with conjugation.

Order 1. Holotricha. Without adoral zone; cilia over all or part of the body.

Suborder 1. Gymnostomata. Mouth at surface or in a pit, closable, without special cilia, often with trichites.

Suborder 2. Trichostomata. Mouth leading into a cytopharynx provided with special ciliary rows; not closable.

Suborder 3. Hymenostomata. Cytopharynx present, provided with one or more undulating membranes.

Suborder 4. Astomata. Mouthless, parasitic.

Suborder 5. Apostomea. Parasitic, life cycles complex.

Order 2. Spirotricha. With an adoral row of membranelles, beginning to the right of the peristome and passing around to the left.

Suborder 1. Heterotricha. Body clothed with short cilia mostly all over, limited in some cases.

Suborder 2. Oligotricha. Body naked or with a few large bristles.

Suborder 3. Hypotricha. Cilia confined to the ventral surface, generally in the form of cirri.

Order 3. Peritricha. Adoral row beginning to the left of the peristome and passing around to the right; no other cilia except one or more posterior girdles in some forms; mostly sessile, often colonial.

Order 4. Chonotricha. Cilia confined to the anterior end, not membranelles; anterior end funnel-like, mostly spirally coiled like a cornucopia; epizoic on crustacean gills.

Class V. Suctoria or **Acineta.** Cilia present only in young stages; adults without mouth, with tentacles, mostly sessile.

III. GENERAL MORPHOLOGY AND PHYSIOLOGY

1. Form and Size.—Although many rhizopods lack definite form except such as is conferred by the shell when present, most Protozoa exhibit a fixed shape and size characteristic for each species. A great variety of shapes occurs, but spherical, oval, and elongated forms, often more or less flattened, are most common. All types of animal symmetry are represented among the Protozoa. The lobose rhizopods and the Foraminifera are asymmetrical and anaxial; spherical symmetry obtains in the Heliozoa and Radiolaria; radial symmetry is noted in many sessile forms, as the choanoflagellates; but the majority display bilateral symmetry, generally imperfect, with definite anterior and posterior ends and dorsal and ventral surfaces. The anterior end is that one directed forward in locomotion; the ventral surface is arbitrarily defined as that which bears the mouth opening. Distinction between the two surfaces is most evident in the hypotrichous ciliates that crawl on the ventral surface (Fig. 55*C*).

The majority of the Protozoa are of small or microscopic size; they range from 2 or 3 micra (a micron is $\frac{1}{1000}$ mm.) to several centimeters in length or diameter. The largest Protozoa are found among the Radiolaria and Foraminifera, especially the latter, in which the shells may reach a diameter of 2 to 10 or 15 cm. Among fresh-water species, *Spirostomum ambiguum,* 4.5 mm. long, is notable for its size.

2. General Structure of the Cytosome.—The protozoan cytosome consists of a transparent, colorless or faintly tinted, viscous hyaloplasm or ground substance in which are imbedded numerous microsomes, and which commonly also contains fibrils, droplets, vacuoles, ergastic substances, plastids, and other elements enumerated in Chap. I. Although a few amoeboid forms appear to be structurally simple, specific organelles are differentiated in the majority of the Protozoa and serve specific functions.

The cytosome is commonly differentiated into a clear surface layer, the *ectoplasm,* and an inner mass, the *entoplasm* (or *endoplasm*) (Fig. 6). The ectoplasm is devoid or nearly so of granules, often shows a high degree of differentiation, and is probably a protein gel. Apparently the degree of ectoplasmic rigidity determines the body shape for when the ectoplasm is fluid the animal necessarily takes a spherical form whereas with a stiff surface, a variety of shapes can be maintained. The ectoplasmic surface may consist simply of the ectoplast (page 7) but usually is differentiated into a definite membrane, the *pellicle* or *periplast* (Fig. 6). This may be structureless or present spiral or longitudinal striations (Fig. 7A) or in connection with the insertion of cilia may exhibit alternating ridges and grooves (Fig. 55E) or a pattern of square, rhomboidal, or polygonal depressions bounded by ridges (Figs. 7B, C, 55A). In the ciliate *Blepharisma,* Nadler found that removal of the pellicle did not affect the shape or behavior of the animal; the pellicle was reformed. Thin, obviously lifeless, secreted membranes on the external surface of the ectoplasm are termed *cuticle.*

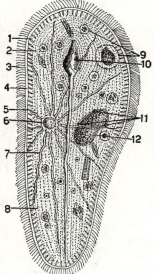

Fig. 6.—A protozoan, *Frontonia,* a holotrichous ciliate, viewed from the ventral surface. (*After Tönniges,* 1914.) 1, ectoplasm; 2, entoplasm; 3, cilia; 4, pellicle; 5, trichocysts; 6, contractile vacuole; 7, feeding canals of vacuole; 8, lines of attachment of cilia; 9, food vacuoles; 10, cytopharynx; 11, micronuclei; 12, macronucleus.

The chief locomotor organelles, the *cilia* and *flagella,* are filamentous projections of living ectoplasm which spring from granules, the *basal bodies* (Fig. 7C), embedded in the ectoplasm, and pierce the pellicle. The various granules and fibrils associated with cilia and flagella are considered later.

Beneath the pellicle the ectoplasm may show much differentiation, particularly in ciliates, where it contains the basal bodies of the cilia, various fibrils, and other structures such as *trichocysts* (Fig. 6, page 165).

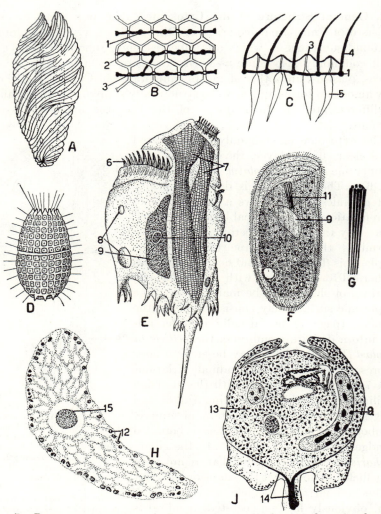

Fig. 7.—Protozoan structures. A. *Euglena ehrenbergii*, showing the striated pellicle separated from the body. (*After Hamburger*, 1911.) B. Surface view of the pellicle of *Paramecium multimicronucleatum*, showing the hexagonal depressions and beneath (in black) the basal bodies of the cilia connected by the interciliary fibrils. C. Section through the same, showing also the trichocysts attached to the sides of the hexagons. (*Both after E. E. Lund*, 1933.) D. The ciliate *Coleps* with an armor of small square plates in the ectoplasm. (*After Conn*, 1905.) E. *Ophryoscolex*, from the stomach of sheep, with two skeletal plates in the ectoplasm; these plates consist of a layer of prisms made of a cellulose-like material. (*After Dogiel*, 1927.) F. *Chilodonella* (= *Chilodon*), from life, with a circlet of trichites at the mouth. G. the trichites enlarged. H. The gregarine *Monocystis*, parasite of earthworms, after osmic acid treatment, showing the Golgi bodies. (*After Hirschler*, 1917.) J. A peritrichous ciliate, *Carchesium*, in longitudinal section, with mitochondria. (*After Fauré-Fremiet*, 1910.) 1, basal body; 2, interciliary fibril; 3, tip of trichocyst; 4, cilium; 5, trichocyst; 6, adoral zone of membranelles; 7, skeletal plates; 8, contractile vacuoles; 9, macronucleus; 10, micronucleus; 11, trichites; 12, Golgi bodies; 13, mitochondria; 14, myonemes; 15, endosome.

In a few forms skeleton is present in the ectoplasm, e.g., the plates of the little ciliate *Coleps* (Fig. 7*D*) and the armor of the Ophryoscolecidae (Fig. 7*E*) and Cycloposthiidae, remarkable ciliates parasitic in the digestive tracts of horses and cattle.

Contractile fibrils or *myonemes* located usually in the ectoplasm but sometimes extending into the entoplasm occur in the more complex ciliates (Fig. 7*J*) and in gregarines, generally as a layer of longitudinal fibers, sometimes in successive layers running at right angles to each other. The myonemes are employed to some extent in locomotion but serve chiefly to contract the body with reference to external or internal conditions. Much investigation of protozoan myonemes has failed to elucidate the mechanism of the contraction, which is presumably of the same nature as muscle contraction in general.

The entoplasm is a fluid granular mass composed fundamentally of hyaloplasm bestrewed with microsomes and containing one to many nuclei, various organelles, and inclusions. The hyaloplasm may be dense and uniform or vacuolated with various sizes of watery spheres. Protozoa tend to become highly vacuolated when aging, dying, starving, or under other adverse conditions. Fibrillar and supporting structures are usually absent from the entoplasm. Hardened rods termed *trichites* are found in association with the mouth in many gymnostomatous ciliates (Fig. 7*F*, *G*) and some flagellates as *Peranema* (Fig. 27*G*, *P*) and these project into the entoplasm and serve to strengthen the food passage.

The most common organelles of the entoplasm are the *chromoplasts* and the *food* and *contractile* vacuoles. Chromoplasts or *chromatophores* are of wide occurrence in flagellates as variously shaped bodies (Fig. 9). They nearly always contain chlorophyll and when composed wholly of this substance are termed *chloroplasts;* but frequently yellow, brown, red, or other pigments are also present, masking the green color. Chromoplasts function as in plants in the manufacture of carbohydrates. Associated with and often embedded in the chromoplasts are bodies called *pyrenoids* (Fig. 9), probably also concerned in carbohydrate production.

Food vacuoles are simply spherical cavities in the entoplasm containing digesting food and fluid (Fig. 6). They can hardly be considered formed organelles.

The contractile vacuole (Figs. 6, 8) is characteristic of fresh-water Protozoa and marine and parasitic ciliates but is lacking in other marine and parasitic groups. It is a vacuole that rhythmically fills with a clear fluid, attains a certain size, and then collapses to invisibility, discharging its contents to the exterior, directly or by way of the cytopharynx. The intervals between successive contractions vary from a few seconds to several minutes in different Protozoa and also depend on temperature, and chemical content and osmotic pressure of the medium. In parasites and marine species the rate is notably slow, presumably because of the high osmotic pressure of their surroundings. The mechanism of the contraction is unknown but probably consists chiefly in a gelation of the encircling cytoplasm. In the naked rhizopods the apparatus is usually a simple vacuole that rolls around in the entoplasmic currents, but in other protozoans the vacuoles generally occupy fixed positions, in or just beneath the ectoplasm, and in ciliates the system may attain considerable complication, comprising one to several canals (Fig. 6) that collect fluid and discharge droplets whose union forms the vacuole. The number of vacuoles varies from one to several and may be constant for the species. In most protozoans, the vacuole is not a permanent structure but is formed anew after each contraction by the fusion of minute entoplasmic droplets or small vacuoles. The collecting canals when present and the pore seem to be of more permanent nature; in some cases a canal leads from the vacuole to the pore (Figs. 61*B*, 64*C*). Pieces of protozoans so cut as to lack a vacuolar system quickly reform one and the same happens in normal fission.

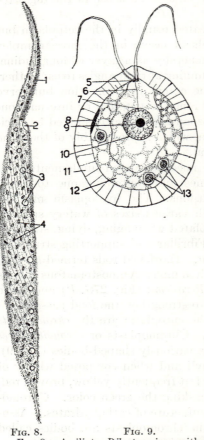

Fig. 8.   Fig. 9.

Fig. 8.—A ciliate, *Dileptus gigas*, with numerous contractile vacuoles and numerous nuclei, from life, nuclei after haematoxylin staining.

Fig. 9.—A flagellate, *Haematococcus*, showing flagellar attachments. (*After Elliott*, 1934.) 1, band of trichocysts; 2, mouth; 3, contractile vacuoles; 4, nuclei; 5, basal bodies of flagella; 6, rhizoplast; 7, centriole; 8, stigma; 9, endosome; 10, nucleus; 11, cell wall of cellulose; 12, cup-shaped chloroplast; 13, pyrenoids.

Mitochondria as small entoplasmic rods, ovals, or spheres have been reported for all groups of Protozoa (Fig. 7*J*). Bodies of various shapes have been identified in many Protozoa as *Golgi bodies* but most of these identifications are probably erroneous and Golgi bodies have been found with certainty only in gregarines (Fig. 7*H*) and some flagellates. Some authors regard the parabasal bodies of certain flagellates as Golgi apparatus and Nassonov and others locate it in the wall of the contractile vacuole.

Granules, spheres, or other bodies not belonging to any of the foregoing categories are usually either digesting food or ergastic substances. The latter include all three kinds of organic food—carbohydrates, lipids, and proteins. Some flagellates store starch but carbohydrates are usually stored as *glycogen* or as *paramylum*, which differs somewhat chemically from ordinary starch. Glycogen has been demonstrated by chemical test in *Pelomyxa, Paramecium, Vorticella* and many parasitic forms (Fig. 2*H*). Paramylum bodies, often of curious shapes (Fig. 27*C, D*) are common among the green flagellates. A kind of carbohydrate called *leucosin* occurs in some of the lower orders of flagellates (Fig. 23*D*). *Oil* droplets, serving both as stored food and as aids in floating, are common in the Radiolaria and Dinoflagellata. Fat spherules strewn throughout the entoplasm (Fig. 2*G*) have been demonstrated by chemical means in many different Protozoa. *Protein* spheres and *volutin* grains (Fig. 2*F*) are not uncommon and *crystals*, probably usually organic in nature, are also found in Protozoa. In a detailed study of the cytoplasmic constituents of *Amoeba proteus*, Mast and Doyle identified: small spherical or oval bodies, probably mitochondria, large spherical refractive bodies with a protein-lipid shell, showing reactions similar to Golgi bodies; plate-shaped crystals composed of the amino acid leucin; bipyramidal crystals containing magnesium and probably a derivative of the amino acid glycine; and droplets of neutral fat.

3. The Nucleus.—The protozoan nucleus is far more varied in form and construction than the metazoan nucleus and, further, can present different appearances at different phases of the life cycle. It consists of the *nuclear membrane*, the *nuclear sap* or *nucleoplasm*, *chromatin* granules, and *plastin*, probably identical with the plasmosomes of metazoan nuclei. Protozoan nuclei are *vesicular* or *massive;* the former, commonly spherical, sometimes oval or biconvex, usually consist of a central body, the endosome (Binnerkörper of German writers) encircled by a zone of nuclear sap (Fig. 9). The endosome may consist of chromatin alone, or partly of chromatin and partly of plastin, often in a definite pattern, or wholly of plastin. The chromatin may occur in the endosome or in the nuclear sap or attached to the nuclear membrane. In some nuclei there are several endosomes while a few vesicular nuclei lack endosomes altogether. Vesicular nuclei with central endosomes are common in rhizopods, flagellates, and Sporozoa, and the micronuclei of ciliates are often of this type. Massive nuclei, best illustrated by the ciliate macronucleus (Fig. 6), are more solid and uniformly constructed of evenly distributed chromatin granules. One or more endosomes may be present. Besides the usual rounded or oval shapes, ciliate macronuclei often assume unusual forms—elongated, bent like a horseshoe, moniliform (like a string of beads), or branched (Figs. 65*A*, 63*C*, and 67*A, G*).

The protozoan cytosome is usually uninucleate but many Radiolaria, and isolated forms in other groups, such as *Pelomyxa, Opalina, Actinosphaerium, Loxodes, Dileptus, Calonympha,* are regularly multinucleate (Figs. 8, 43*A*, and 61*A*).   In many other forms multinuclearity occurs temporarily at certain phases of the life cycle and is merely an indication of an approaching multiple fission.   According to R. Hertwig, Goldschmidt, Schaudinn and others, chromatin passes out from the nucleus into the cytosome in some Protozoa, particularly the shelled Lobosa, and there accumulates as granules and networks called *chromidia* (Fig. 1*L*). It is further claimed that these chromidia may aggregate into nuclei that serve in reproductive processes.   Doubt has been thrown upon all this work by the fact that in some of these cases tested by the Feulgen method[1] the chromidial net has failed to give a chromatin reaction. Several workers are of the opinion that the alleged chromidia or chromidial nets are of mitochondrial nature.

The whole class Ciliata is bi- to multinucleate and in addition has two sorts of nuclei, a single large massive *macronucleus* (sometimes several) and one to many (about 80 in *Stentor coeruleus*) small, often vesicular, *micronuclei* (Fig. 6).   The macronucleus is regarded as the *somatic* nucleus, which discharges the usual nuclear functions, while the micronucleus is *generative*, concerned only in reproduction.   This nuclear dimorphism in ciliates has been very puzzling to protozoologists and has led some of them to postulate two kinds of chromatin, the vegetative *trophochromatin* and the generative *idiochromatin*.   In uninucleate forms, both kinds are assumed to reside in one nucleus.   This *binuclearity hypothesis* of Goldschmidt has not met with much favor owing to the difficulty of applying it to the metazoan nucleus.   Another attempt to explain the variety and complexity of nuclear conditions in Protozoa is the *polyenergid* theory of Max Hartmann.   The term *energid*, as used by its inventor, the botanist Sachs, meant a simple nucleus plus the cytoplasmic zone that it controls functionally.   Hartmann modified the word to mean any nucleus or part of a nucleus that with surrounding cytoplasm can reconstitute an individual.   Such nuclei are *monoenergid*.   Multinucleate Protozoa are considered *polyenergid* organisms.   An apparently single nucleus that undergoes multiple division in reproduction by sporulation is regarded as a polyenergid nucleus.   Here, again, the theory, although of value in considering certain phenomena in Protozoa, lacks general applicability.   But it helps in visualizing the Protozoa as complex organisms, rather than as simple cells.

The conception of *karyoplasmic relation* (*Kernplasmarelation*) of R. Hertwig was already mentioned (page 5).   It was based on a study

[1] This is a recently developed chemical test for chromatin that has proved very useful in identifying nuclear (i.e., chromatic) substance in cells.

of the Protozoa; the volumes of nucleus and cytosome were measured at different times in the life cycle and under different conditions of temperature, nutrition, external medium, etc. The theory asserts that normally a definite ratio exists between nuclear and cytoplasmic mass, that the ratio varies with changes in conditions, and that excess of cytoplasmic mass leads to cell division. Multinuclearity and elongated, moniliform, and branched nuclei are regarded as methods of increasing the nuclear surface, thus permitting the continuance of larger cytoplasmic masses. The idea undoubtedly possesses a certain value.

The Protozoa have constituted the chief material for investigation of the function of the nucleus, since many of them can be cut into nucleated and nonnucleated parts that survive long enough for study. *Amoeba* and other rhizopods and ciliates have furnished the chief materials. Nonnucleated parts survive but a short time. Enucleated portions of *Amoeba* may live for several days. Movement is never quite normal, and often decidedly abnormal. Food is never actively ingested but may be enclosed accidentally, whereupon according to most observers it is not digested.[1] Response to stimuli is abnormal. Shelled rhizopods cannot replace the shell in the absence of the nucleus. Nonnucleated parts of ciliates are incapable of regenerating the missing structures while this is readily accomplished by nucleated portions. In general, then, in the absence of a nucleus, behavior and activities are not normal, survival is brief, and constructive power has been lost.

4. Encasements and Shells.—Recent work has shown that the capacity to secrete tectin, a mucus-like substance, is widespread among the Protozoa and is employed as a temporary protective or anchoring device. Many Protozoa, however, are enclosed in more or less permanent secreted coverings. These may consist of organic material alone or of an organic matrix in which are embedded minerals or foreign bodies such as sand grains. The organic substance is either a gelatinous material or cellulose or tectin (pseudochitin); true chitin is seldom present.[2] The chief minerals found in shells are silica and calcium carbonate, but others may occur. These protective coverings may adhere closely to the surface or may be loose encasements. The former vary from simple soft gelatinous or tectinous envelopes to a hardened armor or cuirass such as the cellulose plates of the dinoflagellates (Fig. 10A). Such armors may be

---

[1] Becker's report of digestion of *Euglena* by enucleated Amoebae constitutes the sole exception.

[2] The chemical nature of the gelatinous substance cannot be stated; it is probably mucus-like. Cellulose is a complex starch compound. Tectin or pseudochitin is a glycoprotein, a combination of protein and carbohydrate, similar chemically to mucin (slime). Chitin is nonprotein and consists of acetic acid united to glucosamine (the sugar glucose with one OH group replaced by NH_2). Chitin is uncommon among Protozoa.

variously sculptured or ornamented. More common are those coverings, separated by a space from the contained protozoan. These may consist of gelatinous envelopes or tectinous membranes or bell-, vase-, or beaker-shaped cases or loricae of tectin (Fig. 10*B, C*); or shells and skeletons composed principally of lime or silica or foreign particles embedded in an organic matrix (Fig. 40*E*). Among the best known examples are the shells of the shelled Lobosa (Fig. 10*E*) and of the Foraminifera (Fig. 41)

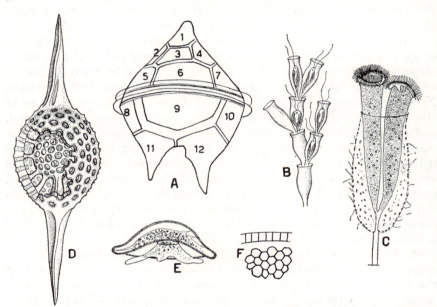

FIG. 10.—Types of protozoan encasements. *A*. A dinoflagellate, *Peridinium*, with an armor of cellulose plates. (*After Barrows*, 1918.) *B*. A chrysomonadine flagellate, *Dinobryon*, attached in vase-like cellulose cases. (*After Kent*, 1880.) *C*. A peritrichous ciliate, *Cothurnia*, occurring in couples in a tectinous case with adherent foreign particles, from life, Atlantic Coast. *D*. Siliceous shell of a radiolarian, composed of two concentric lattice spheres. (*After Haeckel*, 1887.) *E*. One of the shelled Lobosa, *Arcella*, with a bowl-shaped shell composed of siliceous prisms set in tectin, from life, seen from the side. *F*. The prisms of the shell, magnified, seen from the side and in surface view. 1, apical plate; 2–4, accessory plates; 5–7, precingular plates; 8–10, postcingular plates; 11–12, antapicals.

and the elaborate skeletons of the Radiolaria (Fig. 10*D*). The latter also often penetrate into the interior of the animal. Any of these encasements can be readily replaced and reformed. In the category of secreted protective coverings belong also the cyst walls (Fig. 15) formed by Protozoa when they pass into a dormant state, the walls of spores, etc.

5. Kinetic Elements.—Under this name will be grouped bodies and fibrils concerned in mitotic division, i.e., granules or other bodies that initiate mitosis and act as the poles of the spindle or are concerned in mitosis. These are of great variety in the Protozoa, and since they have not yet been homologized in the different groups a bewildering assortment of names has been applied to them. Kinetic bodies occur in both the nucleus and cytosome. Those within the nucleus are termed *endobasal bodies, intranuclear bodies,* and other names. The entire endosome may function as an endobasal body pulling apart into a dumbbell-shaped body (Fig. 22) that takes the place of a mitotic figure; or the endobasal body may consist of a granule similar to and behaving like a centriole; or the kinetic element of the nucleus may consist of a mass like a centrosphere that forms *polar caps* (Fig. 16*D*) at the two ends of the nucleus in division. The kinetic elements of the cytosome are also of many sorts and may or may not be of nuclear origin. In some Protozoa regular cytoplasmic centrioles with surrounding centrospheres (Fig. 16*A*) are present as permanent organelles or appear only at the time of division. Or again the division center may consist only of the centrosphere lacking centrioles. In flagellates, which are particularly rich in these kinetic elements, each flagellum is attached to a granule, termed the *basal body* or *blepharoplast.* This granule may be inside the nucleus or attached to the nuclear membrane or in the cytosome but is usually at the point where the flagellum springs from the body. In many cases the blepharoplast acts as a centriole dividing in two at mitosis and drawing apart leaving a connecting strand or *desmose* between the halves. In such cases the blepharoplast is termed *centroblepharoplast* by some authors. In other flagellates there is a separate granule, the *centriole*, often fastened to

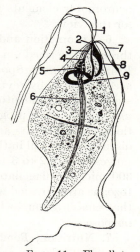

Fig. 11.—Flagellate structure. *Devescovina*, inhabiting the intestine of termites. (*After Kirby*, 1927.) 1, 3 anterior flagella; 2, blepharoplast; 3, rhizoplast; 4, centriole; 5, nucleus; 6, axostyle; 7, trailing band flagellum; 8, chromatic basal rod; 9, parabasal body coiled around nucleus.

the nuclear membrane, and connected by a fibril, the *rhizoplast*, with the basal body of the flagellum (Figs. 9, 16*H*), and this centriole initiates mitosis; but Cleveland's work renders it probable that basal body, rhizoplast, and centriole should be regarded simply as an elongated centriole. Additional problematical filamentous, rod-shaped, or oval bodies attached to the blepharoplasts, such as *parabasal bodies, parastyles, axostyles, chromatic rods,* etc., occur in some flagellates. Some of these structures are illustrated in the accompanying figure (11) of *Devescovina*, a polymastigote flagellate inhabiting the intestine of termites. This animal has four flagella that spring from a blepharoplast (really composed of fused blepharoplasts), a rhizoplast extending from the blepharoplast to the nucleus where it terminates on a small centriole, an axostyle encircled by the nucleus, a parabasal body, which makes a turn around the nucleus, and a chromatic basal rod. The axostyle is apparently a supporting structure but the function of the two other bodies is unknown. It is assumed by some that these various fibrils, rods, and granules in flagellates constitute a conductile system, and consequently they are classed as neuromotor elements (see below); but there seems little factual support for this view.

6. Locomotion and Locomotory Organelles.—The Protozoa progress through the medium in three different ways. Characteristic of the Rhizopoda, many Sporozoa, and some other forms is *amoeboid movement*, accomplished by cytoplasmic protrusions, the *pseudopodia*. In the second type, filamentous projections, *cilia* or *flagella*, collectively termed *undulipods*, cause progression by their beating. A third mode of locomotion, *gliding*, occurs among some Sporozoa. These various methods are discussed in detail in the account of the classes. The speed of locomotion ranges from 0.2 to 3 micra per second in various amoeboid forms; 15 to 300 micra in flagellates; and 400 to 2000 in most ciliates. Many protozoans are provided with devices such as oil drops or projecting processes that enable them to keep afloat, and some secrete gas bubbles for this purpose.

7. Nutrition, Food-intake, and Digestion.—Nutrition is *holophytic, saprozoic, holozoic,* or *mixotrophic. Holophytic* or *autotrophic* nutrition is identical with the photosynthesis of plants, in which carbohydrates are synthesized from water and carbon dioxide with the aid of chloroplasts and the energy of sunlight. Proteins are then built up by combining nitrogenous salts with carbohydrates. Holophytic nutrition is widespread among the chlorophyll-bearing flagellates, some of which can therefore live in the light in a solution containing nothing but inorganic salts, provided one of these is nitrogenous, such as ammonium nitrate. Others, however, require an organic source of nitrogen such as amino acids even in the light, and all the holophytic protozoans when in the dark live by the saprozoic method and must therefore be provided with organic nutrients, such as amino acids, peptones, and sugars. Many green forms have not been successfully cultivated in the dark. Saprozoic forms are those which do not ingest solid food but subsist entirely on dissolved substances in the medium. Here belong the majority of the parasitic Protozoa and a number of free-living colorless flagellates. The dissolved substances are absorbed through the entire surface or possibly through limited regions. Some of the free-living saprozoic flagellates can flourish in a surprisingly simple medium; thus *Polytoma* can build up starches and proteins from such simple substances as acetic or butyric acid and ammonium salts; and the little *Chilomonas* has been cultivated in a solution composed of magnesium sulphate, ammonium chloride, potassium acid phosphate, and sodium acetate, from which it is claimed that the acetate can be omitted if silicon is present as a catalyzer and the carbon dioxide supply is adequate; but this result has been disputed. Most saprozoic forms must be supplied with amino acids, peptones, etc. The term mixotrophic, or mesotrophic, is applied to forms that combine the holophytic and saprozoic methods. The majority of the free-living Protozoa are holozoic, i.e., they ingest solid food in the form of other organisms, as bacteria, yeasts, algae, protozoans, and small metazoans. There have been many attempts in recent years to cultivate the holozoic Protozoa in a medium free from other organisms, or particulate food Success has been attained with a number of ciliates of the genera *Glaucoma, Colpidium, Colpoda, Loxocephalus, Trichoda, Chilodonella,* and with the green *Paramecium, P. bursaria;*[1] these forms, normally bacteria feeders, can be grown in sterile media containing organic nutrients, such as yeast extract, peptones, bouillon, etc. Other bacteria-feeding ciliates, as *Paramecium caudatum,* can be cultivated on sterile particulate food, as dead bacteria and yeasts. No nongreen ciliate has been grown in a purely inorganic medium. A soil amoeba has been cultured in a medium consisting of inorganic salts, peptone, and dextrose (Reich, 1935).

The holozoic mode of nutrition leads to the specialization of food-catching and food-ingesting organelles. The regular locomotor organelles usually serve for the capture of prey but additional structures may occur. Among the rhizopods food is ingested at any point of the surface, being embraced by pseudopods and drawn into the cytosome (Figs. 12*A*, 37). In flagellates and ciliates a definite region becomes specialized for food intake. In its simplest form, seen in some flagellates, this consists of a region at the base of the flagellum (Fig. 12*B*). In the next stage there is a simple mouth opening or cytostome, probably primitively terminal but often shifted to a lateral position, which leads into the entoplasm (Fig. 12*C*). In raptorial forms the entoplasmic food passage may be supported by a circlet of trichites termed the *pharyngeal basket* (Fig. 7*F, G*). Then a tubular or funnel-shaped passage, the *cytopharynx,* also called *gullet* and *esophagus,* develops, extending from the surface deep into the entoplasm (Fig. 12*C*). Finally a portion of the body surface, the *peristome,* may be specialized for directing food into the cytopharynx (Fig. 12*D*), and both cytopharynx and peristome come to be provided with special ciliary tracts or undulating membranes for creating water currents that sweep the food into the cytopharynx.

[1] It is now known that several of these ciliates were misidentified and that they are in fact identical, belonging to an undescribed species now named *Tetrahymena geleii* (Furgason, 1940, Arch. Protistenk., vol. 40)

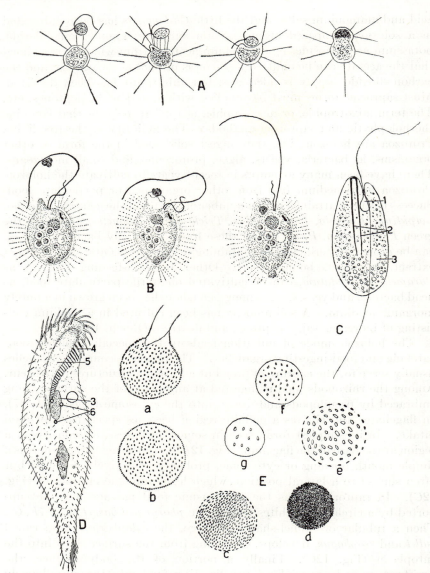

Fig. 12.—Food-catching structures and activities.   *A.* A heliozoan *Raphidocystis*, capturing a *Chilomonas* by pseudopods followed by protoplasmic engulfment; the process required 18 minutes.   (*After Wetzel, 1926.*)   *B.* A monad, *Monas vestita*, engulfing food brought by the flagella to a special area at their base; the animal is anchored by delicate tectinous filaments.   (*After Reynolds, 1934.*)   *C.* A euglenoid flagellate, *Entosiphon*, with one locomotory and one trailing flagellum, a pair of trichites, and a food-ingesting gullet, from life.   *D.* An hypotrichous ciliate, with a food-ingesting depression, the peristome, bordered by special food-catching membranelles, from life.   *E.* Cycle of changes in the food vacuole of *Paramecium*, after neutral red staining, from life.   *a,* vacuole being released from the gullet end, colored pale red (acid) and covered with neutral red granules from the

The ingested food may lie directly in the entoplasm but is usually enclosed in a *food* or *gastric vacuole* with fluid consisting partly of water included when the food was engulfed and partly of entoplasmic secretion. In ciliates the food vacuoles are moved along in a more or less definite course by entoplasmic currents. The assertion of some workers that a definite "digestive tube," along which the vacuoles pass, exists in ciliates is a mistake. The contents of the vacuoles undergo alteration and digestion by means of acids, alkalies, and enzymes secreted from the surrounding entoplasm. Often entoplasmic granules, stainable with neutral red, probably mitochondria, attach themselves to the vacuole wall and seem to play some role in digestion (Fig. 12E). Changes of reaction in the vacuoles have been studied by feeding dyes or dyed foods which indicate acidity or alkalinity by change of color (Fig. 12E). In most Protozoa, the food vacuoles pass through two phases, an early acid phase and a later alkaline phase, although in some cases the acid phase cannot be demonstrated. Report of an additional brief alkaline phase preceding the acid phase in some ciliates is probably erroneous. It is generally stated that during the acid phase the prey is killed and the contents of the vacuole concentrated. The acid is inorganic, probably hydrochloric, and in *Paramecium* was found by Nirenstein to attain a concentration of 0.3 per cent but in most Protozoa is more dilute. Howland in *Actinosphaerium* reported an increase in acidity in the food vacuoles from an original pH of 6.9 to one of 4.3. A recent suggestion that the acidity results from the death of the prey and not from a secreted acid is plausible; but meets the difficulties that the acid is inorganic in nature according to several workers and is omitted in some Protozoa. Most or all of the digestion occurs during the alkaline phase in which the vacuole swells again through intake of water (Fig. 12E). Its contents dissolve and pass into the entoplasm. In rhizopods, indigestible remnants lag into the rear and are emitted and left behind as the animal flows onward; in flagellates and ciliates they are generally ejected at a more or less definite point, the *cytopyge* (Fig. 57C). This is usually detectable only when in use, but in some ciliates a canal leads to the cytopyge.

As in all animals, digestion is performed by enzymes, which are secreted into the food vacuoles from the entoplasm. Proteases, i.e., protein-splitting enzymes, have been demonstrated in many Protozoa and seem usually to be similar to trypsin, acting in alkaline medium. Pepsin-like proteases requiring an acid medium have also been found in

---

cytoplasm; *b*, same vacuole free in the cytoplasm; *c*, vacuole condensing, stains deep red; *d*, vacuole fully condensed, stains very deep red, strongly acid; *e*, vacuole expanding again, stains orange, turning alkaline; contents partly dissolved; *f*, vacuole yellow, fully alkaline, contents mostly gone; *g*, vacuole about to be discharged from the cytopyge, yellow, with a few indigestible remnants. 1, gullet; 2, trichites; 3, nucleus; 4, row of membranelles; 5, peristome; 6, micronuclei.

rhizopods.   Amylases (starch-digesting enzymes) are of wide distribution in Protozoa.   There is evidence that some Protozoa, such as the flagellates inhabiting the intestine of wood-eating termites and cockroaches, and the complicated ciliates found in the stomachs of cattle and horses, can digest cellulose, an ability which is usually lacking in animals.   Proof that Protozoa can digest lipins is scanty although the common occurrence in them of stored fats and oils implies the ability to utilize these as foods. Direct evidence is available only for amoebas, which have been seen to digest injected droplets of cod-liver, olive, cottonseed, and other oils, and also the fat droplets contained in ingested prey (Dawson and Belkin, 1927; Mast, 1938).

8. Respiration.—In Protozoa respiratory exchange presumably occurs by diffusion through the surface.   No proof exists of any specific respiratory function of the contractile vacuole.   The majority of Protozoa are aerobic, take in oxygen and give off carbon dioxide like other animals, and gradually become immotile and die in an oxygen-free atmosphere. The oxygen consumption of a single *Paramecium caudatum* is given as 0.00385 cu. mm. per hour by Necheles, 0.0052 by Kalmus, 0.00073 by Zweibaum, 0.00049 by Howland and Bernstein; the wide variation in these results makes it impossible to place any reliance on the figures. Other data available are: 0.001 for *Paramecium multimicronucleatum* (Mast, Pace, and Mast); 0.00113 for *Actinosphaerium* (Howland and Bernstein); 0.0025 for *Spirostomum* (Specht); and 0.000017 for *Chilomonas* (Mast, Pace, and Mast).   Imperfections of methods and the presence of bacteria cast doubt on the value of most of these data.   The most accurate determination of protozoan respiration is that of R. H. Hall (1938), who, using bacteria-free cultures and a medium containing only salts, found an oxygen intake for *Colpidium campylum* of 112.5 cu. mm. of oxygen per million animals per hour at 19.8°C.   Mast, Pace, and Mast reported a respiratory quotient of 0.71 for *Paramecium* and 0.31 for the saprozoic *Chilomonas*, an indication that the latter uses up some of the carbon dioxide that it produces.   The oxygen consumption of *Paramecium* is increased two- to threefold by the ingestion of food and decreased by starvation (Lund).   The oxygen intake of ciliate Protozoa appears to be unaffected by the presence of potassium cyanide (which lowers the respiratory rate of all metazoans tested) but this is not the case with flagellates.   Mud- and sewage-dwelling protozoans are probably more or less anoxybiotic and the same is true of endoparasitic or endocommensal Protozoa, i.e., they obtain or can obtain their energy from some other reaction than union with free oxygen, probably from the breakdown of glycogen into lactic acid.   The presence of abundant glycogen has been demonstrated for many parasitic Protozoa.   Oxygen may even be harmful to protozoans inhabiting the interior of other animals; thus the flagellate commensals of the termite intestine can be killed without harm to the host by placing the host in a high oxygen atmosphere.

9. Excretion and the Contractile Vacuole.—Excretion is here defined as the concentration and elimination of metabolic wastes other than the respiratory gases. The most important excretions are nitrogenous and result from the utilization of proteins. The nitrogenous wastes of Protozoa seem to vary with the species; thus *Paramecium* and *Spirostomum* are reported to give off urea and ammonia; *Didinium*, ammonia and some uric acid; *Glaucoma*, ammonia and amids; and *Bodo*, ammonia. Parasitic forms that metabolize chiefly carbohydrates such as trypanosomes give off ammonia and a variety of organic acids. Ammonia is apparently the most common nitrogenous waste of Protozoa.

Many workers have assigned a specific excretory function to the contractile vacuole. This view originated with the claim of Griffiths (1889) that he had demonstrated by chemical test the presence of uric acid in the vacuoles of *Amoeba* and other Protozoa. Recent attempts to verify Griffiths' results, using his procedure, were entirely negative, but Weatherby (1927, 1929) with a more sensitive test has found urea in the fluid withdrawn by a micropipette from the vacuole of *Spirostomum*. However, the concentration was too low to warrant assigning a specific excretory function to the vacuole. More acceptable at present is the view that the vacuole regulates the water content of the animal. In a medium of lower osmotic pressure than cytoplasm, as fresh water, water continually passes into the cytosome, and some device to prevent excess hydration is necessary. This view accounts for the lack of a vacuole in many marine Protozoa, its disappearance when a fresh-water protozoan is gradually transferred to sea water, the acceleration of the pulsation rate in media of low osmotic pressure, retardation and stoppage in concentrated media, and similar facts. In marine ciliates where the vacuolar rate is very slow, dilution of the sea water enormously accelerates the pulsation rate but not if the osmotic pressure of the medium is maintained unaltered by addition of a nonelectrolyte. If vacuolar activity is inhibited by means of potassium cyanide, the body swells (Kitching, 1938). Injection of distilled water into amoeba results in increased rate of vacuolar output (Howland and Pollack, 1927). Some workers contend that water does not pass continuously into Protozoa through the surface but enters only or chiefly at the gullet in the formation of food vacuoles (Frisch, 1937). However, Kitching (1939) has shown that the intake of water with food vacuoles is only a fraction of the output of the contractile vacuole in fresh-water Protozoa and as proof of entry of water through the general surface offers the facts that fresh-water forms shrink after addition of sea water and marine protozoans swell in diluted sea water (1938). Furthermore, vacuolar systems exist in Protozoa that do not form food vacuoles, as the green flagellates. However, water intake at the pharynx may be the chief source of excess water in a few species, especially those with thick or protected pellicles. According to Frisch, the rate of pulsation of the posterior vacuole of *Paramecium*, which is near the gullet, is accelerated during feeding, apparently because of the water ingested with the food.

The available facts thus indicate that the vacuolar system serves to regulate the water content of the cytosome, eliminating excess water entering through the surface and with food. The presence of a contractile vacuole in many marine Protozoa offers some difficulty; but Kitching has found that the output from the vacuole is about equal to the intake with food, so that in marine forms excess water originates entirely from the food vacuoles. The rate of pulsation is extremely slow in marine Protozoa. The absence of a vacuole in marine rhizopods may be explained on the assumption that water is ejected with the undigested contents of food vacuoles. Among parasitic forms, the vacuolar system may aid in the diffusion of absorbed food.

The water discharged to the exterior by vacuoles necessarily contains a proportionate amount of metabolic wastes and respiratory gases, but this fact does not justify assigning a specific excretory or respiratory role to the apparatus. However, it must be emphasized that regulation of water content is an important function of excretory systems throughout the animal kingdom. It is not impossible that it is the primary function, and hence in this sense the vacuolar system of Protozoa would constitute the most primitive excretory system.

In 1924, Nassonov reported that the vacuolar wall in several Protozoa blackens with osmic acid and hence resembles a Golgi apparatus, and postulated that the apparatus may have secretory powers. The blackening has been verified for some Protozoa, but in most the vacuolar wall does not contain any lipins. Gatenby and Singh (1938) have found true Golgi material associated with the vacuolar apparatus of two flagellates (*Euglena, Copromonas*) and believe it functions in the collection of water for the vacuole, although they regard this function as secondarily acquired. It thus appears that the cytoplasm of or near the vacuolar wall may have specific power to secrete water.

10. Neuromotor System and Sense Perception.—It was formerly believed that the Protozoa are devoid of conductile specializations, but in recent years there has been demonstrated in many ciliates a so-called *neuromotor system*. This consists primarily of longitudinal ectoplasmic fibrils, the *interciliary fibrils*, which connect the basal bodies of the cilia with each other (Figs. 7*B*, *C*, 55*A*, and 56*H*). Transverse connections between the basal bodies may also occur, and in many forms there are additional longitudinal fibrils, the *interstrial connectives*, midway between the interciliary fibrils (Fig. 13*A*).   All these fibrils may center in a small body, the *motorium*, situated near the cytopharynx (Fig. 13*A*, *B*, and *C*). The surface fibrils continue into the pharynx wall, which generally has a lattice work of longitudinal and circular fibrils, and often additional strands pass from the cytopharynx into the entoplasm (Fig. 13*C*).   It seems highly probable that at least some of these fibrils are conductile in nature, serving to coordinate the cilia, the movements of membranelles and cirri, and food-ingesting activities.   Experimental evidence of the nervous nature of the system has been offered by Taylor, who, after cutting the connectives from the motorium to the five anal cirri in *Euplotes* (Fig. 13*B*), observed lack of coordination and disturbances of locomotion; and by MacDougall, who noted great disturbance of the cilia after the destruction of the motorium in *Chlamydodon*.   Some of the fibrils may be supporting, and in *Boveria* (Fig. 13*A*) the interciliary fibrils also function as myonemes.   Various fibrils from the flagellar basal granules of flagellates have been considered to constitute a neuro-motor system.

Conduction of stimuli certainly occurs in Protozoa, since external agents applied to one point may evoke response at a distant point.   The coordinated movements of cilia in forward and backward locomotion are not understandable without the presence of some conducting mechanism.   Conduction is ectoplasmic, since ciliary coordination in *Spirostomum* is abolished if the ectoplasm is torn but is not affected if the entoplasm is squeezed out of a body region.

Protozoa perceive and respond by movements to factors in the environment such as food, contact, light, chemicals, etc.   Such perception is probably in most cases a general property of the ectoplasm.   According to Mast, light perception in *Amoeba* resides in the inner part of the ectoplasm.   In ciliates the whole surface is equally sensitive to chemicals and heat since portions (*Paramecium*) react the same as intact animals. Cilia and flagella probably function in general as tango- and chemo-receptors; in addition there are in many ciliates special stiff motionless cilia, isolated or in rows, that apparently are receptors of tactile and chemical stimuli (Fig. 13*D*).   The most remarkable sense organelle of Protozoa is, however, the *stigma* or *eyespot* of certain flagellates, which is a photoreceptor and in the Volvocales consists, according to Mast, of a pigment cup, a light-sensitive substance contained within the cup, and sometimes of a lens-like pellicular thickening (Fig. 13*E*).   Still more astonishing is the eyespot of some dinoflagellates as *Pouchetia* (Fig. 25*H*) with its large spherical lens.

In general, then, Protozoa behave as if they had a nervous system, showing perception, conduction, and response; and in at least many

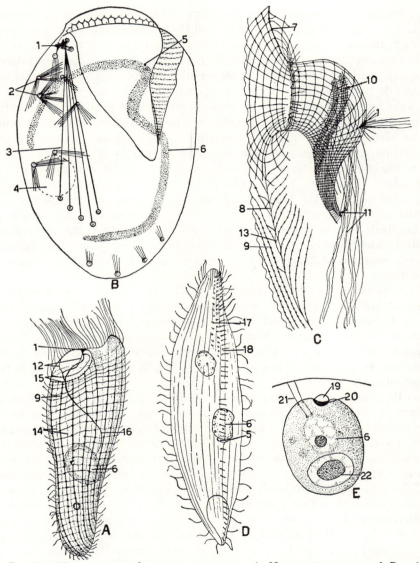

FIG. 13.—Neuromotor and sensory structures.   A. Neuromotor system of *Boveria teredini*, a ciliate parasitic in the shipworm *Teredo* (clam).   (*After Pickard*, 1927.)   Each dot is the basal body of a cilium; these are connected by the interciliary fibrils, here also acting as myonemes, and by transverse connectives which meet the interstrial fibrils between the interciliary fibrils.   B. Neuromotor system of *Euplotes* (*after Yocum*, 1918), showing fibers attached to the base of each cirrus, and the five fibers cut by Taylor which extend from the motorium to the anal cirri.   C. Neuromotor system of the cytopharynx and adjacent parts of *Paramecium* (*after E. E. Lund*, 1935); the basal bodies of the cilia are connected by the interciliary fibrils and transverse connectives; the body interciliary fibrils meet at the pre- and postoral sutures.   D. The ciliate *Trachelophyllum*, with a long

cases differentiated organelles serving these functions appear to be present, although it must be emphasized that such functions also reside in apparently undifferentiated protoplasm.

11. Behavior.—This term usually refers to movements elicited by changes in external factors. Response is of two general sorts, depending on whether the external change is perceived merely as an alteration of intensity or concentration or whether also its location plays a role. In the former case, the response, termed a *phobotaxis*, is general and undirected; in the latter there is a directed reaction or *topotaxis*, with respect to the location of the agent. Reactions to particular agents are named by combining the name of the agent with the word *taxis*, as phototaxis, chemotaxis, thigmotaxis, thermotaxis, rheotaxis, galvanotaxis and geotaxis, responses to light, chemicals, contact, heat, water currents, electric currents, and gravity, respectively. The receptors of such stimuli are similarly named photo-, chemo-, tango- etc., receptors.

The majority of protozoan reactions are phobotaxes and are of the same general character throughout the phylum. Upon encountering an unfavorable medium or condition or when touched, the animal stops, retreats, turns at an angle to its previous course, and then resumes locomotion in the new direction (Fig. 14*A*). The details for each species depend upon its form and symmetry and type of motor organelles. This general phobotactic reaction is also called the *avoiding reaction,* and the method of escaping unsuitable conditions and finding more satisfactory ones by repetitions of the avoiding reaction is named the "trial-and-error" method. This behavior is exclusively negative. Favorable conditions elicit no response, but the animal is able to remain in such conditions by giving the avoiding reaction whenever it chances to leave them. By these means, Protozoa, presented with a choice of conditions or a gradient in one condition, in the course of time aggregate in a favorable situation, which is then called the "optimum" of that agent.

Chemotaxis is universal among Protozoa. To most chemicals an avoiding reaction is given. Some, particularly weak acids, elicit a so-called positive response, i.e., the animal fails to react on entering a favorable concentration but gives the avoiding reaction if about to leave. In this way large numbers of ciliates aggregate in a drop or ring of optimum concentration. Earlier statements that only the anterior end of

row of tactile bristles and two short rows of chemoreceptive bristles. (*After Gelei,* 1933.) *E.* One zooid of a *Eudorina* colony to show the photoreceptor. (*After Mast,* 1916.) 1, motorium; 2, cirrus bases with fibers; 3, five fibers from the motorium to the anal cirri; 4, contractile vacuole; 5, micronucleus; 6, macronucleus; 7, preoral suture; 8, postoral suture; 9, interciliary line; 10, penniculus (eight ciliary rows in the pharynx wall); 11, postpharyngeal fibers and accessory motorium; 12, oral ring; 13, loop for cytopyge; 14, interstrial lines; 15, fibers of the adoral zone; 16, pharyngeal fiber; 17, chemoreceptive bristles; 18, tangoreceptive bristles; 19, lens-like thickening; 20, pigment cup; 21, flagella; 22, pyrenoid.

Paramecium is sensitive to chemicals have not been verified by recent workers (Horton, Koehler).

Most ciliates and colorless flagellates are indifferent to light but some select an optimum of moderate light intensity. *Amoeba* gives an avoiding reaction to bright light. The green flagellates are highly sensitive to light, a special case discussed below.

When placed in a temperature gradient, most Protozoa respond and select an optimum temperature by trial and error. For *Paramecium* the optimum is 24 to 28°C. The optimum depends, however, on the temperature at which the animals were previously kept and can also

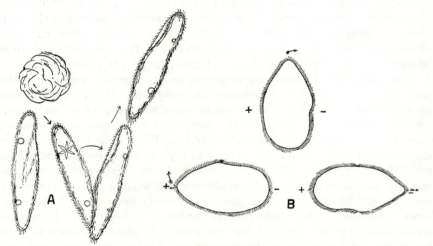

Fig. 14.—Reactions of Protozoa. *A*. Avoiding reaction of *Paramecium* on striking an obstacle, from life; the animal bounces backward, swerves in the direction opposite the peristome and proceeds in a new direction. *B*. Galvanotactic response of *Opalina ranarum*, ciliate from the frog's intestine (*after Wallengren*, 1903), showing ciliary beat in different positions with reference to the poles of the current.

be altered by other conditions. Recent results indicate that the entire surface is equally thermosensitive. Local applications of temperatures above or below the optimum elicit an avoiding reaction.

To localized touch, an avoiding reaction is generally given, but positive thigmotaxis, in which the animals come to rest in contact with objects, is common among Protozoa. Agitation or vibration causes rhizopods to withdraw their pseudopodia and round up, induces contraction in ciliates with myonemes, and more rapid swimming in other forms.

A few cases of positive rheotaxis, swimming against a water current, are known. *Paramecium* exhibits negative geotaxis, i.e., swims upward, particularly when carbon dioxide has accumulated in the medium.

Different investigators have failed to reach any agreement as to the means by which *Paramecium* perceives the direction of gravity.

Directed reactions or topotaxes are the exception in Protozoa. The active pursuit of food may belong here and perhaps positive thigmotaxis. But the two most striking examples are the light response of the green flagellates and galvanotaxis. In the former case any change in the direction of light affects the eyespot, and this change in turn is somehow conveyed to the flagella, which alter their beat so as to turn the organism with its axis in line with the light rays. Although green flagellates are generally positive to light, their reaction can be changed to a negative one by chemicals, preceding light conditions, etc. Galvanotaxis furnishes the best example of a directed response. Most Protozoa when subjected to a constant electric current turn and swim or crawl toward the cathode. The turning apparently results from the direct action of the current on the cilia or other locomotor organelles. The cilia on the cathodal side beat forward, those on the anodal side backward, and the animal is thus turned to face the cathode (Fig. 14*B*).[1] Rhizopods put out pseudopods on the cathodal side and withdraw them from the anodal side.

The topotaxes were formerly called *tropisms*, defined as forced involuntary orientation with respect to a source of energy. Tropisms were explained thus: whenever an external agent acted unsymmetrically upon the two halves of a bilaterally symmetrical animal, it set up an unequal intensity of chemical reaction in the two sides, and this chemical difference caused the locomotor apparatus to react to different degrees on the two sides, more strongly on the side away from the agent, forcing the animal to turn until its axis was parallel to the direction of the agent. J. Loeb and his supporters attempted energetically to prove that all animal reactions are of this forced compulsory kind. Originally opposed by Jennings, who showed through careful observation that the majority of the lower organisms react by the trial-and-error method, Loeb's idea has met with less and less acceptance until now very few reactions of Protozoa are considered to be of the compulsory type, and the word tropism has gradually come to be restricted to the growth responses of plants and sessile animals and to the reactions of the latter.

12. Encystment.—The secretion of a protective wall under unfavorable conditions or during reproduction is widespread among the fresh-

[1] This explanation appears to the author inadequate, since it fails to explain why animals facing the anode do not continue toward the anode. Further, when the response of organisms to other agents, as light, is reversed, galvanotaxis is also reversed, the animals proceeding to the anode, and this could not happen if galvanotaxis resulted simply from the direct action of the current on cilia and flagella. The author believes the explanation of galvanotaxis must be sought in the same factors that maintain polarity.

water and parasitic Protozoa and rare in marine forms.   The ordinary cyst arises as follows.   The animal becomes spherical, loses its organelles such as cilia, flagella, food-catching mechanisms, and myonemes, and ejects food vacuoles and similar bodies.   The rounded protoplasmic mass then undergoes reduction in size chiefly through the expulsion of water by the contractile vacuole, which continues to pulsate for some time but eventually also disappears.   Around the animal, which often rotates continuously while secreting the cyst, there appear layers of a gelatinous material; this hardens into the outer cyst wall or *ectocyst* (Fig. 15*A*, *C*) often spiny or warty and sometimes colored yellow or brown.   Inside this, a thin transparent *endocyst* is secreted.   Chemical tests have shown that the ectocyst is carbohydrate in some forms, tectinous or keratin-like in others.   Minerals such as silica may also be incorporated (Fig. 23*L*).

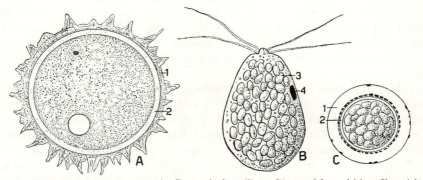

Fig. 15.—Protozoan cysts.   *A.* Cyst of the ciliate *Pleurotricha.* (*After Ilowaisky.* 1924.)   *B. Polytomella agilis.*   *C.* Same, freshly encysted. (*After Doflein,* 1920.)   1. ectocyst; 2, endocyst; 3, starch bodies; 4, stigma.

Many fresh-water Protozoa readily encyst under natural or labora- tory conditions, while others seldom or never pass into this state.   The ordinary *protective* cyst is formed under unfavorable circumstances such as lack of food, lack of oxygen, drying, heat, cold, fouling of the medium, changes in acidity and alkalinity, injurious chemicals, or accumulation of metabolic wastes; and can be induced in the laboratory by application of such conditions.   Internal changes, such as rich feeding, may also induce encystment.   In some Protozoa, encystment ensues, apparently for the purpose of digestion, after intake of large food bodies, resulting in *diges- tion* cysts.   Another kind of cyst is the *reproduction* cyst, within which fission occurs (Figs. 17*D*, 61*M*).   Nuclear degeneration followed by reorganization has also been reported with the designation of such cysts as *regeneration* cysts.   Emergence from the cyst, or *excystment,* occurs under favorable conditions, such as adding fresh oxygenated water of proper acidity or fresh culture medium.   First the contractile vacuole appears, followed by cilia and other organelles.   The entocyst dissolves, probably through enzyme action, and the ectocyst is ruptured by the assaults of the contained animal, now enlarged through intake of water. The escaped protozoan quickly regains normal structure and shape although in some cases on emergence it resembles an ancestral form and passes through a series of changes.

The cysts of Protozoa occur attached to grasses, vegetation, and other objects, in the soil, etc., and may be disseminated by various agents but do not float about in the air to any extent.   In Puschkarew's experiments, air inoculation of sterile cultures resulted in only 13 species, chiefly small amoebas and flagellates and one ciliate (*Colpoda*).   Frequently, sterile cultures exposed to the air fail to develop any Protozoa.   Encysted Protozoa may survive drying for long periods.   In most cases dry cysts remain viable for several months to 5 years, but Hausman recovered flagellates from material dried 20 years, and Goodey upon culturing museum specimens of old dry soils obtained *Colpoda* from soils 38 years old and amoebas and small flagellates such as *Monas, Bodo, and Cercomonas* from 49-year-old specimens.   The cysts of *Colpoda* are not injured by high vacuum if gradually produced and if very dry will stand the temperature of liquid air ($-180°C.$) for $13\frac{1}{2}$ hours, 70°C. for 26 hours, and 106°C. for 1 hour.   Some cysts hatched even after $12\frac{1}{2}$ days in liquid air (Taylor and Strickland, 1936).

13. Nuclear Phenomena of Division.—The former belief that division in Protozoa is chiefly amitotic and that approaches to the mitotic method represent primitive stages has been shown by more careful cytological studies to be erroneous.   Most Protozoa divide mitotically, and departures from the typical procedure are probably modifications rather than stages in evolution.   Genuine amitosis is limited to the macronucleus of ciliates (Fig. 3*A*).   In Protozoa the mitotic figure is usually entirely of nuclear origin (Figs. 16*F, H, K* and 38*F, H*).

Protozoan mitoses have been classified by Belar (1926)[1] into *eumitotic, paramitotic,* and *cryptomitotic* types.   The eumitoses resemble the ordinary karyokinesis, and there may be a complete mitotic figure of cytoplasmic origin and chromosomes that behave typically (Fig. 16*A–C*). Variations from this type include the origin of the centrioles from the nuclear membrane and the absence of centrioles, with centrospheres or polar caps serving as the poles of the spindle; and also the entire lack of cytoplasmic granules or areas acting as poles.   In another series of forms, which include most Protozoa, the mitotic figure is entirely enclosed inside the nuclear membrane and may have centrioles and centrospheres (Fig. 38*F*) or centrioles alone (Fig. 16*H*) or polar caps (Fig. 16*D, K*) or

[1] For the details of protozoan mitosis, this classical paper of Belar's should be consulted.

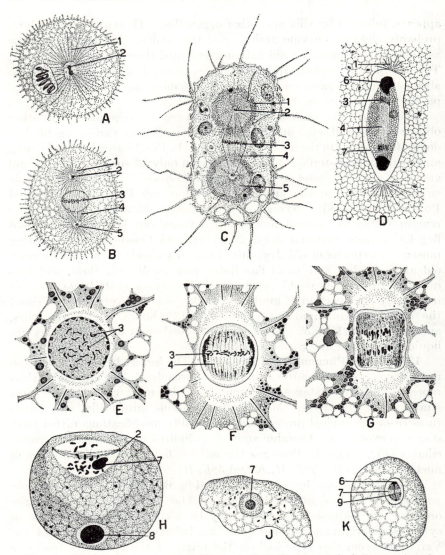

FIG. 16.—Nuclear phenomena of division.   *A, B, C.* Division of the heliozoan *Acantho-cystis aculeata,* showing typical mitotic figure of cytoplasmic origin.   (*A and B after Schaudinn,* 1896; *C after Stern,* 1924.)   *D. Amoeba verrucosa* in division (*after Gläser,* 1912); an intranuclear mitosis with polar caps, spindle, and chromosomes arising entirely from the endosome, astral rays cytoplasmic.   *E, F, G.* Stages in the division of the nucleus of the heliozoan *Actinophrys* (*after Belar,* 1923), an intranuclear mitosis without polar structures. *H. Eudorina* in division (*after Hartmann,* 1921); the endosome plays no part; spindle, centrioles, and chromosome arise in the nucleus.   *J.* An amoeba, *Valkampfia magna; K.* the same in division (*after Jollos,* 1917); polar caps and desmose come from the endo-some; there are no definite chromosomes.   1, aster; 2, centriole; 3, chromosomes; 4, spindle; 5, centrosphere; 6, polar cap; 7, endosome; 8, pyrenoid; 9, desmose.

entirely lack polar structures (Fig. 16*E*–*G*). Figure 16*D* is a case with an intranuclear figure with polar caps and astral rays in the adjacent cytoplasm. In all these variations of the eumitotic type there is a spindle with definite chromosomes that behave typically.

Under the term paramitotic, Belar has included those cases where the chromosome behavior is atypical, displaying irregularities in position on the spindle or manner of dividing. The achromatic figure may exhibit any of the variations described above. The name cryptomitosis is applied to cases where the achromatic figure is more or less evident but definite chromosome formation is lacking and the chromatic division is practically amitotic.

The endosome plays a variable role. In some forms both centrioles and chromosomes come from the endosome; this kind of division is called *promitosis* by some authors. Again the endosome may furnish only the chromosomes (*mesomitosis*); or, as in euglenoid flagellates, the whole endosome acts as a centriole (*haplomitosis*, Fig. 22*A*–*D*). In many cases, the endosome, being composed of plastin, plays no role in division but disappears (Fig. 16*H*).

Whereas in many Protozoa there is no formation of distinct chromosomes, in others chromosomes of specific shape and number appear at each division. The numbers in known cases range mostly from a few to 50, but in some Radiolaria more than a thousand chromosomes are formed. Such nuclei are considered polyenergid (page 54) by certain authors.

14. Asexual Reproduction and Division of the Cytosome.—Four types of asexual reproduction are generally recognized in Protozoa: *binary fission, budding, multiple fission,* and *plasmotomy*. Binary fission, or division into two approximately equal parts, constitutes the usual method. The nucleus divides by any of the methods indicated above, the cytoplasm by a constriction. In flagellates and peritrichous ciliates, fission is longitudinal and initiated at the anterior end (Figs. 17*A* and 65*C*–*E*); in other ciliates, the fission plane is transverse (Fig. 17*B*, *C*). Organelles either divide also, or one daughter cell retains them and the other must regenerate them, or each cell receives some of the old organelles and regenerates the others, or the organelles disappear (Fig. 17*E*) and are reformed by both offspring. Some Protozoa, e.g., *Colpoda* and *Tillina*, divide only in the encysted state (Figs. 17*D* and 61*M*).

Budding in Protozoa is a form of fission in which one of the products is unlike the mother animal and undergoes differentiation either before or after it becomes free. The bud is usually, but not necessarily, smaller than the other fission product. Budding is rare and sporadic except in the Suctoria (Fig. 67) where it is the regular mode of reproduction. In *exogenous* budding, one to many buds are constricted off to the exterior.

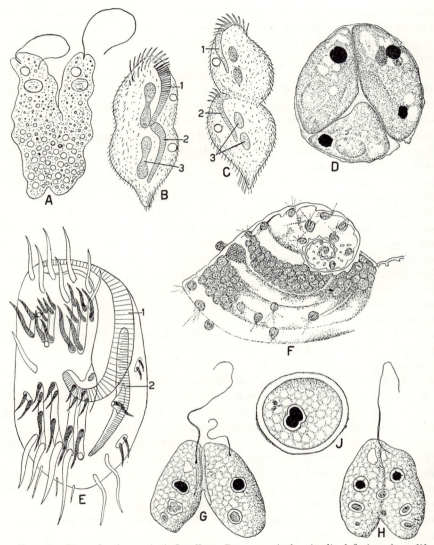

Fig. 17.—Reproduction.   *A.* A flagellate, *Peranema*, in longitudinal fission, from life.
B and *C.* A hypotrichous ciliate in transverse fission, from life, showing formation of new
adoral zone in the posterior daughter and amitotic division of the two macronuclei.   *D.* The
ciliate *Tillina*, dividing while encysted.   (*After Gregory*, 1909.)   *E.* *Euplotes* in early
fission, showing groups of new cirri (cross-hatched) forming to replace the old ones which
are shed.   (*After Griffin*, 1910.)   *F.* The foraminiferan *Peneroplis*, sporulating into amoeboid young.   (*After Winter*, 1907.)   *G, H.* A flagellate, *Copromonas subtilis*, in hologamy;
J. The resulting encysted zygote.   (*After Dobell*, 1908.)   1, old adoral zone; 2, new adoral
zone; 3, nucleus.

In *endogenous* budding the buds are liberated into internal spaces or *brood chambers* where they may divide before they escape to the exterior.

Multiple division or *sporulation* is the division simultaneously into a number of offspring (Fig. 17*F*). Previous to multiple fission, the protozoan always becomes multinucleate, usually by a rapid succession of ordinary nuclear divisions, rarely by the fragmentation of the nucleus simultaneously into a number of parts. The nuclei usually assume a peripheral position, cytoplasm constricts around each one, and the protozoan falls apart into as many offspring as there are nuclei. The number may be very large, running into thousands. Any remnant of the mother cell disintegrates. Multiple fission is termed *schizogony* or *agamogony* when occurring in an asexual cycle where the products develop directly into adults. It is called *sporogony* when following sexual fusion and *gamogony* when the products are sex cells. Various names are applied to the offspring resulting from multiple fission. When asexual they are included under the name *agamete*. When incased in a shell or other resistant covering they are usually termed *spore* and in this condition may remain viable for a long time. Motile products of multiple fission are often called *swarm spores* or *swarmers;* if flagellate, *flagellospores;* when amoeboid, *pseudopodiospores* or *amoebospores,* etc. Sporulation is common in Foraminifera, Radiolaria, and Sporozoa.

Plasmotomy is the division of a multinucleate protozoan into two or more parts without any nuclear division, the nuclei simply being distributed among the products. It occurs in the opalinids and some other forms.

15. Sexual Reproduction.—Two kinds of sexual process occur in Protozoa: *copulation* or *syngamy,* the fusion of two sex cells; and *conjugation* or temporary contact of two protozoans with nuclear exchange.

In syngamy the two uniting cells are called *gametes.* Gametes display all degrees of differentiation. They may not differ morphologically from the ordinary individual and are recognized as gametes only by their behavior. Such sexual fusion of two ordinary mature protozoan individuals is termed *hologamy* and is known for a few flagellates and rhizopods (Fig. 17*G–J*). When the fusing individuals are young, the phenomenon is termed *paedogamy.* Ordinarily, however, copulation occurs between special gametes differing in size and often morphology from the parent organism and from agametes. When the copulating gametes are alike in size and form they are termed *isogametes* and their union is *isogamy.* Isogamous gametes are generally produced by multiple fission or a succession of binary fissions and often escape as flagellate swarmers that fuse in pairs (Fig. 28*E*). Isogamy is common in the Foraminifera, the Phytomonadina, and the gregarines. Usually, however, the two fusing gametes differ in size, morphology, and behavior.

Differing gametes are called *anisogametes* (Fig. 18*B*, *C*) and their fusion is *anisogamy*. All possible grades of difference be-

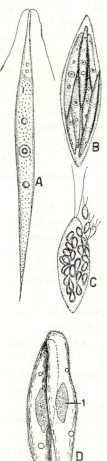

tween a copulating pair of anisogametes exist in Protozoa, from a slight size difference to the extreme case of union of a small, active, generally flagellated, *male gamete* or *microgamete* produced by multiple fission or a succession of binary fissions, with a large, passive, immotile, food-filled *female gamete* or *macrogamete* (Fig. 51*L*). Such fully differentiated gametes are really spermatozoa and eggs. They occur in the Phytomonadina and the Sporozoa. Where the fusing gametes are products of one parent cell, the union is termed *autogamy* (Fig. 44*D–G*). The cell resulting from the fusion of two gametes is termed the *fertilized egg* or *zygote* or *oöspore*, and its nucleus formed by the union of the nuclei of the gametes is the *synkaryon*. The zygote may develop directly into the adult or may first encyst and emerge as a young animal; or frequently it undergoes multiple fission or repeated divisions often within a cyst wall into agametes of various types that escape and grow to the adult form.

In conjugation, two protozoans attach by the mouth region (Fig. 18*D*), exchange nuclear material by way of the attachment, and then separate and continue their ordinary existence. This sexual conduct is limited to the subphylum Ciliophora where it will be considered in detail.

Both in gamete formation and in conjugation a reduction of chromosomes occurs, and this may, as in *Actinophrys*, be almost identical in all cytological details with reduction in the sex cells of Metazoa. In most Protozoa as in other animals the gametes are haploid and the zygote and all other stages diploid; but it appears that in some Sporozoa only the zygote is diploid and the gametes and entire life cycle are haploid. Reduction in these cases takes place in the first divisions of the zygote.

A curious phenomenon observed in some rhizopods is the fusion, generally partial, of two or more animals. The nuclei remain distinct and the organisms separate again unchanged sooner or later. The behavior is thus nonsexual and is known as *plasmogamy* or cytoplasmic

Fig. 18.—Reproduction, continued. *A. Chlorogonium*, one of the Volvocales, having anisogamous gametes; *B.* Same, producing macrogametes; *C.* Same, giving off microgametes, (*After Stein*, 1878.) *D. Paramecium* in conjugation, from life. 1, macronucleus.

union. In some cases it serves the purpose of digestion of large prey (Fig. 44*B*, *C*).

16. Regeneration.—The capacity for regeneration or replacement of lost parts is widespread among the Protozoa and is normally displayed by many forms at fission (Fig. 17*E*) or excystment, cases of so-called physiological regeneration. Parasitic Protozoa so far as tested have but slight regenerative power. The behavior of experimentally cut pieces of free-living rhizopods and ciliates has been studied by many workers, who agree that nucleated pieces of sufficient size reform proportional missing parts and may assume normal shape, often within a few hours (Fig. 19*A*). Old organelles may be retained or may be shed or absorbed and entirely new ones differentiated; the latter is the rule in the more highly differentiated ciliates, as the Hypotricha. Enucleated pieces may regenerate to some extent, but as a rule a fragment of nucleus is essential for the completion of the process, probably not because of any specific action of the nucleus on regeneration but because of the necessity of the nucleus for survival and constructive metabolism. In ciliates a piece of the macronucleus is required for regeneration, and hence genera with elongated or numerous macronuclei furnish the most suitable material, as *Stentor, Spirostomum, Dileptus, Uroleptus, Euplotes,* etc. In such forms, Sokoloff found that pieces $\frac{1}{50}$ to $\frac{1}{75}$ of the original volume can regenerate completely. Size of piece and in some species level of the body represented in the piece affect the rate and result of regeneration. A proper proportion of ectoplasm, entoplasm, and nucleus in the piece is the most important factor, especially the quantity of ectoplasm, since this must cover the cut surface quickly to prevent disintegration and must reform most of the missing organelles. Whether a micronucleus is essential for the regeneration of pieces of ciliates has not been definitely settled; according to the results of Young on *Uronychia* and Tittler on *Uroleptus,* some regeneration can occur in pieces devoid of a micronucleus, but complete regeneration is not possible in such pieces. Considerable reorganization of the macronucleus may occur during regeneration. Isolated nuclei are unable to create cytoplasm and perish. In hypotrichous ciliates, where all old organelles are shed or absorbed at regeneration and fission, the new organelles arise in a small definitely located area, termed the *regeneration field,* and from there migrate to their eventual locations (Fig. 19*A*). Whether the conception of a regeneration field can be generally applied to Protozoa remains to be seen. Regenerative power is least shortly after fission in ciliates and increases to the next fission (Calkins, 1911; D. B. Young, 1922).

17. Genetics.—An assemblage of organisms derived by asexual reproduction from a single ancestor is called a *pure line* or *clone.* In Protozoa, study of clones derived from random individuals has shown

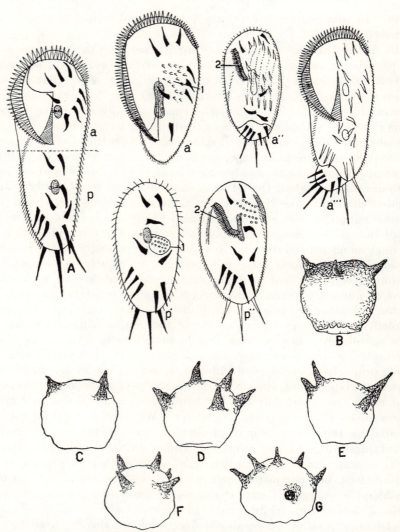

Fig. 19, *A.*—Regeneration of *Stylonychia*. (*After Dembowska,* 1925.)   The animal has an adoral zone of membranelles, 18 cirri, and three tail bristles; it was cut across as shown in *A*, into anterior (*a*) and posterior (*p*) halves.   The regeneration of the *a* half is shown in *a′, a″,* and *a‴*.   A group of 18 new cirri appear in the center of the piece (*a′*), the old adoral zone is shed and a new one formed (*a″*) and the old cirri are pushed off at the posterior end while the new ones spread to their definitive positions (*a‴*).   Similar changes occur in the posterior piece (*p′* and *p″*).   1, Group of new cirri; 2, new adoral zone; old cirri black, new ones white.

Fig. 19, *B–G.*—*A.* Splitting of a clone into new forms. (*After Jennings,* 1916.)   *B.* Shell of the parent *Difflugia,* one of the shelled Lobosa.   *C–G.* Members of the different families derived by asexual reproduction from the animal in *B.*

that each species can be split into a number of clones that differ in size, shape, rate of fission, frequency of conjugation, resistance to heat and cold and chemicals, number of contractile vacuoles, and other characters. Such diverse clones, originally obtained in *Paramecium* by Jennings, have since been isolated in many protozoan species. The shelled Lobosa furnish the most favorable material because of the ease of study of the variations of the shells. Under a given set of environmental conditions, the characters of a clone are constant within the normal range of variation and are inherited. Alteration of the environment induces alterations in the clone. The first attempts, headed by Jennings, to obtain diverse clones within a clone by cultivating the extreme variations, gave negative results, and it was concluded that clonal variations are not inheritable. But further researches, in some of which again the shelled Lobosa proved suitable material, showed that some of the clonal variations are inheritable so that clones may be split into new clones (Fig. 19*C–G*). Thus each species continues to diversify itself. Among the causes that have been suggested for the splitting of species into clones and clones into new clones are nuclear reorganizations and recombinations at endomixis (page 176) and conjugation, alterations in the karyoplasmic ratio, and environmental changes. On the last matter the most pretentious experiments are those of Jollos with *Paramecium*. Resistance to high temperature and injurious chemicals, developed by a slow process of acclimatization, and decrease in fission rate induced by calcium salts, were inherited if the exposure to these conditions had been sufficiently prolonged. The inheritance of the induced alteration persisted for a long time after return to normal cultural conditions, but eventually the acquired properties were lost.

From these interesting researches on Protozoa[1] we get a picture of organisms constantly changing in morphology and physiology in correlation with internal reorganizations and environmental alterations.

18. Ecological Considerations.—In discussing animal habitats and distribution, certain ecological terms are convenient. Aquatic animals may be classified into *pelagic* or *limnetic* types that occupy the open waters of oceans, seas, and lakes, and are independent of the bottom, and *benthonic* types which live in or on the bottom. Pelagic organisms are again divisible into the *plankton*, including the smaller and microscopic floating and swimming forms that are moved about by winds, waves, tides, and currents and are incapable of directed locomotion; and the *nekton*, the larger swimming animals whose movements are independent of the physical forces at work in the water. In fresh water the nekton consists practically wholly of fish; in the ocean it comprises fish, aquatic

---

[1] For a fine review of this work the student is referred to the article by Jennings, Genetics of the Protozoa, in *Bibliographia Genetica*, vol. 5, 1929.

mammals, and some large crustaceans and cephalopods. In the ocean pelagic life is conveniently divided into *epipelagic* animals, occupying the upper strata of the open waters, say to about 200 m. depth, and the *bathypelagic* types, which inhabit the deeper waters. Floating forms living at the surface have been termed *neuston*, and pelagic forms typical of shallow water near the shores of oceans are referred to as *neritic*. The benthos or bottom of the ocean is divisible into the shallow-water or *littoral* zone comprising the continental shelf extending 5 to 250 miles off shore and roughly to about 200 m. depth; the *archibenthal* zone, down to about 1000 m. depth; and the *abyssal* zone, including the remaining bottom, which runs in general to about 6000 m., and the *ocean deeps*, relatively small basins in the ocean bottom 6000 to over 10,000 m. in depth. The lower part of the littoral, 40 to 200 m., is often called *sublittoral*.

Fresh-water habitats classify as *lentic* or standing-water bodies: lake-pond-swamp series, and *lotic*, or running-water formations: brook-stream-river series. Among the smaller lentic environments, such as pools, ditches, ponds, and swamps, the animals are practically all littoral and benthonic. Only in the larger ponds and in lakes is the fauna divisible into pelagic and benthonic types. The divisions of the benthos in lakes are naturally much smaller than in the ocean and an abyssal zone is practically nonexistent. Lake bottoms are divided by Welch into *littoral*, comprising the zone of rooted vegetation, *sublittoral*, from this level down to the zone of relatively constant physical conditions, and the *profundal*, including the latter zone.

The Protozoa inhabit water everywhere. In the ocean they display some distribution with reference to temperature, salt content, light, and depth. There are definite warm- and cold-water species and benthonic and plankton forms. The plankton Protozoa are often provided with floating devices in the form of oil drops and projecting processes or skeletal spicules. The dinoflagellates constitute an important part of the epipelagic fauna of the ocean, the Radiolaria are epi- and bathy-pelagic, and the Foraminifera and other rhizopods are mostly littoral benthonic types. Fresh waters everywhere contain Protozoa, but they are least abundant in lotic and most abundant in lentic habitats, especially those where decay exists. Most of the fresh-water species are cosmopolitan, i.e., occur all over the world, but their local distribution is governed by factors such as light, temperature, acidity, salts, oxygen content, degree of putrefaction, etc. Protozoa are also abundant in damp soils, wet mosses, fecal deposits, etc., and readily excyst and encyst as the water content of such habitats changes. The term *coprozoic* is applied to Protozoa characteristic of fecal pools, *sapropelic* to those of the bottom slime in foul waters. The cysts of Protozoa seem to be ubiquitous; they have been found in desert sands, on dry mountain heights, and in the dust of glaciers and icebergs. They remain viable for months and years (page 71), hatch quickly in the presence of even minute amounts of water, and encyst again when dried. It has been estimated that more than a million Protozoa may inhabit 1 g. of garden soil. Whether the soil Protozoa play any role in enriching the soil has not been satisfactorily determined.

Protozoa display considerable power of acclimation to environmental factors. Although most Protozoa die at temperatures of 30 to 40°C., some species inhabit hot springs that range from 40 to 65°C., and many can by sufficiently gradual change become adjusted to high temperatures. The most noted experiment of this sort is that of Dallinger and Drysdale who by slow elevation of temperature extending through 7 years were able to acclimate three species of small flagellates to 70°C. Protozoa can live at 0 to −4°C. if freezing does not occur, but actual enclosure in ice is generally although not invariably fatal. Protozoa acclimate to gradual changes in salt content and a few fresh-water species have been transferred by degrees to salt water, losing their contractile vacuole in the process.

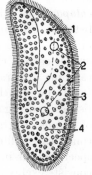

FIG. 20.—The green *Paramecium*, *P. bursaria*, with endoplasm filled with symbiotic zoochlorellae, from life. 1, peristome; 2, contractile vacuoles; 3, trichocysts; 4, zoochlorellae.

Relationships with other organisms are the same as in Metazoa. *Symbiosis*, better called *mutualism*, the close association of different organisms with mutual benefit, is illustrated in Protozoa by the green algal cells or *zoochlorellae* (Fig. 20), and the brown or yellow cells, *zooxanthellae*, believed to be flagellates, both of which live and multiply in the entoplasm of Protozoa. Zoochlorellae should not be confused with the green chloroplasts of flagellates, for they can exist independently as algae. The host can be freed from them and reinfected with them and can live without them like any other protozoan. The zoochlorellae utilize the carbon dioxide and the nitrogenous and phosphorous wastes given off by their hosts and in return furnish oxygen and synthesized food and may even be digested by the host in times of hunger. The zooxanthellae are mostly flagellates of the orders Chrysomonadina and Dinoflagellata; their physiological relations to the host are probably the same as those of the zoochlorellae. Protozoa themselves may live symbiotically with metazoans, as in the case of the flagellate inhabitants of the intestine of termites, which digest cellulose for their hosts.

The term *commensalism* is applied to animal companionships or associations where neither form appears to receive evident benefit or injury, except that food may be shared, and either *ecto-* or *entocom-*

mensalism may occur. Many examples of ectocommensals or *epizooic* species, i.e., species habitually living upon the surface of other animals, which they appear to use simply as a substratum, occur in Protozoa, such as vorticellids on tadpoles, and *Trichodina* and *Kerona* on Hydra. Among entocommensals or *entozoic* forms may be listed the apparently harmless protozoan inhabitants of the intestine of many animals. Naturally there is no sharp line between entocommensals and entoparasites.

Parasitism is the association of different organisms, of which one, the *parasite*, receives evident benefit, while the other, the *host*, is unbenefited or injured by the association. Parasites inhabiting the external surfaces of their hosts are called *ectoparasites*, those dwelling in the interior, *entoparasites*. Entoparasites may live in any of the body spaces or between cells in tissues and organs as *intercellular* parasites or in the interior of cells as *intracellular* parasites. The entoparasitic life usually entails certain changes: saprozoic nutrition with loss of mouth and food-catching apparatus, augmentation of motor organelles in parasites that swim about in body fluids, loss of these in those which lie quiescent in tissues and organs, anoxybiotic respiration in many cases, development of organs of attachment, resistance to digestive fluids, and occurrence of complicated life histories, often involving cyst formation. Parasitic species occur in all the classes of Protozoa and one class, the Sporozoa, consists exclusively of entoparasites. Members of practically all animal groups may serve as hosts as may also various plants. The Protozoa themselves are parasitized by other Protozoa, bacteria, and fungi, and reproductive phases of these parasites have often been mistaken as those of the host.

Bioluminescence or *phosphorescence*, the emission of flashes of light by organisms without the production of heat, is notably illustrated among protozoans by the Radiolaria and the Dinoflagellata, which latter are in fact responsible for many of the smaller sparks seen along ocean shores. The light emanates from certain granules but the process has not been analyzed in Protozoa where, unlike conditions in Metazoa, oxygen does not seem to be necessary.

Since Protozoa when food is adequate regularly reproduce by asexual methods in which the body is subdivided, any one individual does not live as such very long, usually a fraction of a day to a few days. When fission is inhibited as by lack of food, an individual protozoan may live up to 2 or 3 weeks probably. Forms that reproduce by sporulation and in which therefore the adult must grow from a small agamete or zygote have a longer existence, up to several weeks.

IV. CLASS FLAGELLATA OR MASTIGOPHORA

1. Definition.—The Flagellata are Protozoa that are flagellate, permanently or temporarily, in the adult state or which, by the production of flagellate young, indicate a derivation from typical flagellates. The flagellates are extremely difficult to separate from rhizopods, algae, and sporozoans.

2. General Characters.—The form is usually definite and simple, oval, spherical, or elongated, with differentiated anterior end. Symmetry is generally radial, but bilateral and irregular types occur.

Form is maintained in many species by a firm pellicle often ridged spirally or longitudinally (Figs. 7A and 24G). Many are provided in addition with shells, cases, and armors, which may adhere closely as the cellulose plates of the dinoflagellates (Fig. 26E) or may consist of loose encasements (Fig. 10B) of jelly, tectin, cellulose, or silica. Where the pellicle is thin or absent, amoeboid changes of shape obtain, and some species become wholly amoeboid at times, even losing the flagellum. Certain chrysomonads have stiff pseudopods like those of Heliozoa. Some forms frequently indulge in worm-like contractions and expansions called "*metabolic*" or *euglenoid* movements (Fig. 21A).

The cytosome usually lacks obvious distinction into ectoplasm and entoplasm. The pointed or rounded anterior end may bear a furrow, depression, or gullet-like cavity, but these generally serve for the insertion of the flagella rather than for food intake. Conspicuous organelles are the chromoplasts (Fig. 27) of various shapes, such as disk, band, bowl, and cup forms. They may consist entirely of chlorophyll, as in the Euglenoidina and Phytomonadina, lending to the animals a pure green color; but very often the chlorophyll is masked by red, brown, or yellow pigments of the carotin and xanthophyll groups of plant pigments. The chromoplasts are usually accompanied by pyrenoids (Fig. 21C). In many flagellates a red eyespot or stigma occurs near the anterior end (Fig. 27). It consists of a cup of carotin pigment called *hematochrome* and is believed to shade a light-sensitive substance located in the cup and overlain in some forms by a lens-like thickening. The whole constitutes a sensory organelle for light perception. Hematochrome can also occur in some species (*Haematococcus pluvialis*, Fig. 9) free in the cytosome, not contained in chromoplasts, to such extent that the animals may impart a red color to their habitat and cause the phenomena of red snow, red rain, etc. Hematochrome is said to develop only when the medium is poor in nitrogen and phosphorus and to disappear when these substances are supplied. Other organelles are the pharyngeal rods or trichites found in *Peranema* (Fig. 27P), *Entosiphon* (Fig. 27G) and other colorless euglenoids, the axostyles, parastyles, cytostomal fibers, and other rods and filaments of uncertain function (Figs. 21B, 33 and 34), and the various fibrils and granules more directly related to the flagella. Contractile vacuoles, widespread in fresh-water forms, consist of a simple vacuole discharging into the cytopharynx (when present) and reformed after each discharge from the fusion of small vacuoles (Fig. 26L). Tricho-

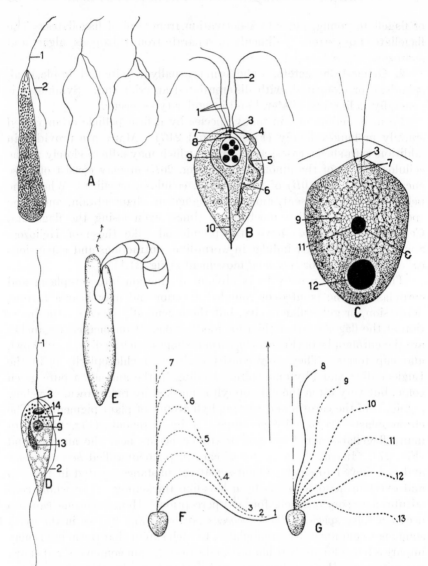

Fig. 21.—Flagellate structure and movements.   A. *Heteronema*, a colorless euglenoid, showing euglenoid contraction, from life.   B. *Trichomonas buccalis* (*after Hinshaw*, 1926), a polymastigote flagellate with axostyle, undulating membrane, and centriole on the nuclear membrane.   C. One zooid of a *Eudorina* colony, showing flagellar attachments and intranuclear centriole.   (*After Hartmann*, 1921.)   D. A protomonad, *Proteromonas* (= *Prowazekella*) *lacertae*, from the rectum of a lizard, with parabasal body.   (*After Grassé*, 1926.)   E. *Euglena deses*, showing cone traced by the flagellum.   (*After Ulehla*, 1911.)   F, G. A monad, showing action of the flagellum (*after Krijgsman*, 1925): F. recovery stroke, successive stages in 1–7; G. backward lash, successive positions in 8–13.   1, locomotory flagella; 2, trailing flagellum; 3, blepharoplasts; 4, cytostome; 5, undulating membrane; 6, basal rod; 7, rhizoplast; 8, centriole; 9, nucleus; 10, axostyle; 11, endosome; 12, pyrenoid; 13, parabasal body; 14, perirhizoplastic ring (nature unknown).

cysts, of the same types as those of ciliates, occur in a number of flagellates (Figs. 24F and 25G). The nucleus is generally single and vesicular with a central endosome (Fig. 21C) but may be massive as in dinoflagellates (Fig. 24K). Assimilation products consist of starch, paramylum, glycogen, leucosin, and other forms of carbohydrates, and oil and fat drops.

The chlorophyll-bearing flagellates are exclusively or chiefly holophytic, and some species can flourish in the light on inorganic salts; but most require or are benefited by the addition of sugars and split products of proteins (page 58) and can become wholly saprozoic. The colorless flagellates are either saprozoic or holozoic. Holozoic nutrition is seen mostly among the colorless euglenoids, the free-living protomonads, and the dinoflagellates. In amoeboid phases, flagellates ingest prey after the manner of rhizopods. In other holozoic flagellates, food is generally engulfed at the anterior end, directly by a region near the flagellar base (Fig. 12B), or by way of a differentiated mouth, depression, or cytopharynx as in the colorless euglenoids (Fig. 27G, O, P). Some of the latter are provided with hard rods, the pharyngeal rods or trichites, which lie alongside the cytopharynx and assist in food intake (Fig. 27G, P). Currents created by flagellar undulations may waft small food objects toward the cytosome; or the flagellum may entangle the prey and draw it to the animal. The flagellar tip is apparently often used as a sense organ for the detection of food and the mouth rim is also chemically sensitive. Practically nothing is known of the details of digestion.

The flagellates inhabit water everywhere and are among the most typical and abundant plankton forms of salt and fresh waters. The free-living forms embrace solitary, sessile, and colonial types. Sessile forms may be fastened directly by a stalk or live free or attached inside vase-like or tubular cases that may be secreted upon one another to produce branching colonies with a flagellate occupying the open end of each branch (Figs. 10B and 30L). Other colonial types are free-swimming plates or spheres of a few to many thousand individuals, held together by gelatinous or cellulose secretions (Fig. 29). The class also includes many parasites, some, the trypanosomes, of great importance to man.

In their possession of chlorophyll, their holophytic mode of nutrition, and their synthesis of carbohydrates with the aid of light, the flagellates betray a close relationship to algae and are generally considered as such in botanical treatises. It is probably impractical to erect any definition for separating the strictly holophytic flagellates from algae; but neither is it possible to isolate them from the animal types of flagellates.

3. The Flagella and Flagellar Movement.—The flagellum is a long delicate filament used for swimming, creating water currents, and as a sensory organelle for exploring the surroundings. The number usually varies from one to four, but numerous flagella occur in some parasitic groups. Where two or more occur, they may be equal in length and similar in function, but often one is the *main* flagellum while the others are smaller *accessory* flagella; or one may be directed backward as a *trailing* flagellum that apparently serves to anchor and steer the animal (Fig. 21*A*, *B*, *D*). In some parasites one of the flagella forms the border of a thin wavy protoplasmic extension called the *undulating membrane* (Fig. 21*B*). Flagella commonly spring from the anterior tip, directly (Fig. 21*C*), or from a groove, pit, or the cytopharynx, often by two roots, as in many euglenoids (Fig. 22*A*); in dinoflagellates the flagella originate from the lateral surface (Fig. 24*G*) and in trypanosomes (Fig. 31*E*) from the posterior end (regarded by some, however, as the anterior end). The flagellum is cylindrical or flat and band-like, and consists of a stiff elastic straight or spiral axial fibril, the *axoneme*, itself possibly a bundle of fibers, and an enclosing protoplasmic *sheath*, continuous with the cytosome and enwrapping the axoneme in a spiral manner, often leaving the axoneme tip free.

Flagellar attachments are often complex, and the subject is still further obscured by the lack of a uniform terminology. A flagellum always originates from a kinetic element (page 57) whose substance is in fact continuous with the axoneme and which may be intranuclear or cytosomal. In the simplest case, exemplified in only a few flagellates, the flagellum springs from the nucleus, either directly (when the nucleus is at the surface) or by way of a rhizoplast. But generally each flagellum is attached to a granule (or two when its root forks), termed the *basal body* or *blepharoplast* (Fig. 21*B*, *C*, *D*). The blepharoplast is generally situated at the surface point from which the flagellum springs but may occur on the nuclear membrane or in the cytosome (Fig. 24*F*), in which cases the axoneme continues as a *rhizoplast*. When the blepharoplast functions as a centriole in division, it is often called *centroblepharoplast*. In other cases there is a separate centriole often fused to the nuclear membrane (Figs. 9 and 21*B*) and this is connected to the basal bodies of the flagella by rhizoplasts. One to many *parabasal bodies* occur in the orders Protomonadina, Polymastigina, and Hypermastigina as rounded, oval, ring-shaped, rod-like, or elongated bodies attached directly or by a thread to the blepharoplasts (Figs. 21*D* and 11). In some cases they react chemically like mitochondria, in others they give the Feulgen test (page 54) for nuclear material, and often they take part in division. It has recently been maintained that they constitute the Golgi apparatus of these flagellate groups. In the Polymastigina, a rhizoplast, or bundle of rhizoplasts, in cases where the flagella are numerous, continues the length of the animal as a rod, the *axostyle*, which is said to stain like flagella and possibly to serve as a steering device (Figs. 21*B* and 33*B*, *C*, *G*). In parasitic flagellates, still other elongated elements may be present attached to the blepharoplasts, such as *parastyles, cytostomal fibers* encircling the cytostome, and *chromatic basal rods* that extend along the attachment of the undulating membrane (Fig. 33*A, D*). It is impossible at present to evaluate and homologize these various structures associated with flagella.

The mechanism of flagellar movement is not understood. The mechanism resides in the flagellum itself, since this continues active when isolated if the basal body is retained. Without the latter, activity ceases almost instantly. Of various explanations of the movement that which assumes contractility in the flagellar sheath seems most tenable. As to the way in which the flagellum accomplishes locomotion, there are three main ideas. Bütschli's screw theory postulates a spiral turning like a screw exerting a propeller action, pulling the animal forward. Metzner, studying currents set up by rotating wires fastened at one end, concluded that a simple flagellar beat in a circle tracing a cone develops sufficient current to pull the animal forward. These theories are rendered doubtful by the direct observations of Ulehla and Krijsman (Fig. 21*E–G*) on swimming flagellates in dark-field illumination in which the area traced by the flagellum appears as a light space. These observers state that the ordinary movement of a flagellum is a sidewise lash, consisting of an effective downstroke with the flagellum held out, and a relaxed recovery stroke in which the flagellum, strongly curved, is brought forward again. As a result the animal moves forward and is also caused to rotate on its longitudinal axis. Other movements observed were wave-like undulations pulling the animal forward when proceeding from tip to base, causing backward movement when progressing from base to tip. When such undulations are spiral they cause rotation in the opposite direction.

4. Behavior.—Free solitary forms swim in a spiral path rotating on the longitudinal axis and keeping always the same surface facing the axis of the spiral. Colonies such as *Volvox* rotate on the antero-posterior axis because of the coordinated oblique beat of all the flagella but are said to move in a straight line without spiraling. Some species move directly forward without rotating by undulating only the flagellar tip in one plane. Many at times absorb or cast off the flagella and then become amoeboid or move by body contortions.

General reactions have been tested chiefly in *Euglena* and *Chilomonas.* These react to mechanical shock, temperature change, and chemicals, and the former reacts to light. The reaction is of the general phobotactic type (page 67). The animal stops or slows down, traces a wider spiral by swinging the anterior end farther out, and starts off in a new direction, or else simply turns at an angle to its former course. The chlorophyll-bearing flagellates react definitely to both intensity and direction of light, and this reaction has been studied extensively, especially in the Phytomonadina.   By causing a shadow to travel over *Euglena* it has been proved that light is perceived only at the anterior end, presumably by the light organelle.   Any change in the direction of light causes the light-sensitive substance to be shaded by the stigma at each rotation, and this stimulus acts to increase the flagellar beat on the side away from the light turning the colony toward the light.   The reaction seems to be a direct orientation of the topotactic sort.   These forms are positive to moderate light intensity and negative to strong light or darkness; but temperature, previous light conditions, etc., modify the reaction.   The colorless flagellates are indifferent to light.

The flagellates readily encyst under even very slight changes of conditions.   Besides forming the ordinary protective cysts, the holophytic flagellates often assume the *palmella* state (Figs. 23*B* and 28*B*) losing their flagella and rounding up into an alga-like cell, in which metabolism continues and reproduction occurs by fission so that extensive green scums on ponds may result, composed entirely of flagellates in the palmella state.

5. **Reproduction.**—The flagellates reproduce almost exclusively by longitudinal fission (Fig. 17*A*).   Fission is transverse in the dinoflagellates (Fig. 26*B–D*).   Fission begins usually by the division of a kinetic element, which may be the basal body of the flagellum, or the centriole when a separate centriole is present (Fig. 16*H*), or a body that issues from the nucleus (Fig. 22*B*).   The kinetic element divides in two and the two halves are often connected by a strand, the *desmose* (Fig. 22*E*), or in some cases by a spindle (Fig. 16*H*).   New flagella grow out from the divided kinetic elements (Fig. 22*B*) or one daughter cell may retain the old flagellum and the other form a new one.   Usually the spindle forms entirely inside the nucleus (Fig. 16*H*) and generally lacks centrioles of its own but frequently comes into relation with the kinetic elements in the cytosome, which act as centrioles, and often the desmose, which seems to be a sort of spindle, takes the place of a regular spindle, or becomes incorporated into or closely associated with the intranuclear spindle (Fig. 22*E*).   The role of the endosome varies.   In some cases spindle, centrioles, and chromosomes develop entirely from the endosome; in others the endosome is composed entirely of plastin, furnishes nothing in mitosis, and disappears (Fig. 16*H*).   In the Euglenoidina (Fig. 22*A–D*) the centrioles arise from a chromatoid body issuing from the nucleus, they become basal bodies and grow out the new flagella, the spindle is represented only by a desmose between the centrioles, and, inside the nucleus, the endosome draws out acting as a kinetic element, while the chromosomes arise from the rest of the nucleus.   In flagellates the chromosomes are usually definite in number and form and behave in typical fashion.   After the nuclear division, the cytopharynx divides and

the animal then divides from the anterior tip posteriorly. Often such structures as axostyles, parabasals, and flagella disappear, and new ones form from the kinetic elements. Fission may occur at some definite hour of the day, and some flagellates divide only in the encysted state, rounding up and losing the flagella beforehand.

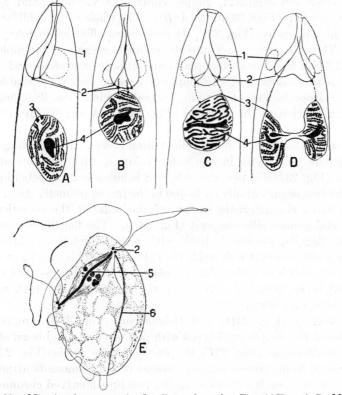

Fig. 22.—Mitotic phenomena in flagellates (see also Fig. 16*H*). *A–D.* Mitosis in *Euglena spirogyra* (*after Ratcliffe*, 1927): *A.* Intranuclear body moves to periphery of nucleus and divides in two. *B.* Nucleus moves near cytopharynx and each intranuclear body again divides forming a new blepharoplast from which a new flagellum grows out. *C.* New flagellum joins the old one, endosome elongates, acting as a spindle. *D.* Nucleus and cytopharynx dividing. *E. Trichomonas batrachorum* in division (*after Dobell*, 1909), with an intranuclear desmose around which the spindle has formed. 1, cytopharynx; 2, blepharoplasts; 3, intranuclear bodies; 4, endosome; 5, desmose; 6, axostyle.

Multiple fission or sporulation is seen chiefly in the trypanosomes and Dinoflagellata. Sexual processes are very rare in flagellates except in the Phytomonadina, described later. One or two cases of hologamy or fusion of two ordinary individuals to an encysted zygote (Fig. 17*G–J*) have been observed, but the fate of the zygote is unknown. Lackey cultivated two common colorless euglenoids, *Entosiphon sulcatum*, and *Peranema trichophora*, for many generations—947 in the former species

—and observed no loss of vitality, no variation in fission rate, and no indications of any sexual process or process of periodic nuclear reorganization.

6. Order Chrysomonadina.—These are typically small, oval forms, solitary or colonial, with one or two flagella, yellow or brown chromoplasts, often red stigmata, simple contractile vacuoles, and a single vesicular nucleus (Figs. 23 and 24A–B). The whole order exhibits strong amoeboid tendencies (Fig. 23C, J) and shows affinities in many directions. Thus they may pass into the palmella stage and resemble algae (Fig. 23B); or lose the chromoplasts and appear as protomonads; or by loss of both flagella and chromoplasts become indistinguishable from typical rhizopods. In one group, axopods encircle the flagellum, suggesting a relation to the Heliozoa (Fig. 23G). A number are provided with gelatinous coverings or enclosed in vase-shaped or tubular cases or protected by skeletons of silica or lime often beset with projecting spines. Nutrition is holophytic in the colored forms, with the formation of leucosin (Fig. 23D–F), never starch, and is holozoic in amoeboid phases. Reproduction occurs wholly by fission in the free or palmella state.

The most characteristic feature of the order is the secretion of a unique endogenous siliceous cyst (Fig. 23L). The flagellate rounds up, loses its flagella, surrounds itself with a thick gelatinous layer, and secretes a siliceous cyst wall inside the cytosome. This cyst has a funnel-shaped opening into which the cytoplasm outside the cyst wall eventually withdraws, forming a plug for the opening. The cyst may be ornamented with spines.

Chromulina (Fig. 23D) and *Ochromonas* (Fig. 23E) are common examples of the simple oval types with one or two large brown chromoplasts; *Mallomonas* (Fig. 23F) is spiny. *Synura uvella* (Fig. 23A), in fresh water, forms free-swimming spheres of chrysomonads attached at their inner ends, each with two flagella, two brown curved chromoplasts, a red stigma, and a spiny cuticle. In *Dinobryon*, (Fig. 10B) also of fresh water, the tiny animals may occupy vase-like cellulose cases fastened into a branching colony. The family *Silicoflagellidae*, marine, are provided with a siliceous skeleton in the form of rings or latticework, often spiny (Fig. 23M). In the family Coccolithophoridae (Fig. 23N) variously shaped pieces of calcium carbonate are embedded in an investing membrane inclosing the flagellate. These pieces, called *coccoliths*, were known in the ocean sediments long before their origin from flagellates was discovered. The chrysomonads lead directly to a group of filamentous brown algae (Chrysophyceae), such as *Phaeothamnion* (Fig. 24A), the cells of which contain two brown chromoplasts, can give rise to endogenous siliceous cysts like those of chrysomonads, and at times release free-swimming flagellate swarmers (Fig. 24B) that closely

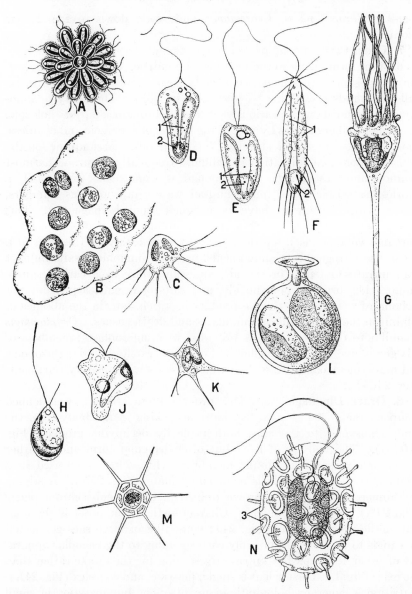

Fig. 23.—Chrysomonads. *A. Synura uvella.* (*After Conn,* 1905.) *B. Synura* in the palmella stage. *C.* Synura in an amoeboid phase. (*After Pascher,* 1912.) *D. Chromulina.* *E. Ochromonas.* *F. Mallomonas.* (*After Conrad,* 1926.) *G. Cyrtophora,* a chrysomonad resembling a heliozoan with stiff pseudopods. (*After Pascher,* 1918.) *H. Ochromonas.* *J* and *K.* Same, passing into an amoeboid phase. (*After Pascher,* 1918.) *L.* Cyst of *Chromulina* (*after Conrad,* 1926), containing two animals. *M.* A silicoflagellate, from life, California Coast. *N.* A coccolithophorid, *Coccochrysis.* (*After Conrad,* 1926.) 1, the two yellow chromoplasts; 2, leucosin body; 3, coccolith.

resemble *Chromulina* or *Ochromonas* and settle down to found new colonies.

7. Order Cryptomonadina.—These are small oval flagellates generally of constant form owing to the presence of a cuticle. They have a gullet-like depression from which two flagella spring and which bears in its walls little rods resembling trichocysts (Fig. 24*F*). They may be holophytic, provided with variously colored chromoplasts; or holozoic, ingesting small organisms by way of the gullet; or saprozoic and colorless. Food reserves consist of starches, fats, and oils. Assumption of the palmella stage and formation of cellulose frequently occur. The most common and best known cryptomonad is *Chilomonas* (Fig. 24*F*), a colorless saprozoic form, found in foul waters in enormous numbers, whose synthetic powers have been much studied (page 59). This animal can synthesize starches, fats, proteins, and protoplasm from inorganic compounds if silicon is present as a catalyzer (Mast *et al.*). It can use nitrogen from amino acids, urea, or ammonium salts but not from nitrates, nitrites, or the air, and can utilize as a carbon source amino acids, urea, carbon dioxide, and salts of organic acids, but not carbonates. The usual reserve product is starch, but, in the absence of sulphur in the medium, fat accumulates and death ensues. *Cryptomonas* is similar to *Chilomonas* but is provided with chloroplasts; members of this genus live as zooxanthellae in Foraminifera, Radiolaria, rhizopods, and many metazoans, escaping at times as free-swimming cryptomonads (Fig. 24*C–E*).

8. Order Dinoflagellata.—This order centers about a well-defined group characterized by two flagella, one trailing in the body axis, the other transverse to the axis, both typically occupying grooves (Fig. 24*H, G*). The body is of fixed but often irregular form and is either naked or enclosed in a simple membrane (Fig. 24*G*) or encased in a cellulose cuirass of two shells or of many plates (Fig. 25*N*). A stigma and numerous small yellow, brown, or infrequently greenish chromoplasts (Fig. 24*K*) are usually present. Characteristic of the order is the non-contractile *pusule* system (Fig. 24*J*) consisting of large sacs connected by canals to the exterior, possibly corresponding to the vacuolar apparatus of other Protozoa but apparently serving for the intake rather than the exit of fluid. The nucleus is single, massive, and complex (Fig. 24*K*). Nutrition is generally holophytic or mixotrophic, but ingestion of small organisms in an amoeboid manner at the ventral flagellar furrow has been repeatedly observed. Some through loss of chromoplasts have become entirely holozoic and partly or completely amoeboid in form and behavior. Others pass the greater part of their existence as round floating bodies enclosed in a cellulose membrane and simulating algae (Fig. 25*A*). A large number are ecto- or entoparasites existing chiefly in a nonflagellate cyst-like condition (Fig. 25*J–L*). Finally, many of the zooxanthellae, especially those of the Radiolaria, are believed to be dinoflagellates (Fig. 24*C–E*). All these aberrant forms indicate their relationship to the typical dinoflagellates by their production of young with characteristic dinoflagellate features (Fig. 25*E*, *M*).

Doflein recognizes three subdivisions of the order. To the Adinida belong a few forms, chiefly marine, with simple oval bodies, naked or enclosed in a cellulose membrane or a cellulose shell of two valves. Two flagella spring from the anterior end, one held forward, the other transversely.

The suborder Dinifera includes all the typical dinoflagellates. In these there is a ventral longitudinal groove, the *sulcus*, from which the *longitudinal flagellum* springs, trailing downwards; and a transverse or spiral groove, the *girdle* or *annulus*, which may make several spiral turns around the body (Fig. 24*H*) and in which the *transverse flagellum*, springing at the junction of sulcus and girdle, plays in wave-like undulations. In armored forms, the grooves are accentuated by thin projections of the armor. The longitudinal flagellum is said to cause forward progression, the transverse to impart rotation. The animals swim in an upright or oblique position in a bouncing jerky fashion, rotating on the long axis. Reproduction occurs by longitudinal fission in the free state or in a cyst, or by multiple fission in a cyst. The cysts usually hatch into swarmers resembling *Glenodinium* or *Gymnodinium* (Fig. 24*G*, *L*).

The typical dinoflagellates may be roughly divided into unarmored and armored groups. The former, placed chiefly in the family *Gymnodiniidae*, are naked or encased in a single cellulose membrane. They are yellow, brown, or of a variety of delicate colors and are very abundant in the ocean below the surface. A few species occur in great numbers in fresh water, such as species of *Glenodinium* (Fig. 24*L*) and *Gymnodinium* (Fig. 24*G*), oval forms with typical sulcus, girdle, and flagella. *Polykrikos* (Fig. 25*F*) is a curious form consisting of a chain of two, four, or eight individuals produced by incomplete fission. This genus also bears trichocysts, as do likewise some other genera (Fig. 25*G*). *Pouchetia* (Fig. 25*H*) has a remarkably developed light-perceiving organ with a large lens-like body. Some of the unarmored forms have degenerated into spherical floating algal-like cells that form crescent-shaped cysts from which a number of swimming *Gymnodinium-* or *Glenodinium*-like young emerge (Fig. 25*A–E*). Most remarkable are the parasitic *Gymnodiniidae* studied chiefly by Chatton. They live on the surface or in the intestine of various marine pelagic animals, particularly copepods, as round or pyriform sacs (Fig. 25*J*) often stalked and attached to the host by root-like extensions or as oval bodies lying in the interior. They reproduce by sporulation into a few to several hundred *Gymnodinium*-like

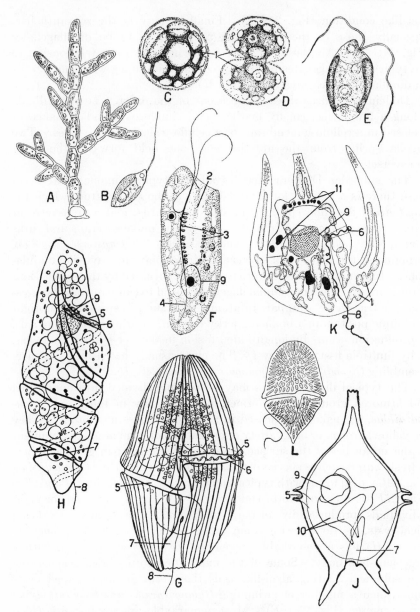

Fig. 24.—Chrysomonads, cryptomonads, dinoflagellates.   *A.* The brown alga *Phaeo-thamnion.*   *B.* Free chrysomonad stage of the same.   (*After Pascher,* 1925.)   *C.* A zoöxanthella from the foraminiferan *Peneroplis,* with one brown chromoplast and starch bodies.   *D.* the same in fission.   *E.* The same, free as a cryptomonad (*Chrysidella*) with one curved chromoplast.   (*After Winter,* 1907.)   *F. Chilomonas paramecium,* a crypto-monad (*after Prowazek,* 1903), with long rhizoplast and pharyngeal trichocysts.   *G.* A typical unarmored dinoflagellate, *Gymnodinium costatum.*   (*After Kofoid and Swezy,* 1921.)   *H.* An unarmored dinoflagellate, *Cochlodinium,* in which both grooves make spiral

swarmers (Fig. 25K–M). In some genera one cell remains behind and continues to give off cells that sporulate young (Fig. 25L).

The armored or thecate dinoflagellates are divisible into two families, the Dinophysidae and the Peridiniidae. The former, marine, have an armor composed of two main lateral valves sutured along the median sagittal plane (Fig. 25O). The girdle, displaced very near the apical pole, has wide projecting lists, and other regions of the armor also may bear wing-like extensions, so that these forms present a very bizarre appearance. The Peridiniidae (Figs. 25N, 26E, and 10A) are typical and abundant plankton forms of oceans and inland waters. They are encased in a cuirass composed of a number of cellulose plates, often porous and variously ornamented, which differ in pattern in different genera but follow the general plan of a circlet of *precingular* plates above the girdle, *postcingular* plates below the girdle, and *apical* and *antapical* plates at the two poles, respectively. Growth is permitted by the interpolation of cement at the sutures. Reproduction occurs usually by binary fission (Fig. 26B–D), in which the armor separates along certain definite sutures in a transverse plane and each daughter animal retains part of the old armor and secretes the remainder. In some forms, the animal casts off the armor, becomes a naked swimmer like *Gymnodinium*, and divides only in this state. The fresh-water species encyst at certain seasons of the year, secreting a cellulose cyst inside the armor. These cysts remain viable for years and upon hatching pass through *Gymnodinium* and *Glenodinium* stages. *Ceratium* is said to bud off small individuals at the sulcus. Sexual processes have been suspected, but good evidence is lacking. The typical genera with many species and varieties are *Peridinium* (Figs. 10A and 26E) and *Ceratium* (Figs. 24K, 25N, and 26A), the former rounded or polygonal, or with one short horn above, two below; the latter known by the three long horns, one apical, two basal, straight or recurved. In *Ceratium*, at fission, the apical horn of one product may remain locked in the girdle of the other and in this way long chains (Fig. 26A) may be formed of which the two original fission products constitute the ends.

The Cystoflagellata, formerly regarded as a separate order of flagellates, include only three species, of which the most important and common is *Noctiluca miliaris* (or *scintillans*) (Fig. 26F). This is a large gelatinous sphere, often 1 mm. or more in diameter, floating on the sea, usually near shores, often in vast numbers. There is a ventral depres-

---

turns. (*After Kofoïd and Swezy*, 1921.) J. View of *Peridinium*, to show the pusule system. (*After Haye*, 1930.) K. Section through *Ceratium*, to show internal structure. (*After Schütt*, 1895.) L. *Glenodinium*, from life. 1, chromoplast; 2, cytopharynx; 3, trichocysts; 4, rhizoplast; 5, annulus; 6, transverse flagellum; 7, sulcus; 8, longitudinal flagellum; 9, nucleus; 10, pusule system; 11, fat spheres.

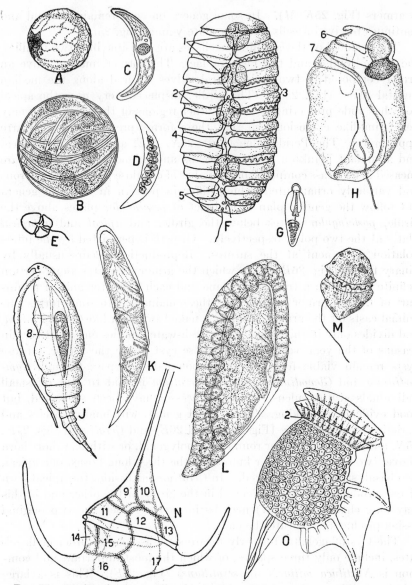

Fig. 25.—Dinoflagellates, continued.   *A. Gymnodinium lunula*, a floating alga-like sphere.   *B.* Same producing crescentic cysts.   *C.* One of the crescentic cysts free.   *D.* Same, giving rise to eight gymnodinid swarmers.   *A–D.* (*After Kofoid and Swezy, 1921, modified from Dogiel.*   *E.* One of the swarmers free. (*After Lebour, 1925.*)   *F. Polykrikos*, an unarmored dinoflagellate with 8 grooves and flagella and four nuclei.   *G.* A trichocyst of *Polykrikos*.   (*After Kofoid and Swezy, 1921.*)   *H. Pouchetia*, showing the enormous photoreceptor with lens. (*After Schütt, 1895.*)   *J. Cyclops*, containing a parasitic dinoflagellate, *Blastodinium*, in the intestine.   *K.* The parasite enlarged.   *L.* The same, in process of sporulating gymnodinid young, with two persistent cells (trophocytes) which continue to sporulate.   *M.* One of the gymnodinid young free. (*All after Chatton, 1920.*)   *N.* A

sion, representing the sulcus, which bears a rudimentary longitudinal flagellum and leads to the mouth near which springs a thick motile *tentacle*, apparently not a flagellum. From a central clump of protoplasm containing the nucleus delicate strands run through the watery interior to the periphery. Nutrition is holozoic. The animal is noted for its phosphorescence and is responsible for much of the phosphorescence of ocean shore waters. Reproduction occurs, after disappearance of all structure, by binary fission and by gamete formation. In the latter process the protoplasm collects into a multinucleate surface disk, and this elevates into numerous little uninucleate buds, each of which constricts off as a gymnodinid isogamete with one long trailing flagellum (Fig. 26*G*, *H*). These fuse in pairs, but the fate of the resulting zygote has not been followed.

The other cystoflagellates are the rare *Leptodiscus medusoides* and *Craspedotella pileolus* (Fig. 26*J*), umbrella-shaped masses resembling little medusae and swimming like medusae by contractions of marginal myonemes. Each has one rudimentary flagellum.

9. Order Euglenoidina.—These flagellates are of moderate size and definite form with a pellicle often striated or ridged (Fig. 27*B*, *D*, *H*). Some in which the pellicle is soft and yielding habitually display euglenoid movements, but in others the pellicle is so rigid that alteration of shape is impossible. The anterior end bears a red stigma in green forms and is provided with a pit or cytopharynx from which one or two flagella emerge and which serves for food intake in holozoic types. Each flagellum is fastened to the wall of the cytopharynx, often by two roots (Fig. 26*K*), and a special granule may occur at the fork of the roots. The vacuole system situated near the stigma is erroneously described in textbooks as "complex." The large contractile vacuole discharges into the expanded gullet base, often unnecessarily termed reservoir, and has no continuity with the succeeding vacuole. Just before the vacuole collapses there appear near it or around it a few to many small vacuoles (Fig. 26*L*) which do not, as usually stated, discharge into the vacuole, but fuse together to form the next vacuole (Hyman, 1938). The vacuolar system therefore does not differ from that of other Protozoa. The members of the order are colorless or provided with few to numerous chloroplasts of various shapes (Fig. 27). The green forms are wholly or partly holophytic and also utilize or even require dissolved organic nutrients, and most can become wholly saprozoic. The colorless genera are mostly

typical armored dinoflagellate, *Ceratium tripos*. (*After Jörgenson,* 1911.) *O. Dinophysis.* (*After Kofoid and Skogsberg,* 1928.) 1, nucleus; 2, annulus; 3, transverse flagellum; 4, sulcus; 5, longitudinal flagellum; 6, lens; 7, pigment cup; 8, parasite; 9, and 10, apical plates; 11, 12, 13, precingular plates; 14, 15, 17, postcingular plates; 16, antapical plate. There are two apicals, two precingulars, two postcingulars and one antapical on the other side.

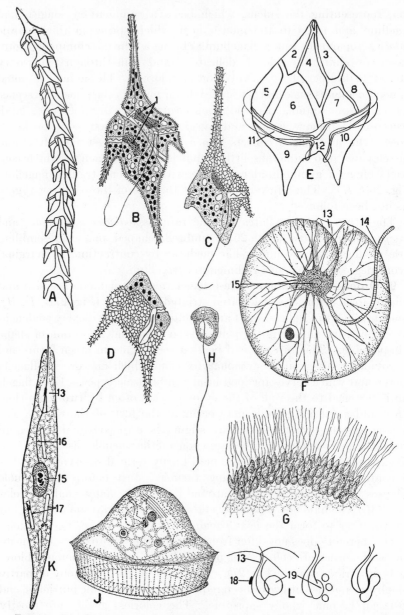

Fig. 26.—Dinoflagellates, continued, Euglenoidina.   A. Chain of *Ceratium*, formed by fission.   (*After Jörgenson*, 1911.)   B. Ceratium in fission, showing diagonal line of separation of the plates.   C. The anterior daughter, and D, the posterior daughter, old plates with pattern.   (*After Lauterborn*, 1895.)   E. Peridinium, showing armor of cellulose plates (*after Barrows*, 1918); for back view see Fig. 10A.   F. Noctiluca.   (*After Pratje*, 1921.)   G. Noctiluca forming gametes.   H. One of the gametes.   (*After Robin*, 1878.)   J. Craspedotella.   (*After Kofoid*, 1905.)   K. Euglena acus (*after Hall and Jahn*, 1925), showing

holozoic, ingesting other Protozoa, algae, diatoms, etc., and some are provided with pharyngeal rods (Fig. 27*G*, *P*) or some other form of trichite lying alongside the cytopharynx. The principal reserve product is paramylum, often stored in definite bodies of unusual shapes, as rods, links, etc. (Figs. 2*E*, 27*C*, *D*). The nucleus is single and vesicular with a central endosome. Encystment is common, and many pass into the palmella stage for long periods. Reproduction occurs by longitudinal fission in the free (Fig. 17*A*) or palmella state and in typical cases is initiated by a centriole (intranuclear body) issuing from the nucleus (Fig. 22*A–D*). This divides to furnish the new basal bodies from which new flagella or flagellar roots sprout and which for a time at least remain connected with the nuclear membrane by rhizoplasts. No mitotic figure appears, but the endosome acts as a division center pulling in two, and chromosomes form around the endosome. Sexual processes are absent except in *Scytomonas* where hologamy has been observed.

This order includes the common fresh-water flagellates seen in laboratories. *Euglena*, elongated and more or less metabolic (Fig. 27*A*, *C–E*), *Phacus*, flattened and stiff (Fig. 27*M*, *N*), and *Lepocinclis* (Fig. 27*B*, *H*), bottle-shaped or oval with a rigid striated pellicle, are the best known green forms with red stigmata, common everywhere in standing waters. *Trachelomonas* (Fig. 27*J*, *K*) with numerous species is enclosed in a brown rounded or oval, often spiny, shell with an anterior collar through which the single flagellum emerges. Among the commoner colorless genera are *Astasia* (Fig. 27*O*) with one flagellum, *Peranema* (Fig. 27*P*) with a pharyngeal rod, one free flagellum, and one flagellum fastened to the pellicle, and *Entosiphon* (Fig. 27*G*), *Heteronema* (Fig. 21*A*), and *Anisonema* with two flagella, one trailing. Some *Euglenas* and *Euglena*-like genera, green or colorless with one to several flagella, inhabit the rectum of tadpoles.

The genus *Euglena* comprises a number of species (about one hundred) that vary much in size, shape, and structural details. Most are of simple fusiform shape, but some are very much elongated and may be much flattened (Fig. 27*C*). The pellicle may be smooth or more frequently is marked by spiral striations or ridges or spiral rows of tubercles (Fig. 27*D*) said to discharge mucus. Depending on the rigidity of the pellicle, the body may be very flexible and capable of pronounced euglenoid movements or may exhibit little change of shape. The long flattened forms often twist their bodies into a spiral (Fig. 27*C*). The majority

flagellar attachments. *L.* Three stages in the vacuolar contraction of *Phacus*, from life; as the vacuole fuses with the gullet, three small vacuoles appear and these unite together to form the next vacuole. 1, dividing chromosomes in telophase; 2–4, apical plates; 5–8, precingular plates; 9–10, postcingular plates; 11, cingulum; 12, sulcus; 13, cytopharynx; 14, tentacle; 15, nucleus; 16, rhizoplast; 17, paramylum bodies; 18 stigma; 19, contractile vacuole.

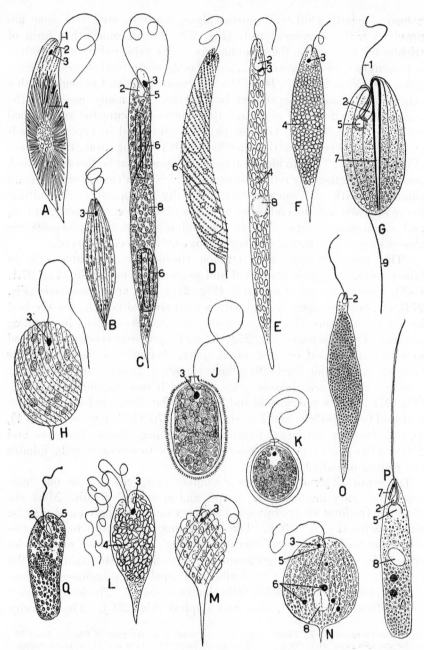

Fig. 27.—Some Euglenoidina, from life, collected around New York City. *A. Euglena viridis*, note stout form and radiating chloroplasts. *B. Lepocinclis marssonii*. *C. Euglena oxyuris* with two link-shaped paramylum bodies. *D. Euglena spirogyra* with spiral rows of tubercles in the periplast. *E. Euglena deses* (?). *F. Euglena proxima* (?). *G. Entosiphon*

range between 50 and 100 micra in length, but there are several very small species between 25 and 50 micra, as *E. minima* and *E. gracilis*, and a few very large ones, 200 or more micra long.   The largest form is *E. oxyuris* (Fig. 27*C*), which may attain a length of nearly 500 micra.

The anterior end contains the flask-shaped cytopharynx, to one side of which is found a mass of red hematochrome granules, the stigma, serving to shade a light-sensitive region.   Near the enlarged base ("reservoir") of the cytopharynx occurs the contractile vacuole, described above. The single flagellum emerging from the narrowed neck of the cytopharynx may be very short or as long as or longer than the body and apparently is readily shed or absorbed.   It is fastened to the wall of the cytopharynx base by two roots (Fig. 26*K*) each anchored in a blepharoplast; at the point of forking of the roots there is a granule.   The cytosome contains a few to many green chloroplasts of various shapes, as disks, ovals, stars, rods, and bands.   In several species, long slender rod-shaped chloroplasts are arranged in one or more radiating groups, giving the impression of star-shaped chloroplasts.   The textbook species, *E. viridis*, usually misidentified and less common in many localities than several other species, is recognizable by its plump form and single group of slender chloroplasts radiating from a central point (Fig. 27*A*).   Typically there is a pyrenoid in the center of each chloroplast, and this may be enclosed in a sheath or two hemispherical shells of paramylum.   Paramylum also occurs free in the cytosome as bodies of various shapes—disks, ovals, rods, and links.   Several of the larger species, as *E. oxyuris* (Fig. 27*C*), have a conspicuous link-shaped paramylum body in each end.   The cytosome also contains mitochondria and volutin grains, and Golgi material has been reported in the vicinity of the vacuolar apparatus. The nucleus occurs near the middle of the body and is spherical with a central endosome.   The latter acts as spindle during division, while the chromosomes come from the zone around the endosome (Fig. 22*A–D*). The chloroplasts also divide, either during or after fission.   Reproduction occurs by longitudinal fission in the free or encysted state.   *Euglena* very readily encysts, forming both thin- and thick-walled cysts within which fissions may occur.   Such a palmella stage is of regular occurrence in some species and may coat large areas with a green scum.   There is no evidence of any sexual process in *Euglena*.

In certain species, as *E. rubra* and *E. sanguinea*, the cytosome contains numerous hematochrome granules.   These forms are red in the

---

ovatum with hairpin-shaped trichite.   *H. Lepocinclis ovum.   J* and *K.* Two species of *Trachelomonas*, with a brown shell.   *L. Eutreptia viridis.   M. Phacus pyrum.   N. Phacus orbicularis.   O. Astasia.   P. Peranema trichophora*, with two trichites.   All green with a red stigma, except *G, O, P.   Q.* A chloromonad, *Coelomonas.   (After Poisson,* 1935.)   1. flagellum; 2, cytopharynx; 3, stigma; 4, chloroplasts; 5, contractile vacuole; 6, paramylum body; 7, trichite; 8, nucleus; 9, trailing flagellum.

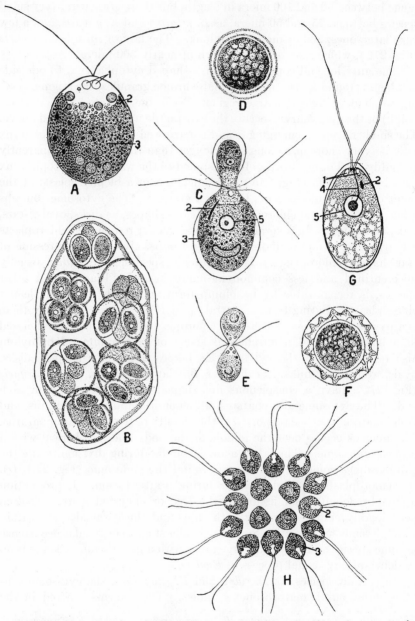

Fig. 28.—Phytomonads. *A. Chlamydomonas*, from life. *B. Chlamydomonas* in the palmella state. *C.* Anisogametes of *C. braunii.* *D.* Resulting zygote. *E.* Isogametes of *C. perty*, fusing. *F.* Resulting zygote. (*B–F, after Goroschankin, 1892.*) *G. Polytoma uvella.* (*After Entz, 1918.*) *H. Gonium*, from life. 1, contractile vacuole; 2, stigma, 3, cup-shaped chloroplast; 4, rhizoplast; 5, nucleus.

sunlight, which induces dispersion of the granules, and green in the dark, or in shady spots, or on cloudy days because of the retreat of the granules to the interior. Color changes require but a few minutes.

The *Euglenas* take no solid food but subsist entirely by autotrophic plus saprozoic nutrition (see review by Hall, 1939). It is not unequivocally established that any species of *Euglena* can grow in the light on an inorganic medium; but some species have been so grown with only an extremely minute trace of organic material such as peptone. Most species appear to require at least amino acids in the medium, and some need more complex organic substances such as peptones. In the dark, *Euglenas* must of course have complex organic nutrients; chloroplasts and pyrenoids degenerate and disappear.

10. Order Chloromonadina.—This is a small, little-known group of moderate size with metabolic and amoeboid bodies, pale green chloroplasts, two flagella, one trailing, and oil, never carbohydrates, as the assimilation product (Fig. 27*Q*).

11. Order Phytomonadina or Volvocales.—These are small oval or elongated flagellates of fixed form, enclosed in a cellulose membrane, usually with two rather short equal flagella, red stigma, one large cup-shaped chloroplast, two small contractile vacuoles, and simple vesicular nucleus (Figs. 9, 21*C* and 28*A*). The group is chiefly in fresh water, single or colonial, with holophytic, saprozoic, or mixotrophic nutrition. Cyst and palmella formation occur. Reproduction is asexual by division within the membrane and sexual with all grades of isogamous and anisogamus gametes. The zygote is generally enclosed in a thick spiny shell and undergoes reduction in its first divisions.

The family Chlamydomonadidae includes the typical single forms, oval with two flagella, green, like *Chlamydomonas* (Fig. 28*A*), *Chlorogonium* (Fig. 18*A*), and *Haematococcus* (Fig. 9), or colorless, like *Polytoma* (Fig. 28*G*) and *Polytomella* (Fig. 15*B*). Some species may be colored red by hematochrome as *Chlamydomonas nivalis*, inhabiting melting snow, and *Haematococcus pluvialis*, whose sudden appearance in rain pools gives rise to the myth of red rain. The colorless forms are saprozoic and have been much experimented on with artificial media (page 58). This family reproduces asexually in a nonflagellate palmella-like state by two or three divisions into agametes that are simply small replicas of the parent (Fig. 28*B*). The smaller isogametes arise by a greater number of divisions; they fuse in pairs to form the thick-shelled zygote (Fig. 28*E*, *F*), which after a dormant period divides into several young like the parent except in size. Anisogametes also occur in some species, differing from each other and the parent primarily in size (Fig. 28*C*). In one species both iso- and anisogametes are said to be given off, depending on the number of divisions of the parent cell. Thus parents, agametes, isogametes, and anisogametes differ from each other only in

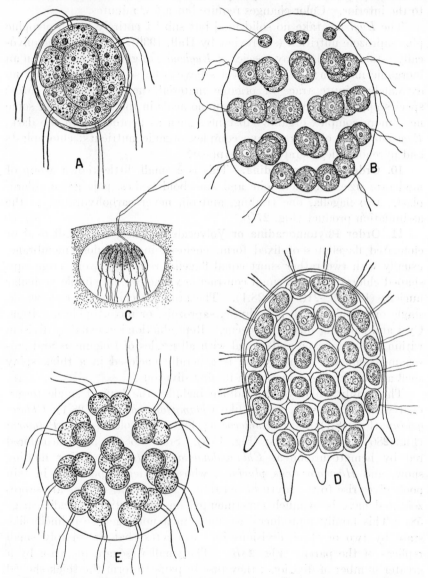

Fig. 29.—Colonial phytomonads. *A. Pandorina*, from life. *B. Pleodorina illinoisensis.* *C.* Sperm mass of the same. (*Both after Merton*, 1908.) *D. Platydorina caudata.* (*After Kofoid*, 1899.) *E. Eudorina*, from life.

size, and sexual differentiation is believed to have originated among such flagellates primarily through size differences.

The colonial Phytomonadina, included in the family *Volvocidae*, entirely fresh-water, consist of flat, oval, or spherical colonies of 4 to 128 cells in most genera, several hundred to over twenty thousand in *Volvox*. The individuals or zooids resemble *Chlamydomonas*, having two (four in *Spondylomorum*) flagella, a red stigma, two contractile vacuoles, large curved chloroplast, and cellulose membrane. The zooids may hold together loosely but generally are enclosed in a common gelatinous or cellulose membrane or embedded in a jelly; in *Volvox* they are also connected by protoplasmic bonds (Fig. 30*B*). Common genera are *Gonium* (Fig. 28*H*) forming flat squares of 4 to 16 cells; *Pandorina*, a sphere of 16 cells closely placed; *Eudorina* (Fig. 29*E*) of 32 cells near the surface of a jelly sphere; *Platydorina* (Fig. 29*D*) of 32 individuals arranged in a flat oval of jelly with scalloped posterior border; *Pleodorina* (Fig. 29*B*) with as many as 128 zooids on the surface of the jelly sphere; and *Volvox* (Fig. 30*A*) of hundreds or thousands of minute flagellates on the surface of a jelly ball often over 2 mm. in diameter. All the colonies are polarized since they swim always with one region, hence called the anterior pole, forward. Furthermore, in *Pleodorina* and *Volvox*, the zooids of the anterior pole are incapable of reproduction, may be smaller than the others (*Pleodorina*, Fig. 29*B*), and have larger light organelles, these grading in size to the posterior pole. Nutrition is holophytic. The group is noted for its reaction to light (page 69). In all the genera except *Pleodorina* and *Volvox*, every zooid is capable of both asexual and sexual reproduction; but in *Volvox* and still more markedly in *Pleodorina* the zooids at the anterior pole are sterile and may also differ morphologically from the others. Asexual reproduction takes place by the repeated division of the zooid into a miniature colony (Fig. 30*A*) that escapes by rupture of the parent. Sexual reproduction is universal. In the simpler forms like *Gonium*, the zooids themselves may become free and serve as isogamous gametes; or gametes may arise by fissions. Various degrees of anisogamy exist, reaching the extreme in *Eudorina*, *Pleodorina*, and *Volvox* where some zooids enlarge slightly or greatly to *macrogametes* or *eggs* (Fig. 30*C*) and others by repeated fissions produce plates or spheres of small biflagellate *microgametes* or *sperm* (Fig. 29*C*). In some species the sexes are separate, each colony producing only one kind of gamete. The zygote (Figs. 28*D*, *F* and 30*D*) develops a thick spiny shell, often red or orange, and after a dormant period hatches either as a small colony or as a biflagellate cell that later divides into a colony.

The Phytomonadina are of great interest in many respects of which not the least is their approach to multicellular organization. All grades of organization are presented from the loose association of like zooids as in *Spondylomorum* to colonies like *Pleodorina* and *Volvox* with their

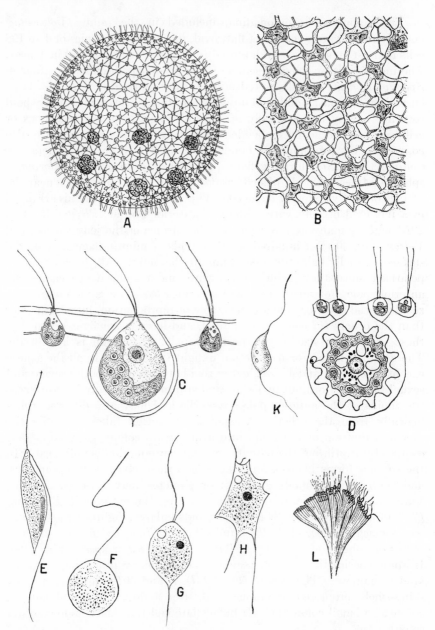

Fig. 30.—Phytomonads, continued; protomonads. A. *Volvox*, from life, with six daughter colonies. B. *Volvox globator*, surface view, showing protoplasmic connections between the zooids and gelatinous encasement of each. (*After Janet*, 1922.) C. *Volvox aureus*, two zooids and a macrogamete from the side. (*After Janet*, 1922.) D. *Volvox globator*, zygote. (*After Janet*, 1922.) E, F, G. Monads, from life, from foul water. H. Amoeboid phase of *G*, a few minutes later. K. *Cercomonas*. (*After Kent*, 1881) L. *Rhipidodendron*. (*After Blochmann*, 1895.)

anterior sterile somatic cells and posterior reproductive cells. The differentiation of anterior and posterior poles, the coordination of the flagella of all the zooids in swimming, and the cellular differentiation just mentioned all bespeak an organization higher than that of a colony and approaching that of a multicellular individual.

12. Order Protomonadina.—We here begin the consideration of flagellates of distinctly animal nature. This order comprises small colorless flagellates, mostly naked, often amoeboid or euglenoid, with usually one or two flagella, one often trailing, solitary, colonial, or parasitic. The free-living forms are mostly holozoic, usually taking in food directly by pseudopod formation (Fig. 12*B*) but in some cases by a simple mouth. The numerous parasitic species are saprozoic. Reproduction occurs by longitudinal fission and in addition by multiple fission in some parasitic species. Sexual reproduction is usually absent, but hologamy has been seen in some monads.

This order includes the flagellates often known as *monads* (Figs. 12*B* and 30*E–K*), by which one understands small, colorless, naked oval amoeboid forms with one to three flagella, one often trailing. They occur in foul waters and feces and may be unimportant intestinal inhabitants of man and other animals. Among the familiar genera are *Oicomonas, Rhizomastix*, and *Monas* (Figs. 12*B*, and 30*E–G*). Colonial forms include *Anthophysis* (Fig. 31*A*), forming spherical colorless colonies on the tips of slimy brown stalks from which they may break away as swimming, rotating spheres; *Dendromonas*, with single zooids terminating branching stalks; and *Rhipidodendron* (Fig. 30*L*) with zooids in the ends of gelatinous tubes.

The family Craspedomonadidae consists of the interesting *choanoflagellates*, so called from the thin transparent collar that encircles the base of the single flagellum (Fig. 31*B, D*). They are sessile, single (Fig. 31*B*), or colonial (Fig. 31*D*), usually enclosed in a soft investment or firm vase-like case fastened directly or by a stiff stalk. The structure of the collar is disputed. The collar is a food-catching device. Minute food particles, chiefly bacteria, upon touching the outer surface of the basal half of the collar, adhere and are slowly passed down the outside of the collar into the cytosome. The group is predominantly of fresh water. The colonial *Proterospongia* (Fig. 31*C*) forms a gelatinous mass with collared individuals at the surface and collarless interior amoeboid zooids derived from inwandered surface zooids. *Proterospongia* is regarded as a link between choanoflagellates and sponges. The choanoflagellates in turn probably came from Heliozoa, since the collar appears to arise through the fusion of axopods.

To the Protomonadina belongs also the *Bodo* group, colorless flagellates similar to monads but of more complicated structure with a

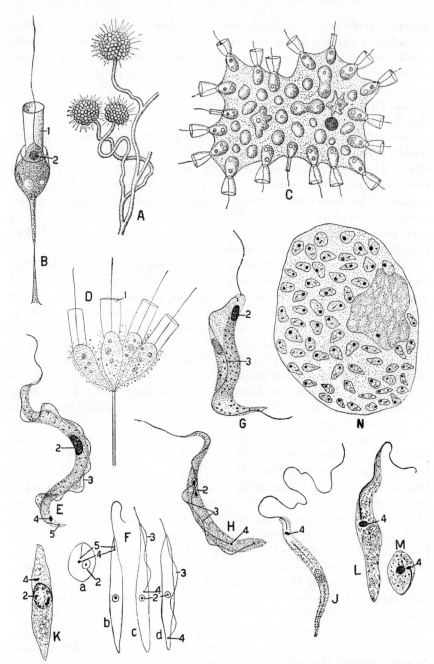

Fig. 31.—Protomonads.   *A. Anthophysis.*   (*After Kent, 1881.*)   *B.* A choanoflagellate. (*Codosiga, after Lapage,* 1925.)   *C. Proterospongia.*   (*After Kent,* 1881.)   *D.* A colonial choanoflagellate, *Codonosiga,* from life, with a gelatinous envestment.   *E. Trypanosoma*

cytostome, conspicuous parabasal body near the flagellar base or the nucleus, and two to four flagella, one trailing and often fastened to the cytosome or forming the border of an undulating membrane. They live free in foul water or feces or inhabit the mucous membranes of the intestinal or urogenital tracts. Here belong *Bodo*, mostly free-living, *Proteromonas* (= *Prowazekella*, Fig. 21*D*) from the colon of reptiles and amphibia, and *Trypanoplasma* (Fig. 31*G*), trypanosome-like parasites in the blood of fishes, transmitted by leeches, in which they undergo several changes of form. The cercomonads (Fig. 30*K*) have one to three anterior flagella and a trailing flagellum which is fastened to the body surface and becomes free at the posterior tip.

The most important protomonads from the human standpoint are the *trypanosomes*, family Trypanosomatidae or Herpetomonadidae, blood parasites of man and other vertebrates. They are typically (Fig. 31*E*) of elongated form, pointed at one or both ends, with one flagellum springing from a basal granule located in front of, near, or behind the vesicular nucleus. The basal granule is accompanied by another granule, variously called blepharoplast, kinetoplast, kinetonucleus, etc., shown by the Feulgen test (page 54) to contain chromatin and regarded by some as a parabasal body. The entire family is parasitic and saprozoic; they utilize sugars mainly and give off acids and ammonia but are not entirely anoxybiotic. Reproduction occurs by longitudinal fission (Fig. 31*H*), involving the division of the kinetoplast, basal body, and nucleus; the old flagellum is retained by one daughter and reformed in the other from the new basal body. Typical trypanosomes may also undergo multiple fission, splitting after several nuclear divisions into a number of offspring arranged in a rosette.

The trypanosomes are markedly polymorphic, presenting different morphologies under different conditions. Four chief types (Fig. 31*F*) are recognized. The *Leishmania* form is rounded or oval with kinetonucleus and rhizoplast but no flagellum. The *Leptomonas* stage is elongated with a short flagellum springing from anteriorly located kinetic elements. In the *Crithidia* form the kinetic elements are more central in front of the nucleus, and the flagellum emerging on the surface runs forward as the border of a short undulating membrane. Finally in the *Trypanosoma*

---

remaki, from the blood of the pike. (*After Minchin*, 1909.) *F*. Diagrams of trypanosome forms. (*After Wenyon*, 1913.) *a*, Leishmania type; *b*, Leptomonas type; *c*, Crithidia type; *d*, Trypanosoma type. *G*. *Trypanoplasma*, from the pike. (*After Minchin*, 1909.) *H*. *Trypanosoma gambiense* in longitudinal fission. (*After Robertson*, 1913.) *J*. *Herpetomonas pediculi*, from the intestine of the human body louse. (*After Fantham*, 1912.) *K*. *Leishmania tropica*, enlarged, from slide. *L* and *M*. Stages of *Crithidia*, from the intestine of a horsefly. (*After Patton*, 1909.) *N*. A white blood cell taken from an oriental sore, filled with *Leishmania tropica*. (*After Patton*, 1913.) 1, collar; 2, nucleus; 3, undulating membrane; 4, kinetonucleus; 5, basal body.

type, the kinetic elements are situated in the posterior end,[1] and the flagellum runs nearly the entire body length on the edge of an undulating membrane, becoming free near the anterior tip. Each genus of the family may assume two or more of these forms.

Generic definitions in trypanosomes depend upon complete knowledge of the life history, and hence generic placement remains uncertain in many cases. The genus *Leishmania* comprises those forms which have only leishmania and leptomonas stages and alternate between a vertebrate and an invertebrate host. They live in the leptomonas stage in insects and in vertebrates in the leishmania form as an intracellular parasite of the reticulo-endothelial system. *L. donovani* is the causative organism of a serious oriental disease, kala azar, in which the parasite invades the cells of the liver, spleen, lymph glands, bone marrow and other parts with resultant swelling. Oriental sores or boils are caused by *L. tropica* (Fig. 31*K, N*). These two diseases are probably transmitted by blood-sucking flies of the genus *Phlebotamus*.

The genera *Crithidia, Leptomonas,* and *Herpetomonas,* which may be referred to as herpetomonads, are confined to invertebrate hosts and pass from one to another by way of cysts voided in the feces. *Leptomonas* has only leishmania and leptomonas stages, *Crithidia* (Fig. 31*L, M*) has also the crithidial stage, and *Herpetomonas* (Fig. 31*J*) displays in addition the complete trypanosome form; but these distinctions are more or less uncertain. They inhabit chiefly the intestine of arthropods, mostly insects. The best-known forms are *Crithidia gerridis* from the water strider, *Leptomonas ctenocephali* from the dog flea, and *Herpetomonas muscarum* from the intestine of houseflies. A number of herpetomonads, sometimes placed in the separate genus *Phytomonas,* inhabit the milk vacuoles in the latex cells of plants with milky juice such as milkweeds, euphorbias, and dogbanes and are transmitted from plant to plant by way of plant-sucking bugs. They assume leishmania and leptomonas stages and therefore would fall into the genus *Leptomonas,* but for their mode of transmissal.

The genus *Trypanosoma* (Fig. 31*E, H*) includes the typical blood parasites of vertebrates, living free in the blood stream but also occurring in other systems. They are transmitted from vertebrate to vertebrate by blood-sucking invertebrates, such as leeches, ticks, and insects, in whose intestine they undergo a definite cycle of development, requiring a number of days, before they become again infective to vertebrates. Only in the vertebrate do the full trypanosomatic characters appear— the elongated form, posterior position of the kinetic bodies, and long flagellum and undulating membrane. In the invertebrate host and in

---

[1] Regarded by some as the anterior end; this is improbable since fission begins at the end opposite the kinetic elements.

artificial cultures, leishmanic, leptomonad, crithidial, and modified trypanosomatic types obtain.

Trypanosomes occur in all classes of vertebrates but are pathogenic only to man and domestic mammals, probably representing recently acquired hosts. In their natural wild hosts, the big-game mammals of tropical countries, they are relatively harmless. The cause of their extreme harmfulness to man and domestic mammals is obscure but may consist in the liberation of toxins. The pathogenic trypanosomes are confined to tropical countries.

As an example of a trypanosome life cycle, that of *T. lewisi* (Fig. 32), nonpathogenic in the rat, may be presented, as this has been thoroughly studied. Rats become infected by licking from their fur or skin freshly deposited feces of the rat flea. After an incubation period of several days in some unknown part of the body, the parasites appear in the rat's blood and multiply rapidly for 1 to 2 weeks by equal and unequal fission and multiple fission with rosette formation. Multiplication then ceases because of the formation in the rat of a reproduction-inhibiting antibody ("ablastin" of Taliaferro). The trypanosomes then decline in numbers rapidly at first, more slowly later, until after a week to several months, the rat is free from them and thereafter immune to the infection. The disappearance of the trypanosomes is caused by a trypanocidal antibody, produced chiefly in the spleen. When fleas suck the blood of an infected rat during the multiplicative phases, they ingest trypanosomes, 25 per cent of which persist in the flea, where they undergo a cycle occupying about 5 days. They penetrate into the epithelial cells of the flea stomach, there altering to rounded or oval flagellate bodies that sporulate into many trypanosomiform young (Fig. 32, *4*). These escape into the stomach and may repeat the cycle. Eventually they transform into crithidians and pass into the rectum, where they swim about or adhere to the rectal walls, undergoing many changes of form (Fig. 32, *8*). They multiply immensely by longitudinal fission, and some finally change into trypanosome-like forms that pass out with the feces.

The chief pathogenic trypanosomes of man are *T. gambiense* and *T. rhodesiense*, causative organisms of African sleeping sickness,[1] characterized in early stages by fever, enlarged lymph glands, an anemia, and later, after the trypanosomes have invaded the central nervous system, by nervous symptoms, lethargy, and death. The disease is transmitted from man to man, or other mammals to man, by blood-sucking tsetse flies of the genus *Glossina*, in whose digestive tract a cycle of changes ensues, best known for *T. gambiense*. A multitude of slender forms originating by fission of the ingested trypanosomes work their way into the salivary

---

[1] Must not be confused with ordinary "sleeping sickness" or encephalitis, having no relation to trypanosomes.

glands where they assume the crithidial type and continue to multiply. After several days trypanosomiform individuals again appear that are infective to the mammalian host when injected into the blood by the

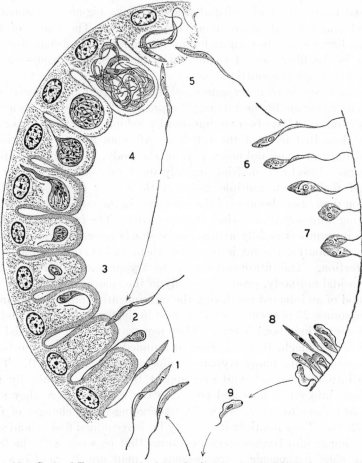

Fig. 32.—Cycle of *Trypanosoma lewisi* in the digestive tract of the flea. (*After Minchin and Thomson*, 1915, some stages omitted.) 1, trypanosomes as taken up by flea from rat; 2, trypanosomes entering stomach cells of flea; 3, curved shape in stomach cells; 4, various stages in the multiple fission of the trypanosome in the stomach cell; 5, daughter trypanosomes escaping from stomach cell; they may reenter a stomach cell as at 2 and repeat the cycle or may proceed into the rectum; 6, trypanosomes attached to rectal wall change into a short form; 7, which multiplies by fission; 8, various types found attached to rectal wall; 9, form which leaves flea in feces and is infective to rat.

bite of the fly. Other pathogenic trypanosomes have a similar history, seen to be much less complicated than that of *T. lewisi.*

There are a number of other pathogenic trypanosomes. Chagas disease of South America, in which the parasites multiply inside the muscles, the heart, and the nervous system, causing dangerous swellings, is due to *T.* (or *Schizotrypanum*) *cruzi*, transmitted by a bug, *Triatoma megista*. *Trypanosoma brucei*, transmitted by species of *Glossina*, causes nagana fever of a variety of African domestic mammals. The surra disease of India, attacking horses, mules, cattle, and camels, is due to *T. evansi*, transmitted probably by tabanid flies. *T. equiperdum*, instigator of the dourine disease of horses and mules, differs from the others in having no alternate invertebrate host, being transferred directly in coition. Other pathogenic trypanosomes all with a cycle in blood-sucking flies are *T. equinum*, causing the disease mal de caderas of horses in South America; *T. congolense*, pathological to African domestic mammals in general; and *T. vivax*, disease-producing in cattle, sheep, and goats.

Nonpathogenic trypanosomes also occur in mammals, such as *T. primatum* of anthropoid apes, *T. theileri* of cattle, *T. melophagium* of sheep, and many species in bats. To other vertebrate classes, the parasites are harmless. Those of birds are large with long pointed tails and are probably transmitted by mosquitoes. Similar trypanosomes occur in the blood of turtles, crocodiles, snakes, and lizards. They are transmitted between aquatic hosts by leeches, between land forms by blood-sucking insects. *T. rotatorium*, the chief trypanosome of frogs, a large, broad species, is acquired in the tadpole stage by way of leeches, exists in the tadpole in the crithidial form, and changes to the typical trypanosome after metamorphosis of the tadpole into a frog. Trypanosomes are widespread in fishes with leeches as the intermediate hosts.

13. Order Polymastigina.—This group comprises oval and elongated forms with two to eight, generally four, or else many flagella, a delicate pellicle permitting much change of form, and often parabasal bodies, axostyles, and similar elements. A slit-like or elongated mouth may be present. There are one to many nuclei. Reproduction occurs by longitudinal fission involving a characteristic type of mitosis (Fig. 22*E*) with extranuclear centrioles connected by a fiber (*desmose.*) Cyst formation is common and serves in the transmission of parasitic forms from host to host. Nutrition is holozoic or saprozoic. The majority are commensal or parasitic in the intestine or arthropods, especially insects, and vertebrates, including man.

The simpler members of this order possess typically four flagella, one of which is a trailing flagellum and may form the border of an undulating membrane. In *Chilomastix* (Fig. 33*A*), the trailing flagellum lies in the elongated cytostome. This genus has numerous species that inhabit the intestine of various vertebrates and pass from host to host by way of cysts in the feces. *C. mesnili* is one of the common flagellate inhabitants of the human intestine. *Tetramitus* is a free-living form with four flagella and trough-like cytostome. *Eutrichomastix* (formerly

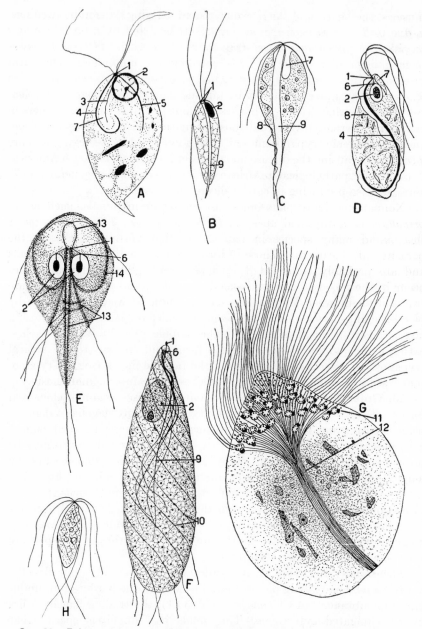

Fig. 33.—Polymastigina.   A. *Chilomastix mesnili*, from slide.   (*Courtesy Dr. D. H. Wenrich.*)   B. *Eutrichomastix lacertae*, from lizard intestine.   (*After Wood*, 1935.)   C. *Trichomonas*, from frog rectum, from life.   D. *Trichomitis*, from termite intestine.   (*After Kofoid and Swezy*, 1919.)   E. *Giardia enterica*.   (*After Kofoid and Swezy*, 1919.)   F. *Pyrsonympha*, from the termite intestine.   (*After Powell*, 1928.)   G. *Calonympha*, from termite intestine.   (*After Janicki*, 1915.)   H. *Hexamita*, from frog rectum, from life.   1,

Trichomastix, Fig. 33*B*) with three forward flagella, one trailing flagellum, mouth slit, and axostyle projecting posteriorly as a pointed tail, occurs in the intestine of various mammals, birds, reptiles, fish, and insects. *Trichomonas* (Figs. 21*B* and 33*C*) with numerous species is one of the most common protozoan inhabitants of the intestine of all groups of vertebrates as well as occurring in leeches and termites. This and related genera have three to five free flagella, a trailing flagellum bordering an undulating membrane, mouth, parabasal body, large axostyle, and a *chromatic basal rod* running along the attachment of the undulating membrane to the body. Most species feed on bacteria, yeasts, and similar forms found in their habitats. Cysts are lacking, and transmission occurs in the free state. In man there are three chief species, *T. vaginalis* in the vagina, *T. hominis* in the colon, and *T. buccalis* in the mouth. *T. vaginalis* has been accused of causing various ailments in women, including abortion, but the evidence for anything beyond an annoying itch or burning in some patients is inconclusive. *T. foetus* of cattle is, however, responsible for abortions and other pathological conditions of the female tract.

There are a number of polymastigotes that inhabit the intestine of termites as commensals such as *Streblomastix* with six flagella, *Trichomitus* (Fig. 33*D*) with four flagella, *Janickiella* with four flagella and an axostyle and others. In *Devescovina* (Fig. 11) and several related genera there are four flagella, one trailing, a prominent axostyle that embraces the nucleus, and an elongated parabasal body that makes one or more spiral turns around the axostyle. Among the more interesting commensals of termites are the genera *Dinenympha* and *Pyrsonympha* (Fig. 33*F*) in which the four to eight flagella are fastened in a spiral course to the periplast for the greater part of their length to form the *flagellar cords* by means of which the body is kept in constant undulation. The axostyle has the form of one to several filaments.

A group of polymastigotes termed Diplozoa includes curious bilaterally symmetrical flagellates with doubled structures, i.e., two nuclei, two axostyles, two groups of flagella, etc. *Hexamita* (Fig. 33*H*) found in stagnant water and the intestine of cold-blooded vertebrates, is an oval form with eight flagella and two axostyles. *Giardia* (Fig. 33*E*) parasitic in the intestine of vertebrates, has a flattened, very bilateral body, with a ventral sucking disk, two vesicular nuclei, two parabasals, two axostyles, and four pairs of flagella whose rhizoplasts make complicated loops through the cytosome. Oval cysts are formed that regularly contain

blepharoplast; 2, nucleus; 3, peristomal flagellum; 4, parabasal body; 5, parastyle; 6, centriole; 7, peristome; 8, undulating membrane; 9, axostyle; 10, flagellar cords; 11, group made up of nucleus, parabasal body, blepharoplast, and rhizoplast; 12, axostyle formed of combined rhizoplasts; 13, rhizoplasts; 14, peristomial fiber.

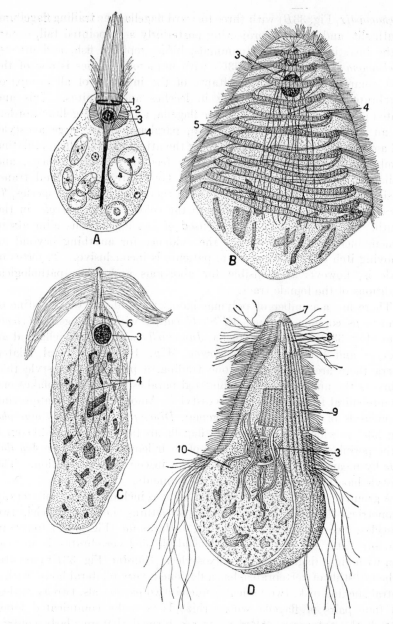

Fig. 34.—Hypermastigina. *A. Lophomonas* from the cockroach intestine. (*After Kudo*, 1926.) *B. Macrospironympha*, from the intestine of a wild cockroach, having numerous thread-like axostyles, and two deeply imbedded spiral bands bearing flagella. (*After Cleveland*, 1934.) *C. Rhynchonympha*, from a wild cockroach, with two bands of flagella, two centrioles at the ends of fibers, and numerous axostyles. (*After Cleveland*, 1934.) *D. Trichonympha*, from the termite intestine. (*After Kirby*, 1932.) 1, ring of

four nuclei indicating the beginning of fission; these pass out in the feces and are the means of transmission. *Giardia enterica* (Fig. 33*E*) is the most common intestinal flagellate of man, especially of children.

The chief intestinal flagellates of man are then *Chilomastix mesnili*, *Trichomonas hominis*, and *Giardia enterica*. They live in various parts of the intestine in the active swimming state, feeding on the intestinal flora or saprozoically. *Chilomastix* and *Giardia* are transmitted by cysts in the feces, *Trichomonas* only in the active state; but in any case, the active flagellates are seen in the stools only in diarrhoeic conditions. That any of the intestinal flagellates are primarily harmful seems very doubtful but they may effect some injury when intestinal disease is present. The incidence of infection is generally given as 5 to 15 per cent for *Giardia*, 3 to 5 per cent for *Chilomastix*, and 0.2 to 1 per cent for *Trichomonas*, rising to 10 per cent in insanitary conditions.

The remaining polymastigotes, frequently called Polyzoa, comprise complicated forms, commensal in the intestine of termites, which exhibit a multiplication of the essential polymastigote structures. The anterior end contains numerous groups, each composed of a nucleus, a parabasal body, two to four flagella, and a rhizoplast. The rhizoplasts converge to form an axial bundle, the axostyle. Typical forms are *Calonympha* (Fig. 33*G*) and *Stephanonympha*.

14. Order Hypermastigina.—This order includes the most complex flagellates, inhabitants of the intestine of termites and cockroaches, large oval forms with numerous flagella, many elongated parabasal bodies, axostylar filaments, extranuclear centrioles, and a single nucleus. The flagella may occur in a terminal tuft as in *Lophomonas* (Fig. 34*A*) found in the domestic cockroach, or in two or four elongated groups at the anterior end as in *Barbulonympha* and *Rhynchonympha* (Fig. 34*C*), found in a wild woods cockroach, or over most or all of the body in longitudinal grooves as in *Trichonympha* (Fig. 34*D*) or in spiral or double spiral bands as in *Holomastigotoides*, from termites or *Macrospironympha* (Fig. 34*B*) from a woods cockroach. The anterior end often forms a projecting *rostrum* topped by a clear ectoplasmic *cap* and covered with thick ectoplasm. Two centrioles (Fig. 34*C*) frequently depend from the rostrum and from this region probably attached to the membrane formed by the union of the numerous basal bodies of the flagella hang the thread-like parabasal bodies and axostylar fibrils. Fission is initiated by the centrioles, which give rise to a spindle. The rostrum divides followed by the rest of the body, and the old parabasals, axostyles,

basal bodies of flagella; 2, parabasal body; 3, nucleus; 4, axostyle; 5, spiral bands to which flagellar roots extend through thick layer of ectoplasm; 6, centriole; 7, cap, part of 8, rostrum; 9, surface ridges and grooves; the flagella spring from the grooves; 10, parabasal bodies. In *D*, part of the surface is cut away to show the interior.

flagellar bands, etc., disappear, and new ones form in relation to the centrioles.

The relation of these remarkable flagellates to their wood-eating termite and cockroach hosts has been extensively studied by Cleveland, who has shown that the flagellates digest wood for their hosts, since the latter when deprived of their flagellate inhabitants (through exposure to warm temperatures or high oxygen atmospheres) starve and die on their regular wood diet. In the woods cockroach, the chitinous intestinal lining forms a closed tube (peritrophic membrane) separated from the gut wall and containing the food and the flagellates; and since the food does not come into contact with the intestinal epithelium, it seems that it must be digested entirely by the flagellates. The ingestion of bits of wood by the posterior region of the flagellates has been witnessed by several observers. The flagellates are thus symbionts vital to the life of their hosts. At the time of moult, they are shed in the termites which regain them by licking other individuals; but in the cockroach, they encyst and the cysts are eaten by the young.

15. Order Rhizomastigina.—This order has been created for several colorless flagellates, unplaceable elsewhere, which are permanently amoeboid, closely resembling amoebas, but at the same time possess a long flagellum. Here belong *Mastigamoeba* (Fig. 35), *Mastigina*, and *Mastigella*.

V. CLASS RHIZOPODA OR SARCODINA

1. Definition.—The Rhizopoda are Protozoa in which pseudopodia serve as the sole means of locomotion and food intake during the whole or part of the life cycle. Many forms are impossible to separate from flagellates as they may become flagellate under certain conditions or give off flagellate young.

2. General Characters.—The rhizopods are on the whole much less highly organized than the flagellates. In contrast to the definite form and radial or bilateral symmetry of the latter, the rhizopod body is either irregular and devoid of symmetry or exhibits spherical symmetry and in either case is without antero-posterior organization or any differentiation of surfaces (Fig. 36). When not spherical the body form changes constantly owing to the temporary nature of pseudopodia or may be more or less shaped by an enclosing shell. The cytosome is usually obviously divisible into ecto- and entoplasm and generally lacks a definite pellicle, again in contrast to the flagellates. Skeletons and shells, often very elaborate, or other secreted coverings are common, and in fact the class as a whole specializes in the direction of skeleton rather than in cytosomal differentiation. There are one to many nuclei and in fresh-water forms one to several simple contractile vacuoles without contributing vacuoles or canals. Nutrition is holozoic, formed food being captured and ingested by the pseudopodia at any point. Asexual reproduction predominates, chiefly by binary fission, but also by multiple fission, budding, and plasmotomy. Sexual processes are known for some species and groups. In many cases the life cycle includes the production of flagellate swarmers, and some forms are flagellate at times in the adult state, thus evincing a close relationship to the Flagellata. The Rhizopoda are mostly solitary and free living, but parasitic and colonial forms occur. They are cosmopolitan, inhabiting salt and fresh waters and damp terrestrial environments.

FIG. 35.—Rhizomastigida. *Mastiga-moeba.* (*After Calkins*, 1901.)

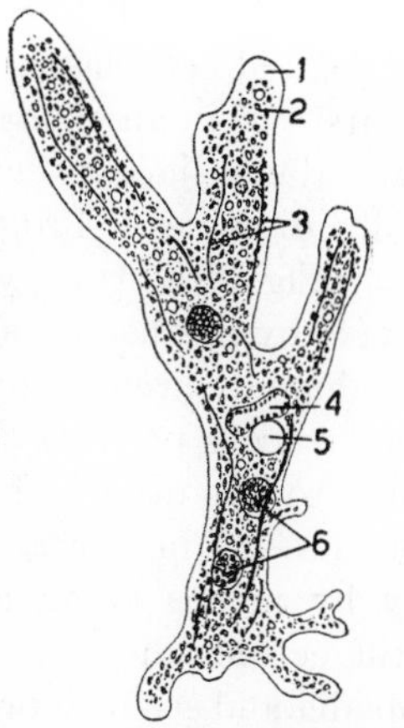

FIG. 36.—Lobosa. *Amoeba proteus,* from life. 1, ectoplasm; 2, entoplasm; 3, ectoplasmic ridges; 4, nucleus (side view); 5, contractile vacuole; 6, larger food bodies.

3. Pseudopodia.—These protoplasmic extrusions assume various shapes that are generally classified into four types. *Lobopods* are broad to cylindrical with rounded tips and are usually composed of both ectoplasm and entoplasm. More slender shapes with pointed tips and composed of ectoplasm are called *filopods.* Thread-like pseudopodia that branch and anastomose into networks are termed *reticulopods* or *rhizopods.* Ray-like pseudopodia stiffened by a central axial rod are named *axopods;* they serve for food capture rather than locomotion. A given pseudopodial form is more or less constant for each species or group but can be somewhat altered by changes in chemical content, acidity, osmotic pressure, etc., of the medium. Thus in hypotonic media, pseudopodia tend to be broad or sheet-like, in hypertonic media, slender and ray-like.

4. Amoeboid Movement.—Progression by means of pseudopodia, or *amoeboid movement*, as it is commonly called, is regarded as the most primitive kind of animal movement or contractility and hence has been the object of much investigation in the thought that light might thereby be thrown on the general nature of contractility. It is indeed probable that a thorough understanding of the mechanism of amoeboid movement would also elucidate the nature of muscle contraction. The investigations and theories concern lobopods and filopods, since only these types serve primarily for locomotion.

In amoeboid progression, the pseudopodia, i.e., lobopods, are formed in two general ways, the *profluent* (Fig. 38K) and the *eruptive* (Fig. 38M). In the former, the ectoplasm bulges as a blunt projection into which, as it extrudes, the endoplasm flows in an even manner. In the eruptive type, limited to small forms and probably associated with a very thin layer of gelated ectoplasm, the surface breaks, and ectoplasm and entoplasm burst out in an explosive manner forming a round pseudopod that overflows the adjacent ectoplasmic surface (Fig. 38M). The latter eventually dissolves. Progression by the profluent method may be of the *lobose* (Fig. 38K) type, with several pseudopodia in advance, or of the *limax* type, by means of a single large pseudopodium (Fig. 38O). Eruptive pseudopodia are usually single. In any case the animal moves in a somewhat zigzag path as the pseudopodia tend to extrude first to one side, then to the other. In most amoeboid forms only the tips of the pseudopodia are in contact with the substratum to which they cling possibly by means of an adhesive secretion. However, forms with a very stiff ectoplasm or a definite tough cuticle are unable to extrude pseudopodia and seem to progress by rolling with the entire lower surface in contact with the substratum.

Of various proposed explanations of amoeboid movement, only the two principal ones will be considered: the *surface-tension* theory and the *change-of-viscosity* theory. The former is associated with the names of Berthold, Bütschli, Verworn, and Rhumbler. It argues that, since protoplasm is fluid, there must exist at the surface of a protoplasmic mass a tension acting to make the mass spherical. Wherever on such a sphere the surface tension is locally lowered, as by external or internal changes, an outflow will occur. In such a projection the fluid will flow forward in the center and back along the sides, so-called fountain streaming. Supporters of the theory have shown that drops of certain chemical mixtures will move in amoeboid fashion because of local decreases in surface tension and that in some amoeboid forms fountain streaming can be observed in active pseudopodia. The majority of rhizopods, however, exhibit no such currents during locomotion. Furthermore, the theory assumes a fluid surface, whereas in most amoeboid forms the ectoplasm is gelatinized. Therefore while the surface-tension theory may apply to some very fluid rhizopods, the change-of-viscosity theory is more acceptable for most of them. Briefly mentioned by several early workers, this theory was first strongly advocated by Hyman (1917) and also adopted by Pantin (1923–1926) and Mast (1925).[1] Broadly stated, the theory considers an amoeboid form to consist of an outer gelatinized layer and an inner fluid mass. A local liquefaction of the gelated layer causes an outflow at that point. As the outflow progresses, its sides gelatinize again so that a pseudopodium consists of a gelatinized tube with a fluid interior and tip. Only the tip touches the substratum (Dellinger, 1906). The local liquefaction probably results from a local chemical reaction (release of acid according to Pantin) that renders the protoplasm more fluid either directly by change of colloidal phase or indirectly through imbibition of water. The process of gelation, which may be accompanied by loss of water but more probably is simply a colloidal change, involves a contraction that helps squeeze the pseudopodium forward. The entire ectoplasm as long as it is in the gel state also has contractile properties, and this is particularly evidenced at the rear end where short, obviously solidified projections accumulate. It is generally postulated that at pseudopodial tips entoplasm is being converted into ectoplasm (ento-ectoplasmic process of Rhumbler) whereas elsewhere in the body ectoplasm becomes entoplasm again.

5. Ingestion, Digestion, and Egestion of Food.—Nutrition is holozoic, consisting of algal cells and filaments, other protozoans, small metazoans such as rotifers and nematodes, and, in fact, any small organisms. The little flagellate, *Chilomonas paramecium*, and other similar flagellates appear to constitute the favorite food of large amoebas, and some amoebas feed almost exclusively on diatoms. No definite regions or organelles for food intake are present; the food is captured by pseudopodia, usually by the formation of a *food cup*, in which a pseudopodium embraces the object from each side while a thin sheet advances over it from above pinning it to the substratum (Fig. 37A, C). The cup is then completed below and the food enclosed. The food cup may advance always in contact with the prey, a method called *circumfluence* and generally employed by axopods and reticulopods, which seem to exude sticky and paralyzing substances upon the prey. Axopods in capture

---

[1] In relation to his interpretation of the sol-gel theory, Mast has coined the terms plasmasol and plasmagel. These terms have been widely adopted and used as practically synonymous with entoplasm and ectoplasm, meanings that were certainly not Mast's intention. By plasmasol, Mast means the fluid part of the entoplasm; plasmagel seems in general to mean the outer (gelated according to Mast) part of the entoplasm plus the inner part of the ectoplasm. The outer most hyaline part of the ectoplasm is considered by Mast to be fluid, a view the author finds unacceptable. Other details of Mast's theory differ from the view presented here.

and enclosure of food undergo liquefaction into ordinary cytoplasm. Lobopods and filopods employ circumfluence (Fig. 37*D*) in the ingestion of immotile prey but capture active prey by *circumvallation* (Fig. 37*A, C*), i.e., by throwing out a wide food cup that embraces the prey without touching it and includes a large amount of water. The behavior thus varies according to the type of food and other circumstances. By repeated circumfluent movements long algal filaments can be rolled up inside the cytoplasm. Other minor modes of food intake are *import* (Fig. 37*B*) where the object sinks passively into the body and *invagination* in which it is drawn into a deepening depression. Ingested food is

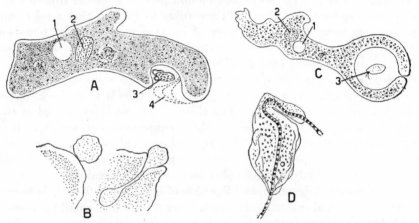

Fig. 37.—Food intake in lobose rhizopods. *A. Amoeba proteus* ingesting *Chilomonas* by circumvallation; dotted lines show successive stages of closure of the food cup, seen from the side. (*After Kepner and Taliaferro,* 1913.) *B.* Import method of food intake by amoeba. (*After Mattes,* 1924.) *C.* Food cup of *Amoeba dubia,* closing around a *Chilomonas,* seen from above, from life. *D.* An amoeba ingesting an algal filament by circumfluence, beginning to roll up the filament. (*After Rhumbler,* 1898.) 1, contractile vacuole; 2, nucleus; 3, food object; 4, successive positions of food cup.

usually carried into the general mass of the entoplasm for digestion but may be digested by pseudopodia at the point of capture as is usually the case with reticulopods. Digestion occurs in food vacuoles by means of enzymes as already described. The death of active prey requires 3 to 60 minutes. The ability to digest proteins is widespread among rhizopods. Some, as *Pelomyxa* and *Endamoeba,* can digest starch, storing the products as glycogen, and others can probably handle cellulose. Fat utilization has been demonstrated only for *Amoeba* (page 62). Indigestible remnants are extruded at any point where they happen to reach the surface.

6. Behavior.—Reactions have been studied chiefly in *Amoeba* and closely related forms. To mechanical shock, localized touch, most chemicals, media differing from the culture fluid, temperatures other than the optimum, and bright light or darkness, a general negative phobotactic reaction is given. The animal ceases movement, and after a brief interval puts out new pseudopodia and resumes locomotion in some other direction than that from which the stimulus is applied. There is evidence that the stimulus may be transmitted from the point of application. When placed in a constant electric current, amoebas withdraw pseudopods from the anodal side and move toward the cathode. Positive response, the emission of pseudopodia toward the stimulating condition, may be given to contact, food, and some chemicals. According to Schaeffer (1916–1917), Amoeba can sense thoroughly washed particles of insoluble materials like carbon and glass without touching them as evidenced by the emission of short pseudopodia in their direction. Such nonnutritive particles are generally not ingested but may be, particularly if agitated. *Amoeba* can discriminate between nutritive and nonnutritive particles and can distinguish different food animals. Thus Mast and Hahnert (1935) report that *Amoeba* can discriminate between *Chilomonas* and *Monas* and selects the former in preference to the latter. Food cups may be formed toward dissolved nutrients and when the animals are immersed in simple salt solutions.

7. Order Lobosa.—This order comprises the typical amoeboid forms with lobose or filose pseudopods, never with axopods or reticulopods. The form at rest approaches the spherical and is irregular and constantly changing in movement. The cytosome is obviously divisible into a hyaline ectoplasm, scanty in some forms, and a granular entoplasm (Fig. 36). The varying relative viscosity of these two regions affects the form of the pseudopods. Apart from secreted shells, the ectoplasm is naked, covered only with the ectoplast, but in a few species, as *Amoeba verrucosa* (Fig. 38*N*), is provided with a definite tough pellicle that almost inhibits amoeboid movement. One to several simple contractile vacuoles are present in fresh-water forms but lacking in marine and parasitic Lobosa. They usually occupy no fixed position but roll about in the entoplasmic currents, commonly lagging to the rear when about to discharge. The vacuole may reform in the place of discharge, from a remnant of the preceding vacuole or by the fusion of minute vacuoles, or may arise *de novo*, without reference to the preceding vacuole. So-called excretory granules are associated with the contractile vacuole in some species of amoebas (see Mast, 1938) but their role is unexplained. There are one to many vesicular nuclei, usually with central endosomes. Nutrition is holozoic even in parasitic forms, which however are possibly also saprozoic. A number of species harbor symbiotic zoochlorellae. Binary fission (Figs. 38*A–E* and 40*C*) is the regular mode of reproduction, but other methods may occur. The nuclear division is never a simple amitosis as formerly believed; usually an intranuclear spindle forms with (Fig. 16*D*, *K*) or without (Fig. 38*H*) polar caps, which may originate

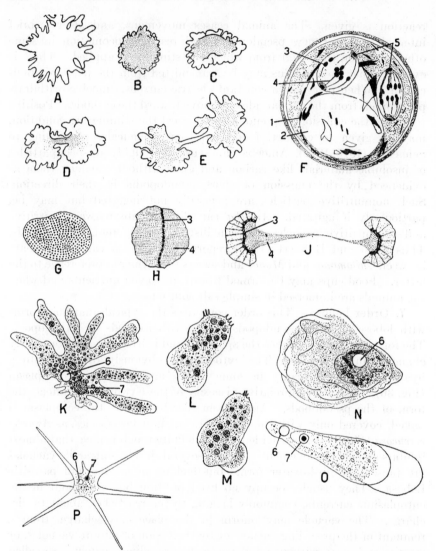

Fig. 38.—Lobose rhizopods. *A–E. Amoeba dubia* in fission. (*After Botsford*, 1926.)
F. Endamoeba coli in division inside cyst, showing two intranuclear spindles with polar
centrospheres. (*After Swezy*, 1920.) *G, H, J.* Division of the nucleus in a large type of
amoeba. (*After Belar*, 1926.) *G.* Resting nucleus showing the surface chromatin granules;
these do not participate in the mitosis. *H.* Chromatin band across center of spindle.
J. Telophase with polar caps. *K–P.* Pseudopod types in amoebas, from life. *K. Amoeba
dubia*, with lobose pseudopods. *L, M.* Guttula type with explosive pseudopod. *N.*
Verrucosa type with very low broad pseudopods. *O.* Limax type shown in two positions.
P. Radiosa type. 1, chromatoid bodies; 2, glycogen mass; 3, chromosomes; 4, spindle.
5, centrospheres; 6, contractile vacuole; 7, nucleus.

from the endosome, sometimes with centriole-like intranuclear granules (Fig. 38F), sometimes with extranuclear centrospheres (Fig. 16D). Multinucleate species may divide by plasmotomy or else all of the nuclei undergo mitosis. Multiple division (Fig. 40B) may occur, and hologamy is common among the shelled Lobosa. Encystment is general throughout the order.

The Lobosa are divided into the naked and shelled forms, given in some texts as separate orders. The naked forms are constantly changing lumps of protoplasm and include all those rhizopods known as amoebas. A large number of species have been assigned to the genus *Amoeba*, although attempts to split this genus into a number of genera have not been wanting (Schaeffer, 1926). The various amoebas range in size from a few to 1500 micra and vary greatly in viscosity of ectoplasm, quantity of ectoplasm, thickness of surface membrane, shape, length, and manner of formation of the pseudopods, number and structure of nuclei, type of mitosis, etc. Several pseudopodial types are recognized: *lobose* or finger-shaped (Figs. 36 and 38K); *stellate* or *radiosa* type, slender and pointed (Fig. 38P); *guttula* type, broad rounded eruptive pseudopodia (Fig. 38L, M); *limax* type with a single broad pseudopod (Fig. 38O); and *verrucosa* type (Fig. 38N), where the stiff pellicle reduces the pseudopods to low, slowly changing bulges. Any one species is capable of considerable variation of pseudopodial type under different conditions or alteration of the chemical constituents of the medium. Thus amoebas having lobose pseudopods when in contact with a substratum put out long slender ones when floating free in the water.

The amoebas are typically bottom dwellers in fresh and salt waters, damp soils, and foul materials. They readily form thick-walled spherical cysts. In addition to the usual binary fission (Fig. 38A–E), multiple division into many small amoebas has been reported and also the formation after many nuclear divisions of numerous internal uninucleate cysts which, escaping by disintegration of the mother amoeba, hatch into minute amoebas. In either case the small amoebas are said to undergo several changes of form, passing into *radiosa* or *guttula* types before assuming the typical appearance. The work of Johnson (1930) and Halsey (1936) indicates that these accounts are erroneous as far as concerns the larger free-living species such as *A. proteus* and *dubia;* but multiple fission may occur in some of the smaller forms and of course in parasitic amoebas. A sexual process is known only for the binucleate *Amoeba* (or *Sappinia*) *diploidea*, whose two nuclei originate from the cytoplasmic union of two individuals enclosed in a common cyst; these two nuclei fuse only at the next encystment. Plasmogony or temporary cytoplasmic union also occurs among the naked Lobosa.

Division of the naked Lobosa into genera and species is difficult and usually requires long study and cultivation, and determination of the mode of mitosis. Most free-living forms with typical pseudopods are put in the genus *Amoeba*, although this genus cannot be said to have been accurately defined. Of the large amoebas, around 500 micra across, there are two well-recognized species in the United States: *A. proteus* (Fig. 36) with ridged pseudopods and disk-shaped biconcave nucleus, and *A. dubia* (Fig. 38*K*) with oval nucleus and smooth pseudopods. In both the nucleus is peculiar in having numerous chromatic blocks visible in life (Fig. 38*G*). These are strewn throughout the nucleus in *A. dubia* and appear to give rise to the chromosomes at mitosis; in *A. proteus* they are superficial and there is a central endosome from which the chromosomes originate. The mitosis of these species has been described by Dawson, Kessler, and Silberstein (1935, 1937); there is an intranuclear spindle with polar caps. The numerous moderate to small amoebas, often of *limax*, *guttula*, or *radiosa* types, seen in protozoan cultures are probably distinct species but are difficult to identify. They have ordinary vesicular nuclei with a central endosome (Figs. 1*B* and 38*O*).

Schaeffer (1926) contends that the name *Amoeba* is invalid and must be replaced by *Chaos*. His argument runs as follows. The first recorded sight of an amoeba is that of Rösel von Rosenhof (1755). This amoeba of Rösel's was named *Volvox chaos* by Linnaeus in the 10th ed. of his Systema Naturae, the starting point for all scientific names. In a later edition he changed this name to *Chaos protheus*. Since nomenclatorial rules permit the same generic name for plants and animals, the valid name of Rösel's amoeba would seem to be *Volvox chaos;* but if this be not admitted, then the name becomes *Chaos chaos*. The question then hinges on the identity of Rösel's animal. Schaeffer maintains that it is identical with the rhizopod named *Pelomyxa carolinensis* by H. V. Wilson in 1900, a very large form 1.5 to 3 mm. long with numerous nuclei. This species has recently been rediscovered and is now under cultivation in several laboratories. Schaeffer further contends that *Pelomyxa carolinensis (Chaos chaos)* and *Amoeba proteus* belong to the same genus, i.e., *Chaos*, that *A. proteus* is identical with an amoeba described by O. F. Müller in 1786 under the name *diffluens*, and consequently that the correct name of *A. proteus* is *Chaos diffluens*. Zoologists have been unwilling to accept these changes for the reason that the entire matter rests upon the correct identification of old species. It is extremely difficult, if not impossible, to recognize with certainty old descriptions and figures of species. If the name *Chaos* be not admitted, the next available generic name is *Amiba* of Bory de St. Vincent (1822) and this appears to be the valid spelling of the genus; the spelling *Amoeba* is of later date (Ehrenberg, 1831). If Schaeffer's contentions are correct, the name of the species usually called *Amoeba proteus* would be either *Chaos diffluens* or *Amiba diffluens*.

Schaeffer has further split up the free-living amoebas among a number of genera, most of which rest on very slight grounds and have received practically no acceptance. Thus the species *dubia* is placed in the genus *Polychaos*, *verrucosa* in *Thecamoeba*, *vespertilio* in *Mayorella*, etc. Whether any of these names shall become eventually acceptable must depend upon the concerted opinion of protozoologists. Some division of the numerous species placed in the genus *Amoeba* is probably desirable.

Some other genera of the naked free-living Lobosa that may be mentioned are: *Hyalodiscus* with thin hyaline sheets between the pseudopods; *Pelomyxa*, very large slow forms with two to many nuclei and numerous inclusions (Fig. 39*C*); *Hartmanella* and *Valkampfia*, small limax-type amoebas (Fig. 16*J*), feeding on bacteria in foul waters or feces or inhabiting the intestine, distinguished mainly by their type of mitosis; and *Paramoeba*, said to sporulate into chrysomonad-like biflagellate swarmers.   One group (family Bistadiidae) represented chiefly by *Naegleria*, can under certain conditions transform into flagellates with one to three flagella.   Jones (1937) has reported that *Naegleria* is in reality a stage of a myxomycete (group of fungi with amoeboid and flagellate young stages which fuse to a multinucleate plasmodium resembling a large amoeboid protozoan).[1]   Here may be listed forms of uncertain position, often included under the name Protomyxidea, sometimes regarded as a separate order, sometimes grouped with the Heliozoa. Typical forms are *Nuclearia* and *Vampyrella* (Fig. 39*A*, *B*) with filopods, feeding on algae by puncturing the cells and sucking out the contents (Fig. 39*B*), forming cysts with cellulose walls within which sporulation into amoeboid young occurs.

There are a number of parasitic amoebas, chiefly intestinal inhabitants of man and other animals.   These are now assigned mostly to the genus *Endamoeba* (including *Entamoeba*),[2] represented in man by *E. histolytica* and *E. coli* in the colon and *E. gingivalis* in the mouth; species also occur in the intestine of all classes of vertebrates and in insects and leeches. They are transmitted directly from host to host by means of cysts passed in the feces.   Only *E. histolytica* (Fig. 39*D*) is pathological, being the causative agent of amoebic dysentery in man, in which the amoebas invade and destroy the intestinal mucosa, induce abscesses, and may spread into the liver, spleen, lungs, and brain with abscess formation. Severe cases are characterized by diarrhoeic stools containing blood, mucus, and free and encysted amoebas.   The amoebas feed on blood corpuscles, tissue debris, bacteria, and yeasts.   After multiplication by

---

[1] The myxomycetes under the name Mycetozoa are often considered to be an order of the Class Rhizopoda and as such are described in many zoological books. Since the plasmodium eventually puts forth sporangia filled with spores, we here regard the myxomycetes as fungi and omit them from consideration.

[2] The name *Endamoeba* was created by Leidy in 1879 for the amoeba of the cockroach, *E. blattae;* the name *Entamoeba* dates from Casagrandi and Barbogallo (1895) for *E. coli*.   That *Endamoeba* has priority over *Entamoeba* is self-evident, but this fact alone does not justify inclusion of *Entamoeba* in *Endamoeba*.   To settle this question it must be decided whether *E. blattae* and *E. coli* really should be placed in the same genus, and on this point protozoologists have never come to a definite decision.   If the two are congeneric then the name is *Endamoeba;* but if they are not, then *Entamoeba* is valid for the human intestinal amoebas.

ordinary binary fission, small precystic individuals arise that encyst as smooth spherical cysts containing eventually four nuclei (Fig. 39E).

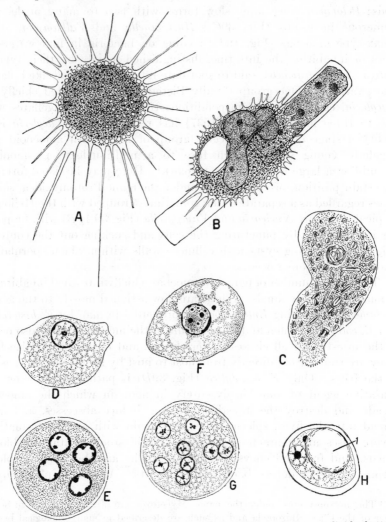

Fig. 39.—Some naked Lobosa. *A. Vampyrella* in motion. *B.* Same individual attacking an algal filament, having drawn out the sap (into a large vacuole) and the chloroplast of one cell, about to attack the next cell, from life. *C. Pelomyxa*, from life, note numerous inclusions. *D. Endamoeba histolytica*, from human intestine, stained preparation. *E.* Cyst of *E. histolytica*. *F. Endamoeba coli*, stained, from human intestine. *G.* Cyst of *E. coli*. *H.* Cyst of *Iodamoeba bütschli*, human feces, showing glycogen body 1, from slide. (*Courtesy of Dr. D. H. Wenrich.*)

According to Dobell (1928) the cyst hatches to a quadrinucleate amoeba that divides mitotically to produce finally eight uninucleate amoebulae; at each division only one of the original four nuclei divides, and the others are distributed among the two daughter cells in all possible combinations. *Endamoeba coli* (Fig. 39*F*) with an eight-nucleate cyst (Fig. 39*G*) and *E. gingivalis* of which the cysts have not been seen are harmless entocommensals feeding on bacteria, yeasts, etc. Dobell (1938) states that the cysts of *E. coli* hatch to a multinucleate amoeba with four to eight nuclei (since some nuclei may degenerate) and this divides without nuclear division directly into uninucleate amoebulae. The cysts of these intestinal amoebas usually contain deeply staining elongate bodies known as *chromatoid bodies* (Fig. 38*F*). Other harmless amoebas of the human intestine are: *Endolimax nana* with ovoid four-nucleate cysts; *Iodamoeba bütschlii* (also called *williamsi*), whose uninucleate cysts have a characteristic large glycogen body (Fig. 39*H*); and *Dientamoeba fragilis*, a binucleate amoeba of which the cysts are unknown. The incidence of the human intestinal amoebas in European and American whites is about as follows: *E. histolytica*, 5 to 10 per cent; *E. coli*, 10 to 50 per cent; *Iod. bütschlii*, 1 to 10 per cent; and *Endolimax nana*, 0.5 to 10 per cent. In backward communities and native tropical populations, the incidence may be much higher.

Intestinal amoebas very similar to and probably identical with those of man occur in monkeys and apes. Among the intestinal amoebas of lower animals, the best known are *Endamoeba ranarum* in frogs and *Endamoeba blattae* from the cockroach. A tentative life cycle for the latter has been described by Morris (1936). The small precystic individuals become multinucleate cysts that excyst after being eaten by roaches, breaking up into many uninucleate amoebulae, possibly of the nature of gametes. These amoebulae grow to a small-sized form that may carry on a secondary cycle of encystment and excystment before finally attaining the adult size, possibly by fusion in pairs. *Hydramoeba hydroxena* is a large amoeba that is ectoparasitic on hydra, loosening and devouring cells and soon killing the host.

The shelled Lobosa are simply amoebas enclosed in protective coverings that vary from a gelatinous or membranous encasement to shells or tests composed of siliceous prisms or plates or of foreign particles embedded in a gelatinous or tectinous matrix. The shells are of simple shape, mostly oval, urn-, or bowl-like with a single opening or *pylome* through which the clear lobose or filose pseudopods protrude. There are generally a single nucleus, sometimes more, and one to several contractile vacuoles. This group is supposed to have extranuclear chromatin as chromidia (Fig. 1*L*, page 54). In fission, the encasements if soft also divide; otherwise, part of the cytosome exudes from the pylome and secretes a new shell before separation occurs (Fig. 40*C*). Where the shell embodies foreign fragments, these are stored up by the parent prior to fission and emitted into the daughter at the time of division. Encystment within the shell is common.   Sporulation into naked amoebulae (Fig. 40*B*), which leave the parent and later secrete their own shells, has been reported as well as the production of amoeboid anisogametes that

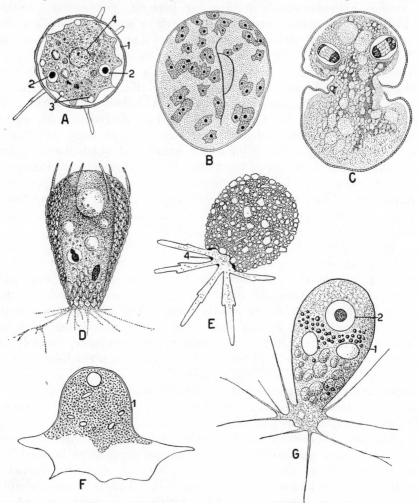

Fig. 40.—Some shelled Lobosa.   *A. Arcella* from life, seen from above; side view, Fig. 10*E*.   *B. Arcella* sporulating into numerous amoeboid young.   *C. Arcella* in binary fission; the two nuclei in mitosis with polar caps; part of the cytoplasm exudes from the pylome and secretes a new shell.   (*B and C after Elpatiewsky, 1907.*)   *D. Euglypha* with a shell of little siliceous scales.   (*After Leidy, 1879.*)   *E. Difflugia*, from life, with a case made of rock grains.   *F. Cochliopodium*, from life, with a membranous case.   *G. Chlamydophrys.*   (*After Belar, 1921.*)   1, shell; 2, nucleus with endosome; 3, contractile vacuole; 4, pylome.

copulate in pairs.   Hologamy appears to be widespread among the shelled Lobosa; the zygote issues as one or more naked young that form a shell later.   The curious *Trichosphaerium*, probably best assigned to the shelled

Lobosa, having a soft jelly hull with radiating lime spicules and several apertures, was found by Schaudinn (1899) to have the following life cycle: numerous amoeboid agametes produced by multiple fission grow up into forms with a simple jelly hull, and these sporulate into biflagellate isogametes that copulate in pairs to form a zygote developing directly into the adult.

The shelled Lobosa are primarily fresh-water inhabitants, common in ponds, sphagnum bogs, and fecal deposits. *Cochliopodium* (Fig. 40*F*), *Chlamydophrys* (Fig. 40*G*), and *Pamphagus* are examples of types with a simple thin membranous test. The very common *Arcella* (Figs. 10*E*, 40*A*) has a yellow to brown bowl-like shell, composed of siliceous prisms set in tectin (Fig. 10*F*), smooth or with dimples or with horns. It has two vesicular nuclei and several peripherally located contractile vacuoles. At fission half of the cytoplasm exudes and secretes a new shell, recognizable by its lighter color, in such a way that the pylomes of parent and daughter shells face each other (Fig. 40*C*). *Difflugia* (Fig. 40*E*), *Centropyxis*, and *Nebela* have pyriform shells made of foreign particles set in an organic matrix; these particles are ingested prior to fission, and in *Nebela* consist of plates of other Testacea used as food. In *Euglypha* (Fig. 40*D*) the test is composed of secreted siliceous scales and spines, and in *Quadrula* of squarish plates.

8. Order Foraminifera.—This order is distinguished by reticulopods (branching and anastomosing pseudopods) and is here limited to such types of rhizopods. A few naked amoeboid fresh-water forms of uncertain position as *Protomyxa* may be included here by virtue of their reticulopods. All others are invested with a shell or test that is one-chambered (*monothalamous, unilocular*) or many-chambered (*polythalamous, multilocular*), and *imperforate* (with one or a few openings, Fig. 41*E*) or *perforate* (with many pores, Fig. 41*N*). The test is composed of a gelatinous or pseudochitinous secretion, or of sand grains, sponge spicules, or other foreign bodies embedded in such secretions (Fig. 41*J*) or in the majority of species of calcium carbonate in the form of the mineral calcite. Calcareous shells consist of 90 per cent calcium carbonate and 10 per cent silica, magnesium sulphate, and other minerals. Unilocular shells (Fig. 41*F*, *J*) are of simple spherical, oval, tubular, spiral, or branched shapes, and expand continuously with the growth of the animal. Multilocular tests consist of a series of successively larger chambers, sometimes irregularly arranged but generally following each other in a definite sequence. Such regular arrangements classify into the following types: *nodosaroid* (Fig. 41*A*, *B*), chambers in a straight line like beads or inclosing one another; *spiral* (Fig. 41*D*), chambers coiled in a flat or conical spiral like a snail's shell; *cyclic* (Fig. 41*E*), chambers concentric; *textularid* (Fig. 41*C*), chambers in two or three alternating rows

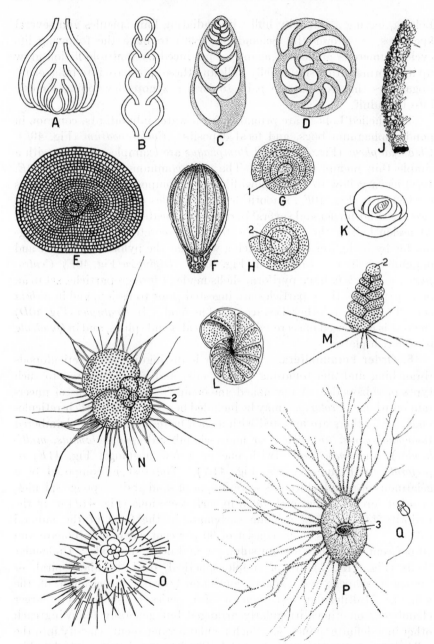

FIG. 41.—Foraminifera.   A and B. Diagrams of nodosaroid types of shell.   C. Diagram of textularid type of shell.   D. Of spiral type.   (After Carpenter, 1862.)   E. Cycloid type of shell, Discospirulina.   F. Lagena.   G. Cornuspira, microscleric.   H. Cornuspira, megascleric.   J. Saccorhiza, with irregular shell of sand grains.   K. Type of shell of the family Miliolidae.   L. Elphidium (= Polystomella), spiral type of shell.   M. Textularia,

like a braid; and finally irregular and mixed types. The shell may be ornamented with sculpturing and protuberances.

The majority and most typical foraminiferal shells are multilocular, perforate, calcareous, and spiral (Fig. 41L, N, O). The chambers are separated internally by calcareous septa pierced by one or more openings. The walls are perforated with numerous pores (whence the name Foraminifera or pore-bearers), and in many forms elaborate canal systems run in the walls. The animal starts life with one chamber termed the *proloculus* but with growth outflows from the main opening and secretes a new larger chamber. This process continues throughout life, resulting in a succession of chambers of steadily increasing size. In the higher forms, each species is dimorphic, having two types of shells, *megascleric* (Fig. 41H, M, N) with a large proloculus and *microscleric* (Fig. 41G, O) with a small one.

The cytosome occupies all the chambers passing through the openings in the septa. The protoplasm is viscous and granular, frequently with many small inclusions, lacks a distinct ectoplasm, and contains one to many nuclei. Contractile vacuoles are absent in marine species. The protoplasm extends through the mouth of the shell and through the pores in perforate shells to form a layer over the exterior that by secretion continually adds to the thickness of the shell and from which the pseudopods extend. These are long and filamentous, very viscous and contractile, uniting into networks (Fig. 41N, P) and exhibiting vigorous streaming movements. The food consists of small organisms caught and apparently paralyzed by the pseudopodial network, enclosed and often digested at the point of capture. Many forms contain symbiotic zoochlorellae and zooxanthellae.

The Foraminifera so far as known reproduce exclusively by multiple division, involving an alternation of generations. Early incomplete accounts of the life cycle by Schaudinn and Lister based on *Elphidium* (= *Polystomella*) have been recently verified by Calvez (1938) and others. The adult foraminifer is dimorphic as already mentioned; some individuals are *schizonts* or *agamonts*, destined for asexual reproduction, and others are *gamonts*, which give rise to gametes. In the simpler monothalamous foraminifers, the two forms cannot be distinguished morphologically (Fig. 42H, J). In the typical polythalamous genera, the schizonts have microscleric shells and the gamonts have megascleric ones (though exceptions occur). The schizonts or microscleric individuals early become multinucleate and when adult undergo multiple fission into mononuclear young, which soon begin the secretion of megascleric shells

megascleric, alive, Bermuda. *N. Globigerina*, megascleric, alive, California. *O*. Spiny type of *Globigerina*, microscleric. *P. Gromia*. (*After Jepps*, 1926.) *Q*. Supposed flagellospore of same. 1, first microscleric chamber; 2, first megascleric chamber; 3, pylome.

and then escape from the parent shell (Fig. 42A–C). These megascleric individuals develop into gamonts, although it appears that a few may become schizonts in some species. These gamonts remain uninucleate until mature and then, following complicated nuclear reorganization processes, undergo sporulation into multitudes of minute (2 to 5 micra long) biflagellate isogametes (Fig. 42J, K). These have two unequal flagella; they fuse in pairs to a zygote that develops directly into a schizont.

In some genera, the gametes are *amoeboid*, not flagellate. The life cycle of one of these, *Patellina* (Fig. 42A–G), has been beautifully worked out by Myers (1935). The microscleric individuals sporulate into 12 amoeboid agametes (Fig. 42B) that secrete megascleric shells and associate in groups of two or more (Fig. 42C). Each megascleric individual divides into eight amoeboid isogametes (Fig. 42D) that copulate in pairs (Fig. 42E); the resulting zygotes develop microscleric shells (Fig. 42F) and escape as young microscleric animals.

The association of two or more foraminifers appears to be a common phenomenon and in at least many cases is related to sexual reproduction. Preceding gamete formation a cyst may be secreted around the group of shells. It is known for some that a gamete fuses only with a gamete from one of the other individuals in the group and in fact this cross-fertilization appears to be the purpose of such associations.

A few naked species and forms with simple oval tectinous shells such as *Gromia* (Fig. 41P) and the similar *Allogromia* and *Lieberkühnia* inhabit fresh water, but the group as a whole is marine. The Foraminifera are typically bottom dwellers, although some are pelagic and may be provided with spines as a floating device (Fig. 41O). The shells range mostly from 20 to 50 micra to 2 to 5 mm. in diameter, but a few may reach 10 to 15 cm. or even more in width. Among the more primitive forms, such as the astrorhizids, the test is composed chiefly of foreign particles and may be branched as in *Astrorhiza* but more commonly is rounded, oval, or tubular (Fig. 41J). Monothalamous shells are illustrated by the bottle-shaped *Lagena* (Fig. 41F) and the spirally coiled *Cornuspira* (Fig. 41G, H). A cycloid type with the rings partially subdivided into tiny chambers is seen in *Discospirulina* (Fig. 41E). Among polythalamous types, the Nodosariidae have chambers in a row as in *Nodosaria*, diagrammed in Fig. 41B or enclosing each other as in *Frondicularia*, diagrammed in Fig. 41A; in the Textulariidae (Fig. 41C, M), the chambers alternate; in the Miliolidae (Fig. 41K), the chambers make a half spiral and somewhat enclose each other; the Rotaliidae display the typical spiral succession of chambers exemplified by the beautiful sculptured *Elphidium* (Fig. 41L); and in the Orbulinidae the spirally arranged chambers are bulbous as in the pelagic genus *Globigerina* (Fig. 41O, N). The Foraminifera occur in the ocean in such enormous

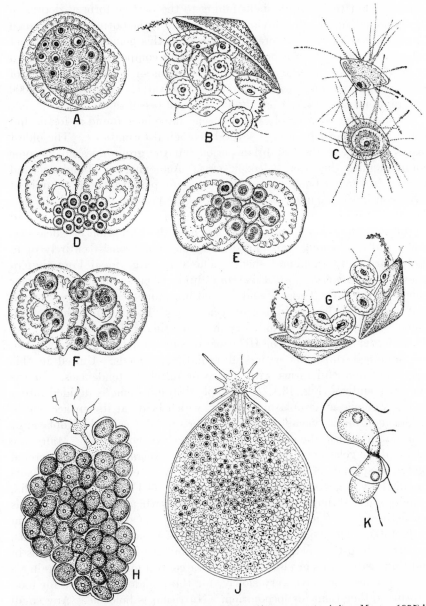

Fig. 42.—Foraminiferan life cycles. *A–G. Patellina corrugata* (*after Myers*, 1935):
A, microscleric individual in process of asexual sporulation into 12 megascleric young; *B*,
escape of megascleric young; *C*, two young megascleric individuals; these tend to adhere
in groups of two to ten; *D*, megascleric individuals have each given rise to eight amoeboid
isogametes; *E*, isogametes copulating in pairs to form zygotes; *F*, young microscleric individuals beginning to form their shells; *G*, Escape of microscleric young. *H–J, Iridina,*
monothalamous genus (*after Calvez*, 1938). *H*, asexual sporulation into amoeboid young
which become sexual individuals or gamonts; *J*, Gamont (= megascleric adult of dimorphic
species) sporulating into gametes. *K*. The biflagellate gametes fusing.

numbers that their empty shells falling to the bottom form at depths of 2500 to 4500 m. the most obvious components of the bottom mud, termed *Globigerina ooze* from the prevalence in it of this genus, although other calcareous shells are also present. This mud composes about one-third of the ocean floor. At greater depths calcareous shells dissolve because of the increased carbon dioxide content of the water. As many as 50,000 foraminiferal shells may occur in one gram of ocean sand.

A very large number of extinct species have been found as fossils and many species persist through several geological formations. The oldest fossils go back to the Cambrian period but the group does not become common until the later Paleozoic eras. Achieving an abundance and variety in the Carboniferous and Cretaceous periods, the Foraminifera have continued common in the rocks to the present time, and the late Tertiary species are identical with living forms. During Jurassic and Cretaceous times they contributed much to the formation of calcareous rocks and chalk, and some chalks and limestones consist entirely or in large part of foraminiferal shells. The very large fossil Foraminifera known as *Nummulites* (now *Camerina*), up to 19 cm. across, reached their height in the early Tertiary and formed limestone beds in Europe, Asia, and northern Africa. In recent years fossil Foraminifera have been much employed in the oil industry in correlating rock strata.

9. Order Heliozoa.—The Heliozoa, or sun animalcules (Figs. 43, 44), are spherical rhizopods with stiff radiating axopods. United in this group are doubtful forms with lobose or flagellate tendencies. In the typical members (Fig. 43*A*, *B*) the spherical cytosome is divided into a highly vacuolated ectoplasm or *cortex*, which bears at its surface one to several contractile vacuoles, and a denser granular central entoplasm or *medulla* in which the one to many nuclei are contained. Many are enclosed in gelatinous envelopes in which foreign objects or secreted plates or spicules of silica (Fig. 43*D*, *E*) may be embedded; or are surrounded by a tectinous lattice sphere (Fig. 44*A*). The pseudopodia, which project through the skeletal investments when present, are axopods consisting of a stiff axial rod clothed with a layer of streaming protoplasm (Fig. 43*C*). The axial rods, said to consist of bundles or tubes of fibrils, penetrate into the medulla where they terminate free or on a nucleus in multinucleate forms or else converge to a central granule. The animals are motionless or move very slowly, for the pseudopodia serve for food capture rather than for locomotion. Nutrition is holozoic. Any small animals that happen to touch the axopods adhere and are quickly paralyzed, possibly by a toxic secretion. The axopods may shorten, conveying the prey to the main mass of the animal (Fig. 12*A*), or they may melt around the prey into ordinary cytoplasm (Fig. 44*A*), which then slowly retracts into the animal. Plasmogamy is commonly practiced in

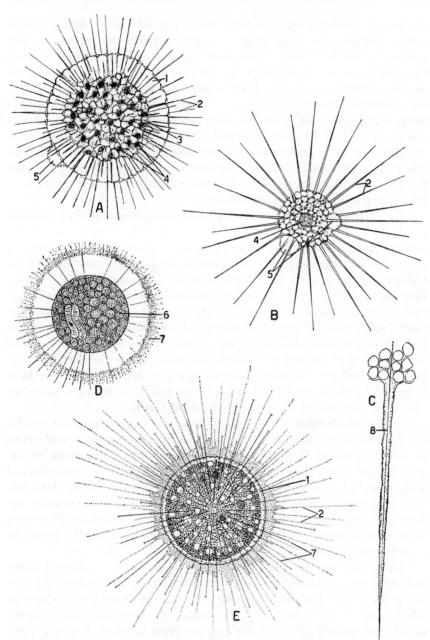

FIG. 43.—Heliozoa. *A. Actinosphaerium*, from life. *B. Actinophrys*, from life. *C.* Highly magnified living axopod of *Actinosphaerium* to show axial rod. *D. Heterophrys*, from life, filled with symbiotic algae and with minute siliceous spicules on the surface of a gelatinous hull. *E. Acanthocystis*, with siliceous spicules. (*After Leidy*, 1879.) 1, ectoplasm; 2, axopods; 3, entoplasm; 4, nucleus; 5, contractile vacuole; 6, zoochlorellae; 7, siliceous spicules; 8, axial rod.

the capture and digestion of large prey (Fig. 44*B*, *C*). Many species harbor zoochlorellae (Fig. 43*D*). Asexual reproduction occurs in uninucleate forms by binary fission involving a regular mitotic division of the nucleus; or by plasmotomy without nuclear division in multinucleate species. *Acanthocystis* (Fig. 43*E*) is said to bud off amoeboid or biflagellate young that grow into adults. A remarkable form of hologamy called *autogamy* or self-fertilization has been thoroughly established for *Actinophrys* (Fig. 44*D–G*) and *Actinosphaerium* in which the animal after withdrawing its pseudopods and secreting a gelatinous cyst divides into two daughter cells. These undergo two typical maturation divisions like those of metazoan sex cells and then fuse to an encysted zygote that later hatches into a young heliozoan.

The Heliozoa are predominantly fresh-water forms, free or fastened by stalks. Many texts include in the group doubtful forms that other authors assign to the Lobosa or elsewhere. Among these are several forms, called *Helioflagellidae*, that pass into a flagellate condition, either losing or retaining the axopods; and a group of species parasitic in amoeboid phases in algae and flagellates, producing flagellate free forms that may assume a heliozoan-like appearance. Of the typical Heliozoa the most familiar are the small uninucleate *Actinophrys* (Fig. 43*B*) and the large multinucleate *Actinosphaerium* (Fig. 43*A*), sun-like protozoans with well-defined cortical and medullary regions. *Heterophrys* (Fig. 43*D*) has a jelly hull with embedded siliceous spicules; *Acanthocystis* (Fig. 43*E*) is known by the radiating siliceous spines; and the beautiful *Clathrulina* (Fig. 44*E*) is enclosed in a latticed sphere of tectin.

10. Order Radiolaria.—The Radiolaria are characterized (Figs. 45, 46) by the sharp division of the body into *central capsule* and *extracapsular cytoplasm* (Fig. 45*A*, *B*), regions possibly equivalent to the ectoplasm and entoplasm of other rhizopods. The majority are spherical with spherical symmetry, and nearly always provided with skeletons. The pseudopodia are axopods or filopods. Contractile vacuoles are wanting. The Radiolaria are among the larger Protozoa ranging from 50 micra to several millimeters in diameter or even, in colonial forms, to several centimeters.

The central capsule, the essential part of a radiolarian, consists of the *intracapsular cytoplasm* and the enclosing *central capsule membrane*, rarely wanting. The former contains one to many nuclei, which may be when single very large and polyenergid in character. The capsule membrane, usually spherical but also occurring in other shapes, is composed of tectin and is pierced either by numerous evenly distributed pores or by one to three groups of pores called *pore fields* (Figs. 45*G* and 46*E*). The pores allow continuity of the intra- and extracapsular protoplasms. The latter, a broad zone, consists chiefly of a gelatinous material, the

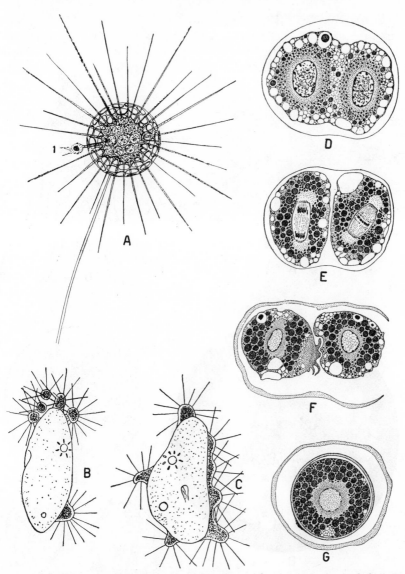

Fig. 44.—Heliozoa (continued). *A. Clathrulina*, with a tectinous latticed shell, from life; at 1, a small ingested protozoan. *B. Raphidocystis* attacking *Paramecium*, around which they unite in plasmogony *C* for purposes of digestion. (*After Wetzel*, 1926.) *D–G*, Process of autogamy in *Actinophrys* (*after Belar*, 1923): *D*, encysted animal divides; *E*, each daughter undergoes maturation divisions with intranuclear spindles; *F*, left daughter acts as male, other as female; *G*, resulting zygote.

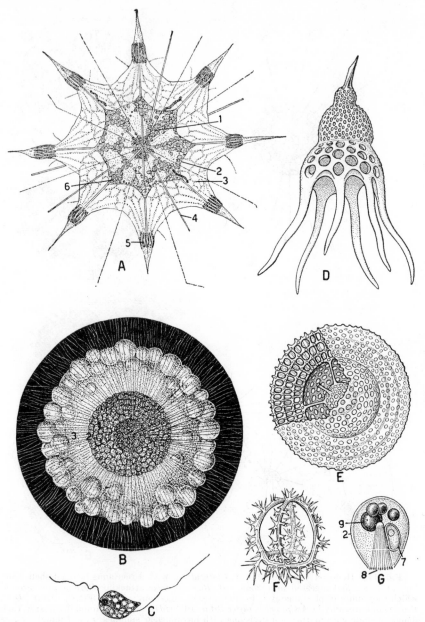

Fig. 45.—Radiolaria.   *A. Acanthometra*, typical of the Acantharia.   (*After Moroff and Stiasny*, 1909.)   *B. Thalassicola*, without skeleton, one of the Spumellaria, showing radiating pseudopodia.   (*After Huth*, 1913.)   *C.* Biflagellate isogamete of a radiolarian.   (*After Le Calvez*, 1935.)   *D.* Helmet shape of skeleton, order Nassellaria.   *E.* Skeleton type of concentric lattice spheres and disks, order Spumellaria.   *F.* Ring type of skeleton of many Nassellaria.   *G.* Central capsule of a nassellarian, with one pore field.   (*D–G, after Haeckel*, 1887.)   1, central capsule; 2, central capsule membrane; 3, extracapsular protoplasm; 4, skeletal spicules; 5, myofrisks; 6, zooxanthellae; 7, nucleus; 8, pore field; 9, oil drops.

calymma, (Fig. 45*A*, *B*), usually forming the walls of large vacuoles filled with a watery fluid, which give the animal a bubbly, frothy appearance. The extracapsular protoplasm lacks nuclei and usually contains "yellow cells," symbiotic zooxanthellae very characteristic of the Radiolaria, formerly supposed to be algae, now known in many cases to be modified dinoflagellates or chrysomonads. More common in the central capsule but also occurring in the calymma are fat drops, oil spheres, crystals and a variety of other inclusions, and pigment granules, generally red, yellow, or brown, sometimes blue. From the central capsule or the pore fields or from a zone (matrix) just outside the capsule membrane a denser protoplasm extends outward like a net or as rays through the calymma to issue at the surface as fine radiating pseudopodia, usually axopods, which may branch or anastomose. The central capsule is capable of independent existence and can regenerate the rest of the organism. Nutrition is holozoic, although the assimilative powers of the zooxanthellae may be utilized.

A skeleton is nearly always present, radiate or concentric or of both types intermingled, composed of silica except in the Acantharia where it is made of strontium sulphate or calcium aluminum silicate. The radiating type (termed *astroid* by Haeckel) (Fig. 45*A*) confined to the suborder Acantharia, consists of long spines or needles radiating from the center of the central capsule and embraced where they leave the calymma by a circlet of myonemes, termed *myofrisks*, which serve to move the spines and contract the calymma. Concentric skeletons, arranged concentrically with reference to the capsule membrane, take the form either of separate spicules lying free in the calymma (*beloid* type) or of lattice spheres (*spherical* type), occurring anywhere inside the body or enclosing it, often present as a concentric series of several spheres one inside the other (Figs. 10*D* and 45*E*). All possible combinations of radiating spines and lattice spheres occur, together with innumerable ornamentations such as spines, thorns, hooks, etc., rendering the radiolarian skeleton one of the most wonderful and exquisite objects in nature. Besides the more common lattice spheres, helmet (Fig. 45*D*), disk, bell, and other shapes of lattices abound. The skeleton, especially the latticed types, has been explained by postulating deposition of minerals along the planes and angles of contact of the vacuoles of the protoplasm.

Asexual reproduction by binary fission involves first the nucleus, which when polyenergid may produce hundreds of chromosomes, then the central capsule, and finally the calymma. When possible, the skeleton is also divided and each daughter regenerates the missing half. When the skeleton is indivisible, one daughter cell issues forth and secretes an entire new skeleton. In many Radiolaria, after the breaking up of the nucleus into numerous nuclei, sporulation into biflagellate swarmers (Fig. 45C), probably isogametes, has been observed. Reported anisogamous swarmers are probably escaped zooxanthellae. The complete history is unknown in any case.

The Radiolaria are exclusively marine and chiefly pelagic; the bubbly calymma, oil and fat drops, and spreading pseudopodia and skeletal

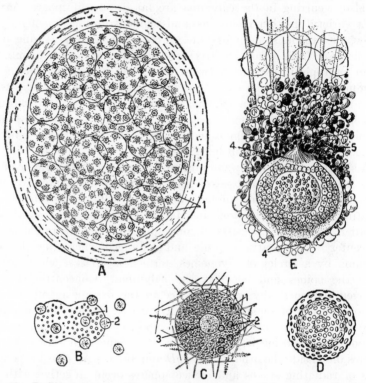

Fig. 46.—Radiolaria (continued).   *A.* Colonial radiolarian, *Sphaerozoum*, order Spumellaria, a bubbly gelatinous mass with numerous central capsules. *B, C, D.* Enlarged central capsules of three genera of such colonial radiolarians: *B*, dividing central capsule of *Collozoum*, without skeleton; *C*, central capsule of *Sphaerozoum*, enlarged from *A*, with loose spicules; *D*, central capsule of *Collosphaera*, enclosed in a lattice sphere. *A–D*, from life, Bermuda, tow. *E.* Portion of a member of the order Tripylea, showing central capsule with three pore fields and the dark phaeodium. (*After Haeckel*, 1887.) 1, central capsule; 2, zooxanthellae; 3, oil drop; 4, pore fields; 5, phaeodium.

spines all serve as aids to floating.   They are able to ascend and descend by altering the degree of extension of the calymma and pseudopods, and are said to sink below the surface in stormy weather.   Their distribution is related to external factors, as there are warm- and cold-water forms, littoral and oceanic species, surface dwellers, and those inhabiting deep water down to 5000 m. (over 3 miles).   The bottom mud in the deeper parts of the ocean where calcareous shells dissolve consists largely of siliceous skeletons of the Radiolaria, sponges, and diatoms and is called the radiolarian ooze. It occupies 3 to 4 per cent of the ocean floor. The many species presenting a wonderful array of skeletal patterns are usually grouped into four suborders. The Acantharia are characterized by the distribution of pores throughout the capsule membrane, and a skeleton of radiating spines mostly of strontium sulphate, often united outside the animal by latticework. *Acanthometra* (Fig. 45*A*) is one of the best known representatives of this group. In the Spumellaria or Peripylea the capsule membrane is also pierced throughout with pores, but the skeleton is absent or composed of silica as loose concentrically arranged spicules or lattice spheres (Fig. 45*E*). Here belong the beautiful *Thalassicola* (Fig. 45*B*) without skeleton and the colonial Collidae, forming large spherical or cylindrical bubbly gelatinous masses containing numerous central capsules (Fig. 46*A*). The principal genera are *Collozoum* with naked central capsules (Fig. 46*B*), *Sphaerozoum*, capsules surrounded by loose spicules (Fig. 46*A*, *C*), and *Collosphaera*, capsules enclosed in a lattice sphere (Fig. 46*D*). The Nassellaria or Monopylea have a central capsule with a single pore field (Fig. 45*G*) and skeletal types such as Fig. 45*D* and *F*. The Tripylea or Phaeodaria are characterized by a central capsule with typically three pore fields (Fig. 46*E*), a mass of dark pigment, the *phaeodium*, lying near the main pore field, and a variously formed siliceous skeleton.

The Radiolaria are a very ancient group and among the oldest fossils known, said to occur in Pre-Cambrian rocks in Brittany. Only the Spumellaria and Nassellaria are preserved in the rocks. As far back as the Tertiary, where the most abundant display of fossil Radiolaria occurs, the skeletons are preserved unaltered and are practically identical with present species. In older formations the silica has been replaced by other minerals and the species are different. Radiolarian skeletons contribute largely to siliceous rocks such as chert.

VI. CLASS SPOROZOA

1. Definition.—The Sporozoa are entoparasitic Protozoa transmitted mostly by walled spores usually produced by multiple fission except in blood-inhabiting forms, which sporulate into naked young.

2. Other Characters.—The sporozoans are inter- or intracellular parasites of vertebrates and most invertebrate phyla; each species is more or less limited to a specific host. They commonly pass from host to host by means of young or zygotes enclosed in hard walls and known as *spores*, but, where the transmission is direct, as by blood-sucking intermediate hosts, the infecting stages are naked. The body in vegetative phases is oval or rounded or often elongated and worm-like, motionless or exhibiting amoeboid, euglenoid, or gliding movements. The cytosome is uninucleate in young stages but becomes multinucleate either before or at the time of multiple fission. It may be differentiated into ectoplasm and entoplasm and in gregarines has myonemes and special adhesive organelles, but in general formed structures are absent. There are no contractile vacuoles. Nutrition is strictly saprozoic by absorption over the whole surface or in some gregarines apparently at the anterior end. Typically both sexual and asexual reproduction involve multiple fission in which the animal after becoming multinucleate by a series of rapidly ensuing mitoses breaks up into a number of offspring, agametes or gametes. The growing vegetative parasite is called a *trophozoite*. When this, upon attaining full size, undergoes multiple fission directly into agametes, it is called a *schizont* or *agamont*, the multiple fission is termed *schizogony* or *agamogony*, and the agametes are known as *merozoites*. These reinfect the host and grow up either into another generation of schizonts which repeat the schizogonic cycle or develop into *gamonts*, also termed *gametocytes*, which produce the gametes directly or by a multiple fission called *gamogony*. The zygote, also called *oöcyst*, or if motile, *oökinete*, usually again undergoes multiple fission, known as *sporogony*, either into naked young, the *sporozoites*, which infect directly, or into walled *spores*, from which one to many sporozoites emerge under proper conditions. The life cycles of many Sporozoa include an alternation of schizogony and sporogony, often in relation to change of hosts. The gregarines and coccidians differ from all other animals in that the reduction of the chromosomes occurs in the first division of the zygote, which alone is diploid; all other stages of the life cycle are haploid as in higher plants; but it is not certain that this phenomenon is true for all members of these orders.

The Sporozoa are often divided into two subclasses, the Telosporidia, with elongated sporozoites and no polar capsules in the spores, and the Neosporidia, in which the sporozoites are amoeboid and the spores bear polar capsules. In some recent texts, the divergence of these two groups is considered sufficient to warrant their separation as classes of Protozoa. In such case the Telosporidia are called class Sporozoa in the restricted sense and the remaining orders are united under the name Amoebosporidia. The name Sporozoa is here employed in the older sense with the understanding that it includes an arbitrary assemblage of little related forms; only the Telosporidia constitute a natural group. The Telosporidia fall into three orders: Gregarinida, Coccidia, and Haemosporidia.

3. Order Gregarinida.—The gregarines (Figs. 47 and 48) are mostly extracellular parasites of worm-like form in which the life cycle consists only of sporogony with the production of walled spores containing eight sporozoites, except in a few instances where schizogony occurs preceding sporogony. They inhabit the digestive tract, coelomic spaces, and other cavities of echinoderms, mollusks, tunicates, annelids, arthropods and other invertebrates, being probably absent from vertebrates. The young parasite (sporozoite or merozoite) is usually intracellular but as it grows protrudes from or leaves the cell, and the matured schizonts or gamonts either adhere externally to the digestive or coelomic lining, or have the knobby, pointed, hooked, or root-like anterior end (Fig. 47A, B, F) anchored in one or more cells, or move about freely in the body spaces. The grown trophozoites vary from 10 micra to 16 mm. in length and are usually of elongated, worm-like shape (Fig. 47A–F). They move in amoeboid fashion or by worm-like bendings and contractions or by a peculiar gliding movement, much studied but little understood. The old view that a column of mucus accumulating behind the animal pushed it forward is now discredited; more recent observers incline to regard the gliding as caused by delicate contraction waves along the myonemes. The gregarines may attain a considerable degree of differentiation. The ectoplasm in the more complicated forms is said to consist of four layers: an outer tough cuticle often longitudinally ridged (Fig. 47C), a mucus-secreting layer discharging through pores into the surface grooves, the ectoplasm proper, and an innermost zone of myonemes, termed the *myocyte*, which may consist of both circular and longitudinal fibrils as well as bundles extending into the entoplasm. The anterior end may be provided with spines, hooks, filaments, etc., of cuticular origin, used in adhesion (Fig. 47A, B, F). The dense granular entoplasm is loaded with inclusions, such as paraglycogen bodies, protein and volutin granules, and fat spheres. Mitochondria and true Golgi bodies (Fig. 7H) are present. The gregarines are uninucleate in young stages, becoming multinucleate either before or as multiple fission approaches.

In most gregarines the sporozoites develop directly into gamonts, schizogony being absent. The gamonts tend to adhere in chains of two or more individuals (Fig. 47D). The adherence of two gregarines, known as *syzygy*, anticipates gamogony, for the later history shows that the anterior member is female, the posterior male. Gamogony follows the same course in all members of the order. The mature male and female gamonts, often distinguished by cytosomal differences, if not already in syzygy, adhere in couples, round up, and encyst within a common cyst wall, often embedded in jelly (Fig. 47H, J.) Inside the cyst, the gamonts without fusing undergo multiple fission into a number of gametes, all those from one gamont being of the same sex (Fig. 47K, N). A considerable amount of parent cytoplasm remains unused and constitutes the *residual body*. The usually rounded gametes appear to be isogamous, but in some species the male gametes are pointed or tailed or even

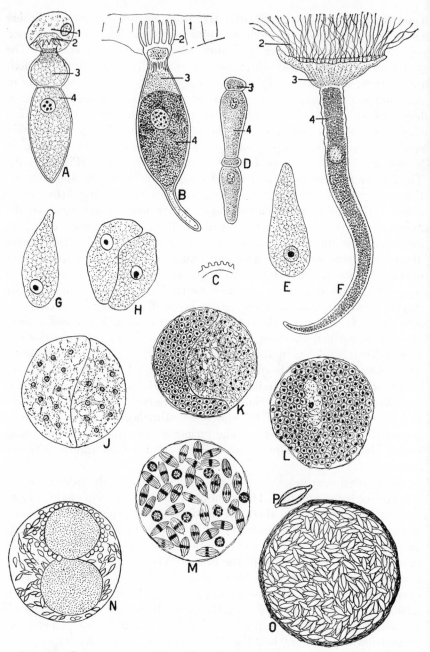

Fig. 47.—Gregarines. *A. Actinophilus*, from centipede gut, from slide. (*Courtesy Dr. D. H. Wenrich.*) *B.* Gregarine from a grasshopper gut, from slide. (*Courtesy Dr. D. H. Wenrich.*) *C.* Section of the cuticle of *B*, showing ridges. *D. Gregarina*, from the gut of a mealworm. (*After Brendt*, 1902.) *E. Monocystis*, acephaline gregarine from the

flagellate (Fig. 47N). The gametes fuse in pairs (Fig. 47L), and the resulting zygotes each transform into a walled body, formerly termed *pseudonavicella*, now usually called *spore*, of various shapes: oval, rectangular, pyriform, fusiform, sometimes with spines or long tails (Fig. 48U–X). Each zygote becomes one single spore within which multiple fission into a bundle of eight (in a few cases one) elongate sporozoites occurs (Fig. 47M). All these processes take place within the original cyst (Fig. 47O), which now or previously is discharged by way of the feces or genital or excretory ducts or possibly only by death of the host. In many forms the exact details of the transfer from host to host are unknown. The residual body often assists the rupture of the cysts either by swelling or as in the genus *Gregarina* by forming tubes, the *sporoducts*, which, turning inside out, penetrate cyst wall and jelly and serve as conduits for the exit of the spores (Fig. 48Y). The latter can resist prolonged drying. They hatch, when ingested by proper hosts, into worm-like sporozoites, which by gliding and myoneme movements attain their accustomed sites. In most gregarines the infection simply passes from one individual to another of the same species but in a few there is an alternation of hosts. Owing to the lack of schizogony in most gregarines, the parasites do not multiply within the host and consequently cause little damage.

The gregarines fall into two suborders, the Schizogregarinaria and the Eugregarinaria. The schizogregarines are a small group, inhabiting the digestive tract and its appendages in annelids, arthropods, and tunicates and multiplying by one or more schizogonic cycles before the typical gamogony sets in. Examples are *Schizocystis* (Fig. 48A–H), a worm-like form in the intestine of a midge that sporulates as in Fig. 48B, before entering on the typical sexual cycle with anisogametes (Fig. 48D–H); and *Ophryocystis* (Fig. 48J–N) from the Malpighian tubules of beetles where each gamont produces only a single gamete (Fig. 48M), and one spore (Fig. 48N) results. The eugregarines, which lack schizogony, comprise the majority and more typical members of the order and are divisible into *acephaline* and *cephaline* types. The former, characterized by simple undivided bodies, inhabit the body spaces of various invertebrates. Representative are *Monocystis* and related genera (Fig.

seminal vesicles of earthworms. *F. Pterocephalus. G–M.* Life cycle of a gregarine, based on *Lankesteria planariae*, acephaline gregarine found in planarians, somewhat diagrammatic: *G*, mature gregarine; *H*, association of two gamonts; *J*, nuclear multiplication; *K*, further nuclear divisions, the left gamont (probably male) more advanced than the right one, having formed gametes; *L*, zygotes resulting from the fusion of gametes from the two gamonts; *M*, each zygote has formed a spore containing eight sporozoites. *N.* Gamete formation in two gamonts of a species of *Monocystis*, showing difference between male and female gametes. (*After Hoffmann,* 1909.) *O.* Ripe cyst of *Monocystis*, full of spores, from seminal vesicle of an earthworm. *P.* One of the spores enlarged. 1, host tissue; 2, epimerite; 3, protomerite; 4, deutomerite.

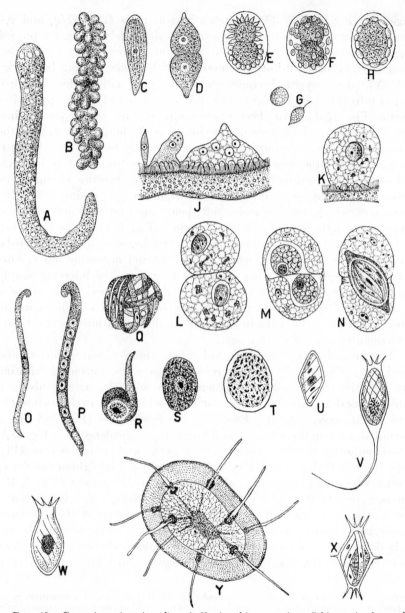

Fig. 48.—Gregarines (continued). *A-H*. A schizogregarine, *Schizocystis*, from the intestine of the midge *Ceratopogon* (*after Leger*, 1909): *A*, the mature schizont; *B*, schizont undergoing schizogony; *C*, mature gamont; *D*, gamonts in syzygy; *E*, inside the cyst, each gamont undergoes multiple fission into gametes, which are anisogamic; *G*, male and female gametes enlarged; *F*, gametes have fused to zygotes; *H*, each zygote has formed a sporocyst. *J-N*. A schizogregarine, *Ophryocystis*, parasitic in the Malpighian tubules of beetles (*after Leger*, 1907): *J*, stages of growth of the parasite; *K*, gamont; *L*, two gamonts in syzygy; *M*, each gamont produces a single isogamete; *N*, the two gametes have united to a zygote

47E, N, O), which occupy the center of the sperm balls in the seminal vesicles of earthworms, and *Lankesteria* (Fig. 47G), occurring in planarians, insects, ascidians, etc. The cephaline gregarines comprise the most complex members of the order with the body divided into an anterior *epimerite* furnished with a knob, point, teeth, hooks, filaments, etc. (Fig. 47A, B, F) for anchorage in the host cells, and a worm-like remainder, often separated by an ectoplasmic partition into a short anterior *protomerite* and a long posterior *deutomerite* containing the nucleus (Fig. 47A, B, D, F). In this group the ectoplasm and myonemes reach their greatest differentiation. The cephaline gregarines inhabit chiefly the intestine of arthropods. Representative is the genus *Gregarina* (Fig. 47D) with many species in cockroaches, meal worms, and other insects, with a simple epimerite and cysts emptying through sporoducts (Fig. 48Y).

4. Order Coccidia.—The Coccidia are intracellular parasites of epithelial cells of annelids, mollusks, arthropods, and vertebrates, with complex life cycles involving an alternation of schizogony and sporogony, sometimes with change of host. They inhabit principally the lining epithelium of the intestine or its appendages such as the bile duct, liver, or Malpighian tubules but may also parasitize the kidneys, testes, and linings of blood vessels and coelomic spaces. The young sporozoites and merozoites are elongated and motile like gregarines. They quickly enter an epithelial cell, become rounded and motionless, and grow into schizonts that undergo schizogony into numerous merozoites (Fig. 49F–J). These differ slightly from sporozoites. They reinfect additional host cells, and, as schizogony may be repeated many times, the host may become heavily infected and suffer serious or fatal damage from the destruction of its cells. Often, however, the host appears to become adjusted to the inroads of the parasite through regeneration of new cells. After repeated schizogony, the merozoites develop into gamonts (Fig. 49K). The female gamont enlarges into a large spherical macrogamete or egg packed with food (Fig. 49O) reserves while the male gamont or microgametocyte divides into two, four, or many microgametes (Fig. 49L–N). The zygote encysts, being then termed *oöcyst*, and undergoes sporogony into a variable number (one, two, four, or many) of bodies called *sporoblasts* that, secreting cyst walls, become *sporocysts* or *spores* within which a final division into one, two, four, or many sporozoites occurs (Fig. 49P–R). Thus the oöcyst contains walled

which becomes a single spore containing eight sporozoites. *O–T. Selenococcidium*, a coccidian resembling a gregarine (*after Leger and Duboscq*, 1910): *O*, mature worm-like schizont; *P*, same, preparing for schizogony; *Q*, schizogony; *R*, alteration to rounded macrogametocyte; *S*, mature macrogamete; *T*, formation of microgametes. *U–X.* Various types of gregarine spores. (*After Leger*, 1892.)   *Y.* Cyst of *Gregarina* with sporoducts. (*After Bütschli.* 1881.)

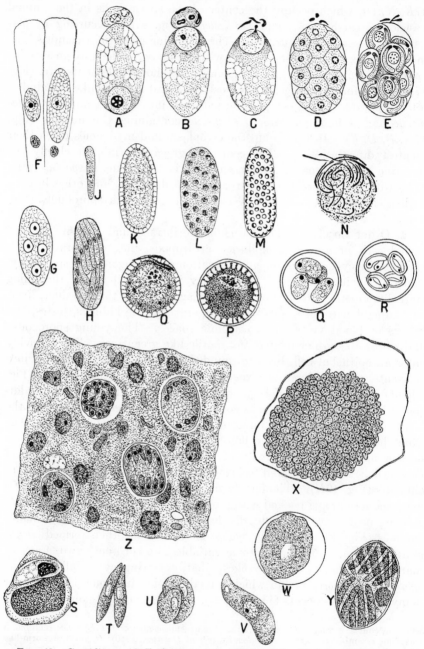

Fig. 49.—Coccidians. *A–E.* Sporogony in *Adelea* (*after Greiner*, 1921): *A*, male gametocyte attached to macrogamete; *B*, male gametocyte producing four sperm; *C*, one of the sperm penetrating the macrogamete (egg); *D*, fertilized egg divides into sporoblasts; *E*, each sporoblast becomes a sporocyst forming two sporozoites. *F–R.* Life cycle of a

spores (sporocysts) each of which contains one or more sporozoites. The sporozoites escape when the oöcysts are ingested by the proper host. The foregoing is the typical history, which may be modified in blood-inhabiting forms. The majority of the coccidians are confined to a single host; only the blood-dwelling genera and a few others pass through an intermediate host.

The Coccidia are divided into two suborders, the Adeleidea and the Eimeridea. In the former, the larger female gamont and the smaller male gamont adhere or encyst together, as in gregarines, and the male gamont then divides into two or four nonflagellate microgametes, one of which fertilizes the egg (Fig. 49*A–E*). The number of sporocysts and contained sporozoites is variable and in some cases, as *Haemogregarina*, the oöcyst produces the sporozoites directly without sporocyst formation (Fig. 50*A–L*). To the Adeleidea belong the true blood coccidians, formerly called haemogregarines, comprising the genera *Karyolysus*, inhabiting the endothelial lining of the blood vessels of lizards and snakes; *Hepatozoon* (Fig. 49*S–Z*) living in the cells of the liver, spleen, bone marrow, etc., of mammals; and *Haemogregarina* (Fig. 50*A–L*), parasitizing the red blood corpuscles of turtles, possibly other reptiles, and fish. These forms pass through schizogonic cycles in the situations mentioned but the gamonts penetrate red and white blood corpuscles and develop no further unless ingested by a blood-sucking invertebrate, such as ticks, mites, or leeches. Gamogony and sporogony ensue in the invertebrate host, and the reinfection of the primary vertebrate host is accomplished either by ingestion of infected mites and ticks or by the bite of an infected animal.

In the Eimeridea or typical coccidians, the gamonts remain separate, and the microgametocyte produces by multiple fission numerous small, slender, biflagellate microgametes that swim to the large immotile macrogametes (Figs. 49*F–R* and 50*M–Q*.) Certain genera exhibit a true alternation of hosts; the details are known only for *Aggregata;* its schizogonic cycles occur in the intestine of crabs, and gamogony and sporogony occur in squids which feed on crabs. *Schellackia* in the digestive tract

---

typical coccidian, *Eimeria sp.* from centipede intestine, from slide (*courtesy Dr. D. H. Wenrich*): *F*, growth of trophozoite in the epithelial cells of the host; *G*, beginning of schizogony; *H*, schizogony; *J*, single merozoite that reinfects intestinal cells; *K*, gametocyte; *L–N*, male gametocyte forming numerous sperm; *O*, female gametocyte developed from *K*, being fertilized; *P*, oöcyst with a cyst wall; *Q*, oöcyst has formed four sporocysts; *R*, each sporocyst becomes a cyst and produces two sporozoites. *S–Z*. Life cycle of *Hepatozoon* (*after Miller*, 1908): *S*, Merozoite in a white blood cell of the rat; *T*, such merozoites, when ingested by rat ticks sucking the rat's blood, develop into elongated gametes that fuse in pairs; *U*, fusion of gametes; *V*, resulting oökinete, which penetrates into the tick's tissues where it encysts to an oöcyst *W* and sporulates into numerous sporoblasts *X*, each of which becomes a sporocyst *Y* and sporulates into numerous sporozoites; these, injected into the rat by the tick's bite, infect various tissues and cells of the rat but undergo schizogony only in the liver; *Z*, section of the liver of an infected rat with various stages of schizogony.

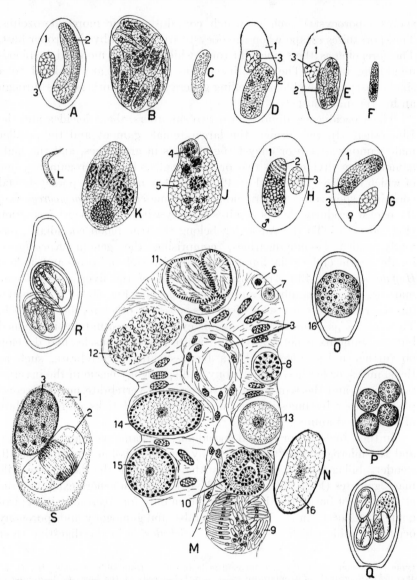

Fig. 50.—Coccidians (continued). *A–L.* Life cycle of *Haemogregarina stepanowi,* parasite of the blood corpuscles of turtles (*after Reichenow,* 1910): *A,* mature worm-like parasite in red blood cell of turtle; *B,* same in schizogony; *C,* one of the merozoites; this reinfects corpuscles; *D,* type of trophozoite that gives rise to gametes; *E,* same in schizogony; *F,* small merozoites from *E;* these become female, *G,* and male, *H,* gametocytes; *J,* male gametocyte adheres to mature female gamete and gives off sperm into it; *K,* zygote sporulates directly into sporozoites; *L,* single sporozoite.   Stages *J–L* take place in leeches by whose bite turtles become infected with the sporozoites.   *M–Q.* Life cycle of the rabbit coccidian, *Eimeria stiedae,* from slide (*courtesy of Dr. D. H. Wenrich*): *M,* section of a bile passage of the rabbit, showing coccidians in the epithelium; 6–7, young trophozoites; S stage of schizogony; 9, schizogony of large type cyst; 10–12 stages of formation of sperm

of lizards, and *Lankesterella* in the lining of the blood vessels of frogs pass through both schizogony and gamogony in the situations mentioned; but the sporozoites penetrate the blood corpuscles (Fig. 50*S*) and are transmitted to new hosts by way of bloodsucking mites and leeches, in which however they undergo no changes. These two genera are often classed among the haemogregarines. Other Eimeridea are confined to a single host that becomes infected by eating infected feces. The typical genus is *Eimeria* (formerly called *Coccidium*), with numerous species inhabiting arthropods and all classes of vertebrates but particularly domestic birds and mammals, characterized by round or oval oöcysts containing four spores each with two sporozoites (Figs. 49*R*, 50*Q*). Species of *Eimeria* live usually in the epithelial cells of the digestive tract, bile ducts, and liver, less often in other organs. In these sites all stages of the life cycle are passed and the oöcysts are discharged with the feces. Usually the division of the zygote into four spores occurs after discharge outside the host. Eimerians cause the disease *coccidiosis* in mammals, with severe digestive symptoms, sometimes fatal, but often subsiding into a mild chronic condition. Best known is the liver coccidiosis of rabbits, in which all stages of the parasite (*Eimeria stiedae*) except spore formation can be found in the epithelium of the bile passages (Fig. 50*M*, *N*). Coccidiosis of man by species of *Eimeria* has been reported several times, but the oöcysts seen in the feces apparently originated in ingested food. The related genus *Isospora* in which the oöcysts contain two spores each with four sporozoites (Fig. 50*R*) does, however, occasionally parasitize the digestive tract of man and is common in cats, dogs, birds, frogs, and other vertebrates.

5. Order Haemosporidia.—The Haemosporidia are intracellular parasites of the blood corpuscles or other parts of the blood system of vertebrates in which the schizogonic cycle is passed; the development of the gametes and sporogony occur only in a blood-sucking intermediate host. There are no cyst walls at any stage, and the naked sporozoites come directly from the zygote. The type genus is *Plasmodium* (including *Laverania* and *Proteosoma*), causative organism of human and bird malaria with the following cycle (Fig. 51). The sporozoites penetrate red blood corpuscles where they grow as amoeboid organisms (Fig. 51*A–C*), passing through a ring stage in the case of human malaria (Fig. 52*B*, *H*). Black pigment granules, products of the digestion of

---

from male gametocyte; 13, young female gametocyte; 14, longitudinal section, and 15, cross-section of mature female gametocyte or egg. *N*, the fertilized egg, note shell; *O*, oöcyst after leaving the rabbit; *P*, division of oöcyst into four sporoblasts; *Q*, each sporoblast forms a sporocyst with two sporozoites. (*O–Q, after Wasielewski,* 1904.) *R*. Oöcyst of *Isospora*, having two sporocysts each with four sporozoites. (*After Dobell,* 1919.) *S. Lankesterella* in red blood corpuscle of a frog, from slide. (*Courtesy Dr. D. H. Wenrich.*) 1, host blood corpuscle; 2, parasite; 3, nucleus of host corpuscle or tissue; 4, male gametocyte; 5, female gametocyte.

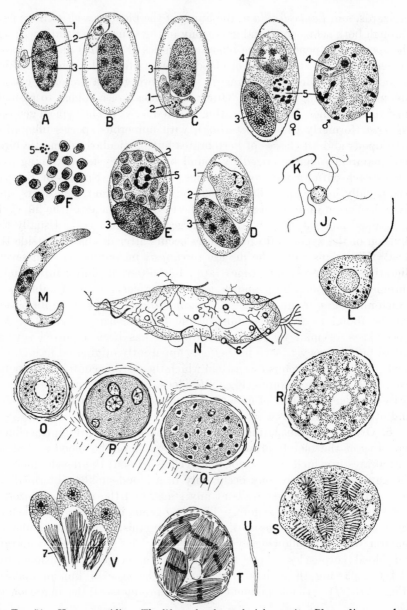

Fig. 51.—Haemosporidia.　The life cycle of a malarial parasite, *Plasmodium sp.*, from the canary bird and the mosquito *Culex*, from slides.　(*Courtesy of Dr. Clay Huff, except J, K, L, N after Neumann, 1909.*)　*A*. Young trophozoite in the red blood corpuscle of the canary bird, 8 A.M.; *B*, noon; *C*, 8 P.M.; *D*, 4 A.M.; showing growth of the parasite; *E*, 6 A.M., beginning of schizogony; *F*, 8 A.M. 24 hours after *A*; the merozoites set free will infect other corpuscles.　*G*. The female, and *H*, the male gametocyte; these develop from stages like *D*.　*J*. Male gametocyte producing sperm; *K*, one of the sperm.　*L*. Fertilization of the female gamete.　*M*. Fertilized egg or oökinete.　*N*. Stomach of the mosquito

hemoglobin, appear in their cytoplasm (Figs. 51E and 52D, J). The mature schizonts undergo multiple fission into a number of merozoites (Figs. 51E, F and 52D, J) that escape by rupture of the infected corpuscle and enter new corpuscles, repeating the schizogonic cycle indefinitely. Sooner or later some of the merozoites develop into gamonts (gameto-cytes), distinguishable as male and female (Figs. 51G, H and 52E, F), and these develop no further until taken into the stomach of a mosquito. Here the female gamont matures into a female gametocyte or egg and the male gamont divides into four or eight long slender spermatozoa.[1] The latter become free (Figs. 51J, K and 52L) and one fertilizes the egg (Fig. 51L). The zygote known as an oökinete (Fig. 51M) becomes elongated and amoeboid and works its way through the stomach wall until it lies under the outermost layer (Fig. 51N, O). Its nucleus then multiplies (Fig. 51P, Q), the cytoplasm becomes reticulate (Fig. 51R), the numerous nuclei arrange themselves on the surface of the cytoplasmic strands, and around each nucleus a sporozoite forms (Fig. 51S) so that the ripe oöcyst becomes packed with bundles of sporozoites (Fig. 51T). These escape by rupture of the oöcyst and migrate into the salivary glands of the mosquito (Fig. 51V) whence they are discharged into a vertebrate host during the act of bloodsucking.

After infection with sporozoites through the bite of a mosquito, a latent period of 10 to 12 days elapses (in human malaria) before the parasites become sufficiently numerous in the blood to evoke the first attack of chills and fever characteristic of malaria.   These attacks recur at intervals of 48 or 72 hours, corresponding to the length of the schizo-gonic cycle of the different species of human *Plasmodium*.   The attack of chills and fever coincides with the release of merozoites into the blood (as the parasites are at the same stage when injected they tend to reach schizogony simultaneously), and seems to result from toxins discharged into the blood by the rupture of infected corpuscles.   About a week after the first attack, the gamonts are seen and require 3 to 6 days to mature to the stage in which they are infective to mosquitoes.   Ripening of the gametes and fertilization occur in the mosquito stomach within a few

---

[1] The usual account, that the spermatozoa are put out from the surface of the male gamont as long slender processes, appears to be incorrect according to the recent work of O'Roke (1930).

Culex with nine cysts of bird malaria on its outer surface.   *O–T*. Development of the oöcysts embedded in the outer surface of the stomach: *O*, the oöcyst before nuclear division; *P*, *Q*, stages of nuclear multiplication; *R*, continued nuclear division, the cytoplasm is becoming net-like; *S*, the sporozoites begin to appear on the edges of the cytoplasmic strands; *T*, the ripe oöcyst, filled with bundles of sporozoites.   *U*. A single sporozoite.   *V*. Three cells of the salivary glands of the mosquito containing sporozoites.   1, red blood corpuscle of canary bird; 2, the parasite; 3, the nucleus of the corpuscle; 4, nucleus of the gametocyte; 5, the pigment granules resulting from destruction of hemoglobin by the parasite; 6, oöcysts on mosquito stomach; 7, sporozoites.

hours. The length of the cycle in the mosquito varies from 10 to 20 days, depending on temperature; the development of the parasite is suppressed below 16°C. The mosquito appears to suffer no damage from the parasites although the stomach may be literally covered with as many as 30 or 40 oöcysts, each releasing 1000 to 10,000 sporozoites.

Three different species of malarial parasite, distinguished by various morphological details, are recognized for man. In *Plasmodium vivax*, causative organism of the ordinary benign tertian malaria, the schizogonic cycle occupies 48 hours, while in quartan malaria, due to *P. malariae* (Fig. 52*A–F*), the cycle is 72 hours. In both species, the entire asexual cycle is passed in the circulating blood, the gamonts are spherical (Fig. 52*E*, *F*), and the disease is seldom fatal. In the third species, *P. falciparum* (Fig. 52*G–L*), organism of malignant or tropical tertian malaria, the schizogonic cycle requires about 48 hours but the infected corpuscles tend to adhere in clumps and stick in the capillaries (Fig. 52*G*) of various organs, in which locations most of the stages must be sought. Only the ring stage of the schizont (Fig. 52*H*) and the gamonts, known from their shape as *crescents* (Fig. 52*K*), are found in the circulating blood. Because the masses of infected corpuscles block the capillaries of important organs, this type of malaria is serious and often fatal. The schizonts at the segmenting stage (Fig. 52*J*) are easily distinguished from the other types of malaria by their much smaller size.

All human malaria is transmitted only by mosquitoes of the genus *Anopheles*. The disease is characteristic of the warmer countries of the earth and corresponds in distribution to the habitat of the species of mosquito concerned. In the two less serious types of malaria, the symptoms gradually subside and the parasites apparently disappear although enough remain to cause sudden recurrences. The natives of malarial countries acquire a certain amount of immunity as a result of repeated infections.

Species of *Plasmodium* also occur in other mammals, particularly apes, monkeys, bats, and small rodents and carnivores, and are likewise found in birds and lizards where they were formerly referred to under the name *Proteosoma*. Those of birds (Fig. 51), particularly common in the sparrow tribe, belong to several species of *Plasmodium* and are transmitted only by mosquitoes of the genus *Culex* or related genera. The asexual cycle requires only 24 hours. As they can be grown in canary birds, the bird malarial parasites have furnished excellent material for laboratory studies of malaria. The work of Taliaferro and his associates on bird malaria has shown that after a great initial multiplication, the parasites decline sharply until they become undetectable and that this destruction results from the ingestion of the parasites by white blood corpuscles and other types of phagocytic cells. These results indicate

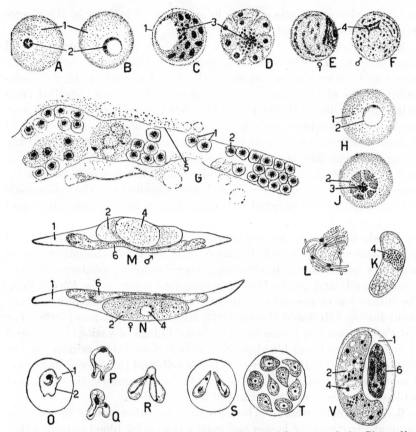

FIG. 52.—Haemosporidia (continued).   *A–F*. Stages of human malaria, *Plasmodium malariae*, as seen in smears of human blood: *A*, early stage; *B*, ring stage; *C*, beginning of schizogony; *D*, division of parasite into merozoites; note that the merozoites about fill the corpuscle; *E*, female gametocyte; *F*, male gametocyte.   *G–L*. Some stages of *Plasmodium falciparum*, agent of human malignant tertian malaria, from slides.   (*Courtesy Dr. Milton Halpern.*)[1]   *G*, capillary of the human brain filled with infected corpuscles; the parasite is recognized by the conspicuous black pigment granules derived from hemoglobin; *H*, ring stage in the circulating blood; *J*, formation of merozoites in a brain capillary; note that the merozoite group is much smaller than the corpuscle; *K*, crescentic gametocyte from the circulating blood; *L*, formation of sperm from male gametocyte; this will take place in a blood smear as the blood cools.   *M*. Male, and *N*, female gametocyte of *Leucocytozoon*, inside the blood corpuscles of the duck, from slide.   (*Courtesy of Dr. E. C. O'Roke.*)   *O–T. Babesia canis* (*O–S* after *Nuttall and Smith*, 1907; *T* after *Breinl and Hindle*, 1908): *O*, the parasite in a red blood corpuscle of the dog; *P–S*, stages of division; *T*, several parasites in a blood cell.   *V*, *Haemoproteus*, crescentic gametocyte in a red blood cell of the pigeon.   1, red blood corpuscle; 2, the parasite; 3, pigment granules; 4, nucleus of parasite; 5, capillary; 6, nucleus of blood corpuscle.

[1] Dr. Halpern, city pathologist of New York, studied a large number of cases, many of them fatal, among drug addicts, who were transmitting the disease among themselves by using a hypodermic syringe for injecting the drug.

that immunity to malaria consists in an increased activity of the phagocytic elements of the body.

Some other genera of the Haemosporidia are *Haemoproteus* and
Leucocytozoon. In *Haemoproteus,* found in birds and reptiles, the
schizogonic cycles are passed as in the blood coccidians in the endothelial linings of the blood vessels and only the gamonts, called from
their sausage shape *Halteridium* (Fig. 52*V*) parasitize the blood corpuscles. The complete cycle is known for *H. columbae* of pigeons and
H. lophortyx from a California quail; gamogony and sporogony occurring
in bloodsucking flies (*Lynchia*) are similar to those of *Plasmodium.* A
similar life cycle was found by O'Roke (1934) for *Leucocytozoon anatis,*
cause of a serious disease of wild and domestic ducks. The schizogonic
stages inhabit the endothelial cells of capillaries in the lungs, liver, and
spleen, and only the gametocytes (Fig. 52*M, N*) are seen in the circulating blood, where they appear as oval bodies in the much altered red
blood corpuscles. The cycle is completed in black flies (*Simulium*) where
formation of gametes, fertilization, encystment of oökinetes in the
stomach wall, and production of sporozoites occur as in *Plasmodium.*
The utilization of general endothelial tissue by these parasites and the
recent finding (Huff and Bloom, 1935; Kikerth and Mudrow, 1938) that
bird *Plasmodium* can parasitize endothelial linings of various organs and
all types of blood and blood-forming cells indicate that primitively the
Haemosporidia inhabited various types of cells and the present limitation
of some to red blood corpuscles is a specialized characteristic. Relation
to blood coccidians is also evidenced by these facts.

6. The Piroplasmoses.—These are diseases, often serious, of domestic
mammals, particularly horses and cattle, caused by blood parasites that
seem to belong to the Haemosporidia. The parasites are exceedingly
minute oval or pyriform organisms found inside the red blood corpuscles
where they multiply by longitudinal binary fission (Fig. 52*O–T*). They
are transmitted only by ticks of the family Ixodidae [genera *Boöphilus*
(= *Margaropus*), *Ixodes, Dermacentor, Rhipicephalus, Hyalomma, Haemo-
physalis*] as was first shown in 1893 in a famous investigation
of Texas cattle fever by two American workers, T. Smith and F.
L. Kilbourne. This was also the first demonstration of the transmission of a protozoan disease by a bloodsucking arthropod. The
disease of piroplasmosis is characterized by fever, anemia, jaundice, and
bloody urine ("red water"). The organisms concerned are usually
grouped into two families: the Babesiidae, including the genera *Babesia*
(= *Piroplasma*) and *Nuttallia,* and the Theileriidae, for *Theileria.* The
complete life cycle of a *Babesia* has been described only for *B. bigemina,*
causative agent of Texas cattle fever, by Dennis (1932). The organisms
in the red blood cells of cattle are apparently gametocytes. In the tick's

stomach, these alter to vermiform isogametes and fuse in couples to a motile oökinete, which works its way into the developing eggs in tne ovary of the tick (*Margaropus annulatus*). Inside an egg, the oökinete encysts to an oöcyst, within which multiple fission occurs into amoeboid sporoblasts. These wander throughout the developing embryo and at the time of hatching of the young tick or later sporulate into numerous sporozoites that infect the salivary glands and are injected into the mammalian host by the tick's bite. However, Regandanz and Reichenow (1931) were unable to find any stages except simple binary fission in either dog or tick in *Babesia canis*, transmitted by *Dermacentor*, and believe the babesias are rhizopods, and Reichenow (1935) thinks Dennis is in error, having confused stages of two different parasites. But Ivanic (1937) has reported typical schizogony like that of the malarial parasites in the spleen of horses infected with *Babesia caballi*. It is probable that the babesias are Haemosporidia. In *Theileria* this has been definitely established. Details have been worked out by Cowdry and associates (1932, 1933) for a cattle theileriosis of Africa, termed East Coast fever, caused by *Theileria parva* and transmitted by the tick *Rhipicephalus;* and by Sergeant and asssociates (1936) for another cattle disease of the Mediterranean region caused by *T. dispar* trans-- mitted by ticks of the genus *Hyalomma*. Schizogony occurs in the cells of the reticulo-endothelial system. The round, oval, or elliptical parasites in the red blood corpuscles are gametocytes. When ingested by the tick, these invade the epithelial cells of the gut, where later forms believed to be zygotes are seen. These zygotes migrate to the salivary glands where they become sporonts, giving rise to a number of sporoblasts, each of which sporulates into numerous sporozoites. There are still many gaps in these accounts.

Minute bodies termed *Anaplasma*, apparently consisting entirely of chromatin, have been seen in the red blood cells of cattle and other animals and are believed by some to be related to the piroplasms. *Anaplasma* seem to be transmitted by ticks and bloodsucking flies.

7. Subclass Cnidosporidia and Order Myxosporidia.—The Cnidosporidia include all sporozoans in which the spores contain *polar capsules,* oval bodies resembling nematocysts, enclosing a spirally coiled thread (Fig. 53*A, G*) that under the action of digestive juices discharges by turning inside out and fastens the spore to the walls of the digestive tract. The spores hatch into amoeboid young that early begin to produce spores in their interior. The group is divided into the three orders Myxosporidia, Actinomyxidia, and Microsporidia.

The Myxosporidia parasitize almost exclusively fish, both fresh and salt water. They inhabit hollow organs, as the gall and urinary bladders, in which case they are actively amoeboid; or they live in connective

Fig. 53.—Myxosporidia.   *A*. A myxosporidian spore, of *Leptotheca*.   *B*. Trophozoite of *Leptotheca*.   *C*. Trophozoite of *Ceratomyxa*.   *D*. Trophozoite and *E*, spore, of *Myxidium*. *F*. Section of fish gill showing cyst of *Henneguya* containing spores; *G*. one of the spores of *Henneguya* enlarged.   *H*. *Myxobolus* in the muscles of a fish.   *J*. Spore of *Ceratomyxa*. (*A, F, G, From slides, courtesy of Dr. D. H. Wenrich; B–E, J, after Davis, 1917; H, after Keysselitz,* 1908.)   *K–P*. Process of spore formation in *Ceratomyxa drepanopsettae* (*after Awerinzew,* 1908): *K*, pansporoblast has divided into two large and two small cells; *L*, each large cell has fused with a small cell to form a zygote; two vegetative nuclei are seen;

tissue or among the cells of the gills, kidneys, liver, spleen, etc., where they either soon become encysted by layers of host tissue or spread diffusely, even dividing into fragments. They are mostly harmless to the host but may cause damaging tumor-like masses (Fig. 53F). The spore hatches into a single uninucleate amoeboid young (really a zygote) that soon becomes multinucleate, possibly multiplying by fission or plasmotomy; but in the majority of species spore formation constitutes the sole mode of reproduction. Each spore is enclosed in a shell made of two valves (Fig. 53A) and consists of one, two, or four, usually two, polar capsules and one or two amoeboid masses, termed *sporoplasm*, that are gametes before they fuse (Fig. 53A), a zygote after fusion (Fig. 53G, J). The spores are of various shapes (Fig. 53A, G, J, E) and may have long processes said to assist floating. Each parasite produces two to many spores, often beginning while immature and continuing throughout its growth. The process of spore formation is complex and in the best known cases proceeds as follows: It begins by an endogenous budding in which a nucleus is cut off with a bit of cytoplasm in the interior of the parasite. This cell, called the *pansporoblast*, divides into two large and two small cells. The two small cells take no direct part in spore formation. In *Myxobolus*, the two large cells divide until each produces a group of six cells or nuclei; but in *Ceratomyxa*, each divides so that two large and two small cells, really anisogametes, result (Fig. 53K). These fuse in pairs to zygotes (Fig. 53L), and each zygote divides into a group of six cells (Fig. 53N). The subsequent history is the same for both genera. In each group of six, two cells become valve cells, forming the valves of the spore, two become polar capsules, and the remaining two are isogametes that sooner or later fuse to form the amoeboid zygote or sporoplasm (Fig. 53O, P). Thus commonly each pansporoblast gives rise to two spores. The fertilization is seen to be a paedogamous autogamy.

A few common genera are illustrated in Fig. 53. *Leptotheca* (Fig. 53B) with elongated pseudopodia at one end occurs chiefly in the body cavity of fish and has rounded spores (Fig. 53A). *Ceratomyxa* (Fig. 53C) with many species in the gall bladder of fish produces transversely elongated spores (Fig. 53J), generally two. *Myxidium* (Fig. 53D) is abundant in the gall and urinary bladders and kidneys of fish, sometimes reptiles; the spores (Fig. 53E) have the polar capsules pointed in opposite directions. *Henneguya*, mostly in fresh-water fish, may form tumor-like swellings (Fig. 53F), which become filled with the tailed spores (Fig.

M, each zygote has again divided, and *N*, division continues until six cells arise from each; *O, P*, each group of six cells forms a spore; two secrete the polar capsules, two become enclosing valve cells, and two unite to form the amoeboid zygote. 1, polar capsule; 2, capsule-forming cell; 3, valve cell; 4, amoeboid gamete or zygote; 5, suture line of the two valves; 6, large gamete; 7, small gamete; 8, zygotes; 9, vegetative nucleus.

53G). *Myxobolus* (Fig. 53H), widespread in fresh-water fish, dwells in any of the solid organs or tissues, there encysting to form large swellings, which may damage or kill the host and which contain numerous oval spores with one or two polar capsules.

8. Order Actinomyxidia.—This is a small, little-known group, inhabitants of the coelom or digestive tract of fresh-water oligochaetes and marine sipunculids. The spores (Fig. 54A) are three-rayed, composed of three valves often with long tails, three polar capsules, and one to many amoeboid young or a multinucleate mass. The uninucleate young escaping from the spore (Fig. 54B) associate in couples (Fig. 54C) and eventually one gives rise to eight small and the other to eight large gametes (Fig. 54D). These anisogametes fuse in pairs, and each zygote divides to seven nuclei or cells (Fig. 54E). Of the seven, three give rise to polar capsules, three to the valves, and the seventh undergoes division to a multinucleate mass (Fig. 54F) that eventually forms 24 sporozoites (Fig. 54G). Thus each cyst (Fig. 54D) comes to contain eight spores (Fig. 54H), which unfold as at Fig. 54A on escape. The foregoing is the account of Mackinnon and Adam (1924) for *Triactinomyxon* found in *Tubifex*. Other genera are *Tetractinomyxon* and *Hexactinomyxon*.

9. Order Microsporidia.—These are intracellular parasites of various organs and tissues of arthropods and fishes, less often of other groups. The minute spores (Fig. 54N, O), of simple form and structure, contain a long coiled thread, representing a polar capsule of which the wall is missing. The amoeboid young penetrate host cells and there undergo binary or multiple fission into offspring that often adhere in chains. Certain of the parasites become pansporoblasts producing one to a number of spores, but the details of the process have not been well worked out owing to the minute size of all stages. The most important members are *Nosema bombycis*, causative organism of the pébrine disease of silkworms, and *N. apis*, probably agent of disease in bees (Fig. 54M, N). They inhabit the epithelium of the digestive tract. The silkworm disease was investigated in 1865 by Pasteur, sent by the French government to combat the ravages of the malady in the silk-growing districts of southern France and adjacent countries. He discovered the "corpuscles" (spores) and correctly interpreted them as the agents by which the disease was spread although he never understood the true nature of the parasite. Species of *Glugea* produce large cysts in the tissues of fresh-water fish and other vertebrates. *Thelohania* infests mostly arthropods as a minute intracellular parasite. *Mrazekia* parasitizes chiefly the coelomic cells of fresh-water oligochaetes and the fat body of aquatic insects and has elongated spores (Fig. 54O) with a long thread attached to a rod-like base.

10. Subclass Sarcosporidia.—These parasites inhabit the muscles or connective tissue of mammals, and, less often, birds and reptiles.

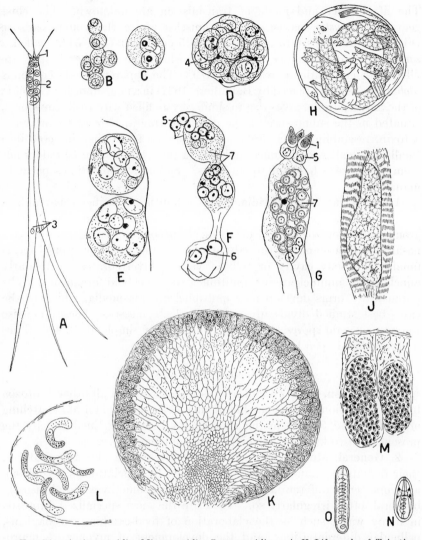

Fig. 54.—Actinomyxidia, Microsporidia, Sarcosporidia.   *A–H*. Life cycle of *Triactino-myxon*. (*After Mackinnon and Adam*, 1924.): *A*, the ripe spore, with three polar capsules and three long valves; *B*, amoeboid young (gamonts) liberated from *A*; *C*, these aggregate in couples; *D*, one in each couple gives rise to large gametes, the other to small gametes and these fuse in pairs, large and small, to a zygote as at 4; *E*, each zygote divides to seven nuclei and forms a spore *F*; three of the nuclei produce the polar capsules at 5, three form the valves at 6, and the other becomes a multinucleate mass at 7; *G*, further development of the young spore; the polar capsules have differentiated; the enclosed mass has become a number of amoeboid young gamonts; *H*, cyst in the host tissues, filled with young spores. *J*. Young *Sarcocystis* in muscle. (*After Moroff*, 1915.)   *K*. Completed cyst of *Sarcocystis* in mammalian muscle, from slide. (*Courtesy Dr. R. P. Hall.*)   *L*. A bit of *K* magnified to show the crescentic spores.   *M*. Epithelial cells of the bee's stomach filled with spores of *Nosema apis*.   *N*. A spore of *Nosema bombycis* (silkworm) enlarged. (*After Stempell*, 1909.)   *O*. Spore of *Mzarekia*. (*After Leger and Hesse*, 1916.)   1, polar capsules; 2, mass containing gamonts; 3, valves; 4, fusion of large and small gamete to a zygote; 5, cells to form polar capsules; 6, cells to form valves; 7, multinucleate mass or sporoplasm.

The life history and mode of transmission are unknown. The chief genus, *Sarcocystis*, parasitizes the muscles where the young parasite (Fig. 54*J*) develops into a large (up to 5 cm.) cyst (Fig. 54*K*) called a *sarcocyst*, made of many chambers of which the peripheral ones are filled with crescentic spores (Fig. 54*L*). The apparently related genus *Globidium*, recently placed by Babudieri (1932) in a new suborder Globidia of the Sarcosporidia, gives rise to similar cysts filled with fusiform spores, situated in the submucosa of the digestive tract. *Sarcocystis* produces a toxin, resembling a bacterial toxin, which is fatal when injected into small mammals such as mice and guinea pigs, but the parasite does not seem to be very harmful to its hosts. Sarcocysts sometimes occur in man.

11. Subclass Haplosporidia.—This group is an artificial assemblage of entoparasitic spore-producing forms that are not assignable to other groups of Sporozoa. One of them, *Rhinosporidium*, associated with nasal polypi in man, has turned out to be a fungus. The typical forms inhabit the body cavity or cells of various invertebrates, particularly annelids, as uninucleate or multinucleate amoeboid organisms. The uninucleate forms develop into multinucleate plasmodia, which in the cases best studied divide up into uninucleate masses. These give rise to one to several spores. The spores are mostly simple, oval, sometimes with tails, and open by a lid.

VII. CLASS CILIATA

1. Definition.—The Ciliata are distinguished from all other Protozoa by the possession throughout life of cilia as locomotor and food-catching organelles; and (except in the Protociliata and a few Euciliata) by the presence of two kinds of nuclei, somatic and generative.

2. General Morphology.—The Ciliata resemble the Flagellata in their definite permanent shape, maintained by a gelatinized ectoplasm, anteroposterior differentiation, and symmetry, sometimes radial, usually bilateral, often irregularly so. They are the most specialized Protozoa in many ways, such as the elaboration of food-catching mechanisms, pellicular differentiations, and the development of myonemes, neurofibrils, and other fibrillar elements. They are mostly solitary free-swimming organisms, but some are temporarily or permanently sessile and may form branching treelike colonies, and a number of ecto- and entoparasites and commensals occur in the class. Some of the sessile forms secrete gelatinous or tectinous cases, of which the best examples are the vaselike cases of the Tintinnidae.

Ectoplasm and entoplasm are distinct, and the former is often highly differentiated into the pellicle and underlying layers. The pellicle in the majority of ciliates is marked by longitudinal or diagonal lines or grooves, which are the places of attachment of the ciliary rows (Figs. 55E, 61, 62, and 63). In some forms, notably *Paramecium* (Figs. 7B, C, and 55A), the pellicle has a pattern of depressed hexagons, squares, or rhomboids bounded by ridges; there are one or two cilia in the center of each depressed area, and the trichocysts open on the ridges. Beneath the pellicle lies the so-called *alveolar* layer, which contains the basal bodies of the cilia and their connections, myonemes when these are present, plates of armor in a few forms like Coleps (Fig. 7D), the Ophryoscolecidae (Fig. 7E), and the Cycloposthiidae (Fig. 64D), and the trichocysts and tectin-secreting granules. The innermost or *cortical* layer is not distinctly marked off from the entoplasm; it contains the contractile vacuoles.

The *trichocysts*, characteristic of the holotrichous ciliates, are minute rods or ovals arranged at right angles to the body surface. They may be evenly distributed throughout the surface, as in *Frontonia* (Fig. 6) and *Paramecium* (Fig. 57C), or limited to a special region as the anterior end (*Dileptus*, Fig. 8) or mouth region (*Didinium*, Fig. 57B), or sometimes occur in little groups (*Loxophyllum*, Fig. 56J). In many Holotricha, granules or rods that are not typical trichocysts, and hence are called *protrichocysts*, are present in the pellicle and seem to be concerned in the production of tectin. The typical trichocysts, on mechanical or chemical stimulation, discharge through pores in the pellicle into elongate filaments (Fig. 56A, G), described by some as of elaborate construction. They are of two general kinds, *cnidotrichocysts* and ordinary trichocysts. The former, as in *Prorodon*, have the structure of a nematocyst (Fig. 56D), consisting of a fine tube coiled inside a capsule. On discharge, the tube turns inside out (Fig. 56E), and a material may be shot out through the tube to form the endpiece. The more common type of trichocyst, such as that of *Paramecium*, has a solid construction, and its mechanism of discharge is not understood. Krüger (1930) has postulated that the undischarged trichocyst (Fig. 56B) contains a highly absorptive layer that on discharge swells greatly, causing the elongation (Fig. 56C). According to the much-quoted work of Tönniges (1914) on *Frontonia*, the trichocysts originate from the nucleus, but this view seems improbable, and Chatton (1931) states that they grow out from the basal bodies of the cilia. The function of the trichocysts is uncertain. In some ciliates, such as *Dileptus* (Fig. 8), they are employed in the capture of prey and apparently secrete a toxic material, but in most ciliates their role is obscure. Mast (1909) suggests that they are discharged to ward off enemies, since he observed that *Paramecium* when attacked by *Didinium* emits a cloud of trichocysts, which push the *Didinium* away and may force it to detach. However, unless the *Didinium* is much smaller than the *Paramecium*, it often retains its hold and devours the

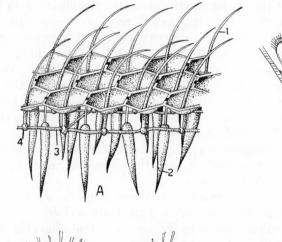

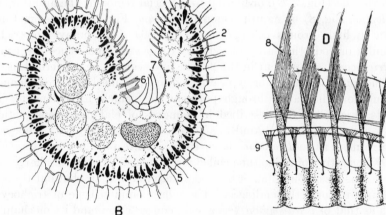

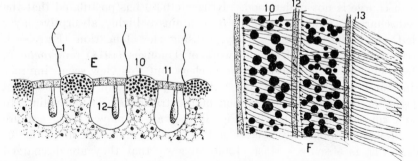

Fig. 55.—Ciliate structure. *A.* View of a small area of the surface of *Paramecium* (*after E. E. Lund,* 1935), to show the hexagonal depressions, trichocysts, and interciliary lines. *B.* Cross section through the cytopharynx of *Paramecium* (*after Gelei,* 1934), showing ciliation of the pharynx. *C. Stylonychia,* from life, side view, showing manner of use of cirri. *D.* Membranelles of *Stentor,* with fibrillar attachments. (*After Gelei,* 1926.) *E.* Section through *Stentor coeruleus.* (*After Schröder,* 1906.) *F.* Surface view of *Stentor,*

latter despite the discharge of trichocysts. The most sensible suggestion is that of Saunders (1925) that locally discharged trichocysts serve to anchor the ciliate while feeding on bacteria. This links the trichocysts to tectin secretion, and probably trichocysts are the final stage in the evolution of the tectin-secreting mechanism.

The cilia are short filaments that spring from the basal bodies in the ectoplasm and pierce the pellicle to the exterior. They commonly occur in longitudinal or diagonal rows and have the same structure and mechanism of movement as flagella, from which they differ in their shorter length, greater numbers, and lack of relation of the basal bodies to mitotic division. The cilia may clothe the entire surface or may be limited to special regions. They may be compounded into complex structures, such as *undulating membranes*, *membranelles*, and *cirri*. Undulating membranes, located in the cytopharynx, consist of one to several rows of cilia adhering sidewise into a delicate membrane whose wave-like undulations help propel food into the cytopharynx (Fig. 61O). In some ciliates the membrane can be greatly protruded (Figs. 57D and 61P) and acts like a scoop in capturing prey. Membranelles (Fig. 55D) are triangular plates composed of two or more rows of cilia fused together and are said to be anchored in the ectoplasm by a complicated array of fibrils (Fig. 55D) attached to their basal bodies. In the Spirotricha and Peritricha a row of membranelles called the *adoral zone* encircles the peristome and passes down into the cytopharynx (Figs. 62, 63, 64, and 65). Cirri, characteristic of the Hypotricha, are large stiff bristles composed of a fused tuft of cilia, are movable in all directions, and are used like legs in crawling (Fig. 55C). The compound nature of all these structures is proved by the numerous basal bodies that underlie them, one for each cilium, and by the fact that they fray out into ordinary cilia (Fig. 56F) under mechanical or chemical manipulation. Besides the ordinary locomotor cilia, many ciliates possess stiff motionless cilia, which are probably sensory (Fig. 13D) and are said to have special fibrils and granules at their bases.

An elaborate system of fibrils, termed the neuromotor system (Figs. 13A, B, C, 56H, and 64A) and connecting the basal bodies of the cilia, has been described for a large number of ciliates. It consists chiefly of the *interciliary fibrils*—longitudinal fibrils that connect the basal bodies of the cilia in each longitudinal row, run in the ectoplasm parallel to the surface, and also extend down the cytopharynx (Fig. 13C). In some forms (Figs. 13A and 56H), additional fibrils, the *interstrial fibrils*, are found halfway between the interciliary fibrils, and *transverse connectives*

showing ciliary rows. (*After Gelei*, 1926.) 1, cilium; 2, trichocyst; 3, interciliary fibril; 4, basal body of cilium; 5, macronucleus; 6, penniculus; 7, other special cilia of cytopharynx; 8, membranelle; 9, fibrillar attachments of membranelles; 10, pigmented stripe; 11, white stripe; 12, myoneme; 13, ciliary row.

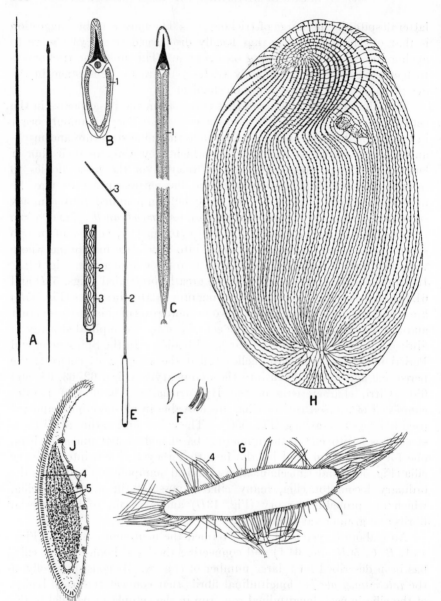

Fig. 56.—Ciliate structure. *A*. Discharged trichocysts of *Frontonia*. (*After Tönniges*, 1914.) *B*. Diagram of undischarged and, *C*, of discharged trichocysts of *Paramecium*. (*After Krüger*, 1930.) *D*. Diagram of undischarged and, *E*, discharged cnidotrichocysts of *Prorodon*. (*After Krüger*, 1936.) *F*. Cirrus, intact, and same, raveled into cilia by acid, of *Euplotes*, from life. *G*. *Paramecium* after discharge of the trichocysts by acetic acid, from life. *H*. Silver-line system of *Colpidium*. (*After Klein*, 1927.) *J*. *Loxophyllum meleagris*, from life, having part of its trichocysts in bundles. 1, swelling substance; 2, tube; 3, end piece; 4, trichocysts; 5, nucleus.

may also occur. This fibrillar system may connect with a body, the motorium, situated near the cytopharynx (Figs. 13*A*, *B*, *C*, and 64*A*). Frequently, additional fibrils extend inward from the cytopharynx (Figs. 13*C* and 64*B*) and may act as anchorage. In the Hypotricha (Fig. 13*B*) fibrils radiate from each cirrus base, but these do not connect with the motorium and are probably not nervous. It is probable that at least some of the fibrils of the neuromotor system are conductile and serve to coordinate ciliary activities (further, page 64); but others are presumably of a supporting nature. A network of fibrils in the ectoplasm nearer the surface than the ciliary fibrils has also been seen in a number of ciliates and is of uncertain function.

In recent years, Klein, a German investigator, has applied a dry-silver method to ciliates and obtains a picture of black networks and lines which he calls the *silver-line system* (Fig. 56*H*). This system appears to be a conglomeration of the pellicular markings, ectoplasmic networks, and neuromotor system.

Myonemes occur in the ectoplasm of many ciliates, especially members of the orders Spirotricha and Peritricha as *Stentor* (Fig. 62*E*) *Spirostomum* (Fig. 63*C*), *Vorticella* (Fig. 65*B*), etc. They are usually longitudinal fibrils, sometimes cross-striated, which run lengthwise the body beneath or near the grooves or lines to which the cilia are attached (Fig. 55*E*) so that when contraction occurs, these lines appear very distinct (Figs. 62*F* and 63*D*). In vorticellids the longitudinal myonemes converge at the base of the bell to form the spiral myoneme of the stalk (Fig. 65*B*). This myoneme of the vorticellid stalk is the largest and best developed myoneme of Protozoa and has been much studied. The peristome may be provided with circular myonemes. The myonemes serve primarily to contract the animal and close up the peristome as a protective measure.

The ciliates are almost wholly holozoic and exhibit the greatest elaboration of food-catching apparatus found among the Protozoa. In their feeding habits, the ciliates fall into two groups, the *raptorial* and the *current-producing* types (*Schlinger* and *Strudler* of German writers). The raptorial forms hunt and ingest large prey, often larger than themselves, while the current producers secure their food by means of ciliary currents. The morphology of the food-catching apparatus therefore follows two lines of development. Primitively the mouth is a mere opening at the anterior end. In the raptorial forms it generally retains this position as in *Coleps* (Fig. 7*D*), or in *Didinium* (Fig. 57*B*), where it is mounted on a projecting proboscis. In both these forms the mouth can be opened as wide as the body diameter. *Didinium* attacks other ciliates, especially *Paramecium*, by fastening the proboscis tip to them and then gradually engulfing them. In many raptorial ciliates the food-ingesting passage is strengthened by a circlet of trichites forming the *pharyngeal basket* resembling the staves of a barrel (Figs. 7*F*, *G*, 57*A*, and 61*C*). From its primitive anterior position the mouth may shift to a lateral or ventral position (Fig. 61*C*, *G*, *H*, *L*) and may form a deep or elongated depression (Fig. 61*F*, *G*), but a definite cytopharynx is lacking. In the current producers, on the other hand, a portion of the surface, named the *peristome*, becomes specialized for maintaining water currents, and the mouth is then shifted ventrally and often posteriorly to receive

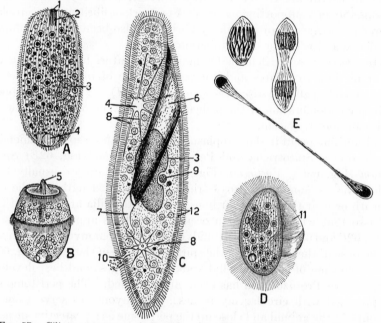

Fig. 57.—Ciliate structure.   *A. Prorodon*, from life, with terminal mouth armed with trichites.   *B. Didinium* (*after Blochmann*, 1895,) with mouth on the tip of a proboscis. *C. Paramecium caudatum*, from life, nuclei after staining, showing peristome leading to cytopharynx.   *D. Pleuronema* (*after Schewiakoff*, 1889), with large undulating membrane. *E*. Division of the micronucleus of *Pleurotricha*. (*After Manwell*, 1928.)   1, mouth; 2, trichites; 3, macronucleus; 4, contractile vacuole; 5, proboscis; 6, peristome; 7, cytopharynx; 8, canals of contractile vacuoles; 9, micronucleus; 10, cytopyge; 11, undulating membrane; 12, trichocysts.

the particles brought by the current.   The peristome may be depressed as an *oral groove* (Fig. 57*C*) or elevated as a *disk* (Fig. 65*B*, *J*).   Its cilia are often longer and more powerful than those elsewhere and may be modified into membranelles (Figs. 62*E*, *G*, 63, and 65), which, encircling the peristome one to several times, produce a powerful current.   In most of these forms a funnel-like cytopharynx (Figs. 57*C* and 62*E*) extends from the peristome down into the entoplasm, and an additional cavity, the *vestibule* (Fig. 65*J*), may be interpolated between peristome and cytopharynx.   The cytopharynx has often either special ciliary tracts (Fig. 55B) or undulating membranes (Figs. 57D, 61O, P) for wafting the food into its base. The food is whirled about in the cytopharynx by such arrangements, small particles such as bacteria are condensed into a ball, and these balls pass from the bottom of the cytopharynx into the entoplasm. In the entoplasm, the food vacuoles follow a definite circuit, interpreted to indicate a slow circulation or *cyclosis* of the entoplasm. Digestion was already described (page 61). Undigested material is generally ejected at a definite point, the *cytopyge* (Fig. 57C), which opens into the cytopharynx or vestibule in the Peritricha and to which in some parasitic ciliates (Fig. 64D) a canal leads. Ciliates can absorb dissolved nutrients or feed on nonliving material (page 59).

Contractile vacuoles are present throughout the ciliates, varying in different species from one to many, occupying fixed positions in the innermost layer of the ectoplasm. Probably a single posterior vacuole represents the primitive condition. In some ciliates, as *Frontonia* (Fig. 6), *Paramecium* (Fig. 57C), *Urocentrum* (Fig. 61G) and others, several long canals encircle the vacuole and at their distal ends collect fluid from special entoplasmic regions. In other cases, as *Stentor* (Fig. 62E), *Spirostomum* (Fig. 63C) and *Bursaria* (Fig. 63B), one very long canal leads to the vacuole, and in many ciliates there are no such feeding channels. Probably the vacuole is never a permanent structure but is formed anew after each contraction by the fusion of small vacuoles that arise in the surrounding entoplasm or are emitted from the proximal ends of the feeding canals. In the Peritricha the vacuole empties into the vestibule, in some cases with the interpolation of a reservoir (Fig. 65L). Each vacuole discharges by a more or less permanent pore through the pellicle, to which an excretory tubule may lead. The Ophryoscolecidae and Cycloposthiidae have highly developed vacuoles, often with tubules that may be encircled by a myoneme (Fig. 64C).

The entoplasm is fluid and granular, vacuolated in some forms, and contains the food vacuoles, food reserves mostly in the form of glycogen and fat, and the nuclei. In a number of species the entoplasm is filled with zoochlorellae, whose role has been especially studied in the green Paramecium, *P. bursaria* (Fig. 20). According to the work of Parker (1926) and Pringsheim (1928) this animal can live and multiply in the light without food in a medium containing the necessary salts, being supplied with food manufactured by its zoochlorellae. If deprived of its zoochlorellae or kept in the dark it dies under such conditions. It feeds like other species of *Paramecium* on bacteria, yeasts, etc., when these are available.

In the majority of ciliates, two kinds of nuclei occur: the *macronucleus* (or *meganucleus*) of somatic functions, and the *micronucleus*, or generative nucleus. The macronucleus is usually large, usually single, of the massive type, and of various shapes—round, oval, elongated, moniliform, or horseshoe-like (Figs. 62E, 63C, and 65B). In some forms, as *Dileptus anser* (Fig. 8), there are many macronuclei and micronuclei. The micronuclei are minute and usually vesicular and vary from one to over eighty in number. Removal of the micronucleus (Taylor, 1923) of *Euplotes* resulted in cessation of fission and death but in several species mutant races devoid of a micronucleus have been found. These live and divide normally but are incapable of conjugation or endomixis, evidence that the macronucleus suffices for ordinary metabolism, while the micronucleus is essential for sexual processes.

3. Asexual Reproduction.—Asexual reproduction occurs almost exclusively by binary fission, transverse in most forms, longitudinal in the Peritricha (Fig. 65C–E). The process is initiated by the micronuclei, which all divide by a modified eumitotic method, with or without polar caps (Fig. 57E). Each micronucleus draws apart into two halves connected for some time by a desmose, and spindle fibers and chromosomes are more or less evident during the division. The macronucleus divides by a simple amitosis, first condensing into an oval shape in cases where it is ordinarily of unusual or elongated form. As the nuclei pull apart, a cytosomal constriction forms and, deepening, cuts the animal into two halves. Usually each half retains such old organelles as fell within its limits and regenerates the others, often at the beginning of fission. Thus the new mouth, cytopharynx, adoral zone, etc., commonly appear in the posterior fission product before fission is completed and often seem to arise by a budding process from the old structures. In many cases, however, there is an extensive dissolution of old organelles and both offspring form new ones at the onset of fission (Fig. 17E). Some ciliates divide only in the encysted state (Figs. 17D and 61M).

4. Encystment.—Encystment, described in detail on page 69, is widespread among the fresh-water ciliates. The ordinary resistant cyst not only enables the protozoan to endure unfavorable conditions, particularly drying, but also furnishes a condition in which dispersal by winds, animals, etc., is readily accomplished. Ciliates may also undergo encystment for fission or digestion of large food objects or apparently for nuclear reorganization. Some, as *Paramecium*, very rarely, if ever, encyst. Probably the reorganization and regeneration processes involved in encystment and excystment accomplish a certain amount of rejuvenescence and renewal of vitality.

5. Sexual Reproduction.—Except in the Protociliata, the sexual process in ciliates takes a peculiar form known as *conjugation* (Fig. 58). The ciliates become sticky and adhere in couples by the mouth region where actual protoplasmic fusion occurs. This connection endures for

a number of hours, during which nuclear changes ensue. The macronucleus may break up into fragments that gradually disappear while
the following changes are in progress or may not disintegrate until
afterward. The micronuclei, which play the important role in conjugation, all divide twice, and these divisions probably correspond to the
maturation divisions of metazoan germ cells, involving a reduction of
chromosomes. All the micronuclei disappear except one in each conjugant (Fig. 58E). This one divides in two and one of its offspring
becomes the *stationary* or *female* micronucleus while the other is the
wandering or *male* micronucleus. The latter from each conjugant crosses
the protoplasmic bridge into the other conjugant (Fig. 58G, J) where it
fuses with the female micronucleus to a synkaryon. The essential
feature of conjugation is thus an exchange of micronuclear material and
a nuclear fusion. The synkaryon now divides a variable number of
times in different species, usually once, twice, or three times, in *Bursaria*
and *Dileptus* many times. Of the products, some remain micronuclei
and others develop into macronuclei so that at conjugation the macronuclei are formed anew from micronuclei. The two conjugants now
separate, being then known as *exconjugants*, and by appropriate divisions,
the nuclear condition typical of the species is restored. Thus the synkaryon may divide only once, and the two nuclei may become the single
macronucleus and micronucleus of the animal so that the normal condition is reached without further change. Or the synkaryon may divide
twice, and two of the products may become macronuclei and two micronuclei. Then, by a cytoplasmic division without nuclear division, each
daughter cell is left with a normal single macro- and micronucleus, as in
Paramecium bursaria; or, if the species has normally two micronuclei, as
in *P. aurelia*, the micronuclei divide while the macronuclei do not, and
each daughter cell then receives one macronucleus and two micronuclei.
In *P. caudatum*, the synkaryon divides three times to produce eight
micronuclei, four of which become macronuclei; and two successive
cytosomal divisions without nuclear divisions ensue, resulting in four
animals, each with the normal single macro- and micronucleus. Various
other possibilities are realized in other species. In forms with numerous
macro- and micronuclei, these in the exconjugants continue to multiply
without cytosomal divisions until the normal condition is restored.

The foregoing account is typical of most ciliate conjugation. The
conjugants are usually indistinguishable from the normal forms, but in
some cases, as *Leucophrys* and *Prorodon*, the conjugants are noticeably
smaller than the regular population, and presumably arise through some
special fissions just before conjugation. More striking are the conditions
in the parasitic *Ophryoscolecidae* (Fig. 59) where by a regular unequal
progamous fission, the last one before conjugation, a large *macroconjugant*

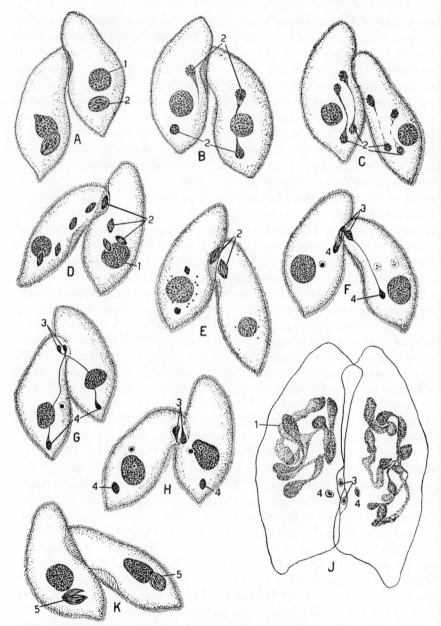

Fig. 58.—Nuclear phenomena of conjugation, *Cryptochilum*. (*After Dain*, 1930.) A. Micronucleus of each conjugant in mitosis. B. Micronucleus has divided. C. Micronuclei dividing again. D. Each conjugant has four micronuclei. E. Three of the four micronuclei degenerate, the fourth ones at the oral groove again undergo mitosis. F. Further stage of mitosis of fourth micronucleus. G. Division continued, one half of each micronucleus has crossed by way of the oral bridge into the other conjugant. H. Mitosis completed, wandering nuclei still at oral bridge. K. Fusion of wandering and stationary

and a small *microconjugant*, differing also in morphological details, are produced. In these forms, also, the wandering micronucleus has a sperm-like shape. At the end of such a series is the anisogamous conjugation of the Peritricha, which may be an adaptation to the sessile mode of life. Here some of the ordinary attached individuals serve as macroconjugants while others by two or more rapidly succeeding fissions give rise to small swimming microconjugants. One of these attaches itself to the side of an ordinary vorticellid (Fig. 65*F*), and the usual micronuclear behavior and exchange occur; in the case of the microconjugant the final micronuclei result from a fourth instead of a third division. The small remnant of the microconjugant left after conjugation dies.

The frequency of conjugation varies greatly in different species of ciliates and different races and clones of the same species. In some it may occur every few weeks or even at intervals of a few days, whereas other ciliates very seldom, if ever, conjugate. In races or stocks of *Paramecium* that are prone to conjugate, conjugation can be induced by starvation following rich feeding (Jennings, 1910; Hopkins, 1921; Giese, 1935), by placing large numbers in a small dish in fresh medium (Sonneborn, 1936), and by the addition of certain salts, notably ferric and

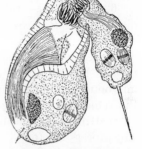

FIG. 59.—Conjugation in an ophryoscolecid, *Opisthotricium* (*after Dogiel* 1925), showing unequal size of conjugants.

aluminum chlorides (Zweibaum, 1912); and it seems in general to ensue after a period of rapid fission. Other races or stocks of *Paramecium* cannot be induced to conjugate by any of the known methods, or they very seldom respond. Induction of conjugation is easier the shorter the time since the last endomixis (see below). If a considerable time has elapsed since this event, conjugation will not occur until after the next endomixis. Increased oxygen consumption and decline of glycogen during conjugation was reported by Zweibaum (1921, 1922) for *Paramecium*. Conjugation accomplishes the same result as fertilization, i.e., the mixture of nuclear materials from two individuals with the creation thereby of new hereditary combinations and possibilities. Other possible effects of conjugation have been the subject of endless argument (see below).

Sonneborn (1938) and Jennings (1939) have shown for several species of *Paramecium* that conjugation will occur only between individuals that differ in some unknown way. Members of the same clone will not

micronuclei. *J.* Stage in the conjugation of *Paramecium* (*after Landis*, 1925), showing exchange of micronuclei at oral connection, and breaking up of macronuclei into vermiform fragments. 1, micronucleus; 2, macronucleus; 3, wandering micronucleus; 4, stationary micronucleus; 5, synkaryon.

conjugate together; members of different clones may or may not. By making conjugation tests it is found that a species consists of several mating types that can be classified into groups. The mating types within each group will conjugate with each other but not with the types of another group. When animals of different mating types within the same group are mixed, the animals agglutinate in clumps and then members from the two types conjugate. Each group of mating types has characteristic conditions of temperature and time of day when conjugation occurs, and usually some time must have elapsed since the last conjugation. Further investigation along these lines may lead to an understanding of the original nature of sexual differences.

6. Endomixis.—In 1914, Woodruff and Erdmann announced the discovery in *Paramecium aurelia* of a regularly recurring nuclear reorganization that they termed *endomixis*. The nuclear changes in endomixis strongly resemble those in conjugation, but a nuclear fusion appears to be lacking. The macronucleus fragments and dissolves. The micronuclei divide several times; most of the products disappear, and the remaining ones reconstitute new micronuclei and macronuclei that are distributed by means of fission until the normal condition is attained. The process was found to occur every 25 to 35 days and to be accompanied by a decline in fission rate and an increased volume, opacity, viscidity, and sluggishness of the animal, a state usually called *depression*, and previously seen by other workers. As in the case of conjugation the endomictic interval varies in different stocks and under different conditions. The interval is not so regular as originally supposed and may vary in *P. aurelia* from 4 to 129 days. Conjugation delays endomixis but rise of temperature favors it (Sonneborn). The occurrence of endomixis during free life has been verified for some other species of *Paramecium,* but in most forms studied, as *Didinium, Spathidium, Uroleptus, Dileptus, Stylonychia,* the process takes place only in the encysted state, in which indeed nuclear reorganizations have long been known. In some ciliates endomixis is certainly absent, and no such changes have been observed in such flagellates and rhizopods as have been subjected to continuous cultivation over long periods. This lack of universality of the process renders doubtful the obvious interpretation that in ciliates the macronucleus wears out through the vicissitudes of ordinary life and must be replaced at intervals.

Diller (1936) has been unable to verify the account of Woodruff and Erdmann of the nuclear changes in endomixis and believes they have confused two processes, *autogamy* and *hemimixis*. In autogamy the micronuclei divide as in conjugation to form eight or more, of which two fuse to a synkaryon; the macronucleus degenerates and new macro- and micronuclei arise from the divisions of the synkaryon. In hemimixis

he macronucleus undergoes degenerative changes, giving off chromatin
alls into the cytoplasm or breaking up into fragments; how a new
nacronucleus forms is not explained in Diller's account.

**7. Life Cycles and the Physiological Significance of Conjugation
nd Endomixis.**—The question whether Protozoa can continue to mul-
iply indefinitely by binary fission without decline of health or vitality
as been the object of intensive research for more than 50 years. Because
f their commonness and ease of cultivation, ciliates have been most

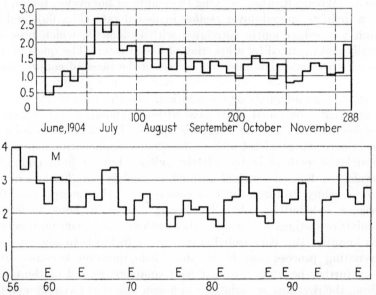

Fig. 60.—Graphs of variations in fission rate of ciliates; number of fissions per day on
he vertical, days on the horizontal. The fission rate is averaged for 5-day periods, and
ach short length of the graph is such a period. Upper graph: variations of fission rate in
clone of the hypotrich *Gastrostyla steinii*, cultivated for 6 months. (*After Woodruff and
Baitsell*, 1911.) Lower graph: variations in fission rate of a clone of *Paramecium aurelia*,
howing the occurrence of endomixis (*E*) at each period of low fission rate. (*After Wood-
uff*, 1917.) These variations in fission rate are probably the result of fluctuations in
ultural conditions, except possibly the association of low fission rate with endomixis.

mployed as material; clones are grown on depression slides and fission prod-
cts transferred at intervals to fresh slides. The early work of Maupas
nd R. Hertwig abroad, and of Calkins in this country, in which a variety
f ciliate species were used, lead to the result that after a certain number
f asexual generations, a clone declines in vitality and fission rate, shows
n unhealthy appearance, and finally dies out. These workers therefore
oncluded that Protozoa like Metazoa are subject to senescence and
leath and have a definite life cycle consisting of a limited number of
generations (about several hundred), unless conjugation intervenes.
Conjugation was regarded as a necessary rejuvenating factor. Although

Calkins's later work and some other researches supported these contentions, other investigators, particularly Woodruff and his students and Enriques, showed that the early results were attributable to bad and inadequate cultural conditions and that with careful attention to medium, at least some ciliates can propagate indefinitely by binary fission without conjugation. Thus Woodruff has maintained since 1907 a clone of *Paramecium aurelia*, which has now reached about 15,000 generations without decline of vitality or of fission rate and which has not conjugated. Woodruff, while denying the reality of life cycles, found, however, a definite up-and-down *rhythm* in fission rate (Fig. 60), and this rhythm was subsequently correlated with endomixis, which process is generally accompanied by a lowering of fission rate. The question then arose whether endomixis may not be taking the place of conjugation as a rejuvenating factor and whether clones can multiply indefinitely without either endomixis or conjugation. In the case of *P. aurelia* it appears that continued existence without endomixis is impossible (Sonneborn) and therefore that this species does have a definite life cycle in accordance with Calkins's views. In Sonneborn's experiments with delayed endomixis by selecting clones having long endomictic intervals, the longest survival without endomixis was 303 generations. However, many Protozoa can under adequate environmental conditions propagate indefinitely solely by binary fission without undergoing endomixis or conjugation or any other nuclear reorganization process so far as known. But it is probable that every fission is to some degree a rejuvenating process and hence the whole question becomes futile. It may further be suggested that with complete control of the culture medium, the rhythms or variations in fission rate that have been emphasized by Woodruff will disappear except possibly in the few species that regularly undergo endomixis.

There remains the question of the physiological effect of conjugation. This has been studied by comparing the vitality, longevity, and fission rates of clones reared from exconjugants and nonconjugants from the same original clone. The results have shown that in some ciliates, as *Uroleptus* and *Spathidium*, conjugation does prolong the life of a clone restore waning vitality to at least some extent, and may accelerate the fission rate. In exconjugants artificially separated before the micronuclear exchange had occurred, these rejuvenating effects still obtain, as shown by Calkins in *Uroleptus*, and thus seem to result from the renewal of the macronucleus. Jennings's comparison of clones reared from exconjugants and nonconjugants in Paramecium demonstrated a much greater occurrence of inheritable variations in the exconjugant lines, a result indicating the importance of conjugation in the production of diversities.

8. Behavior and Other Experimental Results.—The ciliates swim in a spiral path rotating upon the longitudinal axis, making one spiral turn to each rotation so that the same surface of the animal always faces the axis of the spiral. The width of the spiral, the closeness of the turns, and the direction of rotation (whether to right or left) vary with and are constant for the species. The spiraling and the rotation result from the fact that in ordinary forward progression the ciliary beat passes diagonally backwards in a wave that takes a spiral course. As a result the animal would swim in circles were it not also thrown in rotation in a direction opposite to that of the ciliary wave. The ciliary wave can be reversed as in backward locomotion. The coordination in the action of the cilia and the changes of beat under various conditions indicate some correlating mechanism, probably the neuromotor apparatus. The most remarkable conditions are seen in the Hypotricha where each of the large cirri can be moved in all directions either independently of or in correlation with the others, acting like legs in crawling.

The ciliates are sensitive to heat, chemicals, and contact but are indifferent to light unless they contain zoochlorellae. All the cilia probably act as sensory receptors but there are also special stiff sensory bristles (Fig. 13D). Some longer nonmotile cilia at the posterior tip of *Paramecium* have been thought to exercise a steering function. To most chemicals, localized contact, and temperatures other than the optimum a general phobotactic or avoiding reaction is given. The animal darts backward, turns at an angle to its former course and swims in a new direction, repeating this behavior until the stimulating factor ceases to act. Positive reactions such as aggregation in a favorable location are likewise phobotactic—the animal fails to react upon entering the region but gives an avoiding reaction if about to leave and so remains within a circumscribed area. Genuine directed or topotactic reactions probably occur to food, contact at times, in seeking partners at conjugation, and to electric current (page 69). Negative geotaxis (a swimming upward) is manifested by *Paramecium* (page 68) and a few other ciliates.

The ability of ciliates to discriminate food from other particles has been much studied, particularly in current-producing types, such as *Paramecium* and *Stentor*. These forms will ingest inert particles like carmine, India ink, indigo, glass, and at first sight appear to swallow anything brought by the ciliary currents. Experiment, however, has shown that ciliates can discriminate between nutritive and nonnutritive particles. When offered mixtures of carmine and bacteria or egg yolk, *Paramecium* takes in the nutritive material and rejects the carmine. When drops of carmine or carbon and bacterial suspensions are placed on a slide with *Paramecium*, the animals gather in and feed on the bacteria and similarly choose between drops of different species of bacteria.   Larger nonnutritive particles are more apt to be rejected than smaller ones.   When *Stentor* is offered mixtures of food organisms with starch grains, sulphur grains, carbon, or carmine, the food organisms are ingested and the nonnutritive particles mostly rejected (Schaeffer). *Stentor* does not choose between living and killed food organisms of the same species but does choose between different species, selecting certain ones.   *Bursaria* when offered a mixture of normal yolk particles and those stained with toxic dyes ingests the former and rejects the latter to a large extent (Lund, 1914).   While ciliates very commonly take in nonnutritive particles, the vacuoles formed of these are very soon ejected from the cytopyge.   The rejection of particles is accomplished by the reversal or other coordinated action of the cilia involved in food catching. The behavior of a raptorial ciliate is exemplified by Mast's account of *Didinium* (1909).   This animal (Fig. 57*B*) has an anterior conical projection, the *proboscis* or *seizing organ*, strengthened by a bundle of fibers (trichites?) anchored deep in the cytosome, and bearing the mouth at its tip.   When hungry, *Didinium* darts rapidly about until it comes in contact with a suitable prey whereupon the proboscis adheres, the mouth opens widely, and the proboscis retracts drawing the prey into the interior.   Protozoans much larger than *Didinium* can be ingested. *Didinium* can necessarily eat only those protozoans to which the proboscis will adhere on contact, as *Paramecium, Frontonia, Colpidium,* and *Colpoda;* attachment fails to occur on contact with such forms as *Stentor, Spirostomum,* and hypotrichous ciliates.   Apparently some property of the pellicle determines which forms shall fall prey to *Didinium.*   The results indicate that food discrimination in ciliates depends in part or in some species on tactual properties such as shape, size, weight, or surface texture of the available particles or food animals and in other cases on chemical properties.

Many examples of modifiability and variety of behavior and some of alleged learning have been noted in ciliates.   *Paramecium* when fed for some time on carmine particles "learns" to reject the carmine and forms no more or very few carmine vacuoles.   The behavior is lost in 2 or 3 days and is not transmitted to fission products.   Shaking or disturbance is generally less effective after several repetitions if these are sufficiently close together.   *Paramecium* confined in a capillary tube that barely permits it to turn around "learns" by repeated trials to turn much more quickly than at first (Day and Bently, 1911).   It is probable, however, that the accumulation of carbon dioxide in the capillary tube softens the pellicle, and this is presumably the explanation of the result (Buytendijk, 1919).   In recent years workers at the University of Marburg under Alverdes (Bramstedt, 1935; Soest, 1937; Alverdes, 1938) have reported the formation of associations in various ciliates, as *Para-*

mecium, Stylonychia, Stentor, and *Spirostomum.* In these investigations
the contrasting factors employed were light and darkness, cold and
optimum temperature, rough and smooth substratum, etc., and electric
shocks and shaking were used as punishments. One or two examples of
these experiments may be given. A slide was so arranged that half
was heated to 42°C. and the other half kept at 15°C.; in addition the
warm half was illuminated and the cold half darkened. *Paramecia*
placed on such a slide turned back into the cold-dark half whenever they
happened to swim towards the warm-light half (avoidance of warm water).
After 1 to 1½ hours of this "training" the entire slide was put at 15°C.,
but the *Paramecia* continued to turn back on reaching the lighted half.
As *Paramecium* normally shows no reaction to differences in light intensity, it was concluded that the animals had formed an association between
light and warm temperature (Bramstedt). Similarly, *Paramecium,
Spirostomum,* and *Stylonychia* will "learn" to turn back from a dark-light
boundary into the dark half if they are punished when they pass into the
light half by shaking or an electric shock. The contrary experiment,
trying to teach the animals to avoid the dark half, fails. Ordinarily
these ciliates show no reaction to light, although the experiments indicate
that they can perceive light differences. *Stylonychia* may similarly be
taught to associate light with a rough substratum and dark with a smooth
substratum. These associations are retained only about 15 minutes.
Bramstedt further found that *Paramecium* confined in small vessels of
definite shape follows the contour of the wall and if then transferred to a
vessel of different shape continues for about 15 minutes to swim in a
path resembling the shape of the previous container. The foregoing
types of experiments have been repeated by Grabowski (1939), who
although verifying the results opposes the interpretation and thinks that
small chemical differences to which the animals respond may arise during
the experiment between the two halves of the slides.

There has been much study of the changes ensuing in cultures made
of natural materials containing Protozoa or their cysts. It is found that
such cultures change progressively in acidity and exhibit a regular succession of protozoan forms replacing each other. This merely indicates
that each species requires a certain combination of external factors for
its best development. The speed of bacterial fermentation, which in
turns depends on the quantity of fermentable food present, is one of the
most important factors in protozoan culture. Much recent work
revolves around the question opened by T. B. Robertson, whether Protozoa excrete a substance favorable to their own reproduction. Robertson claims that two or more ciliates divide more rapidly than one in the
same (small) amount of medium and, postulating that protozoans secrete
an autocatalyst favoring fission, assigns this result to a greater retention

of autocatalyst by each animal when several are present in a restricted medium. Various repetitions and modifications of this experiment on the relation of fission rate to initial number of animals and quantity of culture medium have yielded conflicting results, a few in accord with Robertson's contention (Petersen, 1929, using large volumes; Yocom, 1928; Johnson, 1933, in part), but the majority contrary (Cutler and Crump, 1923–1925; Greenleaf, 1926; Myers, 1926; Jahn, 1929; Petersen, 1929, with small volumes; Beers, 1933; Johnson, 1933, in part). Even those whose results agreed with those of Robertson have been unwilling to accept his interpretation. Probably the whole question is one of proper medium and concentration of food supply. In a medium faulty in physicochemical makeup or too concentrated as regards food supply, a larger number of individuals in a limited space is obviously advantageous as they can more rapidly alter the medium to a favorable condition. Thus the pH of the medium is of importance (review by D. H. Johnson, 1936). Most ciliates grow best in a medium of pH 6.0 to 8.0 but some species have their optimum growth at a higher acidity (4.8 to 6.0). The metabolism of Protozoa modifies the pH of the medium so that the greater the initial number within a limited space, the more rapidly will they bring the medium to a more favorable acidity. Again, W. H. Johnson (1933) using *Oxytricha* found that the concentration of bacteria was an important factor in division rate so that in too high a concentration reproduction is retarded. Under such conditions additional individuals in a limited space would favor growth through reducing the number of bacteria. However, with other ciliates, e.g., *Paramecium* (Johnson, 1936) and *Glaucoma* (Harding, 1937), multiplication is greater the higher the concentration of bacteria. Different factors no doubt operate in limiting or favoring growth in different genera, but under optimum conditions it is probable that Robertson's phenomenon would be absent. Perhaps the best experimental attack was that of Beers (1933), who, using *Didinium* and *Stylonychia* in an artificial salt medium to which an adequate supply of food organisms was added daily, failed to obtain any differences in fission rates among cultures ranging from one to eight individuals in 0.02 to 0.16 cc. of medium.

Another mode of attack upon this problem is to compare the fission rate of the same initial number of animals in fresh culture medium and in "conditioned" medium, i.e., culture fluid in which the same protozoan has already lived for varying periods of time. Both negative (Reich, 1938) and positive (Mast and Pace, 1938) results have been reported. It is probable that in general slight conditioning of the medium is favorable to animal growth whereas considerable conditioning or crowding is unfavorable. Usually in the early stages of protozoan cultures, growth and multiplication are rapid until a maximal population for the particular space is reached, and thereafter the population declines in fission rate and numbers through death. Since the work of Woodruff (1911) it has been generally accepted that the metabolic products of Protozoa are depressing and toxic to themselves and that this is the cause of the decline of cultures. Woodruff's result is disputed by Johnson and Hardin (1938) who report that *Paramecium* multiplies as rapidly in old as in fresh culture medium. The whole question of the action of conditioned medium is at present an open one requiring further investigation.

The genetics of ciliates accords with that of other Protozoa (page 77). From any wild species a number of clones can be isolated, and within a clone inheritable variations may result from nuclear reorganizations as in endomixis and conjugation or from unknown causes. Among the inherited changes are size, fission rate, and number of contractile vacuoles.

9. Subclass Protociliata.—The Protociliata or opalinids differ from the typical ciliates in almost every respect except the possession of cilia. They are entocommensals in the intestine of tadpoles and adults of the anuran Amphibia (frogs, toads) and occasionally of other cold-blooded vertebrates. They are simple oval cylindrical or flattened forms, completely clothed with cilia, and devoid of mouth and contractile vacuoles. In some forms (Fig. 61*B*) long convoluted noncontractile canals or a series of vacuoles, supposed to have an excretory function, are present. The group is bi- or multinucleate, but all the nuclei are alike. Asexual reproduction occurs by plasmotomy, sexual by gametes. Conjugation is lacking. At the time of egg laying of their hosts, the opalinids divide into small forms that encyst, pass out in the feces, and, when ingested by tadpoles, excyst, and then may divide into anisogamous gametes. The zygote either encysts again and passes out to infect other tadpoles or develops at once into the adult. Metcalf, the chief student of the group, has divided the opalinids into four genera: *Protoopalina* (Fig. 61*B*), with two nuclei and cylindrical body; *Zelleriella*, binucleate but flattened; *Cepedea*, oval and multinucleate; and *Opalina* (Fig. 61*A*) multinucleate and very flattened though of oval outline. The evolutionary changes among the opalinids have been utilized to elucidate the phylogenetic relationships among their amphibian hosts.

10. Subclass Euciliata and Order Holotricha.—This subclass includes all the typical ciliates with dimorphic nuclei, conjugation, feeding apparatus, and contractile vacuoles. The order Holotricha comprises those with simple cilia, which may clothe the entire surface or be limited to certain areas. The suborder Gymnostomata includes the raptorial types with a closable mouth situated at the surface or forming a pit or slit, without definite peristome. Among the simple oval types with a terminal mouth are *Coleps* with ectoplasmic plates (Fig. 7*D*) and rows of cilia between the plates and *Didinium* (Fig. 57*D*) with two or more girdles

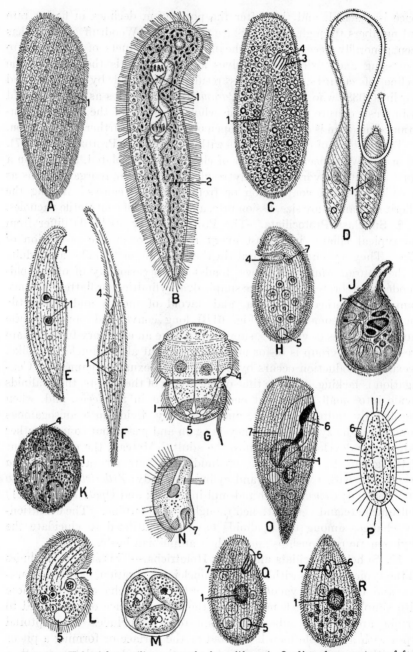

Fig. 61.—Holotrichous ciliates, mostly from life. *A. Opalina*, from rectum of frog, multinucleate species. *B. Protoopalina intestinalis (after Metcalf, 1909)*, with two nuclei and long excretory canal. *C. Nassula* with lateral mouth and trichites. *D. Lacrymaria*, extended and contracted. *(After Conn, 1905.)* *E. Loxodes. F. Lionotus. G. Urocentrum*

of cilia and mouth on the tip of a proboscis armed with long fibers (tricho-cysts?). In both genera the mouth can be opened as wide as the body diameter and large prey ingested. *Didinium* feeds almost exclusively on *Paramecium*, encysts in the absence of food, and undergoes endomixis while encysted but can be cultivated indefinitely by fission if the food supply is adequate. Many of the gymnostomatous ciliates have a pharyngeal basket, as *Prorodon* (Fig. 57*A*), with terminal mouth and basket, and *Chilodonella* (Fig. 7*F*) and *Nassula* (Fig. 61*C*), with ventral mouths and baskets. A number of genera have the anterior end elon-gated into a sort of proboscis, often very flexible, with a round or slit mouth at its base. Here belong *Trachelius* (Fig. 61*J*), *Loxodes* with beak-like anterior end (Fig. 61*E*), and *Lionotus* (Fig. 61*F*), *Loxophyllum* (Fig. 56*J*), and *Dileptus* (Fig. 8) with a long flexible proboscis armed with trichocysts. *Lacrymaria* (Fig. 61*D*) with an exceptionally long serpen-tine proboscis or "neck" differs in the terminal position of the mouth.

The Trichostomata include those Holotricha with a definite cyto-pharynx not provided with undulating membranes and situated at the bottom of a peristomal depression. The wall of the cytopharynx and peristome are provided with special ciliary tracts. The most familiar genus of this group is *Paramecium* (see below). Other genera are the small *Colpoda* (Fig. 61*L, M*) and *Tillina* (Fig. 17*D*) both of which divide only while encysted, and *Plagiopyla* (Fig. 61*H*).

Paramecium, the most familiar and studied protozoan genus, is characterized by the oral groove or peristome, a deep depression beginning at the anterior end and extending obliquely backward to the right, so that a cross section through the anterior half of the animal is crescentic (Fig. 55*B*). There are about ten species (Wenrich, 1928; Ludwig, 1931): *caudatum* (Fig. 57*C*), *aurelia*, *multimicronucleatum*, *bursaria* (Fig. 20), *nephridiatum*, *trichium*, *putrinum*, *calkinsi*, *polycaryum*, and *woodruffi*. These differ in size, shape, number of micronuclei, vacuolar apparatus, and other details. The size ranges from about 300 $m\mu$ for the largest species (*caudatum*, *multimicronucleatum*) to about 80 $m\mu$ for the smallest (*trichium*). There are two types of body shape: the *aurelia* type (Fig. 57*C*), resembling in outline the sole of a shoe, broadest behind the middle, with an elongated anterior portion and rounded anterior end, and the *bur-saria* type (Fig. 20), slightly flattened with beak-like anterior end curved to the right and rest of the body of about the same width throughout.

---

turbo. *H. Plagiopyla nasuta. J. Trachelius ovum. (After Blochmann,* 1895.) *K. Ichthyophthirius multifiliis. (After Bütschli,* 1889.) *L. Colpoda. M.* same, dividing while encysted. *(After Rhumbler,* 1888.) *N. Microthorax. (After Blochmann,* 1895.) *O.* Unidentifiable ciliate with large undulating membrane in the cytopharynx. *P. Cyclidium,* with projecting undulating membrane. *Q. Colpidium. R. Glaucoma pyriformis.* 1, nucleus; 2, excretory canal; 3, pharyngeal basket of trichites; 4, mouth; 5, contractile vacuole; 6, undulating membrane; 7, cytopharynx. The micronuclei can usually not be seen in living ciliates.

The body is covered with a pellicle that is sculptured into hexagonal, rhomboidal, or squarish depressions (Figs. 7B, C and 55A) bounded by ridges on which the trichocysts open. From the center of each depression springs a cilium whose base pierces the pellicle to reach the basal body situated in the alveolar layer of the ectoplasm. The ciliation is uniform except for a few longer cilia often present on the posterior end. The depressions and consequently the cilia are arranged in longitudinal rows.

In the alveolar stratum of the ectoplasm lies the neuromotor system running parallel to the body surface. It consists primarily of the interciliary fibrils, each of which is a longitudinal strand connecting the basal bodies of the cilia of a longitudinal row. The interciliary fibrils curve around the cytopharynx (Fig. 13C) meeting at an angle above and below it to form the *preoral* and *postoral sutures* (Fig. 13C), of which the latter makes a ring around the cytopyge. Pellicular markings and neuromotor fibrils continue into the cytopharynx where the latter form a system of radiating and circular fibrils passing through the basal bodies (Fig. 13C), making a latticework. The radiating fibrils extend only a short distance outside the entrance of the cytopharynx. Attached to the left dorsal wall of the cytopharynx is the neuromotorium consisting of two masses from which fibrils pass into the entoplasm. In the dorsal wall of the cytopharynx near its inner end is a chain of about five granules, from which a bundle of *postesophageal fibers* extends posteriorly into the entoplasm. The foregoing account is taken from the work of E. E. Lund (1933).

In addition to the neuromotor fibrillar system there have been described in *Paramecium* two systems of ectoplasmic networks, an outer and an inner. The outer net (part of Klein's silver-line system) is situated in the pellicular ridges, which it faithfully follows (and is nothing but these ridges, in the opinion of E. E. Lund). The inner net (*infraciliary net* of Gelei, 1937) is located at the level of the basal bodies of the cilia. These nets have no connection with the neuromotor system and are believed to be of a supporting nature.

Occupying the greater part of the alveolar layer of the ectoplasm are the trichocysts, carrot-shaped bodies evenly distributed over the animal, attached by their slender necks to the anterior and posterior ridges of the pellicular polygons (Fig. 55A). Upon certain kinds of stimulation they are ejected to the exterior, altering in the process to long slender rods. Their function and mode of discharge were already discussed (pages 165).

The vacuolar system occupies a fixed position in the innermost layer of the ectoplasm on the dorsal side of the animal. It commonly consists of two vacuolar apparatuses, one in each body half, but *P. multimicronucleatum* frequently has one to five extra apparatuses. Each apparatus consists of the pore and a circlet of several radiating canals (Fig. 57C). These canals are often very long, much longer than they appear in the living animal, tapering at their distal ends into fine canals that receive fluid from many minute vacuoles. The canals run parallel to the surface but may extend somewhat into the entoplasm. At their proximal ends, each canal has a swollen portion or *ampulla* from which a fine *injector canal* proceeds toward the pore. Drops of fluid emitted from the ends of the injector canals at each emptying of the canals unite to form the contractile vacuole, which is thus a temporary structure formed anew after each discharge. The pore (two or more may be present in *P. nephridiatum*) appears to be a permanent structure whose inner end closes again after each discharge. The relative rates of pulsation of the anterior and posterior vacuoles have been the subject of considerable argument (see Frisch, 1937). The statement often seen that they contract alternately is erroneous; usually the posterior vacuole has a faster rate than the anterior one, but this is caused by its proximity to the cytopharynx. Intake of water at the cytopharynx with food vacuoles accelerates the rate of the posterior vacuole. In *P. trichium* there are no feeding canals, but instead vesicles open into the contractile vacuole; a long convoluted tube leads from each vacuole to the pore.

At the posterior end of the oral groove, the funnel-shaped cytopharynx leads into the entoplasm. The ciliation of the cytopharynx is rather complicated (Gelei, 1934). Contrary to usual opinion there is no undulating membrane. The outer part of the cytopharynx (*vestibule* of Gelei) has the same structure as the ectoplasm in general, except that there are often two cilia in each depression and the posterior edge is devoid of cilia. The ciliation extends more deeply along the left than along the right wall of the vestibule (Fig. 55B). The next part or pharynx proper is a curved tube that is devoid of cilia on its right wall (Fig. 55B). Along the left wall runs the *penniculus,* a curved band of eight parallel rows of cilia arranged in two groups of four rows each (Figs. 13C and 55B). In the dorsal wall is another band composed of four rows of long cilia paralleling the penniculus; this may be called the *quadrulus.* No doubt the movements of the penniculus and quadrulus have given rise to the conception of undulating membranes. Gelei is of the opinion that the quadrulus serves to direct the finer food particles into the esophagus whereas the penniculus handles larger objects. The innermost narrowed end of the cytopharynx, termed *esophagus* by Gelei, is extremely short; the entrance into it is considered by some the true or original mouth, sunk inward.

The cytopyge is a definite pore situated on the right side near the inner end of the cytopharynx in the aurelia group of species, at the posterior end in the bursaria group.

The macronucleus is a large oval solid body in the entoplasm near the middle of the animal. There is a single micronucleus in the form of a small solid ball resting in a depression in the macronucleus in the species *caudatum, bursaria,* and *trichium.* The other species have two to four or more micronuclei of the vesicular type with a central endosome.

The entoplasm of *Paramecium* presents no especial features; it contains much fat and glycogen. In *P. bursaria,* it is filled with zoochlorellae, which confer a green color on this species. Several investigators have studied the biology of this animal (page 171). The food of *Paramecium* consists essentially of bacteria but larger organisms can be ingested. *Paramecium* can live on a single species of some kinds of bacteria but not on any species and discriminates between bacterial species when a choice is presented. Although Phelps (1934) could not succeed in growing *P. aurelia* in a bacteria-free medium or on dead bacteria, Glaser and Coria (1933) were able to cultivate *P. caudatum* in a medium composed of liver extract, dead yeast, and pieces of fresh rabbit kidney. So far no species of *Paramecium* except the green one has been successfully cultivated in a nutrient medium devoid of particulate food, but this need not be alive.

As most points in the biology of *Paramecium* are discussed elsewhere in this chapter, it remains to consider encystment. The green *Paramecium* probably encysts, but encystment of the other species is a rare occurrence and has never been witnessed for any species except *caudatum.* Encystment of *P. caudatum* was reported by Ivanic (1926) and Michelson (1928) but the work of the former is questionable. Michelson failed to induce encystment of *P. caudatum* by any of the ordinary methods that would be applicable in nature. Encystment was finally obtained under extraordinary conditions, in agar. The cysts are stated to resemble sand grains. Cleveland noted a few cysts formed when *Paramecia* (species not stated) were injected into the rectum of frogs. Contrary to general opinion, *Paramecia* cannot be obtained from dry hay or other dry materials, since drying does not induce encystment of *Paramecium.*

In the Hymenostomata the cytopharynx is provided with one or more undulating membranes that may project conspicuously, as in *Pleuronema* (Fig. 57D) and *Cyclidium* (Fig. 61P), acting as food scoops. These two forms execute springing movements by means of their long cilia. *Colpidium* (Fig. 61Q) with lateral and *Glaucoma* (Fig. 61R) with ventral mouth are small oval forms with a projecting ectoplasmic lip on one side of the mouth margin. The curious *Urocentrum turbo* (Fig. 61G) has two broad ciliary girdles and a tail tuft by which it may adhere and so execute pendulum movements. In the little *Microthorax* (Fig. 61N) there is a posterior cytopharynx and a firm pellicle through which protrude widely spaced rows of cilia. The ciliate figured in Fig. 61O is notable for the large and conspicuous undulating membrane. *Frontonia* (Fig. 6) with a very long slit-like peristome, long vacuolar canals, and sometimes zoochlorellae belongs to the Hymenostomata.

The group Astomata consists of mouthless entoparasites, not clearly related to the other Holotricha, inhabiting invertebrates. They are oval to elongated forms, completely clothed with cilia, often with elongated macronuclei (Fig. 62A, B) frequently with a clinging structure or adhesive organ at the anterior end, and with several contractile vacuoles. They reproduce by transverse fission or may divide off small individuals from the posterior end. Chains may result from the incomplete separation of such buds. Conjugation has been observed. Representative forms are *Anoplophrya* (Fig. 62A) without adhesive organ and *Hoplitophrya* with a hook-like trichite (Fig. 62B) for adherence to the host's intestine. Some other genera such as *Haptophrya* have a sucker-like adhesive organ. The Astomata live in the digestive tract of annelids, the liver of mollusks, and the body cavity of annelids and crustaceans.

The family Foettengeridae, a holotrichous group of uncertain relationships, placed by its chief investigator Chatton (1935) in a special suborder Apostomea, are parasitic ciliates with complicated life histories. The adult *Foettengeria* (Fig. 62C) lives inside the coelenteron of sea anemones. After some time it emerges and encysts, undergoing multiple fission into numerous ciliated young, whose ciliary pattern differs from that of the adult. These young ("tomites" of Chatton) encyst upon some crustacean (Fig. 62D), and, when such an infected crustacean is eaten by a sea anemone, the cyst hatches and the young grow up into the mature foettengerid. A number of other genera have been described. most of which pass their free lives entirely in or on crustaceans.

The free-living suborders of the Holotricha also include a number of ecto- and entocommensals and parasites. The best known is *Ichthyophthirius multifiliis* (Fig. 61K), an oval, completely ciliated form with terminal mouth, parasitic on the skin of fish where it becomes embedded in white pustules, and may be fatal by making the skin susceptible to fungus growth. The pustules eventually rupture and the escaped ciliate encysts and undergoes multiple fission into many (up to 1000) tiny ciliates that again invade the skin of fish. In the mature ciliate, the micronucleus seems to be embedded inside the macronucleus. Wenrich (1924) has described a species of the free-living genus *Amphileptus* that inhabits the gills of tadpoles and ingests masses of cells from the gills. *Conchophthirius*, closely resembling *Colpoda*, and *Ancistruma* and *Boveria* (Fig. 13A), with long cilia leading to the posterior mouth, live as harmless commensals in the mantle cavity of bivalve mollusks whose food they share. Entocommensal Holotricha are common in the digestive tract of the horse, cow, and other mammals, and in the intestine of sea urchins.

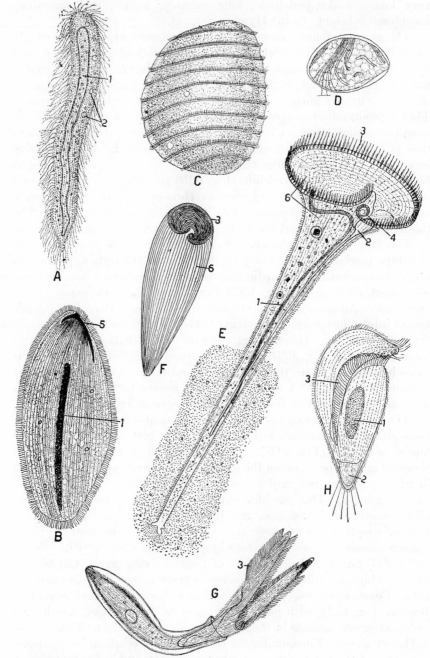

Fig. 62.—Parasitic Holotricha, Heterotricha. *A. Anoplophrya*, from a fresh-water oligochaete. (*After Pierantoni*, 1909.) *B. Hoplitophrya*, from the intestine of an earth-worm, from slide. (*Courtesy, Dr. D. H. Wenrich.*) *C. Foettengeria*, from a sea anemone

11. Order Spirotricha.—Here are included all ciliates with an adoral zone of membranelles beginning on the right side or the anterior edge of the peristome and passing along its left edge into the cytopharynx. The membranelles are large triangular plates composed of fused cilia (Fig. 55D) and produce a powerful current. There is a large peristome consisting either of a disk-like anterior end (*Stentor*, Fig. 62E) or of a triangular or elongated depression. A vestibule may be interposed between peristome and cytopharynx, and an undulating membrane is generally present. The order is variously divided in different texts; here three groups will be considered: Heterotricha, Oligotricha, and Hypotricha.

The suborder Heterotricha embraces those Spirotricha in which the body is clothed with short cilia. Here belong several of the best known and most investigated genera of Protozoa. *Stentor* (Fig. 62B) has an elegant trumpet-shaped body with a broad peristome encircled by the row of membranelles, which leads by way of a vestibule into the spirally coiled cytopharynx. The blue species (*S. coeruleus*, Fig. 1F) is characterized by alternating blue and white ectoplasmic stripes (Fig. 55E, F) of which the blue stripes consist of pigment and the white stripes are underlain by a myoneme and an interciliary fibril. In the several smaller colorless species (Fig. 62E), some of which have a basal loose gelatinous investment, the myonemes are not very evident in the extended state but become conspicuous on contraction (Fig. 62F). They run lengthwise on the body and in concentric curves on the peristome. The stentors are generally attached but often break loose and swim about in a semicontracted condition. They feed chiefly on small ciliates that after being trapped in the vestibule are driven into the cytopharynx. The macronucleus is very elongated (Fig. 62E) or moniliform (Fig. 1F), there are several to many micronuclei (to 80 in *S. coeruleus*), and the single contractile vacuole is generally fed by a very long canal. The bottle animalcule, *Folliculina* (Fig. 62G), marine, resembles *Stentor* but has two wing-like extensions of the peristome and secretes a vase-like tectinous case fastened to plants or other animals. This genus can undergo much change of form, often escaping from its case as an oval swimming ciliate without the arms. Upon settling down again, it reforms the case and differentiates into its typical morphology. *Spirostomum* (Fig. 63C, D) is a long slender heterotrich with an elongated peristome, moniliform nucleus, and highly developed myonemes. In the large stout oval *Bursaria* (Fig. 63B) the adoral zone is inside the very

---

(*after De Morgan*, 1924); D, same, encysted (*after Chatton and Lwoff*. 1935). *E. Stentor*, probably *roeseli*, from life, with a gelatinous tube. *F. Stentor* contracted, showing myonemes. *G.* The bottle animalcule, *Folliculina*. (*After Stein*, 1878.) *H, Metopus*, from life. 1, nucleus; 2, contractile vacuole; 3, adoral zone of membranelles; 4, cytopharynx; 5. attachment hook; 6, myonemes.

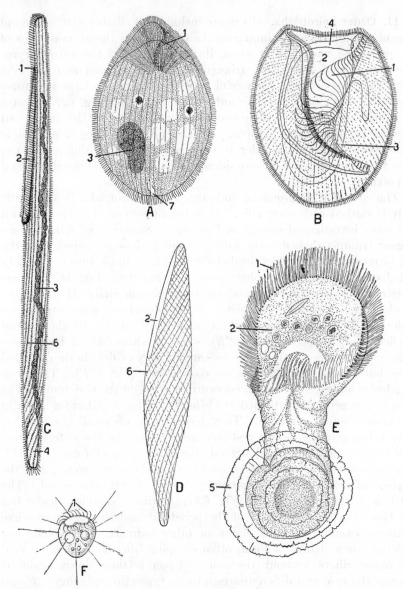

Fig. 63.—Heterotricha, Oligotricha. *A. Balantidium*, from the intestine of a chimpanzee, from slide. (*Courtesy Dr. D. H. Wenrich.*) *B. Bursaria.* (*After Brauer*, 1886.) *C. Spirostomum*, from life; *D*, same, contracted, showing the myonemes. *E. Lichnophora.* (*After Stevens*, 1903.) *F. Halteria.* (*After Kent*, 1881.) 1, adoral zone; 2, peristome; 3, nucleus; 4, contractile vacuole and canal; 5, adhesive disk; 6, myonemes; 7, cytopyge.

capacious funnel-shaped peristome. *Metopus* (Fig. 62*H*) with many species is characterized by the spiral depressed adoral zone, and the somewhat similar *Caenomorpha* has in addition a long tail and anterior cirri. *Blepharisma* is a small oval form with an elongated peristome like that of *Spirostomum* but differing in being provided with a projecting undulating membrane; the common species, *B. undulans*, is peach colored.

The Heterotricha include several well-known ecto- and entocommensals. *Lichnophora* (Fig. 63*E*) with a stentor-like expanded peristome edged by the adoral spiral has its posterior end modified into an adhesive disk by which it clings to a variety of marine animals as a harmless commensal. In some species, the adhesive disk is ciliated so that the animal can move about over its host. *Nyctotherus* (Fig. 2*H*), a common intestinal commensal of various invertebrates and vertebrates, particularly frogs, also very occasionally found in man, is a bean-shaped ciliate with the adoral zone leading down into a lateral notch. *Nyctotherus cordiformis* multiplies by binary fission in the rectum of frog tadpoles. When the tadpole is about to metamorphose, smaller preconjugant forms arise and these conjugate in pairs with the usual ensuing nuclear exchange. The large exconjugants found in the rectum of the newly metamorphosed frog undergo binary fission to ordinary-sized individuals that encyst. The cysts hatch when eaten by tadpoles (Wichterman, 1937). In *Balantidium* (Fig. 63*A*) an intestinal inhabitant of various animals, chiefly frogs and mammals, the oval ciliated body has a large peristomal depression at the anterior end. *B. coli*, whose natural host is the pig, in which it is transmitted in the encysted state, may infect human beings who handle pigs and may by invading the intestinal wall cause severe symptoms.

In the suborder Oligotricha, the body cilia are greatly reduced or absent, and the adoral row of membranelles encircles the circular raised or depressed peristome occupying the anterior end and bearing the mouth opening. Among the free-living forms are the minute jumpy fresh-water *Halteria* (Fig. 63*F*), making quick springs by means of its long bristles, and the Tintinnidae (Fig. 64*A*), marine ciliates with feathery membranelles, which inhabit vase-shaped gelatinous or tectinous cases often including foreign particles. Here may be placed the remarkable entocommensals of the digestive tract of hoofed mammals, relegated by some to a separate suborder of Spirotricha (Entodiniomorpha). They are among the most complicated protozoans. Besides the peristomial circlet of cirrus-like membranelles, one or more girdles or groups of membranelles may occur elsewhere (Fig. 64*D*). The body is generally of irregular form, often with one or more lobes or spine-like projections at the posterior end (Figs. 7*E*, and 64*B*), which may be movable by a complicated array of myonemes (Fig. 64*B*); sometimes also there are lobes around the mouth. Beneath

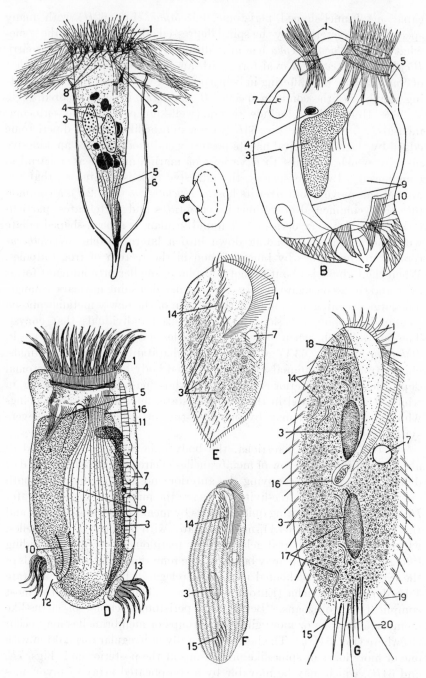

Fig. 64.—Oligotricha, Hypotricha.   *A. Favella*, a tintinnid.   (*After Campbell*, 1926.)
B. Diplodinium, an ophryoscolecid.   (*After Kofoid and MacClennan*, 1932.)   *C.* Contractile

the tough pellicle the ectoplasm is supported by a fibrillar network and contains in many genera one to five skeletal plates (Figs. 7E, and 64D), some long and narrow, others broad. These plates are composed of little polygonal prisms made of a cellulose-like material impregnated with glycogen, so that the skeleton serves as a depository of food reserves. The entoplasm is limited to an internal sac separated from the thick ectoplasm by a membrane stiffened by a fibrillar network. The cytopharynx, also provided with myonemes, leads into this entodermal sac (Fig. 64D) from the side of whose lower end a rectal canal, encircled by myonemes, extends to the cytopyge (Fig. 64B, D). These ciliates therefore could almost be said to have a digestive tract. Bunches of myonemes proceed inward from the membranelles (Fig. 64B, D) and an extensive neuromotor system, including the fibrils already mentioned, has been described for members of the group. In fact the conception of a neuromotor apparatus originated through Sharp's study of the structure of an ophryoscolecid (Epidinium ecaudatum, then called Diplodinium). One to fifteen contractile vacuoles are present with canals, sometimes encircled by a myoneme (Fig. 64C), leading to the external pore. There are an elongated macronucleus and one micronucleus. Reproduction occurs by ordinary binary fission. Conjugation in many cases is preceded by a special fission into a large and a small conjugant (Fig. 59). Resistant cysts are lacking, and infection of new hosts occurs by ingestion of active parasites in the food or drinking water.

These parasites are divided into the family Ophryoscolecidae, in which the extra membranelles are limited to the anterior end, and the Cycloposthiidae, where there are posterior coils of membranelles, usually two. The former family, including the genera Entodinium, Epidinium, Diplodinium (Fig. 64B), Ophryoscolex (Fig. 7E) and many others, inhabits the rumen and paunch of ruminants such as cattle, sheep, goats, antelope, deer, etc., often occurring in millions; the Cycloposthiidae, typified by Cycloposthium (Fig. 64D) live in the intestine and caecum of herbivorous mammals, including horses, tapirs, elephants, and apes. The relation of these ciliates to their hosts has been much studied, and various ideas have been suggested: that they digest cellulose for their hosts, prepare plant proteins, agitate the digesting food, and keep down bacteria and fungi. The work of Becker and his associates in Iowa disproves these suggestions, for they have shown that the hosts digest cellulose and plant proteins equally well regardless of the presence or absence of the ciliates,

vacuole of Cycloposthium, showing spiral myoneme around the exit. (After Strelkow, 1929.) D. Cycloposthium, from the horse. (After Dogiel, 1925.) E. Onychodromus, F. Urostyla (after Conn, 1905), primitive types of Hypotricha. G. Stylonychia, from life. 1, adoral zone; 2, motorium; 3, macronucleus; 4, micronucleus; 5, myonemes; 6, case; 7, contractile vacuole; 8, neuromotor fibrils; 9, entoplasmic sac; 10, rectal tube; 11, skeletal rod; 12, cytopyge; 13, posterior group of membranelles; 14, frontal cirri; 15, anal cirri; 16, cytopharynx; 17, ventral cirri; 18, peristome; 19, marginal cirri, 20, caudal cirri.

which therefore classify as harmless commensals. They can digest protein, starch, and probably cellulose.

The third suborder of the Spirotricha, the Hypotricha, includes many of the most common and familiar marine and fresh-water ciliates. They are oval forms, strongly flattened dorsoventrally, with a marked differentiation of the ventral surface for creeping. The dorsal surface is mostly devoid of cilia or bears only stiff, presumably sensory, bristles. The ventral surface lacks cilia and is provided with cirri. In the more primitive forms, as *Urostyla* (Fig. 64*F*) and *Onychodromus* (Fig. 64*E*) there are several rows of cirri on the ventral surface, but the cirri gradually become restricted to a few ventral groups, at first with the retention of the marginal row as in *Oxytricha* and *Stylonychia* (Fig. 64*G*), finally with the loss of all cirri except a few groups definite in position and number as in *Euplotes* (Fig. 65*A*). At the anterior end of the ventral surface is a large depressed triangular peristome bordered by the adoral zone and leading into a cytopharynx supplied with an undulating membrane. The adoral zone begins at the right anterior angle of the peristome and passes along the anterior end and down the left margin of the peristome into the cytopharynx. The cirrus groups in the more specialized genera (Figs. 64*G*, and 65*A*) comprise an anterior *frontal* or *sternal* group, a median *ventral* group, an *anal* (or *transverse*) group often of five large cirri in a row, and *caudal* cirri in some cases attached to the posterior margin. *Stylonychia* (Fig. 64*G*) has three, and *Euplotes* (Fig. 65*A*) four such caudal bristles. There are generally two or more oval macronuclei, each accompanied by one or more micronuclei, but *Euplotes* (Fig. 65*A*) has a very long curved macronucleus. Fission and conjugation are typical. Some other common genera are: *Uroleptus*, long and slender, with ventral cirrus rows and two to many macronuclei; *Strongylidium* with spiral cirrus rows; *Holosticha*, oval, with one to three cirrus rows and a row of anal cirri; *Gastrostyla*, with frontal and anal groups; *Oxytricha*, similar to *Stylonychia* but without caudal bristles; *Uronychia* with large anal cirri and marginal cirri reduced to a few large bristles; and the small rounded *Aspidisca* having the adoral zone somewhat concealed under a fold and cirri reduced to large frontoventral and anal groups. *Kerona* inhabits the surface of Hydra apparently as a harmless ectocommensal. The Hypotricha have been much used in studies of regeneration, life cycles, and heredity.

12. Order Peritricha.—In this group the cilia have been still further reduced and most species retain only the adoral zone; in some there is also a posterior circlet of cilia, but otherwise the body is naked. The body is typically bell- or vase-shaped attached by a short to long stout or slender stalk (Figs. 65 and 66). The anterior end forms a broad circular flat or bulging peristome or *disk* separated by a groove from a *collar* or lip. In this groove runs the adoral zone, which begins on the disk, circles around to the right (i.e. counterclockwise) 1½ to several (Fig. 66*C*) times, and then descends into the vestibule (Fig. 65*B*). The adoral zone is composed of an inner and an outer circlet of cilia (Fig. 65*B*), which are not membranelles but adhere more or less after the manner of an undulating membrane. The inner circlet stands erect, is double in at least some species (not so shown in Fig. 65*B*), and keeps up a constant undulation. The outer circlet is single, inclines outward like a shelf, and guides the food into the vestibule. At the right edge of the vestibule the inner and outer circlets separate; the former passes down into the vestibule along its inner wall, the latter along the outer wall (Fig. 65*L*), becoming a strong undulating membrane. Between the disk and the collar at one place is a large cavity, the *vestibule*, where the disk is raised considerably above the collar, with the result that the beginning of the adoral zone is higher than its end. The vestibule continues into the interior as a funnel-like cytopharynx (Fig. 65*L*). The pellicle of the bell is often marked with circular parallel striations (Fig. 65*B*), which apparently are not myonemes, and is tuberculate in some species of *Vorticella*. The interior contains numerous food vacuoles and the elongate curved macronucleus near which there is a single micronucleus. There are one or two contractile vacuoles that open into the vestibule, often with the interposition of a small reservoir (Fig. 65*L*), and the cytopyge also discharges into the vestibule. The collar is provided with circular myonemes forming a sphincter, and longitudinal myonemes, visible chiefly in the base of the bell, converge to form the spiral muscle band of the vorticellid stalk. Upon contraction (Fig. 65*G*) the collar closes over the disk, and the stalk is thrown into spirals by the shortening of its muscle.

Reproduction occurs by binary fission, which is longitudinal, whereas that of other ciliates is transverse, a fact suggesting that the peristome of the Peritricha corresponds to the dorsal surface of other ciliates. At the onset of fission, the collar closes over the peristome (Fig. 65*C*), and the elongated macronucleus condenses to an oval shape. The peristome then shows a vertical constriction, and this rapidly extends to the stalk (Fig. 65*D*). One daughter develops a posterior girdle of cilia (Fig. 65*E*) and swims away, later growing a new stalk and attaching. When exposed to unfavorable conditions, vorticellids also put out such a posterior ciliary circlet, detach from their stalks, and swim away. Conjugation (Fig. 65*F*) is characterized by the production of small microconjugants through several fissions of some of the bells; these attach to the sides of the ordinary bells, and the usual nuclear changes ensue.

There are a few motile Peritricha with permanent posterior girdles, as *Telotrochidium* (Fig. 66*E*), which swims about rapidly by its posterior circlet with the posterior end in advance. This form has never been observed to attach. Other similar types are epizoic and possibly ecto-

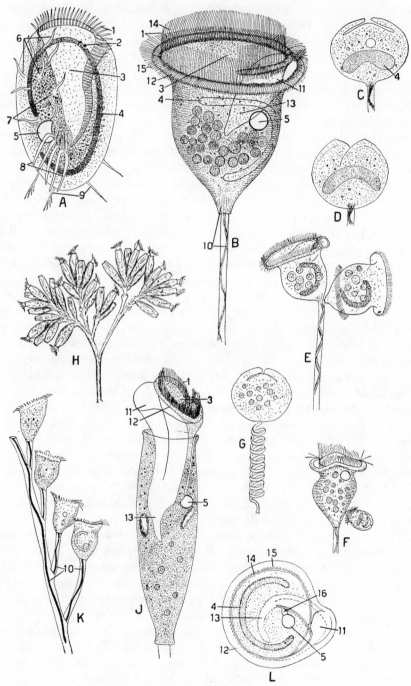

FIG. 65.—For legend see opposite page.

parasitic, comprising the genera *Urceolaria*, *Cyclochaeta*, and *Trichodina* (Fig. 66*H*). They inhabit the surface of a variety of animals, as hydras, sponges, planarians, tadpoles, and fish, where they glide about by means of the posterior circlet. The body is short and broad, circular in section, with the posterior end modified into a concave disk, strengthened by a ring, often toothed, and edged with a circlet of cilia.

The remaining and majority of the Peritricha do not have any posterior girdle except on the occasions mentioned above and are with few exceptions permanently attached by a posterior disk or a stalk. In the most primitive types, as *Scyphidia* (Fig. 66*D*), the posterior end forms an adhesive disk, the *scopula*, by which the animal is fastened to various objects, often other animals. This scopula is a concavity bordered by a projecting rim and containing cilia-like projections, often arranged in concentric circles. The stalk of the Peritricha is a secretion, probably tectinous, of the scopula. The rim secretes the wall of the stalk, and the concavity gives rise to fine tubes that seem to come from protrichocysts associated with the cilia-like projections. These tubes may fill the whole interior of the stalk (*Epistylis*) or the periphery only, leaving the center empty (*Zoöthamnium*), or may be reduced to short lengths arranged in a spiral on the inside of the stalk wall (*Vorticella*).

Among the stalked Peritricha, the family Epistylidae is characterized by the noncontractile stalk. Some genera are solitary as *Rhabdostyla*, resembling a single *Epistylis*, and *Pyxidium*, resembling an *Opercularia* individual. *Epistylis* (Fig. 66*A*) and *Opercularia* (Fig. 65*H*, *J*) form branching colonies with stiff stems, fastened to various objects. Each bell of *Epistylis* resembles a *Vorticella*, but in some species the adoral zone encircles the peristome several times (Fig. 66*C*). *Opercularia* (Fig. 65*J*) differs in the stalked peristome and delicate membrane bordering the large vestibule. The family Vorticellidae is distinguished by the spiral muscle band (spasmoneme) of the stalk. This consists of a band of myonemes enclosed in a larger sheath continuous with the pellicle of the bell and fastened in a spiral course to the inner surface of the wall of the stalk. The family includes the solitary *Vorticella* (Fig. 65*B*) with numerous species, some epizoic on tadpoles, etc.; and the colonial genera *Zoöthamnium* (Fig. 66*B*) with spasmonemes continuous throughout the colony so that all the bells contract together, and *Carchesium* (Fig. 65*K*), in which each bell has a separate spasmoneme. The family Vaginicolidae

---

Fig. 65.—Hypotricha, Peritricha. *A. Euplotes*, from life. *B. Vorticella*, from life. *C–E.* Stages of fission of *Vorticella*, from life. *F. Vorticella* in conjugation. (*After Kent*, 1881.) *G. Vorticella* contracted, from life. *H.* Colony of *Opercularia*. *J.* Single individual of same, from life. *K.* Small part of a colony of *Carchesium*, showing myoneme arrangement. (*After Conn*, 1905.) *L.* Peristome of *Vorticella*. (*After Noland and Finley*, 1931.) 1, adoral zone; 2, micronucleus; 3, peristome; 4, macronucleus; 5, contractile vacuole; 6, frontal cirri; 7, ventral cirri; 8, anal cirri; 9, caudal cirri; 10, myonemes; 11, vestibule; 12, collar; 13, cytopharynx; 14, inner circlet of adoral zone; 15, outer circlet; 16, reservoir.

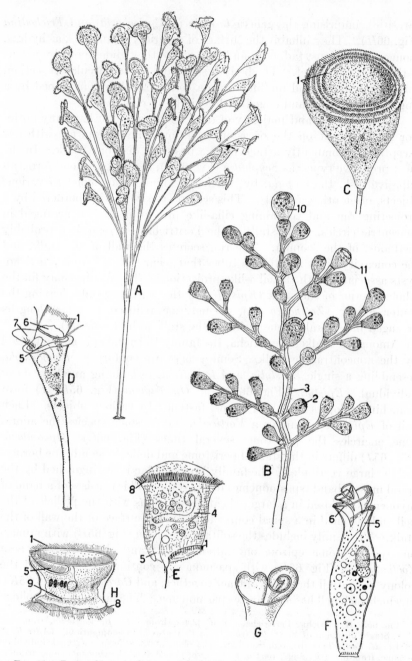

Fig. 66.—Peritricha.   A. Colony of *Epistylis*, from life.   B. Colony of *Zoöthamnium arbuscula*, from life.   C. One zooid of *Epistylis* (not same species as A), showing several spiral turns of adoral zone. (*After Conn*, 1905.)   D. An epizoic peritrich, *Scyphidia*

comprises several genera such as *Vaginicola*, *Pyxicola*, and *Cothurnia* (Fig. 10*C*), which live alone or in couples in delicate tectinous cases fastened directly (*Vaginicola*) or by a short stalk (*Cothurnia*), and closable by a lid in some forms (*Pyxicola*).

New colonies arise in the following manner. Bells (any bell in most species, only certain bells in a few, see below) develop a posterior ciliary girdle, detach from their stalks, and swim away. On finding a suitable spot, each attaches, loses the posterior girdle, grows a new stalk, and gives rise to the entire colony by repeated fissions of itself and its daughters. One of each pair of fission products grows a new stalk, and the old stalk also lengthens. As the fissions take place in a definite way, a certain colony shape with a specific pattern of branching results.

In a few colonial Peritricha, *Systilis* and certain species of *Zoöthamnium*, the bells of the colony show a remarkable degree of differentiation. Conditions in *Z. alternans* (Fig. 66*B*) have been described by Fauré-Fremiet (1930) and Summers (1938). The colonies are founded by the large median axillary bells, which detach and swim away as *migratory ciliospores*. After swimming for several hours, these attach by the scopula, grow a new stalk, and divide unequally into a larger bell, which becomes the *terminal macrozooid*, and a smaller bell or *microzooid*. The latter at its first fission gives rise to a *median axillary microzooid* and a *branch microzooid*. The branch microzooid and its daughters form the first branch. The terminal macrozooid continues to elongate and at its second fission again produces a larger macrozooid and a smaller microzooid, and the latter again divides into a median axillary microzooid and the second branch microzooid. These processes take place in such a way that successive branches alternate. A macrozooid always remains at the summit of the axis of the colony but grows smaller with repeated fissions. The median axillary microzooids may divide once; only they or their immediate daughters become migratory ciliospores, as a rule. Only the terminal macrozooid, of which each colony has one, becomes a macroconjugant. The microconjugants are transformed terminal microzooids of the branches. Each colony thus consists of four kinds of individuals: the single terminal macrozooid; the median axillary microzooids, which can become migratory ciliospores; the terminal branch microzooids, which resemble the macrozooid morphologically and can metamorphose into microconjugants; and the ordinary vegetative microzooids, some of which

---

terebellae. (*After Fauré-Fremiet*, 1920.) *E.* A free-swimming type of Peritricha, *Telotrochidium*, from life. *F. Spirochona gemmipara.* *G.* Enlarged view of peristome. (*After R. Hertwig*, 1877.) *H. Trichodina.* (*After Conn*, 1905.) 1, adoral zone; 2, median axillary microzooids (become migratory ciliospores); 3, myoneme; 4, macronucleus; 5, cytopharynx; 6, peristome; 7, vestibule; 8, posterior circlet of cilia; 9, supporting ring of adhesive disk; 10, terminal macrozooid (becomes macroconjugant); 11, terminal branch microzooids (become microconjugants).

may also become ciliospores or microconjugants. The experiments of Summers have shown that if the terminal macrozooid or terminal branch microzooids are cut off, adjacent bells will assume their functions and morphology. These results indicate that the bells of the colony do not differ qualitatively but that their functions and morphology result from position and other correlative factors. The terminal macrozooid exercises a controlling influence on the colony, chiefly of a restraining nature. When it conjugates, this control diminishes, so that branches below the conjugant grow out of all proportion. The fate of conjugant macrozooids is not clearly known. After a quiescent period they divide; one of the daughters remains as the terminal macrozooid and the other possibly becomes a migratory ciliospore.

13. Order Chonotricha.—This is a small group of ciliates often placed in the Peritricha to which, however, they bear no close relationship. They are exclusively epizoic on the gills of amphipods, to which they are fastened by a basal disk or by a stalk. The body is vase-shaped and has a funnel-like ciliated peristome often spirally coiled (Fig. 66G). There is no adoral zone. Asexual reproduction occurs by the formation of lateral buds. In conjugation adjacent individuals fuse by their peristomes and one absorbs the other; the nuclear changes are insufficiently known. The principal genus is *Spirochona* (Fig. 66F, G), common on amphipods in fresh and salt waters.

VIII. CLASS SUCTORIA

The Suctoria, also called *Acineta*, are devoid of cilia or other locomotor organelles in the adult stage and lack a mouth, being provided with tentacles for food capture and intake (Fig. 67). They are rounded, oval, inverted conical, or branched sessile protozoans, fastened directly or by a stalk to objects or often to other animals. Several genera are provided with a delicate case. The stalk is secreted by a scopula as in the Peritricha. The tentacles spring from the whole surface or from the free end (Fig. 67B, F) or occur in groups (Fig. 67A, H) and have knobbed (Fig. 67B) or pointed (Fig. 67F) ends. They consist of an outer contractile sheath, which probably contains very fine myonemes and is thrown into folds on contraction, and an inner stiff tube, which extends deeply into the general entoplasm. The knob when present is permeated with fine radial canals. The food consists of small animals, such as protozoans and rotifers, which adhere to the tentacle ends when they happen to strike them (Fig. 67C) and are paralyzed by a toxic secretion from the tentacles. Their contents are then sucked in by way of the tentacular canal, but it is not known how the suction is produced. There are one to several contractile vacuoles, a single oval, elongated or branched (Fig. 67A, G) macronucleus, and one to several micronuclei.

Encystment is common, occurring when food is scarce. Asexual reproduction takes place by exogenous or endogenous budding with the production of a ciliated young, called an embryo. In the most primitive case, exemplified in some species of *Podophrya*, the entire suctorian withdraws its tentacles, develops cilia, and leaves its stalk as a ciliated protozoan resembling a holotrich with longitudinal rows of cilia. In other cases of exogenous budding, the distal half of the animal may absorb its tentacles, put out cilia, and swim off; or a number of small elevations may sprout from the distal surface, become ciliated, and constrict off as ciliated embryos as in the Ephelotidae (Fig. 67*F*). In internal or endogenous budding (Fig. 67*D*), a space, the brood chamber, appears in the interior of the suctorian, either by invagination from the outside or by a split, and, into this chamber, adjacent cytoplasm protrudes and develops into a ciliated embryo, sometimes several, released by a sudden evagination. In all budding processes the nuclei behave as in the ordinary binary fission of ciliates. The macronucleus extends into each bud (Fig. 67*G*) and divides directly while the micronuclei undergo a form of mitosis. The embryos (Fig. 67*E*) commonly bear several circlets of cilia and may also have extra tufts or groups of cilia. The future ventral surface may be provided with an adhesive disk. The embryos swim about for a few hours, fasten by the ventral surface, lose their cilia, and develop tentacles. In some Suctoria, in addition to the ciliated embryos, nonciliated vermiform buds may be given off internally or externally. Conjugation occurs by the adhesion and eventual fusion of two adjacent suctorians with nuclear changes as in typical ciliates.

The suctorians are very common everywhere in fresh and salt water, often as ectocommensals of a variety of animals. In *Acineta* (Fig. 67*H*), the knobbed tentacles are grouped into two, sometimes three, clusters, while the otherwise similar *Paracineta* (Fig. 67*B*) bears them all over the distal surface. *Podophrya*, of fresh water, with the same general appearance, has knobbed tentacles distributed over the entire body. *Ephelota*, and related genera, often epizoic on hydroid stems, are characterized by two sorts of tentacles, the pointed grasping kind and some short knobbed tentacles (Fig. 67*F*). In *Dendrosomides* (Fig. 67*A*) and allied genera, the body, stalked or not, is irregularly branched into elongate arms bearing groups of knobbed tentacles. *Dendrocometes* (Fig. 67*C*, *D*) gives off arms whose ends branch into short pointed tentacles. The curious *Ophryodendron* (Fig. 67*J*) bears a cluster of tentacles on the end of a highly retractile arm. Some true parasites occur among the Suctoria. *Sphaerophrya* lives in the entoplasm of various ciliates such as *Paramecium* and *Stentor* and gives off ciliated embryos that develop into rounded suctorians with several knobbed tentacles. These attach to and embed themselves in new hosts and then lose their tentacles. *Pottsia*

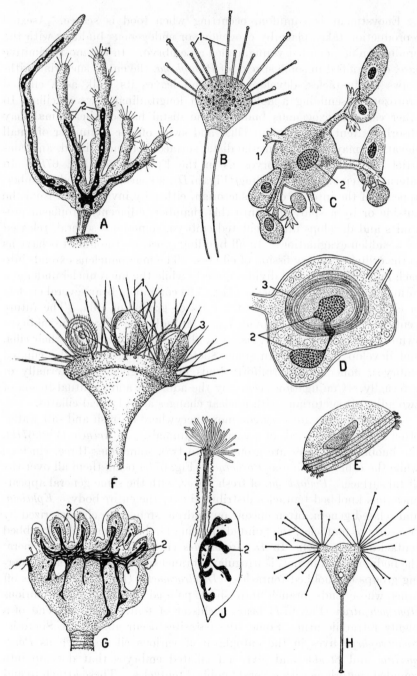

FIG. 67.—Suctoria.   A. *Dendrosomides*.   (*After Collin,* 1912.)   B. *Paracineta*, fastened to a hydroid, from life.   C. *Dendrocometes*, feeding on a ciliate.   D. Same, forming an

occurs on *Folliculina* and *Cothurnia* as a rounded body with four tentacles sunk into the host; the embryo has three girdles of cilia and two tentacles by which it fastens to new hosts. *Endosphaera* inhabits the interior of vorticellids as a rounded organism giving off embryos by way of a canal through the pellicle; tentacles are not present at any stage.

The derivation of the Suctoria from ciliates is clearly indicated by their dimorphic nuclei and ciliated young and by the occurrence of conjugation. They are usually considered to be related to the Peritricha from their possession of scopula and stalk and the arrangement of the cilia on the embryos into several circlets. Kahl, however, has recently maintained (1931) that they derive from primitive Holotricha of the *Prorodon* type by way of such ciliates as *Actinobolina* (= *Actinobolus*) a curious holotrich that can put out tentacle-like extensions supported by an internal fiber and employed in "fishing" for food. The animal can withdraw the tentacles by rolling up the fibers in its interior, and it then swims about like an ordinary ciliate. Relation to Holotricha is further indicated by the ciliary arrangement on the embryos of the most primitive Suctoria such as *Podophrya*, where the cilia occur in longitudinal rows, not in girdles.

IX. GENERAL AND PHYLOGENETIC CONSIDERATIONS

Among the Protozoa there occur all grades of differentiation from the simple construction and indefinite form of the amoeboid rhizopods to the complicated morphology of the hypermastigote flagellates and the spirotrichous and peritrichous ciliates. It seems clear that differentiation begins with the stiffening of the ectoplasm, which then confers definite form and symmetry upon the animal and leads to anteroposterior differentiation. With the presence of a hardened surface, some provision must be made for food intake, and there appear first a simple mouth opening and later the complicated devices seen among the ciliates, especially those which feed by producing water currents. Such mechanisms reach their height among the spirotrichous and peritrichous ciliates with their peristomes, zone of membranelles, and cytopharynx with its special ciliation. The current type of feeding seems to lead gradually to a sessile life as exemplified in some of the Heterotricha and in the Peritricha. Along with food-catching elaboration there frequently occur other differentiations, such as the formation of myonemes and fibrils of one

---

internal bud. *E.* The bud escaped. (*After Pestel*, 1931.) *F. Ephelota gigantea*, giving off exogenous buds. (*After Noble*, 1929.) *G. Ephelota gemmifera*, with buds, showing branching nucleus. (*After Collin*, 1912.) *H. Acineta*, with two bunches of tentacles. (*After Kent*, 1881.) *J. Ophryodendron*. (*After Collin*. 1912.) 1, tentacles; 2, macronucleus; 3, bud.

sort and another. Only one group of ciliates, the Hypotricha, has specialized along the line of more efficient controlled locomotion; there we find powerful cirri capable of a variety of movements and probably operated by a neuromotor mechanism. The flagellates contrast with the ciliates in the slight differentiation of food-taking structures, and they seem on the other hand to have undergone elaboration in the way of kinetic elements. The numerous flagella of the polymastigote and hypermastigote flagellates are presumably an adaptation for locomotion in the thick contents of the digestive tract.

It is now generally accepted that the Flagellata stand at the bottom of both the plant and animal kingdoms. It has been seen that the green flagellates, such as euglenoids and Volvocales, are practically inseparable from green algae, which may be regarded as derived directly from the holophytic flagellates. Such groups as the chrysomonads form a continuous series with filamentous brown algae many of which give off swarmers identical in structure with *Chromulina* and *Ochromonas*. Within any of the holophytic flagellate orders, colorless animal forms may arise by loss of chloroplasts, and by further loss of the flagella typical rhizopods appear. Some flagellates have adopted a parasitic mode of life with sporulation as a method of asexual reproduction, thus suggesting affinities with the Sporozoa.

The flagellates themselves appear to be a heterogeneous assemblage of groups that have probably arisen from a number of different sources, possibly bacteria and spirochaetes, many of which are provided with flagella. The arrangement into orders is a more or less arbitrary matter. Some of these orders are well-defined and center about typical members; but as has been seen there are many species whose placing in the recognized orders is very difficult.

The rhizopods like the flagellates constitute an arbitrary assemblage of forms having in common the pseudopodial method of locomotion and food capture. It is probable that the various orders of rhizopods have arisen independently from different groups of flagellates, i.e., the class is polyphyletic. In particular the Chrysomonadina seem to be ancestral to several types of rhizopods; some by loss of flagella and chromoplasts become naked Lobosa and others by developing axopods lead to the Heliozoa whose flagellate affinities are further displayed by the helioflagellates. The Foraminifera are evidently related to the shelled Lobosa, from which in fact some of them can scarcely be distinguished. The Radiolaria are more sharply defined than most other rhizopod orders but again suggest flagellate relationships by their production of flagellate swarmers. Both the Radiolaria and the Foraminifera occur as fossils in the oldest rocks and have undergone but slight morphological changes since those remote periods.

The Sporozoa again are a heterogeneous group of which the different orders have probably had separate origins. The Telosporidia seem to constitute a natural assemblage for which many authors assign a flagellate ancestry because of the flagellate form of the sporozoites and the presence of flagella on the microgametes, those of the Haemosporidia resembling protomonads. The schizogregarines are considered the most primitive group of the Telosporidia from which the eugregarines have been derived by loss of the schizogonic cycle. There seems little doubt that the coccidians have originated from the gregarines as indicated by the very similar mode of sporogony in the Adeleidea and the gregarines, in both of which groups the gamonts encyst together in couples. Many authors further mention *Selenococcidium* (Fig. 48*O–T*) as a link between the gregarines and the coccidians. This form has extracellular, worm-like schizonts, like those of the schizogregarines. The close relationship of the Haemosporidia to the Eimeridea is indicated by the similarity of their life cycles, which differ chiefly in the loss of cyst walls in the former through transmission by way of an intermediate host, avoiding exposure to external conditions. The haemosporidian habit of dwelling in the blood stream may be seen originating in the blood coccidians (haemogregarines) which parasitize the endothelial cells of the blood vessels or of highly vascular organs. At first only the gamonts parasitize the blood corpuscles but in *Haemogregarina* all stages have come to occupy the blood cells, and there is a loss of cyst walls as in the Haemosporidia. The relations of the remaining groups of Sporozoa are very obscure. The amoeboid form of the sporozoites suggests a rhizopod ancestry. The nature and origin of the polar capsules of the Cnidosporidia are unsolved questions, but it may be pointed out that certain flagellates have quite similar cnidotricho-cysts (Fig. 25*G*).

The Ciliata differ so markedly from the other Protozoa in their possession of cilia, nuclear dimorphism, and sexual phenomena that their relation to them remains problematical. The relation of the opalinids to the Euciliata is equally enigmatic, although it has been suggested that the opalinids are not ciliates at all but hypermastigotes whose flagella have been shortened down to ciliary length. Within the Euciliata, the simpler Holotricha with a complete uniform ciliation and simple terminal mouth presumably represent the original forms from which the other groups have diverged along many lines by loss and specialization of the cilia and elaboration of the food-catching mechanism.

The Protozoa as acellular organisms compare favorably with the lowest multicellular animals. They may have one or more layers of myonemes that correspond to the muscle sheath of coelenterates, they may have a system of ectoplasmic fibrils conductile in nature, the ophryoscolecids could almost be said to possess a digestive tract, composed of mouth, cytopharynx, entoplasmic sac, rectal tube, and anus (page 195), and sensory bristles and a highly differentiated photoreceptor may be present. Complete sexual differentiation is attained within the phylum and many forms even exhibit the equivalent of embryonic development, giving off, as in dinoflagellates and suctorians, young that resemble an ancestral form and must pass through a series of changes before they attain the adult morphology.

Bibliography

TEXTBOOKS AND TAXONOMIC WORKS AND ARTICLES

Beardsley, A. E. 1902. Notes on Colorado Protozoa. Amer. Micros. Soc. Trans. 23. **Blochmann, F.** 1895. Die mikroskopische Tierwelt des Süsswassers. I. Protozoa. **Brumpt, E.** 1922. Précis de Parasitologie. **Calkins, G. N.** 1901. Marine Protozoa from Woods Hole. U. S. Fish Comm. Bul. 21. 1901. The Protozoa. 1926, 1933. Biology of the Protozoa. **Conn, H. W.** 1905. A preliminary report of the Protozoa of the fresh waters of Connecticut. Conn. State Geol. Nat. Hist. Survey Bul. 2. **Craig, C. F.** 1926. A manual of the parasitic Protozoa of man. **Dobell, C. C.** 1909. Researches on the intestinal Protozoa of frogs and toads. Quart. Jour. Micros. Sci. 53. 1925–1926. Intestinal Protozoa of monkeys. Rpt. Med. Res. Council Protistol. 31, 35. **Dobell, C. C.,** and **F. W. O'Connor.** 1921. The intestinal Protozoa of man. **Doflein, H.,** and **E. Reichenow.** 1927–1928. Lehrbuch der Protozoenkunde. **Edmondson, C. H.** 1906. The Protozoa of Iowa. Davenport Acad. Sci. Proc. 11. 1912. Protozoan fauna of high mountain lakes of Colorado. Colo. Univ., Studies 9. 1920. Protozoa of Devil's Lake. Amer. Micros. Soc. Trans. 39. **Entz, G.** 1884. Über die Infusorien des Golfes von Neapel. Mitth. Zool. Sta. Neapel 5. **Fantham, H. B.** 1919–1925. Parasitic Protozoa found in South Africa. So. African Jour. Sci. 16–23. **Gajewskaja, N.** 1933. Zur Ökologie, Morphologie und Systematik der Infusorien des Baikalsees. Zoologica 32, Heft 83. **Hegner, R. W.** 1926. The interrelations of Protozoa and the utricules of Utricularia. The Protozoa of the pitcher plant. Biol. Bul. 50. 1927. Host-parasite relations between man and his intestinal Protozoa. **Hegner, R. W.,** and **W. H. Taliaferro.** 1924. Human protozoology. **Jennings, H. S.** 1899. Protozoa of Lake Erie. U. S. Fish. Comm. Bul. 19. **Kent, W. S.** 1880–1881. Manual of the Infusoria. 3 vols. **Knowles, R.** 1928. An introduction to medical protozoology. **Kolle, W.,** and **A. Wassermann.** 1930. Handbuch der pathogenen Mikroorganismen. 10 vols. **Kudo, R.** 1926. Protozoa parasitic in frogs. Amer. Micros. Soc. Trans. 41. 1931. Handbook of protozoology. **Landacre, F. L.** 1908. Protozoa of Sandusky Bay and vicinity. Ohio Acad. Sci. Bul. 4. **Minchin, E. A.** 1912. Introduction to the study of the Protozoa. **Nöller, W.** 1922. Die wichtigsten parasitischen Protozoen des Menschen und der Tier. Parasiten der Haus und Nutztieren I. (ed. by Ostertag, Wolffhügel, und Nöller). **Prowazek, S.,** and **W. Nöller.** 1925. Handbuch der pathogenen Protozoen. **Sandon, H.** 1927. The composition and distribution of the protozoan fauna of the soil. **Smith, I.** 1915. Infusoria of Kansas. Kans. Univ. Bul. 16. **Stein, F.** 1878. Die Organismus der Infusionstiere. 1888. Freshwater Infusoria. Jour. Trenton Nat. Hist. Soc. 1. **Swarczensky, B.** 1928–1930. Zur Kenntnis der Baikalprotistenfauna. Arch. Protistk. 64, 65, 69. **Wenrich, D. H.** 1924. Protozoa from the skin and gills of tadpoles. Amer. Micros. Soc. Trans. 43. **Wenyon, C. M.** 1926. Protozoology. 2 vols. **Wood, W. F.** 1935. Some observations on the intestinal Protozoa of California lizards. Jour. Parasitol. 21.

PROTOZOA

General

Alverdes, F. 1922. Untersuchungen über begeisselte und beflimmerte Organismen. Arch. Entwickl. Mech. Organ. 52. 1922. Zur Localisation des chemischen und thermischen Sinnes bei Paramecium und Stentor. Zool. Anz. 55. 1923. Über Galvanotaxis und Flimmerbewegung. Biol. Zentbl. 43. 1923. Neue Bahnen in der Lehre von Verhalten der niederen Organismen. **Andrews, J.,** and **M. Paulsen.** 1931. The incidence of human intestinal Protozoa. Amer. Jour. Med. Sci. 181. **Becker, E. R.** 1926. The role of the nucleus in the cell functions of amoebae. Biol. Bul. 50. **Beers, C. D.** 1927, 1935. Encystment in Didinium. Jour. Morph. 44; Arch. Protistk. 84. 1933. Relation of density of population to rate of reproduction in Didinium and Stylonychia. Arch. Protistk. 80. **Belar, K.** 1926. Die Formwechsel der Protistenkerne. Ergeb. Zool. 6. **Blättner, H.** 1925. Reizphysiologie von Spirostomum. Arch. Protistk. 53. **Bodine, J. H.** 1921. Hydrogen ion concentration of protozoan cultures. Biol. Bul. 41. **Botsford, E.** 1926. Contractile vacuole of amoeba. Jour. Expt. Zool. 45. **Bramstedt, F.** 1935. Dressurversuche mit Paramecium und Stylonychia. Ztschr. Vergleich. Physiol. 22. **Brandt, T.** 1923. Encystierung von Vorticella und hypotrichen Infusorien. Arch. Protistk. 47. 1935. Die stoffwechsel der Protozoen. Ergeb. Biol. 12. **Bresslau, E.** 1921. Die exper. Erzeugung von Hüllen bei Protozoen. Naturwissenschaften 9. 1924. Neues über das Tektin. Verh. Deut. Zool. Gesell. 29. **Buchner, P.** 1921. Tiere und Pflanze in intrazellularer Symbiose. **Buddenbrock, W.** 1916. Criticism of the tropism theory of J. Loeb. Jour. Anim. Behavior 6. **Caldwell, L.** 1933. Inherited diversities at endomixis in Par. Jour. Expt. Zool. 66. **Calkins, G. N.** 1911. Regeneration and cell division in Uronychia. Jour. Expt. Zool. 10. 1906. The protozoan life cycle. Biol. Bul. 11. **Causey, D.** 1929. Incidence of infection with intestinal Protozoa. Science 70: 102. **Cleveland, L. R.** 1924. Symbiotic relations between intestinal Protozoa of termites and their host. Biol. Bul. 46. 1926. Symbiosis among animals with special reference to termites and their intestinal flagellates. Quart. Rev. Biol. 1. **Crozier, W. J.** 1928. Tropisms. Jour. Gen. Psychol. 1. **Cunha, A. M.,** and **J. Muniz.** 1928. La réaction nucleaire de Feulgen chez les Protozoaires. Soc. Biol. [Paris] Compt. Rend. 99: 1339. **Daniel, G. E.** 1931. Respiratory quotient of Balantidium coli. Amer. Jour. Hyg. 14. **Darby, H. H.** 1929. Effect of hydrogen ion concentration on the sequence of protozoan forms. Arch. Protistk. 65. **Dawson, J. A.,** and **M. Belkin.** 1929. The digestion of oils by Amoeba proteus. Biol. Bul. 56. **Dawson, J. A., M. Belkin,** and **W. H. Mitchell.** 1929. The viability of certain infusorian cysts. Amer. Nat. 63. **Day, H. C.** 1927. Contractile vacuole of Amoeba. Jour. Morph. 44. 1930. Contractile vacuole of Spirostomum and Par. Physiol. Zool. 3. **Day, L. M.,** and **M. Bently.** 1911. Learning in Par. Jour. Anim. Behavior. 1. **Deflandre, G.** 1929. Mouvements propres, pistes, et vitesses de déplacement de quelques Protistes. Ann. Protistol. 2. **Degen, A.** 1905. Kontraktile Vacuole. Bot. Ztg. 63. **Dembrowski, W.** 1925. Regeneration von Stylonychia. Arch. Mikro. Anat. 104. **Dobell, C. C.** 1909. Chromidia and the binuclearity hypothesis. Quart. Jour. Micros. Sci. 53. **Dogiel, V.** 1925. Die Geschlechtsprozesse bei Infusorien. Arch. Protistk. 50. **Efimoff, W.** 1924. Über Ausfrieren und Überkältung der Protozoen. Arch. Protistk. 49. **Elliott, A. M.** 1933. Isolation of Colpidium in bacteria-free cultures. Biol. Bul. 65. 1935. Growth of Colpidium. Arch. Protistk. 84. **Fauré-Fremiet, E.** 1910. Mitochondries des Protozoaires. Arch. Anat. Micros. 11. 1911. Appareil nucleaire, chromidies, mitochondries. Arch. Protistk. 21. **Fermor, X.** 1913. Encystierung bei Stylonychia. Zool. Anz. 42. **Feulgen, F. B.** 1924. Über die Nuclealfärbung. Arch. Gesam. Physiol. Mensch. Tiere 203. **Fine, M.** 1912. Chemical properties of hay infusions, acidity, protozan sequence. Jour. Expt. Zool. 12. **Fraenkel, G.** 1931. Die Mechanik der Orientierung der Tiere im Raum. Biol. Rev. Cambridge Phil. Soc. 6. **Fritsch, F.** 1929. Evolutionary sequence and affinities among the Protophyta. Biol. Rev. Cambridge Phil. Soc. 4. **Gatenby, J. G.**, and S. King. 1925. Nature of the contractile vacuole. Nature [London] 115: 157. **Gelei, J.** 1925. Nephridialapparate bei dem Protozoen. Biol. Zentbl. 45; Arch. Protistk. 64. **Glaser, R. W.**, and **N. Coria.** 1933. Culture of Par. caudatum free from living microorganisms. Jour. Parasitol. 20. **Goldschmidt, R.** 1905. Die chromidia der Protozoen. Arch. Protistk. 5, also 8. **Goetsch, W.**, and **L. Scheuring.** 1926. Parasitismus und Symbiose der Algengattung Chlorella. Ztschr. Morph. Ökol. Tiere 7. **Goodey, T.** 1913. Excystation of Colpoda. Roy. Soc. London, Proc. 86 B. 1915. Remarkable retention of vitality of Protozoa in old stored soils. Ann. Appl. Biol. 1. **Gregory, L.** 1909. Life history of Tillina magna. Jour. Expt. Zool. 6. **Greenleaf, W.** 1926. Influence of volume of culture medium and cell proximity on the rate of reproduction of Infusoria. Jour. Expt. Zool. 46. **Greenwood, M.** 1886–1888. Digestion process in some rhizopods. Jour. Physiol. 7, 8. **Greenwood, M.** and **E. Saunders.** 1894. Role of acid in protozoan digestion. Jour. Physiol. 16. **Griffiths, A. B.** 1889. Uric acid in the contractile vacuoles. Roy. Soc. Edinb., Proc. 16. **Hartmann, M.** 1909. Polyenergide Kerne. Biol. Zentbl. 29. 1911. Die Konstitution der Protistenkerne. **Hartmann, M.** and **S. Prowazek.** 1907. Blepharoplast, caryosom, und centrosome. Arch. Protistk. 10. **Hartog, M.** 1888. Functions and homologies of the contractile vacuole in plants and animals. Brit. Assoc. Ad. Sci., Rpt. 58. **Hausman, L.** 1934. Revivification of certain species of Protozoa after twenty years of encystment. Amer. Nat. 68. **Haye, A.** 1930. Exkretionsapparat bei den Protisten. Arch. Protistk. 70. **Hegner, R. W.** 1919. Heredity, variation, and the appearance of diversities during the vegetative reproduction of Arcella. Genetics 4. 1920. Relation between nuclear number, chromatin mass, cytoplasmic mass and shell characteristics of Arcella. Jour. Expt. Zool. 29. **Herfs, A.** 1922. Die pulsierende Vakuole der Protozoen. Arch. Protistk. 44. **Hertwig, R.** 1903. Über Korrelation von Zell- und Kerngrösse. Biol. Zentbl. 23. **Hetherington, A.** 1932. Constant culture of Stentor. Arch. Protistk. 76. 1933. Culture of some holotrichous ciliates. Same, 80. 1936. Precise control of growth in a pure culture of a ciliate, Glaucoma pyriformis. Biol. Bul. 70. **Hill, J. C.** 1933. Golgi apparatus of Protozoa. Roy. Micros. Soc. Jr. 53. **Hirschler, J.** 1927. Studien über die sich mit osmium schwärzenden Plasmakomponenten einiger Protozoen-arten. Ztschr. Zellf. Mikro. Anat. 5. **Hogue, M. J.** 1923. Contractile vacuoles in amoebae. Jour. Elisha Mitchell Soc. 39. **Holmes, S. J.** 1907. The behavior of Loxophyllum and its relation to regeneration. Jour. Expt. Zool. 4. **Horton, F. M.** 1935. The reactions of isolated parts of Par. Jour. Expt. Zool. 12. **Hovasse, R.**, and **G. Teissier.** 1923. Sur la position systématique des xanthelles. Soc. Zool. France Bul. 48. **Howland, R. B.** 1924. Experiments on the contr. vacuole of Amoeba and Par. Jour. Expt. Zool. 40. 1924. Excretion of nitrogenous waste as a function of the contr. vacuole. Jour. Expt. Zool. 40. 1928. Colorimetric determination of hydrogen-ion concentration in the gastric vacuoles of Actinosphaerium. Anat. Rec. 38. **Howland, R. B.** and **A. Bernstein.** 1931. Method for determining oxygen consumption of a single cell. Jour. Gen. Physiol. 14. **Ilowaisky, S.** 1926. Cysten der Hypotrichen. Arch. Protistk. 54. **Ishikawa, H.** 1913. Wundheilungs- und Regenerations-vorgänge bei Infusorien. Arch. Entwick. Mech. Organ. 35. **Jennings, H. S.** 1904. External discharge of the contr. vacuole. Zool. Anz. 27. 1906.

Behavior of the lower organisms. 1920. Life and death, heredity and evolution of the simplest organisms. 1929. Genetics of the Protozoa. Bibliog. Genet. 5. **Johnson, D. F.** 1936. Isolation of Glaucoma in bacteria-free cultures. Arch. Protistk. 86. **Jirovic, O.** 1927. Die Nuclealreaktion bei einigen Protozoen. Arch. Protistk. 59. **Kalmus, H.** 1927. Die Atmung von Par. Biol. Zentbl. 47. **Kanitz, A.** 1907. Der Einfluss der Temperatur auf die pulsierende Vakuole. Biol. Zentbl. 27. **Kater, J., and R. Burroughs.** 1926. Cause and nature of encystment in Polytomella. Biol. Bul. 40. **King, S. D.** 1927. The Golgi-apparatus of Protozoa. Roy. Micros. Soc. Jour. 47. **Kitching, J. A.** 1934. Physiology of contractile vacuoles. I, II. Jour. Expt. Biol. 11. **Kofoid, C. A.** 1929. The Protozoa of the human mouth. Jour. Parasitol. 15. **Kofoid, C. A., E. McNeil, and M. Kopac.** 1931. Chemical nature of the cyst wall in human intestinal Protozoa. Soc. Expt. Biol. Med. Proc. 29. **Koehler, O.** 1934. Verhalten von Paramecium-Teilstücken. Zool. Anz. Sup. 7. **Kühn, A.** 1919. Die Orientierung der Tiere in Raum. **Le Dantec.** 1890–1891. Recherches sur la digestion intracellulaire chez les Protozoaires. Inst. Pasteur [Paris], Ann. 4, 5. **Lloyd, F.** 1928. The contractile vacuole. Biol. Rev. Cambridge Phil. Soc. 3. **Luck, J. M., G. Sheets, and J. Thomas.** 1931. The role of bacteria in the nutrition of Protozoa. Quart. Rev. Biol. 6. **Lwoff, A.** 1923. Sur la nutrition des Infusoires. Acad. Sci. Compt. Rend. 176: 928. 1929. La nutrition de Polytoma et le pouvoir de synthèse des Protistes hétérotrophes. Les Protistes mésotrophes. Acad. Sci. Compt. Rend. 188. 1932. Recherches biochemique sur la nutrition des Protozoaires. **Lwoff, A., and M. Lwoff.** 1929. Le pouvoir de synthèse de Chlamydomonas et l'Haematococcus en culture pure à l'obscurité. Soc. Biol. [Paris], Compt. Rend. 102. **Lwoff, A., M. Lwoff, and N. Roukhelman.** 1926. Formes d'azote dans une culture pure d'Infusoires. Acad. Sci. Compt. Rend. 183. **Lynch, V.** 1919. The function of the nucleus of the living cell. Amer. Jour. Physiol. 48. **Mast, S. O.** 1927. Structure and function of the eye-spot in unicellular and colonial organisms. Arch. Protistk. 60. 1932. Localized stimulation, transmission of impulses and the nature of response in Amoeba. Physiol. Zool. 5. **Mast, S. O., and W. Doyle.** 1936. Structure, origin, and function of cytoplasmic constituents in Amoeba. Arch. Protistk. 86. **Mast., S. O., W. Doyle, and D. Pace.** 1933. Synthesis from inorganic compounds of starch, fats, proteins, and protoplasm in Chilomonas. Protoplasma 20. **Mast, S. O., W. Doyle, D. Pace, and L. Mast.** 1936. The effect of sulphur on the rate of respiration and on the respiratory quotient in Chilomonas. Jour. Cell. Compar. Physiol. 8. **Metchnikoff, E.** 1889. Recherches sur la digestion intracellulaire. Instit. Pasteur [Paris] Ann. 3. **Middleton, A. R.** 1915. Heritable variations and the results of selection in the fission rate of Stylonychia. Jour. Expt. Zool. 19. **Morgan, T. H.** 1902. Regeneration of proportionate parts in Stentor. Biol. Bul. 2. **Mouton, H.** 1902. Recherches sur la digestion chez les amibes et sur leur diastase intracellulaire. Instit. Pasteur [Paris] Ann. 16. 1903. Sur une diastase proteolitique extraite des Infusoires ciliés. Soc. Biol. [Paris] Compt. Rend. 55. **Nadler, J. E.** 1929. Notes on the loss and regeneration of the pellicle in Blepharisma undulans. Biol. Bul. 56. **Nassonov, D.** 1924. Der Exkretionsapparat der Protozoa als homologen des Golgischen Apparates. Arch. Mikros. Anat. 103. **Nirenstein, E.** 1905. Beiträge zur Ernährungs-physiologie der Protisten. Ztschr. Allg. Physiol. 5, also 10. 1925. Über die Natur und Stärke der Säureabscheidung in den Nahrungsvacuolen von Par. Ztschr. Wiss. Zool. 125. **Pascher, A.** 1918. Flagellaten und Rhizopoden in ihren gegenseitigen Beziehungen. Arch. Protistk. 38. **Peters, A. W.** 1907. Chemical studies on the cell and its medium. Amer. Jour. Physiol. 17. **Peters, R. A.** 1920. Growth of Par. in sterile culture medium. Jour. Physiol. 53. 1921. The substances needed for the growth of a pure culture of Colpidium. Jour. Physiol., 55. **Phelps, A.** 1934. Studies on the nutrition of Par. Arch. Protistk. 82. 1936. Growth of Protozoa in pure culture. Jour. Expt. Zool. 72. **Pringsheim, E.** 1921. Zur Physiologie saprophytischer Flagellaten (Polytoma, Astasia, Chilomonas). Beitr. Allg. Bot. 2. **Puschkarew, B.** 1913. Über die Verbreitung der Süsswasserprotozoen durch die Luft. Arch. Protistk. 28. **Reich, K.** 1935. Cultivation of a sterile amoeba. Jour. Expt. Zool. 69. **Reichenow, E.** 1928. Ergebnisse mit der Nuclealfärbung bei Protozoen. Arch. Protistk. 61. **Rhumbler, L.** 1888. Die verschiedenen Cystenbildungen und die Entwicklungsgeschichte der holotrichen Infusoriengattung Colpoda. Ztschr. Wiss. Zool. 46. **Robertson, T. B.** 1923. The chemical basis of growth and senescence. **Roskin, G.,** and **L. Levinsky.** 1926. Die Oxydasen und Peroxydasen bei Protozoen. Arch. Protistk. 56. **Rumjantzew, A.** 1922. Chromidial-substanz bei Difflugia. Arch. Russ. Protistol. 1. **Schaudinn, F.** 1911. Gesammelte Arbeiten (contains mitosis Centropyxis). **Shapiro, N.** 1927. The cycle of hydrogen-ion concentration in the food vacuoles of Par., Vorticella, and Stylonychia. Amer. Micros. Soc. Trans. 46. **Sokoloff, B.** 1924. Das Regenerationsproblem bei Protozoen. Arch. Protistk. 47. **Specht, H.** 1934. Aerobic respiration in Spirostomum and the production of ammonia. Jour. Cell. Compar. Physiol. 5. **Staniewicz, W.** 1910. Études expèr. sur la digestion de la graisse dans les infusoires ciliés. Bul. Acad. Sci. Cracow. Cl. Math. Nat. Sci. B. **Stempell, W.** 1914. Über die Funktion der pulsierenden Vacuolen. Zool. Jahrb., Abt. Zool. Physiol. 34; Arch. Protistk. 48. **Stocking, R. J.** 1915. Variation and inheritance of abnormalities occurring after conjugation in Par. Jour. Expt. Zool. 19. **Stolc, A.** 1900. Über die Verdauung und Bildung der Kohlenhydrate bei Pelomyxa. Ztschr. Wiss. Zool. 68. **Stolte, H. A.** 1922. Verlauf, Ursachen, und Bedeutung der Enzystierung bei Blepharisma. Verh. Deut. Zool. Gesell. 27. **Taliaferro, W. H.** 1926. Host resistance and types of infections in trypanosomiasis and malaria. Quart. Rev. Biol. 1. 1929. The immunology of the parasitic infections. **Taylor, C. V.** 1920. Demonstration of the function of the neuromotor apparatus in Euplotes. Calif. Univ. Pubs., Zool. 19. 1923. The contractile vacuole in Euplotes, an example of the sol-gel reversibility of cytoplasm. Jour. Expt. Zool. 37. **Thinmann, K. V.,** and **H. Barker.** 1934. Studies on the excystment of Colpoda. Jour. Expt. Zool. 69. **Verworn, M.** 1889. Psychophysiologische Protisten-Studien. 1891. Die physiologische Bedeutung der Zellkerne. Arch. Gesam. Physiol. Mensch. Tiere. 51. **Van Herwerden, M.** 1917. Über das Volutin und seine chemische Zusammensetzung. Folia Microbiol. [Delft] 5. **Wachendorff, T.** 1911. Das Gaswechsel von Colpidium. Ztschr. Allg. Physiol. 13. **Weatherby, J. H.** 1927. The function of the contractile vacuole in Par. Biol. Bul. 52. 1929. Excretion of nitrogenous substances in Protozoa. Physiol. Zool. 2. **Wenrich, D. H.** 1935. Host-parasite relations between parasitic Protozoa and their hosts. Amer. Phil. Soc. Proc. 75. **Wenrich, D. H.** *et al.* 1932. Results of a protozoological survey of 401 college freshmen. Jour. Parasitol. 19. **Yocom, H. B.** 1928. The effect of quantity of culture medium on the division rate of Oxytricha. Biol. Bul. 54. **Zingher, J.** 1933. Fetteinschlüsse bei einigen Protozoen. Arch. Protistk. 81. **Zuelzer, M.** 1919. Der Einfluss des Meerwasser auf die pulsierende Vakuole. Arch. Entwickl. Mech. Organ. 29.

RHIZOPODA

Leidy, J. 1879. Fresh-water Rhizopoda of North America. U. S. Geol. Survey Terr. Rept. XII. **Pénard, E.** 1902. Faune rhizopodique du Bassin du Léman. **Wailes, G. H.,** and **J. Hopkinson.** 1919. British Freshwater Rhizopoda and Heliozoa.

AMOEBOID MOVEMENT

Dellinger, O. 1906. Locomotion of amoebae and allied forms. Jour. Expt. Zool. 3. **Edwards, J. G.** 1923–1924. Effect of chemicals. Jour. Expt. Zool. 38; Jour. Expt. Biol. 1. **Hopkins, D. L.** 1928. Effect of physical and chemical factors. Jour. Morph. 45. **Jensen, P.** 1902. Die Protoplasmabewegung. Ergeb. Physiol. 1, Abt. 2. **Hyman, L. H.** 1917. Metabolic gradients in Amoeba and their relation to amoeboid movement. Jour. Expt. Zool. 24. **Loeb, L.** 1921. Amoeboid movement, tissue formation, and consistency of protoplasm. Amer. Jour. Physiol. 56. **Mast. S, O.** 1925. Structure, movement, locomotion, and stimulation in Amoeba. Jour. Morph. 41. 1929. Mechanics of locomotion in Amoeba. Protoplasma 8. **Pantin, C.** 1923. Physiology of amoeboid movement. I. Jour. Mar. Biol. Assoc. 13; Jour. Expt. Biol. 1, 3. **Rhumbler, L.** 1905. Zur Theorie der Oberflächenkräfte der Amöben. Ztschr. Wiss. Zool. 83. **Schaeffer, A. A.** 1920. Amoeboid movement. **Spek, T.** 1925. Die Protoplasmbewegung. Handbuch Nor. Path. Physiol. 8, part 1. **Tiegs, O. W.** 1928. Surface tension and the theory of amoeboid movement. Protoplasma 4.

NAKED LOBOSA

Arndt, A. 1924. Rhizopodien Studien. Arch. Protistk. 49. **Bach, F.** 1923. Affen Entamöben. Arch. Schiffs Tropen Hyg. 27. **Beers, C.** 1926. The cleaving of ciliates by Amoeba. Science 64: 90. **Causey, D.** 1925. Mitochondria and Golgi bodies in Endamoeba gingivalis. Calif. Univ., Pubs. Zool. 28. **Chalkley, A. W., and G. Daniel.** 1933. The relation between form of the living cell and the nuclear phases of division in Amoeba proteus. Physiol. Zool. 6. **Chambers, R.** 1920. Dissection and injection studies on Amoeba. Soc. Expt. Biol. Med. Proc. 18. **Craig, C. F.** 1911. The parasitic amoebae of man. 1934. Amebiasis and amoebic dysentery. **Dawson, J. A., W. Kessler,** and **J. Silberstein.** 1935. Mitosis in Amoeba dubia. Biol. Bul. 69. **Dobell, C.** 1914. Cytological studies on three species of Amoeba. Arch. Protistk. 34. 1919. The amoebae living in man. **Edwards, J.** 1925. Formation of food-cups in Amoeba induced by chemicals. Biol. Bul. 48. **Folger, H. T.** 1927. Response of Amoeba to mechanical shock and sudden illumination. Biol. Bul. 53. **Fortner, H.** 1934. Untersuchungen an Pelomyxa. Arch. Protistk. 83. **Gläser, H.** 1912. Über die Teilung einiger Amöben. Arch. Protistk. 25. **Greeff, R.** 1874. Pelomyxa palustris. Arch. Mikros. Anat. 10. **Grosse-Allermann, W.** 1900. Amoeba terricola. Arch. Protistk. 17. **Gruber, K.** 1912. Untersuchungen an Amoeba proteus. Arch. Protistk. 25. **Halsey, H. R.** 1936. The life cycle of Amoeba proteus and dubia. Jour. Expt. Zool. 74. **Hartmann, M.** 1910–1914. Untersuchungen über parasitische Amöben. Arch. Protistk. 18, 24, 34. **Hartmann, M.** and **K. Nägler.** 1908. Amoeba diploidea. Gesell. Naturf. Freunde. Berlin, Sitzber. 112. **Hausman, L. A.** 1920. Life History of Amoeba proteus. Biol. Bul. 38. **Heilbrunn, L. V.** 1929. Absolute viscosity of Amoeba protoplasm. Protoplasma 8. **Hogue, M.** 1914. Valkampfia. Arch. Protistk. 35; Amer. Jour. Hyg. 1. **Hopkins, D. L.** 1926. Effect of hydrogen ion concentration on Amoeba proteus. Nat. Acad. Sci. Wash., Proc. 12. 1929. Effect of the substratum and cations. Jour. Morph. 48. **Howland, R.** 1924. Dissection of the pellicle of Amoeba verrucosa. Jour. Expt. Zool. 40. **Hulpieu, H., and D. Hopkins.** 1927. Life history of Amoeba proteus. Biol. Bul. 52. **Ivanic, M.** 1925. Fortpflanzungserscheinungen einiger Süsswasseramöben. Arch. Protistk. 50. 1934. Vampyrellidium. La Cellule 43. **Janicki, C.** 1912, 1918, 1932. Paramoeba. Ztschr. Wiss. Zool. 103, 131, 142. **Jepps, M.,** and **C. Dobell.** 1918.

Dientamoeba fragilis. Parasitol. 10. **Johnson, P.** 1930. Reproduction in Amoeba proteus. Arch. Protistk. 71. **Jollos, V.** 1917. Untersuchungen zur Morphologie der Amöbenteilung. Arch. Protistk. 37. **Jones, J.** 1928. Life cycle of Amoeba proteus. Arch. Protistk. 63. **Kepner, W. A.**, and **W. H. Taliaferro.** 1913. Reactions of Amoeba proteus to food. Biol. Bul. 24. **Kessel, J. F.** 1923. Infection of rats and mice with the common intestinal amoebae of man. Calif. Univ., Pubs. Zool. 20. **Leiner, M.** 1923. Das Glycogen in Pelomyxa. Arch. Protistk. 47. **Lloyd, F.** 1927. Behavior of Vampyrella. Mich. Acad. Sci. Arts, Letters, Paper 7. **Mast, S. O.**, and **W. Doyle.** 1936. Structure, origin, and function of cytoplasmic constituents in Amoeba proteus. I, II. Arch. Protistk. 86. **Mast, S. O.**, and **W. Hahnert.** 1935. Feeding, digestion, and starvation in Amoeba proteus. Physiol. Zool. 8. **Morris, S.** 1935. Studies of Endamoeba blattae. Jour. Morph. 59. **Okado, Y.** 1930. Über den Bau und die Bewegungsweise von Pelomyxa. Arch. Protistk. 70. **Parsons, C. W.** 1926. Behavior of Amoeba proteus. Quart. Jour. Micros. Sci. 70. **Reynolds, B.**, and **J. B. Looper.** 1929. Hydramoeba hydroxena. Jour. Parasitol. 15. **Rhumbler, L.** 1898. Bewegung, Nahrungsaufnahme, Defäkation, Vacuolen-Pulsations, und Gehäusebau bei Lobosen Rhizopoden. Arch. Entwicki. Mech. Organ. 7. 1910. Die verschiedenartigen Nahrungsaufnahmen bei Amöben. Arch. Entwickl. Mech. Organ. 30. **Sanders, E. P.** 1931. Life cycle of Entamoeba ranarum. Arch. Protist. 74. **Schaeffer, A. A.** 1916. Behavior of Amoeba towards fragments of glass, carbon, etc. Biol. Bul. 31. 1916. On the feeding habits of Amoeba. Jour. Expt. Zool. 20. 1916. Characters of Amoeba proteus, A. discoides, and A. dubia. Arch. Protistk. 37. 1917. Choice of food in Amoeba. Jour. Anim. Behavior. 7. 1917. Reactions to light. Biol. Bul. 32. 1926. Taxonomy of the amebas. Carnegie Instit. Wash., Pub. 345. 1926. Recent discoveries in the biology of Amoeba. Quart. Rev. Biol. 1. **Scheel, C.** 1899. Fortpflanzung der Amöben. Festschr. von Kupffer. **Schubotz, H.** 1905. Amoeba blattae und Amoeba proteus. Arch. Protistk. 6. **Stolc, A.** 1910. Über kernlose Individuen und kernlose Teile von Amoeba. Arch. Entwickl. Mech. Organ. 29. **Swezy, O.** 1920. Endamoeba coli. Calif. Univ., Pubs. Zool. 20. **Valkampf, E.** 1905. Amoeba limax. Arch. Protistk. 5. **Willis, H. S.** 1916. Influence of the nucleus on the behavior of Amoeba. Biol. Bul. 30. **Yorke, W.**, and **A. Adams.** 1926–1927. Observations on Entamoeba histolytica. Ann. Trop. Med. Parasitol. 20, 21. **Wilson, C.** 1916. Life history of a soil amoeba. Calif. Univ., Pubs. Zool. 16.

SHELLED LOBOSA

Awerinzew, S. 1907. Die Struktur und die Chemische Zusammensetzung der Gehäuse bei den Süsswasserrhizopoden. Arch. Protistk. 8. **Belar, K.** 1921. Thecamöben der Chlamydophrys-gruppe. Arch. Protistk. 43. **Cavallini, F.** 1926. Asexual cycle in Arcella. Asexual cycle in Centropyxis. Jour. Expt. Zool. 43. **Deflandre, G.** 1928. Le genre Arcella. Arch. Protistk. 64. 1929. Le genre Centropyxis. Arch. Protistk. 67. **Elpatiewsky, W.** 1907. Zur Fortpflanzung von Arcella. Arch. Protistk. 10. **Fermor, X.** 1913. Entwicklungsgeschichte von Arcella. Arch. Protistk. 31. **Goette, A.** 1916. Lebenscyclus von Difflugia. Arch. Protistk. 37. **Hegner, R. W.** 1919–1920. Papers on heredity in Arcella. Jour. Expt. Zool. 29, 30; Genetics 4. **Hertwig, R.** 1899. Encystierung und Kernvermehrung bei Arcella. Festschr. von Kupffer. **Ivanic, M.** 1934. Zweiteilung, multiple Teilung, und Encystierung bei Euglypha. Arch. Protistk. 82. 1935. Kopulation bei Cochliopodium, Kopulation bei Süsswasserthalamaphoren im allgemeinen. Biol. Zentbl. 55. **Jennings, H. S.** 1916. Heredity, variation, selection in Difflugia. Genetics 1. **Khainsky, A.** 1910. Arcella. Arch. Protistk. 21. **Mac-**

Kinlay, R. 1936. Nebela. Roy. Micro. Soc. Jour. 56. **Martini, E.** 1905. Arcella. Ztschr. Wiss. Zool. 79. **Pateff, P.** 1926. Fortpflanzungserscheinungen bei Difflugia, Clypeolina. Arch. Protistk. 55. **Schaudinn, F.** 1899. Generationswechsel von Trichosphaerium. Kgl. Preuss. Akad. Wiss. Berlin, Anhang. **Stump, A.** 1935. Feeding of Difflugia. Biol. Bul. 69. 1936. Influence of test materials on reproduction in Pontigulasia. Biol. Bul. 70. **Swarczewsky, B.** 1908. Fortflanzungserscheinungen bei Arcella. Arch. Protistk. 12. **Zuelzer, M.** 1904. Difflugia. Arch. Protistk, 4.

FORAMINIFERA

Awerinzeff, S. 1903. Struktur der Kalkschalen mariner Rhizopoden. Ztschr. Wiss. Zool. 74. **Brady, H. B.** 1884. Report on the Foraminifera. Challenger Rpts., Zool. 9. **Carpenter, W. B., W. K. Parker, and D. R. Jones.** 1862. Introduction to the Study of the Foraminifera. Ray Society. **Cushman, J. A.** 1910. Monograph of the Foraminifera of the N. Pacific Ocean. U. S. Natl. Mus., Bul. 71. 1918. Foraminifera of the Atlantic Ocean. U. S. Natl. Mus., Bul., 104. 1920. Observations on living specimens of Iridia. U. S. Natl. Mus., Proc. 57. 1925. Introduction to the morphology and classification of the Foraminifera. Smithsn. Inst. Misc. Collect. 77. 1927. Reclassification of the Foraminifera. Cushman Lab. Foramin. Res., Contrib. 3. 1928. Foraminifera, their classification and economic use. Cushman Lab. Foramin. Res., Spec. Publ. 1. **Galloway, J. J.** 1933. A manual of the Foraminifera. **Hofker, J.** 1930. Foraminifera of the Siboga Expedition Siboga Rpt. IVa. 1930. Foraminifera des Golfes von Neapel. Staz. Zool. Napoli. Pubbl. 10. **Jepps, M.** 1926. Gromia. Quart. Jour. Micros. Sci. 70. **Lister, J. J.** 1894. Life-history of Foraminifera. Roy. Soc. London Proc. 56. 1895. Roy. Soc. London, Phil. Trans. 186 B. 1906. Brit. Assoc. Adv. Sci., Pres.. address. **Myers, E.** 1934. The life history of Patellina corrugata, a foraminifer. Bul. Scripps Inst. Oceanogr. Tech. Ser. 3, No. 15. **Rhumbler, L.** 1911–1913. Die Foraminifern der Plankton-Expedition. Ergeb. Plank. Exped., 3, Abt. L. **Schaudinn, F.** 1903. Polystomella. Arb. Kaiser. Gsndhtsamt. 19. **Winter, F. W.** 1907. Untersuchungen über Peneroplis. Arch. Protistk. 10.

HELIOZOA

Belar, K. 1921. Befruchtung von Actinophrys sol. Verh. Deut. Zool. Gesell. 26. Formwechsel von Actinophrys. Biol. Zentbl. 41. 1923–1924. Untersuchungen an Actinophrys sol. I, II. Arch. Protistk. 46, 48. **Boissevain, M.** 1908. Über Kernverhältnisee bei Actinosphaerium. Arch. Protistk. 13. **Cienkowsky, L.** 1867. Clathrulina. Arch. Mikros. Anat. 3. **Hertwig, R.** 1898. Kernteilung, Richtungskörperbildung, und Befruchtung bei Actinosphaerium. Akad. Wiss. Munich, Abhandl. Math.-Physik. Kl. 19, part III. 1904. Über physiologische Degeneration bei Actinosphaerium. Festschr. Haeckel. **Howland, R.** 1928. Grafting and reincorporation in Actinosphaerium. Biol. Bul. 54. **Looper, J. B.** 1928. Food reactions of Actinophrys. Biol. Bul. 54. **Pénard, E.** 1904. Les Héliozoaires d'eau douce. **Roskin, G.** 1925. Über die Axopodien der Heliozoa. Arch. Protistk. 52. **Rumjantzew, A., and E. Wermel.** 1925. Protoplasmabau von Actinosphaerium. Arch. Protistk. 52. **Schaudinn, F.** 1896. Über das Centralkorn der Heliozoen (Acanthocystis). Verh. Deut. Zool. Gesell. 6. **Stern, C.** 1924. Untersuchungen über Acanthocystideen. Arch. Protistk. 48. **Wetzel, A.** 1926. Zur Morphologie und Biologie von Raphidocystis. Arch. Protistk. 53.

RADIOLARIA

Borgert, A. 1909. Fortfplanzung der tripyleen Radiolarian, speciell von Aulocantha. Arch. Protistk. 14. **Brandt, K.** 1885. Die Koloniebildenden Radiolarien. Fauna Flora Golf. Neapel 13. 1902. Beiträge zur Kenntnis der Colliden. Arch. Protistk. 1. **Bütschli, O.** 1906. Chemische Natur der Skelettsubstanz der Acantharia. Zool. Anz. 30. **Cayeux, L.** Radiolaires precambriens. Soc. Géol. France, Bul., Ser. 3, Vol. 22. **Chatton, E.** 1923. Les Péridiniens parasites des Radiolaires. Acad. Sci. [Paris], Compt. Rend. 177. **Haeckel, E.** 1862, 1887. Die Radiolarien. 1887. Radiolaria collected by the Challenger. Challenger Rpts., Zool. 18. **Hertwig, R.** 1879. Der Organismus der Radiolarien. **Hovasse, R.** 1923. Les Péridiniens intracellulaires-zooxanthelles et Syndiniums-chez les Radiolaires coloniaux. Soc. Zool. France, Bul. 48. **Huth, W.** 1913. Zur Entwicklungsgeschichte der Thalassicolen. Arch. Protistk. 30. **Le Calvez, J.** 1935. Flagellispores du Radiolaire Coelodendrum. Arch. Zool. Expt. Gén. 77. **Moroff, T.** 1910. Thalassicolla. Festschr. R. Hertwig, I. **Moroff, T.,** and **G. Stiasny.** 1909. Acanthometron. Arch. Protistk. 16. **Popofsky, A.** 1904. Die Acantharien der Plankton-Expedition. Ergeb. Plank. Exped. III, f. **Schewiakoff, W.** 1902. Chemische Natur der Skelette der Radiolaria-Acanthometrea. Ztschr. Naturw. 75. 1926. Acantharia Fauna Flora Golf. Neapel 37.

FLAGELLATA

General

Alexieff, A. 1924. Sur le corps parabasal, l'axostyle, et les mitochondries chez les flagellés. Arch. Russ. Protistol. 3. **Bütschli, O.** 1906. Beiträge zur Kenntnis des Paramylons. Arch. Protistk. 7. **Dellinger, O.** 1909. The cilium as a key to the structure of contractile protoplasm. Jour. Morph. 20. **Duboscq, O., et Grassé, P.** 1933. L'appareil parabasal des flagellés. Arch. Zool. Expt. Gén. 73. **Francé, R. A.** 1893. Zur Morphologie und Physiologie der Stigmata. Ztschr. Wiss. Zool. 56. **Fritsch, F. E.** 1935. The structure and reproduction of the algae. I. **Geitler, L.** 1928. Morphologie und Entwicklungsgeschichte der Pyrenoide. Arch. Protistk. 56. **Grassé, P.** 1926. Flagellés parasites. Arch. Zool. Expt. Gén. 65. **Hausman, L. A.** 1920. Manipulation and identification of the free-swimming Mastigophora of fresh waters. Amer. Nat. 54. **Janicki, C.** 1911. Zur Kenntnis des Parabasalapparates bei parasitischen Flagellaten. Biol. Zentbl. 31. **Klebs, G.** 1883. Über die Organisation einiger Flagellatengruppen. Bot. Instit. Tübingen Untersuch. I. 1892. Flagellatenstudien. Ztschr. Wiss. Zool. 55. **Kofoid, C. A.** 1920. Intestinal protozoan infections in U. S. Army Troops. Amer. Gastroent. Assoc. Trans. **Krijgsman, B.** 1925. Beiträge zum Problem der Geisselbewegung. Arch. Protistk. 52. **Kühn, A.** 1921. Morphologie der Tiere in Bildern. I. Flagellaten. **Metzner, P.** 1920. Zur Mechanik der Geisselbewegung. Biol. Zentbl. 40. **Pascher, A.** 1914. Über Flagellaten und Algen. Ber. Deut. Bot. Gesell. 32. 1922. Morphologische Entwicklung der Flagellaten zu Algae. Ber. Deut. Bot. Gesell, 42. **Pascher, A.,** and **A. Lemmermann.** Die Süsswasser-Flora Deutschlands, Osterreiches, und der Schweiz. 2. Flagellatae. 3. Dinoflagellatae. 4. Volvocales. **Prowazek, S.** 1903. Flagellaten-Studien. Arch. Protistk. 2. **Schiller, J.** 1926. Die planktonische Vegetationen des Adriatischen Meeres. Arch. Protistk. 53. **Ulehla, V.** 1911. Ultramikroskopische Studien über Geisselbewegung. Biol. Zentbl. 31. **Wager, H.** 1899. Eyespot and flagellum of Euglena. Linn. Soc. [London] Jour. Zo.l. 27.

CHRYSOMONADINA, CRYPTOMONADINA, CHLOROMONADINA

Belar, K. 1916. Protozoenstudien II. (about Chilomonas). Arch. Protistk. 36. **Conrad, W.** 1926. Chrysomonadines. Arch. Protistk. 56. **Doflein, F.** 1917. Rhizochrysis. Zool. Jahrb. Abt. Zool. Physiol. 40. 1921. Mitteilungen über Chrysomonadinen. Zool. Anz. 53. **Haye, A.** 1930. Dinobryon. Arch. Protistk. 72. **Jennings, H. S.** 1900. Reactions of Chilomonas. Amer. Jour. Physiol. 3. **Kepner, W. A.**, and **J. Edwards.** 1916. Nucleus of Chilomonas. Biol. Bul. 31. **Korshikov, A. A.** 1929. Studies on chrysomonads. Arch. Protistk. 67. **Lohmann, H.** 1902. Die Coccolithophoridae. Arch. Protistk. 1. 1913. Über Kokkolithophoriden. Verh. Deut. Zool. Gesell. **Mast, S. O.**, et al. 1933-36. Metabolism of Chilomonas. Protoplasma. 20; Arch. Protistk. 85; Jour. Cell. Compar. Physiol. 8. **Nägler, K.** 1912. Chilomonas. Arch. Protistk. 25. **Pascher, A.** 1912. Über Rhizopoden und Palmella-stadien bei Chrysomonaden. Arch. Protistk. 25. 1925. Die braune Algenreihe der Chrysophyceen. Arch. Protistk. 52. **Poisson, R.** 1935. Observations sur une chloromonadine au genre Coelomonas. Arch. Zool. Expt. Gén. 77. **Schiller, J.** 1926. Coccolithophoraceen. Arch. Protistk. 53. **Schulz, P.** 1928. Beiträge zur Kenntnis fossiler und rezenter Silicoflagellaten. Bot. Arch. 21. **Ulehla, V.** 1911. Cyathomonas. Ber. Deut. Bot. Gesell. 29.

DINOFLAGELLATA

Apstein, C. 1906. Pyrocystis lunula. Wiss. Meeresunter. Abt. Kiel 9. 1910. Knospung bei Ceratium. Internatl. Rev. Hydrobiol. 3. **Barrows, A.** 1918. Skeletal variations in Peridinium. Calif. Univ., Pubs. Zool. 18. **Borgert, A.** 1910. Kern- und Zellteilung bei Ceratium. Arch. Protistk. 20. **Chatton, E.** 1914. Les cnidocysts der Peridinien Polykrikos. Arch. Zool. Expt. Gén. 54. 1920. Les Peridiniens parasites, morphologie, reproduction, ethologie. Arch. Zool. Expt. Gén. 59. **Cienkowski, L.** 1873. Noctiluca. Arch. Mikros. Anat. 9. **Dogiel, V.** 1906. Beiträge zur Kenntnis der Peridineen. Mitth. Zool. Sta. Neapel 18. **Entz, G.** 1921. Mitotische Teilung von Ceratium. Arch. Protistk. 43. 1925. Über Cysten und Encystierung der Süsswasser-Ceratien. Arch. Protistk. 51. 1926. On chain formation in Ceratium. Biol. Hungar. 1. Morphologie und Biologie von Peridinium. Arch. Protistk. 56. 1927. Süsswasser-Ceratien. Arch. Protistk. 58. **Fauré-Fremiet, E.** 1910. Le tentacle de la Noctiluca. Soc. Zool. France Bul. 35. **Goor, A.** 1918. Die Zytologie von Noctiluca. Arch. Protistk. 39. **Gross, F.** 1934. Biologie und Entwicklungsgeschichte von Noctiluca. Arch. Protistk. 83. **Hall, R. P.** 1925. Mitosis in Ceratium. Calif. Univ., Pubs. Zool. 28. **Harvey, E. B.** 1917. A physiological study of Noctiluca. Nat. Acad. Sci. Wash., Proc. 3. **Hertwig, R.** 1877. Über Leptodiscus medusoides. Jenaische Ztschr. 11. **Hovasse, R.**, and **G. Teissier.** 1923. Péridiniens et Zooxanthelles. Acad. Sci. Compt. Rend. 176. **Huber, G.**, and **F. Nipkow.** 1922. Die Entwicklung von Ceratium. Ztschr. Bot. 14. **Ishikawa, O.** 1894. Noctiluca. Tokyo Imp. Univ., Col. Sci., Jour. 6. **Jollos, V.** 1910. Dinoflagellaten Studien. Arch. Protistk. 19. **Jörgensen, E.** 1911. Die Ceratien. Internatl. Rev. Hydrobiol. Ser. 2, Sup. Vol. 4. **Kofoid, C. A.** 1905. Craspedotella. Mus. Compar. Zool. Harvard, Bul. 46. 1907. The plates of Ceratium. Zool. Anz. 32. The structure and systematic position of Polykrikos. Zool. Anz. 31. 1908. Exuviation, anatomy, and regeneration in Ceratium. Calif. Univ., Pubs. Zool. 4. 1909. On Peridinium steinii. Arch. Protistk. 16. 1920. A new morphological interpretation of the structure of Noctiluca. Calif. Univ., Pubs. Zool. 19. **Kofoid, C. A.**, and **T. Skogsberg.** 1928. The Dinophysoidae. Harvard Mus. Compar. Zool. Mem. 51. **Kofoid, C. A.**, and **O. Swezy.** 1921. The free-living unarmored Dinoflagellata. Calif. Univ. Mem. 5. **Lebour, M.** 1925. The dinoflagellates of northern seas. Mar. Biol. Assoc. **Lemmermann, E.** Peridiniales. Kryptogamenflora der Mark Brandenburg. 3. **Peters, N.** 1927. Das Wachstum des Peridiniumpanzers. Zool. Anz. 73. **Pratje, A.** 1921. Noctiluca, Morphologie und Physiologie. Arch. Protistk. 42. **Schütt, F.** 1895. Die Peridineen. Ergeb. Plank. Exped. 4, M, a. 1896. Peridiniales. in Engler and Prantl. Natür. Pflanzenfamilien I, Abt. I.

EUGLENOIDINA

Baker, C. L. 1933. Cytoplasmic components of Euglena. Arch. Protistk. 80. **Baker, W. B.** 1926. Life history of Euglena agilis. Biol. Bul. 51. **Bancroft, F. W.** 1913. Heliotropism, differential sensibility, and galvanotropism in Euglena. Jour. Expt. Zool. 15. **Bracher, R.** 1919. Euglena deses. Ann. Bot. [London] 33. **Bretschneider, L.** 1925. Phacus. Arch. Protistk. 53. **Brown, V. E.** 1930. Cytology and fission of Peranema. Quart. Jour. Micros. Sci. 73. **Bütschli, O.** Über Cyanophyceen (structure of flagellum). Arch. Protistk. 1. **Causey, D.** 1926. Mitochondria in Euglena. Calif. Univ., Pubs. Zool. 28. **Conrad, W.** 1934. Monographie du genre Lepocinclis. Arch. Protistk. 82. **Dangeard, P.** 1901. Recherches sur les Eugleniens. Le Botan. 8. **Deflandre, G.** 1926–1927. Monographie du genre Trachelomonas. Rev. Gén. Bot. 38, 39. **Dreżepolski, R.** 1925. Connaissance des Eugléniens de la Pologne. Kosmos [Lwow] 50. **Franzé, R.** 1893. Stigmata der Mastigophoren. Ztschr. Wiss. Zool. 56. **Gojdics, M.** 1934. Morphology and division of Euglena deses. Amer. Micros. Soc. Trans. 53. **Grassé, P.** 1925. Vacuome et appareil de Golgi des Euglénes. Acad. Sci. [Paris], Compt. Rend. 181. **Günther, F.** 1928. Bau und Lebensweise der Euglenen. Arch. Protistk. 60. **Haase, G.** 1910. Euglena sanguinea. Arch. Protistk. 20. **Hall, R. P.** 1929, 1933, 1934. Articles on Peranema. Jour. Morph. 48; Arch. Protistk. 81; Amer. Micros. Soc. Trans. 53. **Hall, R. P., and W. Powell.** 1927, 1928. Peranema. Amer. Micros. Soc. Trans. 46; Biol. Bul. 54. **Hamburger, C.** 1911. Studien über Euglena ehrenbergii. Heidelberg. Akad. Wiss. Math. Nat. Kl., Sitzber. IIB. **Hegner, R. W.** 1923. Euglenoidina in the digestive tract of tadpoles. Biol. Bul. 45. **Khawkine, W.** 1886. Recherches sur Astasia et Euglena. Ann. Sci. Nat. Ser. 6, 19, Ser. 7, 1. **Lackey, J. B.** 1929. Entosiphon and Peranema. Arch. Protistk. 66, 67. 1934. Comparison of structure and division of Distigma and Astasia. Biol. Bul. 67. **Loefer, J. B.** 1931. Heteronema acus. Arch. Protistk. 74. **Mainx, F.** 1928. Morphologie und Physiologie der Eugleninen. Arch. Protistk. 60. **Mast, S. O.** 1912. Reactions of Peranema. Jour. Anim. Behavior 2. **Prowazek, S.** 1903. Die Kerntheilung des Entosiphon. Arch. Protistk. 2. **Ratcliffe, H.** 1927. Mitosis in Euglena spirogyra. Biol. Bul. 53. **Schaeffer, A. A.** 1918. New flagellate Jenningsia. Amer. Micros. Soc. Trans. 37. **Schmitz, F.** 1884. Chromatophoren. Jahrb. Wiss. Bot. 15. **Skvortzav, B.** 1928. Gattung Phacus. Ber. Deut. Bot. Gesell. 46. **Tannreuther, G.** 1923. Nutrition and reproduction in Euglena (also Peranema). Arch. Entwickl. Mech. Organ. 52. **Ternetz, C.** 1912. Euglena gracilis. Jahrb. Wiss. Bot. 51. **Walton, L. B.** 1915. Euglenoidea of Ohio. Ohio Biol. Survey Bul. 4. **Wager, H.** 1900. Eye-spot and flagellum in Euglena. Linn. Soc. [London] Jour. Zool. 27. **Wilson, C. N.** 1928. Trachelomonas. Amer. Micros. Soc. Trans. 47. **Zumstein, H.** 1900. Euglena gracilis. Jahrb. Wiss. Bot. 34.

VOLVOCALES

Chatton, E. 1911. Pleodorina californica. Bul. Sci. France Belg. 44. **Dangeard, P.** 1900. Pandorina. Le Botan. 7. **Delsman, H.** 1918. Egg cleavage of

Volvox. Roy. Acad. Sci. Amsterdam. Proc. 21. **Doflein, F.** 1918. Polytomella agilis. Zool. Jahrb. Abteil. Anat. Ontog. Tiere. 41. **Elliott, A. M.** 1934. Haematococcus pluvialis. Arch. Protistk. 82. **France, R.** 1894. Die Polytomen. Jahrb. Wiss. Bot. 26. **Goroschankin, J.** 1891. Chlamydomonas. Soc. Imper. Natur. Moscow, Bul. 4, 5. **Harper, R. A.** 1912. Colony in Gonium. Amer. Micros. Soc. Trans. 31. **Hartmann, M.** 1918–1924. Formwechsel der Phytomonadinen (Eudorina). Arch. Protistk. 39, 43, 49. **Janet, C.** 1922. Le Volvox. **Klein, L.** 1889. Volvox. Ber. Deut. Bot. Gesell. 7; Jahrb. Wiss. Bot. 20. **Kofoid, C. A.** 1898. Pleodorina illinoisensis. 1899. Platydorina. Ill. Nat. Hist. Survey, Bul. 5. **Kuschakewitsch, S.** 1931. Entwicklungsgeschichte von Volvox. Arch. Protistk. 73. **Lander, C.** 1929. Oögenesis and fertilization in Volvox. Bot. Gaz. 87. **Mainx, F.** 1929. Geschlechterverteilung bei Volvox. Arch. Protistk. 67. **Mast, S. O.** 1907, 1916, 1926, 1927. Papers on light reactions and eye spots of Volvocales. Jour. Compar. Neurol. 17; Jour. Expt. Zool. 20; Ztschr. Vergleich. Physiol. 4; Arch. Protistk. 20. **Merton, H.** 1908. Pleodorina. Ztschr. Wiss. Zool. 90. **Meyer, A.** 1896. Plasmaverbindungen und Membranen von Volvox. Bot. Ztg. 54. **Oltmanns, F.** 1904–1905. Morphologie und Biologie der Algen. I. Volvocales. **Overton, E.** 1889. Volvox. Bot. Zentlbl. 39. **Pocock, M. A.** 1933. Volvox in S. Africa. So. African Mus. Ann. 16. **Powers, J. H.** 1907, 1908. New species of Volvox. Amer. Micros. Soc. Trans. 27, 28. **Ryder, J.** 1889. Polar differentiation of Volvox. Amer. Nat. 23. **Schreiber, E.** 1925. Physiologie und Sexualität höher Volvocales. Ztschr. Bot. 17. **Shaw, W.** 1894. Pleodorina. Bot. Gaz. 19. **Zimmermann, W.** 1920. Entwicklungsgeschichte und Zytologie von Volvox. Jahrb. Wiss. Bot. 60. 1925. Ungeschlechtliche Entwicklung von Volvox. Naturwissenschaften 13.

PROTOMONADINA

Balfour, A. 1906. Herpetomonas parasites in fleas. Jour. Hyg. 6. **Basile, C.** 1921. Leishmania, Herpetomonas, and Crithidia in fleas. Parasitol. 12. **Becker, E. R.** 1923. Papers on Crithidia and Herpetomonas. Jour. Parasitol. 9. **Berliner, E.** 1909. Flagellaten Studien. Arch. Protistk. 15. **Boeck, W. C.** 1917, 1919. Giardia microti. Calif. Univ., Pubs. Zool. 18, 19. **Bresslau, E., and L. Scremin.** 1924. Die Kerne der Trypanosomen und ihr Verhaltnis zur Nuclealreaktion. Arch. Protistk. 48. **Bruce, D.,** et al. 1910–1914. Trypanosome diseases of domestic animals in Uganda, in Nyassaland. Roy. Soc. London, Proc., Ser. B. 82, 83, 87, 88. **Burck, C.** 1909. Choanoflagellaten. Arch. Protistk. 16. **Chatton, E., and A. Leger.** 1911. Eutrypanosomes, leptomonas et leptotrypanosomes chez Drosophila. Soc. Biol. [Paris] Compt. Rend. 70. **Coventry, F.** 1925. Reaction product which inhibits reproduction of Tryp. lewisi. Amer. Jour. Hyg. 5, further 12. **De Saedeleer, H.** 1927, 1929. Craspédomonadines. Soc. Roy. Belg. Ann. 58, Rec. Inst. Zool. Torley-Rousseau 2. **Dobell, C. C.** 1908. Structure and life-history of Copromonas. Quart. Jour. Micros. Sci. 52. **Donovan, C.** 1913. Kala-azar, its distribution and probable mode of infection. Indian Jour. Med. Res. 1. **Duke, H. L.** 1914. Wild game as a trypanosome reservoir. Arch. Protistk. 32. **Ellis, W.** 1929. Researches on Choanoflagellata. Soc. Roy. Zool. Belg. Ann. 60. **Fantham, H. B.** 1912. Herpetomonas pediculi. Ann. Trop. Med. Parasitol. 6. 1926. Latex herpetomonads. Linn. Soc. [London] Proc. 138. **Franca, C.** 1914, 1920. La flagellose des Euphorbes. Arch. Protistk. 34, Inst. Pasteur, [Paris], Ann. 34. **Franchini, G.** 1922. Trypanosomes des euphorbes. Bul. Soc. Path. Exot. 15. **Geiger, A.** et al. 1930. The glycolytic power of trypanosomes. Ann. Trop. Med. Parasitol. 23, 24. **Hartmann, M., and W. Nöller.** 1918. Tryp. theileri. Arch. Protistk. 38. **Hoare, C.** 1923. Exper. study of sheep trypanosome.

Parasitol. 15. **Kühn, A.** 1915. Bodo edax. Arch. Protistk. 35. **Lapage, G.** 1925. Notes on the choanoflagellate Codosiga. Quart. Jour. Micros. Sci. 69. **Laveran, A.** 1917. Leishmanioses. **Mesnil, F.** 1912. Trypanosomes et trypanosomiasis. **Martin, C.** 1913. Intestinal trypanoplasmas of fishes. Quart. Jour. Micros. Sci. 59. **McCulloch, I.** 1915. Papers on Crithidias. Calif. Univ., Pubs. Zool. 16, 18, 19. **Minchin, E. A.** 1908. Development of trypanosomes in the tsetse-flies. Quart. Jour. Micros. Sci. 52. 1909. The structure of Trypanosoma lewisi. Quart. Jour. Micros. Sci. 53. 1909. Flagellates parasitic in the blood of fresh-water fishes. Soc. Zool. London, Proc. 1. **Minchin, E. A.,** and **J. D. Thomson.** 1915. The rat trypanosome and its relation to the rat flea. Quart. Jour. Micros. Sci. 60. **Nöller, W.** 1913. Die Blutprotozoen des Wasserfrosches. Arch. Protistk. 31. **Novy, G.,** and **MacNeal, W. J.** 1905. On the trypanosomas of birds. Jour. Infect. Dis. 2. **Ogawa, M.** 1913. Trypanosomen des Frosches. Arch. Protistk. 29. **Patton, W. S.** 1909–1922. Papers on Herpetomonas, Crithidia, Rhynchoidomonas. Arch. Protistk. 12, 15; Indian Jour. Med. Res. 8, 9; Bul. Soc. Path. Exot. 3. 1922. Kala-azar and oriental sore problem. Indian Jour. Med. Res. 9. **Porter, A.** 1909. Papers on Herpetomonas and Crithidia. Parasitol. 2, 4, 7; Quart. Jour. Micros. Sci. 65. **Reynolds, B.** 1927. Bicosoeca kepneri. Amer. Micros. Soc. Trans. 46. 1934. Observations on Monas vestita. Arch. Protistk. 81. **Robertson, M.** 1913. Life history of Trypanosoma gambiense. Roy. Soc. London, Phil. Trans., Ser. B. 203. **Roskin, G.,** and **S. Schischliaiewa.** 1928. Die Kernteilung bei Trypanosomen. Arch. Protistk. 60. **Soule, M. H.** 1925. Respiration of Tryp. lewisi and Leishmania tropica. Jour. Infect. Dis. 36. **Taliaferro, W. H.** 1926. Host resistance and types of infection in trypanosomiasis and malaria. Quart. Rev. Biol. 1. 1926. Variability and inheritance of size in Tryp. lewisi. Jour. Expt. Zool. 43. **Wenyon, C. M.** 1913. Observations on Herpetomonas muscae-domesticae. Arch. Protistk. 31. 1922. Leishmaniasis. Trop. Dis. Bul. 19. **Yamasaki, S.** 1924. Leptomonas ctenocephali Tryp. lewisi und pathogene Trypanosomenarten im Hundefloh. Arch. Protistk. 48

POLYMASTIGINA

Andrews, J. M. 1925. Morphology and mitosis in Trichomonas termopsidis. Biol. Bul. 49. **Belar, K.** 1921. Protozoen Studien III. Arch. Protistk. 43. **Bunting, M.** and **D. H. Wenrich.** 1929. Amoeboid and flagellate phases of Tetramitus. Jour. Morph. 47. **Cleveland, L. R.** 1928. Tritrichomonas of man. Amer. Jour. Hyg. 8. **Connell, F. H.** 1932. Gigantomonas, a trichomonad from Kalotermes. Calif. Univ., Pubs. Zool. 37. **Fedorowa, T.** 1923. Pyrsonympha und Dinenympha. Arch. Russ. Protistol. 2. **Geiman, Q.** 1935. Chilomastix of man and other mammals. Jour. Morph. 57. **Hegner, R. W.** 1923– . Papers on Giardia, Trichomonas and Chilomastix. Amer. Jour. Hyg. 2, 3, 4, 5, 7, 8. Jour. Parasitol. 2, 14. **Hinshaw, H.** 1926. Morphology and mitosis of Trichomonas buccalis Calif. Univ., Pubs. Zool. 29. **Janicki, C.** 1915. Die Gattungen Devescovina, Parajoenia, Stephanonympha, Calonympha. Ztschr. Wiss. Zool. 112. **Kirby, H.** 1924. Morphology and mitosis of Dinenympha. Calif. Univ., Pubs. Zool. 26. 1927. Staurojoenina. Calif. Univ., Pubs. Zool. 29. 1933. Comparative morphology of devescovinid flagellates of termites. Jour. Parasitol. 20. **Kofoid, C. A.** 1920. Nomenclature of human intestinal flagellates. Calif. Univ., Pubs. Zool. 20. **Kofoid, C. A.,** and **O. Swezy.** 1920. Morphology and mitosis of Chilomastix mesnili. Calif. Univ., Pubs. Zool. 20. 1926. Proboscidiella. Calif. Univ., Pubs. Zool. 28. **Powell, W. N.** 1928. Morphology of Pyrsonympha. Calif. Univ., Pubs. Zool. 31. **Reuling, T.** 1921. Morphologie von Trichomonas vaginalis. Arch. Protistk. 42. **Wenrich, D. H.** 1921. Structure and division of Trichomonas muris. Jour. Morph. 36.

HYPERMASTIGINA

Cleveland, L. R. 1925. Toxicity of oxygen for Protozoa. Biol. Bul. 48. 1925. Method by which Trichonympha ingests solid particles oi wood. Biol. Bul. 48. 1928. Symbiosis between termites and their intestinal Protozoa. Biol. Bul. 54. 1934. The wood-feeding roach Cryptocercus, its Protozoa, and the symbiosis between Protozoa and the roach. Amer. Acad. Arts Sci., Mem. 17. 1935. Centrioles in Pseudotrichonympha. Biol. Bul. 69. 1938. Longitudinal and transverse fission in flagellates. Biol. Bul. 74. **Cutter, D.** 1920. Joenopsis. Quart. Jour. Micros. Sci. 64. **Duboscq, O.** 1928. Protistes parasites des termites du France. V. Spirotrichonympha. Arch. Zool. Expt. Gén. 67. **Duboscq, O.,** and **P. Grassé.** 1924–1925. Protistes parasites des termites du France. Soc. Biol. Compt. Rend. 90, 92, 93. Acad. Sci. [Paris] Compt. Rend. 180. 1927. Flagellés de Calotermes. Arch. Zool. Expt. Gén. 66. **Kirby, H.** 1926. Intestinal flagellates of Cryptotermes. Calif. Univ., Pubs. Zool. 29. 1932. Genus Trichonympha. Calif. Univ., Pubs. Zool. 37. **Koidsumi, M.** 1921. Intestinal Protozoa found in the termites of Japan. Parasitol. 13. **Kofoid, C. A.** and **O. Swezy.** 1919. Parasites of the termites. Calif. Univ., Pubs. Zool. 20. **Kudo, R.** 1926. Lophomonas blattarum. Arch. Protistk. 53. **Leidy, J.** 1877. Intestinal parasites of Termes flavipes. Acad. Nat. Sci. Phila., Proc. 29. 1881. Parasites of the termites. Acad. Nat. Sci. Phila., Jour. 8. **Mackinnon, D.** 1926. Holomastigotoides. Quart. Jour. Micros. Sci. 70. **Porter, J. F.** 1897. Trichonympha and other parasites of Termes. Harvard Univ., Mus. Compar. Zool. Bul. 31.

RHIZOMASTIGINA

Becker, E. R. 1928. Streaming and polarity in Mastigina. Biol. Bul. 54. **Calkins, G. N.** 1901. Some Protozoa from Van Cortlandt Park, N. Y. Amer. Nat. 35. **Goldschmidt, R.** 1907. Lebensgeschichte der Mastigamöben, Mastigella, Mastigina. Arch. Protistk. Sup. 1. **Klug, C.** 1936. Gattungen Mastigamoeba, Mastigella, Cercobodo, Tetramitus, Trigomonas. Arch. Protistk. 87.

SPOROZOA

General

Auerbach, M. 1910. Die Cnidosporidien. **Joyet-Lavergne, P.** 1931. La sexualisation cytoplasmique. Rev. Gén. Sci. 42. **Naville, A.** 1931. Les sporozoaires. Soc. Hist. Nat. Genéve, Mem. 41.

GREGARINIDA

Berndt, A. 1902. Kenntnis der im Darme der Larve von Tenebrio lebenden Gregarinen. Arch. Protistk. 1. **Bhatia, B.** 1924. Mode of infection of earthworms by monocystid parasites. Roy. Micros. Soc. Jour. **Brasil, L.** 1905. Monocystidées. Arch. Zool. Expt. Gén. Ser. 4, Vols. 3, 4. **Bütschli, O.** 1881. Zur Kenntnis der Gregarinen. Ztschr. Wiss. Zool. 35. **Crawley, H.** 1902. Progressive movements of gregarines. Acad. Nat. Sci. Phila., Proc. 54. **Fantham, H. B.** 1908. The schizogregarines. Parasitol. 1. **Hesse, E.** 1909. Monocystidées des oligochaetes. Arch. Zool. Expt. Gén. Ser. 5, Vol. 3. **Hoffmann, R.** 1909. Über Fortpflanzungerscheinungen von Monocystiden der Lumbricus. Arch. Protistk. 13. **Jameson, A.** 1920. The chromosome cycle of gregarines. Quart. Jour. Micros. Sci. 64. **Kamm, M.** 1922. Synopsis of the polycystid gregarines of the world. Ill. Biol. Monog. 7. **Kuschakewitsch, S.** 1907. Gregarinen des Mehlwurmdarm. Arch. Protistk. Sup. 1. **Léger, L.** 1892. Recherches sur les gregarines. Tablettes

Zool. 3. 1906. Le genre Ophrocystis. Arch. Protistk. 8. 1909. Le genre Schizocystis. Arch. Protistk. 18. **Leger, L.**, and **O. Duboscq.** 1910. Selenococcidium. Arch. Zool. Expt. Gén. Ser. 5, Vol. 5. 1915. Spirocystis. Arch. Protistk. 35. **Lühe, M.** 1904. Bau und Entwicklung der Gregarinen. Arch. Protistk. 4. **Martiis, L.** 1927. Sul miocito e sui movimenti delle Gregarine Monocistidae. Arch. Protistk. 58. **Mühl, D.** 1921. Morphologie und Physiologie der Mehlwurmgregarinen. Arch. Protistk. 43. **Mulsow, K.** 1911. Monocystis rostrata. Arch. Protistk. 22. **Prell, H.** 1921. Die Bewegung der Gregarinen. Arch. Protistk. 42. **Ray, H.** 1930. Gregarines of the genus Selenidium. Parasitol. 22. **Schellack, C.** 1912. Die Gregarinen. in Prowazek and Nöller Handb. path. Protozoen. **Schwarczewsky, B.** 1910. Lankesteria sp. in Turbellarien des Baikalsees. Festschr. R. Hertwig. I. **Siedlicki, M.** 1899. Monocystis ascidiae (Lankesteria). Acad. Sci. Cracovie. Bul. **Troisi, R.** 1933. Acephaline gregarines of some oligochaete annelids. Amer. Micros. Soc. Trans. 52. **Vandel, A.** 1921. Lankesteria planariae. Soc. Biol. Compt. Rend. 84. **Wasielewski, T.** 1904. Studien und Mikrophotogramme zur Kenntnis der pathogenen Protozoen. I. Coccidien. **Watson, M.** 1916. Studies on gregarines. Ill. Biol. Monog. 2.

Coccidia

Andrews, J. M. 1926. Coccidiosis in mammals. Amer. Jour. Hyg. 6. **Becker, E. R.** 1935. Coccidia and coccidiosis of domesticated, game, and laboratory animals and man. **Dobell, C.** 1919. Coccidia parasitic in man. Parasitol. 11. 1925. Life history and chromosome cycle of Aggregata eberthi. Parasitol. 17. 1926. Species of Isospora in man. Parasitol. 18. **Greiner, J.** 1921. Gametenbildung und Befruchtung von Adelea ovata. Zool. Jahrb., Abt. Anat. Ontog. Tiere 42. **Hadley, P.** 1911. Eimeria avium. Arch. Protistk. 23. **Henry, D.** 1932. Coccidiosis of the guinea pig. Calif. Univ., Pubs. Zool. 37. **Metzner, R.** 1903. Coccidium cuniculi. Arch. Protistk. 2. **Miller, W. W.** 1908. Hepatozoon. Hyg. Lab. Bul. Wash. 46. **Moroff, T.** 1908. Die bei den Cephalopoden vorkommenden Aggregata Arten. Arch. Protistk. 11. **Mowry, H.** 1935. Exogenous cycle of Eimeria carinii. Amer. Micros. Soc. Trans. 54. **Naville, A.** 1925. Cycle sporogonique des Aggregata. Rev. Suisse Zool. 32. **Nöller, W.** 1912. Lankesterella. Arch. Protistk. 24. 1913. Die Blutprotozoen des Wasserfrosches. Arch. Protistk. 31. 1920. Befruchtung und Sporogonie von Lankestrella. Arch. Protistk 41. **Pérard, C.** 1924. Coccidies et les coccidioses du lapin. Inst. Pasteur [Paris], Ann. 38, 39. **Pixell-Goodrich, H.** 1914. Sporogony and systematic position of the Aggregatidae. Quart. Jour. Micros. Sci. 60. **Reichenow, E.** 1910. Haemogregarina stepanowi. Arch. Protistk. 20. 1912. Die Haemogregarinen. Prowazek-Nöller Handbuch. Path. Protozoen. 2. 1913. Karyolysus lacertae. Arb. Kaiser. Gsndhts. Amte 45. 1919. Karyolysus und Schellackia. Sitzber. Gesell. Naturf. Freunde Berlin. 1921. Die Hämococcidien der Eidechsen. Arch. Protistk. 42. 1921. Die Coccidien. Prowazek-Nöller Handbuch. Path. Protozoen 3. **Sambon, L.**, and **C. Seligmann.** 1907. Haemogregarines of snakes. Trans. Pathol. Soc. London. 58. **Schaudinn, F.** 1900. Generationswechsel der Coccidien. Zool. Jahrb. Abt. Anat. 13. **Schellack, C.** 1913. Adelina. Arb. Kaiser. Gsndhts. Amte 45. **Shellack, C.**, and **Reichenow, E.** 1915. Adela ovata. Arb. Kaiser. Gsndhts. Amte 48. **Thomson J.**, and **A. Robertson.** 1926. Passage of fish coccidea through the human intestine. Brit. Med. Jour. 1. **Tyzzer, E.** 1929. Coccidiosis in domestic birds. Amer. Jour. Hyg. 10. Coccidiosis in gallinaceous birds. Amer. Jour. Hyg. 10. **Wenyon, C. M.** 1926. Coccidiosis of cats and dogs and the status of the Isospora of man. Ann. Trop. Med. Parasitol. 17; Parasitol. 18.

HAEMOSPORIDIA

Adie, H. 1924. The sporogony of Haemoproteus columbae. Bul. Soc. Pathol. Exot. 17. Aragao, H. 1908. Haemoproteus columbae. Arch. Protistk. 12. Boyd, G. 1925. Course of infections with Plasmodium precox. Amer. Jour. Hyg. 5. Breinl, A., and E. Hindle. 1908. Morphology and life history of Piroplasma canis. Ann. Trop. Med. Parasitol. 2. Brumpt, E. 1920. Les Piroplasmes des bovidés. Bul. Soc. Path. Exot. 13. 1924. Les Theileries. Ann. Parasitol. Humaine. Compar. 2. Dennis, E. 1932. Life cycle of Babesia bigemina of Texas cattle-fever in the tick. Calif. Univ., Pubs. Zool. 36. Gonder, R. 1911. Theileria und Babesia. Arch. Protistk. 21. Grassi, B. 1901. Die Malaria. Hartman, E. 1927. Three species of bird malaria, P. precox, P. cathemerium, P. inconstans. Arch. Protistk. 60. 1929. Asexual cycle in Leucocytozoon. Jour. Parasitol. 15. Hegner, R. et al. 1919. Experimental studies of bird malaria. Quart. Rev. Biol. 4. Hintze, R. 1901. Lankesterella. Zool. Jahrb., Abt. Anat. Ontog. Tiere. 15. Huff, C. 1927. Infectivity of plasmodia of birds for mosquitoes. Amer. Jour. Hyg. 7. Huff, C. and W. Bloom. 1935. A malarial parasite infecting all blood and blood-forming cells of birds. Jour. Infect. Dis. 57. Nocht, B., and M. Mayer, 1918. Die Malaria. Neumann, R. 1909. Die Übertragung von Plasm. precox auf Kanarienvogel und die Entwicklung der Parasiten im Magen und der Speicheldrüsen diser Stechmühe. Arch. Protistk. 13. Nuttall, G. 1913. Piroplasmosis. Parasitol. 6. Nuttall, G., and G. Graham-Smith. 1904–1907. Canine piroplasmosis. Jour. Hyg. [London] 2, 6, 7. O'Roke, E. 1930. Morphology, transmission, and life history of Haemoproteus lophortyx. Calif. Univ., Pubs. Zool. 36. 1934. A malaria-like disease of ducks caused by leucocytozoon. Mich. Univ., School Forestry Conserv. Bul. 4. Regandanz, P., and E. Reichenow. 1931. Die Entwicklung von Babesia canis in Dermacentor. Arch. Protistk. 79. Ross, R. 1898. Report on the cultivation of Proteosoma in grey mosquitoes (discovery of mosquito cycle of malarial parasite). Indian Med. Gaz. 33. Schaudinn, F. 1902. Plasmodium vivax. Arb. kaiser. Gsndhts. Amte 19. Smith, T., and F. Kilbourne. 1893. Investigations into the nature, causation, and prevention of Texas or southern cattle-fever. U. S. Bur. Anim. Indus. Ann. Rpt. 8, 9. Taliaferro, L. G. 1925–1928. Papers on bird malaria. Amer. Jour. Hyg. 5; Jour. Prev. Med. [London] 2. Taliaferro, W. H. 1929. The immunology of the parasitic infections. Taliaferro, W. H., and L. G. Taliaferro. 1934. Plasmodium brasilianum in monkeys. Amer. Jour. Hyg. 20. Taliaferro, W. H. et al. Papers on bird malaria. Jour. Prev. Med. [London] 2, 3, 5. Amer. Jour. Hyg. 2. Yakimoff, W. 1931. Revision der Gattung Piroplasma. Arch. Protistk. 74.

MYXOSPORIDIA

Awerinzew, S. 1908. Die Sporenbildung bei Ceratomyxa drepanopsettae. Arch. Protistk. 14. 1911. Sporenbildung bei Myxidium. Arch. Protistk. 23. Davis, H. S. 1917. Myxosporidia of the Beaufort region. U. S. Bur. Fisheries, Bul. 35. Keysselitz, G. 1908. Myxobolus pfeifferi. Arch. Protistk. 11. Kudo, R. 1919. Studies on Myxosporidia. Ill. Biol. Monog. 5. Papers on Myxosporidia in Jour. Parasitol. 3, 4, 5. 1933. A taxonomic consideration of Myxosporidia. Amer. Micros. Soc. Trans. 52. Mavor, J. W. 1916. Parasite of the pike, Myxidium lieberkühni. Biol. Bul. 31. Schröder, O. 1910. Sphaeromyxa. Arch. Protistk. 19. Schuurmans-Stekhoven, J. 1920. Die Gattung Myxobolus. Arch. Protistk. 31. Thélohan, P. 1895. Recherches sur les Myxosporidies. Bull. Sci. France Belg. 26.

ACTINOMYXIDIA

Caullery, M., and **F. Mesnil.** 1905. Recherches sur les Actinomyxidies. Arch. Protistk. 6. **Granata, L.** 1925. Gli attinomissidi. Arch. Protistk. 50. **Ikeda, I.** 1912. Life history of Tetractinomyxon. Arch. Protistk. 25. **Léger, L.** 1904. Sur le genre Triactinomyxon et les Actinomyxidies. Soc. Biol. [Paris], Compt. Rend. 56. **Mackinnan, D.,** and **D. Adam.** 1924. Life history of Triactinomyxon. Quart. Jour. Micros. Sci. 68.

MICROSPORIDIA

Cépède, C. 1924. Mrazekia piscicola, parasite du Gadus. Soc. Zool. France Bul. 49. **Fantham, H. B.,** and **A. Porter.** 1912. Microsporidiosis, a protozoal disease of bees due to Nosema apis. Ann. Trop. Med. Parasitol. 6. **Hertwig, M.** 1923. Ventriculus of the honey-bee with reference to infection with Nosema apis. Jour. Parasitol. 9. **Korke, V.** 1914. On a Nosema parasitic in the dog flea. Indian Jour. Med. Res. 3. **Kudo, R.** 1916. Structure and life history of Nosema bombycis. Imp. Seric. Expt. Sta. Japan, Bul. 1. 1920. Structure of some microsporidian spores. Jour. Parasitol. 6. 1922. Microsporidia parasitic in mosquitoes. Jour. Parasitol. 8. Thélohania. Arch. Protistk. 49; Jour. Parasitol. 11. 1924. Biologic and taxonomic study of the Microsporidia. Ill. Biol. Monog. 9. **Léger, L.,** and **E. Hesse.** 1906. Sur la structure de la spore des microsporidies. Soc. Biol. [Paris] Compt. Rend. 79. 1924. Microsporidies nouvelles parasites des animaux. Trav. Lab. Pisc. Grenoble Univ., Ann. 14. **Mattes, O.** 1928. Thélohania. Ztschr. Wiss. Zool. 132. **Stempell, W.** 1909. Über Nosema bombycis. Arch. Protistk. 16.

SARCOSPORIDIA

Alexieff, A. 1913. Recherches sur les Sarcosporidies. Arch. Zool. Expt. Gén. 51. **Babudieri, B.** 1932. I. Sarcosporidi e le Sarcosporidosi. Arch. Protistk. 76. **Bertram, A.** 1892. Beiträge zur Kenntnis der Sarcosporidien. Zool. Jahrb. Abt. Anat. Ontog. Tiere 5. **Erdmann, R.** 1910. Entwicklung der Sarcocystis muris. Gesell. Naturf. Freunde Berlin, Sitzber. **Hahn, C. A.** 1913. Sporozoan parasites of certain fishes. U. S. Bur. Fisheries Bul. 33. **Moroff, T.** 1915. Zur Kenntnis der Sarcosporidia. Arch. Protistk. 35. **Scott, J. W.** 1930. The Sarcosporidia, a critical review. Jour. Parasitol. 16.

HAPLOSPORIDIA

Caullery, M., and **F. Mesnil.** 1905. Recherches sur les Haplosporidies. Arch. Zool. Expt. Gén. Ser. 4, Vol. 4. **Debaisieux, P.** 1920. Haplosporidium chitonis, H. nemertis, et le groupe des Haplosporidies. La Cellule 30. **Granata, L.** 1914. Ciclo evolutivo di Haplosporidium limnodrili. Arch. Protistk. 35. **King, E.** 1926. Haplosporidium chitonis. Quart. Jour. Micros. Sci. 70. **Pixell-Goodrich, H.** 1915. Minchinia, a haplosporidian. Zool. Soc. London, Proc. 2.

CILIATA

General

Alverdes, F. 1938. Die Marburger Untersuchungen über das Lernvermögen nieder Tiere. Zool. Anz. Sup. 11. **Becker, E. R.,** and **M. Talbot.** 1927. The protozoan fauna of the rumen and reticulum of American cattle. Iowa State Col. Jour. Sci. 1. **Biggar, R.** 1932. Studies on ciliates from Bermuda sea-urchins.

Jour. Parasitol. 18. **Brodsky, A.** 1924. Die Trichocysten der Infusorien. Arch. Russ. Protistol. 3. **Buisson, J.** 1923. Les Infusoires ciliès du tube digestif de l'homme et des mammifères. Paris. **Bullington, W.** 1925. Spiral movement in ciliate Infusoria. Arch. Protistk. 50. **Buytendijk, F. J.** 1919. Acquisition d'habitudes par des êtres unicellulaires. Arch. Néerl. Physiol. Homme Anim. 3. **Chambers, R., and J. A. Dawson.** 1925. Structure of the undulating membrane in Blepharisma. Biol Bul. 48. **Chatton, E.** 1911. Ciliés parasites des Cestes et des Pyrosomes. Arch. Zool. Expt. Gén. Ser. 5, Vol. 8. **Chatton, E., and A. Lwoff, and M. Lwoff,** L'origine infraciliare et la genèse des trichocysts et des trichites chez les ciliés Foettingeriidae. Acad. Sci. [Paris], Compt. Rend. 193. **Cuénot, L.** 1891. Protozoaires commensaux et parasites des echinodermes. Rev. Biol. France Nord 3, 4. **Dangeard, P.** 1900. Les zoochlorelles du Par. bursaria. Le Botan. 7. **Dawson, J. A.** 1919. Experimental study of an amicronucleate Oxytricha. Jour. Expt. Zool. 29. **Enriques, P.** 1907. La conjugazione e il differenziamento sessuale negli Infusori. Arch. Protistk. 9. **Gelei, J.** 1926. Zur Kenntnis des Wimperapparates. Zeit. Gesam. Anat. Abt. I, vol. 81. 1929. Sensorischer Basalapparat der Tastborsten. Zool. Anz. 83. 1932. Die reizleitenden Elemente der Ciliaten. Arch. Protistk. 77. 1933. Tastborsten bei den Ciliaten. Arch. Protistk. 80. **Gray, J.** 1928. Ciliary movement. **Hetherington, E.** 1933. Culture of some holotrichous ciliates. Arch. Protistk. 80. **Hsiung, T. S.** 1930. Monograph on the Protozoa of the large intestine of the horse. Iowa State Col. Jour. Sci. 4. **Jennison, M., and J. Bunker.** 1934. Analysis of the movement of cilia by high-speed photography. Jour. Cell. Compar. Physiol. 5. **Jacobsen, I.** 1931. Fibrilläre Differenzierungen bei Ciliaten. Arch. Protistk. 75. **Kahl, A.** 1933–1934. Ciliata entocommensalia et parasitica-ciliata libera et ectocommensalia in Die Tierwelt der Nord- und Ost-See (ed. by G. Grimpe). Teil II, C3, C4. 1935. Die freilebenden und ektocommensalen Infusorien in Die Tierwelt Deutschlands (ed. by F. Dahl). **Klein, B. M.** 1927. Die Silberliniensystem der Ciliaten. Arch. Protistk. 58; 65. 1932. Das Ciliensystem in seine Bedeutung für Lokomotion, Koordination und Formbildung. Ergeb. Biol. 8. **Krüger, F.** 1936. Die Trichocysten der Ciliaten im Dunkelfeldbild. Zoologica 34. **Lepsi, J.** 1926. Die Infusorien des Susswassers und Meeres. **Loefer, J.** 1936. Bacteria-free culture of Par. bursaria. Jour. Expt. Zool. 72. **Lund, E. E.** 1935. Correlation of the silver line and neuromotor apparatus of Par. Calif. Univ., Pubs. Zool. 39. **Maier, H.** 1903. Über den feineren Bau der Wimperapparate. Arch. Protistk. 2. **Maupas, E.** 1888. Recherches expér. sur la multiplication des Infusoires ciliés. Arch. Zool. Expt. Gén. Ser. 2, Vol. 6. **Mitrophanow, P.** 1905. Trichocysts des Paramécies. Arch. Protistk. 5. **Pénard, E.** 1922. Études sur les Infusoires d'eau douce. **Peschkowsky, L.** 1927. Skelettgebilde bei Infusorien. Arch. Protistk. 57. **Pickard, E.** 1927. Neuromotor apparatus of Boveria teredinidi. Calif. Univ., Pubs. Zool. 29. **Rammelmeyer, H.** 1931. Biologie einiger Raubeninfusorien. Arch. Protistk. 73. **Schuberg, A.** 1905. Über Cilien und Trichocysten. Arch. Protistk. 6. **Taylor, C. V.** 1923. Removal of micronucleus. Science 58. **Ten Kate, C.** 1927. Fibrillensystem der Ciliaten. Arch. Protistk. 57. **Wetzel, A.** 1925. Vergleichend cytologische Untersuchungen an Ciliaten. Arch. Protistk. 51. **Woodruff, L. L.** 1921. Micronucleate and amicronucleate races of Infusoria. Jour. Expt. Zool. 34. 1925. The physiological significance of conjugation and endomixis in the Infusoria. Amer. Nat. 59. 1926. Eleven thousand generations of Paramecium. Quart. Rev. Biol. 1. 1935. Physiological significance of conjugation in Blepharisma. Jour. Expt. Zool. 70. **Woodruff, L. L., and G. Raitsell.** 1911. Rhythms in the reproductive activities of Infusoria. Jour. Expt. Zool. 11.

PROTOCILIATA

Gatenby, J. B., and S. D. King. 1925. Opalina ranarum a flagellate. Nature [London] 116. Metcalf, M. M. 1907. Excretory organs of Opalina. Arch. Protistk. 10. 1909. Opalina. Arch. Protistk. 13. 1923. Opalinid ciliate Infusorians. U. S. Natl. Mus. Bul. 120. 1928. The Opalinidae and their significance. Nat. Acad. Sci. Wash., Proc. 15.

HOLOTRICHA

Beers, C. D. 1926. Life cycle in Didinium nasutum. Jour. Morph. 42. Amer. Nat. 63. Bozler, E. 1924. Über die Morphologie der Ernährungsorganelle und die Physiologie der Nahrungsaufnahme bei Paramecium. Arch. Protistk. 49. Brown, V. E. 1930. Neuromotor apparatus of Par. Arch. Zool. Expt. Gén. 70. Brumpt, E. 1913. Conjugaison d'Anoplophrya. Arch. Parasit. 16. Buschkiel, A. 1911. Ichthyophthirius. Arch. Protistk. 21. Calkins, G. N. 1915. Didinium. Jour. Expt. Zool. 19. Calkins, G. N., and S. W. Cull. 1907. The conjugation of Par. caudatum. Arch. Protistk. 10. Causey, D. 1926. Mitochondria in ciliates. Calif. Univ., Pubs. Zool. 28. Cépède, C. 1910. Infusoires astomes. Arch. Zool. Expt. Gén. Ser. 5, Vol. 3. Chatton, E., and M. Chatton. 1925. La conjugaison du Glaucoma. Acad. Sci. [Paris], Compt. Rend. 180. 1931. La conjugaison du Par. caudatum. Acad. Sci. [Paris], Compt. Rend. 193. Chatton, E., and A. Lwoff. 1935. Les Ciliés Apostomes. 1935. Arch. Zool. Expt. Gén. 77. Cheissin, E. 1930. Astomata aus dem Baikalsee. 1931. Ancistridae und Boveridae. Arch. Protistk. 70, 73. Cleveland, L. R. 1927. Encystment of Par. in the rectum of frogs. Science 66. Dain, L. 1930. Die Conjugation von Cryptochilum. Arch. Protistk. 70. De Garis, C. F. 1935. Heritable effects of conjugation in Par. Jour. Expt. Zool. 71. Dembowski, J. 1929, 1931. Vertikelbewegungen von Par. Arch. Protistk. 66, 74. Gaw, H. 1936. Physiology of the contractile vacuole in ciliates. Arch. Protistk. 87. Emory, F. E. 1928. Metabolism of amino-acids by Par. Jour. Morph. 45. Geiman, Q. 1931. Coleps. Amer. Micros. Soc. Trans. 50. Gelei, J. 1934. Die feinere Bau des Cytopharynx von Par. Arch. Protistk. 82. Giese, A. 1935. Role of starvation in the conjugation of Par. Physiol. Zool. 8. Goodey, T. 1913. Excystation of Colpoda. Roy. Soc. London, Proc. 86 B. Hamburger, C. 1903. Trachelius ovum. Arch. Protistk. 2. Hausman, L. A. 1921. Fresh water and marine gymnostominan Infusoria. Amer. Micros. Soc. Trans. 40. Heidenriech, C. 1935. Parasitische Ciliaten aus Anneliden. Arch. Protistk. 84. Hertwig, R. 1904. Conjugation in Dileptus gigas. Gesell. Morph. Physiol. Sitzber. 20. Hood, C. L. 1927. Zoochlorellae of Frontonia. Biol. Bul. 52. Hopkins, H. S. 1921. Conditions of conjugation in diverse races of Par. Jour. Expt. Zool. 34. Ivanic, M. 1926. Über die mit den Reorganisations-prozessen der Bewegungs- und Nahrungsaufnahmeorganellen verbundenen Ruhestadien von Par. Zool. Anz. 68. 1934. Vermehrungs- und Wiedervermehrungsruhestadien von Chilodon. Arch. Protistk. 82. Jennings, H. S. 1910. What conditions induce conjugation in Par? Jour. Expt. Zool. 9. Jennings, H. S., and G. T. Hargitt. 1910. Characteristics of the diverse races of Par. Jour. Morph. 21. Johnson, W. 1929. Reactions of Par. to known hydrogen ion concentration. Biol. Bul. 57. Joseph, H. 1907. Kernverhältnisse von Loxodes rostrum. Arch. Protistk. 8. Kalmus, H. 1927. Atmung von Par. caudatum. Biol. Zentbl. 47. 1931. Paramecium, das Pantoffeltierchen. Kanda, S. 1914. Geotropism of Par. and Spirostomum. Biol. Bul. 26, 34. Kasaneff, W. 1910. Loxodes rostrum. Arch. Protistk. 20. Khainsky, A. 1910. Par. caudatum. Arch. Protistk. 21. Kidder, G. 1933. Genus Ancistruma. Arch.

Protistk. 81. 1934. Conchophthirius. Biol. Bul. 66. **King, R.** 1928. Contractile vacuoles in Par. trichium. Biol. Bul. 55. 1935. Cont. vacuole of Par. multimicronucleata. Jour. Morph. 58. **Krüger, F.** 1930. Trichocysten von Par. caudatum. Arch. Protistk. 72. 1931. Trichocysten von Frontonia. Arch. Protistk. 74. **Landis, E.** 1920. Amicronucleate race of Par. caudatum. Amer. Nat. 54. 1925. Conjugation of Par. multimicronucleata. Jour. Morph. 40. **Losina-Losinsky, L.** 1931. Zur Ernahrungsphysiologie der Infusorien (Par. caudatum). Arch. Protistk. 74. **Ludwig, W.** 1931. Gattung Paramecium. Zool. Anz. 92. **Lynch, J. E.** 1929, 1930. Ciliates from the intestine of Strongylocentrotus. Calif. Univ., Pubs. Zool. 33. **Macdougall, M.** 1928. Neuromotor apparatus of Chlamydodon. Biol. Bul. 54. **MacLennan, R.** 1936. Dedifferentiation and redifferentiation in Ichthyophthirius. I. Neuromotor system. Arch. Protistk. 86. **Mast, S. O.** 1909. Reactions of Didinium. Biol. Bul. 16. Conjugation and encystment in Didinium. Jour. Expt. Zool. 23. **Maupas, E.** 1885. Sur Coleps hirtus. Arch. Zool. Expt. Gén. Ser. 2, Vol. 3. **McNally, E.** 1926. Nassula. Biol. Bul. 51. **Metalnikow, S.** 1912. Digestion intracellulaire chez les Protozoaires (Par.). Arch. Zool. Expt. Gén. Ser. 5, Vol. 9. **Michelson, E.** 1928. Existenzbedingungen und Cystenbildung bei Par. caudatum. Arch. Protistk. 61. **Mitrophanow, P.** 1905. Trichocystes des Paramécies. Arch. Protistk. 5. **Moore, E.** 1924. Endomixis and encystment in Spathidium. Jour. Expt. Zool. 39. **Morgan, W.** 1925. Foettingeria actiarum. Quart. Jour. Micros. Sci. 68. **Necheles, H.** Respiration rate of Par. ref. in Winterstein Handbuch. der Vergleich. Physiologie, 2, Part 2: 931. **Nirenstein, E.** 1910. Über Fettverdauung und Fettspeicherung bei Infusorien. Ztschr. Allg. Physiol. 10. 1925. Natur und Stärke der Säureabscheidung in den Nahrungsvacuole von Par. Ztschr. Wiss. Zool. 125. **Noland, L.** 1925. Genus Coleps. Amer. Micros. Soc. Trans. 44. **Parker, R.** 1926. Symbiosis in Par. bursaria. Jour. Expt. Zool. 46. **Pênard, E.** 1917. Le genre Loxodes. Rev. Suisse Zool. 25. **Pierantoni, U.** 1909. Struttura, biologia e sistematica di Anoplophrya. Arch. Protistk. 16. **Prandtl, H.** 1906. Conjugation von Didinium. Arch. Protistk. 7. **Pringsheim, E.** 1915. Kultur von Par. bursaria. Biol. Zentbl. 35; Arch. Protistk. 64. **Prowazek, S.** 1909. Konjugation von Lionotus. Zool. Anz. 34. **Prytherch, H.** 1923. Ichthyophthirius disease of fishes. U. S. Comm. Fish. Rpt. Appen. IX. **Rees, C.** 1922. Neuromotor apparatus of Par. Calif. Univ., Pubs. Zool. 20. **Rhumbler, L.** 1888. Colpoda. Ztschr. Wiss. Zool. 46. **Saunders, J.** 1925. Trichocysts of Par. Biol. Rev., Cambridge Phil. Soc., 1. **Schewiakoff, W.** 1889. Beiträge zur Kenntnis der Holotrichen Ciliaten. Bibliog. Zool. 1. 1896. Organisation et classification des Infusoires Holotricha. Acad. Imp. Sci. St. Petersburg, Mém. C. Sci. Phys. Math. 4. **Sonneborn, T. M., and R. S. Lynch.** 1934. Hybridization and segregation in Par. aurelia. Jour. Expt. Zool. 67. **Spencer, H.** 1924. Par. calkinsi. Jour. Morph. 39. **Studitsky, A.** 1930. Dileptus gigas. Arch. Protistk. 70. **Tannreuther, G.** 1926. Prorodon. Biol. Bul. 51. **Thon, K.** 1905. Didinium. Arch. Pritistk. 5. **Tönniges, C.** 1914. Die Trichocysten von Frontonia. Arch. Protistk. 32. **Visscher, J.** 1923. Feeding reactions in Dileptus. Biol. Bul. 45. 1927. Neuromotor apparatus in Dileptus. Jour. Morph. 44. **Wenrich, D. H.** 1926. Par. trichium. Jour. Morph. 43. 1928. Eight well-defined species of Par. Amer. Micros. Soc. Trans. 47. 1929. Actinobolus vorax. Biol. Bul. 56. **Woodruff, L. L.** 1911. Par. aurelia and Par. caudatum. Jour. Morph. 22. 1917. Rhythms and endomixis in various races of Par. aurelia. Biol. Bul. 33. 1921. Par. calkinsi. Biol. Bul. 41. **Woodruff, L. L., and R. Erdmann.** 1916. Periodic reorganization process in Par. caudatum. Jour. Expt. Zool. 20. **Woodruff, L. L., and H. Spencer.** 1923. Par. polycarum. Soc. Expt. Biol. Med. Proc. 20. 1924.

Spathidium, significance of conjugation. Jour. Expt. Zool. 39. **Zweibaum, J.** 1912, 1921-1922. Papers on conjugation in par. Arch. Protistk. 26, 44.

HETEROTRICHA

Andrews, E. A. 1914. The bottle-animalcule, Folliculina. Biol. Bul. 26, 39; Amer. Nat. 55; Jour. Morph. 38. **Bishop, A.** 1923. Observations on Spirostomum. Quart. Jour. Micros. Sci. 67, 69, 71. **Blättner, H.** 1926. Reizphysiologie von Spirostomum. Arch. Protistk. 53. **Brauer, A.** 1886. Bursaria. Jenaische Ztschr. Naturw. 19. **Calkins, G. N.,** and **R. Bowling,** 1928, 1929. Studies on Dallasia. Biol. Bul. 55; Arch. Protistk. 66. **Dierks, K.** 1926. Stentor coeruleus. Arch. Protistk. 54. **Fauré-Fremiet, E.** 1932. Division et morphogénèse chez Folliculina. Bull. Biol. France Belg. 66. **Hamburger, C.** 1908. Conjugation von Stentor. Ztschr. Wiss. Zool. 90. **Johnson, H.** 1893. Morphology and biology of the Stentors. Jour. Morph. 8. **Lund, E. J.** 1914. The relations of Bursaria to food. Jour. Expt. Zool. 16. **McDonald, J.** 1922. On Balantidium coli and B. suis with an account of their neuromotor apparatus. Calif. Univ., Pubs. Zool. 20. **Morgan, T. H.** 1900. Regeneration of proportionate structures in Stentor. Biol. Bul. 2. **Mulsow, W.** 1913. Conjugation von Stentor coeruleus. Arch. Protistk. 28. **Poljansky, G.** 1928. Conjugation von Bursaria. Zool. Anz. 79. **Schaeffer, A.** 1910. Selection of food in Stentor. Jour. Expt. Zool. 8. **Schmähl, O.** 1926. Die Neubilding des Peristoms bei der Teilung von Bursaria. Arch. Protistk. 54. **Schröder, O.** 1907. Stentor coeruleus. Arch. Protistk. 8. **Schuberg, A.** 1887. Bau der Bursaria. Morph. Jahrb. 12. 1891. Stentor coeruleus. Zool. Jahrb., Abt. Anat. Ontog. Tiere. 4. **Schwartz, V.** 1935. Regeneration und Kerndimorphismus von Stentor. Arch. Protistk. 85. **Stevens, N. M.** 1903. Lichnophora and Boveria. Arch. Protistk. 3. **Stolte, H.** 1924. Blepharisma. Arch. Protistk. 48.

HYPOTRICHA

Baitsell, G. 1912, 1914. Reproduction of hypotrichous Infusoria. Jour. Expt. Zool. 13, 16. **Bovard, J.** 1907. Condylostoma. Calif. Univ., Pubs. Zool. 3. **Calkins, G. N.** 1919-1921. Uroleptus mobilis, division, conjugation, vitality. Jour. Expt. Zool. 27, 29, 31, 34. **Dawson, J.** 1926. Life cycle of Histrio. Jour. Expt. Zool. 46. **Fermor, X.** 1912. Encystierung bei Stylonychia. Zool. Anz. 42. **Gelei, J.** 1929. Sensorische Basalapparat der Tastborsten und der Syncilien bei Hypotricha. Zool. Anz. 83. **Gregory, L.** 1923. Conjugation of Oxytricha. Jour. Morph. 37. **Griffin, L.** 1910. Euplotes worcesteri. Philippine Jour. Sci. 5. **Ilowaisky, S.** 1926. Cysten der Hypotrichen. Arch. Protistk. 54. **Ivanic, M.** 1928. Vermehrungscysten von Chilodon. Arch Protistk. 61. 1931. Encystierungsvorgang von Euplotes. Zool. Anz. 95. **Lund, E. E.** 1935. Neuromotor system of Oxytricha. Jour. Morph. 58. **Manwell, R.** 1928. Conjugation, division, and encystment in Pleurotricha. Biol. Bull. 54. **Plough, H.** 1916. Genus Aspidisca. Amer. Micros. Soc. Trans. 35. **Sterki, V.** 1878. Morphologie der Oxytrichinen. Ztschr. Wiss. Zool. 31. **Taylor, C. V.** 1928. Protoplasmic reorganization in Uronychia during fission and regeneration. Physiol. Zool. 1. **Turner, J.** 1930. Division and conjugation in Euplotes. Calif. Univ., Pubs. Zool. 33. **Wallengren, H.** 1900. Vergleichende Morphologie der hypotrichen Infusorien. Bih. Svenska Vet. Akad. Handl. 26. 1902. Neubildung und Resorbtionsprocesse bei den Theilung der hypotrichen Infusorien. Zool. Jahrb. Abt. Anat. Ontog. Tiere. 15. **Woodruff, L. L.** 1905. Life history of hypotrichous Infusoria. Jour. Expt. Zool. 2. **Yocum, H. B.** 1918. Neuromotor apparatus of Euplotes. Calif. Univ., Pubs. Zool. 18.

OLIGOTRICHA

Becker, E. R. 1932. Present status of problems relating to the ciliates of ruminants and Equidae. Quart. Rev. Biol. 7. **Braune, R.** 1914. Untersuchungen über die im Wiederkäuermagen vorkommenden Protozoen. Arch. Protistk. 32. **Bretschneider, L.** 1934. Strukturlehre der Ophryoscoleciden. Arch. Protistk. 82. **Campbell, A. S.** 1926. Cytology of Tintinnopsis, Studies on Fovella. Calif. Univ., Pubs. Zool. 29. **Dogiel, V.** 1925. Geschlechtsprozesse bei Ophryoscoleciden. Arch. Protistk. 50. 1927. Monographie der Ophyroscolecidae. Arch. Protistk. 59. **Entz, G.** 1909. Organisation und Biologie der Tintinniden. Arch. Protistk. 15. **Kofoid, C. A., and A. S. Campbell.** 1929. Conspectus of marine and fresh-water ciliata belonging to the suborder Tintinnoidea. Calif. Univ., Pubs. Zool. 34. **Kofoid, C. A., and R. MacLennan.** 1930-1932. Ciliates from Bos indicus. Calif. Univ., Pubs. Zool. 33, 37. **Krascheinnikow, S.** 1929. Exkretionsapparat einiger Ophryoscolecidae. Ztschr. Zellforsch. Mikros. Anat. 8. **Laackmann, H.** 1906. Fortpflanzung der Tintinnen. Zool. Anz. 30. **MacLennan, R.** 1934. Glycogen reserves in Polyplastron. Arch. Protistk. 81. **Sharp, R. G.** 1914. Diplodinium ecaudatum with an account of its neuromotor apparatus. Calif. Univ., Pubs. Zool. 13. **Strelkow, A.** 1929. Morphologie und Skelett der Gattung Cycloposthium. Arch. Protistk. 68, 75. **Trier, H.** 1926. Der Kohlehydratstoffwechsel der Panseninfusorien. Ztschr. Vergleich. Physiol. 4. **Weineck, E.** 1934. Die Celluloseverdauung bei den Ciliaten des Wiederkäuermagens. Arch. Protistk. 82.

PERITRICHA

Bresslau, E. 1919. Systilis. Biol. Zentbl. 39. **Cavallini, F.** 1931. La gemmazione in Trichodina. Arch. Protistk. 75. **Danisch, F.** 1921. Reizbiologie und Reizempfindlichkeit von Vorticella. Ztschr. Allg. Physiol. 19. **Diller, W. F.** 1928. Binary fission and endomixis in Trichodina. Jour. Morph. 46. **Fabre-Domerque, R.** 1893. Les Trichodines. Le Nature [Paris] 14. **Fauré-Fremiet, E.** 1905. La structure de l' appareil fixateur chez les Vorticellidae. Arch. Protistk. 6. 1920. Scyphidia terebellae. Soc. Zool. France Bul. 45. 1930. Growth and differentiation of the colonies of Zoothamnium. Biol. Bul. 58. **Fortner, H.** 1926. Morphologie und Physiologie des Vorticellenstieles. Ztschr. Wiss. Zool. 128. **Fulton, J.** 1923. Trichodina. Boston Soc. Nat. Hist., Proc. 37. **Furssenko, A.** 1929. Lebenszyklus und Morphologie von Zoothamnium. Arch. Russ. Protistol. 3. **Greer, N. M.** 1916. Opercularia. Amer. Micros. Soc. Trans. 35. **Kepner, W. A., and Pickens, A. L.** 1925. Trichodina steini. Biol. Bull. 49. **Noland, L., and H. Finley.** 1931. Taxonomy of genus Vorticella. Amer. Micros. Soc. Trans. 50. **Popoff, M.** 1908. Gametenbildung und Konjugation von Carchesium. Ztschr. Wiss. Zool. 89. **Prowazek, S.** 1903. Fibrilläre Strukturen der Vorticellinen. Arch. Protistk. 2. **Schröder, O.** 1906. Vorticella. Arch. Protistk. 7. **Shumway, W.** 1926. Scyphidia clymenellae, an endoparasitic peritrich. Jour. Parasitol. 12. **Wetzel, A.** 1927. Trichodina pediculus. Ztschr. Morph. Ökol. Tiere 9.

SUCTORIA

Chatton, E., and A. Lwoff. 1927. Pottsia infusoriorum, acinétien parasite des Folliculines et des Cothurnies. Bul. Inst. Oceanogr. Monaco. No. 489. **Collin, B.** 1912. Étude monographique sur les Acinétiens. Arch. Zool. Expt. Gén. 51. **Farkas, B.** 1924. Beiträge zur Kenntnis der Suctorien. Arch. Protistk. 48. **Gönnert, R.** 1933. Über Systematik, Morphologie, Entwicklungegsechichte, und Parasiten einiger Dendrosomidae. Arch. Protistk. 86. **Hickson, S. J., and J. Wadsworth.**

1902. Dendrocometes paradoxus. Quart. Jour. Micros. Sci. 45. **Kahl, A.** 1931 Über die verwandtschaftlichen Beziehungen der Suktorien zu den prostomen Infusorien. Arch. Protistk. 73. **Lapage, G.,** and **J. Wadsworth.** 1916. Dendrocometes paradoxus II. Quart. Jour. Micros. Sci. 61. **Lynch, J.,** and **A. E. Noble.** 1931. Genus Endosphaera. Calif. Univ., Pubs. Zool. 36. **Noble, A. E.** 1929. Two new species of Ephelota. Calif. Univ., Pubs. Zool. 33. 1932. Tokophrya. Univ. Calif., Pubs. Zool. 37. **Pénard, E.** 1920. Infusoires tentaculifères. Soc. Phys. Nat. Hist. Genéve, Mem. 39. **Pestel, B.** 1931. Morphologie und Biologie von Dendrocometes paradoxus. Arch. Protistk. 75. **Root, F. M.** 1914. Reproduction and reactions to food of the suctorian Podophrya. Arch. Protistk. 35. 1922. New suctorian from Woods Hole. Amer. Micros. Soc. Trans. 41. **Sand, R.** 1899. Étude monographique sur le groupe des Infusoires tentaculifères. Soc. Belg. Micros., Ann. 24, 25. **Schulz, E.** 1931–1933. Kenntnis mariner Suctorien. Zool. Anz. 96, 97, 103. **Swarczewski, B.** 1928. Die an den Baikalgammariden lebenden Infusorien. I. Dendrosomidae. II. Dendrocometidae. III. Discophryidae. IV. Acinetidae. Arch. Protistk. 61–63.

CHONOTRICHA

Canu, E. 1886. Sur le genre Spirochona. Bul. Sci. France Belg. 17. **Hertwig, R.** 1877. Über Bau und Entwicklung der Spirochona gemmipara. Jenaische Ztschr. Naturw. 11. **Swarczensky, B.** 1928. Spirochona elegans. Arch. Protistk. 61.

ADDENDA

Beers, C. D. 1937. Viability of ten-year-old Didinium cysts. Amer. Nat. 71. **Bernheimer, A. W.** 1938. Crystalline inclusions of Protozoa. Amer. Micros. Soc. Trans. 57. **Browne, K. M. R.** 1938. Golgi apparatus and other cytoplasmic bodies in Spirostomum. Roy. Micros. Soc. Jour. Ser. 3, Vol. 58. **Burrows, H.** 1938. Growth of Chilomonas in inorganic and acetate solutions. Protoplasma 31. **Byrd, E. E.** 1937. Intestinal parasites in fecal samples from 729 college freshmen. Jour. Parasitol. 23. **Calvez, J. Le.** 1938. Recherches sur les Foraminifères. Arch. Zool. Expt. Gén. 80. **Cowdry, E. V.,** and **A. W. Ham.** 1932. East coast fever. I. Life cycle in ticks. Parasitol. 24. **Cowdry, E. V.,** and **W. B. C. Banks.** 1933. East coast fever. II. Behavior of the parasite in susceptible animals. Parasitol. 25. **Cutler, D. W.,** and **L. M. Crump.** 1923–1925. Rate of reproduction in artificial cultures of Colpidium. Biochem. Jour. 17, 18, 19. **Dawson, J. A., W. R. Kessler,** and **J. Silberstein.** 1937. Mitosis in Amoeba proteus. Biol. Bul. 72. **Diller, W. F.** 1936. Nuclear reorganization processes in Paramecium aurelia. Jour. Morph. 59. **Dobell, C.** 1928. Life-history of Entamoeba histolytica. Parasitol. 20. 1938. Life-history of Entamoeba coli. Parasitol. 30. **Doyle, W. L.,** and **J. P. Harding.** 1937. Excretion of ammonia by Glaucoma. Jour. Expt. Biol. 14. **Fowell, R. R.** 1936. Fibrillar structures of Protozoa with special reference to Selenidium. Roy. Micros. Soc. Jour. 56. **Frisch, J. A.** 1937. The rate of pulsation and the function of the contractile vacuole in Paramecium. Arch. Protistk. 90. **Gatenby, J. B.** and **B. N. Singh.** 1938. Golgi apparatus of Copromonas and Euglena. Quart. Jour. Micros. Sci. 80; La Cellule. 47. **Gelei, J. v.** 1937. Eine neues Fibrillensystem im Ectoplasma von Paramecium. Arch. Protistk 89. 1938. Paramecium nephridiatum. Arch. Protistk. 91. **Giese, A. C.,** and **M. A. Arkoush.** 1939. Sexual differentiation in Paramecium. Physiol. Zool. 12. **Grabowski, A.** 1939. Lernvermögen von Paramecium. Ztschr. Tierpsychol. 2. **Greenleaf, W. E.** 1926. Influence of volume of culture medium and cell proximity on rate of reproduction of Infusoria. Jour. Expt. Zool. 46. **Grimwald, E.** 1928. L'action de la substance allélocatalitique apparait-elle dans les cultures du Colpidium? Acta Biol. Experiment. 3. **Hall, R. H.** 1938. Oxygen consumption of Colpidium. Biol. Bul. 75. **Hall, R. P.** 1939. Trophic nature of the plant-like flagellates. Quart. Rev. Biol. 14. **Harding, J. P.** 1937. Quantitative studies on Glaucoma. Jour. Expt. Biol. 14. **Hayes, M. L.** 1938. Cytological studies on Dileptus anser. Amer. Micros. Soc. Trans. 57. **Hoare, C. A.** 1933. New ophidian and avian Coccidia with a review of the classification of the Eimeroidea. Parasitol. 25. **Holter, H.,** and **W. L. Doyle.** 1938. Enzymatic studies on Protozoa. Jour. Cell. Compar. Physiol. 10, 12. **Hornby, H. E.** 1934. Classification of piroplasms of domestic animals. 12th Internatl. Vet. Cong. N. Y., Vol. 3. **Ivanic, M.** 1937. Multiple Teilung bei Piroplasmen der Familie Babesiidae. La Callule 46. **Jahn, T. L.** 1929. Relation of density of population to growth rate of Euglena. Biol. Bul. 57. **Jennings, H. S.** 1937. Formation, inheritance, and variation of the teeth in Difflugia. Jour. Expt. Zool. 77. 1938. Sex reaction types and their inter-relations in Paramecium bursaria. Nat. Acad. Sci. Wash., Proc. 24, 1939. Genetics of Paramecium bursaria. I. Mating types. Genetics. 24. **Johnson, D. F.** 1936. Isolation of Glaucoma in bacteria-free cultures and growth in relation to pH. Arch. Protistk. 86. **Johnson, W. H.** 1933. Effects of population density on rate of reproduction in Oxytricha. Physiol. Zool. 6. 1936. Nutrition and reproduction of Paramecium. Physiol. Zool. 9. **Johnson, W. H.,** and **G. Hardin.** 1938. Reproduction of Paramecium in old culture medium. Physiol. Zool. 11. **Jones, P. M.** 1937. Soil amoeba (Naegleria) coalesce to form a plasmodium. Amer. Nat. 71. **Kikerth, W.,** and **L. Mudrow.** 1938. Die endothelialen Stadien der Malariaparasiten. Zentbl. Bakt. [etc.] Abt. I, Original 142. **Kitching, J. A.** 1938. Mechanism of movement of food vacuoles in peritrich ciliates. Arch. Protistk. 91. 1938–1939. Physiology of contractile vacuoles. Jour. Expt. Biol. 15, 16. Biol. Rev., Cambridge Phil. Soc. 13. **Lawrie, N. R.** 1935. Nitrogenous metabolism and respiration of Bodo. Biochem. Jour. 29. **Loefer, J. B.** 1936. Bacteria-free culture of Para-mecium bursaria and concentration of the medium as a factor in growth. Jour. Expt. Zool. 72. 1938. Effect of hydrogen-ion concentration on the growth and morphology of Par. bursaria. Arch. Protistk. 90. **MacLennan, R. F.** 1936. Dedifferentiation and redifferentiation in Ichthyophthirius. Arch. Protistk. 86; Jour. Expt. Zool. 76. **Madson, H.** 1938. Coccidia of East Greenland hares with a revision of the Coccidia of hares and rabbits. Meddelelser om Grønland. 116. **Mast, S. O.** 1938. Contractile vacuole in Amoeba proteus. Biol. Bul. 74. **Mast, S. O.,** and **D. M. Pace.** 1938. Effect of substance produced by Chilomonas on rate of reproduction. Physiol. Zool. 11. Relation of hydrogen ion concentration to rate of reproduction of Chilomonas. Jour. Expt. Biol. 79. **Müller, R.** 1936. Die osmoregulatorische Bedeutung der kontraktilen Vakuolen. Arch. Protistk. 87. **Myers, E. C.** 1927. Relation of density of population to survival and reproduction in Paramecium. Jour. Expt. Zool. 49. **Myers, E. H.** 1936. The life cycle of Spiril-lina. Roy. Micros. Soc. Jour. Ser. 3, Vol. 56. 1938. Present state of our knowledge concerning the life cycle of the Foraminifera. Nat. Acad. Sci. Wash., Proc. 24. **Petersen, W.** 1929. Relation of density of population to rate of reproduction in Paramecium. Physiol. Zool. 2. **Phelps, A.** 1936. Growth of Protozoa in pure culture. Effect of different concentrations of nutrient materials. Jour. Expt. Zool. 72. **Reich, K.** 1938. Allelocatalytic effect in Amoeba cultures free of bacteria. Physiol. Zool. 11. **Reichenow, E.** 1935. Übertragungsweise und Entwicklung der Piroplasmen. Zentbl. Bakt. [etc.] Abt. I, Original 135. **Reynolds, M. E. C.** 1932. Regeneration in an amicronucleate infusorian. Jour. Expt. Zool. 62. **Schulz, E.** 1936. Reaktionen des Ciliaten Trachelomonas auf mechanischen Reize. Zool. Anz.

116. Sergent, E., A. Donatien, L. Parrot, and F. Lestoquard. 1936. Cycle evolutif de Theileria dispar du Boeuf chez la tique Hyalomma. Inst. Pasteur Algérie, Arch. 14; Instit. Pasteur [Paris], Ann. 57; Acad. Sci. [Paris], Compt. Rend. 202. Soest, H. 1937. Dressurversuche mit Ciliaten. Ztschr. Vergleich. Physiol. 24. 1938. Haben einzeller ein Gedächtnis? Mikrokosmus (Stuttgart) 31. Sonneborn, T. M. 1936. Factors determining conjugation in Par. aurelia. Genetics. 21, 22. 1937. Induction of endomixis in Par. aurelia. Biol. Bul. 72. Extent of the inter-endomictic interval in Par. aurelia. Jour. Expt. Zool. 76. 1938. Mating types in Par. aurelia. Amer. Phil. Soc. Proc. 79. Delayed occurrence and total omission of endomixis in selected lines of Par. aurelia. Biol. Bul. 74. Sonneborn, T. M., and R. S. Lynch. 1934. Hybridization and segregation in Par. aurelia. Jour. Expt. Zool. 67. Subramaniam, M. K., and R. G. Aiyar. 1937. Golgi apparatus and vacuome in Protozoa. Indian Acad. Sci. Proc. 6. Summers, F. M. 1938. Form regulation in Zoothamnion alternans. Aspects of normal development in Zoothamnium alternans. Biol. Bul. 74. Taylor, C. V., and A. G. R. Strickland. 1936. Effects of high vacua and extreme temperatures on cysts of Colpoda. Physiol. Zool. 9. Taylor, C. V. and W. H. Ferguson. 1938. Structural analysis of Colpoda duodenaria. Arch. Protistk. 90. Tittler, I. A. 1938. Regeneration and reorganization in Uroleptus. Biol. Bul. 75. Turner, J. P. 1937. Studies on Tillina. Amer. Micros. Soc. Trans. 56. Wenrich, D. H. 1937. Dientamoeba fragilis. Jour. Parasitol. 22, 23. Wichterman, R. 1937. Division and conjugation in Nyctotherus cordiformis. Jour. Morph. 60.

CHAPTER IV

PHYLUM MESOZOA

1. Introduction.—Discovered in 1839, the Mesozoa have since constituted a taxonomic puzzle. Formerly serving as a sort of catchall for a variety of small enigmatic animals not assignable to any of the regular groups, the Mesozoa with increased knowledge emerge as an assemblage with well-defined and rather remarkable characteristics. These features are such that the Mesozoa cannot be included in any other phylum but whether their peculiarities are primitive or the result of parasitic degeneration cannot be decided. Van Beneden, one of the leading students of the group, took the former view, regarding these animals as intermediate in structure between Protozoa and Metazoa, and therefore invented for them the name Mesozoa, in 1877. Hatschek (1888) noted the similarity of their structure to that of the planula larva of coelenterates, altered the name to Planuloidea, and treated them with coelenterates. Most zoologists regard them as degenerate flatworms and hence append the Mesozoa to the phylum Platyhelminthes.

The Mesozoa in general have a solid two-layered construction, but their two layers do not correspond to the ectoderm and entoderm of Metazoa, for the inner layer (often comprising a single elongated cell) has no digestive functions. It is reproductive and gives rise to agametes. Therefore it can be said that structurally the Mesozoa have not reached the stage of a gastrula (with entoderm) but have remained at the stage of a morula or stereoblastula, whence Hartmann's name Moruloidea. As far as their anatomy is concerned, the Mesozoa are certainly simpler than any other Metazoa, but as already intimated this simplicity is probably not primitive. The Mesozoa also stand alone among cellular animals in that they reproduce by means of agametes.

2. Definition.—The Mesozoa are cellular endoparasites that during all or part of the life cycle are composed of an outer cell layer or syncytium, enclosing one or more reproductive cells. They have a complicated life cycle involving an alternation of asexual and sexual generations. The phylum is divided into two orders, the Dicyemida or Rhombozoa and the Orthonectida. These are united into the class Moruloidea by Hartmann.

3. The Dicyemida.—The dicyemids are very common parasites, known since 1839, in the nephridia of cephalopod mollusks (squids and

233

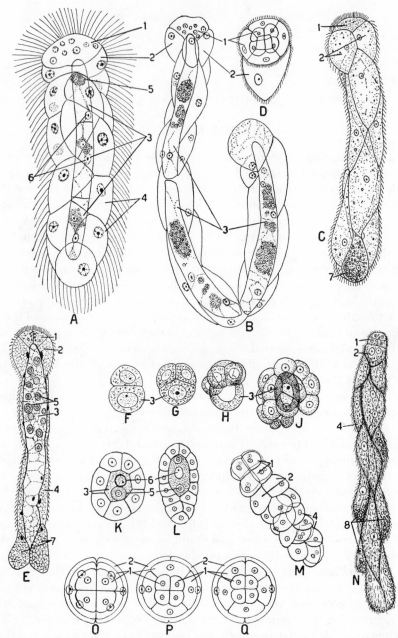

Fig. 68.—Life cycle and morphology of dicyemids. *A.* Larval stage with three axial cells (*Pseudicyema truncatum* from *Sepia*). *B.* Stem nematogen, develops directly from *A. C.* Nematogen of *P. truncatum. D.* Head of same, showing the two tiers of polar cells and one parapolar cell. *E.* Optical section of nematogen of *P. truncatum. F–M.* Development of a nematogen from an agamete: *F,* two-cell stage; *G,* the smaller cell has

octopuses). The ordinary form of the parasite or *primary nematogen* (Fig. 68*C*) is a minute vermiform ciliated animal, up to 6 or 7 mm. long, composed of a limited and definite number of cells, usually not more than 25. These cells comprise an outer ciliated layer and a single elongated internal cell (Fig. 68*E*). As the terms ectoderm and entoderm cannot be employed with regard to the Mesozoa, the outer cells are called the peripheral or *somatic* cells or *somatoderm* and the inner cell is termed the *axial cell*. The body can be roughly divided into a slightly distinct anterior end or *head* and an elongated *trunk*. The somatoderm of the head consists of eight or nine *polar cells* (Fig. 68*D*, *O–Q*) disposed in two tiers termed the *polar cap* or *calotte*. These polar cells may be radially arranged or may be displaced "ventrally" and then exhibit bilaterality. The most anterior trunk cells, next to the polar cells, hence termed *parapolar* cells, usually two in number (Fig. 68*C*), are intermediate in size and appearance. The remaining trunk cells, about 10 to 15 in number, definite for each species, are large highly vacuolated cells provided with long cilia and often containing inclusions. In *Pseudicyema truncatum* (Fig. 68*C*, *E*) there are 14 trunk cells, of which the last two (*uropolar cells*) are rich in inclusions. The axial cell is a very elongated cylindrical or fusiform cell, also with a highly vacuolated cytoplasm (Fig. 68*E*). It is originally uninucleate (Fig. 68*J*) but soon undergoes a sort of endogenous division and becomes filled with germ cells that in the nematogenic stage are always agametes. The cytoplasm of the axial cell and some of the nuclei retain a vegetative function and serve to nourish the agametes.

The typical dicyemids have been classified by Nouvel (1933) into three genera. In *Dicyema* (Fig. 68*O*), the polar calotte consists of two tiers of four cells each, arranged oppositely. *Pseudicyema* (Fig. 68*D*, *P*) has also eight polar cells, but the two tiers alternate, and in *Dicyemennea* the second tier is made of five cells (Fig. 68*Q*). Gersch (1938) doubts the validity of the genus *Pseudicyema*.

Despite the efforts of several prominent zoologists, the life cycle of the dicyemids has not yet been elucidated. In modern times, three accounts have been published, that of Hartmann (1907) that of Lameere (1916–1922), and that of Gersch (1938). These accounts differ in certain important particulars, and it is now clear that Hartmann was in error in

---

divided; *H*, the larger cell is being enclosed by the progeny of the smaller cell; *J*, continuation of enclosing process; *K*, optical section, the larger or axial cell completely enclosed has given rise to an agamete; *L*, later stage, axial cell with two agametes; *M*, young nematogen, entire view, all cells complete. *N*. Rhombogen stage of a dicyemid, with verruciform cells (*Dicyema typus* from the Octopus). *O–Q*. Heads of the three typical dicyemid genera. *O*, *Dicyema*; *P*, *Pseudicyema*; *Q*, *Dicyemennea*. (*A*, *B*, *after Lameere*, 1916; *C–N*, *after Whitman*, 1882; *O–Q*, *after Nouvel*, 1933.) 1, polar cap; 2, parapolar cells; 3, axial cell; 4, trunk cells; 5, agamete; 6, vegetative nucleus; 7, uropolar cells (peculiar to *P. truncatum*); 8, verruciform cells.

several matters.[1]   Gersch has verified the findings of Lameere (1916) and Nouvel (1933) that the infusoriform stage is an asexual larva, not a male, but differs from Lameere and Hartmann in his interpretation of the infusorigens.   Lameere and Nouvel worked with *Pseudicyema truncatum* (Fig. 68*C*), common in the kidneys of the European squid, *Sepia officinalis*, and Gersch studied chiefly *Dicyema typus* from the octopus.

According to Lameere, the earliest stage, found in the kidneys of very young squids, is a ciliated larva with eight polar, three parapolar, seventeen somatic, and three axial cells (Fig. 68*A*).   Each of the axial cells contains two nuclei, one a vegetative nucleus and the other generative. The latter soon acquires cytoplasm and separates as a germ cell, really an agamete.   The larva grows into an elongated vermiform individual called by Lameere the *stem nematogen* (Fig. 68*B*).   It has the same number and arrangement of cells as the larva, but the agametes have multiplied to form groups of cells that develop inside the stem nematogen into ordinary nematogens (Fig. 68*C*).   Gersch denies the existence of the stem nematogen and maintains that the earliest parasites seen in very young cephalopods are identical with the ordinary nematogens.

The ordinary nematogens (Fig. 68*C*) as already described have eight or nine polar, two parapolar, one axial, and 10 to 15 somatic cells.   The axial cell already contains a number of agametes (*axoblasts* of Gersch), which arise as follows.   The nucleus of the axial cell divides; one daughter remains as the nucleus of the axial cell; the other becomes the progenitor of all the agametes and multiplies by repeated fissions.   Eventually each agamete begins to develop into a nematogen.   In this development no indication of any maturation process has been observed by any of the authors.   Hence these cells are agametes and not parthenogenetic eggs. The development of an agamete into a nematogen (Fig. 68*F–M*) is a simple process resembling the cleavage of an egg.   The agamete divides into two unequal cells (Fig. 68*F*); the larger cell becomes the axial cell; the smaller one divides to form all the somatic cells, and these gradually enclose the axial cell (Fig. 68*H–K*).   The axial cell soon divides into two unequal cells of which the smaller becomes the progenitor of all the agametes.   When the nematogens have completed their differentiation, they leave the mother nematogen and wander about in the kidney fluid.   Each one soon gives rise within itself to another generation of nematogens.

---

[1] The author cannot help remarking on the way in which the German workers have treated the French investigators.   Hartmann and other Germans completely ignored the French work and continued to present Hartmann's erroneous account long after Lameere had maintained that the infusoriform type was a larva, not a male. Gersch throughout his paper continually belittles the work of the French, glosses over Hartmann's errors, and attempts to exaggerate the originality of his own findings.

The production of nematogens continues throughout the growth of the host but ceases when the host attains sexual maturity, and the parasite then assumes a new form termed a *rhombogen* (Fig. 68*N*). The rhombogens may arise by direct transformation of nematogens (then called *secondary* rhombogens) or may come from agametes inside the last generation of nematogens (*primary* rhombogens). Nematogens and primary and secondary rhombogens have the same essential structure and the same numbers and arrangements of cells but differ in their cell inclusions and in the type of offspring they produce. In rhombogens some of the somatic cells become packed with inclusions of the nature of yolk (lipoprotein balls) and glycogen and then often project conspicuously as the so-called *verruciform* or wart-like cells (Fig. 68*N*). The agametes of the axial cell of rhombogens no longer develop into nematogens; many of them degenerate but some cleave in the same manner as for the formation of nematogens. However, after a ball of cells has been produced, the development ceases and the outer cells round up and separate off, while the central cell continues to produce more outer cells, and these again separate.

The nature of these cell balls or clusters inside the rhombogen, which will be called *infusorigens*, remains the chief point of dispute in the various accounts. According to Hartmann, the infusorigens are females, and the cells that separate from them are true eggs that undergo maturation and must be fertilized. According to Lameere, they are hermaphrodites; the surface cells are eggs as in Hartmann's account, but the central cell is a mother spermatogonium that divides into several spermatogonia, and these undergo an ordinary spermatogenesis. Gersch asserts that the infusorigens are degenerate nematogens without any sexual character. It seems probable that Gersch's view is correct.

The cells that are given off from the surface of the infusorigens, termed *pseudo-eggs* by Gersch, cleave to form a ball of cells that differentiates into a free-swimming ciliated larva, the *infusoriform larva*, or *swarmer* of Gersch (Fig. 69*A*, *g-l*). These larvae were erroneously considered by Hartmann to be males. Lameere, Nouvel, and Gersch all agree that they are nonsexual larvae that function to spread the parasite to a presumably intermediate host.

The infusoriform larva (Fig. 69*C*, *D*) is of short oval form, covered externally by several large ciliated cells and two unciliated anterior or *apical* cells; each apical cell contains a very large refringent body, shown by Nouvel to consist of uric acid. The interior cells of the larva are termed the *urn* and comprise four granular *central* cells held by two curved *capsule* cells and bounded anteriorly by a small cavity covered by four *cover* cells and two small ciliated cells situated under the two apical cells. The central and capsule cells are filled with granules and spherules of the

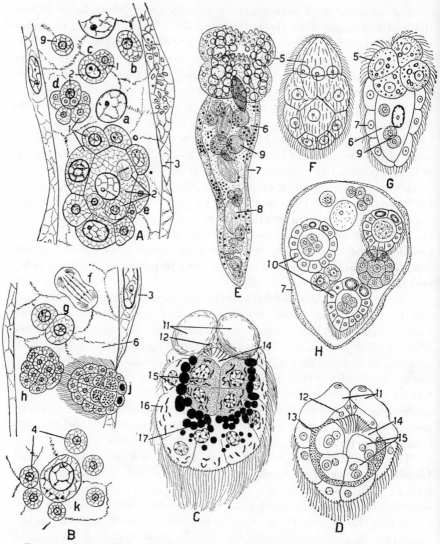

Fig. 69.—Dicyemids (continued).   *A.* Diagrammatic view of part of the axial cell of a rhombogen showing formation of an infusorigen: *a*, vegetative nucleus; *b*, agamete; *c*, division of agamete into future central and surface cells; *d*, further cleavage; *e*, completed infusorigen, considered female by Hartmann, hermaphrodite by Lameere, degenerated nematogen by Gersch.   *B.* Part of axial cell of a rhombogen showing development of the infusoriform larva: *f*, agamete from surface layer of infusorigen; *g*, first division of same; *h*, later cleavage stage, *j*, completed infusoriform larva; *k*, degenerating infusorigen, breaking up into cells.   *A* and *B*, (*after Hartmann, 1907*).   *C.* General view and *D*, horizontal section of the infusoriform larva of the dicyemids.   (*After Nouvel, 1933.*)   *E–H. Conocyema polymorpha* (*after van Beneden, 1882*).   *E*, mature nematogen filled with embryos of nematogens; *F*, one of the embryos enlarged; *G*, transformation of embryo into a nematogen; *H*, rhombogen stage containing infusoriform embryos.   1, outer cells; 2, central cell (spermatogonium of Lameere); 3, somatoderm of rhombogen; 4, pseudo-

nature of food reserves (the large black balls in Fig. 69C are yolk spheres). The infusoriform larvae leave their mother rhombogens and escape from the host into the sea water. Their further history is unknown, but it is to be presumed that they enter some intermediate host in which the sexual phases of the life cycle occur. It is also not known how young cephalopods become infected.

After having given off a succession of pseudo-eggs, the infusorigens degenerate and according to Gersch, the rhombogens also degenerate. In earlier accounts it was stated that the rhombogens might again function as nematogens and that the last pseudo-eggs may develop into nematogens.

If Gersch's account is correct, the entire cycle of the dicyemids in their cephalopod hosts is asexual, and the sexual phases, if they occur, must take place in some other animal.

Besides the typical dicyemids to which the foregoing account is applicable there are two species, known as heterocyemids, that differ considerably from the former. They are rare parasites of the kidneys of cephalopods. One of them, *Conocyema polymorpha* from the octopus, is known chiefly from the researches of van Beneden (1882). The nematogen (Fig. 69E) is unciliated and has four large polar cells filled with inclusions and a trunk composed of an axial cell enclosed in a few flat somatic cells. The axial cell contains the usual agametes and developmental stages. The agametes give rise directly to ciliated larvae (Fig. 69F), which have an axial cell, four polar cells, and several somatic cells. They transform directly into adult nematogens (Fig. 69G) through the alteration of the polar cells and the loss of cilia. The rhombogen (Fig. 69H) lacks polar cells and consists of a thin layer of somatic cells and a large axial cell filled with infusoriform larvae in various stages of development. The infusoriform larvae are identical with those of typical dicyemids.

The other heterocyemid, *Microcyema vespa*, from *Sepia*, has been studied extensively by Lameere (1916). The earliest stage in *Sepia* is a ciliated form with three axial cells, practically identical in appearance with the same stage of the typical dicyemids (Fig. 68A). This transforms directly into a stem nematogen (Fig. 70A) by loss of cilia and the cell walls of the somatic layer. The stem nematogen is thus an irregular form with a syncytial layer over the three axial cells. The axial cells contain agametes and developmental stages, and these develop into ciliated larvae (Fig. 70B) composed of ten somatic cells enclosing one

eggs; 5, polar cells; 6, axial cell; 7, trunk cell; 8, embryo of nematogen; 9, agametes; 10, infusoriform larvae; 11, refringent body of apical cells; 12, ciliated cover cells of urn; 13, capsule cells of urn; 14, cavity of urn; 15, central cells of urn; 16, mitochondria; 17, lipoprotein balls.

axial cell.   The somatic layer of the larva becomes amoeboid and syncytial (Fig. 70C), and the larva passes into an amoeboid phase (Fig. 70D).   These amoeboid forms are young nematogens and grow into the typical nematogens (Fig. 70E) with a syncytial somatic layer over a single axial cell.   The nematogens produce not only larvae of the type of Fig. 70B but also larvae of the type of Fig. 70F, known from their discoverer as *Wagener's larvae*.   Wagener's larva attaches to the host tissue by its anterior cilia and transforms into a nematogen by way of stages illustrated in Fig. 70G and H.   Thus, in *Microcyema*, nematogens come from either larval type, but those derived from Wagener's larvae give rise only to such larvae.   The rhombogens are very like the nematogens and produce infusorigens and infusoriform larvae as in the typical dicyemids.

Gersch claims that the heterocyemids are merely degenerative stages of the dicyemids.   However, the details that have been described for them can hardly be disposed of in this manner, although no doubt there are errors in the existing accounts.

The biology of the dicyemids has been studied by Nouvel (1933). The younger stages swim about in the fluid of the host kidneys, but the mature forms adhere by the cilia of the polar cap to the spongy kidney tissue.   They do not damage the host tissue and appear to be harmless inhabitants of the kidneys.   They presumably absorb nutritive substances such as albumin and amino acids known to be present in the nephridial fluid of cephalopods, and in addition their somatic cells phagocytize and digest particulate matter, such as the host's spermatozoa, found in this fluid.   During their growth, the nematogens accumulate protein bodies in their somatic cells, and during the rhombogen stage these protein reserves become charged with lipoids of the nature of lecithin and so form yolk material.   The verruciform cells are simply somatic cells enlarged through the accumulation of such lipoprotein bodies.   Glycogen is also present in abundance in the somatic cells of the rhombogen.   These food reserves in the rhombogen are utilized in the formation of the infusoriform larvae that when mature contain protein granules in the central cells of the urn, lipoprotein balls in the capsule cells, and much glycogen in the surface ciliated cells.   Glycogen also occurs in young nematogens.   These reserves are utilized in the swimming activities of young nematogens and infusoriform larvae.   It is probable that anoxybiotic respiration obtains in all stages except the infusoriform larvae, which require oxygen.   Other stages probably metabolize glycogen with the liberation of lactic acid.   Mitochondria occur abundantly in the somatic cells at all stages, and vacuoles stainable with neutral red are concerned in the accumulation of protein reserves.

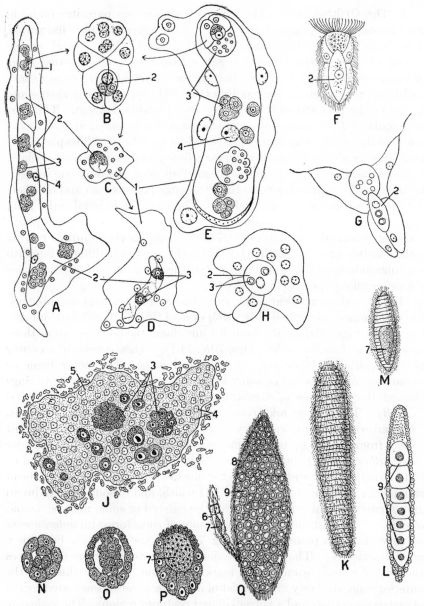

Fig. 70.—*Microcyema*, orthonectids. *A. Microcyema vespa*, stem nematogen. *B.* Larva of same. *C.* Amoeboid phase developed from *B.* *D.* Young nematogen, amoeboid stage. *E.* Mature nematogen. *F.* Wagener's larva. *G* and *H.* Stages of development of Wagener's larva into a nematogen. (*After Lameere, 1916, 1917, except F, after van Beneden, 1882.*) *J.* Male plasmodium of *Rhopalura ophiocomae* from a brittle star. *N–P.* Stages of development of male of same; *Q,* fertilization of same species. *K.* External view of female. *L.* Longitudinal section of female. *M.* External view of male of *R. julini* from an annelid. (*J, N–P, K–M. After Caullery and Mesnil, 1901; Q, after Caullery and Lavallée, 1908.*) 1, trunk syncytium; 2, axial cells; 3, agametes and embryos; 4, vegetative nucleus; 5, plasmodium; 6, male; 7, testis; 8, female; 9, ovocytes.

4. The Orthonectida.—The orthonectids are rare parasites found in the internal spaces and tissues of various invertebrates—flatworms, nemerteans, brittle stars, annelids, and a clam. The several species belong with one exception to the genus *Rhopalura*. The asexual stage or agamont differs widely from that of the dicyemids. It consists of a multinucleate amoeboid plasmodium (Fig. 70*J*) spread in the tissues and spaces of the host where it may effect considerable damage. Thus the plasmodia of *R. granosa*, found in the clam *Heteranomia*, and *R. ophiocomae* in the brittle star destroy the gonads of their hosts. The plasmodia reproduce by simple fragmentation for a time and then give rise asexually to males and females. Usually a plasmodium produces only one sex, but in some species both sexes come from the same plasmodium and in others the sexual forms are hermaphrodites. The sexual individuals arise from certain nuclei of the plasmodium that become encircled with cytoplasm and then constitute agametes (Fig. 70*J*). These cleave to form a morula (solid blastula or stereoblastula) of which the outer cells differentiate into the somatoderm of the sexual adults and the inner mass of cells becomes the primordial sex cells (Fig. 70*N*, *O*).

The sexual forms bear some resemblance to dicyemid nematogens. They are minute elongated (Fig. 70*K*) or oval (Fig. 71*A*) ciliated animals, the males (Figs. 70*M*, 71*B*) about 0.1 mm. long, the females two or three times longer than the males (Figs. 70*K*, 71*A*). They consist of an outer ciliated epithelial layer and an inner cell mass. The outer layer or somatoderm is composed of many small cells and is marked off into rings through the occurrence of circular grooves at intervals (Figs. 70*K*, *M* and 71*A*, *B*). These rings may consist of one, two, or more rows of cells. They are constant for each sex of each species, but vary in different species from about 5 up to 50 or more; the very peculiar extremely slender *Stoecharthrum giardi* found in annelids is 0.8 mm. long, is composed of 60 to 70 equal rings, and resembles a string of beads. The rings may be of equal (Fig. 70*K*) or unequal (Fig. 71*A*) width, and in some species broad and narrow rings alternate. All may be ciliated or some may be devoid of cilia. The most anterior ring or group of rings forms an *anterior cone* on which the cilia point forward (Fig. 71*A*); on the rest of the body they point backwards. The most posterior ring or group of rings constitutes the *posterior cone*, often clearly marked off, and, between this and the anterior cone, the body may consist of a narrow anterior unciliated region of one or more rings and a longer ciliated posterior region. The males are smaller and with fewer rings than the corresponding females (Figs. 70*Q*, *M* and 71*B*) but present the same general body regions. In some species, refringent bodies, probably food reserves, occur in definite situations as those of the anterior cone in the male in Fig. 71*B*.

The interior (Figs. 70Q, L and 71A) differs from that of the dicyemids in that it consists of several to many cells, up to two or three hundred. In the female the interior cells may be arranged in a single row (Fig. 70L) or in two or three rows or may form a mass of many cells (Fig. 71A). These interior cells are all ovocytes. In the male, similarly, there is an internal cluster of cells that are spermatogonia and give rise to sperm. Hermaphroditic species resemble the females of the dioecious species but have a testis anterior to the mass of eggs.

As already mentioned the sexually mature forms develop from agametes inside the parasitic plasmodium. When finished the sexual animals escape from their host and swim about in the sea water where fertilization occurs by contact of the male with the female (Fig. 70Q) and the discharge of sperm into her by way of a genital opening present behind the middle. The fertilized eggs develop inside the female into ciliated embryos (Fig. 71C) that somewhat resemble the infusoriform larvae of the dicyemids. Like the latter they escape free into the sea water and serve to reinfect new hosts of the same kind. As shown by Caullery and Lavallée (1912) for R. ophiocomae, the ciliated larvae on penetration into new hosts apparently lose their somatic layer. The interior cells probably scatter, and each one apparently gives rise to a plasmodium. Thus the plasmodia of the orthonectids presumably correspond to the axial cells of the nematogens of dicyemids.

5. Other Supposed Mesozoa.—Formerly a number of minute and peculiar animals were assigned to the Mesozoa, but most of these have now been shown to belong to other groups, or else other affinities have been suggested for them. Thus Trichoplax and Treptoplax, which have the construction of planulae, were found actually to be modified planulae of Hydroidea. Haplozoon (Fig. 71D), several species of which are parasitic in the intestine of marine annelids, was made the basis of a special group of Mesozoa (Catenata) by Dogiel, 1908. It begins as a single cell provided with a stylet and a tuft of filaments as organelles of attachment; by repeated divisions it forms behind itself a chain of cells or a flattened body consisting of several straight or oblique rows of cells. The hindermost of these cells are continually freed as reproductive bodies whose further history is unknown. It is now considered highly probable from the work of Chatton that Haplozoon is a parasitic dinoflagellate and that its division into a multicellular body is a process of colony formation (compare Fig. 71D with Fig. 25L). Amoebophrya is a parasite in the interior of Radiolaria where it forms the so-called spiral bodies. When free it is a cylindrical organism encircled many times along its length by a spiral furrow bearing cilia. The multinucleate interior has a central and a peripheral space. Amoebophrya is obviously a protozoan. Nere-

cheimeria(= *Lohmannella*) occurs in the gonads of the tunicate *Fritillaria* and in its earliest stage consists of a multinucleate plasmodium anchored into the host tissues by branching amoeboid processes at one place. As the parasite grows, the nonpseudopodial side extends as a hollow conical

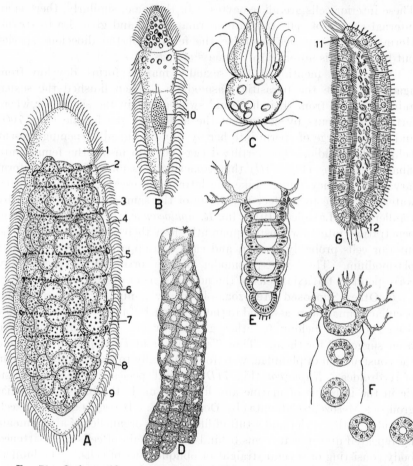

FIG. 71.—Orthonectids and some supposed Mesozoa. *A. Rhopalura granosa* from the clam *Heteranomia*, mature female. *B.* Male of same. *C.* Embryo of same. (*After Atkins*, 1933.) *D. Haplozoon.* (*After Dogiel*, 1908.) *E* and *F.* Stages of *Neresheimria.* (*After Neresheimer*, 1904.) *G.* Longitudinal section of *Salinella.* (*After Frenzel*, 1892.) 1, anterior cone; 2–7, body rings; 8, posterior cone; 9, mass of ovocytes; 10, testis; 11, mouth; 12, anus.

projection that becomes divided by constrictions into a series of rings (Fig. 71*E*). These are given off as hollow spheres (Fig. 71*F*) and presumably serve for reproduction. *Neresheimeria* is probably also a parasitic dinoflagellate allied to *Paradinium*, which has a multinucleate amoeboid phase parasitic in copepods and also discharges rounded reproductive bodies.

Still unclassifiable is *Salinella*, a minute animal 2 mm. long, discovered by Frenzel (1892) in a culture made from material coming from salt beds in the Argentine. *Salinella* consists of a single layer of cells enclosing a digestive cavity opening at one end by the mouth, at the other by the anus (Fig. 71*G*). Mouth and anus are encircled by long bristles, the somewhat flattened ventral surface is heavily ciliated, the convex dorsal surface bears sparse bristles, and the cells are also ciliated on the side facing the digestive cavity. The food consists of detritus digested in the cavity. Asexual reproduction occurs by transverse fission. What appeared to be a sexual process, consisting of the adherence and subsequent encystment together of two individuals was frequently observed but could not be followed further. The unicellular young, resembling a hypotrichous ciliate, seen in the culture possibly come from such cysts. From the rather complete description of *Salinella* given by Frenzel it is evident that this animal is not a mesozoan and does not fit into any other animal phylum. It seems to be most nearly allied to the Protozoa and possibly should be made the basis of a new phylum. It differs from all other known Metazoa in lacking interior cells but is obviously of a higher grade of organization than a colonial protozoan such as *Volvox*. *Salinella* might be regarded as an experiment in metazoan organization of a type different from the usual method of relegating some of the cells to the interior to serve as entoderm.

6. Phylogenetic Considerations.—Concerning the affinities of the Mesozoa proper there are two principal views: that they have degenerated from one of the lower metazoan phyla and that they are truly primitive. With regard to the former view, only coelenterates and flatworms need to be considered. By some, mesozoan structure is interpreted as planuloid, and a coelenterate ancestry is therefore suggested. This view really hinges on whether the interior cells can be regarded as entoderm or not. Among the dicyemids the development of the various stages follows the same course and consists in the covering over of one cell by the others. This process has been likened by some zoologists to an epibolic gastrulation, while others regard such embryos as remaining at a stereoblastula stage. Among the orthonectids the development of the sexual adults takes place by a process identical with entoderm formation by secondary delamination (see Chap. V). But as the interior cells never differentiate into functional entoderm, the Mesozoa can be said to have remained at a morular or stereoblastular stage of structure. In any event, there is nothing about their structure or life history to suggest coelenterates, and the idea of coelenterate affinity has little weight today.

Most zoologists incline to the view that the Mesozoa are degenerate flatworms. This view rests chiefly on the resemblance of their life cycle to that of the digenetic trematodes. In both groups there is a ciliated larva and there are simplified vermiform stages that reproduce by an asexual method. But the trematode miracidium comes from a fertilized egg and the infusoriform larva from an agamete and furthermore there is no structural resemblance at all between these larvae. Neither is there any anatomical resemblance between the orthonectid sexual adults and an adult trematode. It is difficult to suppose that the Mesozoa have any affinities with flatworms, especially in view of the fact that parasitic animals very commonly present complicated life cycles, so that the occurrence of such cycles cannot be taken as evidence of relationship.

Lameere (1922) asserts that the Mesozoa are degenerate Echiuroidea but gives very few grounds for this opinion. Similarities mentioned are the occurrence of small ciliated males in the echiuroid *Bonellia* and the like position of the female genital opening in echiuroids and orthonectids.

Although it is not likely that the simplicity of the Mesozoa is wholly primitive it is still more improbable that they are degenerate representatives of some higher phylum. They seem to be more nearly related to the Protozoa than to any other phylum. Among their primitive and protozoan characteristics are the occurrence of cilia throughout most of the life cycle, the differentiation of the cells into somatic and reproductive cells only as in *Volvox*, the endogenous position of the reproductive elements as in many Protozoa, and the retention by the surface cells of the power of intracellular digestion. Complicated life cycles with alternation of asexual and sexual phases are of common occurrence among the Sporozoa.

If the structural features of the Mesozoa could be shown to be original and not degraded, the group would be of the utmost phylogenetic significance, as a stage between Protozoa and Metazoa. They would furnish proof that the first step in metazoan organization is the relegation of reproductive cells into the interior, that the original metazoan had a solid, not a hollow construction, and that the gastraea theory of Haeckel is definitely erroneous. But since it is impossible to decide on existing evidence that the anatomy of the Mesozoa is primitive in nature, their taxonomic position remains problematical. They are here taken at their face value as of a grade of construction lower than that of coelenterates and are hence placed in an isolated position between Protozoa and Porifera. This placing should not be taken to confer upon the Mesozoa any especial phylogenetic significance, although the author believes that their characters are in the main primitive and not the result of parasitic degeneration.

Finally it is clear that the Mesozoa constitute a well-defined group and should no longer be regarded as a convenient dumping place for any peculiar organisms of uncertain affinities

Bibliography

Atkins, D. 1933. Rhopalura granosa, orthonectid parasite of Heteranomi? Jour. Mar. Biol. Assoc. 19. **Borgert, A.** 1897. Kenntnis der Sticholonche und

Acanthometridenarten vorkommenden Parasiten (Amoebophrya). Ztschr. Wiss. Zool. 63. **Caullery, M.,** and **A. Lavallée.** 1905. Les larves ciliées d'un Orthonectide. Soc. Biol. [Paris] Compt. Rend. 57. 1908. La fécondation et le développement de l'oeuf des Orthonectides. Arch. Zool. Expt. Gén. Ser. 4, Vol. 8. 1912. Le cycle évolutif des Orthonectides. Bul. Sci. France Belg. 46. **Caullery, M.,** and **F. Mesnil.** 1899. Stoecharthrum giardi. Sur trois orthonectides nouveaux. Acad. Sci. [Paris], Compt. Rend. 128. 1901. Recherches sur les Orthonectides. Arch. Anat. Micros. 4. **Dogiel, V.** 1908. Catenata, eine neue Mesozoengruppe. Ztschr. Wiss. Zool. 89, 94. **Frenzel, J.** 1892. Salinella. Arch. Naturgesch. 58, pt. 1. **Gersch, M.** 1938. Der Entwicklungszyklus der Dicyemiden. Ztschr. Wiss. Zool. 151. **Giard, A.** 1880. The Orthonectida. Quart. Jour. Micros. Sci. 20. **Hartmann, M.** 1907. Generationswechsel der Dicyemiden. Acad. Roy. Belg., Cl. Sci. Mém. 1. **Julin, C.** 1882. Mesozoaires. Arch. Biol. 3. **Krumbach, T.** 1907. Trichoplax die umgewandelte Planula einer Hydromeduse. Zool. Anz. 31. **Lameere, A.** 1916–1919. Connaissance des Dicyemides. Bull. Biol. France Belg. 50, 51, 53. 1922. L'histoire naturelle des Dicyemides. Brussels Acad. Roy. Belg. Bul. Cl. Sci. Ser. 5, Vol. 8. **Mesnil, F.** and **M. Caullery.** 1905. Développement des ovules et des larves ciliées d'un orthonectide hermaphrodite. Soc. Biol. [Paris] Compt. Rend. 57. **Metschnikoff, E.** 1881. Orthonectiden. Ztschr. Wiss. Zool. 35. **Neresheimer, E.** 1904. Lohmannella. Ztschr. Wiss. Zool. 76. 1908. Mesozoen. Zool. Zentbl. 15. **Nouvel, H.** 1931. Accumulation et utilisation du glycogène chez les Dicyémides. Arch. Zool. Expt. Gén. 71. 1932. Les Dicyémides d'*Octopus* *vulgaris.* Bul. Inst. Océanogr. Monaco. No. 599. 1933. Cytologie, physiologie et biologie des Dicyémides. Ann. Inst. Océanogr. Monaco. 13. **Shumway, W.** 1924. Haplozoon. Jour. Parasitol. 11. **Van Beneden, E.** 1876. Recherches sur les Dicyémides. Brussels Acad. Roy. Belg. Bul. Cl. Sci. 41, 42. 1882. Histoire des Dicyémides. Arch. Biol. 3. **Whitman, C. O.** 1882. Embryology, life-history, and classification of the dicyemids. Mitt. Zool. Stat. Neapel. 4.

CHAPTER V

INTRODUCTION TO THE LOWER METAZOA

I. ORIGIN OF THE METAZOA

No direct proof exists of the origin of the Metazoa from the Protozoa, but such origin besides being necessitated by the principle of evolution is strongly indicated by the facts of embryonic development, in which each metazoan passes from an acellular to a cellular condition. There are two principal ways in which the Metazoa might have been derived from the Protozoa: first, by the appearance of cell boundaries in a multinucleate syncytium; and second, by colony formation. Both views have been advocated by various prominent zoologists, but the former has met with little acceptance because of a lack of supporting evidence; the latter is generally held, since it accords best with the facts of embryonic development.

The following types of colonies occur among the Protozoa: linear, arboroid (branching in a tree-like manner), plate-like, and spherical. The first two may be disregarded, since their loose type of construction and the lack of correlation between the cells are unfavorable for progression toward a multicellular individuality. Colonies composed of more closely associated cells, such as the flattened to spherical types occurring in flagellates, and particularly in the Phytomonadina, suggest themselves as more likely subjects for speculation. The plate form such as *Gonium* (Fig. 28*H*) was favored by Bütschli as the ancestral metazoan type. He postulated that this became two-layered by cutting off a lower plate of cells and then curving into a sphere, an idea for which there is a little evidence. More plausible are the theories that derive the Metazoa from spherical flagellate colonies. The solid colony or morula such as *Synura* (Fig. 23*A*) or *Pandorina* was favored by Lankester as the ancestral form, whereas Haeckel derived the Metazoa from the hollow *Volvox*-like condition (Fig. 30*A*). Both theories accept the Flagellata as the most probable ancestral group.

The belief in the flagellate ancestry of the Metazoa rests upon a number of grounds. First, it has been seen that the flagellates are a highly plastic group from which in all probability the entire plant kingdom and all the other protozoan classes have originated. Then, the flagellates display a great tendency toward the formation of compact colonies, and these resemble stages in the embryonic development of the Metazoa. Further, in some of the Phytomonadina, such colonies exhibit

248

a high degree of individualization with the differentiation of an anterior pole and an anteroposterior axis, appearance of anatomical differences among the zooids with respect to the axis, and limitation of reproduction to certain posterior cells of the colony. Such colonies would be regarded as Metazoa were they not connected by all gradations with unicellular forms. Very striking is the fact that the lowest metazoan phylum, the sponges, produces flagellated larvae and further possesses a type of cell, the choanocyte, that closely resembles a choanoflagellate. In the coelenterates the tendency of the entoderm to put out flagella is noteworthy. Finally may be recalled the evolution of sexual reproduction in the Phytomonadina, with the differentiation in this group of typical metazoan-like sex cells by the gradual alteration of ordinary flagellate protozoans. And the spermatozoan so evolved, which may be regarded as a modified flagellate (Fig. 72*A*, *B*), has been retained in nearly all the metazoan phyla; in short, the occurrence of flagellate, i.e., tailed, spermatozoa almost universally among the Metazoa is regarded by many as evidence of the descent of the Metazoa from the Flagellata.

Most writers on phylogeny have accepted Haeckel's derivation of the Metazoa from the hollow *Volvox*-like flagellate colony and consequently picture the common ancestor of the Metazoa as a little hollow ball (Fig. 72*E*) composed of a single layer of flagellated cells, swimming about with one pole directed forward and having an anteroposterior axis from this pole to the opposite one. This hypothetical organism was termed by Haeckel the *blastaea* and is generally believed to be reproduced in the development of Metazoa as the *blastula* stage.

The first differentiation occurring in such an organism is the specialization of certain cells as sex cells, a process already seen in *Volvox*. The early differentiation of the sex cells is a phenomenon still seen in many animals. In other cases the later origin of the reproductive cells from cells that have preserved an undifferentiated or embryonic character, as the archaeocytes of sponges or the interstitial cells of coelenterates, may be a reminiscence of the same phenomenon. There is probably a general tendency for the sex cells to pass into the interior.

Since even the simplest Metazoa are two-layered or *diploblastic*, the next step must have been the formation of an inner layer serving digestive functions. The fact that the lower metazoans are diploblastic was discovered in the medusae by T. H. Huxley in 1849 and confirmed for hydroids in 1853 by Allmann, who invented the terms *ectoderm* and *entoderm* for the two "membranes" of these animals. In his great work on the calcareous sponges published in 1872, Haeckel described the two-layered construction of the ascon sponges, and this particular discovery started him on the long train of phylogenetic speculations with which zoological teaching has become so thoroughly imbued.

In the blastaea, the flagellated somatic cells not only are locomotory and perceptive but also must capture and digest food. All theories of the mode of transformation of the one-layered into the two-layered condition start from the assumption that the separation of locomotory and digestive functions would be advantageous, and vary according to the author's conception of the mode of feeding of the blastaea. Lankester argued that food would be passed into the inner ends of the cells of his solid morula and that these ends would then be cut off as an internal digestive layer, the mouth and digestive cavity developing later (Fig. 72C, D). However, this mode of entoderm formation is very rare, and the theory found no acceptance. Most opponents argued that an entoderm would be of no value without a mouth for taking in food; but this objection is not cogent since food can be passed from the surface to the interior cells, a process still seen in sponges and coelenterates. The majority of writers assumed that the posterior cells of the blastaea became specialized in food getting, either because the organism fed by swimming along the bottom or because the beating of the flagella would tend to drive particles toward the posterior pole. On the basis that the posterior cells of the blastaea took on digestive functions, Haeckel postulated the formation of the two-layered condition by the bending of the posterior half of the blastaea into the anterior half, producing a two-walled cup, of which the inner entodermal sac was termed primitive intestine (*Urdarm* in German), its opening to the exterior primitive mouth or *protostoma* (*Urmund* in German) (Fig. 73M). These terms have been generally replaced by Lankester's names *archenteron* and *blastopore*. Haeckel named this hypothetical two-layered organism the *gastraea* and made it the basis of his famous *gastraea theory*, which asserts that the gastraea is the common ancestor of all the Metazoa, that it is reproduced in their embryology as the *gastrula* stage, that the two layers of the gastraea are retained throughout the Metazoa as ectoderm and entoderm, and that the entoderm is fundamentally formed by invagination, all other modes being secondary modifications of invagination. Haeckel's ideas were opposed at the time of their promulgation by many workers, among them Metschnikoff, who, having discovered that digestion is intracellular and phagocytic in the lower Metazoa, pointed out that the ancestral metazoan would not have required a digestive sac or mouth. He believed that certain cells of the blastaea might develop strong phagocytic tendencies and wander into the interior which would then become filled up with amoeboid cells embedded in a gelatinous material (Fig. 72F, G). He thus considered the ancestral metazoan to be a solid gastrula, consisting of an external ectoderm enclosing an interior mass having digestive functions (Fig. 72G). Thus both Metschnikoff and Lankester agreed that the original diploblastic ancestor was solid rather than hollow; the former termed the

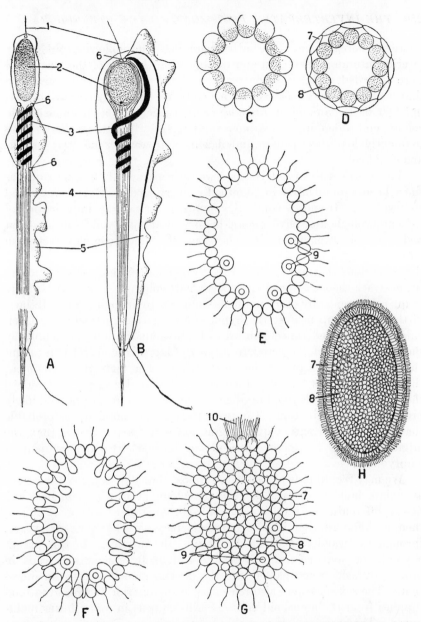

Fig. 72.—Comparison of A, a spermatozoon, and B, a polymastigote flagellate. (*After Alexieff*, 1924.) C and D. Diagrams of entodermal formation by primary delamination according to Lankester's theory. E–G. Diagrams of formation of the entoderm by multipolar ingression (*according to Metschnikoff's theory*): E, hypothetical ancestral blastaea, with germ cells in the interior; F, stage of multipolar ingression; G, hypothetical stereogastrula or planuloid ancestor of the Eumetazoa. H. Planula larva of a hydroid, from life, example of an actual stereogastrula. 1, acrosome of sperm; flagellum of flagellate; 2, nucleus; 3, spiral filament of sperm, parabasal body of flagellate; 4, axial filament of sperm, axostyle of flagellate; 5, undulating membrane; 6, centriole-like granules; 7, ectoderm; 8, entoderm; 9, germ cells; 10, sensory bristles.

organism *parenchymula,* the latter *planula.* The hollowing out of the interior into an archenteron and the breaking through of the blastopore were regarded as later, secondary processes. Metschnikoff considered that his theory was greatly strengthened by the discovery by Saville Kent in 1880 of the organism *Proterospongia* (page 107), a choanoflagellate colony embedded in a gelatinous matrix, in which the collared cells frequently lose their collars and flagella and wander into the jelly as amoeboid cells.

The gastraea theory of Haeckel won acceptance at the time and has since been promulgated in practically every textbook of zoology and embryology. It and its corallaries represent a masterly simplification of the embryologic and phylogenetic history of animals and furnish a clear and plausible explanation of the stages by which complex metazoan structure might have been achieved. But it is probably one of those simplifications that are too beautiful to be true. The chief objection to the gastraea theory is that in metazoan embryology the entoderm is more frequently formed by other methods than it is by invagination. In fact, in the very group nearest the hypothetical gastraea, namely, the Coelenterata, the entoderm seldom arises by invagination but commonly by the inwandering of the ectoderm, and the larva (Fig. 72*H*) is a parenchymula or planula rather than a gastrula. The facts of development thus support Metschnikoff's theory rather than Haeckel's and indeed the wandering of cells to fill up spaces seems a far more natural and likely process than invagination. Contrary to Haeckel's opinion it is probable that entoderm formation by invagination is a derived rather than the original method and represents one of those short cuts common in embryology.

We may regard it as plausible to suppose that the Metazoa arose from an axiate hollow spherical flagellated colony in which there occurred first a differentiation into somatic and reproductive cells (Fig. 72*E*) and then a differentiation into locomotor-perceptive and nutritive types, through the wandering of the latter into the interior. In this parenchymula or stereogastrula, food was caught by the surface cells in protozoan fashion and passed into the interior amoeboid cells for digestion. The sex cells were also relegated to the interior and received food supplies from the amoeboid cells, as still happens in many lower metazoans. The anterior pole probably bore special sensory cells or a tuft of sensory cilia. Such an organism may be considered the common ancestor of the coelenterates and flatworms (Fig. 72*G*).

The three lowest metazoan phyla, the Porifera, the Cnidaria, and the Ctenophora, are commonly stated to have remained at the gastrular level of construction and are usually considered to be two-layered or diploblastic groups. As will appear shortly, these phyla are not strictly diploblastic except for the class Hydrozoa of the phylum Coelenterata. The real bases of distinction between these groups and the higher Metazoa will be explained later.

II. GENERAL CHARACTERS OF THE METAZOA

The Metazoa differ from the Protozoa in being composed of numerous cells differentiated into many sorts for the performance of different functions; in the arrangement of at least part of their cells into layers; in their higher grade of individualization, expressing itself, except in sponges, in the formation of a nervous system, whose centralization in one part of the body conditions this part as an anterior end or head; and in the occurrence of a process of embryonic development in the life history. We have already seen in the Protozoa that a high degree of morphological differentiation can be attained within one continuous protoplasmic mass; but obviously the cellular construction of the Metazoa permits a much greater degree of diversification, since different cells can follow different lines of specialization. Again the layered construction of the Metozoa leads to differentiation, since the various layers come into diverse environmental relations. Almost universally the surface layer exposed to external conditions specializes first into protective functions, then into sensory and nervous structures; while the internal layer becomes digestive. Cells and layers in an intermediate situation tend to assume supporting and contractile roles. The layered construction also favors the formation of different organs at different depths. The correlation of numerous cells into one harmonious whole seems to depend in large part upon the formation of a nervous system, since the chief integrating mechanism in animals consists of the transmission of stimuli and commands from one part of the body to another. Such transmission can occur in undifferentiated protoplasm; but it is probable that even in the Protozoa paths are morphologically differentiated from the rest of the cytosome to serve as lines of transmission, although these do not reach the grade of a definite nervous system. Nervous tissue in some unknown way accomplishes transmission much more rapidly than ordinary protoplasm and consequently is much more efficient. A transmissive system to attain its greatest efficiency must be centralized, and such centralization takes the morphological form of a head containing the main nervous mass, or brain. Characteristic of the Metazoa is the amazing process of embryonic development by which the fertilized egg passes through a series of changes culminating eventually in the formation of the adult metazoan. Hints of such a process already appear in the Protozoa where swarmers may be given off that differ considerably from the parent form and attain the latter by undergoing some degree of transformation. Apparently simpler is the formation of colonial types as in the Phytomonadina where the zygote or vegetative cell becomes an adult by repeated cell divisions. None of these processes seem comparable in complexity to the case in metazoans where in the development of the egg one sees an aggregate of cells molded into successive forms definite for the species.

It is frequently stated that the Metazoa differ further from the Protozoa in the separation of the body into a *somatic* part, which carries on the regular life activities and eventually dies, and a *germinal* part, which is immortal by means of sexual reproduction. But in this matter the Protozoa do not seem to differ from the Metazoa so much as in some of the other points mentioned, since, as already seen, all the phenomena of sexual reproduction occur among the Phytomonadina, including the limitation of sex cell formation to specific cells in particular regions of the colony. The idea of the rigid separation of soma or body and germ originated with Weismann and has been of great influence in biological thought; but today it seems physiologically unsound in view of the high capacity of the body cells of the lower forms for regeneration, of the relations of the sex glands to other endocrine glands in vertebrates, and of the proved origin of the sex cells directly from body cells in many animals.

The Metazoa when studied morphologically are seen to present various degrees of complexity of structure. It is believed that these different stages of anatomical elaboration actually represent in a general way the steps by which the higher animals evolved from the lower ones. We may consider that the first true Metazoa were diploblastic animals, devoid of organs, consisting of an outer ectodermal epithelium, and an inner entodermal mass; some of the cells at times differentiated into sex cells. Soon, however, both layers gave off gland, muscle, and primitive connective tissue cells; sensory and nerve cells were apparently of later origin. The majority of these various sorts of cells came from the ectoderm. Connective tissue of *ectodermal* origin came to lie between the ectoderm and entoderm forming a mesenchyme. The main step in the evolution toward a higher type of structure came through the formation from the *entoderm* of a *third* layer, the *mesoderm*, adding to the original mesenchyme and eventually replacing it. Animals with a mesoderm of entodermal origin are called *triploblastic*. The mesoderm furnished space and material for the formation of many organs impossible to the two-layered animal. It took over the formation of muscular, supporting, reproductive, and circulatory systems, freeing the ectodermal and entodermal epithelia from the task of producing these types of tissues. The ectoderm thereupon specialized in skin and nervous structures, the entoderm in the digestive tract and its various elaborations. Very shortly after or possibly simultaneously with the appearance of the mesoderm, the metazoan body became *coelomate*, i.e., a space or system of spaces developed in the mesoderm. Since all the higher animals are coelomate, this step seems to have been of importance. The coelom apparently facilitates the reproductive and excretory functions and very probably aids other organs by giving them space in which to carry on their activities. The final anatomical step in the evolution of the Metazoa is the segmentation of the body.

In the original diploblastic condition there were no organs or differentiated functional systems, unless the archenteric sac could be regarded as a digestive system. Nervous, muscular, and supporting systems appeared in a simple form rather early, but there was but little definite formation of organs and organ systems until the mesoderm came into existence. Thereupon there were rapid strides in the differentiation and elaboration of systems already present; in the formation of new systems, first the reproductive and excretory and later the circulatory and respiratory systems; and in the production of organs by aggregation of tissues.

The exact steps in the evolution of the various grades of invertebrate structure are not and presumably never can be known. Statements about them are inferred from anatomical and embryological evidence and in no case should be regarded as established facts. It must further be remembered that evolution does not proceed in a straight line but rather as a branching tree; any particular grade of structure may therefore present several variations, with some features emphasized in one group of animals, others in another.

III. DEVELOPMENT THROUGH THE GASTRULA STAGE

The life history of a metazoan from the egg through sexual maturity is termed *ontogeny*. It is divisible into two periods: the *period of embryonic development*, sometimes termed *morphogenesis*, and the *period of growth*. During the former the fertilized egg undergoes a series of changes that result in the formation of a young animal like the parent except as regards the reproductive system and related sexual characters. The developing organism, when enclosed within protective coverings or the parent body, is termed an *embryo*. When, before development is completed, it becomes free and leads an independent life, it is called a *larva*. A sudden marked change during the course of development is known as *metamorphosis*. During the second part of ontogeny, the growth period, the organism increases in size, undergoes minor anatomical changes, and matures its reproductive system, with which process is associated the appearance of certain characters, called the *secondary* sexual characters.

The period of embryonic development may again be divided into the following stages: the period of *cleavage* or *segmentation;* the period of *formation of the germ layers;* the period of formation of organs, or *organogenesis;* and the period of histological differentiation, or *histogenesis.* We are here concerned only with the first two parts of the developmental process.

The course of early development is intimately related to the construction of the egg. The egg is definitely organized. It has radial symmetry, often also distinct evidences of bilateral symmetry. The main axis of symmetry is termed the *polar axis,* the ends of which are named the *animal* and *vegetal* (or *vegetative*) poles, respectively. Along the polar axis there generally exists an arrangement of visible materials; furthermore, the invisible ground substance also possesses a polarized organization, for when the visible materials are disarranged by centrifuging eggs, the development is usually not affected. The organization of the egg is related to the future organism, in that certain parts of the embryo are formed from certain regions of the egg. This *germinal localization,* as it is called, varies in degree in different eggs, being so marked in some that removal of portions of the egg results in specific defects of the embryo; whereas, in the case of other eggs, normal larvae may develop despite such operations. In any case, the difference is chiefly one of time, since those eggs not at first sharply localized with respect to the future embryo, become so as development proceeds.

The principal visible materials of eggs are ergastic food supplies, called *deutoplasm* or *yolk,* consisting mostly of fats and proteins. Eggs are classified according to the amount and distribution of the yolk. When the yolk is slight in amount, it is also more or less evenly dispersed; such eggs are variously termed *isolecithal, alecithal* or *homolecithal* (Fig. 73*A*). Larger amounts of yolk tend to accumulate in one region of the egg, either the vegetal half (Fig. 73*B, C*) or the center (Fig. 73*D*), leaving most of the protoplasm in the animal half or the periphery, respectively. Eggs with vegetal yolk are termed *telolecithal* (Fig. 73*C*), with central yolk, *centrolecithal* (Fig. 73*D*).

The egg begins its development by undergoing *cleavage* or *segmentation,* i.e., by dividing mitotically many times in rapid succession into cells of continuously diminishing size, called *cleavage cells* or *blastomeres.* The arrangement of the blastomeres, i.e., the *cleavage pattern,* depends in part upon the amount and distribution of the yolk, since the mitotic figures are generally shifted into the more protoplasmic portions and away from the more yolky portions of the egg. The protoplasmic portions therefore divide into smaller cells than the yolky portions, and, further, they divide more frequently. The cleavage pattern also depends in part upon what seem to be hereditary factors.

When the entire egg divides up into blastomeres, the cleavage is spoken of as *total* or *holoblastic* and is said to be *equal* when the cleavage cells are approximately of the same size (Fig. 73*E*), and *unequal* (Fig. 73*F*) when they differ considerably. Holoblastic equal cleavage (Fig. 73E) is characteristic of isolecithal eggs; holoblastic unequal cleavage (Fig. 73F, G) is characteristic of moderately telolecithal eggs, the cells then grading in size from the smaller protoplasmic ones in the animal half to the large yolky ones in the vegetal half (Fig. 73G). In holoblastic cleavage, the first two cleavages are *meridional*, at right angles to each other, dividing the egg into four quarters as one would divide an apple. The third cleavage is transverse, at right angles to the other two, and is *equatorial*, i.e., through the center of the egg in isolecithal eggs, and *latitudinal*, i.e., shifted toward the animal pole, in telolecithal eggs. The further cleavages tend to alternate between meridional and transverse planes until a considerable number of cells of ever-diminishing size has been produced. Holoblastic cleavage may be further classified according to the symmetry relations of the cleavage pattern. The cleavage is said to be *radial* (Fig. 73E) when symmetrical with reference to the polar axis, resulting in tiers of cells on top of each other; *spiral* when diagonal to the polar axis (Fig. 73F), so that successive tiers alternate; *dissymmetric* or *biradial* (Fig. 73H) when symmetrical with regard to the first cleavage plane; *bilateral* (Fig. 73J) when exhibiting bilateral symmetry; and *irregular* when the pattern is indefinite. The spiral type (Fig. 73F, G) is of great importance among invertebrates and characterizes several large phyla. In this type, the spindles for the third cleavage, instead of being erect, are inclined diagonally, so that the resulting upper tier of four cells is displaced sidewise, resting in the angles between the four lower cells. When to the observer looking down upon the animal pole, the four upper cells are displaced in a clockwise rotation, the cleavage is said to be *right-handed* or *dextrotropic;* when displaced counterclockwise, the spiral displacement is called *left-handed* or *levotropic.* In spiral cleavages there tends to be an alternation of dextrotropic and levotropic divisions. Holoblastic cleavage is also termed *determinate* when the various cells play definite exact roles in the production of the embryo and *indeterminate* when the cleavage pattern bears no definite relation to the embryo. Spiral cleavage is always markedly determinate.

In very yolky eggs, most of the protoplasm is collected in a disk or film at the animal pole (Fig. 73C), and this alone undergoes cleavage; the remaining yolk-filled part of the egg shows no division. Such cleavage is termed *discoidal* or *meroblastic* (Fig. 73K) and results in a disk of cells resting upon the yolk. In most centrolecithal eggs, only the peripheral layer of protoplasm cleaves, a kind of cleavage termed *superficial,* producing a membrane one cell thick enclosing the yolk (Fig. 73P). In both meroblastic and superficial cleavage, the cleavage planes form primarily at right angles to the surface and are often incomplete leaving the cells in partial continuity with the yolk.

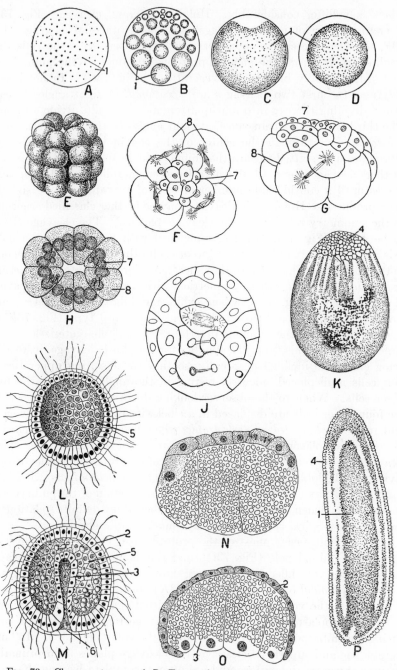

Fig. 73.—Cleavage types. A–D. Types of eggs according to yolk distribution, diagrams: A, isolecithal; B, telolecithal with holoblastic cleavage; C, telolecithal with mero-

The end stage of the period of cleavage is termed the *blastula*. In the case of holoblastic cleavage, the cells generally draw apart leaving a central cavity and forming a surface layer, generally single in invertebrates. Such a blastula (Fig. 73L) is termed a *coeloblastula*, sometimes *archiblastula*, and its cavity is called the *blastocoel*, or *primary body cavity*. When the word blastula is used without qualification, a coeloblastula is meant. The coeloblastula resulting from holoblastic equal cleavage is termed *adequal*, meaning that the cells of the wall are of about the same size throughout. After holoblastic unequal cleavage, the coeloblastula is *inequal*, as the wall of the vegetal half is thicker than that of the animal half and the blastocoel is reduced in volume and displaced toward the animal pole (Fig. 73N). The wall of an inequal coeloblastula may also be several cell layers thick, but this is unusual in invertebrates. In some cases, the blastula fails to develop a central cavity and is then termed a solid blastula or *stereoblastula* (also spelled *sterroblastula*) (Fig. 74G). In a stereoblastula, the blastomeres may reach from the surface to the center; or separate blastomeres may occupy the interior (Fig. 74G). The latter condition is called a *morula* in some texts; but the word morula is also often used for late cleavage stages before the blastocoel has appeared. In meroblastic cleavage the blastula stage consists of a disk or film of cells resting upon the yolk (Fig. 73K); and in superficial cleavage it consists of a membrane one cell thick enclosing the central yolk (Fig. 73P). These types of blastulae are called *discoblastula* and *periblastula*, respectively. They necessarily lack a blastocoel.

Although cell division continues throughout embryonic development, the period of cleavage is usually regarded as terminated with the formation of the blastula. There follows the period of formation of the *germ layers*, i.e., of cell strata from which the tissues and organs of the adult arise. The first step in the formation of the germ layers consists in the transformation of the single-layered blastula into a double structure

---

blastic cleavage; *D*, centrolecithal. *E*. Holoblastic equal cleavage, also of the radial type, note tiers of cells on top of each other; holothurian egg. (*After Selenka*, 1883.) *F* and *G*. Cleavage of egg of the type of Fig. *B*, illustrating holoblastic unequal spiral cleavage, egg of the snail *Crepidula* (*after Conklin*, 1897): *F*, 16-cell stage seen from the animal pole; note alternating tiers of cells; *G*, later stage seen from the side; note gradation in cell size from animal to vegetal pole. *H*. Holoblastic unequal cleavage of the biradial type, egg of the ctenophore *Beroë*. (*After Ziegler*, 1898.) *J*. Holoblastic adequal cleavage of the bilateral type, embryo of the rotifer *Asplanchna*. (*After Jennings*, 1896.) *K*. Meroblastic cleavage of egg of the type of Fig. *C*, illustrating a discoblastula, egg of a cephalopod mollusk. (*After Watase*, 1891.) *L*. A coeloblastula, resulting from cleavage of the type of *E*, holothurian embryo. (*After Selenka*, 1883.) *M*. Same, in the gastrula stage, illustrating a typical gastrula, entoderm formed by embolic invagination. *N*. Inequal blastula of *Crepidula;* section of an embryo like Fig. *G*. *O*. The same later, showing entoderm forming by epiboly, ectoderm growing down over the large yolky entoderm cells. (*M and N after Conklin*, 1897.) *P*. Periblastula, resulting from superficial cleavage of eggs of the type of *D;* egg of a fly. (*After Noack*, 1901.) 1, yolk; 2, ectoderm; 3, entoderm; 4, blastoderm (=cellular part of the embryo); 5, blastocoel; 6, blastopore.

consisting of an outer cell layer, the *ectoderm*, and an inner layer or mass, the *entoderm*. Ectoderm and entoderm are called the two *primary germ layers*, the process of entoderm formation is termed *gastrulation*, and an embryo or larva composed of ectoderm and entoderm is known as a *gastrula*. The entoderm may arise in several different ways.

1. *By Invagination or Emboly.*—In this process, usual in adequal coeloblastulae, the posterior or vegetal region of the blastula bends inward as if pushed by a finger into a sac that may or may not touch the outer wall (Fig. 73*M*). In the former case, the blastocoel is obliterated; in the latter case, which usually obtains in invertebrates, the blastocoel remains surrounding the invaginated sac. The entodermal sac is termed *primitive intestine* or *archenteron*, its opening at the vegetal pole termed the *blastopore, protostoma,* or *primitive mouth*. Entoderm formation by invagination was regarded by Haeckel as the primitive method, the gastrula so formed as the original type, hence termed *archigastrula*, and all other kinds of entoderm formation and gastrulae as secondary and derived. This viewpoint has been generally accepted and is commonly presented in textbooks and adopted in phylogenetic speculations; but it appears to the author to rest upon inadequate grounds.

2. *By Epiboly.*—Here the animal cells grow down over the vegetal cells, enclosing the latter as entoderm (Fig. 73*O*). This mode usually follows unequal holoblastic cleavage, where the yolk-laden vegetal cells are apparently too inert to carry out the active process of invagination and is obviously a modification of the latter method. The end result is the same as by invagination—a two-walled gastrula with archenteron and blastopore (Fig. 74*A*).

3. *By Involution.*—In this case cells turn under and extend beneath the ectoderm to form the entoderm (Fig. 74*K*). This type of entoderm formation is common in meroblastic eggs and appears to be a further modification of epiboly. The place of inturning of the margin of the disk of the discoblastula is more or less related to the symmetry of the future embryo. The gastrula so formed has neither typical archenteron nor blastopore and may be called a *discogastrula* (Fig. 74*K*).

4. *By Delamination.*—This word is not very exact, being generally used to cover all other modes of entoderm formation than the preceding types. For exactness, it is therefore necessary to distinguish several kinds of delamination.

    a. Primary Delamination.—In this, the original meaning of the word delamination and for which the term was invented by Lankester, the inner halves of the cells of the coeloblastula are cut off by cleavage planes parallel to the surface and become the entoderm (Fig. 74*E, F*). Primary delamination was proposed by Lankester as the original mode of entoderm formation, but entoderm formation purely by this method is

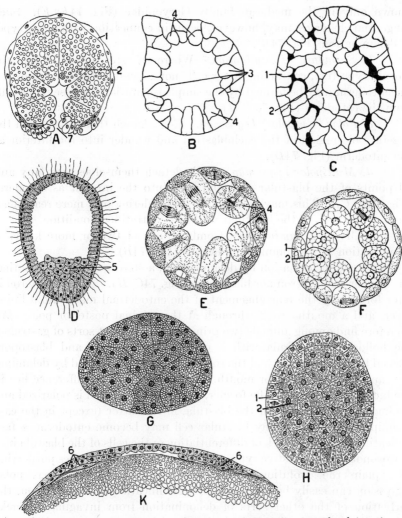

Fig. 74.—Entoderm formation (continued). *A*. Epibolic gastrula, later stage of Fig. 73*O*, *Crepidula*. (*After Conklin*, 1897.) *B*. Formation of the entoderm in the egg of *Hydra*, partly by multipolar ingression, partly by primary delamination. *C*. Completed stereogastrula of *Hydra*. (*B and C after Brauer*, 1891.) *D*. Entoderm formation by unipolar ingression; egg of the hydroid *Clytia*. (*After Metschnikoff*, 1887.) *E* and *F*. Entoderm formation by primary delamination in a geryonid medusa (*after Metschnikoff*, 1882, 1886): *E*, coeloblastula with tangential cleavages beginning; *F*, the resulting stereogastrula. *G* and *H*, Entoderm formation by secondary delamination in the hydroid *Clava*, (*after Harm*, 1903): *G*, stereoblastula or morula; *H*, the interior cells of the same separate from the surface layer as entoderm. *K*. Entoderm formation by involution, further stage of Fig. 73*K*. (*After Watase*, 1888.) 1, ectoderm; 2, entoderm; 3, cells migrating into interior; 4, cells undergoing primary delamination; 5, unipolar ingression; 6, involution.

known only in the medusan family Geryonidae (Fig. 74*E*, *F*). Such tangential cleavages may, however, occur in connection with other types of delamination (Fig. 74*B*).

b. Secondary Delamination.—Where a stereoblastula of the morula type (i.e., containing inner cells not touching the surface) exists, the entoderm may be formed by the simple separation of these inner cells from the ectoderm (Fig. 74*G, H*).

c. Polar (Unipolar) Ingression.—Cells detach themselves from the vegetal pole region of the coeloblastula and wander into the interior as the entoderm (Fig. 74*D*).

d. Multipolar Ingression.—Cells detach themselves from any and all points of the blastular wall and pass into the interior as entoderm (Fig. 74*B, C*). This may be an active inwandering or a mere rearrangement of the cells of the blastular wall into a stratified condition.

e. Mixed Delamination.—Combinations of two or more kinds of delamination are of common occurrence (Fig. 74*B*).

In entoderm formation by delamination, a stereogastrula results that has neither archenteron nor blastopore (Fig. 74*C, H*). An archenteron is later formed by the rearrangement of the entodermal mass into a lining layer, and a mouth breaks through at the original posterior pole. We therefore find among animals two principal and distinct sorts of gastrulae: the hollow archigastrula with a primary archenteron and blastopore formed by invagination; and the solid stereogastrula formed by delamination and lacking cavity or mouth. A more disturbing difference lies in the fact that whereas, in the former, entoderm formation is polarized and confined to certain cells of the blastula, in the latter (except in the case of unipolar ingression) any blastular cell may become entoderm, a fact indicating a complete lack of differentiation of the cells of the blastula into sensorimotor and digestive types and nullifying all the theories purporting to explain the evolution of the two-layered state. Whereas polar ingression can easily be conceived as a modification of invagination, the derivation of the other sorts of delamination from invagination lacks plausibility. Furthermore, it is in the lowest metazoan phyla, the Porifera and Cnidaria, whose embryology might be expected to conform most nearly to the original type, that entoderm formation by delamination and the production of stereogastrulae are of most common occurrence.

The Haeckelian idea of entoderm formation by invagination is universally accepted as the original mode, and all other methods as derived. For reasons already stated (page 252), entoderm formation by ingression seems the more probable and natural original method, and entoderm formation by invagination a derived shortened way of achieving the two-layered condition that is a necessary preliminary to further complication. At any rate there is no adequate basis for the assurance with which invagination is commonly declared to be the primary mode of entoderm formation. It would at least be more reasonable to state that the available evidence does not justify any definite conclusion on the matter. It does appear certain that the first step in the evolution toward a more complex morphology is the change of some cells from a surface to an interior position. The method by which this is accomplished, whether by infolding or inwandering, does not appear to be of importance; what is important is that a functional difference is thereby established through a difference in relation to the external world. The degree of complexity attained by the gastrula is not great; but it is of interest to note that further elaboration is accomplished by a repetition of this same process—the relegation of still more cells to the interior as the mesoderm or so-called third germ layer. This pushes itself between ectoderm and entoderm again either through infolding or inwandering; and from the layers and cell masses so established, a variety of organs arise again fundamentally by these same two methods. In place of the perennial transcendental search for one original primitive mode of germ-layer formation, we might perhaps substitute the view that infolding and inwandering (better designated as the *epithelial* and *mesenchymal* modes of tissue and organ formation) are two methods by which increase in structural complexity is accomplished in animals. All the evidence seems to the author to indicate that the mesenchymal mode is the primitive one (see Chap. IX further); but in any event both were present in Metazoa rather early, one or the other is employed according to circumstances, and a part formed epithelially in one animal may arise mesenchymally in another, even related, form.

In many invertebrates the embryo at the blastula or gastrula or slightly later stage becomes flagellated or ciliated and escapes as a free-swimming larva (Fig. 72*H*). Different types of larvae are characteristic of different groups of animals. Larvae are believed in many cases to approximate ancestral forms, and consequently much phylogenetic speculation has been based upon their characters.

IV. THE DIPLOBLASTIC PHYLA

The term *diploblastic*, meaning two-layered, is commonly applied to those groups of lower invertebrates which consist essentially of two epithelia, an outer and an inner one. These two epithelia are called ectoderm and entoderm. But ectoderm and entoderm are embryological terms, and the body epithelia of even the simplest Eumetazoa differ considerably from the corresponding larval layers. The author therefore proposes that the names ectoderm and entoderm be limited to developmental stages and that a uniform terminology be adopted for the covering and digestive epithelia of adult invertebrates. It is suggested that the covering epithelium be called *epidermis* throughout the invertebrates and the lining of the digestive tract in general be called *gastrodermis*. These words have the further advantage that they avoid embryological implications, i.e., the gastrodermis need not necessarily be entodermal throughout.

Now in fact the three lowest metazoan phyla—Porifera, Cnidaria, and Ctenophora—are not really diploblastic, with the exception of the coelenterate class Hydrozoa. All the others are actually three-layered or triploblastic, having a cellular stratum between epidermis and gastrodermis (Fig. 75*B*). This stratum consists of some type of connective tissue. If one frees oneself from outworn theories dating from Haeckel, one sees at once that there is no essential difference between a cross section of a sea anemone (Fig. 75*B*) commonly called "diploblastic" and a cross section of a flatworm commonly called "triploblastic." And the same is found to be true on impartial examination of the other alleged diploblastic groups except Hydrozoa. In sponges, for instance, a mesenchyme, often very abundant, exists between the outer and inner epithelia; it originates in common with the epidermis and consists of a gelatinous matrix in which there are embedded several types of amoeboid cells capable of functioning in a variety of ways. In the coelenterates the jelly between epidermis and gastrodermis is devoid of cellular elements only in the class Hydrozoa, and even in this group the undifferentiated interstitial cells could be regarded as a sort of mesenchyme. In Scyphozoa this middle layer is a jelly containing cells and fibers, and in Anthozoa it is either a gelatinous mesenchyme or a fibrous connective tissue; in both groups the cellular elements appear to be derived chiefly from the ectoderm, although the entoderm may contribute in some forms. Among the Ctenophora the mesenchyme reaches a high degree of development, containing connective tissue and muscle cells. In the older accounts the cells of the ctenophore mesenchyme were stated to be of entodermal origin; but it is now thought probable that they come from the ectoderm. Thus in the three so-called diploblastic phyla, a cellular layer, chiefly of ectodermal origin, is present between epi- and gastrodermis (except in Hydrozoa). The terms diploblastic and triploblastic will therefore be abandoned altogether, and a better basis for distinguishing the lower from the higher Metazoa will be sought.

It was first pointed out by the brothers O. and R. Hertwig (1882) that the mesoderm originates in two ways: as a loose connective tissue, which they called *mesenchyme,* and as an epithelium, the *mesoblast,* now designated *mesothelium.* Mesenchyme comes from epithelial cells that detach themselves from the epithelium (Fig. 75*A*), become amoeboid, and wander into interior spaces as primitive connective tissue cells.

The Hertwigs noted that a mesenchymal mesoderm occurs in the so-called diploblastic as well as in the higher phyla, that it may remain connective tissue or may differentiate into other types of cells, and that its time of origin in the embryo is unrelated to the usual sequence of developmental events. They attempted to draw a sharp distinction between groups of animals in which the mesoderm is mesenchymal at its inception and those

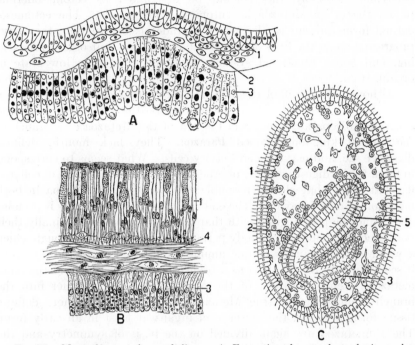

Fig. 75.—Mesenchyme and mesothelium. *A.* Formation of mesenchyme by inwandering of ectoderm cells, in the alcyonarian *Sympodium.* (*After Kowalevsky and Marion,* 1883.) *B.* Cross section through the body wall of a sea anemone showing the three-layered condition; between ectoderm and entoderm is a thick layer of connective tissue containing amoeboid cells; from slide. (*Courtesy of A. E. Galigher.*) *C.* Simultaneous formation of mesothelium and mesenchyme from the archenteron of an echinoderm embryo. (*After Selenka,* 1876.) The archenteron gives off a mesothelial pouch (future water vascular system), and also some of its cells wander into the interior as mesenchyme. 1, ectoderm; 2, mesenchyme; 3, entoderm; 4, connective tissue layer; 5, mesothelial pouch.

where it begins as epithelium. This idea is now known to have been mistaken, since in many groups mesoderm may originate by both methods but it contains the germ of a distinction that still seems to hold. There are apparently two sorts of mesoderm that cannot be homologized with each other. The one kind arises from the embryonic ectoderm and hence is termed the *ectomesoderm,* also the *larval mesoblast.* It is always mesenchymal, never epithelial, and is the only sort of mesoderm occurring in the three so-called diploblastic phyla. It is, however, also formed in several triploblastic phyla where it plays a minor role, since the great mass of their mesoderm is of the second type, i.e., of entodermal origin, and may be either mesenchymal or epithelial (Fig. 75C).

The Porifera, Cnidaria, and Ctenophora cannot therefore be accurately characterized as "diploblastic" phyla; but rather as phyla in which the mesoderm is chiefly an ectomesoderm and exclusively mesenchymal. Possibly they should be designated as ectomesodermal phyla, the other Metazoa as entomesodermal phyla. The ectomesodermal forms present a relatively low grade of construction; they have progressed along the lines of cellular differentiation, but organs are lacking, and hence functional systems have remained in a low state of organization.

Although the Porifera resemble the other ectomesodermal groups in the foregoing respects, their many peculiarities have led zoologists generally to separate them from the rest of the Metazoa as a branch of the animal kingdom, named Parazoa. They lack mouth, definite digestive sac, and nervous and sensory cells. What seems to correspond in them to the digestive lining of other metazoans is composed of collared flagellate cells that closely resemble choanoflagellate protozoa in both morphology and behavior. The embryonic history of sponges is peculiar and cannot be homologized with that of other metazoans. Finally their porous construction with a body permeated with channels through which a water current runs is unique among animals. For all these reasons it seems best to regard them as a branch diverging early from the main metazoan stem. The rest of the Metazoa are put together into the branch Eumetazoa, or true Metazoa, characterized by more definite tissue formation and the presence of organs at least in an early form. The Eumetazoa are again divided on the basis of symmetry and the relations and mode of origin of the mesoderm and coelom.

The ectomesodermal groups of the Eumetazoa present a certain uniformity and are often included in the one phylum Coelenterata. We here prefer to consider the Ctenophora as a separate phylum. These groups possess digestive, nervous, and muscular systems in simple form. The digestive system has achieved the greatest advance, being provided with a mouth and a definite cavity, which is usually greatly branched and serves for distribution as well as digestion of food. For this reason it is generally termed a *gastrovascular* system. In these groups there also begins a structure universal throughout the higher Metazoa, namely, a *stomodaeum* or initial section of the digestive tract formed by inturned ectoderm. However, the digestive tube consists only of the lining epithelium; an anus is absent, the mouth serving as both entrance and exit; and the process of digestion is chiefly or wholly intracellular, i.e., follows the protozoan method. The nervous system consists of a net throughout the body wall with some centralization in a ring encircling the mouth. Probably in correlation with the radial symmetry there is thus no definite development of a head or anterior end containing a concentrated mass of nervous tissue. Sense organs may, however, reach a high degree of differentiation. The muscular system consists of layers of fibrils that in the lower coelenterates may not be completely separated from the epi- and gastrodermal epithelial cells from which they arise; in ctenophores there are separate muscle cells of mesenchymal origin. The sex cells originate from indifferent cells or from the epidermal or gastrodermal epithelium; and may go through their maturation in more or less definite reproductive organs (gonads). The blastoporal end of the larvae becomes the oral end of the adult.

In addition to their general lack of or low state of development of organs and organ systems, the coelenterates and ctenophores contrast with the other Eumetazoa in the following particulars: They are characterized by primary *radial* or *biradial* symmetry, whereas all the other Eumetazoa are *bilateral*. By primary symmetry is meant that the symmetry type of the embryo or larva is retained throughout ontogeny. On the basis of symmetry, the Eumetazoa may therefore be divided into the radiate forms or *Radiata*, a term going back to Cuvier, including now only the Cnidaria and the Ctenophora; and the bilateral forms or *Bilateria* embracing all the other phyla of the Eumetazoa. These terms will hereinafter be employed as here defined. Another difference between the Radiata and the majority of the Bilateria is that in the former no body spaces exist between epidermis and gastrodermis; these layers are in contact or connected by mesenchyme. The sole cavity in the body is the cavity of the digestive tract, and for this reason the Radiata are often designated the *Enterocoela*. The contrasting term for the rest of the Eumetazoa is *Coelomocoela* or *Coelomata* to indicate the occurrence of spaces other than the cavity of the gut. This terminology is objectionable, however, because the nature of the spaces in question is uncertain in some groups, and furthermore in certain phyla, such as the Platyhelminthes and Nemertinea, no such spaces actually exist but are assumed on theoretical grounds. Still other names for these eumetazoan groupings are based on the relations of the larval and adult axes of symmetry. In the development of the Radiata, the larval axis is retained as the adult axis of symmetry and the blastoporal end becomes the oral surface, developing a mouth or retaining the blastopore as mouth. Hatschek suggested the name *Protaxonia* for the radiate phyla, to express this persistence of the larval axis, and *Heteraxonia* for the bilateral phyla in which the larval and adult main axes of symmetry do not coincide. A certain amount of speculation is, however, involved in the latter idea. Altogether the terms Radiata and Bilateria seem the most suitable.

The Radiata may then be characterized as animals in which cell and tissue differentiation have made considerable progress, but in which only a slight amount of organ formation has occurred; in which symmetry is of the radial or biradial or radiobilateral type; in which the digestive tube lacks an anus and is the sole cavity in the body, no space being present between epidermis and gastrodermis; in which the nervous system is poorly concentrated and no definite head has been developed; in which the mesoderm is always mesenchymatous and chiefly of ectodermal origin; and in which the larval axis of symmetry is retained as the anteroposterior axis of the adult, the anterior end of the larva becoming aboral, the posterior end, oral, and the blastopore serving typically as mouth.

V. THE GERM-LAYER THEORY

A *germ layer* may be defined as an embryonic cell stratum from which adult organs arise. The facts of embryology seem to indicate that the formation of germ layers is preliminary to organogenesis. Ordinarily organs do not arise directly from the cleavage cells, although it is difficult to see why this should not occur. The development of layers before organogenesis is more pronounced in indeterminate development. In cases of determinate cleavage or *mosaic development*, as such development is often termed, there is a direct relation between the blastomeres and the future organs, but even in such cases the blastomeres become arranged in layers before differentiating into the organs for which they are predestined. It is probable that the layered condition of the early embryo is simply necessitated by the fact that the external and lining layers of animals cannot be other than epithelia.

The ectoderm and the entoderm are called the *primary germ layers;* the former is always epithelial, the latter may start out as a cell mass but eventually becomes epithelial. From the entoderm arises the so-called third germ layer, the *mesoderm*, which pushes in between ectoderm and entoderm. It is never actually a single layer; if epithelial it is double, consisting of *somatic* and *splanchnic* layers; and if mesenchymal, it is a stratum several cells thick. After formation of the mesoderm, the ectoderm and entoderm are often considered no longer primary, and are then together with the mesoderm called *secondary* germ layers. Again, the names *ectoblast* or *epiblast* and *entoblast* or *hypoblast* have been proposed for the secondary ectoderm and entoderm, although earlier authors employed a reverse usage that really seems more logical, terming the primary layers ectoblast and entoblast and the derived ones ectoderm and entoderm. Now these terms are considered synonymous and those ending in -blast have more or less passed out of usage. The secondary entoderm has more recently been designated *enteroderm*, to express the fact that the gut is its chief derivative.

The fact that the young (vertebrate) embryo consists of parallel layers struck the attention of the early students of embryology such as K. F. Wolff, writing in 1759–1764, and Pander, in 1817. The eminent embryologist, von Baer, whose leading work appeared in 1828, noted the organs that came from these layers (in the chick) and distinguished four layers: the outer, forming skin and nervous system; the second, source of flesh and bones; the third, or vascular layer; and the fourth gut-forming layer. Remak, 1851–1854, reduced the layers to three—outer sensory, middle motor, and inner trophic—and although these names are obsolete, the layers have since been considered with respect to their functions as three in number. The idea of a homology or correspondence of these layers throughout the animal kingdom seems to have originated with Huxley who in 1849 compared the two layers of coelenterates with the outer and inner layers of vertebrates. This germ-layer theory, or idea of the correspondence of the germ layers throughout the Metazoa, received strong support from the many studies on the embryology of various animals that were made after 1850 and was brilliantly urged by Lankester and Haeckel, the latter adopting it as one of the prominent parts of his phylogenetic speculations.

The germ-layer theory states that in the development of all Metazoa first the two primary germ layers, ectoderm and entoderm, and then in the higher Metazoa the third layer, mesoderm, are formed; that these layers were formed originally if not now in the same way throughout the Metazoa; that from each of them the same organs are produced; and, in short, that these layers are everywhere homologous. Any embryonic processes deviating from this formula are regarded as modified or derived processes.

As regards the homology of the ectoderm and entoderm, it has already been seen that the entoderm may arise in various ways. Further, in some cases it comes from a definite, predetermined region of the blastula— the posterior cells—while in others, as in multiple ingression, any blastular cell may become entoderm. To avoid these discrepancies, it might be assumed that the germ-layer theory holds only after entoderm formation. This view encounters the difficulty that the gastrula presents a variety of form, and in some cases simple inspection does not suffice to determine which cells or layer is entoderm. Still more at variance with the theory is the embryonic history of sponges, where an apparently typical invagination gastrula or a stereogastrula is formed. But in the former, it is the anterior half that invaginates, i.e., the half that generally throughout the Metazoa becomes ectoderm; and in the stereogastrula, the inner mass, which in coelenterates is entoderm, in sponges migrates later to the outer surface and becomes the covering epithelium. As regards the history of the mesoderm, even less conformity to the theory is encountered.

The mesoderm may be formed in various ways in different animals, and at different times, and in many cases in more than one way in the same organism. As already stated, it is chiefly of ectodermal origin in the radiate phyla, and of entodermal or both entodermal and ectodermal origin in the bilateral groups. It may begin as mesenchyme or mesothelium, and each may later assume the other tissue form. In some cases, as in echinoderms, part of the mesoderm arises before the entoderm does. The mesoderm may at its initiation consist of whole layers or masses; or as in the groups with determinate cleavage may be derived from a single cell.

From the foregoing facts it is clear that the germ layers cannot be defined or homologized on the basis of their mode of formation or their topographical relations. There remains the criterion of the kinds of organs formed from them. Here a difference appears between the radial and bilateral phyla, for, in the former, structures such as muscles, which in the latter are of mesodermal origin, come from the ectoderm and entoderm. Naturally as the mesoderm has not yet been formed as a definitive layer, ectoderm and entoderm in the Radiata must perform the functions later taken over by it. Among the Bilateria there is greater uniformity as to the fate of the germ layers, although various discrepancies occur, such as the failure of the ectoderm to remain as the surface covering in some parasitic worms and the origin of the excretory system from different germ layers in different phyla. Nevertheless, among the Bilateria it generally holds true that the ectoderm produces the skin and its derivatives, nervous system, and the end sections of the gut, the entoderm becomes midgut and its derivatives, and the mesoderm is the source of the connective tissues, muscles, and blood vessels. Among the higher Metazoa there is then a wide correspondence between the germ layers as regards their fate and function in ontogeny. In fact a germ layer, as pointed out by Braem, can only be identified by its end products.

Among the chief objections raised to the germ-layer theory is the fact that, in budding, regeneration, and embryonic grafting, organs come from different germ layers than is the case in development. In bryozoans and tunicates, the buds develop very differently from the embryo, entoderm serving as ectoderm, etc. Similar facts are well known from studies of the histology of regenerating parts. The extensive and brilliant work of the Spemann-Mangold school on grafts in amphibian embryos has shown that any germ layer, if taken at a young enough stage and if placed in the proper circumstances, can form any organs whatsoever. Yet all these facts seem outside the question. The germ-layer theory is not concerned with the possible capacities of embryonic or regenerative cells but rather with the course of normal development, whether or not this follows some similar plan throughout the animal phyla. To this question it seems that a positive answer must be returned.

A more cogent objection arises from the mode of development of eggs with determinate cleavage in which blastomeres or groups of blastomeres proceed almost directly to organ formation without any very definite interpolation of a germ-layer stage. Nevertheless such development is generally regarded as derived and shortened from the indeterminate type. On the other hand, it may well be that the layered condition is adapted to certain other circumstances. Thus the formation of very obvious germ layers appears to happen most commonly in highly yolky eggs where the yolk must be rapidly enclosed by cellular layers in order that it may be utilized by the embryo. In such cases also there is often a precocious and rapid formation of mesoderm to provide a circulation for the yolk sac. Probably both the direct differentiation of blastomeres into organs and a prolonged layered condition are modifications of an original mode of development.

Other ways of looking at embryonic development have been suggested. Most commonly broached is an idea that apparently originated with Reichert in 1843 according to which the organs are regarded as originating from *primordia* or primitive embryonic parts. As soon as such a primordium separates out from the indifferent embryonic material, its fate can be determined. On this basis determinate and indeterminate modes of development are readily reconciled, as the blastomeres are considered primordia in the one case, the germ layers in the other. The latter are primordia from which several primordia may be derived. No attempt is made on this conception to homologize the primordia in different animals. The idea is flexible and can necessarily meet with no exceptions; but it evades the remarkable similarity of embryonic development evidenced in many groups. Still another suggestion is that of O. Hertwig, that each embryonic stage is mechanically conditioned by the preceding one, that a layered condition must necessarily result from further development of the blastula, etc. Yet the innumerable variations in the developmental process speak against such a mechanical theory. Development seems both to conform to and to vary from some general plan.

It may be concluded that no uniformity any longer exists in the mode of formation of the germ layers or in the early processes of development. The available facts are inadequate either to affirm or deny some original uniform method of germ-layer formation, although the evidence favors the mesenchymal mode of origin. On the other hand it can scarcely be doubted that the later stages of development exhibit a certain similarity especially in the Bilateria and that in general each germ layer gives rise to certain definite organs. The doctrine of the homology of the germ layers may therefore be considered as broadly acceptable and if applied with caution may be used in interpreting embryological facts. It must always be borne in mind that a developing embryo is living, plastic, and modifiable, responding to changed conditions by morphological changes. Probably no development at present adheres to its original course, but all ontogenies have undergone changes, such as shortening of some stages, prolongation of others, precocious development of certain parts (heterochronism), and production of larval organs adapted to a free-swimming life. We may assume a general tendency toward cutting short and condensing stages no longer essential to the life of the embryo or to the development of future organs, and toward the precocious or new appearance of useful parts. Every ontogeny is a compromise between an inherited ancestral mode of development and adaptive modifications and adjustments.

VI. THE LAW OF RECAPITULATION

The conformity of embryonic processes throughout the Metazoa at once suggests some underlying principle, and Haeckel with his genius for generalization was not long in supplying one of his brilliantly worded aphorisms to meet the situation. This statement, based on the doctrine of evolution, is called the *biogenetic law* or the *law of recapitulation*. In its briefest form it states that "*ontogeny* (developmental history) *repeats phylogeny* (race history)"; or, in another of Haeckel's phrases, that phylogenesis is the mechanical cause of ontogenesis, which is to say, that animals have an embryonic history because they have a long train of ancestors behind them. Clearly stated, the law of recapitulation asserts that the embryonic stages of a higher animal resemble the adult states of its ancestors and that therefore in its development an animal presents to the observer the successive ancestors that it had in its evolution. On this point of view, every metazoan embryo passes through a blastula and a gastrula stage, because the blastaea and the gastraea were the common ancestors of the Metazoa. Haeckel was not so clear as to the anatomical construction of the later ancestral forms. An important part of the theory is the distinction between ancestral and adaptive characters in development, the former termed *palingenetic*, the latter *coenogenetic*. Palingenetic characters are those directly retained without alteration from the ancestors; coenogenetic characters are acquired adaptive modifications which do not reflect ancestral forms. Haeckel recognized that many developmental features are of this latter sort; but it is not clear by what criteria they are to be distinguished from ancestral characters.

The law of recapitulation was by no means original with Haeckel. The resemblance of the embryos of higher animals to lower animals had been noticed by the Greeks but was not again emphasized until the dawn of modern embryology at the beginning of the nineteenth century. Meckel (1811) stressed this "parallelism" between the embryos of higher animals and adult states of lower ones, and noted that the stages of development resemble the grades of increasing structural complexity into which the lower animals can be arranged.   Von Baer (1828) objected to Meckel's parallelism between embryos and adults, insisting that the embryos of higher forms resemble only the embryos, not the adults, of lower forms.   He expressed the results of his embryological studies in four laws: (1) the general characters of a group of animals appear earlier in development than the special ones; (2) from the more general characters the less general arise successively until the end specific features are produced, i.e., the characters of the class appear first, then the characters of the order, the family, the genus, etc.; (3) an embryo of a definite species tends to diverge from rather than to resemble the embryo of other species; (4) an embryo is not like the adult of a lower form but only like its embryo.   The fourth rule opposes Meckel's idea and Haeckel's recapitulation theory; but the second rule practically admits that embryonic stages correspond to ancestral stages.   Haeckel's recapitulation borrows more directly, however, from F. Müller (1864) whose conception of the relation of phylogeny to ontogeny was somewhat broader than Haeckel's.   He considered that evolution might occur in two ways: by divergence from the ancestral path during development, and by the addition of new stages at the end of development.   Haeckel adopted Müller's second idea for his law of recapitulation, which is therefore more justly designated the Müller-Haeckel law, and invented the conception of coenogenesis to account for Müller's first supposition.

The law of recapitulation has been severely criticized in many quarters since its enunciation and has been rejected altogether by a number of present-day embryologists.   The chief criticism against it has been well summarized by Garstang.   He and many others have pointed out that in evolution adult forms do not succeed each other but that rather, as each animal is the end result of an ontogenetic process, phylogeny consists of a succession of entire ontogenies.   Any evolutionary alteration of an adult animal must be the consequence of some change in its ontogeny.   The ontogenies therefore of animals closely related by descent will remain similar up to a certain point and will then diverge.   In consequence the embryos of the descendant species will never resemble the adults of the ancestors because they diverge during development before they reach the end ancestral condition.   Thus embryonic stages do not resemble adult ancestors but only embryonic stages of the ancestors.   For example, although all the higher Metazoa pass through a gastrula stage, their gastrulae are never anything like an actual adult coelenterate. The general steps by which advance in structural complexity was achieved persist in a simplified form in the ontogenies of the higher animals, but their embryos do not actually reproduce the adult ancestors that culminated each of these steps. The critics of this type therefore reject Haeckel's statement of the law of recapitulation altogether, adopting von Baer's fourth rule as a more correct representation of the facts. They consider that there are no palingenetic characters but that all embryonic characters have been modified from the ancestral ontogenies and are therefore coenogenetic.

Despite these criticisms the law of recapitulation has continued to find favor with some embryologists and with most paleontologists, and has been urged anew by a group of modern Russian comparative anatomists. In embryology there are many cases where parasitic or sessile forms before undergoing their final degenerative changes pass through an ontogenetic stage closely resembling the adults of well-known free-living groups. Many examples, of which the ammonites are notable, are cited by paleontologists where young stages of more recent fossils are very like the adults of geologically older specimens believed to be their ancestors. The most clear-cut analysis of the relation between phylogeny and ontogeny comes from a Russian school headed by A. N. Sewertzoff, who have made an actual extensive comparison between developmental stages and ancestral adults; and it is their work that will now be summarized.[1]

Their studies have shown that the relation between phylogeny and ontogeny (Sewertzoff uses the word *phylembryogenesis* to express this relation) does not follow any one rule but is of several different sorts.

1. Addition, Prolongation, or Anaboly.—In this type, the development follows the ancestral pattern up to the last ancestral ontogenetic stage, to which further new stages are added. It may be represented by the following scheme in which small letters stand for embryonic stages, capitals for the definitive adult stage:

$$a \ b \ c \ d \ D$$
$$a \ b \ c \ d \ e \ E.$$

The descendant follows the ancestral ontogeny through the stage d and then adds on a stage e, which leads directly to the definitive adult stage E. This type of ontogeny, which appears to be widespread among animals, practically conforms to the Müller-Haeckel law of recapitulation, since the stage d of the descendant is identical with the last ontogenetic stage d of the ancestor, which in turn differs but little from the adult ancestral condition D. Strictly speaking, the adult ancestor is not repeated in the ontogeny of the descendants but only the

---

[1] The discussion is drawn from the writings of Sewertzoff, Matveiev, and Jeschikoff.

final ontogenetic stage of the ancestor. Addition also explains von Baer's first and second rules.

2. Deviation.—Here the ontogeny of the descendant follows the ancestral pattern to a certain stage and then diverges along a new line, thus:

$$a \ b \ c \ d \ e \ f \ F$$
$$a \ b \ c \ d_1 \ e_1 \ f_1 \ F_1$$

This mode of ontogeny does not conform to Haeckel's law as regards recent ancestors, which are not repeated, but can in fact be regarded as a case of recapitulation, since the remote ancestors A, B, and C are practically repeated by the stages a, b, and c. Consequently the real difference between addition and deviation is that in the one the near ancestors, and in the other the remote ancestors, are recapitulated. Deviation is identical with von Baer's fourth rule, appears to be of common occurrence, and is the mode of ontogeny accepted by many of the critics of the law of recapitulation.

3. Archallaxis.—Here the development from the beginning deviates from the ancestral pattern so that there is no recapitulation of either embryonic or adult ancestral characters, thus:

$$a \ b \ c \ d \ e \ f \ F$$
$$a_1 \ b_1 \ c_1 \ d_1 \ e_1 \ f_1 \ F_1$$

Such cases conform neither to Haeckel's nor to von Baer's conceptions.

4. Abbreviation.—The end stages of the ancestral ontogeny are omitted so that the definitive adult of the descendant resembles the adult of a remote rather than a recent ancestor:

$$a \ b \ c \ d \ e \ f \ F$$
$$a \ b \ c \ d \ e \ E_1$$

Cases of neoteny, in which a larval form attains sexual maturity and functions as an adult would also fall under this head. By such omission of the end stages of development, structures may also remain in a rudimentary or simple state or disappear altogether.

5. Acceleration.—Here the middle stages of the ancestral ontogeny are dropped out so that the later structures appear in the ontogeny of the descendant at an earlier stage than they did in the immediate ancestors:

$$a \ b \ c \ d \ e \ f \ F$$
$$a \ b \ e_1 \ f_1 \ F_1$$

This process of embryonic acceleration is seen with regard to parts essential to the life of the embryo or larva and also in the case of structures displaying a high degree of progressive evolution.

6. Omission of the early ontogenetic stages and deviation of the later ones:

$$a \; b \; c \; d \; e \; f \; F$$
$$b_1 \; c_1 \; d_1 \; e_1 \; f_1 \; F_1$$

Such omission of early stages may be followed by progressive evolution in the structures concerned or may result in rudimentation of an organ, which then appears in later and later stages of ontogeny in a smaller and smaller condition and may eventually disappear altogether from the ontogeny.

7. Coenogenesis.—This term should be restricted to the appearance of special adaptations, in larval or embryonic life, that are new formations, have no ancestral significance, and disappear during larval or embryonic life.

8. Heterochronism.—Under this name have been included a variety of time displacements in development in which organs appear earlier or later than is the case in the ancestral ontogeny. Some of these cases fit into the foregoing categories, e.g., acceleration, while others have not been sufficiently analyzed.

From the foregoing discussion it is evident that the developmental stages of an animal may resemble adult ancestors or the embryonic stages of an ancestor or may deviate somewhat from either of these or may bear no resemblance at all to an ancestor. The same remark applies to individual parts or organs of embryos. Resemblance to ancestral forms, embryonic or adult, is a common and widespread phenomenon, and consequently the practice of drawing phylogenetic conclusions from the study of development is to a large extent justifiable. Recapitulation in its narrow Haeckelian sense, as repetition of adult ancestors, is not generally applicable; but ancestral resemblance during ontogeny is a general biological principle. There is no need to quibble over the word recapitulation; either the usage of the word should be altered to include any type of ancestral reminiscence during ontogeny, or some new term should be invented.

VII. CELLULAR DIFFERENTIATION

All the various types of cells known in animals make their appearance early in the Metazoa. The principal cell forms of animals are: *epithelial, connective, muscular, nervous,* and *reproductive.* A complex of approximately like cells is called a *tissue.* A combination of two or more kinds of cells or tissues into a functioning whole is termed an *organ.* The radiate phyla are constructed of cells and tissues with but little aggregation of these into organs.

The causes of cell differentiation are unknown but appear to lie primarily in surrounding conditions. It is probable that any cell can transform into any other type of cell under proper circumstances or if acted upon early enough in ontogenesis. But fully differentiated adult cells can also transform into other types. It appears, however, that many animals contain a stock of undifferentiated, somewhat embryonic cells that come into action in cases of injury, regeneration, asexual reproduction, etc., and differentiate into any type of cell.

Epithelial cells are regarded as the most primitive type of metazoan cell since the simplest Metazoa and the early stages of metazoan embryos consist largely of epithelial cells. Epithelial cells are always united by means of protoplasmic bridges or a thin cement into sheets to form *epithelial tissue*, more briefly termed an *epithelium*, which covers and lines all the free body surfaces, both external and internal. The forming of a protective covering is therefore the primary function of an epithelium. Epithelia are *simple*, i.e., composed of a single layer of cells, or *stratified*, consisting of many layers; those of the invertebrates are almost always simple, sometimes *pseudostratified*. The following sorts of epithelia occur in invertebrates; unless otherwise specified they are understood to be simple.

1. *Squamous* or flattened, in which the cells are flattened to a thin layer. This type is most common as the lining of blood vessels and other internal spaces (Fig. 76*H, K*). Such flat internal linings are often designated *endothelia*, but no real basis exists for distinguishing them from external epithelia.

2. *Cuboidal*, composed of squarish cells (Fig. 76*F*).

3. *Columnar*, composed of tall cells (Fig. 76*A, G, M*).

4. *Pseudostratified*, in which some of the cells of a usually columnar epithelium are forced inward so that they barely touch the surface or do not touch it at all, giving an appearance of an epithelium two or three layers thick.

5. *Ciliated*, with the free surface of each cell bearing a number of cilia. Ciliated epithelium is always cuboidal or columnar (Fig. 76*A*).

6. *Flagellated*, with a single long flagellum springing from the free surface of each cell, otherwise much like ciliated epithelium.

7. *Glandular*, when the cells have secretory functions and are filled with the granules that become the secretion (Fig. 76*G*).

8. *Nutritive*, referring to the lining of the digestive tract.

9. *Pigmented*, when containing pigment granules, usually either of the melanin type, brown to black, or of the lipochrome type, red and yellow.

10. *Sensory*, when the cells are altered to sensory cells (Fig. 76*M*).

11. *Germinal*, when giving rise to sex cells.

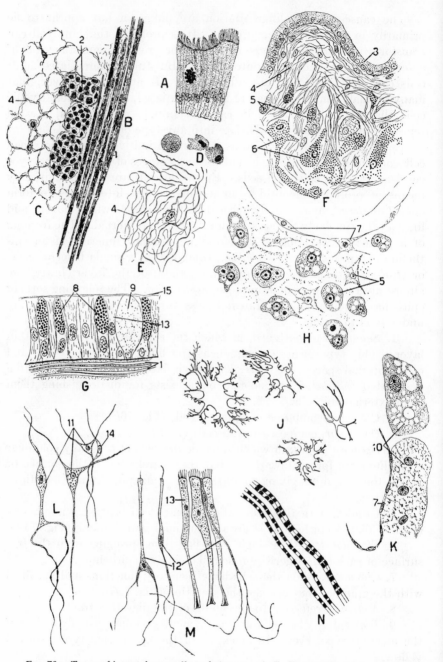

FIG. 76.—Types of invertebrate cells and tissues. A–E. Tissues of a fresh-water clam:
A, columnar ciliated epithelium of the digestive tract; B, smooth muscle bundles, C,
fibrous reticular connective tissue; D, free amoeboid cells; E, fibrous connective tissue, from

Epithelial cells are generally polarized with respect to the free and attached surfaces; the polarity is evidenced by the position of the nucleus and the arrangement of organoids and inclusions. The interior is often granular or fibrillar. The basal end rests upon a basement membrane and is often amoeboid or may be drawn out into muscular fibrils. The free end often bears a border of modified protoplasm that may be condensed or striated ("brush border") or provided with rows of granules. The surface epithelium in invertebrates often secretes a noncellular protective covering, called cuticle (Fig. 76G) when merely a thin flexible membrane, exoskeleton when thick and hard due to impregnation with lime.

Single cells or whole areas of an ordinary epithelium may differentiate into the various sorts specified above. Very common is the formation of single gland cells, also called *unicellular glands* (Fig. 76G). These are filled with granules or spherules that are ejected as secretions useful to the animal, generally enzymes or protective slime. Unicellular glands are generally pyriform or conical with either the broad or the narrow end at the surface. When an epithelial area becomes glandular this may remain flush with the surface or nearly so but commonly invaginates into a tubular or rounded structure termed a *simple* gland. The tubular or rounded (*acinous*) invaginations may branch again to form a *compound* gland. The connection with the surface commonly becomes a *duct*.

Another common differentiation of epithelial cells of the external surface consists in their transformation into *sensory* cells. These may be single or combined in groups to form a *sense organ*, generally with the cooperation of other types of cells. Sensory cells or sense organs may be supplied with nerve fibers from the nervous system or may themselves be actual nerve cells, with an elongated sensory end extending to or beyond the surface and with a more deeply situated cell body from which a fiber runs to the nervous system. For accuracy the latter type is termed *sensory nerve* cell (Fig. 76M).

---

general visceral mass. *F*. Section through the body wall of a snail, showing cuboidal epithelium, fibrous connective tissue, free amoeboid cells, and black pigment cells. *G*. Section through the epidermis of an earthworm, showing gland cells among the regular epithelial cells; smooth muscle fibers below the epithelium. *H*. Section through a freshwater sponge, showing flat squamous epithelium lining a canal and mesenchyme made of free amoeboid cells. *J*. Pigment cells of a shrimp (*after Degner*, 1912); the smallest one is yellow, the largest gray, the two medium ones red. *K*. Fat cells and flat squamous epithelium of a grasshopper, from slide. (*Courtesy A. E. Galigher.*) *L*. Group of four nerve cells and *M*, three sensory nerve cells with three epithelial cells, all from a sea anemone. (*L* and *M* after the Hertwigs, 1879.) *N*. Striated muscle fibers of a crayfish, showing alternating light and dark disks. 1, smooth muscle fibers lengthwise; 2, same in cross section; 3 epithelium; 4, fibrous connective tissue; 5, free amoeboid cells; 6, pigment cells; 7, squamous epithelium; 8, gland cells filled with secretion granules; 9, same after discharge of granules; 10, fat cells; 11, multipolar ganglion cells; 12, sensory nerve cells; 13, columnar epithelial cells; 14, bipolar ganglion cell; 15, cuticle.

The lining of the digestive tract is always an epithelium, and in the radiate phyla this entodermal epithelium constitutes the entire digestive system. The epithelium of the digestive tract serves in whole or in part in food utilization and may be termed a nutritive epithelium. It is commonly a columnar epithelium (Fig. 76A), sometimes ciliated or flagellated, and in the lower forms is interspersed with unicellular glands. In the lower phyla it is both absorptive and digestive, being highly phagocytic and engulfing and digesting food particles like a protozoan. In the higher phyla it is purely absorptive.

The connective or supporting tissues are always located internally between other parts and as the name implies serve to lend strength and firmness to the body. They are characterized by the loose, scattered arrangement of their cells and by the *intercellular* substance—fluid, gelatinous, fibrillar, or hard—in which the cells lie and which they secrete. Connective tissue is in the final analysis of epithelial origin, consisting of cells that have loosened themselves from an epithelium, become amoeboid, and migrated internally. Such primitive connective-tissue cells are termed *amoebocytes* or *mesenchymal* cells. They may exist independently, hardly associated into any proper tissue, or may be held together by a more or less firm intercellular secretion into a definite connective tissue. To the former class belong the blood cells, pigment cells, wandering amoebocytes, etc., of many invertebrates. As definitive connective tissues of invertebrates may be listed *mesenchymal, fatty, fibrillar,* and *chondroid* types.

Scattered amoebocytes that wander about in body fluids and spaces are very common in invertebrates. They constitute the so-called blood cells, resembling the lymphocytes of vertebrates. These usually do not contain the oxygen-carrying chemical, for this in invertebrates is commonly dissolved in the fluid part of the blood. Most of these amoebocytes are simply phagocytic in function; others carry reserve food supplies or gather up excretory matters and convey them to the outside. Some acquire coloring matter and become pigment cells (Fig. 76F, J), which may be stationary or wandering and may develop branching pseudopodia. With independent connective-tissue cells may be classed the cells found in many animals, which are believed to be undifferentiated embryonic cells, variously termed archaeocytes, interstitial cells, parenchyma cells, neoblasts, etc., from which the sex cells differentiate in many cases and which are active in wound repair and regenerative processes.

The most primitive of the definitive connective tissues is the *mesenchyme* (Fig. 76H), which consists of amoeboid cells with blunt or delicate pointed pseudopodia, embedded in a fluid or gelatinous secretion. The pseudopodia may touch or coalesce forming a cellular network. When the cells are closely packed, the mesenchyme is often termed *parenchyma:*

when scattered with much gelatinous secretion between them, the name *collenchyma* is sometimes employed. Mesenchyme is widespread in the embryonic development of Metazoa and is persistent in the adult stage of many invertebrates. From mesenchyme are developed the firmer sorts of connective tissue, such as *fibrillar* (Fig. 76C, E, F), in which fibrils are laid down between the cells, and *chondroid*, where the cells secrete a cartilage-like substance, as in many mollusks (Fig. 1D). *Fatty* connective tissue containing fat deposits is known among invertebrates only in insects (Fig. 76K). True cartilage and bone are absent in invertebrates, which tend to secrete external noncellular rather than internal cell-containing hard parts. But true internal skeleton (*endoskeleton*) formed by the mesoderm occurs in echinoderms.

Muscle cells may originate either from epithelial cells or from mesenchyme. It is generally stated that the most primitive muscle cells are the *epitheliomuscular* cells of coelenterates in which the muscles consist of the elongated fibrillar bases of the epithelial cells and form part of the latter. However, as separate muscle cells exist in sponges, this idea may be doubted. Muscle cells are elongated, often fibrillar, cells that accomplish movement by shortening. The majority of invertebrate muscle cells resemble the smooth muscle cells of vertebrates (Fig. 76B, G). However, advanced types also occur as the diagonally striated muscle cells of mollusks and the cross-striated ones of arthropods (Fig. 76N), which resemble closely in their minute structure the cross-striated muscles of vertebrates. In the lower invertebrates, muscle cells are either isolated or more often arranged in layers, which may be cross, diagonal or longitudinal to the main body axis; but in the higher invertebrates separate *muscles*, i.e., bundles of muscle cells, occur as in vertebrates.

The nerve cells (Fig. 76L) of invertebrates are quite like those of vertebrates, consisting of a *cell body* containing the nucleus, and one to several processes, the *neurites*, springing from the cell body. *Multipolar, bipolar*, and *unipolar* nerve cells, with several, two, or one neurite, respectively, occur in invertebrates. In the lower Metazoa, nerve cells are scattered throughout the body; but in the higher invertebrates they tend to aggregate in a central nervous system as in vertebrates, then supplying the body by means of the neurites only.

The reproductive cells, also termed sex cells, germ cells, gonocytes, etc., are usually regarded as a variety of epithelial cell, but in many cases they come from the indifferent cells of the mesenchyme. In some animals they descend directly from certain embryonic cells that are known as *primordial* germ cells. Some years ago it was general in zoological circles to believe that the germ cells in all animals had some such special line of descent and thus to regard them as composed of some sacred material not to be contaminated with ordinary body protoplasm. This view was one of several originating with Weismann's theory of a rigid separation of body and germinal plasm. Today, however, opinion has swung decidedly in the opposite direction as a result of convincing proof that in many animals, including man, the sex cells come from ordinary mesoderm cells. Cases where the sex cells are produced from a special line of cells (*"germ track"*) have been established in many phyla and may represent the more primitive condition.

The female germ cells, termed *eggs* or *ova*, arise from connective-tissue or epithelial cells by a growth process in which they become filled with food reserves either through engulfing other cells or through being fed by neighboring cells. The male sex cells, or *spermatozoa*, begin in the same way as ordinary cells, but these undergo a striking transformation, the nucleus becoming the oval or elongated head of the spermatozoan, the cytoplasm its long vibratile tail. The process of sex-cell formation is called *gametogenesis*, or *ovogenesis* and *spermatogenesis*, respectively; the unaltered cells immediately ancestral to the sex cells are termed *ovogonia* and *spermatogonia*, respectively; and the last two generations which undergo the maturation divisions (page 14) are called *ovocytes* and *spermatocytes*. In the case of the female sex cells, the cell resulting from the second maturation division is itself the mature egg ready for fertilization; but in the male sex cells, the resultant of the second maturation division is termed a *spermatid* and undergoes the transformation mentioned above into a functional spermatozoan. In most invertebrates the sperm are of the usual flagellate type; but in some peculiar shapes occur, especially in arthropods.

Bibliography

Alexieff, A. 1924. Comparaison entre spermatozoides et flagellés. Arch. Protistk. 49. **Allmann, G. J.** 1853. Anatomy and physiology of Cordylophora. Phil. Trans. London. **Bather, F. A.** 1893. Recapitulation theory in palaeontology. Nat. Sci. 2. **Braem, F.** 1895. Was ist ein Keimblatt? Biol. Zentbl. 15. **Brauer, A.** 1891. Entwicklung von Hydra. Ztschr. Wiss. Zool. 52. **Broman, J.** 1920. Das sogenannte "biogenetische Grundgesetz." **Bütschli, O.** 1883. Bemerkungen zur Gastraea Theorie. Morph. Jahrb. 9. **Conklin, E. G.** 1897. Embryology of Crepidula. Jour. Morph. 13. **Cumings, E. R.** 1910. Palaeontology and the recapitulation theory. Pop. Sci. Monthly. **De Beer, G. R.** 1930. Embryology and evolution. **Degner, E.** 1912. Bau und Funktion der Krusterchromatophoren. Ztschr. Wiss. Zool. 102. **Franz, V.** 1927. Ontogenie und Phylogenie. Abhandl. Theorie Organ. Entwickl. (ed. by Spemann, Vogt, and Romeis), 3. **Garstang, W.** 1922. Recapitulation theory. Jour. Linn. Soc. London Zool. 35. **George, T. N.** 1933. Palingenesis and Palaeontology. Biol. Rev., Cambridge Phil. Soc. 8. **Haeckel, E.** 1874. Die Gasträa Theorie. Jenaische Ztschr. Naturw. 8, 9, 10. 1910. Evolution of man. **Harm, K.** 1903. Entwicklungsgeschichte von Clava. Ztschr. Wiss. Zool. 73. **Hatschek, B.** 1893. Keimblättertheorie. Verh. Deut. Zool. Gesell. 3. **Heider, K.** 1897. Ist die Keimblätterlehre erschüttert? Zool. Zentbl. 4. 1913. Entwicklungsgeschichte und Morphologie der Wirbellosen. 1914.

Phylogenie der Wirbellosen. Kultur der Gegenwart. Teil 3, Abt. 4, Bd. 2 and 4. **Hertwig, O.,** and **R. Hertwig.** 1879. Die Aktinien. Jenaische Ztschr. Naturw. 13. 1882. Die Coelomtheorie. Jenaische Ztschr. 15. **Hurst, C. H.** 1893. Recapitulation theory. Nat. Sci. 2. **Huxley, T. H.** 1849. Anatomy and affinities of medusae. Phil. Trans. London. **Jennings, H. S.** 1896. Early development of Asplanchna. Harvard Univ., Mus. Compar. Zool., Bul. 30. **Jeschikov, J.** 1930. Rekapitulationstheorie. Zool. Jahrb., Abt. Anat. Ontog. Tiere 52. **Kowalevsky, A.,** and **A. Marion.** 1883. Histoire embryogénique des Alcyonaires. Marseille Mus. Hist. Nat. Zool., Ann. 1, Pt. 2. **Lankester, E. R.** 1873. Primitive cell-layers of the embryo. Ann. Mag. Nat. Hist., Ser. 4, Vol. 11. 1877. Embryology and classification. Quart. Jour. Micros. Sci. 17. **Mangold, O.** 1925. Die Bedeutung der Keimblätter. Naturwissenschaften 13. **Matveiev, B.** 1932. Zur Theorie der Rekapitulation. Zool. Jahrb., Abt. Anat. Ontog. Tiere 55. **Metschnikoff, E.** 1882. Entodermbildung der Geryoniden. Ztschr. Wiss. Zool. 36. 1887. Embryologische Studien an Medusen. **Naef, A.** 1920. Über das sogenannte "Biogenetische Grundgesetz." Festschr. Zschokke. 1931. Phylogenie der Tiere. Handb. Vererbungswiss. (ed. by E. Baur and M. Hartmann), Vol. III. **Noack, W.** 1901. Entwicklungsgeschichte der Musciden. Ztschr. Wiss. Zool. 70. **Salensky, W.** 1908. Radiata und Bilateria. Biol. Zentbl. 28. **Schindewolf, O. H.** 1929. Ontogenie und Phylogenie. Paläontol. Ztschr. 11. **Sedgwick, A.** 1894. On von Baer's law and the significance of ancestral rudiments. Quart. Jour. Micros. Sci. 36. **Selenka, E.** 1876. Zur Entwicklung der Holothurien. Ztschr. Wiss. Zool. 72. 1883. Studien über Entwicklungsgeschichte der Tiere. Vol. I. **Sewertzoff, A. N.** 1927. Beziehungen zwischen der Ontogenese und der Phylogenese. Jenaische Ztschr. Naturw. 63. 1931. Morphologische Gesetzmässigkeiten der Evolution. **Von Baer, K. E.** 1828. Über Entwicklungsgeschichte der Tiere. **Watase, S.** 1888. Development of cephalopods. Johns Hopkins Univ. Studies. Biol. Lab. 4. 1891. Jour. Morph. 4. **Ziegler, H. E.** 1898. Studien über Zelltheilung. Arch. Entwickl. Mech. Organ. 7.

CHAPTER VI

METAZOA OF THE CELLULAR GRADE OF CONSTRUCTION— PHYLUM PORIFERA, THE SPONGES

I. THE CHARACTERS OF THE PHYLUM

1. Introduction.—The nature of sponges was debated until well into the nineteenth century, although evidence of their animal nature was adduced in 1765 by Ellis, who saw the water currents and movements of the oscula. As a result, Linnaeus, Lamarck, and Cuvier placed the sponges under Zoophytes or Polypes in their systems, regarding them as allied to anthozoan coelenterates, and many investigators sought to find in sponges the polyps they thought must be there. Although de Blainville (1816) recognized the lack of affinity of sponges with coelenterates and separated them into a group Spongiaria allied to Protozoa, this idea gained little notice, and, through much of the nineteenth century, sponges were placed with coelenterates, usually under the name Coelenterata, or Coelentera, or Radiata. The morphology and physiology of sponges were first adequately understood by R. E. Grant, beginning 1825, who created for the group in 1836 the name Porifera (Latin, *porus*, pore, *ferro*, to bear), by which it is now generally known. Other names in use throughout the nineteenth century were Spongiae, Spongida, Spongiaria, etc. Huxley (1875) and Sollas (1884) proposed the complete separation of sponges from other Metazoa on the grounds of their many peculiarities, but this view did not find its present general acceptance until about the beginning of the twentieth century. Sponges are now recognized as constituting a separate isolated branch of the Metazoa, named Parazoa, after Sollas.

2. Definition.—The Porifera are asymmetrical or radially symmetrical Metazoa of the cellular grade of construction, without organs, mouth, or nervous tissue, with a body permeated with pores, canals, and chambers through which a water current flows, and with one to many internal cavities lined with choanocytes.

3. General Characters.—With the Porifera or sponges we begin the account of the Metazoa or cellular layered animals. The sponges are the lowest of these, having remained at a grade of structure that may be termed cellular, i.e., a loose aggregation of cells hardly formed into tissues. Sponges consist essentially of epithelia and mesenchyme. There are no organs or systems, no mouth or digestive tract, and body functions are performed by the activities of cells acting more or less independently and cooperating but little with each other.

Some sponges exhibit definite form and radial symmetry, having a vase-like shape, but the majority grow irregularly in a plant-like manner, forming flat, rounded, or branching structures, devoid of symmetry. Among the distinguishing features of the phylum is the perforation of the surface by numerous apertures serving for the ingress and egress of water. The *incurrent* openings or *ostia* are small and numerous whereas the *excurrent* openings or *oscula* are few and large. The interior is hollow or is permeated by numerous channels, and all or some of the interior space or spaces is lined by special cells, the *choanocytes* or *collar cells*, which closely resemble the choanoflagellates (page 107), having a single flagellum encircled at its base by a protoplasmic collar. The possession of choanocytes at once distinguishes sponges from all other Metazoa, although choanocyte-like cells occur sparingly in some other animals. Nearly all sponges possess an internal skeleton, secreted by the amoebocytes of the mesenchyme, and consisting of separate crystalline bodies, the *spicules*, or of organic fibers or of both, sometimes with the admixture of foreign particles. The spicules are made of calcium carbonate or of silicic acid. Sponges lack nervous and sensory cells so far as known, but their cells show some differentiation into epithelial, muscle, and possibly gland cells.

All sponges are sessile and incapable of locomotion in the adult state, living fastened to rocks, shells, and other objects, or rarely rolling about on the bottom. They are all marine with the exception of the family Spongillidae, common in ponds and lakes throughout the world. Sponges grow by spreading and branching in a plant-like manner and have high powers of regeneration. A characteristic mode of asexual propagation by means of special cell masses termed *gemmules* occurs. Sexual reproduction is universal with the formation of typical eggs and spermatozoa and the production of free-swimming larvae.

The sponges possess a very low grade of organization, but the slight differentiation of cells for various functions, the cooperation of the cells in producing a functional whole molded into a form more or less characteristic for each species, and particularly the secretion of specific types of skeleton all bespeak a certain amount of individuation and a structural grade somewhat higher than that of a protozoan colony.

II. CLASSIFICATION OF THE PHYLUM

The classification of sponges presents great difficulty, and no one scheme has been unanimously accepted by specialists on sponges. The classification is based chiefly on the type of skeleton, and this serves to mark off rather sharply two groups of sponges, the calcareous and the glass sponges. The remaining siliceous and horny sponges are, however, less clearly delimited, and they are variously subdivided by different specialists. The following arrangement is based on the publications of Topsent, H. V. Wilson, and de Laubenfels.

Class I. **Calcarea** or **Calcispongiae**, the calcareous sponges. Skeleton composed of separate calcareous spicules, one-, three-, or four-rayed, not divisible into megascleres and microscleres.

Order 1. Homocoela, the ascon sponges. Structure asconoid.

Order 2. Heterocoela. Structure syconoid or leuconoid.

Class II. Hexactinellida or **Triaxonida** or **Hyalospongiae**, the glass sponges. Skeleton composed of triaxon (six-rayed) siliceous spicules or some modification of the triaxon form, separate or united into networks; choanocytes limited to finger-shaped chambers arranged in a simple or folded layer; without surface epithelium.

Order 1. Hexasterophora. With hexasters, without amphidisks.

Order 2. Amphidiscophora. With amphidisks, no hexasters.

Class III. Demospongiae. Skeleton of siliceous spicules or horny fibers or both; siliceous spicules not triaxon, generally differentiated into megascleres and microscleres; flagellated chambers mostly small, round, of the leuconoid type.

SUBCLASS I. TETRACTINELLIDA. With tetraxon spicules; no spongin; spicules sometimes wanting.

Order 1. Myxospongida. Without spicules; structure simple.

Order 2. Carnosa or Homosclerophora or Microsclerophora. Megascleres and microscleres not sharply differentiated; mostly without triaenes; asters may be present.

Order 3. Choristida. With long-shafted triaenes; megascleres and microscleres distinct.

Suborder 1. Astrophora. Microscleres include asters.

Suborder 2. Sigmatophora. Microscleres when present are sigmas.

SUBCLASS II. MONAXONIDA. Megascleres monaxonial; with or without spongin.

Order 4. Hadromerina or Astromonaxonellida. Megascleres mostly tylostyles; microscleres when present some form of aster; without spongin.

Order 5. Halichondrina. Megascleres mostly of two or more kinds; microscleres wanting or are rhaphides; with little spongin.

Order 6. Poecilosclerina. Megascleres often of two or more sorts, localized in distribution; reticulate, united by more or less spongin; often with echinating spicules; microscleres include sigmas, chelas, and toxas.

Order 7. Haplosclerina. Megascleres of one kind, diactinal, without special localization; with or without microscleres; spongin generally present.

SUBCLASS III. KERATOSA, the horny sponges. Skeleton composed of spongin fibers, without siliceous spicules.

III. GENERAL MORPHOLOGY AND PHYSIOLOGY

1. External Characters.—The simpler and smaller sponges, particularly those belonging to the Calcarea and Hexactinellida, often exhibit some degree of radial symmetry, having an elongated cylindrical or vase-shaped hollow body fastened at one end and narrowing at the other to a single osculum (Figs. 77*B*, 86*A*, 88*B*, *C*, and 91*A*, *B*, *D*). Many of the Choristida and Hadromerina are more or less spherical with an internal radiating structure (Figs. 97*A*, *B*, 100*A*, *B*). But the great majority of sponges lack definite symmetry and form small to large growths, sometimes cup- or funnel-shaped or fan-like (flabelliform), but more often of irregular form, massive, encrusting, or branching (Figs. 77, 91, 102*J*, and 103*F*) with the surface studded with innumerable pores and bearing many oscula, often on the summit of branches or projections or sometimes sunk into crater-like depressions. The form is very labile, molded

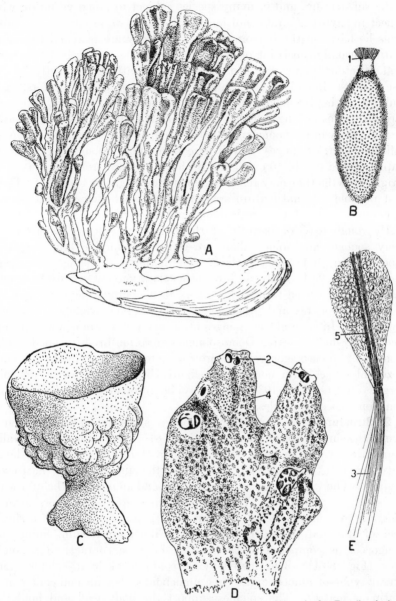

FIG. 77.—Some examples of sponges. *A. Microciona prolifera* (order Poecilosclerina), from life, Atlantic Coast. *B.* A calcareous sponge, *Sycon*, from life, Bermuda. *C.* Neptune's goblet (*Poterion neptuni*, order Hadromerina), dry specimen. *D. Tedania* (order Poecilosclerina), from life, Bermuda. *E.* A hexactinellid sponge, showing root tuft, dry specimen. 1, oscular fringe: 2, oscula; 3, root tuft; 4, dermal pores, or ostia; 5, columella.

to the substratum, and in many species subject to much variation with respect to environmental conditions, particularly water currents. A few forms lie loose on the bottom, but the majority are fastened to a substratum, usually consisting of hard objects, such as rocks, shells, timbers, coral skeletons, plants, etc., to which they are attached directly by the base. Those inhabiting the muddy bottoms of deeper waters, particularly the hexactinellids, are generally fastened to the mud by means of root bundles of long spicules (Figs. 77E and 91B, C). In some forms the main body of the sponge is elevated from the substratum by a slender stalk-like part. Sponges vary in size from small crusts or growths or simple vases a few to 10 or 15 mm. in height to large rounded masses or upright growths that may reach a diameter or height of 1 or 2 m. Their most notable external feature apart from shape is their general porous appearance. Most of the calcareous and siliceous sponges also have a bristly rough exterior because of the projecting spicules whereas the horny sponges and some others are generally slimy in life or with a smooth, hard, or leathery surface. The majority of sponges are of an inconspicuous flesh, drab, or brownish coloration but some are bright orange, yellow or red from the presence of lipochrome pigment in some of the amoebocytes and other colors, such as blue, violet, and black, also occur. In general the sponges of deeper waters are of dull appearance, while shallow water Demospongiae are often brightly hued. The fresh-water sponges, generally of brownish-green color from the presence of zoochlorellae, form encrusting, slightly branching growths on submerged objects (Fig. 103G) and may be recognized by their simple monaxon siliceous spicules.

2. **Structure.**—The structure of sponges is best understood by reference to the simplest or *asconoid* type (Fig. 78). In this there is a radially symmetrical vase-like body consisting of a thin wall enclosing a large central cavity, the *spongocoel*,[1] opening at the summit by the narrowed *osculum*. The wall is composed of an outer and an inner epithelium with a mesenchyme between. The outer or dermal epithelium, here termed *epidermis* to conform to the usage in other animals, consists of a single layer of thin flat cells (Fig. 80A). The inner epithelium, lining the spongocoel, is composed of *choanocytes*, in loose contact, in a single layer (Fig. 80A). The mesenchyme contains skeletal spicules and several types of amoebocytes (free amoeboid cells), all embedded in a gelatinous matrix. The spicules support the body wall and hold the sponge erect. The cells of the mesenchyme originate in common with the epidermis and hence may be considered of the nature of ectomesoderm. The wall of the asconoid sponge is pierced by numerous microscopic

---

[1] The author has coined this term to replace the objectionable names "gastral cavity" or "cloacal cavity" commonly applied to the central cavity of sponges

apertures termed *incurrent pores* or *ostia,* which extend from the external surface to the spongocoel.   Each pore is intracellular, i.e., it is a canal through a tubular cell called a *porocyte* (Fig. 80*A*).   The water current impelled by the flagella of the choanocytes passes through the incurrent pores into the spongocoel and out through the osculum, furnishing in its passage food and oxygen and carrying away metabolic wastes.

The important features of the asconoid structure are the simple wall and the complete continuous lining epithelium of choanocytes, interrupted only by the inner ends of the porocytes (Figs. 78, 79*A*). It will be perceived that the asconoid type of sponge superficially resembles a typical gastrula, and Haeckel cited the asconoid sponges as close approximations to his gastraea, or ideal diploblastic ancestral metazoan. But the asconoid sponges are not diploblastic, having a mesenchymal layer between their two epithelia, and the correspondence of these epithelia with the ectoderm and entoderm of the Eumetazoa is very doubtful.

The asconoid structure occurs in only a very few sponges; the vast majority show a more complicated construction, which can, however, be derived theoretically from the asconoid condition.   The first stage above the asconoid type is termed the *syconoid* type (Fig.

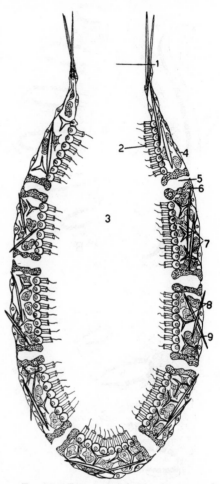

Fig. 78.—Diagram of the simplest type of sponge, the asconoid type. 1, osculum; 2, layer of choanocytes; 3, spongocoel; 4, epidermis, 5, pore through porocyte; 6, porocyte; 7, mesenchyme; 8, amoebocyte; 9, spicule.

79*B*) and is formed by the outpushing of the wall of an asconoid sponge at regular intervals into finger-like projections, called *radial canals*.   At first these radial canals are free projections and the outside water surrounds their whole length, for there are no definite incurrent channels (Fig. 87*A*). But in most syconoid sponges, the walls of the radial canals fuse in such

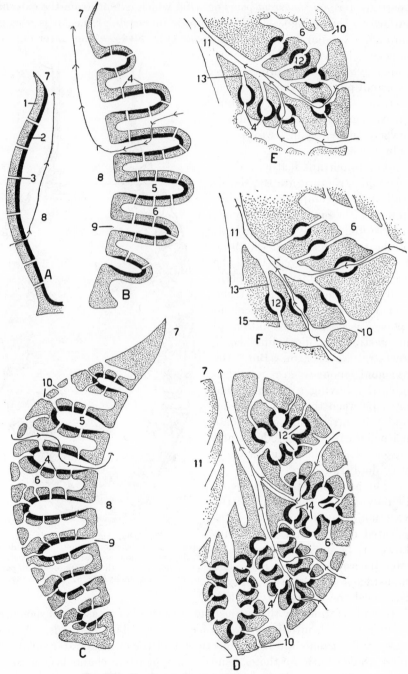

Fig. 79.—For descriptive legend see opposite page.

a manner as to leave between them tubular spaces, the *incurrent canals*, which open to the exterior between the blind outer ends of the radial canals by apertures termed *dermal ostia* or *dermal pores* (Fig. 87*B*). Since these incurrent canals represent the original outer surface of the asconoid sponge they are necessarily lined by epidermis. The radial canals being outpushings of the original spongocoel are necessarily lined by choanocytes, and are therefore better called *flagellated canals*. The interior of syconoid sponges is hollow as in asconoids and forms a large spongocoel, which is lined by a flat epithelium derived from the epidermis. The openings of the radial canals into the spongocoel are termed *internal ostia*. The syconoid sponges retain the radial vase form of the asconoids and the spongocoel opens to the exterior by the single terminal osculum. The wall between the incurrent and radial canals, representing the original wall of the asconoid sponge, is pierced by numerous minute pores called *prosopyles*, which obviously correspond to the incurrent pores of asconoid sponges but apparently are simply intercellular spaces, not channels through porocytes. The surface openings, or dermal pores, clearly do not correspond to any structure in the asconoid type and in the unmodified syconoid sponges are simply spaces guarded by projecting spicules. Syconoid sponges are supported by a spicular skeleton situated in the mesenchyme. The water current in syconoid sponges takes the following route: dermal pores, incurrent canals, prosopyles, radial canals, internal ostia, spongocoel, osculum.

The syconoid sponges differ from the asconoid type in two important particulars: first, in the thick folded walls containing alternating incurrent and radial canals; and, second, in the breaking up of the choanocyte layer, which no longer lines the whole interior but is limited to certain definite chambers (radial canals).

The syconoid structure occurs in two main stages. The first type, illustrated in a few of the heterocoelous calcareous sponges, especially members of the genus *Sycon*, corresponds to the foregoing description (Fig. 79*B*). The external surface is made of the blind outer ends of the radial canals, the spaces between which serve as dermal ostia. In the second stage (Fig. 79*C*), the epidermis and mesenchyme spread over the outer surface forming a thin or thick *cortex*, often containing special cortical spicules. The epidermis becomes pierced by more definite pores that lead into narrowed incurrent canals. These pursue a more or less

---

Fig. 79.—Diagrams of various types of sponge structure. *A*. Asconoid type. *B*. Syconoid type, early stage without cortex. *C*. Final syconoid stage, with cortex. *D*. Leuconoid type with eurypylous chambers. *E*. Leuconoid type with aphodal chambers. *F*. Leuconoid type with diplodal chambers. Choanocyte layer in heavy black, mesenchyme stippled. 1, mesenchyme; 2, choanocyte layer; 3, incurrent pore; 4, prosopyles; 5, radial canal; 6, incurrent canal; 7, osculum; 8, spongocoel; 9, internal ostium; 10, dermal pore; 11, excurrent channel; 12, flagellated chamber; 13, aphodus; 14, apopyle; 15, prosodus.

irregular course through the cortex, branching and anastomosing, before they reach the outer ends of the flagellated chambers, or they may form large cortical spaces, the *subdermal spaces*.

By a continuation of the process of outfolding of the choanocyte layer, the third or *leuconoid* type of canal system (Fig. 79D) results. The choanocyte layer of the radial canals of the syconoid stage evaginates into many small chambers, and these may repeat the process, so that clusters of small rounded or oval flagellated chambers replace the elongated chambers of the syconoid stage. The choanocytes are limited to these chambers. Mesenchyme fills in the spaces around the flagellated chambers, the spongocoel is usually obliterated, and the whole sponge becomes irregular in structure and indefinite in form with the interior permeated by a maze of water channels. The surface is usually covered by an epidermal epithelium (not in hexactinellids) pierced by dermal pores and oscula. The dermal pores lead into incurrent passages that branch irregularly through the mesenchyme, or in many cases the dermal pores may open into large subdermal spaces crossed by columns of spicules supporting the surface layer. The subdermal spaces and incurrent canals lead into the small rounded flagellated chambers by openings still termed prosopyles. The flagellated chambers open by apertures called *apopyles* into excurrent channels, and these unite to form larger and larger tubes, of which the largest lead to the oscula. When the apopyles open directly by wide mouths into the excurrent channels, the system is termed *eurypylous* (Fig. 79D). When a narrow canal, the *aphodus*, intervenes between the chamber and the excurrent canal, the system is called *aphodal* (Fig. 79E). In some cases there is also a narrow tube, the *prosodus*, between the incurrent channel and the chamber; such a condition is *diplodal* (Fig. 79F). Frequently the body of leuconoid sponges is divisible into two regions, an outer *ectosome* devoid of flagellated chambers and composed of cortex or of the dermal membrane and the subdermal spaces; and an inner *choanosome* or *endosome* in which the clusters of flagellated chambers are located (Fig. 96C). The term *cortex* is applied to an ectosome that differs from the choanosome in histological structure or spicule type and arrangement. A *dermal membrane* consists of epidermis plus a thin stratum of mesenchyme.

The main characteristics of the leuconoid system are the limitation of the choanocytes to small chambers, the great development of the mesenchyme, and the complexity of the incurrent and excurrent water passages. The water current takes the following route: dermal ostia, subdermal spaces and incurrent channels, prosodus when present, prosopyles, flagellated chambers, apopyles, aphodus when present, excurrent canals, larger channels, oscula.

The leuconoid structure may be attained by way of asconoid and syconoid stages, but most leuconoid sponges derive from a stage termed a *rhagon* which in turn arises by direct rearrangement of the inner cell mass of the larva. The rhagon is conical, tapering from a broad base to the summit bearing the single osculum (Fig. 96*A*). The spongocoel is bordered by oval flagellated chambers opening into it by wide apopyles. Between the chambers and the epidermis lies a considerable thickness of mesenchyme traversed by incurrent canals and subdermal spaces. The simpler leuconoid types develop directly from the rhagon by outfoldings of the flagellated chambers and the resulting formation of excurrent canals between the chambers and the larger excurrent channels (Fig. 96*B*, *C*).

The vast majority of sponges are constructed on the leuconoid plan, which exhibits innumerable variations and has undoubtedly arisen independently over and over again in different groups of sponges. No doubt the much greater frequency of the leuconoid than the other canal systems may be attributed to the larger size permitted by this type of structure and its greater efficiency in producing a water current.

3. Histology.—The cells of sponges are somewhat differentiated for various functions but with the possible exception of the choanocytes appear to be only slight modifications of a relatively undifferentiated amoeboid cell corresponding to a mesenchyme or primitive connective-tissue cell of higher animals. The surface epithelium or epidermis consists in at least some sponges of large flat polygonal epithelial cells, called *pinacocytes*, each with a thickened central bulge containing the nucleus (Fig. 80*A*, *L*). Seen from above the pinacocytes are closely fitting polygonal cells (Fig. 80*D*), often with inclusions; seen in profile (Fig. 80*L*) they present a central nucleated lump and thin margins continuous with those of adjacent pinacocytes. Pinacocytes (endopinacocytes) also line the incurrent canals and spongocoel of syconoid sponges and the larger canals and spaces of leuconoid sponges. Pinacocytes are highly contractile cells, and, by the withdrawal of the margins into the central bulge, they can greatly reduce the surface area of a sponge. In many sponges the epidermis is not an epithelium of separate cells but a syncytium, a continuous membrane containing scattered nuclei (Fig. 80*E*). This has been designated an *epithelioid membrane* by H. V. Wilson. A definite epidermis is lacking in the Hexactinellida.

In the asconoid sponges, *pore cells* or *porocytes* occur at frequent intervals among the pinacocytes. These are usually said to be modified pinacocytes, but Prenant (1925) derives them from the amoebocytes of the mesenchyme. Porocytes are tubular cells reaching from the epidermis to the spongocoel, pierced by a central canal that acts as incurrent pore (Fig. 80*A*). They usually contain many spherical inclusions and

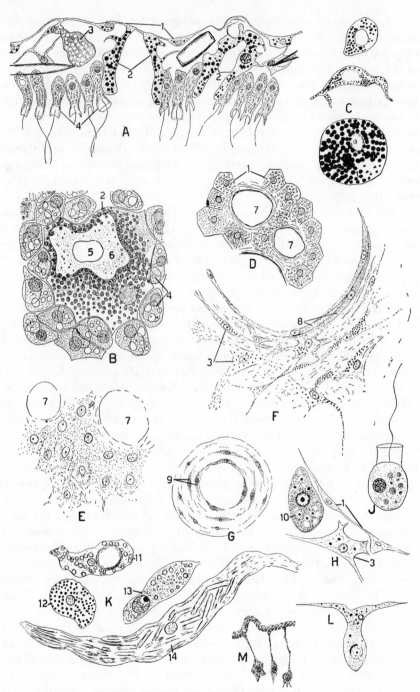

FIG. 80.—For descriptive legend see opposite page.

are highly contractile, effecting closure of the pore by advancing a thin sheet of cytoplasm, called the *pore diaphragm*, from the edge to the center at the outer end of the canal (Fig. 80*B*). According to Prenant, the porocytes are degenerate cells that are eventually cast off. The dermal pores of the syconoid and leuconoid sponges obviously do not correspond to the incurrent pores of asconoid sponges, and their nature is disputed. It is probable that they are usually simply circular openings through the epidermis (Fig. 80*D*), but even so they can be closed by protoplasmic extension of the surrounding cells or of the syncytium in cases where the epidermis is an epithelioid membrane, as well as with the aid of special muscle cells. In fresh-water sponges Brien (1932) found that the dermal pores begin as channels through porocytes, but later the porocytes disappear, leaving the pore as an epidermal opening. The prosopyles are homologous with the incurrent pores of ascon sponges but whether they are intracellular channels through porocytes or simply intercellular spaces has never been determined.

The mesenchyme consists of a gelatinous transparent matrix, commonly called *mesogloea*, presumably of a protein nature, in which free amoeboid cells or *amoebocytes* wander about. When there are much mesogloea and relatively few cells, the mesenchyme is termed *collenchyma;* when the cells are numerous, the name *parenchyma* is applied. The amoebocytes (Fig. 80*C, F, H, K*) are usually of several different kinds in each species of sponge, varying in size, type of pseudopod, and kind of inclusion; those of different species often do not show much correspondence. Types with slender branching pseudopods are called *collencytes* and may be united into a syncytial network. Others have lobose pseudopods and are often packed with granules or spherules or pigment bodies or excretory inclusions (Fig. 80*C, K*). Some of these types have received names; thus pigmented amoebocytes are called *chromocytes*, and those filled with food reserves, *thesocytes;* but it is probable that any of the amoebocytes can serve these functions. Amoebocytes in the act of secreting skeleton are termed *scleroblasts* and according to the nature of

---

Fig. 80.—Histology of sponges. *A*. Cross section through an asconoid sponge, *Leucosolenia*. (*After Prenant*, 1925.) *B*. Porocyte of *Leucosolenia*, with surrounding choanocytes. (*After Minchin*, 1898.) *C*. Types of amoebocytes of *Leucosolenia*. (*After Prenant*, 1925.) *D*. Epidermis of *Leuconia*, with two dermal pores, from slide. (*Courtesy A. E. Galigher*.) *E*. Epithelioid epidermis of *Stylotella* (order Hadromerina), from slide. (*Courtesy Dr. H. V. Wilson*.) *F*. Desmacytes and amoebocytes of *Hircinia* (subclass Keratosa), from slide. (*Courtesy Dr. H. V. Wilson*.) *G*. Prosopyle with encircling myocytes of *Vosmaeropsis* (Class Calcarea). (*After Dendy*, 1893.) *H*. Epidermis and amoebocytes of a fresh-water sponge, from a section. *J*. A choanocyte of *Sycon*, from life. *K*. Amoebocytes of *Microciona*, to scale. (*After Wilson and Penney*, 1930.) *L*. Side view of epidermal cell of *Leucosolenia*. (*After Prenant*, 1925.) *M*. Three gland cells of *Grantiopsis* (Calcarea). (*After Dendy*, 1893.) 1, epidermis; 2, porocyte; 3, amoebocyte; 4, choanocytes; 5, incurrent pore; 6, pore diaphragm; 7, dermal pore; 8, desmacyte; 9, myocytes; 10, archaeocyte; 11–14, types of amoebocytes: 11, globoferous cell or cystencyte; 12, granular amoebocyte; 13, nucleolate cell (archaeocyte); 14, rhabdiferous cell with rod inclusions.

the product are known as *calcoblasts*, *silicoblasts*, or *spongioblasts*. Certain amoebocytes with blunt pseudopods, large nuclei with a conspicuous nucleolus, and often cytoplasmic inclusions are known as *archaeocytes* (Fig. 80*H*, *K*) and are believed by some to represent persistent undifferentiated embryonic cells, which are the sole source of the sex cells and play an important role in regenerative processes. All such fixed morphological ideas should be looked upon with suspicion, but apparently the cells called archaeocytes in sponges are generalized amoebocytes that play a dominant role in reproductive processes and are able to differentiate into all other cell types. *Gland* cells, attached to the surface by long strands (Fig. 80*M*), have been described and presumably secrete slime, but the ability to give off slime is also a general property of the amoebocytes. Long slender cells found in layers in the cortex and around the larger internal channels are called *fiber* cells or *desmacytes* and are common in Demospongiae (Fig. 80*F*). The *myocytes* or muscle cells are fusiform contractile cells resembling the smooth muscle cells of other invertebrates, usually arranged in circular fashion to form a sphincter at the osculum or other openings whose size they can regulate (Fig. 80*G*). The sex cells of sponges differentiate from the amoebocytes, possibly also from choanocytes.

The collar cells or choanocytes (Figs. 80*A*, 85*G*) are rounded or oval cells whose base rests upon the mesenchyme while the free end bears a transparent contractile collar encircling the base of the single long flagellum. The flagellum has the same types of internal attachments as in flagellate Protozoa. The nucleus may be basally or apically situated, and its location has been used as a taxonomic character in Calcarea. The choanocytes are much larger in the Calcarea than in other sponges.

The mesenchyme secretes and contains the skeleton, one of the most important features of sponges.

4. Skeleton.—The skeleton consists of spicules or of spongin fibers or of a combination of both. The spicules or *sclerites* are definite bodies, having a crystalline appearance and consisting in general of simple spines or of spines radiating from a point. They have an axis of organic material around which is deposited the inorganic substance, either calcium carbonate or hydrated silica. They present a great variety of shape, and, as reference to the shape is essential in the description and identification of sponges, a large terminology exists. Here only the principal terms applied to the spicules will be explained.

First, spicules are of two general sorts—*megascleres* and *microscleres*. The megascleres are the larger skeletal spicules that constitute the chief supporting framework of the sponge. The microscleres are the smaller flesh spicules that occur strewn throughout the mesenchyme. The distinction is not absolute and does not hold for the calcareous sponges and some other groups.   Then, spicules are classified according to the number of their axes and rays.   Words designating the number of axes end in -*axon*, those referring to the number of rays end in -*actine* or -*actinal* There are five general types of spicules.

a. *Monaxon.*—These are formed by growth in one or both directions along a single axis, which may be straight or curved.   When growth has occurred in one direction only, as can be recognized by the dissimilarity of the two ends, the spicule is called a *monactinal monaxon*, or, for brevity, a *style*.   Styles are typically rounded (*strongylote*) at one end and pointed (*oxeote*) at the other (Fig. 81, *2*).   Styles in which the broad end is knobbed are called *tylostyles* (Fig. 81, *3*); those covered with thorny processes are named *acanthostyles* (Fig. 81, *1*).   Usually the pointed end of styles projects to the exterior.   Monaxons that develop by growth in both directions from a central point are named *diactinal monaxons*, *diactines*, or, briefly, *rhabds*.   Rhabds pointed at each end are oxeas (Fig. 81, *4*); lance-headed at each end, *tornotes* (Fig. 81, *6*); rounded at the ends, *strongyles* (Fig. 81, *5*); and knobbed at each end, like a pin head, *tylotes* (Fig. 81, *7*).   Microscleric forms of diactins are designated by prefixing micro to the usual name, as *microrhabds*, *microxeas*, and *microstrongyles*.   Special curved types of diactinal microscleres are characteristic of the Sigmatophora and the Poecilosclerina; they may be curved in one plane or spirally twisted.   The most common types are the C-shaped forms, called *sigmas* (Fig. 81, *22*); the bow-shaped ones, or *toxas* (Fig. 81, *23*); and the *chelas* (Fig. 81, *20*, *21*), with recurved hooks, plates, or flukes at each end.   When the two ends are alike, chelas are called *isochelas* (Fig. 81, *20*), when unlike, *anisochelas* (Fig. 81, *21*); both sorts occur in several varieties.   Spirally twisted sigmas are termed *sigmaspires*.   Short spiny microscleric monaxons are known as *streptasters*, of which the principal sorts are the spirally twisted *spirasters* (Fig. 81, *14*), rod shapes or *sanidasters* (Fig. 81, *19*), *plesio-asters* (Fig. 81, *31*) with a few spines from a very short axis, and *amphi-asters* with spines at each end.

b. *Tetraxons.*—Tetraxon spicules, also called *tetractines* and *quadri-radiates*, consist typically of four rays, not in the same plane, radiating from a common point.   By loss of rays they may become three-, two-, or one-rayed; the last two are indistinguishable from diactines and monactines, unless the lost rays are indicated by a remnant of the organic axial thread.   The four rays of the tetraxon spicule may be more or less equal, in which case the spicule is called a *calthrops* (Fig. 81, *8*) or, if a microsclere, a *microcalthrops;* but generally one ray, the *rhabdome*, is elongated, often greatly so, and the three other rays, called *cladi* or *clads*, and together constituting the *cladome*, are short.   Such spicules are termed

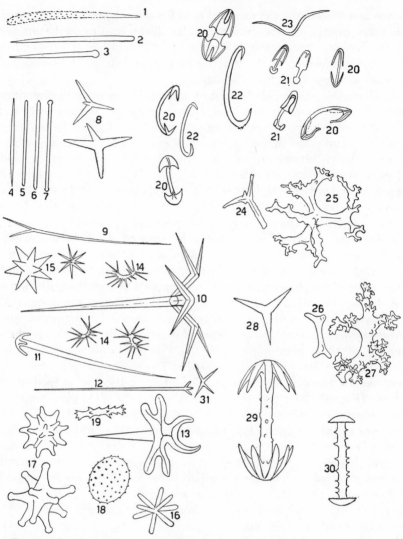

Fig. 81.—Sponge spicules. 1, acanthostyle; 2, style; 3, tylostyle; 4, oxea, 5, strongyle; 6, tornote; 7, tylote; 8, calthrops; 9, diaene; 10–13, triaenes; 10, dichotriaene; 11, anatriaene; 12, protriaene; 13, another kind of dichotriaene; 14, spirasters; 15, oxyasters; 16, strongylaster; 17, spherasters; 18, sterraster; 19, sanidaster; 20–21, chelas; 20, various sorts of isochelas; 21, anisochelas; 22, sigmas; 23, toxa; 24, early and, 25, late stage of a tricrepid desma; 26, early; 27, late stage of a rhabdocrepid desma; 28, triradiate spicule; 29, amphidisk of a hexactinellid sponge; 30, amphidisk of a fresh-water sponge; 31, plesiaster. (24–27 *after Dendy,* 1905.)

triaenes and give the appearance of a crown of three rays, the cladome, at the end of the long rhabdome (Fig. 81, *10–13*). Triaenes occur in a variety of shapes and are named from the form of the cladi and the angle that they make with the rhabdome. The cladi may be forked or branched at their free ends. By loss of one ray from the cladome, a *diaene* (Fig. 81, *9*) results and also occurs in several varieties. The cladome may consist of a simple or scalloped disk instead of cladi, and such disks may occur at both ends of the rhabdome, forming *birotular* spicules, also called *amphidisks* (Fig. 81, *29, 30*).

The *triradiate* or *triactinal* spicule, the most common form of spicule of the calcareous sponges, is regarded as a variety of the triaene, of which the rhabdome has been lost, leaving a cladome of three rays, nearly but not quite in one plane (Fig. 81, *28*). The modifications of the triradiate spicule will be considered with the calcareous sponges.

c. Triaxon.—The *triaxon* or *hexactinal* spicule (Fig. 94) consists fundamentally of three axes crossing at right angles, producing six rays extending at right angles from a central point. From this basic type all possible modifications arise by reduction or loss of rays, branching and curving of the rays, and the development of spines, knobs, etc., upon them. The hexactinal spicule occurs only in the class Hexactinellida.

d. Polyaxons.—These are spicules in which several equal rays radiate from a central point. They are most common among microscleres, where they are known as *asters* and include types with small centers and long rays and others with large centers and short rays. Among the small-centered forms are *oxyasters* with pointed rays (Fig. 81, *15*), *strongylasters* with rounded ends (Fig. 81, *16*), and *tylasters* with knobbed rays. Large-centered forms include *spherasters* with definite rays (Fig. 81, *17*) and *sterrasters* with rays reduced to small projections from the spherical surface (Fig. 81, *18*). Asters grade into the spiny types of monaxons and so are often called *euasters* as a contrasting term to streptasters.

e. Spheres.—These are rounded bodies in which growth is concentric around a center.

A special type of megasclere known as a *desma* occurs in a number of sponges. A desma consists of an ordinary minute monaxon, triradiate, or tetraxon spicule, termed the *crepis*, on which layers of silica have been irregularly deposited (Fig. 81, *25, 27*). The deposited silica at first follows the shape of the crepis but later develops elaborate branches and tubercles not related to the embedded crepis. Desmas are named from the shape of the crepis, as *monocrepid*, *tricrepid*, and *tetracrepid*. They are usually united into a network (Fig. 99*B*, *C*), and such a reticulated skeleton is called *lithistid*.

Spongin skeletons consist of fibers of *spongin*, a protein secretion, arranged either in a network or in a branching fashion. In many Monaxonida the siliceous spicules are bound together by or incorporated in spongin material. The Keratosa have skeletons composed entirely of spongin fibers but often contain foreign bodies.

Spicules are secreted by mesenchyme cells (Fig. 82L), which then become known as *scleroblasts*. The process is best known for calcareous spicules. In the simplest case, that of the monaxon, the spicule begins as a minute sliver of calcium carbonate deposited in a clear space in the interior of a binucleate scleroblast probably arising by the incomplete division of an ordinary scleroblast. The calcium carbonate is believed to be laid down around an organic axial thread, which can be detected with difficulty in the center of the fully formed spicule. The spicule begins between the two nuclei (Fig. 82A), which draw apart as the spicule lengthens until the cell separates into two (Fig. 82C). One cell, the *founder*, is situated at the inner end, the other, the *thickener*, at the outer end of the spicule, since monaxon spicules usually project from the body wall. The spicule is laid down chiefly by the founder, which moves slowly inward, establishing the shape and length. The thickener deposits additional layers of calcium carbonate, also moving inward during this process. When the spicule is completed, both cells wander from its inner end into the mesogloea, the founder first, the thickener later (Fig. 82D). Triradiate calcareous spicules are secreted by three scleroblasts that come together in a trefoil figure and divide in two, each into an inner founder and an outer thickener (Fig. 82E–K). Each pair secretes a minute spicule (Fig. 82E, F), and these three rays are early united into a small triradiate spicule (Fig. 82G). Each ray is then completed in the same manner as a monaxon spicule, the founder traveling toward the tip and completing the length of the ray (Fig. 82H, J). The three thickeners remain for some time at the junction of the rays adding further layers of calcium carbonate (Fig. 82K). In the case of quadriradiate spicules, the fourth ray is added to the forming triradiate spicule by an additional scleroblast. Nothing whatever is known of the actual process of spicule secretion except that the calcium carbonate used is extracted from the surrounding sea water. When placed in calcium-free sea water, the calcareous sponges are unable to secrete spicules, forming only the soft organic axes. Spicules already present dissolve, and the sponge being unable to maintain an upright position without the spicules collapses and degenerates.

The development of siliceous spicules is poorly known and requires further study. It appears that in most cases they are formed completely within one scleroblast, here called silicoblast (Fig. 82M). For the larger types, several silicoblasts may cooperate. The hexactinal spicules of the Hexactinellida arise in the center of a multinucleate syncytial mass (Fig. 94*A*) which is probably formed by repeated nuclear division of an original silicoblast. The silica is laid down in concentric cylinders around a conspicuous organic axial fiber called the *protorhabd* and believed by Dendy to consist of living bacteria-like organisms, a view that has not

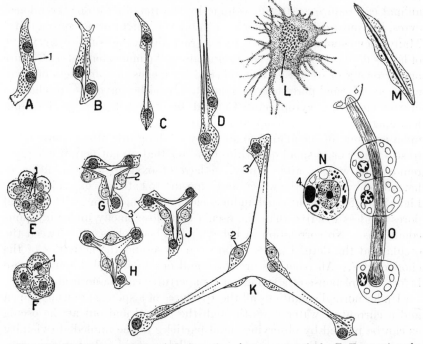

FIG. 82.—Skeleton secretion. *A–D.* Secretion of a monaxon spicule; *E–K*, secretion of a triradiate spicule (*both after Woodland*, 1905): *A*, spicule starting between two nuclei; *B*, spicule lengthened; *C*, nuclei separated into two cells; *D*, spicule end being finished. *E*, triradiate spicule starting as three granules in center of cluster of six cells; *F*, three rays lengthened; *G*, three rays united; *H* and *J*, three founders at the base, thickeners at the tips of the rays; *K*, late stage of the spicule. *L.* A calcoblast. (*After Dendy*, 1893.) *M.* Siliceous monaxon of fresh-water sponge in formation. (*After Evans*, 1901.) *N–O*, spongin secretion in *Reniera* (order Haplosclerina) (*after Tuzet*, 1932): *N*, spongioblast with beginning mass of spongin; *O*, spongioblasts in series secreting a spongin fiber. 1, spicule; 2. founder; 3, thickener; 4, spongin mass.

received acceptance. As the sea water contains only a trace of silica, a sponge must pass enormous quantities of sea water to obtain sufficient silica for its spicules.

Spongin fibers are secreted by mesenchyme cells, then termed spongioblasts (Fig. 82*N*). These arrange themselves in rows and the spongin rod secreted by each fuses with those of adjacent spongioblasts to form a long fiber (Fig. 82*O*). The spongioblasts become vacuolated and degenerate after having secreted a certain amount of spongin.

5. Physiology.—Only scattered, fragmentary observations are available concerning the physiology of sponges. No adult sponge is capable of locomotion, and some are quite devoid of contractile powers, except for changes in the porocytes. The majority, however, can undergo general or localized contraction through alterations in the shape of the pinacocytes, desmacytes, or myocytes. In some ascons, the entire animal can reduce greatly in volume by the rounding up of the pinacocytes, but most calcareous sponges exhibit very slight or no contractility. Many Demospongiae are able to contract the whole surface by virtue of layers of fiber cells in the cortex and along the main channels. Closure or narrowing of oscula is accomplished by means of sphincters of myocytes, and dermal pores may be regulated by either myocytes or changes in the encircling cytoplasm. General body contraction results from handling, disturbance, removal from the water, etc. The oscula close upon exposure of the animal to air as by a falling tide, upon transference to still water or to small quantities of water that do not permit adequate removal of wastes, after injury, in lack of oxygen, upon addition of harmful chemicals to the water, and exposure to extremes of temperature. Light is ineffective, but touch induces closure in some forms. The dermal pores are less reactive than the oscula and close chiefly under injurious conditions. No correlation in behavior has been observed between the oscula and the dermal pores or between these and the activities of the choanocytes. All reactions are slow, and one to several minutes elapse before any response of a sponge or its apertures can be noticed.

Under normal conditions all the apertures of a sponge are widely open and a current of water flows through the animal and out at the oscula as can be proved by observing small particles in the immediate vicinity of an osculum. For *Leucandra*, a small leuconoid calcareous sponge, the water current was found to flow from the osculum at a rate of 8.5 cm. per second and to be detectable 25 to 50 cm. above the osculum. A specimen 10 cm. high and 1 cm. in diameter was estimated to possess 2,250,000 flagellated chambers and to pass 22.5 liters of water per day. Obviously a large sponge with millions of flagellated chambers must pass hundreds of liters of water daily. The rate of the water current in the flagellated chambers is believed to be very slow, about $\frac{1}{100}$ mm. per second. The pressure developed is slight; the water rose only 2–4 mm. in a tube of 1 mm. bore inserted into the osculum in the case of several siliceous sponges (Parker, 1910). The rate of the current through sponges appears to be regulated chiefly by the degree of expansion of the oscula.

The water current is caused by the beating of the flagella of the choanocytes, but, as the flagella do not beat in coordination, the way in which a current is produced is not clearly understood. The most plausible explanation is that of van Tright based on observation of thin expansions of fresh-water sponges. The flagellar movement consists of a spiral undulation passing from base to tip and creating a water current in the same direction. As the choanocytes in each flagellated chamber are grouped near the prosopyle, with their collars more or less pointed toward the apopyle, the water currents tend to flow from the flagellar tips toward the apopyle. The mechanism will obviously be more effective when the apopyles are larger than the prosopyles, as is usually the case in sponges, since the water will tend to seek the larger outlet. Small flagellated chambers are also more efficient than larger ones, since in the latter the flagellar currents will tend to be directed toward the center of the chamber where some degree of stagnation will occur. On the other hand the large size of the outlet in the larger chambers should assist the flow. Obviously the system operates most poorly in the ascon sponges where the flagella must move the mass of water in the large spongocoel; and observation indeed shows that the water current is slow in these forms, despite the advantages gained by the minute size of the incurrent pores (about 9 $m\mu$) and the large size of the choanocytes as compared with other sponges. The leuconoid structure is evidently the most efficient. The current passing at first into narrower and narrower channels is much slowed when it reaches the flagellated chambers, permitting time for food capture and gaseous exchange. Conversely, the current after leaving the chambers is increased in speed, as it flows from the smaller into the larger canals, and is emitted from the osculum with some force because the osculum is generally of less diameter than the final channels. In addition to these mechanisms, the general shape of many sponges increases the efficiency of the current, and may be adapted to take advantage of ocean currents.

Sponges are devoid of sensory or nerve cells; the contractile responses mentioned above are therefore direct reactions to stimuli. The sponge body displays only very slight powers of conductivity. Strong stimuli such as cuts or sharp blows are transmitted not at all or only 3 or 4 mm. at the most. Conductivity is best developed at the osculum where transmission occurs more readily away from than toward the opening. The oscular rim appears to be the most sensitive part of the sponge. In the fresh-water sponge *Ephydatia*, where each osculum occupies the summit of a delicate chimney-like tube, McNair found that stimuli applied at the oscular rim would be transmitted down the chimney, causing contraction or collapse of the latter.

Although many investigators have attempted to study food intake and digestion in sponges by adding carmine particles, milk, starch grains, algal cells, bacteria, etc., to the water, and fixing and sectioning the sponges at various intervals afterward, the results have been unsatisfactory.   The materials fed are found in the choanocytes and amoebocytes, diminishing in the former and increasing in the latter as time passes.   Observations on living sponges by various workers give the following picture of food ingestion and digestion, but the evidence is scanty and inconclusive.   In the calcareous sponges, which have relatively large choanocytes, particles adhere to the outer surface of the collars or are caught between collars and eventually pass into the cytoplasm of the choanocytes.   Here they may be digested in whole or in part but are usually passed on to the amoebocytes of the mesenchyme.   In other sponges probably no digestion occurs in the small choanocytes, but food caught by them is immediately given up to adjacent amoebocytes (Fig. 83).   Some observers state that all the food thus passes through the choanocytes and that none of it goes directly into the mesenchyme through the walls of the incurrent passages; but the latter process seems probable.   Thus, except in Calcarea, digestion is accomplished wholly by the amoebocytes.   In any case, digestion is entirely intracellular as in Protozoa, occurring in food vacuoles, which are acid at first and alkaline later.   Undigestible particles are ejected from the amoebocytes and find their way into the outgoing currents.

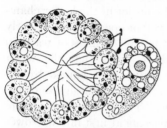

FIG. 83.—Amoebocyte receiving carbon grains from choanocytes in a calcareous sponge, *Grantia.* (*After Pourboix*, 1933.) 1, carbon particles.

The natural food probably consists of minute organisms and organic detritus; there is also evidence that sponges can utilize dissolved nutrients.   Digested food is stored as reserves, chiefly glycogen, fat, and glyco- and lipoprotein masses, in amoebocytes that when thus filled with ergastic bodies are termed *thesocytes.*   Several enzymes have been identified in sponge extracts: protein-digesting enzymes similar to trypsin, pepsin, rennin, and erepsin; lipase; invertase; and amylase in some cases.   Since sponges are permeated with bacteria and other organisms, it is not clear that the enzymes in question really came from the cells of the sponge.

The respiration of sponges is of the usual aerobic type, and sponges die or undergo reduction (see below) if kept in foul water or water deficient in oxygen content or if their dermal pores become clogged with silt.   The oxygen consumed in a given time is dependent on the rate of the water current in the sponge and may be reduced as much as 80 per cent (Hyman, 1916) if the oscula are closed.   This is partly compensated by a supernormal oxygen consumption when the oscula again open.   The rate of oxygen consumption of *Sycon*, a small vase-shaped calcareous sponge, was found to range from 0.16 cc. of oxygen per gram of fresh weight per hour in the smaller specimens to 0.04 in the larger ones.   The upper half (osculum discarded) consumes 10 to 50 per cent more oxygen per gram per hour than the basal half, an indication of a polar physiological difference (Hyman, 1925).

The excretory products have been studied in a few cases, chiefly in siliceous sponges, and have been found to include ammonia and complicated basic nitrogenous substances; urea, uric acid, and other common nitrogenous wastes of higher animals could not be demonstrated. Some observers claim that amoebocytes containing excretory granules and inclusions are discharged by sponges. Some sponges exude mucus or slime, often in large quantities, and most have a characteristic unpleasant odor. Some when handled evoke irritation of the skin and many contain toxic substances that cause various disturbances when injected into other animals and may be fatal, as is the case with the sap of fresh-water sponges injected into mice.

Because of their sessile habit and porous construction, sponges are much utilized by other animals as a substratum and a refuge. Various other sessile animals, as coelenterates, bryozoans, and barnacles may grow upon the surface of sponges. The author found at Bermuda a horny sponge entirely covered with entoproct bryozoans. Although many such associations are probably accidental, the presence of zoanthids on the root tuft of the hexactinellid genus *Hyalonema* is a regular occurrence (Fig. 91*C*). The water passages of sponges are frequently inhabited by a variety of animals, notably annelids and crustaceans. Commensal relations between sponges and crustaceans are common and often of great interest. Shrimps of the family Alpheidae regularly inhabit the interior of sponges and as many as 16,352 shrimps of the genus *Synalpheus* were found by Pearse (1932) in a large loggerhead sponge (*Spheciospongia*, order Hadromerina) at Tortugas. Other shrimps of the family Stenopidae (especially the genus *Spongicola*) live in pairs in the spongocoel of hexactinellid sponges such as *Euplectella* and *Hyalonema*. They enter when young and after growing are unable to escape because of the sieve plate over the osculum. Such glass sponge skeletons with an imprisoned pair of shrimps are said to be used in Japan as wedding gifts to symbolize a marriage lasting until death. Interesting relations exist between sponges of the family Suberitidae (order Hadromerina) and hermit crabs (Paguridae). The sponges regularly grow on snail shells occupied by a hermit crab and finally enlarge to a rounded smooth sponge that completely encloses shell and crab except for the shell opening (Fig. 102*C*). Eventually the shell disappears and the hermit crab continues to occupy a spiral cavity in the sponge lined by smooth firm fibrous tissue (Fig. 102*D*). The relation appears to be of mutual benefit as the sponge is carried about by the crab and protects the crab by its disagreeable taste from fish and other enemies. As some suberitid species are seldom found except with an enclosed hermit crab it is probable that such sponges do not grow unless their larvae happen to attach to a crab-inhabited snail shell. A parasitic relation exists between fresh-water sponges and water mites of the genus *Unionicola* and related genera (Arndt and Viets, 1938). The free-swimming mite female lays her eggs in the tissue of the sponges where the nymphal stages are also passed. Probably a similar parasitism is practised on marine sponges by marine Acarina.

Very curious is the use of sponges by crabs for protective purposes. Crabs of the genus *Dromia* and allied genera have the habit of breaking off pieces of live sponges (also other objects) and holding them with their last pair of legs over their backs pressed closely against the carapace. Other crabs, mostly of the family Majidae (*Inachus, Hyas, Macropodia,* etc.) stick pieces of sponges, algae, hydroids, etc., to their backs and legs by means of an adhesive secretion and are effectively concealed thereby. Often the implanted organisms become permanently fastened and grow normally so that a crab bedecked in this manner looks like an animated submarine garden on a small scale.

Because of their disagreeable taste and odor as well as the bristly spiculation of many forms, sponges are seldom eaten by other animals. Some of the crustacean inhabitants appear, however, to be true parasites feeding on the sponge tissues. Some nudibranchs (mollusks) feed regularly on sponges and may imitate their food sponge in color and appearance. Fish almost universally avoid sponges; hence the protective value of sponges to crustaceans. Sponges may kill other sessile animals (oysters, etc.) by growing over them and cutting off their supply of food and oxygen. The boring sponges (see page 349) may prove fatal to barnacles and other shelled animals.

The smaller sponges live from a few months to several years, while large horny sponges are believed to survive for 50 years or longer. The fresh-water sponges have been kept in aquaria a year or more but in nature are seasonal, dying out in the autumn and growing in the spring from gemmules or other resistant bodies.

Although the individuals of a given sponge species have a general similarity of appearance regardless of habitat, the assemblage of sponge species in a given type of habitat tends to present certain common features. Thus sponges growing in calm water or water where there is much deposition going on are apt to have elevated oscula, while those living in agitated water tend to be of low encrusting type without projections. Flabellate or lamellate types are characteristic of habitats with a constant directed current; the inhalant surface of such sponges faces the current while the oscula are on the downstream side. Deep-water sponges living on muddy bottom have either anchoring root tufts or long projections or spicules to keep them from settling into the ooze.

The vast majority of marine sponges live in shallow water, from the tidal zone down to 50 m., avoiding brackish habitats. The hexactinellids are limited to deeper waters, and some Demospongiae are especially adapted for life on the oozes of deeper parts of the ocean. Sponges are common everywhere throughout the littoral zone of the oceans, but those with spongin fibers are more abundant in tropical and subtropical zones, whereas those with mineral skeletons prevail in colder waters.

6. Regeneration and Other Modes of Asexual Reproduction.— Correlated with their low grade of organization the regenerative power of sponges is high. Any piece is capable of growing into a complete sponge, but the process is slow and months or years may elapse before full size is attained. Still higher powers of regeneration are revealed by a type of experiment devised by H. V. Wilson (1907) and since repeated by many workers. Sponges were squeezed through fine silk cloth and thus broken up into cells and cell clumps (Fig. 84A). Through random amoeboid movements of some of the amoebocytes these gradually adhere into aggregates, often reticular at first (Fig. 84B), finally becoming continuous masses (Fig. 84C). Such *reunition* masses consist of collar cells without collars and the various types of amoebocytes characteristic of the intact sponge. Some of the latter arrange to a covering epidermis (Fig. 84D) within which the choanocytes aggregate to form flagellate chambers and develop collars while the other amoebocytes dispose themselves into the structure typical of the species. Reunition masses composed entirely of choanocytes are incapable of reforming a sponge. Cells from different species may adhere temporarily into reunition masses but soon separate.

Under various adverse conditions many marine and fresh-water sponges collapse and disintegrate leaving only rounded *reduction bodies* (Fig. 84E), which consist of a covering epidermis and an internal mass of amoebocytes (Fig. 84F). All the various types of amoebocytes characteristic of the species occur practically unaltered in this interior mass (Penney, 1933), but the choanocytes show some degree of dedifferentiation. Upon return of favorable circumstances, the reduction bodies can develop into complete sponges. In some sponges, regularly or under adverse conditions, the ends of branches constrict off, round up into balls, and regenerate.

In all fresh-water and some marine sponges, asexual reproductive bodies, known as *gemmules*, are regularly formed as part of the life cycle. The gemmules of fresh-water sponges begin by the gathering of amoebocytes, probably archaeocytes, into groups. Through the cooperation of special nurse cells, or *trophocytes*, these amoebocytes become filled with

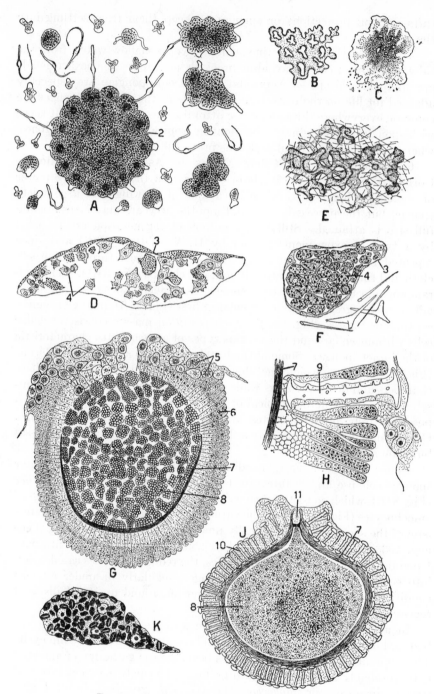

Fig. 84.—For descriptive legend see opposite page.

food reserves in the form of oval bodies composed of glycoprotein or lipoprotein (Fig. 84*K*). Other amoebocytes join the group and arrange in a columnar layer encircling the rounded mass of amoebocytes (Fig. 84*G*). The columnar layer secretes a thick hard inner membrane and later a thin outer one. Meantime scleroblasts throughout the sponge have been secreting amphidisk spicules, and they carry these amphidisks into the columnar layer where they place them radially between the inner and outer membranes (Fig. 84*H*). When the gemmule is finished (Fig. 84*J*), columnar cells, trophocytes, and scleroblasts depart, and the completed gemmule is a small hard ball consisting of a mass of food-laden archaeocytes (Fig. 84*K*) enclosed in a wall composed of two membranes with a layer of amphidisks (lacking in *Spongilla*) between them and pierced by an outlet, the *micropyle*. The fresh-water sponges usually form large numbers of gemmules in the autumn and then disintegrate; the gemmules remain in the remnants of the sponge body or fall to the bottom. They can withstand freezing and a certain amount of drying and hatch, under favorable conditions, in nature usually in spring, when temperatures rise. According to Zeuthen (1939) the gemmules will hatch any time after their formation at a temperature of 21 to 13°C. but require about 2 weeks in late fall and only 3 days in early spring. Upon hatching, the contained cells stream from the micropyle (Fig. 85*A*) and by differentiation and arrangement produce a young sponge. The large multinucleate archaeocytes divide into uninucleate ones and into small cells, the histoblasts, which emerge first (Fig. 85*A*), arrange to form an epidermis, and also differentiate into choanocytes, porocytes, and the linings of internal spaces. These spaces originate by rearrangement. Spicules are secreted by archaeocytes modified into scleroblasts and in about a week after hatching a small complete sponge surrounds the empty gemmule shell (Brien's account, 1932). Many of the uninucleate archaeocytes remain unaltered, serving as phagocytic amoebocytes and parents of sex cells.

The gemmules of marine sponges begin as an aggregation of like cells, presumably archaeocytes, which becomes enclosed by a thin mem-

---

FIG. 84.—Asexual reproduction. *A*. Appearance of *Microciona* tissue 10 minutes after being squeezed through bolting cloth. *B*. Reticulate reunition mass formed from such tissue. *C*. Later stage of the same, practically a young sponge. (*A–C, after Wilson*, 1911.) *D*. Section through a stage like *C*, showing epidermis formed and loose amoebocytes inside. (*After Wilson and Penney*, 1930.) *E*. Reduction bodies of a calcareous sponge. *F*. Section through such a body, showing mass of amoebocytes enclosed in an epithelium. (*After Maas*, 1910.) *G*. Young gemmule of a fresh-water sponge, *Ephydatia*, showing trophocytes and cylindrical layer secreting the inner membrane. *H*. Scleroblast placing its contained amphidisk into the cylindrical layer. *J*. The completed gemmule with surface layer of amphidisks and micropyle. (*G–J after Evans*, 1901.) *K*. One of the archaeocytes of a fresh-water gemmule, showing several nuclei and food bodies. (*After Brien*, 1932.) 1, collar cells; 2, masses of amoebocytes; 3, epidermis; 4, contained amoebocytes; 5, trophocytes; 6, cylindrical layer; 7, inner membrane; 8, mass of archaeocytes; 9, scleroblast with amphidisk; 10, layer of amphidisks; 11, micropyle.

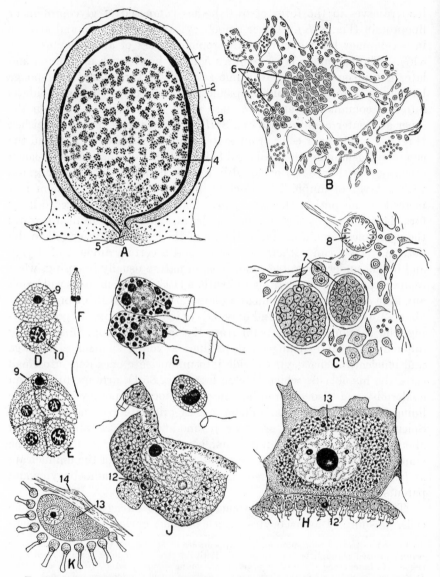

Fig. 85.—Reproduction. A. A gemmule of the fresh-water sponge *Spongilla* (note absence of amphidisks) in process of hatching. (*After Brien*, 1932.) B. Early stages of gemmule formation in the marine sponge *Esperella* (= *Mycale*) (order Poecilosclerina). C. Later stages. (*After Wilson*, 1894.) D–F. Spermatogenesis in *Reniera* (*after Tuzet*, 1930): D, sperm mother cell has divided into a cover cell and the primary spermatogonium; E, latter has divided into four spermatocytes enclosed by cover cell; F, ripe spermatozoon. G–J. Fertilization of the calcareous sponge *Grantia* (*after Gatenby*, 1919): G, spermatozoon approaching two collar cells; H, sperm inside a collar cell, adjacent to an egg; J, collar cell giving up sperm into egg. K. Egg of *Sycon* in situ in the wall of a radial canal. 1, outer membrane of gemmule; 2, inner membrane of gemmule; 3, epidermis of young sponge; 4, food-laden archaeocytes; 5, histoblasts streaming from micropyle, 6, assemblage of

brane of flat cells (Fig. 85B, C). The surface cells of the mass become columnar and flagellated except at the posterior pole, and the gemmule then escapes as a flagellated larva. This swims about for a time, then attaches near the nonflagellated pole, loses the flagella, and becomes a young sponge by rearrangement and differentiation of the interior cells. Remarkably enough these larvae may entirely resemble those arising from fertilized eggs and develop like the latter.

7. **Sexual Reproduction.**—All sponges reproduce sexually by means of typical ova and spermatozoa, but the details are not clearly established. According to the classical account the sex cells come only from archaeocytes that in turn are believed to be persistent embryonic cells. But several authors have described the origin of sex cells from choanocytes, and others maintain that they may arise from any amoebocyte of the mesenchyme. The egg mother cell or ovocyte is first noticed as an enlarged amoebocyte with a large nucleus and conspicuous nucleolus (Fig. 85K). It grows and acquires food stores by engulfing or fusing with other similar amoebocytes or may receive supplies from special trophocytes. Upon attaining full size it undergoes the usual maturation divisions. The formation of sperm has been observed in only a few sponges and in many cases appears to be a rare or sporadic process. In some sponges the sperm mother cell or spermatogonium is described as an enlarged amoebocyte that soon becomes enveloped by one or more flattened cover cells (Fig. 85D, E) derived by division of the mother cell or consisting of other amoebocytes. The whole is called a spermatocyst (Fig. 85E); the enclosed spermatogonium divides two or three times into spermatocytes, which give rise to sperm. Other authors state that the spermatogonia are transformed choanocytes, and Gatenby has described the transformation of an entire flagellated chamber into spermatozoa. The sperm enter other sponges by way of the water current, and the eggs are fertilized in situ. In Calcarea according to Gatenby and others, the spermatozoon enters a choanocyte, which acts as nurse cell (Fig. 85H) and then fuses with the egg, setting free the contained sperm (Fig. 85J). A similar process has been reported by Tuzet for *Cliona* (order Hadromerina) and *Reniera* (order Haplosclerina) where the sperm enters an amoebocyte, which then transfers it to the egg. It is possible that this remarkable kind of fertilization is general for sponges.

The fertilized egg undergoes equal or unequal holoblastic cleavage and develops in situ into a blastula. This becomes flagellated, works its way through the parent tissues into the excurrent system, and goes out from the osculum. After swimming for a few to many hours,

---

archaeocytes to form gemmule; 7, later stages of gemmule; 8, final stage of gemmule, with surface epithelium; 9, cover cell; 10, spermatogonium; 11, yolk bodies of collar cell; 12, sperm inside collar cell; 13, egg; 14, epidermis.

the larva attaches and develops into a small sponge typical of the species.

Although some sponges are apparently dioecious, the majority seem to be hermaphroditic, often, however, giving rise to eggs and sperm at different times. For some it is stated that the eggs are produced in the basal region, the sperm apically. Many, especially those living in shallow water, shed their embryos at definite seasons of the year, whereas the deep-sea forms probably reproduce the year round.

8. Individuality in Sponges.—Whether sponges are individuals or colonies has been much debated. The lack of nervous system and the slight conductivity evidenced by sponges certainly indicate the lowest possible grade of individuality. Yet this very lack of any known coordinating mechanism renders all the more remarkable the molding of sponges into numerous species each with a definite construction and definite types of spicules arranged in particular ways. It is usually stated that each osculum with its contributing portions of the canal system constitutes a sponge individual or person, at least from a physiological point of view. The larger sponges with several oscula are then regarded as colonies of very vaguely indicated individuals.

IV. CLASS CALCAREA OR CALCISPONGIAE

The calcareous sponges form a sharply defined group, readily distinguished from all other sponges by the calcareous nature of their spicules. The Calcarea are of small size, varying from a few to 10 cm. in height, mostly of a drab, inconspicuous coloration, and frequently of bristly texture from the projecting spicules. Typically they are strongly individualized, consisting of solitary or grouped radially symmetrical, vase-shaped bodies, each with a terminal narrowed osculum (Fig. 77B). Some, however, form bushy branching masses (Fig. 86B, C) with many oscula, or compact masses, and a few have slender stalk-like bases (Fig. 86D). The osculum is often encircled by an upstanding collar of long monaxon spicules, termed the *oscular fringe* (Figs. 87G, 88A, B) and the oscular opening may be covered with a sieve membrane. The base is fastened directly to hard objects.

The spicules are composed of crystalline calcium carbonate, chiefly in the form of the mineral calcite, in some cases as aragonite. Analysis of the spicules of *Leucandra* gives about 87 per cent of calcium carbonate, 7 per cent of magnesium carbonate, 3 per cent of water, small quantities of other minerals, and a trace of organic material, believed to form an axial thread in each ray and to cover the spicule with a thin sheath. Axial fiber and sheath are, however, very difficult to demonstrate. The spicules of the Calcarea are separate except in certain species known as the *pharetrone* sponges, where the spicules are united into a network (Fig. 90) or completely enclosed by a calcareous cement.

Calcareous spicules are all megascleres, although each type occurs in a wide range of sizes, and are of three sorts: monaxons, triradiates, and quadriradiates (Fig. 86*H*). The monaxons include both styles and rhabds, the latter often oxeas. The triradiate is the dominant type of calcareous spicule and occurs in many varieties characterized by differences in the lengths and angles of the rays. Triradiate spicules are called *regular* when the three rays and angles are equal (Fig. 86*H*, *15*). When these are unequal the spicule is practically bilaterally symmetrical, having paired *lateral* rays differing in length from or making an angle greater or less than 120 degrees with the third *posterior* or *basal* ray (Fig. 86*H*, *11*). Such spicules are called *sagittal* and also *alate*, as the lateral rays often suggest wings. Alate spicules may also be described as T-shaped, when the lateral rays are depressed (Fig. 86*H*), and Y-shaped or like a tuning fork, when they are erected (Fig. 86*H*, *14*). The three rays of a triradiate are never quite in one plane but outline a low pyramid. Quadriradiates have an additional fourth ray that may be short and thorn-like or long and thick, so that a typical triaene results (Fig. 86*H*, *13*).

The various types of spicules are definitely arranged with respect to the morphology of the sponge to insure adequate protection and support. Monaxons commonly project from the surface, forming a bristly exterior. The osculum often has a special skeletal arrangement consisting of long slender monaxons protruding as the oscular fringe and T-shaped sagittal triradiates forming the oscular rim by the interlacing of their parallel lateral rays (Fig. 87*D*). Where a cortex is present it frequently contains special cortical spicules placed parallel to the surface; or the lateral rays of triradiates or the clads of quadriradiates may parallel the surface making a strong layer while the basal ray projects inward (Fig. 88*D*, *E*). Triradiates or quadriradiates with a short fourth ray occur in the walls and around the internal ostia as supporting spicules.

The class Calcarea includes all three types of structure, asconoid, syconoid, and leuconoid. Here belong all the ascon sponges, most of which are assigned to the genus *Leucosolenia* (including *Clathrina*) with numerous species in shore waters. The ascon sponges are small (up to 10 to 15 cm. high), drab-colored sponges. None of them is a simple solitary ascon tube like Fig. 78, but all of them are colonies of such tubes. In the simplest species of *Leucosolenia*, the colony consists of a few upright tubes each terminating in an osculum and united below by horizontal tubes (Fig. 86*A*). Most species are more complicated, consisting of a confused network of branching tubes from which stand out a few larger erect cylinders bearing an osculum at their summit (Fig. 86*B*, *C*). When

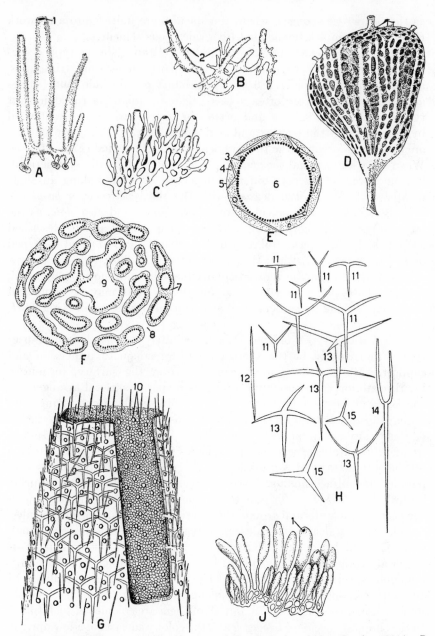

Fig. 86.—Calcarea. *A.* Simple type of *Leucosolenia.* (*After Dendy,* 1891.)   *B.* Branching type of *Leucosolenia,* from life, Atlantic Coast.   *C.* Reticulate type of *Leucosolenia,* from life, California.   *D.* Reticulate type with a pseudoderm. (*After Dendy,* 1891.) *E.* Diagrammatic section through a *Leucosolenia* tube.   *F.* Diagrammatic section through *Leucosolenia* of the type of *D,* with a pseudoderm and pseudopores.   *G.* Oscular end of a *Leucosolenia* tube, showing spicule arrangement.   *H.* Types of spicules of calcareous

any branch attains sufficient size its tip breaks through as an osculum, and the adjacent spicules then rearrange. In a number of species of *Leucosolenia*, the network of tubes converges to one or several oscula (Fig. 86*D*). Finally, in the most complicated species, the outermost tubes fuse together forming a false surface or *pseudoderm* leaving a few large openings or *pseudopores* so that the sponge appears solid and simulates a higher type of sponge; but sections show the network of ascon tubes in the interior (Fig. 86*D, F*). Every part of a *Leucosolenia* colony has the structure shown in Fig. 78 and Fig. 80*A*, with an outer epidermis of separate pinacocytes, inner complete lining of choanocytes, and middle stratum of mesogloea containing amoebocytes and spicules, the whole pierced by numerous pores through porocytes. The wall is filled with tri- and quadriradiate spicules, often of several kinds and sizes in one species, and monaxons projecting to the exterior. Near the osculum, the spicules are of the sagittal type with posterior rays directed away from the osculum and with lateral rays interlaced to form the rim; a few slender monaxons may project as a scanty oscular fringe (Fig. 86*G*).

Besides the genus *Leucosolenia*, Dendy and Row (1913) and de Laubenfels (1936) recognize as ascon genera *Ascute* with giant monaxons, *Ascyssa*, in which all the spicules are monaxon, and *Dendya*, having a central cylinder from which arise numerous radial branches, each covered with short branches. *Dendya* approaches the sycon type.

All the typical syconoid sponges also belong to the Calcarea. Usually they are single vase-shaped forms (Fig. 77*B*), or clusters of such vases, with a large central spongocoel, terminal osculum with or without a conspicuous oscular fringe, and thick wall containing the radial canals and incurrent passages. The sycon structure occurs in several stages and grades imperceptibly into leucon types of Calcarea. In the simplest case, illustrated only by the genus *Sycetta*, the radial canals are wholly separate from each other, and the spaces between them are not organized into definite incurrent canals (Fig. 87*A*). Next the radial canals begin to touch and finally fuse along their entire lengths so that the spaces between them become enclosed to form definite incurrent canals, each bounded by four radial canals (Fig. 87*B*). The incurrent opening may be simply the space left between the outer ends of the radial canals, or this space may be covered over by a dermal membrane pierced by a true dermal pore. Such incurrent openings are guarded by projecting oxeas. These stages are illustrated by the genus *Sycon* (Fig. 87*B, C*),[1] a very

---

[1] According to de Laubenfels (1936) the name *Sycon* must be replaced by *Scypha*.

sponges, from life, except 14. (*After Döderlein,* 1897.) *J. Rhabdodermella,* from life, California, sylleibid type of structure. 1, osculum; 2, buds; 3, flagellate layer; 4, mesenchyme; 5, epidermis; 6, spongocoel; 7, pseudoderm; 8, pseudopore; 9, false spongocoel; 10, ostia; 11, sagittal types of triradiates; 12, oxea; 13, quadriradiates; 14, tuning-fork type; 15, regular triradiates.

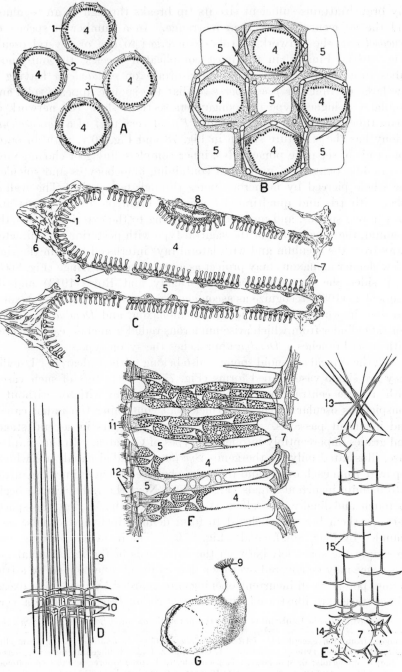

Fig. 87.—For descriptive legend see opposite page.

common genus with numerous species. In the final stage, illustrated by the genus *Grantia*,[1] the dermal membrane spreads over the entire surface of the sponge, forming a cortex of varying thickness, provided with special cortical spicules, most of which are arranged parallel to the surface (Fig. 87*F*). With the development of a cortex the incurrent passages become more irregular and branching, and subdermal spaces may be present. The spongocoel wall may undergo an accumulation of mesenchyme similar to that of the cortex with a resulting retreat of the radial canals and the formation of canals leading from them to the spongocoel. In such cases a special skeleton next to the spongocoel is also developed. Finally the radial canals may branch at their outer ends, leading to further irregularities. In short, with the appearance of a cortex the canal system becomes irregular and lacks taxonomic value so that further generic distinctions are based primarily on type and arrangement of the spicules. Among the genera with syconoid structure and cortex are *Grantiopsis, Grantessa, Heteropia, Sycaltis, Ute, Amphoriscus.*

The cortical types of syconoid sponges lead directly into leuconoid types apparently independently in various families, by way of transitional stages. A common intermediate grade is that known as *sylleibid*, found in such genera as *Rhabdodermella* (Fig. 86*J*), *Leucilla* (Figs. 87*G*, 88*D*) and *Vosmaeropsis*. Here each radial canal is subdivided into elongated flagellated chambers grouped around a common excurrent channel (Fig. 87*D*). This may be considered a primitive leuconoid type. The leuconoid condition may also arise directly from the asconoid without passing through a syconoid stage. The types of asconoids with a pseudoderm correspond to syconoids with a cortex and like the latter tend to evolve toward the leuconoid state, not, however, by branching, but by the anastomosis of the ascon tubes. A transitional type, with elongated chambers, is attained in this way, illustrated by the genera *Leucaltis* (= *Heteropegma*, Fig. 88*E*) and *Leucascus*. By either route the final

---

[1] The little Atlantic Coast sponge sold under the name *Grantia* as class material of a sycon sponge is not a *Grantia* at all, but belongs to the genus *Sycon*.

Fig. 87.—Calcareous sponges (continued), syconoid type. *A*. Diagrammatic vertical section through the wall of *Sycetta*, showing complete separation of flagellated canals. *B*. Vertical section through the wall of *Sycon*, showing formation of incurrent canals. (*After Dendy*, 1893.) *C*. Section along two flagellated canals of *Sycon*, spicules removed, showing histology, from slide. (*Courtesy A. E. Galigher.*) *D*. Arrangement of spicules at the osculum of *Sycon*, from life. *E*. Arrangement of spicules along a radial canal of *Sycon*, from life. *F*. Cross section of *Grantia*, spongocoel to the right, showing cortex with special spiculation. (*After Dendy*, 1893.) *G. Leucilla*, sylleibid type, from life, Bermuda. Black ovals represent choanocytes. 1, choanocyte layer; 2, mesenchyme; 3, epidermis; 4, radial canal; 5, incurrent canal; 6, mass of mesenchyme on outer end of radial canal; 7, internal ostium; 8, amphiblastula in place; 9, monaxons of oscular fringe; 10, sagittal triradiates of oscular rim; 11, cortex; 12, dermal pore; 13, cluster of monaxons at outer end of radial canal; 14, triradiates around internal ostium; 15, sagittal triradiates of radial canal.

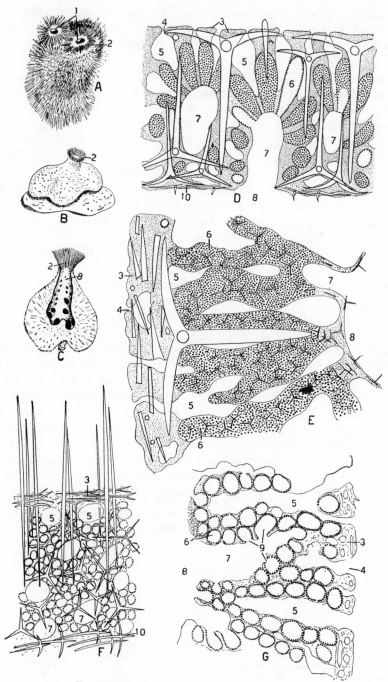

FIG. 88.—For descriptive legend see opposite page.

leuconoid condition with numerous small round chambers strewn in the mesenchyme results as in the genera *Leuconia* (includes *Leucandra*) (Fig. 88*A*–*C*, *F*, *G*) derived from syconoids, and *Leucetta*, derived from asconoids.[1] In the leuconoid Calcarea, the apopyles are always widely open to the excurrent canals and therefore the system remains at the eurypylous stage (Fig. 88*G*).

The histology of the Calcarea presents nothing especial. The epidermis is probably always composed of separate pinacocytes, which, however, may become syncytial around the dermal pores (Fig. 80*D*). The nature of the prosopyles in the higher types is uncertain. The dermal pores are probably intercellular spaces. In the formation of the syconoid and leuconoid systems the choanocytes retreat from the spongocoel, which together with the rest of the excurrent system becomes lined by epidermis migrating in from the exterior. The choanocytes of Calcarea are much larger than those of other sponges and probably play a more active role in digestion. The cell arrangement along each canal of a simple syconoid type is the same as that of an ascon tube (Fig. 87*C*). The cortex consists of an accumulation of mesenchyme, containing special spicules (Figs. 87*F*, 88*E*).

The spiculation is rather monotonous, being confined to the monaxon, tri-, and quadriradiate types. The arrangement of spicules along the radial canals of the genus *Sycon* is shown in Fig. 87*E*; this kind of tubar skeleton when thus made of layers of spicules is said to be *articulate*. In the family Amphoriscidae, containing the genera *Amphoriscus*, *Leucilla* (Fig. 87*G*), and *Rhabdodermella* (Fig. 86*J*), the canal skeleton is of the *inarticulate* type; large triaenes or sagittal triradiates have their cladi in the cortex parallel to the surface while the large thick basal ray is directed toward and almost reaches the spongocoel (Fig. 88*D*). Similar spicules near the spongocoel may send a large basal ray toward the cortex. Such sponges have a hard smooth surface. The cortex of Calcarea often contains small or large monaxons, projecting to form a bristly exterior (Fig. 88*A*, *F*), or large monaxons parallel to the surface or most frequently

[1] Because of this double mode of origin of calcareous leuconoids, de Laubenfels (1936) proposes to abandon the old divisions Homocoela and Heterocoela of the Calcarea and divide them instead into Asconosa, asconoids and their derivatives, and Syconosa, syconoids and their derivatives. The proposal seems sound.

Fig. 88.—Calcarea (continued). Sylleibid and leuconoid types. *A* and *B*. Two species of *Leuconia* (=*Leucandra*) from life, Bermuda. *C*. Median vertical section of *B*. *D*. Cross section of the wall of *Leucilla*, showing typical sylleibid structure, also inarticulate type of skeleton. (*After Dendy*, 1893.) *E*. Cross section of the wall of *Leucaltis* (=*Heteropegma*), stage between asconoid and leuconoid structure. (*After Dendy*, 1893.) *F*. Cross section of *Leuconia*, same sponge as *A*, showing spiculation, from life. *G*. Cross section of *Leuconia*, spicules removed by acid, showing typical eurypylous leuconoid structure, from slide. (*Courtesy of A. E. Galigher.*) 1, osculum; 2, oscular fringe; 3, cortex; 4, dermal pores; 5, incurrent channels; 6, flagellated chambers; 7, excurrent channels; 8, spongocoel; 9. apopyles; 10, spiculation of spongocoel wall.

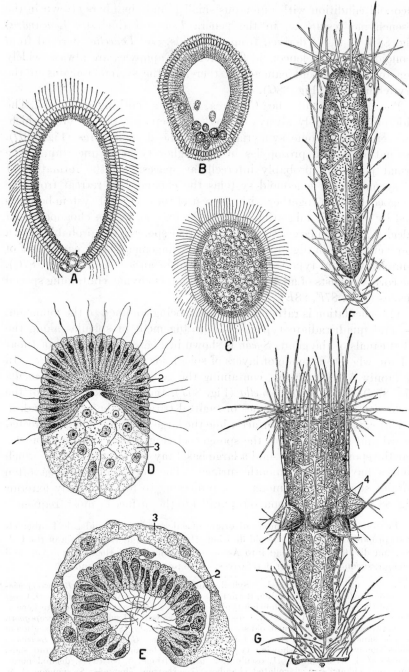

FIG. 89.—For descriptive legend see opposite page.

tri- and quadriradiates parallel to the surface. The interior of the leuconoid types is generally strewn with triradiates, which kind of spicule in fact forms the bulk of the skeleton in most species of Calcarea.

The Calcarea have been much employed in physiological studies on sponges already reviewed (page 302). Some of the Calcarea are highly contractile, with oscula provided with an internal sphincter and very labile pinacocytes, but most seem almost devoid of contractile power and show no visible changes on handling or removal to the laboratory. Some, particularly *Leucosolenia*, are very sensitive to external conditions and will not live when taken from their habitat. Gemmule formation has not been observed in the Calcarea, but reduction bodies may arise under adverse circumstances. Budding is of common occurrence. In some asconoids, the breaking off of the ends of branches is reported as a regular mode of asexual reproduction.

In the Calcarea, according to the best researches, the ova come from amoebocytes of the archaeocyte type (i.e., with a very large nucleus and conspicuous nucleolus). In *Sycon* and *Grantia*, the only forms adequately studied, the first recognizable female germ cells are oögonia. These pass into the cavities of the radial canals where they undergo two mitoses, each producing four ovocytes. These pass through the choanocyte layer into the mesenchyme, where they increase greatly in size, being nourished by special nurse cells or *trophocytes*, which appear to be transformed choanocytes. One such trophocyte attaches to the surface of each ovocyte and eventually fuses with it. In fertilization as already stated, the sperm enters a choanocyte adjacent to a ripe ovocyte. This choanocyte loses its collar and flagellum, becomes amoeboid, and plasters itself to the surface of the ovocyte, which forms a conical depression to receive it (Fig. 85*J*). The sperm in the meantime has lost its tail, and its swollen head becomes surrounded by a capsule. The capsule carrying the sperm head penetrates into the ovocyte, being drawn out into a canal; the sperm-carrying choanocyte then departs (Duboscq and Tuzet, 1937).

The fertilized egg undergoes maturation and cleaves holoblastically. At the 16-cell stage the embryo lies just beneath the maternal choanocyte layer as a flattened disk-shaped body. The fate of the blastomeres has already been fixed by their position with reference to the maternal tissues. The tier of eight cells next to the maternal layer of choanocytes is the future epidermis; the other eight are the future choanocytes. The latter divide rapidly, resembling the micromeres of other metazoan embryos, and

FIG. 89.—Embryology of Calcarea. *A–C*. Stages in the formation of parenchymula of *Leucosolenia* by unipolar ingression. (*After Metschnikoff*, 1879.) *D*. Amphiblastula of a calcareous sponge (*Sycon*). *E*. Same after gastrulation and attachment. (*Both after Hammer*, 1908.) *F*. Later asconoid stage (*Sycandra*). *G*. Same, beginning to put out radial canals. (*Both after Maas*, 1900.) 1, so-called archaeocytes; 2, flagellated cells; 3, granular cells; 4, radial canals.

acquire flagella on their inner ends facing the blastocoel. The future epidermal cells remain undivided for some time, forming a group of eight large rounded cells, similar to macromeres. In the center of this group an opening arises that functions as a mouth and ingests adjacent maternal cells. This stage is hence termed by Duboscq and Tuzet a *stomoblastula*. Now there occurs a process of *inversion*, exactly resembling the same stage in the development of *Volvox*. The embryo turns inside out by way of the mouth, so that the flagellar ends of the flagellated micromeres are brought to the outside. The embryo is now the typical larva of the Calcarea, termed an *amphiblastula*. The greater part of the surface is formed of small, narrow, flagellated cells, and the remainder, usually considered the posterior pole, consists of the group of large, rounded, granular, nonflagellated macromeres. The latter multiply until they come to constitute about half of the larva (Fig. 89*D*). From the blastula stage on, the embryo becomes enclosed in a *trophic membrane*, formed of maternal choanocytes, which supplies the embryo with food.

When completed, the amphiblastula forces its way into the adjacent radial canal and is carried to the exterior. The flagellated hemisphere is directed forward in swimming and also usually bears the polar bodies, so that it appears to correspond to the animal or ectodermal hemisphere of other metazoan embryos. However, an embolic gastrulation ensues in which the flagellated half is invaginated into or overgrown by the granular nonflagellated half (Fig. 89*E*). In some forms a typical gastrula with a blastopore results (Fig. 89*E*), but in others the invaginated flagellate cells form a solid mass in the interior so that the larva is a *stereogastrula* or *parenchymula*. The larva attaches by the blastoporal pole, and in the case of the parenchymula the interior mass hollows out to form the spongocoel. In either case an asconoid type of structure results, termed the *olynthus* stage (Fig. 89*F*). The nonflagellated cells derived from the eight original macromeres become the epidermis (pinacocytes) of the young sponge and also give rise to the scleroblasts and porocytes. The flagellate cells differentiate into choanocytes, archaeocytes, and other types of amoebocytes. Hence the cells of the mesenchyme derive from both embryonic layers.

The foregoing account applies to the Calcarea in general with the exception of some species of *Leucosolenia* where a different type of development has been described (Metschnikoff, 1879; Minchin, 1896). Here the egg cleaves to form a coeloblastula composed entirely of narrow flagellated cells except at the posterior pole, where there is a group of rounded nonflagellated cells (Fig. 89*A*) believed to be archaeocytes and the ancestors of all future archaeocytes of the sponge. These together with adjacent flagellated cells (which thereupon lose their flagella) wander into the interior (Fig. 89*B*) and fill it with a mass of cells (Fig. 89*C*). The resulting larva is thus a stereogastrula or parenchymula (Fig. 89*C*). After some hours of free life, it attaches by the anterior pole and flattens out; the interior cells migrate to the external surface and form the epidermis and mesenchyme, and the flagellated cells are thus enclosed and become choanocytes. A central spongocoel appears, an osculum breaks through, spicules are secreted, and a few days after attachment, a complete asconoid sponge has arisen.

Syconoid genera develop from the olynthus stage by the pushing out of the wall, first at the middle, into radial canals (Fig. 89*G*). The development of the leuconoid Calcarea has apparently never been studied. As already noted, some of them seem to come from the syconoid condition by further branching of the radial canals, whereas others apparently derive directly from the asconoid stage.

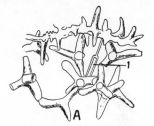

The difficulties of reconciling the foregoing types of development, especially that of the parenchymula, with the ordinary conception of metazoan germ-layer formation will be evident. What appears to be the ectoderm of the sponge larva becomes the internal cells, and what seems to be entoderm is the source of the epidermis.

The Calcarea are exclusively marine and are confined almost entirely to shallow shore waters, some occurring between tide levels, most living a short distance below the surface. They are found throughout the world, but seem to avoid waters too much diluted by fresh water. Some genera, such as

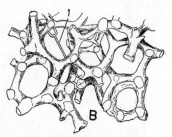

Fig. 90.—A pharetronid sponge, *Petrosoma*. (*After Döderlein*, 1898.) *A*. Early stage of the skeleton, spicules separate. *B*. Later stage, spicules united into a network. 1, tuning-fork spicule.

Leucosolenia, *Sycon*, and *Leuconia*, have a wide distribution, with numerous species.

The Calcarea are poorly preserved as fossils because of the solubility of the spicules in deeper waters and the tendency for the replacement of the spicules by other minerals. Most of the fossils belong to the group termed the *pharetronid* sponges, which began in the Devonian and died out in the Eocene except for a few survivals as the genera *Petrosoma*, *Murrayana*, and *Minchinella*. In these sponges many of the spicules are united into a framework, usually with square meshes, by means of a calcareous cement (Fig. 90). Some of the free spicules have a character-istic tuning-fork shape. In the living genus *Murrayana*, the skeletal fusion has proceeded so far that the spicules are completely embedded

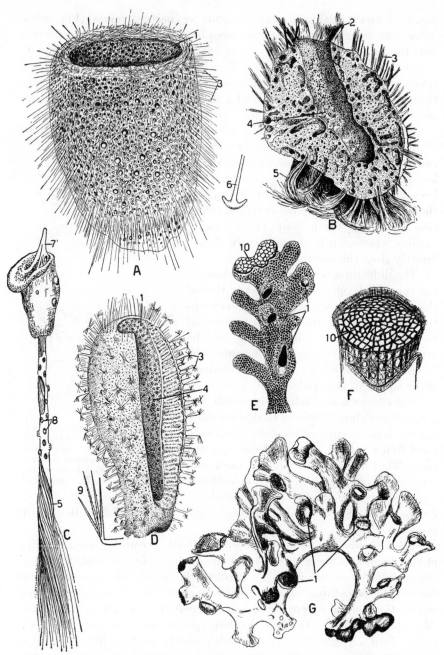

Fig. 91.—Some Hexactinellida. *A. Staurocalyptus*, dry specimen. *B. Pheronema*, longitudinal section. (*After Schulze*, 1887.) *C. Hyalonema*, dry specimen. *D. Rossella*. (*After Schulze*, 1887.) *E.* Branch of *Aphrocallistes*, dry specimen, to show honeycomb dictyonine skeleton, and oscular sieve. *F.* Upper end of *Euplectella*, dry specimen, showing

and concealed by cement. A few fossils of the syconoid type of structure are known from the Jurassic to the present.

V. CLASS HEXACTINELLIDA OR HYALOSPONGIAE

The Hexactinellida or glass sponges are distinguished from all other sponges by the presence of *hexactine* siliceous spicules as well as by certain other peculiarities of structure.   They are mostly strongly individualized, radially symmetrical sponges, with cylindrical, vase-, urn-, funnel-, or similarly shaped bodies, fastened at the base directly or more usually by way of a root tuft of spicules.   The wall of varying thickness encloses a spongocoel opening at the summit by a wide osculum (Figs. 91A, B, D and 92).   The osculum may be covered over by a sieve plate of silica (Fig. 91F) or be bounded by upright spicules (Fig. 91B).   From this general type, the body may vary by widening into a funnel shape and then flattening into a plate or mushroom form, attached by a stalk.   In such cases the osculum is lost as the upper surface is really the spongocoel lining turned outside.   The water current then enters the lower surface and goes out from the upper surface.   Others may flatten laterally into upright plates or curved shell-like shapes in which the water enters one surface and goes out from the other.   Many are elevated from the substratum by a long root tuft (Fig. 91C) or by a stalk-like elongation of the body proper.   Less common than the symmetrical types are branching forms (Fig. 91E, G), which may also assume a lattice appearance by the anastomosing of the branches.   Many are regularly curved rather than erect (Fig. 92) and then exhibit some degree of bilateral symmetry.   The glass sponges are of pale coloration and of characteristic appearance from the projecting glassy spicules, which often occur in tufts and resemble glass wool.   The majority are of moderate size, ranging between 10 and 30 cm; but some reach 1 m. in length, and a few are even much longer because of the excessive elongation of the root spicules.   The Hexactinellida are exclusively marine and limited to the deeper waters of the ocean.

The internal structure differs from that of other sponges.   It consists of a network, the *trabecular net*, made of thin strands outlining large open meshes (Fig. 93D).   The strands appear to be a syncytium formed by the union of the pseudopodia of collencytes, thesocytes, archaeocytes, and other types of amoebocytes.   The external surface apparently lacks a definite epidermis and is composed simply of the trabecular net, thus bearing numerous large openings.   The lining of the spongocoel is of the same nature.   In the midst of the trabecular net are located the flagellated chambers, elongated and finger-like or thimble-shaped, resembling

oscular sieve. G. *Farrea occa*, dry specimen. 1, osculum; 2, marginal prostals; 3, pleural prostals; 4, spongocoel; 5, root spicules; 6, enlarged root spicule of *Pheronema*; 7, gastral cone; 8, symbiotic zoanthids on root tuft of *Hyalonema*; 9, enlarged pleural pentact of *Rossella*; 10, oscular sieve.

the radial canals of the syconoid Calcarea. The chambers are arranged in a single continuous row parallel to the dermal and spongocoel surfaces and straight or folded in and out, as in a simple syconoid or leuconoid arrangement (Fig. 93*A*, *B*). The chambers open into the spongocoel or into excurrent channels by wide apertures. The incurrent and excurrent passages are for the most part only vaguely outlined in the trabecular net;

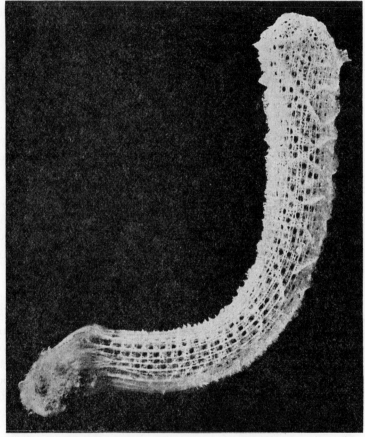

Fig. 92.—*Euplectella*, the Venus's flower basket. (*Photograph courtesy Dr. Ralph Buchsbaum.*)

but when the layer of flagellated chambers is folded, there is usually a large excurrent channel in each fold (Fig. 93*A*, *B*). Typically the wall of a hexactinellid sponge (Fig. 93*A*) then consists of the following regions: dermal surface, subdermal trabecular net, layer of flagellated chambers, subgastral trabecular net, spongocoel.

The Hexactinellida possess a beautiful glass-like skeleton, consisting of separate spicules plus in most cases a network of spicules loosely bound together or fused into a lattice. The skeleton is composed of a non-crystalline hydrated silica, i.e., silicic acid, with the formula $H_2Si_3O_7$ in the case of the long root spicules of *Monoraphis*. Analysis of these spicules gave about 86 per cent silicon dioxide, 9 per cent water, 3 per cent other elements including sodium, potassium, iron, and chlorine, and a small amount of organic matter, named *spiculin*. Each spicule consists of a noticeable axial fiber of spiculin, encircled by cylinders of hydrated silica containing traces of spiculin, and is covered by a sheath of spiculin. The old view that thin cylinders of spiculin alternated with the siliceous cylinders is erroneous. The scanty available evidence indicates that each spicule arises in the center of a syncytial multinucleate scleroblastic mass and is entire from the start, never developing by the fusion of originally separate rays (Fig. 94A, B).

The spicules are divisible into megascleres and microscleres and are all hexactines or some derivative thereof (Fig. 94). The basic *regular* hexactine consists of three axes crossing at right angles, forming six rays of approximately equal length, each provided with an axial fiber (Fig. 94, 1). A common modification is the elongation of one ray, giving a sword-like effect (Fig. 94, 3). When the elongated ray is covered with spines, the name *pinule* is applied (Fig. 94, 4, 5). Various types result from successive loss of rays, often indicated by persistent knobs, bumps, or bases of the axial fibers. Loss of one ray results in the *pentact* spicule, usually consisting of a cross of four rays topping a long, frequently pinulate, basal ray (Fig. 94, 5, 6). By loss of an entire axis, the spicule becomes a *tetract* or simple cross, also called *stauractine*, differing from a quadriradiate calcareous spicule in that the four rays lie in one plane (Fig. 94, 16). *Triacts* occur but are uncommon, whereas *diactines* are abundant and often of great length. They may show their origin from a hexact by the presence near the middle of knobs or branches of the axial fiber but often are indistinguishable from ordinary diactinal monaxons. A common type, called *uncinate*, is covered with short spines directed toward one end (Fig. 94, 7, 8); and others are tipped with recurved hooks. *Monactines*, known by indications of lost rays at one end, also occur; those with a disk or bulb at one end are termed *clavules* (Fig. 94, 10); those with a branched end are called *scopules* (Fig. 94, 9); long monactines with little spines along one end, known as *scepters*, are found among the projecting marginal and pleural prostals of *Pheronema* and its relatives (Fig. 91B).

The microscleres comprise small versions of many of the foregoing types and in addition asters and amphidisks. Asters are regular hexactines with branched rays. These branches are not regarded as true rays since they lack axial fibers. *Oxyhexasters* have the ray ends divided into a few simple straight branches (Fig. 94, 11); in *discohexasters*, the branches are

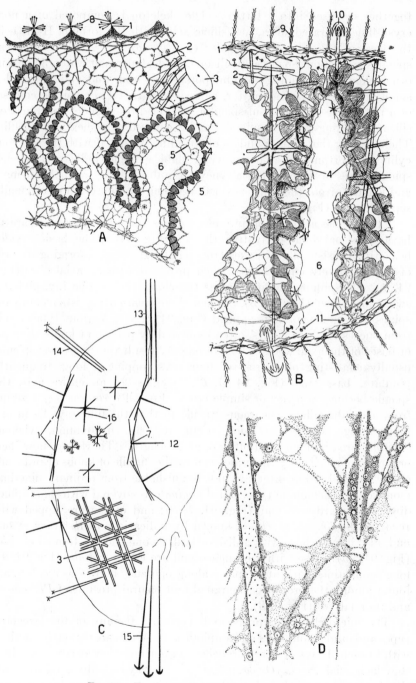

Fig. 93.—For descriptive legend see opposite page.

topped by disks (Fig. 94, *13*); when the branches form brush-like bundles, the name *discoctaster* is applied (Fig. 94, *12*); when these brushes are curved outward, like feather dusters, the aster is called a *plumicome* (Fig. 94, *14*); plumicomes with expanded tips are termed *floricomes* (Fig. 94, *15*); and numerous other variations occur. *Amphidisks* are diactines with ends developed into umbrella-like expansions (Fig. 81, *29*) and occur in a range of sizes.

The spicules are very definitely arranged in the sponge body (Fig. 93C); the Hexactinellida surpass all other sponges in this respect. Spicules projecting from the sponge are termed *prostals* and comprise the long needles, mostly diactines, which encircle the osculum (*marginal* prostals), protrude from the surface singly or in bundles (*pleural* prostals), and form the root tufts (*basal* prostals or anchoring spicules). The pleural prostals may be scepters and uncinates as in *Pheronema* (Fig. 91B) or curious asymmetrical pentacts as in *Rossella* (Fig. 91D). The anchoring prostals comprise one or more dense bundles, often curved or twisted, of long glassy spicules, resembling glass wool and serving to fasten the sponge to the muddy or slimy bottoms on which most of the Hexactinellida live (Fig. 91B, C). The lower end of the root spicules generally bears recurved hooks like the flukes of an anchor (Fig. 91, *17*). These root spicules are often very long as in *Monoraphis* (page 333). The spicules at or beneath the dermal and inner surfaces, termed *dermalia* and *gastralia*, respectively, resemble each other in type and arrangement. They consist chiefly of hexacts and pentacts with the cross of four rays in or near to and parallel with the surface and the long basal ray, often heavily pinulate, projecting inward or outward (Fig. 93C). In many cases the surface is thus effectively protected by the numerous projecting spiny rays of the dermalia. Tetracts also often lie in the dermal and spongocoel surfaces. The spicules strewn throughout the trabecular net, termed *parenchymalia*, consist mostly of regular hexactines, small diactines, the various types of hexasters, and the amphidisks when present. Hexasters and amphidisks may also occur in the dermal and spongocoel surfaces (Fig. 93A, B).

In addition to the free spicules, the skeleton of the majority of the Hexactinellida includes a siliceous network permeating the interior, and

---

Fig. 93.—Structure of hexactinellids. *A.* Section through the wall of *Euplectella*, illustrating one of the Hexasterophora. *B.* Section through the wall of *Hyalonema*, one of the Amphidiscophora. (*A* and *B after Schulze*, 1887.) *C.* Diagram of the spicule arrangement of a hexactinellid, in vertical section. (*Adapted after Schulze*, 1887.) *D.* Trabecular net (*Farrea*) highly magnified. (*After Okada*, 1928.) 1, dermal layer and dermal spicules; 2, subdermal trabecular net; 3, portion of lyssacine (in *A*) or dictyonine (in *C*) skeleton; 4, layer of flagellated chambers; 5, subgastral trabecular net; 6, excurrent channel; 7, gastral layer and gastral spicules; 8, floricome; 9, pinulated pentact; 10, large amphidisks; 11, small amphidisks; 12, spongocoel; 13, marginal prostals; 14, pleural prostals; 15, basal prostals or root spicules; 16, parenchymalia.

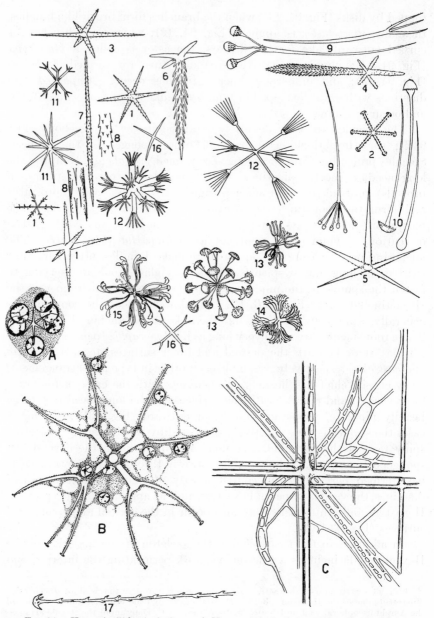

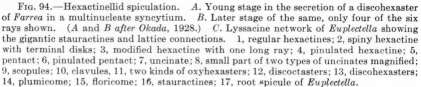

Fig. 94.—Hexactinellid spiculation. *A.* Young stage in the secretion of a discohexaster of *Farrea* in a multinucleate syncytium. *B.* Later stage of the same, only four of the six rays shown. (*A* and *B* after *Okada,* 1928.) *C.* Lyssacine network of *Euplectella* showing the gigantic stauractines and lattice connections. 1, regular hexactines; 2, spiny hexactine with terminal disks; 3, modified hexactine with one long ray; 4, pinulated hexactine; 5, pentact; 6, pinulated pentact; 7, uncinate; 8, small part of two types of uncinates magnified; 9, scopules; 10, clavules, 11, two kinds of oxyhexasters; 12, discoctasters; 13, discohexasters; 14, plumicome; 15, floricome; 16, stauractines; 17, root spicule of *Euplectella.*

running parallel to the surface. In its earlier stages, termed *lyssacine*, this framework is formed by the juxtaposition or interlacing of the elongated rays of hexactines, which may also become united by means of little crossbars of silica (Fig. 94C). Lyssacine networks are usually loose and with irregularly shaped meshes. In the fully developed type, termed *dictyonine*, the rays of regular hexactines fuse at their tips in all six directions through deposition upon them of layers of silica and so form a more or less regular three-dimensional network (Fig. 95A, B). The beautiful glassy hexactinellid skeletons (Fig. 92) often seen in museums consist chiefly of the lyssacine and dictyonine networks, as the loose dermalia, gastralia, and parenchymalia have been lost in drying.

The Hexactinellida, being deep-water forms, have been studied almost entirely from preserved specimens collected in deep-sea dredging expeditions, and consequently little is known of their histology and reproduction, and nothing of their physiology. As already indicated the trabecular net consists of fused amoebocytes of various types. A gelatinous matrix seems to be absent. Myocytes have been reported encircling some openings, but the group is probably as a whole almost devoid of contractile power in correlation with the rigid skeleton. The choanocytes are of usual appearance but are fused basally into a syncytium.

Some hexactinellids reproduce asexually by giving off small buds from almost any part of the surface. The gathering of archaeocytes into groups is of common occurrence throughout the order and is interpreted to represent stages in gemmule formation. The sexual reproduction is poorly known; the most complete account is that of the Okado for *Farrea sollasii*, collected monthly by dredging at 300 m. The ova and spermatozoa come from archaeocytes. The fertilized egg develops into a stereogastrula composed of an outer layer of closely packed cells, many with yolk granules, and an inner jelly containing amoeboid cells, believed to originate from the surface layer (Fig. 95F). Some of the inner amoeboid cells arrange themselves into a layer surrounding a central cavity and become choanocytes. Tetract spicules with long rays appear at the surface (Fig. 95F), and discohexasters form in the interior (Fig. 95G). At this stage the larva probably becomes flagellated, escapes, and settles down. The dictyonine skeleton begins to form in the attached region, and an osculum breaks through. The young sponge (Fig. 95H) thus consists of an oval body with a central spongocoel opening by the osculum and lined by a continuous layer of choanocytes, in which the future flagellated chambers are indicated by protuberances toward the dermal surface, and with a skeleton consisting of surface tetracts, interior hexasters, and the beginning of the dictyonine net. Sexual reproduction probably occurs throughout the year.

The Hexactinellida inhabit all seas but are more abundant in tropical latitudes although extending into polar waters. They are characteristic deep-sea animals, seldom found above 100 m., reaching their greatest

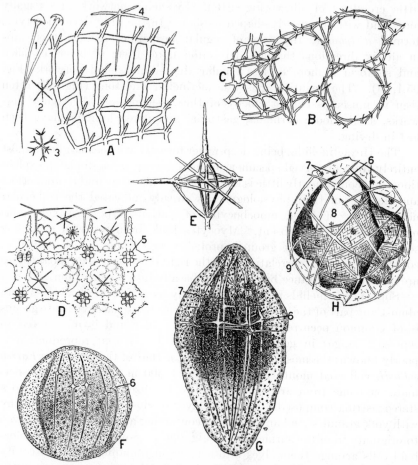

Fig. 95.—Hexactinellida, spiculation, embryology. *A.* Dictyonine framework of *Farrea,* types of loose spicules at the side. *B.* Dictyonine framework of *Aphrocallistes* seen from the surface, showing honeycomb arrangement. *C.* Seen from the side. *D.* Dictyonine framework of *Aulocystis,* with lychnisc joints. *E.* Early stage of a lychnisc joint. (*D* and *E* after Ijima, 1927.) *F.* Early stage of the larva of *Farrea,* stauractines forming. *G.* Later stage of the same, discohexasters have appeared. *H.* Young sponge with osculum and beginning flagellated layer. (*F–H, after Okada,* 1928.) 1, clavules; 2, spiny hexactine; 3, oxyhexaster; 4, pentact; 5, lychnisc joint; 6, stauractine; 7, discohexaster; 8, osculum; 9, flagellated layer.

development between 500 and 1000 m., but having a few representatives at depths as great as 5000 m. (over 3 miles).   Certain ocean deeps are noted for the richness of their hexactinellid fauna—near Japan, the Philippines, the Molucca Islands in the Malay Archipelago, and the

West Indies. The rigid form, open construction, and lack of contractility of these sponges appear to be adaptations to the constant conditions in deep water and probably to the presence of one slow continuous current. Bidder thinks the hexactinellids in nature have a curved attitude facing down the current. The root spicules constitute a device for insuring adhesion to the slimy oozes of the ocean floor in deep waters.

The Hexactinellida are divided into two subclasses or orders, the Amphidiscophora with amphidisk microscleres and the Hexasterophora with astrose microscleres. The former have also the lyssacine type of skeleton, dermalia and gastralia composed of pentactine pinules, and root tufts of monactine anchoring spicules. Among the characteristic genera of the Amphidiscophora are *Pheronema*, *Monoraphis*, and *Hyalonema*. *Pheronema* (Fig. 91*B*) has a thick-walled cup or bowl-shaped body with the spongocoel opening above, pleural tufts, and long twisted root tufts. *Monoraphis* is distinguished by the single gigantic anchoring spicule that may be 2 or 3 m. long and 1 cm. thick. *Hyalonema* (Fig. 91*C*) one of the most common hexactinellid sponges, with numerous species, has usually a rounded or ovoid body with a single root tuft often spirally twisted, the spicules of which continue through the sponge body as an axis or *columella*, often projecting above as the *gastral cone* (Figs. 77*E* and 91*C*). The upper surface bearing the gastral cone has the excurrent openings and may be depressed as a spongocoel, or flush with the surface, in which case there is no spongocoel.

The Hexasterophora are less often fastened by root tufts, being commonly directly attached to a hard object, the root spicules when present are pentactines or diactines, seldom monactines, and the skeleton is often dictyonal throughout or in regions. Among the forms with dictyonine skeleton composed of fused hexactines may be mentioned *Farrea* (Fig. 91*G*), *Eurete*, and *Aphrocallistes* (Fig. 91*E*), with quadrangular, triangular, and honeycomb-like meshes, respectively, to the framework (Fig. 95*A*, *B*). They are mostly branched tubular forms with large lateral oscula and no root spicules. *Aulocystis* is typical of a small group of forms in which the hexactines of the dictyonine framework are *lychniscs*, i.e., a latticework surrounds each node of the dictyonine mesh (Fig. 95*D*, *E*). Genera with a lyssacine skeleton, formed into a framework with irregular meshes include *Euplectella*, *Caulophacus*, *Rossella*, *Rhabdocalyptus*, *Staurocalyptus*. The beautiful glassy skeletons of the genus *Euplectella* (Fig. 92) constitute the Venus's flower baskets often seen in museums. The thin-walled body is of curved tubular form, with root spicules, and a sieve plate (Fig. 91*F*) covering the upper end. Often projecting ledges add to the beauty of the skeleton. The squarish lyssacine meshwork (Fig. 94*C*) that forms the main part of the skeleton consists chiefly of the rays of large four-rayed spicules (Fig. 94*C*), much united by crossbars. The microscleres include oxyhexasters, and floricomes, the latter on the dermal surface (Fig. 93A). *Caulophacus* and relatives have a stalked goblet- or mushroom-like body, sometimes branched. *Rossella* (Fig. 91D), *Rhabdocalyptus*, and *Staurocalyptus* (Fig. 91A) have cup- or sac-like bodies, usually without root spicules, and often "veiled" by long projecting dermalia.

The Hexactinellida, especially the Hexasterophora, are the most abundant of sponge fossils, occurring in the rocks from the Cambrian to the present, reaching their height in the Cretaceous and Jurassic. In the earliest forms, the spicules were tetract, separate or loosely united into lyssacine networks. This fact suggests that the hexactinal spicule was derived from a tetract one by the addition of a third axis. Later the types with dictyonine skeletons predominated and were in fact more abundant in the Triassic than they are today, since living hexactinellids are mostly lyssacine. The dictyonine nets of extinct sponges were made of hexactines that were often lychniscs, a condition found today in only a very few genera and species.

VI. CLASS DEMOSPONGIAE

The Demospongiae are sponges without spicules or with non-hexactinal siliceous spicules or with spongin fibers or with a combination of siliceous spicules and spongin. The forms with siliceous spicules are commonly spoken of as the siliceous sponges, while those with only a spongin skeleton comprise the horny sponges. The canal system is always leuconoid and may be eurypylous, aphodal, or diplodal.

The Demospongiae have not evolved from an asconoid structure but apparently derive from a ground plan termed the rhagon (page 293), having a layer of flagellated chambers opening widely into a central cavity (Fig. 96A). This leads into the simpler siliceous sponges by the folding of the wall and the branching of the flagellated chambers into numerous small ones (Fig. 96B). The final stage consists in the spreading of the dermal membrane over the outer ends of the folds (Fig. 96C).

The class includes several genera completely devoid of skeleton. Some of these are obviously derived from spiculate forms by degeneration of the spicules, but in others the absence of skeleton is regarded as a primitive character by a number of students of sponges, who therefore place these genera (*Oscarella, Halisarca, Hexidella*, and *Bajulus*) in a special order Myxospongida. Other workers believe the loss of spicules is secondary and have transferred these genera to the Keratosa. However, the evidence indicates that at least *Oscarella* and *Halisarca* are primitive sponges, and consequently the order Myxospongida is here retained, regarded as closely allied to the lowest forms with tetraxon spicules.

1. The Tetractinellida.—The siliceous Demospongiae (often called Tetraxonida) are conveniently divisible into the Tetractinellida with

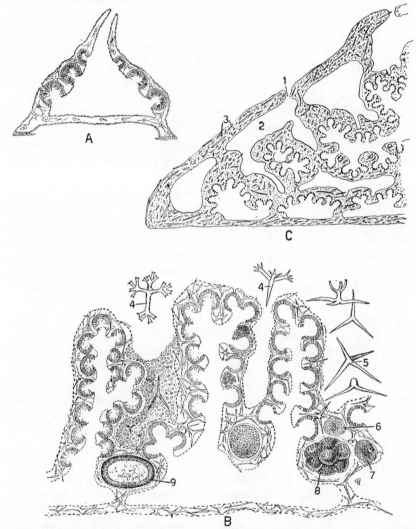

Fig. 96.—Primitive tetractinellids. *A.* Larval stage termed the rhagon. (*After Sollas*, 1888.)   *B.* Simplest type of tetractinellid, *Plakina* (*after Schulze*, 1880), with folded wall and calthrops spiculation; also with embryos.   *C.* Next stage, *Plakortis* (*after Schulze*, 1880), dermal membrane has fused across the folds forming subdermal spaces.   1, dermal pore; 2, subdermal space; 3, dermal membrane; 4, candelabra; 5, calthrops; 6, sperm ball; 7, egg; 8, cleavage stage; 9, larva.

tetraxon megascleres and the Monaxonida with monaxon megascleres, although it must be recognized that this division is artificial since tetraxons grade into monaxons by loss of rays.   The primitive sponges mentioned above without skeleton are here considered as tetractinellid in structure.

The tetractinellid sponges are mostly of solid construction and simple contour, forming rounded, oval, cushion-like, flattened, or encrusting masses, usually without branches or projections. The common shape is that of a somewhat rounded mass (Fig. 97*A*, *C*) attached by one surface to the substratum and bearing one to a few oscula on the opposite surface. Attachment to some hard object is usually direct but sometimes by way of root spicules; some lie free on the bottom. The surface is generally bristly, but some are hard and stony from the numerous spicules in the cortex, and others may be smooth and leathery. The oscula may have a slight rim or be depressed and only occasionally bear a fringe of spicules (Fig. 97*F*). In several genera—*Monosyringa, Tribrachion* (Fig. 97*E*), *Tethyopsis, Kapnesolenia*—the single osculum is at the tip of a long excurrent tube springing from the small rounded body and in *Disyringa* (Fig. 97*F*) there is a similar opposite incurrent tube. The tetractinellids are mostly of small to moderate size; the largest is the cup-shaped *Synops neptuni*, one of the Geodidae, 40 cm. high, taken by the "Challenger" expedition off Brazil. The coloration is mostly of the drab sort, but a range of colors occurs throughout the group. The tetractinellids are exclusively marine and inhabitants chiefly of shore and shallow waters.

The chief structural features of the group are the extensive development of the cortex and the radiating arrangement of the interior (Fig. 97*B*). The more simple genera, as the myxospongids (Fig. 97*H*) and *Plakina* (Fig. 96*B*), lack a cortex and have only a thin dermal layer which follows the folds of the layer of flagellated chambers. But generally the choanosome is covered over by a definite cortex. In the simpler cases (Fig. 96*C*) this consists of a thin dermal layer underlain by large subdermal spaces crossed by columns or trabeculae supported by spicules. Usually, however, the cortex is much thickened and contains a loose or dense fibrous network made up of fusiform fiber cells (desmacytes) running parallel to the surface (Fig. 97*G*). The fibrous net may extend practically throughout the cortex; or, very commonly, it is limited to an inner fibrous layer, while the outer zone consists of a thick gelatinous material containing amoebocytes and forming the collenchymatous layer (Fig. 97*G*). In some cases the collenchymatous layer lies between inner and outer fibrous layers. The cortex commonly contains spicules that may project from the surface or may be embedded in the cortex, sometimes as in *Geodia* (Fig. 98*D*) and *Chondrilla* (Fig. 98*B*), so thickly as to render the cortex hard and stony. Large spaces, the *subcortical crypts*, may be present between cortex and choanosome.

The arrangement of incurrent apertures and channels varies with the development and construction of the cortex. The dermal pores are commonly small and may be evenly distributed over the surface or occur in groups limited to definite areas. When the cortex is absent, the dermal pores lead almost directly into the flagellated chambers (Fig. 96B); when the cortex is thin they open into the subdermal spaces (Fig. 96C). In the case of a thick cortex, each dermal pore generally opens into a canal termed a *chone* (Fig. 98B, D), which penetrates the cortex and is usually provided along its course or at its inner end with a sphincter of myocytes. The dermal pores may also occur in clusters termed *pore areas*, and such pore areas may open into a chone or into an underlying subdermal space, a condition termed *cribriporal* (Figs. 98D, 99D). The oscula are generally simple large apertures with a slight rim but may occur in groups or may be provided with a sieve membrane.

The canal system is leuconoid throughout the group. In the simplest tetractinellids such as *Halisarca* and *Plakina* (Fig. 96B), the sponge consists of a folded wall in which each fold is made up of a thin dermal layer, a layer of small eurypylous flagellated chambers, and a central excurrent channel. In most genera the dermal layer has fused across (Fig. 96C) so as to cover the folds smoothly leaving large subdermal spaces where the depressions were; or more commonly it is thickened into a cortex of special construction, so that the sponge is sharply divisible into ectosome and choanosome (Figs. 97G and 98B, D). The eurypylous condition is retained in many tetractinellids, but others are aphodal or diplodal. In many forms, the canal system has a distinct radiating arrangement. A central spongocoel is usually lacking, although often the larger excurrent channels converge toward the center of the sponge into one or more wide canals leading to the osculum.

A skeleton is absent in the members of the order Myxospongida and also in the genus *Chondrosia*, which is obviously derived from spiculate genera by the loss of spicules; in this sponge support is secured by a very stiff mesogloea. The other tetractinellids are provided with a skeleton of siliceous spicules, consisting of tetraxon and monaxon megascleres and monaxon and astrose or sigmoid microscleres. The typical spicule of the simpler tetractinellids is the calthrops, or tetraxon with four approximately equal rays (Figs. 96B, 98A). This may vary by the branching of the rays, forming types called *candelabra*, (Fig. 96B, 4), and also by the loss of one or two rays. Calthrops may occur in a wide range of sizes (Fig. 98A) so that often there is no distinction between megascleres and microscleres in such sponges (order Carnosa, Fig. 98A). In most tetractinellids, the calthrops are altered into triaenes with very long shafts (rhabdomes) and small cladi (Figs. 97D, 98D, and 99A, B). The most typical sorts of triaenes are the *anatriaenes* with cladi curved downward (Fig. 97G, 4) and the *protriaenes* with cladi pointed up (Fig. 97G, 2). Other types are the *plagio-* and *orthotriaenes* with more or less horizontal

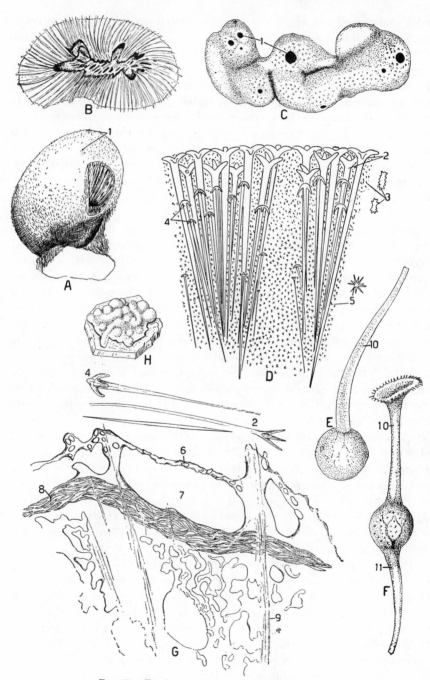

FIG. 97.—For descriptive legend see opposite page.

cladi and the *dichotriaenes* with forked cladi (Fig. 81, *10*). The megascleres also include monaxons, chiefly oxeas, often very long and slender. The characteristic microsclere of the tetractinellids is the aster in all its variations; the large centered forms such as sterrasters and spherasters are particularly developed in certain genera as *Geodia* (Fig. 98*D*, *E*) and *Chondrilla* (Fig. 98*B*, *C*). Other genera are characterized by various types of streptasters. In the suborder Sigmatophora, the microscleres are sigmaspires (Fig. 99*A*), but these may be regarded as spirasters that have lost their thorns.

Each species is characterized by some particular combination and arrangement of the different sorts of spicules. The characteristic arrangement is the occurrence of bundles or columns of spicules radiating from the center of the sponge to the periphery (Fig. 97*B*). These bundles consist of long monaxons and the shafts of triaenes (Figs. 97*D* and 99*A*). The cladi of the triaenes may lie in the cortex (Fig. 97*D*) or may project, forming a bristly surface (Fig. 99*A*), or the cortex may be provided with special small projecting monaxons (Fig. 98*D*). Often, however, the surface is smooth, firm, and leathery or stony with an abundant spiculation in the cortex, composed either of the cladi of triaenes or in some genera of nothing but spherasters closely packed (Fig. 98*B*).

The tetractinellids are divisible into the orders Myxospongida, Carnosa, and Choristida. Under the first are usually listed the four genera *Oscarella*, *Halisarca*, *Hexidella*, and *Bajulus*, but probably only the first two are genuinely primitive, and very likely they should be combined into one genus *Halisarca*. *Oscarella* and *Halisarca* (Fig. 97*H*) are small low encrusting sponges with a lobulated upper surface. Their internal structure is practically identical with that of *Plakina* (Fig. 96*B*) except that spicules are entirely wanting. The basal part of the sponge is filled with eggs and embryos and the peripheral part contains the canal system. Each lobule encloses an excurrent channel surrounded by flagellated chambers and the depressions between the lobules house the incurrent channels. The chambers vary from the eurypylous to the aphodal type but often appear as if diplodal.

Fig. 97.—Tetractinellids. *A.* A typical tetractinellid, *Craniella*, piece removed to show radiating interior, preserved specimen. *B.* Section through a tetractinellid sponge (one of the Craniellidae) showing radiating spicule bundles. *C. Chondrilla*, from life, Bermuda. *D.* Section through two radiating bundles of *Ancorina*, showing pro- and anatriaenes in the bundles and astrose microscleres; microscleres of the cortex are streptasters, magnified at 3, microscleres of the choanosome, oxyasters, magnified at 5. From slide. (*Courtesy Dr. M. W. de Laubenfels.*) *E. Tribrachion. F. Disyringa. G.* Section through the outer part of *Tetilla*, showing ectosome with cribriporal roof, subdermal cavities, and fibrous layer; spicules of the radial bundles above, no microscleres. (*E–G, after Sollas*, 1888.) *H. Oscarella*, with lobulated surface. (*After Schulze*, 1880.) 1, oscula; 2, protriaene; 3, streptaster of cortex; 4, anatriaenes; 5, oxyaster of choanosome; 6, cribriporal roof; 7, subdermal cavity; 8, fibrous layer; 9, radial spicule bundle, spicules thereof enlarged above; 10, oscular tube; 11, incurrent tube.

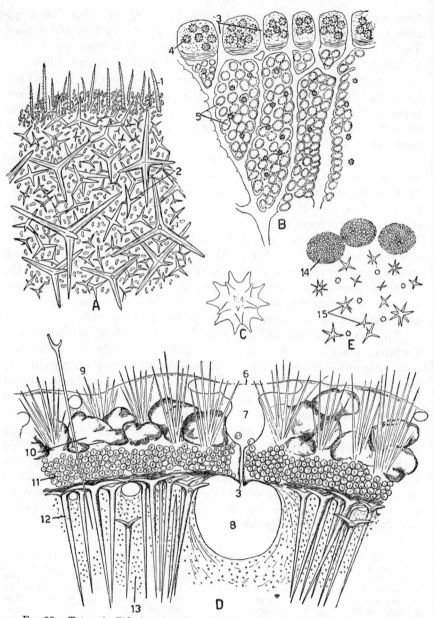

Fig. 98.—Tetractinellida (continued).   *A.* Section of *Pachastrella*, showing spiculation of calthrops, cortex with acanthostyles; from slide.   (*Courtesy Dr. M. W. de Laubenfels.*) *B.* Section through outer part of *Chondrilla* from life, showing the chones and cortex filled with spherasters.   *C.* Spheraster of *Chondrilla*, enlarged.   *D.* Section through *Geodia* showing ectosome with special ectosomal spicule bundles, rock fragments, layer of sterrasters, and chone, and choanosome with triaenes, subcortical crypt, and astrose microscleres.   (*After Sollas,* 1888.)   *E.* Microscleres of *Geodia*, enlarged, from slide.   (*Courtesy*

The order Carnosa comprises those forms with calthrops, including such genera as *Plakina* (Fig. 96*B*), *Plakortis* (Fig. 96*C*), *Thrombus*, *Corticium*, *Corticella*, *Halina*, *Dercitopsis*, and *Pachastrella* (Fig. 98*A*). *Plakina* shows a primitive type of structure without cortex, and *Plakortis* illustrates a stage in the development of cortex. *Chondrilla* (Figs. 97*C* and 98*B*) has lost all the spicule types except spherasters (Fig. 98*C*), which pack the cortex between the chones. The rest of the sponge has scattered asters and is supported mainly by a thick firm mesogloea. The genus *Chondrosia*, devoid of skeleton, has a similar stiff jelly and hence is presumably derived from chondrillid ancestors by loss of the asters.

The order Choristida includes the majority of the genera with a thick and conspicuous cortex and radiating bundles of oxeas and triaenes, typically ana- and protriaenes. The Choristida are divisible into the Astrophora with astrose microscleres and the Sigmatophora with sigmas. Familiar genera with asters include *Ancorina* (Fig. 97*D*), *Thenea*, *Penares*, *Myriastra*, *Stelletta* (Fig. 99*D*), etc. In *Geodia* (Fig. 98*D*), the cortex is packed with sterrasters, and various sorts of asters (Fig. 98*E*) are strewn throughout the choanosome. *Tetilla* (Fig. 97*G*) is defined by de Laubenfels as a genus devoid of microscleres. The Sigmatophora comprise the family Craniellidae, exemplified by *Craniella* (Figs. 97*A* and 99*A*).

A certain number of tetractinellids have lithistid skeletons, i.e., the skeleton is composed of desmas cemented into a framework (Fig. 99*B*, *C*). These were formerly placed in a separate order Lithistida but according to de Laubenfels should be regarded as modified members of the Carnosa and Choristida. In addition to the framework of desmas, these sponges also have triaenes and astrose and various sorts of monaxon microscleres. Some of the genera are *Corallistes* (Fig. 99*B*), *Kaliapsis*, *Pleroma*, *Theonella*, *Vetulina*, and *Discodermia* (Fig. 99*C*).

The details of the development are known only for the more primitive genera as *Halisarca* (Meewis, 1939) and *Plakina* (Schulze, 1880; Maas, 1909). A coeloblastula is formed which escapes as a completely flagellated larva composed of slender crowded cells. This attaches by the anterior half, which invaginates after attachment into the posterior half and becomes the flagellated layer, at first simply outfolding into large flagellated chambers. The resulting stage is similar to a rhagon. The further development has been carefully described for *Halisarca* by Meewis. An osculum breaks through, and from it excurrent canals grow inward connecting with the flagellated chambers. The epidermis and amoebocytes come from the cells of the original posterior half of the larva.

Dr. M. W. de Laubenfels.) 1, acanthostyles; 2, calthrops; 3, chone; 4, spherasters; 5, flagellated chambers; 6, cribriporal roof; 7, subdermal cavity; 8, subcortical crypt; 9, ectosomal spicules; 10, rock grains; 11, layer of sterrasters; 12, triaenes; 13, asters; 14, sterrasters of *Geodia* enlarged; 15, asters of choanosome of *Geodia* enlarged.

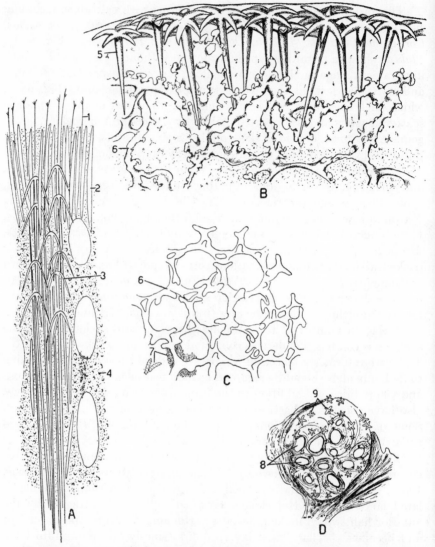

Fig. 99.—Tetractinellida (continued).   *A.* Section through a radial spicule bundle of *Craniella*, showing triaenes and sigmoid microscleres.   *B.* Section through the outer part of a lithistid sponge, *Corallistes*, showing cortical dichotriaenes and desma network of the interior.   (*After Sollas*, 1888.)   *C.* Network of desmas of *Discodermia* with spiny microscleres (shown at only one place).   From slide.   (*Courtesy of Dr. M. W. de Laubenfels.*)   *D.* Cribriporal roof of a subdermal cavity of *Stelletta*, seen from the inner surface, showing also astrose microscleres.   (*After Sollas*, 1888.)   1, protriaenes; 2, oxeas of cortex; 3, anatriaenes; 4, sigmas; 5, dichotriaenes; 6, network of desmas; 7, spiny microscleres; 8, dermal pores of the cribriporal plate; 9, asters.

There is here no inversion of germ layers such as occurs in monaxonids. The developmental history is further evidence for the primitive nature of *Halisarca*.

The tetractinellids are abundantly represented as fossils, chiefly types with lithistid skeletons, of simple shape, beginning in the Cambrian and reaching their height in the Jurassic and Cretaceous. Other types have separate spicules, including calthrops, triaenes, and asters.

2. Monaxonida.—The monaxonid sponges with siliceous monaxon megascleres are the most common of all sponges and are found in abundance throughout the world in shore and shallow waters, down to about 50 m., living attached to objects mostly by means of spongin secretion. The group occurs in a great variety of shapes, from rounded masses (Fig. 100*A*) to bushy, branching types, often with long slender branches (Figs. 77*A*, *D*, 102*J*, and 103*F*). Others are elongated or stalked with club-, funnel-, cup- (Fig. 77*C*) or fan-shaped bodies. Some extend down into the deeper waters, even to depths of 5000 or 6000 m., and some of these deep-water forms are of remarkable appearance, as *Cladorhiza* (Fig. 100*C*). The small rounded body tapers to a pointed base, set into the bottom ooze, and carries a circlet of projections supported by skeleton and evidently serving to prevent sinkage into the mud. Other deep-water forms as *Radiella* (Fig. 100*E*) have an equatorial girdle of long spicules for the same purpose. The monaxonids usually have many oscula, which in branched types are situated on the ends of branches or projections (Fig. 77*D*). In *Polymastia* (Fig. 100*D*) both incurrent and excurrent openings are mounted on tubes (*fistulas*) projecting from the rounded body. The monaxonids vary from quite small forms to large masses, but the majority are of moderate dimensions. The largest known sponges occur in the order Hadromerina; the cake-shaped loggerhead sponge (*Spheciospongia*) from the Gulf of Mexico and the urn-like Neptune's goblet (*Poterion*, Fig. 77*C*) may attain a diameter or height of 1 to 2 m. The monaxonids exhibit a range of coloration, and most of the red or orange sponges fall into this group. The surface is commonly rough or hispid but lacks conspicuously projecting bristles. The group includes the fresh-water sponges, family Spongillidae, order Haplosclerina.

A more or less definite construction is common among the monaxonids; the principal types are the *radiate, plumose,* and *reticulate.* The forms with radiating structure (order Hadromerina) resemble the Choristida, having a thick well-developed cortex and radially arranged bundles (Fig. 100*B*) of megascleric monaxons, mostly tylostyles, but also including oxeas and styles. The plumose or axinellid type (Fig. 101*F*, *G*) is a variant of the radiate type. In the reticulate type (Fig. 100*G*), the spicules are joined by means of spongin into a network that permeates the interior and at the surface commonly opens out into spicule brushes

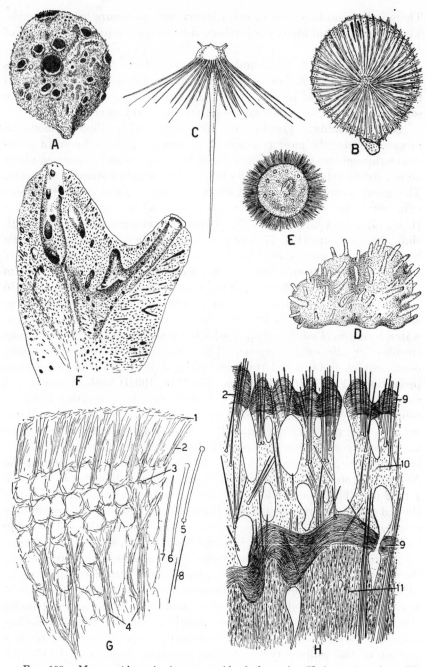

Fig. 100.—Monaxonida. *A.* A monaxonid of the order Hadromerina, from life, Bermuda. *B.* Vertical section through the same, showing radiating bundles of monaxons *C. Cladorhiza.* (*After Ridley and Dendy*, 1887.) *D. Polymastia*, preserved. *E. Radiella.* (*After Ridley and Dendy*, 1887.) *F.* Vertical section of *Tedania*, see Fig. 77*D*, through two

piercing the epidermis. The spicules of monaxonids may also be without definite arrangement, as in *Halichondria* (Fig. 102*A*).

The body is well differentiated into ectosome and choanosome. The former may be tough and fibrous as in *Suberites* (Fig. 100*H*) and its relatives, consisting of one or more layers of desmacytes and containing subdermal spaces. The desmacytes may descend into the choanosome along spicule bundles and canal walls. In other cases the fibrous layers are thin and the cortex consists chiefly of gelatinous mesogloea enclosing various kinds of amoebocytes. In most monaxonids, however, a differentiated cortex is absent, and the ectosome is composed of a thin dermal membrane overlying extensive subdermal spaces (Fig. 103*J*) crossed by columns of spicules or spiculated spongin fibers. The small dermal pores may be scattered over the sponge or limited to pore areas related to the spiculation or the subdermal spaces. Thus a pore area may overlie each subdermal space, and the surface of the sponge may be marked off into rounded or polygonal pore areas that indicate the positions of the subdermal spaces. Dense spiculation of the ectosome also results in the limitation of the pores to separate areas. In some monaxonids, dermal pores occur only in an equatorial zone. In flabellate shapes, the dermal pores may be on one side, the oscula on the other; but this is not always the case. From the subdermal spaces channels lead into the choanosome, which is often permeated with small spaces. The flagellated chambers are of the small rounded type and occur throughout the choanosome embedded in mesenchyme. The canal system is always leuconoid and may be eurypylous, aphodal, or diplodal. There are usually several or many separate oscula, which may be elevated on papillae or have a raised rim or be sunk into depressions. Sometimes the oscula are clustered together. It is not uncommon for the inhalant and exhalant apertures to be indistinguishable.

The spicules are siliceous and generally differentiated into megascleres and microscleres, although either type may be wanting. The megascleres are all monaxons, both styles and rhabds. In a given sponge all the megascleres may be of one kind, but often two or more sorts of megascleres are present. In the order Hadromerina, spongin is lacking, and the megascleres are separate, although often aggregated into radial bundles (Fig. 100*B*). In the other monaxonids, the megascleres are bound together by spongin secretion and usually form a network. Various stages in this process of the binding of some or all of the megascleres by spongin occur (Fig. 101*A–D*). At first only the tips of the spicules are

oscula. *G*. Spiculation of *Tedania*, example of fibroreticulate structure with ectosomal specialization. *H*. Section through a suberitid sponge, showing fibrous layers of ectosome and ectosomal brushes of tylostyles. (*After Ridley and Dendy*, 1887.) 1, tangential ectosomal spicules; 2, ectosomal spicule brushes; 3, choanosomal network; 4, ascending spiculofibers of choanosome; 5–8, spicule types of *Tedania*; 5, tylote; 6, tylostyle; 7, oxea; 8, raphide; 9, fibrous layers of ectosome; 10, ectosome; 11, choanosome.

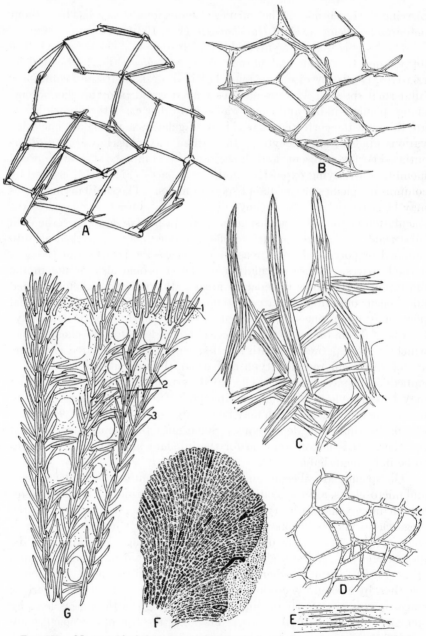

Fig. 101.—Monaxonid skeletons. *A–C.* Types of renierine networks, order Haplosclerina, from life: *A*, spicules bound by spongin at ends only; *B*, spongin covering spicules: *C*, meshes made of bundles of oxeas. *D.* Spicules completely enclosed in spongin. *E.* Part of *D* enlarged. *F.* Vertical section of *Axinella*, showing plumose appearance, preserved specimen. *G.* Part of *F* enlarged showing the echinated ascending spicule tracts and ectosomal brushes of styles. 1, brushes of styles; 2, spiculofibers; 3, echinating spicules of same.

united (Fig. 101*A*), and a regular network results in which the meshes consist of single spicules or a bundle of parallel spicules. Then the spongin gradually extends so as to enclose the spicule bundles in a thin sheath (Fig. 101*B*), and finally definite spongin fibers arise that contain completely enclosed spicules (Fig. 101*C*, *D*). In other cases the spicules are only partly embedded in the spongin fibers and project like spines obliquely toward the surface of the sponge (Figs. 101*G* and 103*A*), an arrangement called *echinating*. Again, spongin fibers may have both enclosed ("*coring*") and echinating spicules (Fig. 103*A*), and these may be of different sorts. The meshes of the network may be all alike and no longer than the spicule length, a type of network known as *renierine* or *isodictyal* (Fig. 101*A*); or there may be long main spiculofibers that run to the sponge periphery (Fig. 101*G*). In branched sponges, each branch may contain one or more main spiculofibers from which secondary fibers are given off. A skeleton of ascending spiculofibers of the echinating type without coring spicules constitutes the plumose or axinellid type (Fig. 101*F*, *G*), named from the genus *Axinella*. The ectosome of *Callyspongia* has a coarse network of spongin fibers with coring spicules enclosing a finer network (Fig. 102*B*). The dominance of spongin over spicule formation may proceed so far that the skeleton becomes a spongin network differing from that of the Keratosa only in the presence of a few spicules in the flesh and fibers at the periphery of the sponge. On the other hand, spongin may be absent and the spicules strewn throughout the flesh without any definite arrangement or but feebly reticulate. The monaxonids also include some forms with lithistid skeletons composed of monocrepid desmas.

There is usually a special ectosomal skeleton, often comprising spicules different in size or type from those of the main body of the sponge. This ectosomal or dermal skeleton may consist of a network or of spicules parallel to the surface or of spicules projecting from the surface. Typically as the spiculofibers of the choanosomal network approach the surface they break up into brush-like bundles that cross the subdermal spaces and may terminate in or beyond the ectosome (Figs. 100*G*, *H* and 101*G*), sometimes carrying along the dermal membrane into tent-like elevations, or *conules*.

The microscleres are astrose in the Hadromerina (Fig. 102*F*, *H*); in other monaxonids, when present, they consist usually of sigmas, toxas, and chelas (Fig. 103*C*, *D*, *E*). Various types of chelas are particularly characteristic, arranged in rosettes in some genera (Fig. 103*G*). Birotulate microscleres (Fig. 81, *30*) are characteristic of the gemmules of fresh-water sponges and are also found in a few marine monaxonids. Microscleres are often absent among the monaxonids, especially in the order Haplosclerina. Foreign bodies are very commonly present.

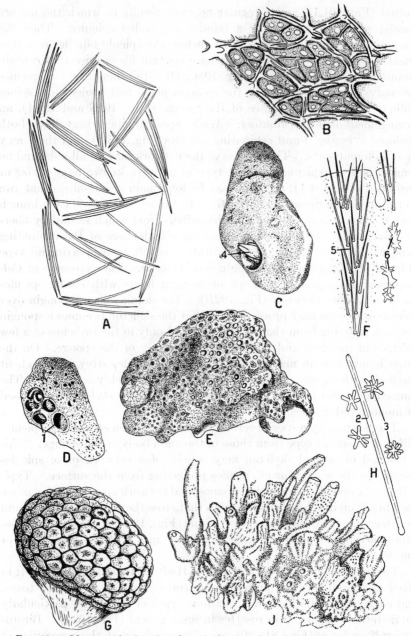

Fig. 102.—Monaxonida (continued).   *A.* Section through *Halichondria* showing the spicules; body surface to the left, showing absence of any special cortical spiculation. *B.* Spongin network of *Callyspongia* with coring spicules, having a coarse network enclosing a finer network (in the ectosome only).   (*From slide, courtesy Dr. M. W. de Laubenfels.*) *C.* A suberitid sponge (*Ficulina*) with an enclosed hermit crab.   *D.* Section of the same,

The monaxonids are divided by some recent workers into the orders Hadromerina, Halichondrina, Poecilosclerina, and Haplosclerina. De Laubenfels (1936) recognizes a fifth order, Epipolasida. The Hadromerina are closely similar to the Choristida in general appearance (Fig. 102*G*) and corticate radiating architecture but lack triaenes. Their megascleres are tylostyles, styles, or oxeas, and the microscleres, when present, are astrose. Typically there are radiating columns of tylostyles with projecting brushes of tylostyles in the cortex, as in *Suberites* (Fig. 100*H*) and *Spirastrella* (Fig. 102*F*). The Suberitidae have a thick fibrous cortex, megascleric tylostyles, and no microscleres (Fig. 100*H*) and are noted for the association of a number of their species with hermit crabs (Fig. 102*C*, *D*). To the Suberitidae belong also *Polymastia* (Fig. 100*D*), with fistulas and radiating tracts of tylostyles and styles, and the very large *Poterion* (Fig. 77*C*). The family Clionidae or boring sponges, with a spiculation of tylostyles and spirasters, inhabit the interior of coral skeletons, mollusk shells, and other calcareous objects (Fig. 102*E*). The larva settles on such objects and in some unknown manner (apparently not by secretion of acid nor with the aid of its spicules) bores and occupies channels in the interior, eventually permeating the entire object and emerging on the surface as a thin layer. Species of *Cliona* are often of a sulphur-yellow color; others are green or purple. A group of genera having oxea-like megascleres is exemplified by *Tethya* (Fig. 102*G*), a genus with a characteristic tuberculate surface, radiating bundles of monaxons, and several types of euasters (Fig. 102*H*).

The Halichondrina generally lack microscleres and have two or more sorts of megascleres—diactines, monactines, or both—intermingled without definite localization. The family Axinellidae have the axinellid structure (Fig. 101*F*, *G*) with ascending spiculofibers of echinating oxeas and styles and a bristly surface caused by projecting ectosomal brushes. *Halichondria*, forming mostly flattened growths with raised oscula (Fig. 102*J*), has a spiculation of various sizes of oxeas strewn throughout the flesh and paralleling the surface (Fig. 102*A*).

The order Poecilosclerina includes the majority of the Demospongiae. The structure is generally reticulate with the spicules united by more or less spongin into a regular network (Fig. 100*G*) or a network with main ascending spiculofibers that may be echinated or cored or both (Fig. 103*A*). There are two or more sorts of monaxon megascleres, one or more kinds in the ectosome, the others in the choanosome. This distinc-

showing spiral cavity formed by snail shell; (*C* and *D* after *Müller*, 1914.)   *E. Cliona*, from life, Atlantic Coast, growing on a piece of coral whose cups can be seen.   *F. Spirastrella*, column of tylostyles, and spirasters enlarged at 6.   *G. Tethya*, preserved.   *H.* Spicules of *Tethya*, styles and euasters.   *J. Halichondria*, from life, Atlantic Coast.   1, spiral cavity formed by snail shell; 2, style of *Tethya*; 3, euasters (strongylasters) of same; 4, claws of hermit crab protruding; 5, tylostyles of *Spirastrella*; 6, spirasters of same.

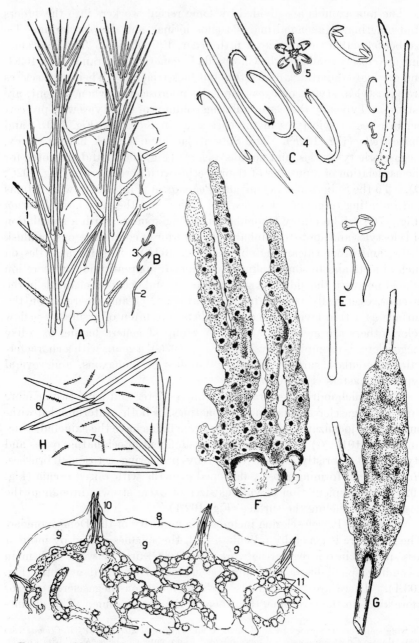

Fig. 103.—Monaxonida (continued).   *A*. Spiculation of *Microciona prolifera* (see Fig. 77*A*) showing spongin fibers with coring styles and echinating acanthostyles.   *B*. Microscleres of same.   *C*. Spicule types of *Paresperella*.   *D*. Spicule types of *Myxilla*. *E*. Spicule types of *Mycale*   (*D* and *E* after de Laubenfels, 1932a.)   *F. Haliclona*, dry

tion between ectosomal monaxons and those of the interior is characteristic of the order.   The microscleres are typically chelas of various types, sigmas, and toxas.   As examples of the range of spiculation a few genera may be mentioned and illustrated.   *Microciona* (Fig. 103*A*, *B*) has dermal and choanosomal styles; ascending spiculofibers of smooth styles with echinating acanthostyles; isochelas and toxas.   *Myxilla* has ectosomal diactines, mostly tornotes; choanosomal styles, often spined; isochelas and sigmas (Fig. 103*D*).   In the very similar *Tedania* (Fig. 100*G*) there are ectosomal tylotes, choanosomal styles and tylostyles, all smooth, and raphides.   *Mycale* (Fig. 103*E*) has coring and echinating smooth monaxons, and anisochelas, sigmas, and toxas as microscleres. In *Paresperella* there are rosettes of anisochelas and very large sigmas (Fig. 103*C*).

Some interesting deep-sea sponges belong to the Poecilosclerina such as *Cladorhiza* (Fig. 100*C*) and *Esperiopsis*, one of the notable finds of the "Challenger" expedition.   In *Esperiopsis*, a long main stalk gives off lateral stalks, each topped by a rounded sponge mass, in a bilateral arrangement.

The Haplosclerina have typically a spiculation of oxeas, occurring in a range of sizes without any definite distinction into megascleres and microscleres nor any special ectosomal spiculation.   The representative marine genus is *Haliclona* (Fig. 103*F*), which according to Burton (1926) includes *Reniera*, *Chalina*, *Pachychalina*, and similar genera.   These very common forms have the renierine or isodictyal skeleton composed of a meshwork of single (Fig. 101*A*) or parallel (Fig. 101*C*) oxeas united by more or less spongin or enclosed in spongin.   The fresh-water sponges, family Spongillidae, logically find place in this order.   They occur throughout the world in ponds, lakes, and slow streams, as low encrusting or slightly branching growths on twigs, plant stems, and other objects (Fig. 103*G*).   Usually they are greenish from the presence of zoochlorellae in their archaeocytes.   The young sponges acquire the zoochlorellae from outside by way of the water current; they are ingested by the choanocytes and then passed on to the amoebocytes.   Although the zoochlorellae are probably of some value to their hosts, it is improbable that they are essential.   Structurally, the Spongillidae consist of a very thin dermal membrane overlying large subdermal spaces (Fig. 103*J*) separated by spicule columns, and a very open interior composed of innumerable water channels lined by pinacocytes and surrounded by sponge tissue consisting of small round eurypylous chambers and two or three kinds

specimen, skeleton as in Fig. 101*C*. *G*. A fresh-water sponge growing on a twig. *H*. Spiculation of a fresh-water sponge, *Spongilla lacustris*. *J*. Section through a fresh-water sponge, showing structure. 1, echinating acanthostyles; 2, toxa; 3, isochela; 4, large sigmas; 5, rosette of anisochelas; 6, oxeote megascleres; 7, microscleric spiny oxeas; 8, dermal membrane; 9, subdermal spaces; 10, spicule column, 11, flagellate chambers.

of amoebocytes, among which the archaeocytes with large nuclei and nucleoli are conspicuous (Fig. 80*H*). There are several oscula, mounted in some forms on delicate chimneys of dermal membrane. The spiculation consists of a network of smooth or spiny large oxeas with small oxeas, often spiny, scattered throughout the flesh (Fig. 103*H*). In addition, in most Spongillidae, birotulates (Fig. 81, *30*) are secreted during gemmule formation. Asexual reproduction by means of gemmules (page 307) prevails among the Spongillidae, although sexual propagation by way of typical larvae also occurs. Reduction has been observed. Many species, distributed among several genera, such as *Spongilla, Myenia, Heteromyenia,* etc., have been recognized.

The order Epipolasida is recognized by de Laubenfels, following the earlier work of Sollas, for sponges similar in general architecture to the Hadromerina (in which order they are usually placed) but differing in an absence of tylostyles. Whether this absence is primitive or the result of loss cannot be stated. *Tethya* (Fig. 102*G, H*) with faintly tylote ends of its styles is an example of the group.

Since spongin is not preservable, fossil monaxonid sponges are known only from the monaxon megascleres of which the earliest occur in the Middle Cambrian. The arrangement of the spicules of some of these fossils suggests that they were bound into fibers by spongin.

3. The Keratosa or Horny Sponges.—The horny sponges are a group in which the skeleton consists exclusively of spongin fibers. They are not sharply demarcated from the monaxonids, since the latter as already mentioned often have conspicuous spongin fibers. The Keratosa are mostly of considerable size and of rounded massive form with a number of conspicuous oscula often mounted on elevated regions of the sponge (Fig. 104*A*). In the genus *Phyllospongia*, the form is leaf-like. The surface is leathery and may be smooth but more often is beset with little elevations termed *conules*. The coloration is dark, chiefly black. The horny sponges characteristically live in the warm waters of tropical and subtropical regions, but small-sized specimens or species may extend into arctic and antarctic zones. They are typically shallow-water forms, inhabiting rocky bottom or some other hard substratum to which they are attached directly by spongin secretion.

The skeleton is typically composed of a network of spongin fibers (Fig. 104*F*) devoid of proper spicules, in which there are often embedded large numbers of rock grains and other fragments (Fig. 104*D*). In some genera, the fibers of the spongin reticulum are all of the same diameter; in others there are numerous larger thicker fibers that pursue a straight course to the surface, elevating it into the tent-like conules just mentioned (Fig. 104*D*). In the genus *Hircinia* (Fig. 104*A, D*), peculiar filaments of unknown nature and function are strewn throughout the sponge. In the family Darwinellidae, separated in many works on sponges into a

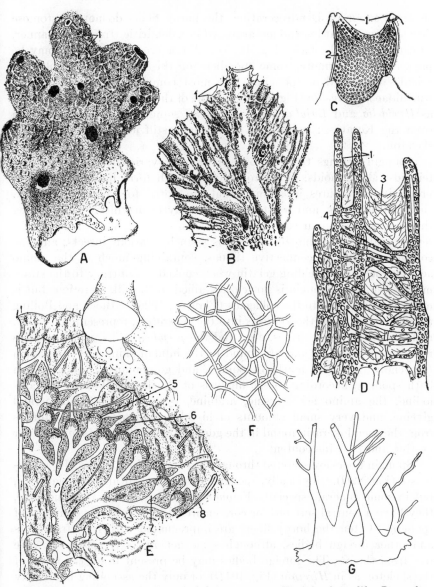

Fig. 104.—Keratosa. *A.* A typical horny sponge, *Hircinia*, from life, Bermuda. *B.* Section through two oscula of the same. *C.* Four conules with membrane between them full of dermal pores. *D.* Skeleton of *Hircinia*, including two conules. *E.* Canal system of *Hircinia*, showing diplodal chambers. (*After Schulze*, 1880.) *F.* Spongin network of a bath sponge. *G.* Skeleton of *Aplysilla.* (*After de Laubenfels*, 1932a.) 1, conules; 2, dermal pores; 3, fibers peculiar to *Hircinia*; 4, spongin fibers filled with rock grains; 5, flagellated chambers; 6, prosodus; 7, aphodus; 8, foreign spicules.

separate suborder Dendroceratina, the horny fibers do not anastomose into a network but instead are arranged in a dendritic (tree-like) manner, spreading from the base (Fig. 104G). A few cross connections may be present. Furthermore, some members of this family have polyaxon spicules composed of spongin. The most common genus of the Darwinellidae is *Aplysilla* (Fig. 104G). Some of the forms devoid of skeleton as *Hexidella* and *Bajulus* are believed by some workers to be derived from the Keratosa; supporting fiber cells or stiff jelly take the place of skeleton.

Spongin belongs to the group of proteins variously known as proteinoids, albuminoids, or scleroproteins, which form hard skeletal and protective structures in animals and are noted for their insolubility, chemical inertness, and resistance to proteolytic enzymes. Here belong the keratins—sulphur-containing proteins such as hair, horn, nails, reptile scales, etc.; the silk secretions spun by various insects; and the collagens, found in connective tissues, containing much of the amino acid glycocoll and yielding gelatin when cooked. Contrary to the statement often seen, spongin is not closely allied to the silk secretions but is more nearly related to the collagens (Clancey, 1926). Block and Bolling (1939) have divided the keratins into the *eukeratins*, represented by hair, nails, feathers, snake scales, etc., and the *pseudokeratins*, which are less resistant to enzymes and are found in the human skin, nervous system (especially the white matter), sponges, and gorgonians. Spongin from bath sponges, according to the analysis of Block and Bolling, contains iodine, the amino acids lysine, arginine, cystine, phenylalanine, and glycine, and very small amounts of histidine and tyrosine. It differs from the pseudokeratin found in the gorgonians chiefly by its much lower cystine and tyrosine content.

Spongin fibers are secreted through the cooperation of rows of spongioblasts (Fig. 82O). Typically, spongin fibers are clear and homogeneous, but in some genera, especially *Verongia* and some of the Darwinellidae, they have a central soft pith or core encircled by concentric cylinders of spongin. Often the horny fibers are impregnated with rock fragments and other foreign bodies, although some genera as *Hippospongia*, are free from them. The foreign bodies may be present in all the fibers of the skeleton as in *Hircinia* (Fig. 104D), or only the ascending fibers may contain them, while the transverse fibers are free from them (*Spongia*). The flesh of the sponge is also very frequently permeated with all sorts of foreign particles.

The surface of the Keratosa consists of a leathery membrane that is apparently nonliving and probably composed of spongin. There are generally numerous dermal pores in the depressions between the conules (Fig. 104C), but the pores may be fewer and scattered. Often large subdermal spaces are present. The canal system of the typical horny sponges is of the diplodal type with small round chambers (Fig. 104*E*), but in the Darwinellidae and some others the eurypylous condition obtains and the chambers may be much elongated, sac-like or tubular. and sometimes branched.

The bath sponges, family Spongiidae, genera *Spongia* (= *Euspongia*) and *Hippospongia*, are thoroughly typical Keratosa. They are typical of (but not limited to) warm shallow waters, with rocky bottom, and are most abundant in the Mediterranean, which furnishes the best quality, the Gulf of Mexico, and the Caribbean and adjacent waters. The sponges are taken by "hooking" with a pronged fork on the end of a long pole, by nude diving, and with the use of diving outfits. They are left lying in shallow water until the flesh has decayed, and then they are squeezed and washed or tread with the feet until only the horny skeleton remains. This may then be bleached or dyed. The familiar sponge of household use consists only of the spongin skeleton and owes its water-holding capacity to the capillary forces of the meshes of the spongin net. Overfishing has much depleted the best Florida sponge grounds, and attempts have been made to restock the habitat by setting out sponge cuttings fastened to cement blocks. Although these require a few years to attain marketable size, such measures will undoubtedly prove beneficial to the industry in the long run. From the known rate of growth of bath sponges, it is estimated that the largest specimens of *Spongia* and *Hippospongia* may be up to 50 years old.

4. Histology.—Histologically the Demospongiae are characterized by the long fiber cells (Fig. 80*F*) that may form one or more fibrous layers in the cortex (Figs. 97*G* and 100*H*) and may occur in the interior along the larger water channels and along spicule tracts. They have contractile powers, being in fact very little different from myocytes, and sponges possessing them will contract considerably upon handling, removal from the water, exposure at low tide, etc. Many Demospongiae possess large amounts of mesogloea and in some, as *Chondrosia* and the forms that lack a skeleton, this jelly furnishes the chief support of the sponge body. The epidermis of the Demospongiae is apparently nearly always syncytial, forming an epithelioid membrane. The Keratosa appear to be clothed in a nonliving tough surface membrane. Each species has several kinds of amoebocytes, among which a type with coarse granules and another with one large globule (cystencyte or globoferous cell) are frequently met with (Fig. 80*K*). Others have colored droplets that give the species a characteristic color. Types with a large nucleus having a conspicuous nucleolus (Fig. 80*H, K*) are presumably identical with the archaeocytes of older literature. Some of the amoebocytes are probably fused into a netlike syncytium in many forms.

5. Reproduction.—Asexual reproduction by means of gemmules (Figs. 84 and 85), which consist essentially of clusters of amoebocytes, is widespread throughout the Demospongiae and is particularly characteristic of the Spongillidae whose gemmules differ from those of marine sponges in being enclosed in a hard shell (Figs. 84*J*, 85*A*). The gemmules of the Spongillidae hatch directly into a young sponge (Fig. 85*A*) whereas those of marine sponges (Fig. 85*B*, *C*) give rise to flagellated larvae which resemble closely in appearance and development the larvae originating from fertilized eggs.

The embryology has been followed in a number of species and except in the simpler tetractinellids already mentioned (page 341) follows a similar course throughout the class. Slightly unequal cleavage results in a solid blastula whose cells increase in size toward the posterior pole (Fig. 105*A*). The superficial cells of the mass alter into long slender flagellated cells, while the interior cells constitute an inner cell mass composed of two or three sorts of amoebocytes embedded in a gelatinous material (Fig. 105*B*). The entire surface may become flagellated but usually the posterior pole remains unflagellated and consists of larger cells continuous with the inner cell mass. Spicules are early formed by scleroblasts of the inner cell mass (Fig. 105*B*). These flagellated stereogastrulae escape, swim about for a few to 24 hours, and then attach near the anterior pole. There then occurs a so-called inversion of layers. The flagellated cells (after loss of the flagella) or at least their nuclei become enclosed, either through their own migrations or through the emergence on the surface of cells of the interior mass. According to the recent account of Wilson (1935), for *Mycale* (order Poecilosclerina), these larvae become syncytial at the time of attachment, and consequently the flagellated cells cannot be traced as such. Their nuclei can, however, be followed; they become the nuclei of the choanocytes. Epidermis and mesenchyme come from the original inner mass, which rearranges into the structure of the sponge (Fig. 105*F*). The young sponge spreads at its margins by sending out a thin sheet of epidermis into which amoebocytes wander (Fig. 105*D*, *E*).

In fresh-water sponges, Brien and Meewis (1938) have found that the fertilized egg cleaves to form a stereoblastula, composed of three sizes of cells, micromeres, mesomeres, and macromeres. The micromeres, at first situated at the anterior pole, spread over the embryo by a sort of epiboly and multiply rapidly so as to form a surface layer of small cells that become flagellated. While the embryo is still enclosed in the maternal tissues, the cells of the inner mass differentiate into collencytes, scleroblasts, choanocytes, and amoebocytes. Choanocytes and scleroblasts come from the large blastomeres or macromeres, which appear to be of the nature of archaeocytes. An interior cavity forms and the embryo escapes as a completely flagellated larva containing spicules, choanocytes arranged in chambers, and other differentiated cell types. After swimming for a few hours to several days, the larva fixes by the anterior pole,

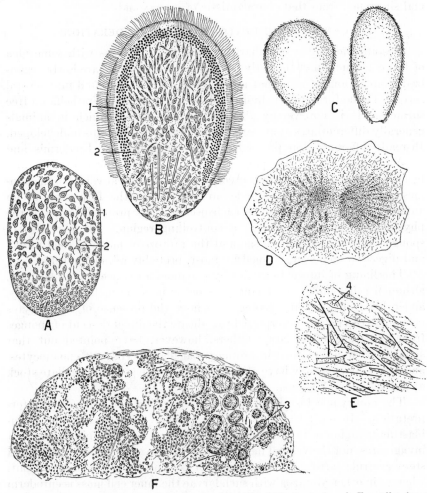

Fig. 105.—Development of Demospongiae. A. Stereogastrula of *Esperella* (now *Mycale*).   B. Swimming larva of the same.   (*A* and *B* after *Wilson*, 1894).   *C.* Swimming larvae of *Tedania*, from life.   D. Young sponge developed from *C.*   E. Growing edge of *D*, showing advancing amoebocytes.   F. Section through young sponge developing from *B*, from slide.   (*Courtesy of Dr. H. V. Wilson.*)   1, flagellated layer; 2, inner cell mass; 3, flagellated chambers; 4, amoebocytes.

and the canal system develops from the cavity already present. The collencytes pass to the exterior to become the epidermis, and the flagellated cells of the surface become enclosed and are phagocytized, playing no role in organogenesis. The development of the Spongillidae thus differs from that of other monaxonids in that there is no "inversion" of the layers and the choanocytes do not come from the surface flagellated cells of the larva; but it is probable that this development is modified and shortened from that characteristic of monaxonids.

VII. GENERAL AND PHYLOGENETIC CONSIDERATIONS

Despite their many peculiarities, sponges furnish us with some idea of the construction of the early Metazoa. The sponges are lowly organized aggregations of cells that are but slightly differentiated into several sorts. Tissue formation is limited to the production of epithelia on free surfaces. It is noteworthy that the surface layer, which in animals generally differentiates at an early stage, in sponges remains undeveloped. Instead, differentiation proceeds in the mesenchyme. Epidermis and mesenchyme originate in sponges from the same embryonic cells, and hence the mesenchyme may be considered theoretically to be an ecto-mesoderm. Sponges have made no progress in the formation of an anterior end or head, although each osculum has probably some of the physiological characteristics of a controlling region. There is also in sponges no proper digestive sac and the protozoan mode of food intake and digestion has been retained by most, probably all, of the cells.

The lining of internal cavities by choanocytes is peculiar to sponges, although cells similar to choanocytes occur in some mollusks, annelids, and other forms. Many zoologists believe the presence of choanocytes in sponges can only be interpreted to indicate the direct descent of sponges from the Choanoflagellata. Others, however, have pointed out that sponge larvae are clothed in ordinary flagellated cells, not choanocytes, and hence sponges may have arisen from the same general flagellate stock as did the other Metazoa.

The embryonic history of sponges is puzzling and difficult of interpretation. In most Calcarea and the simpler tetractinellids the coeloblastula invaginates into a typical gastrula; but it is the animal half that invaginates, not the vegetal half as in other Metazoa. In other sponges a stereogastrula arises by ingression or secondary delamination; but, whereas in other Metazoa with such larvae the inner cell mass is entoderm and hollows out into a digestive sac, in sponges this mass becomes the epidermis and the mesenchyme while the surface epithelium, ectodermal in other Metazoa, transforms into the choanocytes. The one point of agreement between the embryology of sponges and that of the radiate phyla is that the anterior end of the larva becomes the attached end of the adult; but this end in sponges also bears the blastopore when one is present, whereas in the Radiata the blastoporal end is oral. Some zoologists evade these difficulties by postulating the "inversion of the germ layers" in sponges, asserting that the epidermis of sponges is really entoderm, and the choanocyte layer, ectoderm. Such an extreme view will not appeal to many.

It is more reasonable to suppose either that sponges evolved from a different group of flagellates than did the rest of the Metazoa or else that they diverged very early from the general metazoan stem. In either case the divergence occurred at such a primitive state of metazoan organization that the embryology of sponges cannot be expected to bear any resemblance to that of other Metazoa. Attempts to homologize the embryology of sponges with that of Eumetazoa are therefore probably futile. The flagellated sponge larva is probably reminiscent of a colonial flagellated ancestor; this view is greatly strengthened by the recent finding (page 322) that the amphiblastula of syconoid Calcarea undergoes an inversion process identical with that occurring in the development of *Volvox*. The prevalence of stereogastrulae among sponges indicates that the filling of the interior with mesenchyme might have been the common method of achieving complexity among the earliest Metazoa. Sponges have evolved very little beyond the stage of a colonial protozoan, possibly through their early adoption of a sessile mode of life and the inability of their cells to give up their protozoan habits. The failure to develop a mouth and digestive sac and the retention of the original flagellate cells as food getters and current producers lead to the evolution of a unique anatomical type permeated with water channels. With the assumption of the sessile habit, the surface flagellated cells were no longer required to exercise their locomotory function but appear to have been incapable of altering their other protozoan activities. Their relegation to the interior was probably advantageous and may have been accomplished in different ways in the different lines of sponges probably already established. Once the flagellated cells became located in the interior there followed the elaboration of the system of water channels, which is the chief structural feature of sponges. Evolutionary change in sponges has been concerned chiefly with the perfecting of the water system and the development of a skeleton. The mode of production of the skeleton is again protozoan, concerning only single cells or groups of cells.

Concerning the relationship of the three classes of sponges, practically nothing can be said. Within each class evolution has proceeded along many different lines. The Calcarea apparently arose from a simple asconoid sponge, and the leuconoid stage has been reached in this class by more than one route. No evidence is available as to the relationship between the calcareous and the siliceous sponges; the relationship would be by way of the choristid tetractinellids, since only these have spicule types similar to those of Calcarea. The Hexactinellida occupy a very isolated position, but the occurrence of similar amphidisks in hexactinellids and some Demospongiae may point to the origin of the latter from the former. There is some evidence from paleontology and embryology that the tetract is the primitive spicule of the Hexactinellida; this would relate directly to the tetractinellid Demospongiae. Among the Hexactinellida, the forms with loose spicules are evidently the more primitive, from which those with dictyonine networks have evolved. The Demospongiae have seemingly arisen from a simple rhagon-like ancestor with tetraxon spicules and no differentiation into megascleres and microscleres. The earliest type of microsclere, the aster, has apparently been derived from the tetract by the addition of rays. The monaxonid sponges presumably came from tetractinellid ancestors through the alteration of triaenes into monaxons by the loss of the cladi. Among the monaxonids there is evidenced a tendency to the loss of microscleres and the development of spongin binding the spicules together. With increase in spongin content, the spicules progressively disappear, and so the monaxonids lead into the Keratosa with a skeleton purely of spongin. Very likely the Keratosa have arisen from the monaxonids along several different lines. The fresh-water sponges are evidently descended from marine haplosclerine ancestors.

In every group of sponges there is evidenced a tendency for the spicules to fuse into a continuous framework. This is seen among the Calcarea in the pharetronid sponges, in the Hexactinellida in the production of dictyonine skeletons, and in the Demospongiae in the formation of lithistid skeletons in several lines of evolution. It is these fused skeletons that are most apt to persist as fossils, and, since they represent highly evolved types of sponges, the fossil record cannot be expected to throw much light on sponge phylogeny. An opposite tendency toward complete loss of spicules is apparent among the Demospongiae, and forms with reduced spiculation or complete absence of skeleton have evolved in several different lines.

The phylum Porifera is obviously a blind branch of the animal kingdom that has no direct relationship to the Eumetazoa. The origin of the latter is evidently to be sought in some simple swimming colony.

Bibliography

GENERAL

Arndt, W. 1928. Die Spongien als kryptotoxische Tiere. Zool. Jahrb., Abt. Allg. Zool. Physiol. Tiere 45. 1928. Lebensdauer, Altern und Tod der Schwämme. Gesell. Naturf. Freunde Berlin Sitzber. 1930. Schwämme (Porifera, Spongien). Tabulae Biologicae (ed. W. Junk) 6. 1930. Schwämme and Gesundheitswesen. Ztschr. Desinfektions-u. Gesundheitsw. 22. 1933. Die biologische Beziehungen zwischen Schwämmen und Krebsen. Mitt. Zool. Mus. Berlin 19. **Bidder, G. G.** 1923. Relation of the form of a sponge to its currents. Quart. Jour. Micros. Sci. 67. 1933. The energy of flagellate cells. Brit. Assoc. Adv. Sci. Rpt., 103. **Bidder, G. G., and G. S. Vosmaer-Roell.** 1928. Bibliography of sponges, 1751–1913

Cambridge Univ. Press. **Burton, M.** 1928. Comparative study of shallow-water and deep-sea sponges. Jour. Quekett Micros. Club 16. **Cotte, J.** 1904. Nutrition chex les Spongiaires. Bul. Sci. France Belg. 38. **Dendy, A.** 1905. Sponges collected at Ceylon. Herdman Rpt. Pearl Oyster Fish., Part III, Sup. 18. 1926. Origin, growth, and arrangement of sponge spicules. Quart. Jour. Micros. Sci. 70. **Galtsoff, P. S.** 1923. Amoeboid movement of dissociated sponge cells. Biol. Bul. 45. 1929. Heteroagglutination of dissociated sponge cells. Biol. Bull. 57. **Gatenby, J. B.** 1919. Germ cells, fertilisation and early development of Grantia. Linn. Soc. London Jour., Zool. 34. 1920. Further notes on oögenesis and fertilisation of Grantia. Roy. Micros. Soc. Jour. 1927. Further notes, etc. Quart. Jour. Micros. Sci. 71. **George, W. C.,** and **H. V. Wilson.** 1919. Sponges of Beaufort, N. C. U. S. Bur. Fisheries, Bul. 36. **Görich, W.** 1903. Spermatogenese bei den Poriferen. Ztschr. Wiss. Zool. 76. **Huxley, J.** 1911. Regeneration of Sycon. Phil. Trans. Roy. Soc. London 202. 1921. Restitution bodies and free tissue culture in Sycon. Quart. Jour. Micros. Sci. 65. 1921. Differences in viability in different types of regeneration from dissociated sponges. Biol. Bul. 20. **Laubenfels, M. W. de.** 1926. Bispecific conglomerations of sponges. Carnegie Inst. Wash., Yearbook 26. 1932a. Marine and fresh-water sponges of California. U. S. Nat. Mus., Proc. 81. 1932b. Morphology and physiology of Porifera exemplified by Iotrochota. Carnegie Inst. Wash., Tortugas Lab., Publ. 28. 1936. Sponge fauna of the Dry Tortugas with material for a revision of the families and orders of the Porifera. Carnegie Inst. Wash., Tortugas Lab., Publ. 30. **Lendenfeld, R.** 1889. Physiologie der Spongien. Ztschr. Wiss. Zool. 48. **Loisel, G.** 1897. Histophysiologie des Éponges. Jour. Anat. Physiol. 34. **Maas, O.** 1898. Entwicklung der Spongien. Zool. Zentbl. 5. 1899. Reifung und Befruchtung bei Spongien. Anat. Anz. 16. 1910. Involutionserscheinungen bei Schwämmen. Festschr. R. Hertwig, III. **Masterman, A.** 1894. Nutritive and excretory processes in Porifera. Ann. Mag. Nat. Hist., Ser. 6, Vols. 13, 14. **Minchin, E. A.** 1909. Sponge-spicules. Ergeb. Fortschr. Zool. 2. **Müller, K.** 1914. Gemmula-Studien, etc. an Ficulina. Wiss. Meer. Untersuch. Abt. Kiel 16. **Parker, G. H.** 1910. Reactions of sponges. Jour. Expt. Zool. 8. **Pearse, A. S.** 1921. Inhabitants of certain sponges at Dry Tortugas. Carnegie Inst. Wash., Tortugas Lab., Publ. 28. **Pourbaix, N.** 1931. Nutrition chex les Spongiaires. Notes Stat. Océanogr. Salammbo. 23. 1936 Étude histochemique des substances de réserve. Soc. Roy. Zool. Belg., Ann. 65. **Rodriguez, G.** 1930. Symbiose entre la Spongilla et les zoochlorelles. Soc. Roy. Zool. Belg., Ann. 61. **Topsent, E.** 1928. Spongiaires de l'Atlantique et de la Méditerranée, etc. Result. Campagnes Sci. Albert I. Monaco, fasc. 74. **Verrill, A. E.** 1907. Porifera of the Bermuda Islands. Conn. Acad. Arts. Sci., Trans. 12. **Vosmaer, G. C. J.** 1929. Sponges of the Bay of Naples. Porifera Incalcarea. Capita Zoologica 3, 5. **Vosmaer, G. C. J.,** and **C. Pekelharring.** 1898. Nahrungsaufnahme bei Schwämmen. Arch. Anat. Physiol., Physiol. Abt. **Wilson, H. V.** 1894. Gemmule and egg development of marine sponges. Jour. Morph. 9. 1902. Asexual origin of the ciliated sponge larva. Amer. Nat. 36. 1904. Albatross Reports. The sponges. Harvard Univ., Mus. Compar. Zool., Mem. 30. 1907. Some phenomena of coalescence and regeneration in sponges. Jour. Expt. Zool. 5. 1911. Development of sponges from dissociated tissue cells. U. S. Bur. Fisheries, Bul. 30. 1919. Species and sponges. Sci. Monthly, Oct. 1925. Studies on dissociated sponge cells. Carnegie Inst. Wash., Year Book. 24. 1925. Silicious and horny sponges collected by the Albatross. U. S. Natl. Mus. Bul. 100. **Wilson, H. V.,** and **J. T. Penney.** 1930. Regeneration of sponges from dissociated cells. Jour. Expt. Zool. 56. **Woodland, W** 1905. Spicule formation. Quart. Jour. Micros. Sci. 49.

CALCAREA

Bidder, G. 1896. Collar cells of Heterocoela. Quart. Jour. Micros. Sci. 38. Dendy, A. 1891. Organisation and classification of the Calcarea Homocoela. Roy. Soc. Victoria, Trans. 3, Pt. 1. 1893. Structure and classification of the Calcarea Heterocoela. Quart. Jour. Micros. Sci. 35. 1914. Gametogenesis of Grantia. Quart. Jour. Micros. Sci. 60. Dendy, A., and R. Row. 1913. The classification and phylogeny of the calcareous sponges. Zool. Soc. London, Proc. Doederlein, L. 1898. Die Lithonina. Zool. Jahrb., Abt. System, Geog. Tiere 10. Haeckel, E. 1872. Die Kalkschwämme. 3 vols. Hammer, E. 1908. Histologie und Entwicklung von Sycon. Arch. Biontologie 2. Hozawa, S. 1915. Calcareous sponges collected by the Albatross. U. S. Nat. Mus. Proc. 54. 1929. Calcareous sponges of Japan. Tokyo Univ. Facult. Sci., Jour. Sect. IV, Zool. 1, Pt. 5. 1933. Calcareous sponges of Japan. Tohoku Imp. Univ., Sci. Rpt. Ser. IV (Biol.) Vol. 8. Jörgensen, M. 1910. Eibildung, Reifung, Befruchtung, und Furchung bei Syconen. Arch. Zellforsch. 4. Jörgenson, O. 1917. Reproduction in Grantia. Dove Marine Lab., Rpt. 6, 7. Kirkpatrick, R. 1908. New genera of pharetronid sponges. Ann. Mag. Nat. Hist., Ser. 8, Vol. 2. Lendenfeld, R. 1894. Die Kalkschwämme. Ztschr. Wiss. Zool. 53. Maas, O. 1900. Weiterentwicklung der Syconen nach der Metamorphose. Ztschr. Wiss. Zool. 67. Metschnikoff, E. 1879. Spongiologische Studies. Ztschr. Wiss. Zool. 32. Minchin, E. 1892. Anatomy of Leucosolenia clathrus. Quart. Jour. Micros. Sci. 33. 1896. Larva and postlarval development of Leucosolenia. Roy. Soc. London, Proc. 60. 1898. Origin and growth of triradiate and quadriradiate spicules. Quart. Jour. Micros. Sci. 40. 1904. Genus Leucosolenia. Zool. Soc. London, Proc., 1904. Pt. 2. 1908. Formation of spicules in Leucosolenia. Quart. Jour. Micros. Sci. 52. 1909. Relation of the flagellum to the nucleus in collar cells of calcareous sponges. Zool. Anz. 35. Polejaeff, J. 1882. Sperma und Spermatogenesis bei Sycandra. Akad. Wiss. Wien, Math.-Nat. Kl. Sitzber., 86. 1883. Calcarea. Challenger Rpts., Zool. 8. Prenant, M. 1925. Les Porocytes de Clathrina. Trav. Sta. Zool. Wimereux. 9. Schulze, F. E. 1875. Bau und Entwicklung von Sycandra. Ztschr. Wiss. Zool. 25. 1878. Metamorphose von Sycandra. Ztschr. Wiss. Zool. 31. Urban, F. 1906. Kalifornische Kalkschwämme. Arch. Naturgesch. 72, Pt. 1. 1908. Die Calcarea. Wiss. Ergeb. Deut. Tiefsee Exped. 19. 1910. Biologie und Cytologie der Kalkschwämme. Internatl. Rev. Hydrobiol. 3. Volkonsky, M. 1930. Les choanocytes des éponges calcaires. Soc. Biol. [Paris] Compt. Rend. 102, 103; Soc. Zool. France Bul. 55. Webb, D. 1935. Histology, cytology, and embryology of sponges —review of literature since 1914. Quart. Jour. Micros. Sci. 78.

HEXACTINELLIDA

Bidder, G. P. 1930. Attitude of a hexactinellid at the bottom of the sea. Linn. Soc. London, Proc. Ijima, I. 1901–1903. Studies on the Hexactinellida. Tokyo Imp. Univ. Col. Sci. Jour. 15. 1927. Hexactinellida of the Siboga Expedition. Siboga Monog. 6. Kirkpatrick, R. 1910. Hexactinellid sponge spicules and their names. Ann. Mag. Nat. Hist., Ser. 1, Vol. 5. Lendenfeld, R. 1915. Hexactinellida of eastern tropical Pacific. Harvard Univ., Mus. Compar. Zool., Mem. 42. Okada, Y. 1928. Development of Farrea sollasii. Tokyo Univ. Facult. Sci. Jour. Sect. IV, Vol. 2, Pt. 1. Schmidt, J. W. 1926. Lamellierung und Verhalten von organischer und anorganischer Substanz bei den Kieselschwammnadeln. Zool. Jahrb. Abt. Anat. Ontog. Tiere 48. Schulze, F. E. 1887. Hexactinellida. Challenger Rpts., Zool. 21. 1894. Hexactinelliden des Indische Oceans. Akad. Wiss.

Berlin Abhandl. 1899. Amerikanische Hexactinelliden. 1899. Histologie der Hexactinelliden. Akad. Wiss. Berlin Sitzber. Pt. 1. 1909. Hexactinelliden des rothen Meeres. Ber. Comm. Oceanog. Forsch. Zool. Ergeb. 16. 1904. Hexactinellida. Wiss. Ergeb. Deut. Tiefsee Exped. Valdivia 4. **Schulze, P.** 1925. Feinbau der Kieselschwammnadeln. Ztschr. Morph. Ökol. Tiere 4. **Wilson, H. V. and J. T. Penney.** 1930. Rhabdocalyptus. U. S. Nat. Mus. Proc. 76. **Woodland, W.** 1908. Scleroblastic development of hexactinellid and other siliceous sponge spicules. Quart. Jour. Micros. Sci. 52.

DEMOSPONGIAE

Arndt, A. 1926. Bau und Leben der deutschen Süsswasserschwämme. Mikros. Naturfr. 4. **Brien, P.** 1932. Régénération naturelle chez les Spongillidae. Arch. Zool. Expt. Gén. 74. **Brøndsted, H.** 1936. Entwicklungsphysiologische Studien über Spongilla. Acta Zool., 17. **Burton, M.** 1926. Genus Reniera. Ann. Mag. Nat. Hist., Ser. 9, Vol. 17. **Clancey, V.** 1926. Constitution of sponges. Biochem. Jour. 20. **Dendy, A.** 1916–1921. Sealark Reports. Linn. Soc. London, Trans. Zool. 17, Pt. 2, 18, Pt. 1. 1921. The tetraxonid sponge spicule. Acta Zool. 2. **Evans, R.** 1899. Structure and metamorphosis of the larva of Spongilla. Quart. Jour. Micros. Sci. 42. 1901. Ephydatia blembingia with an account of the formation and structure of the gemmule. Quart. Jour. Micros. Sci. 44. **Fiedler, K.** 1888. Ei und Samenbildung bei Spongilla. Ztschr. Wiss. Zool. 47. **Jaffe, E.** 1912. Entwicklung von Spongilla und Ephydatia aus die Gemmula. Die Gemmulae von Spongilla und Ephydatia. Zool. Anz. 39. **Lendenfeld, R.** 1889. Monograph of the horny sponges. 1903. Tetraxonia. Tierreich 19. 1907. Die Tetraxonia. Wiss. Ergeb. Deut. Tiefsee Exped. Valdivia 11. **Maas, O.** 1892. Metamorphose von Esperia. Mitt. Zool. Stat. Neapel 10. 1893. Embryonal-Entwicklung und Metamorphose der Cornacuspongien. Zool. Jahrb. Abt. Anat. Ontog. Tiere. 7. 1898. Metamorphose von Oscarella. Ztschr. Wiss. Zool. 63. 1909. Entwicklung der Tetractinelliden. Verh. Deut. Zool. Gesell. 19. **McNair, G.** 1923. Motor reactions of the fresh-water sponge Ephydatia. Biol. Bul. 44. **Moore, H. F.** 1908. The commercial sponges and the sponge fisheries. U. S. Bur. Fisheries, Bul. 28. 1923. Commercial sponges. Chap. 36 of Marine Products of Commerce (ed. by D. K. Tressler). **Müller, K.** 1911. Reduktionserscheinungen bei Süsswasserschwämme. Arch. Entwickl. Mech. Organ. 32. 1911. Regenerationsvermögen der Süsswasserschwämme. Arch. Entwickl. Mech. Organ. 32. **Old, M. C.** 1932. Spongillidae of Michigan. Mich. Acad. Sci. Papers 15. Delaware fresh-water sponges. Amer. Micros. Soc. Trans. 51. **Penney, J. T.** 1933. Reduction and regeneration in fresh-water sponges. Jour. Expt. Zool. 65. **Potts, E.** 1887. Synopsis of American fresh-water sponges. Acad. Nat. Sci. Phila., Proc. 39. **Pourbaix, N.** 1933. Nutrition chez les Spongillidae. Soc. Roy. Zool. Belg., Ann. 64. 1935. Formation histochemique des gemmules d'Éponges. Soc. Roy. Zool. Belg., Ann. 66. **Ridley, S. O., and A. Dendy.** 1887. Monaxonida. Challenger Rpts, Zool. 20. **Schulze, F. E.** 1877. Die Chondrosidae. Ztschr. Wiss. Zool. 29. 1878. Die Aplysinidae. Ztschr. Wiss. Zool. 30. 1879. Die Spongidae. Ztschr. Wiss. Zool. 32. 1880. Die Plakiniden. Ztschr. Wiss. Zool. 34. **Schulze, P.** 1922. Spongiaria. Biologie der Tiere Deutschlands, Teil 2. 1923. Kieselnadelbildung, besonders bei den Spongilliden. Arch. Zellforsch. 17. **Smith, F.** 1921. Distribution of the fresh-water sponges of N. A. Ill. Nat. Hist. Survey, Bul. 14. **Sollas, W.** 1884. Development of Halisarca. Quart. Jour. Micros. Sci. 24. 1888. Tetractinellida. Challenger Rpts., Zool. 25. **Topsent, E.** 1888–1891. Étude des Clionides. Arch. Zool. Expt. Gén., Ser. 2, Vols. 5, 9. 1891. Spongiaires de Roscoff. Arch. Zool.

Expt. Gén. Ser. 2, Vol. 9. 1894. Spongiaires de France. Tetractinellida. Arch. Zool. Expt. Gén. Ser. 3, Vol. 2. 1900. Spongiaires de France. Monaxonida. Arch. Zool. Expt. Gén. Ser. 3, Vol. 8. (For numerous other papers of this author see Topsent, 1928, above.) **Tright, H. van.** 1919. Physiology of the Spongillidae. Tijdschr. Nederland. Dierk. Vereen. Ser. 2, Vol. 17. **Tuzet, O.** 1930. Fécondation de Cliona. Acad. Sci. Paris, Compt. Rend. 191. 1930. Spermatogénèse de Reniera. Soc. Biol. [Paris] Compt. Rend. 103. 1932. Histologie des Éponges Reniera elegans et simulans. Arch. Zool. Expt. Gén. 74. **Vosmaer, G.** 1911. Spirastrella. Siboga Exped. Monog. 6a. **Weltner, W.** 1907. Spongilliden-Studien. Arch. Naturgesch. 73, Pt. 1. **Wierzejski, A.** 1935. Süsswasserspongien. Mem. Acad. Polonaise Sci. Lettr. Cracovie, Cl. Sci. Math. Nat. Ser. B, Sci. Nat. No. 9. **Wilson, H. V.** 1910. Epithelioid membranes in monaxonid sponges. Jour. Expt. Zool. 9. 1935. Some critical points in the metamorphosis of the halichondrine sponge larva. Jour. Morph. 58.

ADDENDA

Arndt, A. 1936. Die Poriferen von Standpunkt der Strahlungsbiologie. Gesell. Naturf. Freunde Berlin, Sitzber. **Arndt, A., and K. Viets.** 1938. Die biologischen (parasitologischen) Beziehung zwischen Arachnoideen und Spongien. Ztschr. Parasitenk. 10. **Bartsch, R.** 1936. Sponge conservation. Science 83. **Block, R. J., and D. Bolling.** 1939. The amino acid composition of keratins. Jour. Biol. Chem. 127. **Brien, P., and H. Meewis.** 1938. Embryogénèse des Spongillidae. Arch. Biol. 49. **Bronsted, H. O.** 1936. Entwicklungsphysiologische Studien über Spongilla. Creta Zoologica Arg. 17. **Duboscq, O., and O. Tuzet.** 1937. L'ovogénèse, la fécondation, et les premiers stades du développement des éponges calcaires. Arch. Zool. Expt. Gén. 79. 1938. La Collerette des choanocytes chez les éponges calcaires. Soc. Biol. Paris Compt. Rend. 129. 1939. Les diverses formes des choanocytes des éponges calcaires. Arch. Zool. Expt. Gén. 80. **Jewell, M. E.** 1935. An ecological study of the freshwater sponges of northern Wisconsin. Ecol. Monog. 5. **Meewis, H.** 1939. Embryogénèse des Myxospongidae: Halisarca. Arch. Biol. 50. **Zeuthen, E.** 1939. Hibernation of Spongilla. Ztschr. Vergleich. Physiol. 26.

CHAPTER VII

METAZOA OF THE TISSUE GRADE OF CONSTRUCTION—
THE RADIATE PHYLA—PHYLUM CNIDARIA

I. CHARACTERS OF THE PHYLUM

1. Introduction.—As in the case of sponges, the nature of coelenterates was long debated. Aristotle termed them Acalephae or Cnidae (Gr. *akalephe*, nettle; *cnidos*, thread) since he knew they could sting and considered them intermediate between plants and animals, whence the name Zoophyta (Gr. *zoon*, animal, *phyton*, plant) applied to them until relatively recent times. This term Zoophyta, however, included a variety of soft-bodied animals, from sponges to ascidians. Peyssonel (1723) established the animal nature of the coral "insects," since he saw them contract and expand and move their tentacles, and Trembley (1744) gave a similar demonstration for hydras. As a result of such researches, Linnaeus, Lamarck, and Cuvier placed the coelenterates among animals, under their groups Radiata or Zoophyta. In Cuvier's system this included most of the lower invertebrates, with coelenterates split between the Acalephae (medusae, siphonophorans, anemones) and the Polyps (hydroids, bryozoans, anthozoans, sponges). Lamarck's Radiata was limited to medusoid coelenterates and echinoderms, and polypoid coelenterates were termed Polyps. Eschscholtz (1829) divided the Radiata into Zoophyta, Acalepha, and Echinodermata and had the first clear understanding of the Acalepha (medusoid coelenterates); he recognized the groups Ctenophora, Siphonophora, and medusae proper, creating the first two names. Studies on the life cycles of coelenterates, beginning with the work of Sars (1829) on *Aurelia*, demonstrated the relation of the polypoid and medusoid coelenterates, previously considered separate groups. The Bryozoa were definitely removed from the Zoophyta through the studies of Thompson (1831), Ehrenberg (1833), and Johnston (1838), the last creating the name Hydroida. Finally, Leuckart (1847) clearly grasped the fundamental differences between the two great radiate groups, the coelenterates and the echinoderms, and separated them, creating the name Coelenterata (Gr. *koilos*, cavity, *enteron*, intestine, in reference to the fact that the intestine is the sole body cavity). Leuckart's Coelenterata, however, included the sponges and the ctenophores, and this combination was long retained while the coelenterates proper plus ctenophores were often named Acalepha. The proper splitting of Leuckart's Coelenterata was achieved by Hatschek (1888), who recognized three phyla: Spongiaria, Cnidaria, and Ctenophora. We therefore consider Cnidaria to be the most suitable name for the phylum, but the word coelenterates is useful and will be frequently employed. Zoologists who retain the combination of coelenterates and ctenophores call the phylum Coelenterata, subdividing this into Cnidaria for the coelenterates proper and Acnidaria for the ctenophores. We here regard the Ctenophora as a separate phylum. The name Anthozoa comes from Ehrenberg (1833), Hydrozoa from Huxley (1856), and Scyphozoa from Haeckel (1891), who also created many other names used in the classification of medusae. Haeckel's Scyphozoa, however, included the present Scyphozoa and the Anthozoa, so that it would be more just to call this group by the names Acraspeda, Gegenbaur (1856), or Scyphomedusae, Ray-Lankester (1877). Anthozoa is preferable to Actinozoa, as the latter was originated (by Huxley, 1856) to include Anthozoa and Ctenophora.

2. Definition.—The Cnidaria are tentacle-bearing Metazoa with primary radial, biradial, or radio-bilateral symmetry, of the tissue grade of construction, composed essentially of two epithelia with cement or some type of connective tissue between them, with nematocysts of intrinsic origin, and with but one internal cavity, the digestive cavity, opening only by the mouth. More briefly, the Cnidaria are tentacle-bearing Radiata with intrinsic mematocysts.

3. General Characters.—This phylum begins the study of the Eumetazoa or Metazoa proper, having definite form, symmetry, and individuality, with well-developed tissues, usually also with organs, and with a digestive tube opening by a mouth and lined by an ordinary epithelium of entodermal origin. The body surface is continuous, not permeated with macroscopic pores. The lowest Eumetazoa are the radiate phyla, i.e., the Cnidaria and the Ctenophora, radial forms of the tissue grade of construction without a definite head or centralized nervous system and with no internal space except the digestive cavity. The Radiata are constructed essentially of epithelial, muscular, and connective tissues. The polar axis of the larva becomes the oral-aboral axis of the adult and its blastoporal end forms the definitive oral end. The Radiata possess digestive, muscular, nervous, and sensory systems in an elementary stage of development, and often, also, an exoskeleton; but respiratory, excretory, and circulatory systems are wanting and the reproductive system consists simply of sex cells usually aggregated into gonads.

The chief external feature of the Cnidaria is the radial symmetry, which in the Anthozoa is modified into biradial or radiobilateral symmetry through the elongation of the mouth and correlated changes (Fig. 106*H J*). There is one main axis of symmetry, the oral-aboral axis, extending from mouth to base, and the parts are arranged concentrically around this axis (Fig. 106*G*). The parts may be definite or indefinite in number; when definite, the number is usually four or six or some multiple thereof. Very noticeable also are the tentacles, short or slender extensible projections that encircle the oral end in one or more whorls (Fig. 106*A*) and serve for defense and food capture and intake; they are absent in very few members of the phylum.

The phylum is notable for its *polymorphism*, i.e., the variety of form any one species may present. These forms are reducible to two main types, the *polyp* and the *medusa*, which again can be derived from each other. The polyp (Fig. 106*A*) is the sessile form, having the shape of an elongated cylinder fastened at the aboral end, with mouth and tentacles at the free oral end. The medusa, the free-swimming form, contrasts with the polyp in the shortening of the oral-aboral axis, radial expansion, and excessive formation of mesogloea, changes resulting in a gelatinous bell-, bowl-, or saucer-shaped animal with marginal tentacles (Fig. 106*E*). Polyp and medusa occur in a number of morphological variations, several of which may be found in a single species. In the class Hydrozoa, both polypoid and medusoid forms occur, in the Scyphozoa the medusoid type is dominant, while the Anthozoa are exclusively polypoid. Where a species includes both polypoid and medusoid forms, the polyps reproduce exclusively by asexual methods and bud off the medusae or their equivalents, which alone are capable of sexual reproduction. From this fact is derived the idea of *alternation of generations*, also called *metagenesis*, in coelenterates, i.e., that the life cycle consists of an alternation of the asexual polypoid generation with the sexual medusoid generation. It is more probable that the polyp is a persistent larval stage and the medusa the completely evolved coelenterate.

Structurally the Cnidaria consist of a solid body wall enclosing the central digestive cavity. The body wall is composed of an external and an internal epithelium connected by an intermediate layer (Fig. 106*D*). The outer epithelium is usually called ectoderm and the inner one, entoderm, but as already explained (page 264) the terms ectoderm and entoderm will be limited to embryological stages, and the adult epithelia will be called *epidermis* and *gastrodermis*, respectively. The intermediate layer, usually termed *mesogloea*, varies from a thin noncellular cement to a thick gelatinous mass or a fibrous layer; except in the Hydrozoa it contains cellular elements and is therefore really a kind of connective tissue. Characteristic of coelenterates are free undifferentiated *interstitial* cells, which lie among the epithelial cells, give rise to sex cells and nematocysts, and participate in regenerative and reproductive processes. It would be preferable to call all such cells simply mesenchyme cells.

The systems of the Cnidaria are at the tissue grade of construction. The digestive system consists only of an epithelium and has but one orifice, the mouth, serving for food intake and ejection of undigestible material. It is usually called the *gastrovascular system* and its cavity the *gastrovascular cavity*, since it serves both for the digestion and distribution of food. *Coelenteron* is a less cumbersome term for the main cavity and will be frequently employed. Primitively consisting of a simple tube, the digestive system displays throughout the phylum a tendency to complication by putting out branches and pockets and in the Scyphozoa and Anthozoa is divided into compartments by gastrodermal-mesogloeal projections. In the Hydrozoa and Scyphozoa, ectoderm and entoderm meet at the mouth rim; but in the Anthozoa, the ectoderm is turned in for a considerable distance as a muscular introduction to the coelenteron. Such an ectodermal beginning of the digestive tube is known embryologically as a *stomodaeum*, termed *pharynx* or *gullet* in the adult, and is a characteristic feature of the Eumetazoa in general. The muscular system consists chiefly of circular and longitudinal layers of muscle fibrils, which may or may not be parts of the two epithelia. It attains a

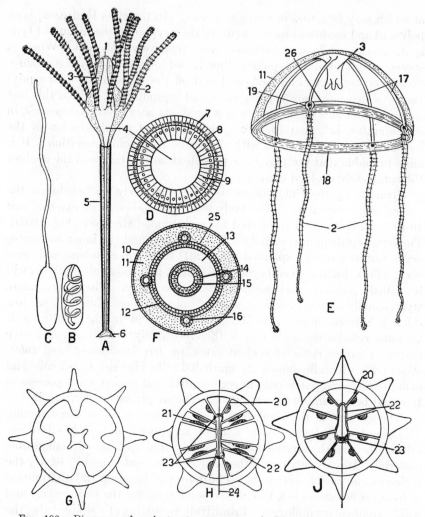

Fig. 106.—Diagrams of coelenterate structure. *A.* Diagram of a hydroid polyp. *B.* Diagram of a nematocyst, unexploded. *C.* Same, exploded. *D.* Diagrammatic cross section of hydroid polyp. *E.* A hydrozoan medusa. *F.* Cross section of a hydrozoan medusa. *G.* Diagram of a hydrozoan or scyphozoan medusa, showing tetramerous radial symmetry. *H.* Diagram of an anthozoan (anemone) showing hexamerous biradial symmetry. *J.* Diagram of an anthozoan (alcyonarian) showing octomerous radiobilateral symmetry. 1, mouth; 2, tentacles; 3, manubrium; 4, gastrovascular cavity; 5, stem with periderm covering; 6, pedal disk; 7, epidermis; 8, mesolamella; 9, gastrodermis; 10, exumbrellar epidermis; 11, mesogloea; 12, subumbrellar epidermis; 13, subumbrellar cavity; 14, epidermis of manubrium; 15, gastrodermis of manubrium; 16, gastrodermal radial canals; 17, radial canals; 18, velum; 19, tentacular bulb with eyespot; 20, septum; 21, muscle band of same; 22, stomodaeum; 23, siphonoglyph; 24, sagittal axis; 25, gastrodermal lamella; 26, ring canal.

high development in some Scyphozoa and Anthozoa. The nervous system comprises one or more networks of nerve cells and neurites located in the deeper parts of both epidermis and gastrodermis. Numerous sensory cells are present in the epidermis, sparingly also in the gastrodermis, and complicated sensory organs of several types occur in medusae. The formation of skeleton is of common occurrence throughout the phylum either as *exoskeleton* secreted on the external surface or as *endoskeleton* formed in the mesenchyme as separate pieces (*sclerites*) or as a continuous mass.

Diagnostic of the phylum are the *nematocysts*, although similar bodies occur in flagellates and as the polar capsules of some Sporozoa (pages 93, 159). The nematocysts found in certain flatworms and snails have been proved to originate from ingested coelenterates. A nematocyst (Fig. 106*B*, *C*) consists essentially of a capsule containing a coiled capillary tube, which on stimulation discharges to the exterior by turning inside out and serves to inject a paralyzing poison into the prey, or to hold it by wrapping around bristles, etc., or is used for adhesion.

The polypoid types are mostly sessile and movably or immovably attached to objects or thrust into a soft substratum, although occasionally they are floating. They are solitary or more often reproduce extensively by asexual processes to form more or less plant-like colonies usually strengthened by skeletal secretions, often hard and massive. The polypoid generation of the Hydrozoa is mostly incapable of sexual reproduction. Medusae are free-swimming and solitary, except for a few cases of budding, and reproduce sexually. The egg usually develops into a ciliated *stereogastrula*, known as a *planula*, which attaches and grows into some sort of polypoid stage. This stage is permanent in the Anthozoa, but in the other classes is often followed by a medusoid stage asexually formed.

The Cnidaria are mostly marine and comprise some of the most familiar and common animals of ocean shores, while also extending to great depths. The fresh-water forms include the well-known hydras, solitary and lacking a medusoid stage, the colonial hydroid *Cordylophora*, the parasitic *Polypodium*, and several fresh-water medusae having a reduced polypoid generation.

II. CLASSIFICATION OF THE PHYLUM

The division of the phylum into the three main classes of Hydrozoa, Scyphozoa, and Anthozoa is universally accepted, but as regards the subdivision of these classes no agreement has been reached.

Class I. **Hydrozoa,** the hydroids and craspedote medusae. Coelenterates with tetramerous or polymerous radial symmetry; polymorphic with both polypoid and medusoid forms, or exclusively polypoid or exclusively medusoid; gastrovascular system without stomodaeum or nematocyst-bearing structures and not divided by projecting ridges or partitions; mesogloea noncellular; sex cells ripening in the epidermis; oral end of the polyp elongated into a hydranth; medusae nearly always craspedote. 2700 species, solitary or colonial, chiefly marine.

Order 1. Hydroida, the hydroids. Polypoid generation well developed, solitary or colonial, budding off free medusae or with structures representing abortive medusae; sense organs of medusae are ocelli and ectodermal statocysts.[1]

Suborder 1. Gymnoblastea or Anthomedusae or Athecata, the tubularian hydroids. Hydranths without hydrothecae; gonophores naked; free medusae tall, bell-like, with ocelli but without statocysts; gonads borne on the manubrium.

Suborder 2. Calyptoblastea or Leptomedusae or Thecaphora, the campanularian hydroids. Hydranths provided with hydrothecae; gonophores enclosed in gonothecae; free medusae flatter, bowl or saucer-shaped, usually with statocysts; gonads borne on the radial canals.

Order 2. Milleporina, the millepores. Hydroid colony occupying the surface layer of a massive calcareous skeleton with pores through which the polyps protrude; polyps dimorphic; dactylozooids elongate, hollow, with capitate tentacles; medusae formed in special cavities, becoming free, devoid of mouth, digestive canals, and tentacles.

Order 3. Stylasterina. Similar to Milleporina but dactylozooids small, solid, without tentacles; gastrozooids and dactylozooids usually arranged in systems; bottom of gastrozooid cup usually with an upright spine; gonophores reduced to sporosacs, developing in special cavities.

Order 4. Trachylina, the trachyline medusae. Craspedote medusae, having as sense organs statocysts and tentaculocysts with entodermal statoliths; tentacles usually inserted above bell margin; with or without a reduced hydroid generation.

Suborder 1. Trachymedusae. Margin smooth, gonads borne on the radial canals.

Suborder 2. Narcomedusae. Margin scalloped by tentacle bases; gonads borne in the floor of the stomach.

Order 5. Siphonophora. Highly polymorphic free-swimming or floating colonies composed of several types of polypoid and medusoid individuals attached to a stem or disk; polypoids without oral tentacles; medusoids never developing into complete medusae and rarely freed.

Suborder 1. Calycophora. Upper end of colony consisting of one or more swimming bells.

Suborder 2. Physophorida. Upper end of colony composed of a float (pneumatophore).

Class II. Scyphozoa or Scyphomedusae, the jellyfish or true medusae. Acraspedote medusae, free-swimming or attached by an aboral stalk; gastrovascular system without stomodaeum, with gastric tentacles, and divided or not into four interradial pockets by four ridges (septa); mesogloea cellular; gonads entodermal; marginal sense organs usually tentaculocysts (rhopalia) with entodermal statoliths; polypoid generation wanting or consisting of a polypoid type (scyphistoma) with gastric tentacles and septa which develops directly into the adult or gives off medusae by transverse fission. Exclusively marine, 200 species.

[1] In regard to many medusae, the hydroid generation from which they presumably came has not been definitely identified; further, the hydroid and medusoid generations may evolve independently, so that often very similar medusae are budded from quite different hydroid types and vice versa. Because of these difficulties it is not yet possible to erect one single scheme of classification for both hydroids and medusae, and often medusae and the corresponding hydroid colony bear different generic names.

Order 1. Stauromedusae or Lucernariida. Attached by an aboral stalk and developing directly from the scyphistoma; marginal sense organs absent or modified tentacles; with septa.

Order 2. Cubomedusae or Carybdeida. Free-swimming form cubical, with four perradial tentacles or tentacle groups, borne on pedalia, and four interradial rhopalia; umbrella margin bent inward as a velarium; with septa.

Order 3. Coronatae (old group Peromedusae in part). Free-swimming, margin scalloped, separated from the bell by a circular furrow; tentacles borne on pedalia; 4 to 32 rhopalia; with septa.

Order 4. Semaeostomeae (with t e next order constituting the old order Discomedusae). Corners of the mouth prolonged into four long frilly lobes; no furrow or pedalia; without septa; margin scalloped; rhopalia 8 or 16.

Order 5. Rhizostomeae. Oral lobes fused, obliterating the mouth; numerous small mouths and canals in the oral lobes; without tentacles or septa; margin scalloped; rhopalia 8 or more.

Class III. Anthozoa. Exclusively polypoid, with hexamerous, octomerous, or polymerous biradial or radiobilateral symmetry; oral end expanded radially into an oral disk; stomodaeum strongly developed, often provided with one or more siphonoglyphs; gastrovascular cavity divided into compartments by complete or incomplete partitions (septa); septa with a nematocyst-bearing edge; mesogloea a mesenchymal or fibrous connective tissue; gonads entodermal in the septa. Solitary or colonial, exclusively marine, 6100 species.

Subclass I. Alcyonaria or Octocorallia. Polyps with eight pinnate tentacles, eight single complete septa, and one ventral siphonoglyph; colonial with endoskeleton.

Order 1. Stolonifera. Polyps not fused, connected by basal stolons or a basal mat, sometimes in addition by simple cross connections; skeleton of separate spicules or spicules fused into tubes.

Order 2. Telestacea. Colony consisting of very long axial polyps, bearing lateral polyps as side branches.

Order 3. Alcyonacea, the soft corals. Lower parts of polyp bodies fused into a fleshy mass, from which only the oral ends protrude; at least some of the polyps reaching the colony base; some dimorphic; skeleton of separate calcareous spicules, not axial.

Order 4. Coenothecalia, the blue coral. Skeleton massive, not of fused spicules, containing erect cylindrical cavities for the polyps and the larger solenial tubes.

Order 5. Gorgonacea, the horny corals, gorgonians, sea fans, sea feathers, etc. With an axial skeleton of calcareous spicules, or of gorgonin, or of both; polyps short, equivalent, rarely dimorphic, borne on the sides of the skeletal axis, not reaching the base.

Order 6. Pennatulacea, the sea pens and sea pansies. Colony consisting of one very long axial polyp and of many lateral polyps, always dimorphic, borne on the sides of the axial polyp; lower part of the axial polyp forming a stalk devoid of polyps; skeleton of separate calcareous spicules.

Subclass II. Zoantharia or Hexacorallia. Tentacles simple, rarely branched, if branched, not eight (except *Dendrobrachia*); septa other than in the Alcyonaria; solitary or colonial; skeleton when present not of loose spicules.

Order 1. Actiniaria, the sea anemones. Septa paired, both complete and incomplete, often in multiples of six; usually with one or more siphonoglyphs; solitary, without skeleton, aboral end often a pedal disk. 1000 species.

Order 2. Madreporaria, the true or stony corals. With a compact calcareous exoskeleton, without a siphonoglyph, otherwise as in Actiniaria, solitary or colonial. 2500 species.

Order 3. Zoanthidea. Septal pairs, except directives, mostly consisting of one complete and one incomplete septum; dorsal directives incomplete; one ventral siphonoglyph; solitary or colonial, without skeleton or pedal disk; mostly epizoic.

Order 4. Antipatharia or Antipathidea, the black corals. Colonial with a thorny, horn-like axial skeleton on which the polyps are borne; septa single, complete, 6, 10, or 12 in number; with six simple or eight branched tentacles and two siphonoglyphs. 150 species.

Order 5. Ceriantharia or Cerianthidea. Long, solitary anemone-like forms, without pedal disk, with numerous simple tentacles in two whorls, oral and marginal; septa numerous, single, complete; siphonoglyph single, dorsal.

III. GENERAL MORPHOLOGY AND PHYSIOLOGY

1. General Features.—The Cnidaria contrast with the Porifera, with which they were at one time united, in their definite form, individuality, and symmetry. The entire phylum exhibits radial symmetry, which is *primary*, i.e., continuous throughout ontogeny. The parts are arranged concentrically around the oral-aboral axis.

In the Hydrozoa and Scyphozoa, all diameters are *apolar*, i.e., with like ends, and any two diameters taken at right angles to each other will be alike and will divide the animal into like halves (Fig. 106*G*). In the Anthozoa, however, radial symmetry tends to be strongly modified in a *biradial* or *bilateral* direction chiefly because of the elongation of the mouth and associated structures. In biradial symmetry (Fig. 106*H*), the diameters are still apolar, but that diameter which constitutes the long axis of the mouth, termed the *sagittal axis*, differs from the *transverse axis*, at right angles to it. Either, however, divides the animal into like halves as there is no differentiation into dorsal and ventral surfaces. In many Anthozoa, the sagittal axis is *heteropolar*, its two ends unlike, dorsal and ventral surfaces are then definable, and the halves obtained by bisecting along the transverse axis differ, if only slightly (Fig. 106*J*). Halves exactly alike are obtainable only by bisection along the sagittal axis and a condition of bilateral symmetry therefore exists in such Anthozoa.

As already noted, the phylum comprises two morphological types, the polyp (Fig. 106*A*, *D*) and the medusa (Fig. 106*E*, *F*). The polyp consists of the base, which may be simply thrust into the substratum as a rounded or pointed end but is usually fastened by an adhesive *pedal disk* or by skeletal secretion or by root-like outgrowths, the *stolons;* of the general cylinder, usually termed *column, stem, stalk,* etc.; and of the oral end, which is elongated into a vase-shaped *hydranth* in the Hydrozoa (Fig. 106*A*) or expanded into an *oral disk* in the Anthozoa (Fig. 185*A*). The mouth is circular in hydrozoan polyps, often elongated with a ciliated groove, the *siphonoglyph,* at one or both ends in anthozoan polyps (Fig. 106*H, J*). The tentacles may be irregularly scattered but commonly occur in one to many circlets; they may be hollow or solid and are heavily armed with nematocysts. Tentacles are absent in the minute polyps *Microhydra* (Fig. 143*E*) and *Protohydra* (Fig. 133*A*), in some parasitic hydroids (as *Hydrichthys,* Fig. 136*B*), in the rhizostome medusae (Fig. 172*C*), in the anemone *Limnactinia,* and in some of the modified polyp forms occurring in polymorphic species. These modifications comprise: loss of mouth and coelenteron with emphasis on tentacular functions (*tentaculozooids*); loss of tentacles and digestive system with emphasis on reproduction (*gonozooids*); development of current-producing devices at the expense of other structures (*siphonozooids*). The polyp wall consists of epidermal and gastrodermal epithelia with a mesogloea between, varying from a thin sheet of cement to a mesenchymal or fibrous connective tissue. The simple tubular coelenteron of hydroid polyps is partly divided by four ridges, or *septa,* in the polypoid larva of the Scyphozoa. Continuation of this process results in anthozoan polyps in septal partitions, some or all of which extend from the body wall to the pharynx. The pharynx, limited to Anthozoa, is a stout tube depending from the mouth into the coelenteron.

The medusa form (Fig. 106*E*) resembles a deep to shallow bowl of gelatin, termed the *bell* or *umbrella;* the convex aboral surface is called the *exumbrella,* the concave oral surface, the *subumbrella.* The tentacles and one or more types of sense organs are borne on the umbrella rim. The mouth hangs from the center of the subumbrella on the end of a tubular, entoderm-lined projection, the *manubrium,* which leads into a low *gastric cavity* or *stomach,* occupying the central region of the bell. The stomach is usually a simple chamber in hydromedusae, but in the lower scyphomedusae its periphery is divided into four perradial gastric pouches by the four interradial septa. From the stomach gastrodermal canals, the *radial* canals, usually four or some multiple thereof in number, lead to a *ring* or *circular* canal running in the bell margin. The arrangement of radial canals, tentacles, and sense organs confers upon medusae a conspicuous *tetramerous* radial symmetry (Fig. 106*F, G*). The four radii, 90 degrees apart, on which the four radial canals or other main structures occur, are termed *perradii,* the sectors between them *interradii,* and the midradius of an interradius, an *adradius.* Ex- and subumbrella are lined with an epithelium of ectodermal origin, and the manubrium, radial, and ring canals are lined with an epithelium of entodermal origin; between these two epithelia is a thick layer of jelly, either a mesogloea or a collenchyme.

In hydromedusae, a circular shelf, the *velum,* projects inward from the bell margin partly cutting off the subumbrellar space (Fig. 106*E*),

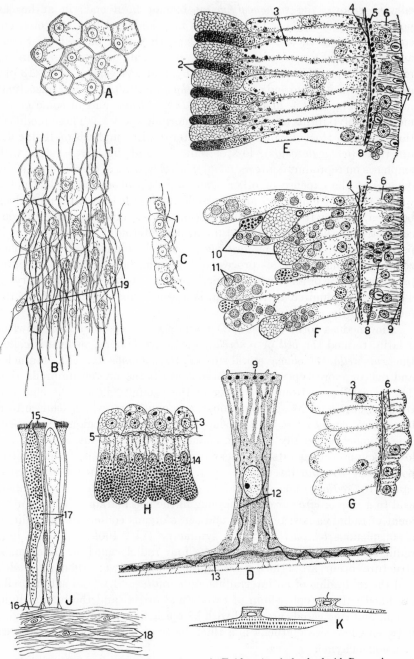

FIG. 107.—Histology of coelenterates.   *A.* Epidermis of the hydroid *Pennaria*, seen from surface view.   *B.* Same seen from the under surface, showing muscle strands.   *C.* Same from the side; obtained by maceration.   *D.* An epitheliomuscular epidermal cell

whence these medusae are known as *veiled* or *craspedote* medusae; the scyphomedusae lack a velum and hence are spoken of as *acraspedote*. The velum contains a highly developed circular muscle band and serves in swimming.

The medusa is the active locomotory stage of the phylum and also is the sexually mature form. Its modifications specialize in one or the other of these two functions. By loss of tentacles, mouth, and reproductive capacity, the medusoid type may become a purely locomotory bell or may be still more modified into a float. On the other hand by gradual degeneration of all structure, the medusoid form comes to serve only for the ripening of the sex cells and ceases to have any independent life.

The Cnidaria are animals of the tissue grade of construction. Anatomically they consist essentially of tissues with no formation of organs except for the somewhat complex sense organs of medusae. The principal tissues of coelenterates are epithelial, muscular, and nervous. The body is composed fundamentally of two epithelia, an outer epidermis of ectodermal origin and an inner gastrodermis of entodermal origin (Fig. 106D). The muscle fibers and nervous tissue occur in the bases of the two epithelia and between the latter is found as a rule some sort of connective tissue.

2. Histology.—The epidermis ("ectoderm") is generally cellular but may be syncytial (Fig. 107). In the former case it consists of epithelial cells (Fig. 107A), also termed *supporting* cells ("Deckzellen" or covering cells in German), which are usually cuboidal or columnar (Fig. 107C–H) but may be very thin and flat as on the exumbrellar surface of medusae or extremely slender and elongated as in anemones (Fig. 107J). Their outer ends frequently bear a layer of granules and may secrete a cuticle or may be ciliated as in anemones (Fig. 107J) or flagellated[1] as in some medusae (Fig. 109G). The cytoplasm generally consists of strands with

---

[1] Workers on coelenterates usually fail to distinguish between cilia and flagella; apparently flagella are rather common in coelenterates and cells and epithelia called ciliated are often really flagellated. In this chapter cells will be spoken of as flagellated when known to be so; otherwise the term ciliated will be employed.

---

of hydra. (*After Gelei*, 1924.) *E–H*. Cross sections of different regions of hydra; *E*, through the hypostome, showing gastrodermal gland cells; *F*, through the stomach region, showing enzymatic gland cells; *G*, through the stalk region, with very vacuolated gastrodermis; *H*, through the pedal disk with epidermal gland cells. *J*. Epidermis and connective-tissue layer of an anemone, from slide. (*Courtesy of A. E. Galigher.*) *K*. Epitheliomuscular cells with striated muscle base from the epidermis of the tentacles of the medusa *Lizzia*. (*After the Hertwigs*, 1879.) 1, muscular base; 2, two types of gland cells; 3, epithelionutritive cells of gastrodermis; 4, muscle bases of same; 5, muscle bases of epidermal cells; 6, epidermis; 7, nematocysts; 8, interstitial cells; 9, granular border of epidermis; 10, types of enzymatic cells of gastrodermis; 11, food vacuoles; 12, supporting fibrils; 13, myoneme of muscular base; 14, epidermal gland cells of pedal disk of hydra; 15, ciliated epidermal cells of anemone; 16, pseudopodial bases of same; 17, mucous gland cells; 18, connective-tissue layer; 19, ganglion cells of epidermis.

fluid-filled spaces between (Fig. 107D). Cell walls are often obscure, and in some coelenterates the epidermis is syncytial. The bases of the epidermal cells reach the mesogloea, to which they are fastened by pseudopodial processes (Fig. 107J). In the epidermis of the exposed parts of hydroid polyps and in that of hydroid medusae except the exumbrellar surface, the cell bases are drawn out into two or more long strands (Fig. 107B) that run in a longitudinal direction just external to or embedded in the mesogloea and contain a contractile fiber or myoneme (Figs. 107D, 108H, and 109H). Supporting cells of this type are called *epitheliomuscular* cells. In the hydras there are always two such basal strands opposite each other with a myoneme extending through them and through the cell base (Fig. 107D). In some Trachylina, and most Scyphozoa and Anthozoa, the bases of the epidermal cells are simply amoeboid and lack contractile extensions (Fig. 107J). Fibrils believed to lend stiffness and elasticity have been found by Gelei (1924) in the epitheliomuscular cells of hydra (Fig. 107D), especially those of the gonads.

The epidermis of tentacles and oral regions always contains an abundance of nematocysts, which with their attendant cnidoblasts are embedded in the supporting cells. Nematocysts also occur in fair numbers in the epidermis of the column or stem of naked polypoid forms and often in the exumbrellar epidermis of medusae, frequently in wart-like clusters or ascending tracts.

Gland cells are frequent in the epidermis of tentacles, oral regions, and the pedal disk (Fig. 107H), and in anthozoans also in the pharynx and exposed parts of the column (Fig. 107J). The epidermis of the pedal disk of hydras consists wholly of gland cells (Fig. 107H) that have muscular basal extensions (hence properly termed *glandulomuscular* cells). In the epidermis of the pedal disk of anemones, supporting cells are scattered among the numerous gland cells. The epidermal gland cells are usually of the *mucous* type, filled with coarse granules before discharge, a network after discharge. The slimy or sticky secretion serves for attachment, protection, entanglement of prey and debris, etc. The second type of coelenterate gland cell, the *granular* type (*Eiweisszellen* of German writers), filled with finer granules or a network, is sparingly present in the surface epidermis although common in the pharyngeal lining (Fig. 185D).

As already mentioned the bases of the epidermal cells in some coelenterates are drawn out into longitudinal muscular strands (Figs. 107B, D, and 109H) which must be thought of as somewhat irregular in shape and arrangement (Fig. 112D). In the remaining coelenterates (Trachylina, Scyphozoa, and Anthozoa) the epidermal muscle fibers usually consist of independent fibers (Fig. 108B, C) that are completely separated from the supporting cells and have sunk into a subepidermal position, forming a layer or bundles close to or embedded in the mesogloea. Such fibers are elongated cells with a central clump containing the nucleus (Fig. 108*B*, *C*). In either the epithelial or independent type of muscle fiber, the fibers may be fastened to the surface of scallops or folds of mesogloea (Fig. 109*G*) and so enormously increased in number; and the independent muscle cells may even sink completely into the mesogloea as bundles consisting of a mesogloeal core coated with a layer of muscle fibers (Figs. 109*C* and 162*E*). The muscle fibers of polypoid coelenterates are generally smooth but in many medusae the circular fibers of velum and subumbrella are cross-striated (Figs. 107*K* and 109*H*) and of complicated cytological structure.

Sensory cells are common in the epidermis of tentacles and oral regions, where they may be interspersed singly between the supporting cells (Fig. 108*J*) or may form, as frequently in medusae, whole patches of sensory epithelium composed chiefly of sensory cells with some supporting cells among them (Fig. 109*A*). The sensory cells of coelenterates are all of the sensory nerve type (page 279), i.e., they are really ganglion cells. They are very elongated cells, smooth or with varicose enlargements, and terminate at or just below the surface in a point or a bulb or one or more bristles or long motile processes resembling flagella (Fig. 109*B*, *E*, *F*). The nucleus occupies a central or basal enlargement. The base of the sensory cells continues into one or more fine fibrils, often beset with varicosities and usually branched; they pass into the general nerve plexus. These sensory nerve cells, sometimes called *palpocils*, presumably serve as general receptors for touch, temperature, chemical qualities, etc., and do not seem to be morphologically differentiated among themselves for these various functions, although in some coelenterates the sense cells of different body parts differ considerably. Free nerve endings having sensory functions and coming from subepithelial sensory ganglion cells have been described for some coelenterates as reaching the surface between the supporting cells; but other workers deny their presence.

The nerve cells, generally called ganglion cells, resemble those of higher animals, being bipolar with two neurites or multipolar with three or more neurites (Figs. 109*G* and 112*A*, *C*). The neurites form slender, often varicose, threads and are not polarized or differentiated into axon and dendrites; they conduct functional impulses in either direction. The epidermal nerve cells are located near the mesogloea and the basal ends of the supporting cells pass through the meshes formed by the neurites (Fig. 109*C*, *G*).

Between or in the supporting cells occur small rounded cells, usually in clumps, the *interstitial* or *indifferent* cells (Fig. 107*E*, *F*), which probably should be regarded as a sort of mesenchyme. They are believed to be

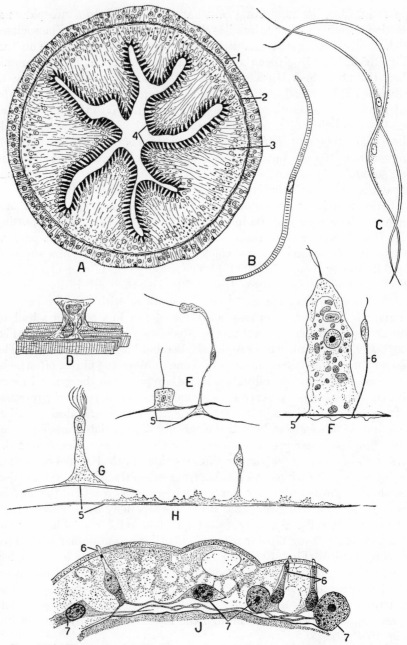

FIG. 108.—Histology of coelenterates (continued). *A.* Cross section through the hypostome of hydra, showing glandular border of the gastrodermis (magnified in Fig. 107*E*). *B.* Independent striated muscle cell of the subumbrellar epidermis of *Lizzia*. *C.* Independent epidermal muscle cells of the oral disk of an anemone. *D.* Subumbrellar

persistent undifferentiated embryonic cells, similar to the archaeocytes of sponges. They arise early in development by the division of ectoderm and entoderm cells, secrete the nematocysts, transform into sex cells and other types of cells, and participate in budding and reparative processes.

The covering layer of coelenterates is thus not a simple epithelium but is composed of three strata: an outer wide stratum comprising the main portions of the supporting cells interspersed with gland and sensory cells, a nervous stratum on a level with the bases of these cells, and an innermost muscle stratum, next to or embedded in the mesogloea (Fig. 109C, G). This stratification is very evident in some coelenterates, notably the Anthozoa, but exists in all and foreshadows the body wall of higher animals, especially if we consider the interstitial cells to constitute a kind of connective tissue.

The gastrodermis ("entoderm") has much the same construction as the epidermis. It consists mainly of large cuboidal or columnar epithelial cells (Fig. 107E–H) called nutritive cells, or nutritive-muscular cells when their bases are drawn out into extensions containing a myoneme (Fig. 108E, F, G). The gastrodermis is markedly columnar and often thrown into folds in those regions where digestion occurs but elsewhere tends to a flattened form. Its cells are generally highly vacuolated and in digestive regions their free ends are filled with food vacuoles and indigestible food remnants (Fig. 107F). The free tips of the nutritive cells bear flagella (Fig. 108E–G), usually two in number, which in older accounts are said to be of pseudopodial nature and readily withdrawn and reformed. Burch (1928), however, finds that they are typical flagella with basal bodies. Throughout polypoid coelenterates the bases of the nutritive cells are drawn out into contractile extensions that run in a circular direction next to the mesogloea. In medusoid forms the gastrodermis usually lacks muscular extensions or a muscular layer, but in Anthozoa the gastrodermal muscles are more strongly developed than the epidermal ones and run in both circular and longitudinal directions. Although gastrodermal muscle fibers are nearly always parts of the gastrodermal cells, they may in Anthozoa separate as independent fibers and in either case may be adherent to folds or plates of mesogloea.

The gastrodermis contains gland and sensory cells similar to those of the epidermis. Near the mouth, gland cells of the mucous type are very

epidermal muscle cell of *Carmarina* (Trachymedusae) with several striated muscle bases. (*After Krasinska*, 1914.) *E.* Gastrodermal nutritive-muscular cells with muscle bases, contracted and extended, from the tentacles of the anemone *Sagartia*. *F.* Nutritive-muscular cell with basal myoneme, and adjacent gastrodermal sensory cell of hydra. (*After Hadzi*, 1909.) *G.* Gastrodermal, and *H*, epidermal epitheliomuscular cells with basal myonemes, tentacles of *Cerianthus.* *J.* Epidermis of the oral disk of hydra, showing sensory nerve cells and ganglion cells of the epidermal nerve net. (*After Hadzi*, 1909.) (*B, C, E, G, H after the Hertwigs*, 1879.) 1, epidermis; 2, layer of muscle bases; 3, gastrodermis; 4, gland cells; 5, myoneme; 6, sensory nerve cell; 7, ganglion cells.

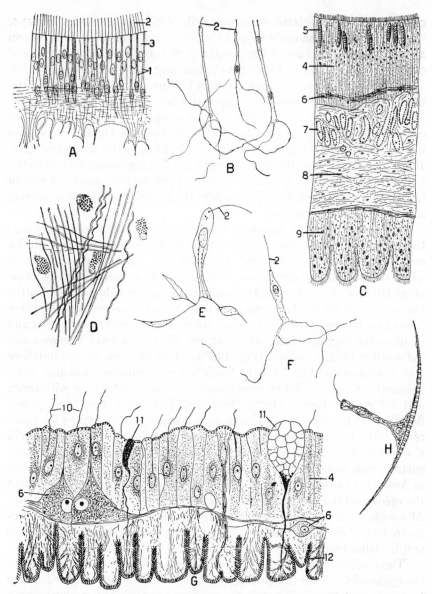

Fig. 109.—Coelenterate histology (continued). *A.* Sensory epithelium, sensory pit on the rhopalium of *Rhizostoma* (Scyphozoa). (*After Hesse*, 1895.)   *B.* Epidermal sensory nerve cells, anemone tentacle.   *C.* Cross section of an anemone tentacle, showing muscle bundles in the fibrous layer.   *D.* Collenchyme of the medusa *Periphylla* (Scyphozoa) showing cells and fibers.   *E.* A gastrodermal sensory nerve cell of hydra. (*After Burch*, 1928.)   *F.* A gastrodermal sensory nerve cell of an anemone. (*B, C, F after the Hertwigs*, 1879.)   *G.* Section through the subumbrellar epidermis of *Pelagia* (Scyphozoa), showing flagellated epidermis, epidermal nerve net, and striated muscle bases mounted on collen- chymal folds.   *H.* A single epidermal cell isolated showing striated muscle base.   (*G and h*

abundant (Figs. 107E and 108A) and may as in the hydras crowd the nutritive-muscular cells to a basal position. They are elongated cells with conical free ends containing the nucleus and secretion granules and a slender base reaching the mesogloea (Fig. 107E, F). They are often of two types, a more slender, dark type containing granules and a broader, paler type filled with a network (Fig. 107E, F); but these may represent different secretion phases of the same kind of gland cells. These mucous cells of the oral gastrodermis are said to be flagellated and to have muscular basal extensions. Their secretion presumably assists in the swallowing of food. In digestive regions the gastrodermis is liberally sprinkled with gland cells of the granular type (Fig. 107F), believed to secrete digestive enzymes. These again taper from a broad free end, which may be flagellated, to a slender base, which may or may not reach the mesogloea. Often these enzymatic gland cells also appear to be of two sorts, a darker granular type and a lighter type with a net-like interior. It is highly probable that some of the presumed gland cells of coelenterates are really storage cells.

Sensory cells similar in appearance to those of the epidermis are not uncommon in the gastrodermis (Fig. 108F). Nematocysts are absent from the general gastrodermis but thickly crowded in certain special structures found in the gastrovascular cavity of Scyphozoa and Anthozoa: the gastric filaments, the septal filaments, and the acontia. Interstitial cells occur sparingly between the bases of the nutritive cells, and in the same location a nerve net, usually less developed than that of the epidermis, may be present. The gastrodermis often contains symbiotic cells, sometimes zoochlorellae as in the green hydra, more often zooxanthellae or "yellow cells"; the latter are especially abundant in corals and anemones.

Between epidermis and gastrodermis lies the mesogloea, so different in the various classes that more exact terms should be employed for it. In hydrozoan polyps it is devoid of cells or fibers and consists of a thin gelatinous membrane for which we may suggest the name *mesolamella*. In medusae, the mesogloea, resembling gelatin, constitutes the bulk of the animal. It is devoid or nearly so of cellular elements in hydromedusae, although crossed by fibers of unknown origin. For such a noncellular gelatinous material, the name *mesogloea* seems really appropriate. The mesogloea of scyphomedusae contains fibers and scattered amoeboid cells (Fig. 109D) and hence is more correctly termed a *collenchyme*. In all medusae, a mesolamella separates the general mass of the mesogloea from both epidermis and gastrodermis. The mesogloea reaches its

after Krasinska, 1914.)   1, sensory nerve cells; 2, sensory hairs of same; 3, epidermal cells between the sensory cells; 4, epidermis; 5, nematocysts of same; 6, epidermal nerve net; 7, muscle bundles; 8, fibrous layer; 9, gastrodermis; 10, flagella of epidermis; 11, gland cells; 12, muscle fibers.

highest differentiation in the Anthozoa, where it is always cellular and varies from a *mesenchyme* consisting of stellate amoeboid cells embedded in a jelly to a *fibrous connective tissue* (Fig. 107*J*) often made of several layers of fibers coursing in different directions, among which are dispersed amoebocytes and connective-tissue cells.

According to the old data of Krukenberg, the mesogloea of medusae (*Aequorea, Rhizostoma*) yields neither gelatin nor mucin and thus is chemically unrelated to connective tissue. The term gelatinous as applied to medusae is then to be taken in a purely descriptive sense. Entire medusae (*Rhizostoma, Aurelia, Chrysaora*) were found to contain 95 to 96 per cent water (not 99.8 per cent as sometimes stated). Teissier (1932) records 96.5 per cent water for *Chrysaora* and the author found around 96.5 per cent for a variety of medusae. In *Cassiopeia*, the water content of the jelly is 94.6 per cent, of the cellular parts, 93.8 per cent (Hatai). The water content of medusae is somewhat dependent on that of the surrounding medium. The data just given apply to sea water of typical salinity and indicate that under such conditions the water content is 94 to 96.5 per cent. In very brackish water, however, with a salt content of less than half that of typical sea water, the water content may rise to 98 per cent (Thill). The solid material of the jelly consists chiefly of salts with probably less than 1 per cent of organic material, mostly protein. From the low nitrogen content of this protein, Hatai suspects that it is chitin.

3. The Nematocysts.—These remarkable structures, also called *stinging cells* and *nettle cells*, are diagnostic of the Cnidaria. They are not cells, but cell organoids and are probably composed of a substance similar to chitin. They are spherical, oval, pyriform, or elongated capsules, generally rounded at one end, narrowed or pointed at the other, containing a coiled tube (usually called "thread") that is fastened to the narrower end and is there continuous with the capsule wall. This attached end of the tube is covered by a little lid or *operculum*. There are two sorts of nematocysts, the *spirocysts* and the nematocysts proper. The spirocysts, limited to the Zoantharia, have thin single-walled capsules, stain with acid dyes, are permeable to water, and contain a long spirally coiled unarmed tube of even diameter (Fig. 110*B, C*). The nematocysts proper, found throughout the phylum, have thick double-walled capsules, stain with basic dyes, are impermeable to water except at discharge, and contain a tube of varied length and construction usually armed at least in part by spiral rows of thorns. Both spirocysts and nematocysts discharge by the eversion (turning inside out) of the tube to the exterior.

The spirocysts are all alike, but the nematocysts occur in numerous varieties whose characteristics have been intensively studied in recent years by R. Weill. He has recognized seventeen different types of nematocysts, based on the characters of the discharged tube. The tube may be a slender filament of the same diameter throughout, or its basal portion may be enlarged into a long or short cylinder, here called *butt* (as the nearest English equivalent of Weill's term *hampe*). The tube may consist only of this butt or may continue beyond the butt as a slender "thread." The butt may present a swollen enlargement either distally or proximally. The tube always bears on its outer surface three spiral ridges that spiral in a clockwise direction if one looks along the tube from the capsular end. Commonly a row of spines or thorns is mounted on each ridge for part or the whole extent of the tube. These spines may be of the same size throughout the tube or larger on the butt or on the swellings of the butt. In some types of nematocysts only the butt is armed with spines, in others the spines are limited to the tube beyond the butt. Presumably the type of nematocyst with a slender tube of even diameter throughout and armed along its whole length with three spiral rows of equal small spines represents the original kind from which varieties with a butt or swelling or unequal size or distribution of spines have been derived.

In undischarged capsules, the tube is usually definitely arranged inside, and this arrangement as well as the features of the discharged tube may serve as a taxonomic character. The butt when present appears as a central rod in the interior of the undischarged capsule, more or less encircled by the coils of the remaining more slender portion of the tube. Since the tube turns inside out on discharge, the armature in the unexploded state is found on its inner surface and is usually not noticeable unless the spines are large.

Weill's classification of nematocysts, based on a study of 119 species belonging to all groups of coelenterates, should prove highly valuable, despite the somewhat formidable names. We here give his main categories:

    I. Tube closed at the end.
        1. *Rhopalonemes*, tube an elongated sac (Fig. 110*A*).
        2. *Desmonemes*, tube thread-like, forming a coil like a corkscrew, also called volvents (Fig. 110*D, H*).
    II. Tube open at the tip, without a butt (haplonemes).
      A. Tube of the same diameter throughout, *isorhizas*, also called glutinants.
        3. *Holotrichous isorhizas*, tube spiny throughout (Fig. 110*F, K*).
        4. *Atrichous isorhizas*, tube devoid of spines (Fig. 110*E, L*).
        5. *Basitrichous isorhizas*, tube spiny at base only.
      B. Tube slightly dilated toward the base, *anisorhizas* (Fig. 110*S*).
        6. *Homotrichous anisorhizas*, spiny throughout, spines equal.
        7. *Heterotrichous anisorhizas*, spiny throughout, spines larger at base (Fig. 110*S*).

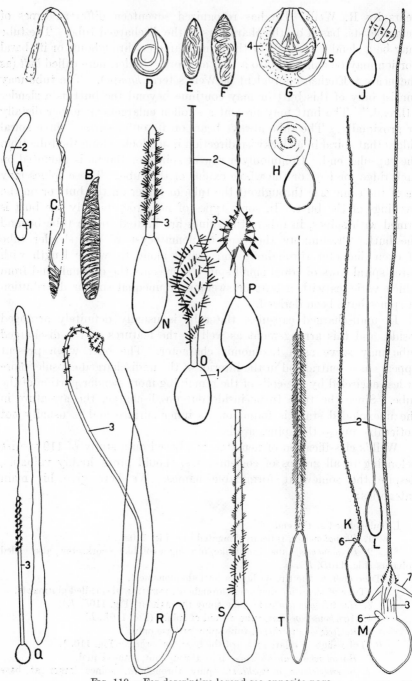

Fig. 110.—For descriptive legend see opposite page.

III. Tube open at tip with a definite butt (heteronemes).

   A. Butt cylindrical, of the same diameter throughout (rhabdoids).

      8. *Microbasic mastigophores,* tube continued beyond the butt, butt not more than three times the capsule length (Fig. 110*T*).

      9. *Macrobasic mastigophores,* as 8, butt four or more times the capsule length (Fig. 110*Q*).

      10. *Microbasic amastigophores,* no tube beyond the butt, butt short as in 8 (Fig. 110*N*).

      11. *Macrobasic amastigophores,* no tube beyond butt, butt long as in 9.

   B. Butt dilated at the summit, euryteles.

      12. *Homotrichous microbasic euryteles,* butt short, spines of butt of equal size (Fig. 110*O*).

      13. *Heterotrichous microbasic euryteles,* butt short, spines unequal on butt (Fig. 110*P*).

      14. *Telotrichous macrobasic euryteles,* butt long, with only distal spines (Fig. 110*R*).

      15. *Merotrichous macrobasic euryteles,* butt long, spines elsewhere than at the ends.

   C. Butt dilated at its base.

      16.[1] *Stenoteles,* also called penetrants (Fig. 110*G, M*).

Rhopalonemes occur only in the Siphonophora. The desmonemes or volvents are found in the hydras, the tubularian hydroids, and some siphonophores. The thick tube on discharge forms a close coil of several turns (five in the hydras) and is employed chiefly in wrapping around bristles (Fig. 111*H*) or other projecting parts of the prey. Minute thorns (Fig. 110*H, J*) occur on the inner side of the coil. In all the other sorts of nematocysts, the tube is open at the tip and is believed to inject a paralyzing substance into the prey. The isorhizas that discharge a simple long slender tube armed or not with spiral rows of spines, often difficult to see, are of wide occurrence, found in hydras, other hydroids, medusae, corals, and anemones. Atrichous isorhizas without spines are characteristic of the Narcomedusae, the Scyphozoa, and the Alcyonaria, and basitrichous isorhizas with basal spines are of common occurrence in

---

[1] Weill recognizes two kinds of rhopalonemes, here omitted, bringing the number of kinds of nematocysts to 17.

Fig. 110.—Nematocyst types. *A.* Rhopaloneme of *Diphyes* (Siphonophora). *B.* Spirocyst of an anemone, from life. *C.* Same, unraveling (not discharged). *D–M.* The nematocysts of hydra (*Hydra littoralis*), from life: *D–G,* undischarged; *D,* desmoneme; *E,* atrichous hydrorhiza; *F,* holotrichous isorhiza; *G,* stenotele inside its cnidoblast; *H–M,* same, discharged; *H,* desmoneme seen from end view showing spiral of thorns; *J,* desmoneme seen from the side; *K,* holotrichous isorhiza; *L,* atrichous isorhiza; *M,* stenotele. *N.* Microbasic amastigophore of the anemone *Sagartia.* *O.* Homotrichous microbasic eurytele of *Pteroclava* (Anthomedusae). *P.* Heterotrichous microbasic eurytele of *Eudendrium.* *Q.* Macrobasic mastigophore of *Millepora.* *R.* Telotrichous macrobasic eurytele of *Pteroclava.* *S.* Heterotrichous anisorhiza of *Tubularia.* *T.* Microbasic mastigophore of an anemone, from life. (*A* and *N–S, after Weill,* 1934. A line at the top indicates that only a part of the tube is shown.) 1, capsule; 2, tube; 3, butt; 4, cnidoblast; 5, its nucleus; 6, lid; 7, stylet.

hydroids and anemones. The mastigophores in which there is a spiny cylindrical butt followed by a slender tube are typical of anemones, zoanthids, and corals, especially the microbasic variety. The amastigophores, differing in the absence of a tube beyond the butt, have the general appearance of a bottle brush and are very characteristic of anemones. The euryteles, with a bulbous swelling at the distal end of the butt, occur in the tubularian hydroids, the Trachymedusae, and the Scyphozoa. The microbasic heterotrichous sort is the most common. The stenotele, or penetrant, is the best-known type of nematocyst, commonly figured in textbooks. It has a relatively large rounded or oval capsule with an obvious lid, a short stout butt about the same length as the capsule, and a long slender tube bearing spirals of small spines. The butt consists of a basal swelling devoid of spines and a distal section bearing three spiral rows of thorns, of which the lowermost one is large and conspicuous and termed a *stylet*. The stenoteles are limited to the class Hydrozoa where they are found in the hydras and other tubularian hydroids, the Milleporina, and the Siphonophora.

The complicated structure of nematocysts is all the more astounding when their minute size is considered. Most capsules range between 5 and 50 $m\mu$ in length and discharge a tube so fine that the details of the spination are often very difficult to ascertain. Larger capsules occur in anemones, corals, and siphonophores. Weill (1934) reports a length of 0.25 mm. for the capsules of the anemone *Actinotryx*, and Iwanzoff (1896) found the capsules of the siphonophore *Halistemma* to reach a length of 1.12 mm., the largest nematocysts known. Such big nematocysts discharge a tube several millimeters long.

The nematocysts are all of one single sort in the Trachylina, the Stylasterina, and some forms scattered in other groups. Other coelenterates have two to four kinds of nematocysts (even five or six in siphonophores), and different types may be found in different stages of the life cycle. The hydras (Fig. 110*D–M*) all have four kinds of nematocysts (desmonemes, stenoteles, holotrichous isorhizas, and atrichous isorhizas). When two or more kinds are present, some types are often more abundant than others, and frequently particular sorts are limited to specific locations in the body, or the various types may be grouped in more or less definite patterns. The studies of Weill have proved the great value of the nematocyst tube as a taxonomic character and as an aid in determining relationships between coelenterate groups and genera. Since groups recognized on other grounds to constitute natural assemblages are found to have similar or identical nematocyst types, it follows that nematocyst characters may be utilized to establish relationships in doubtful cases. Various examples of the application of this principle will appear in the following pages.

The nematocysts are formed inside interstitial cells, which are then termed *cnidoblasts* or *nematocytes*. Because of the minute size of the forming nematocysts as well as other difficulties, the process is not thoroughly understood. The inner wall of the capsule is secreted inside a vacuole that appears in the interior of the cnidoblast, and the outer wall is added later by the cnidoblast. Inside the capsule an elongated body appears, and this differentiates into the tube; the former belief that the tube developed outside the capsule and was later invaginated into the capsule is erroneous (Weill). Meantime the cnidoblast itself undergoes a remarkable differentiation. It becomes fixed in the epidermis by a slender stalk (branched in *Carmarina*) reaching the mesogloea (Fig. 111*B–E*). Its distal part contains the nematocyst, so oriented that the end of discharge lies near the free surface of the cnidoblast. From this surface near the tip of the nematocyst projects a bristle, the *cnidocil*, set in a crater-like elevation often encircled by stiff rods (Fig. 111*A–C*). The cnidocils vary in length with different types of nematocysts. In the periphery of the cnidoblast there usually occurs a circlet of stiff rods probably of a supporting nature and also in many cases a circlet or basketwork of often sinuous fibrils (Fig. 111*A–C*), which extend down the stalk of the cnidoblast to terminate on the mesogloea or to unite to a single fiber so fastened. In the stenoteles of hydras a similar coiled fiber has been termed the "lasso." Many investigators consider this system of fibrils to be contractile, and it is certain that they are of this nature in some coelenterates, as *Physalia*.

Nematocysts commonly develop in regions distant from those where they are to be utilized. Thus the tentacular nematocysts of hydroids originate in interstitial cells of the hydranth body or stem. In medusae the basal enlargements of the tentacles are regular sites of nematocyst formation. The cnidoblasts containing developing nematocysts then migrate by amoeboid movements or are passively transported through the body wall or by way of the gastrovascular cavity to their final situations, being able to traverse the mesolamella. The differentiation of the cnidoblast is completed after the final location is attained.

Nematocysts are most abundant on tentacles where they are usually grouped on warts, knobs, and circular or spiral ridges. In some medusae of the family Cladonemidae the tentacles bear *cnidophores*, contractile stalks having an enlarged hollow tip filled with nematocysts (Fig. 111*G*). In hydras and some other hydroid polyps, the nematocysts of the tentacles occur in groups known as *batteries*. Each battery consists of one or two stenoteles encircled by a number of desmonemes and isorhizas and is enclosed within a single epidermal cell (Fig. 111*F*). Nematocysts are also quite abundant in the epidermis of the oral region but diminish basally, being scanty or absent in aboral regions and absent where the

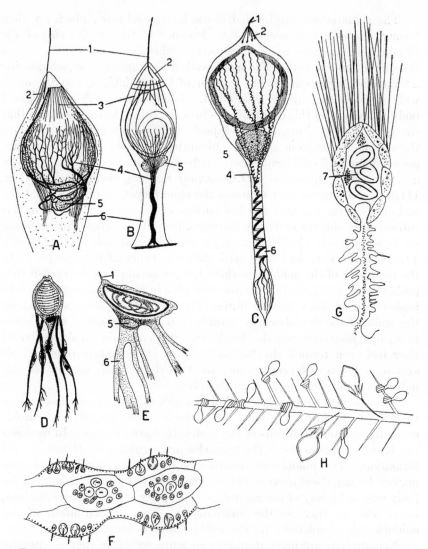

Fig. 111.—Nematocysts (continued).   A and B. Cnidoblasts of *Hydra vulgaris* with contained nematocysts.   A. Stenotele, and B, desmoneme, showing supporting and contractile fibrils.   (*After Gelei*, 1924.)   C. Cnidoblast of *Physalia*, with contractile fibrils. (*After Will*, 1909.)   D. Cnidoblast of *Pelagia*, with several nucleated attachments.   (*After Krasinska*, 1914.)   E. Cnidoblast of *Carmarina*, with a branched stalk.   (*After Iwanzoff*, 1896.)   F. Magnified bit of hydra tentacle, showing epidermal cells with batteries, from life.   G. A cnidophore of *Gemmaria* (see Fig. 121E).   (*After Weill*, 1934.)   H. Tail bristle of a *Cyclops*, pulled away after being captured by hydra, showing desmonemes wound around the hairs, and two stenoteles puncturing the bristle, from life.   1, cnidocil; 2, supporting rods of cnidocil; 3, supporting rods of cnidoblast; 4, fibrillar system, probably contractile; 5, nucleus of cnidoblast; 6, stalk of cnidoblast; 7, nematocysts in hollow end of cnidophore.

body is covered by exoskeleton. They are extremely abundant on internal tentacle-like structures: the gastric filaments, the septal filaments, and the acontia.

The discharge or explosion is believed to result from the proper stimulation of the cnidocil, in nature by the touching of the cnidocil by food, prey, or enemy animals. Both chemical and mechanical factors appear to be involved. In hydra, the juice of *Daphnia* will not discharge the nematocysts (Zick) and in anemones filtered extract of fish skin is but mildly effective (Parker). Most coelenterates react to and swallow pieces of animal flesh or objects soaked in animal juice, but it is not clear whether the nematocysts are discharged to such objects. It is stated, however, that the nematocysts of anemones discharge to pieces cut from other species of anemones but not to pieces of the same species. Other facts indicate that mechanical factors are involved in the stimulation, although touching the cnidocils with a glass rod or other object evokes little or no discharge. Certain nematocysts (desmonemes) are said to discharge only to bristly prey, others only to smooth surfaces. In hydras, the nematocysts are not stimulated by the commensal ciliates (*Kerona, Trichodina*), which run about on the surface and can be seen to bend the cnidocils, but do discharge to other ciliates of similar or even smaller size (Zick). Apparently the cnidocils react primarily to the general mechanical features of objects as texture and shape and secondarily to their chemical emanations. Neither idea, however, explains the fact that when coelenterates are satiated with food the nematocysts apparently fail to explode against the usual food animals. This fact together with some of those just cited have led some authors to postulate a nervous factor in the discharge. Some workers have described nerve endings embracing the nematocyst or an intimate association of sensory cells with nematocysts, but others have failed to find such nervous connections. Further, discharge is strictly local, limited to the region directly stimulated and not transmitted to other regions. Parker's observation that the nematocysts of completely anesthetized anemones discharge as usual indicates an independence of nervous control; but in *Physalia*, where a contraction of the cnidoblast is involved in the discharge, anesthesia inhibits discharge. On the whole, the mechanism of the explosion appears to be nonnervous. Nematocysts isolated from their cnidoblasts do not discharge to natural stimuli (although they can be exploded artificially), and consequently in nature the stimulus is transmitted directly from the cnidocil to the cnidoblast, which then effects some change in the capsular wall.

At discharge, the lid springs open and the tube turns inside out; its base, being continuous with the capsule wall, emerges first, and the rest then follows from base to tip. As the tube everts, the spines unfold to the outside.   In most cases there also issue spiral bands of an adhesive substance (visible only after staining), which swells in water.   Nematocysts can be used only once and after discharge are cast off.

The mechanism of the discharge is uncertain, although evidently the immediate factor is an increased pressure inside the capsule, forcing the tube out.   According to the oldest and most acceptable theory (Iwanzoff, 1896), this increased pressure results from the passage of water into the capsule, augmenting the contents or possibly causing the swelling of a contained colloid.   That the surrounding fluid does enter the capsule on discharge can be proved by using colored solutions (e.g., vital dyes) as agents.   Further, discharge takes place only in a fluid medium.   As the capsules are normally impermeable to water, the stimulation received from cnidocil and cnidoblast must act by increasing the permeability of the capsular wall.   Iwanzoff's theory is supported by experiments in artificially discharging the capsules (Glaser and Sparrow, 1909; Weill, 1934).   Among effective agents may be listed mechanical agitation, uneven pressure, heat, electricity, dilute acids and bases, vital dyes, and dilute solutions or distilled water following more concentrated solutions. Such agents act by injuring the capsule wall, by penetrating directly as in the case of acids and bases, or by a simple osmotic action, in any case involving penetration of fluid into the capsule.   Solutions such as glycerin, xylol, formalin, absolute alcohol, chloroform, and hypertonic solutions are without effect.   A second theory attributes the discharge to the contraction of the fibrillar elements, assumed to be muscular, seen in the cnidoblast.   This factor apparently operates in some cases, as in *Physalia* (G. H. Parker), but the fibrillar systems observed in many nematocysts are not definitely known to be contractile.   A third theory, that of Will (1914), grants the initiation of the discharge by water intake but assigns the completion of the discharge to the swelling of the adhesive material seen clinging to the everted tube.   The mechanics of this theory are obscure, and it has gained little acceptance.   Intake of water into the capsule plus the assistance in some cases of a cnidoblast contraction is the most satisfactory theory on present facts.   The discharge of spirocysts is not understood, as these are normally permeable to water and do not explode on treatments effective with nematocysts; in fact it appears that the natural discharge has never been witnessed, and consequently the function of spirocysts is enigmatical.

Different types of nematocysts apparently serve different purposes. Thus the types with closed ends, as rhopalonemes and desmonemes, can evidently act only for holding prey (Fig. 111*H*).   The atrichous isorhizas of hydra are adhesive, acting to attach the tentacles in locomotion, but the function of the holotrichous isorhizas remains uncertain.   Types with an open tube and a strong armature of spines such as the mastigophores, amastigophores, euryteles, and above all the stenoteles seem adapted for penetration and anchorage in the tissues of prey animals. Direct observation has shown that the tube may penetrate for some distance into soft tissues and can pass through chitinous armor. The capsular contents are ejected from the open tip of the tube. Weill was unable to demonstrate any definite change of volume of the nematocyst on discharge.

The nature of the material ejected from the nematocyst tube is unknown. It is obviously toxic in the majority of nematocysts, having a paralyzing action on the prey and in some cases evoking a burning sensation in the human skin. A number of studies have been made of the physiological action of extracts of coelenterate tentacles and acontia. Different results have been obtained with different methods of extraction. Thus watery extracts of the tentacles of *Physalia, Velella*, medusae and anemones induce somnolence, anesthesia, and death in small experimental animals. Ingestion of dried *Physalia* tentacles is said to be fatal to small vertebrates. This anesthetizing toxin has been named *hypnotoxin*. Alcoholic extracts of nematocyst-bearing parts of anemones produce another set of symptoms—extreme itching and skin irritation in small doses, severe digestive disturbances, prostration, and death in larger doses. The supposed substance having this action was named *thalassin* by its discoverer (Richet, 1902). Still a third group of symptoms, ascribed to a substance *congestin*, has been obtained from glycerin extracts of anemone tentacles, consisting of extreme congestion of the digestive tract with severe digestive disturbances, and death from respiratory interference. These toxins appear to be proteins or mixtures of proteins,[1] and congestin, at least, yields a typical anaphylactic reaction, i.e., light doses become fatal if injected at a 2- to 3-week interval. That an immunity can also be established to these poisons is indicated in the case of the anemone *Adamsia* and the hermit crab to which it regularly attaches (Fig. 195A). Extracts of the tentacles and acontia of *Adamsia* cause tetany and death in the decapod Crustacea on which *Adamsia* regularly feeds, including members of the same genus as the commensal hermit crab; but the latter is entirely immune to the poison, probably through having eaten nematocyst-containing fragments dropped by the anemone. Furthermore, the body fluid of immune crabs can confer immunity on other Crustacea and can neutralize the toxin. Finally may be mentioned tetramine (tetramethylammonium hydroxide), which has been extracted from anemones, probably coming from their nematocysts, and which acts like curare, paralyzing motor-nerve endings.

On the whole it must be concluded that the nature of the nematocyst toxin is unknown, since the extracts mentioned above included tissues

[1] The statement often seen that the nematocyst poison is formic acid has no basis.

as well as nematocysts, and this may account for their protein nature and reactions. Cantacuzene has recently stated (1934) that extracts of *Adamsia* acontia retain their toxic properties after deproteinization.

The "sting" of the majority of the coelenterates is not perceptible to man. This is especially true of the Hydrozoa, which may be handled with impunity, except the Milleporina and the Siphonophora, and also applies to most Anthozoa. The millepores and some corals and gorgonians produce a stinging sensation of short duration, and the sponge divers of the Mediterranean suffer much from skin lesions and deep wounds of the hands caused by an anemone that lives among the sponges. Some siphonophores are very dangerous, and members of this group should not be handled. Most Scyphozoa are harmful and should be approached with caution. *Cyanea*, a common jellyfish of American shores, produces a burning sensation. The most dangerous Scyphozoa are *Dactylometra* and *Chiropsalmus*, inhabitants of warmer waters, whose sting can cause very serious illness and even death. Probably the most dangerous coelenterate is the siphonophore *Physalia* (Portuguese man-of-war) whose long trailing tentacles can inflict severe pain. The injury from these last three coelenterates ranges from a burning pain at the site of contact with the tentacles through skin lesions and eruptions of various sorts, often severe enough to leave scars, to general great pain, fever, prostration, and respiratory interference. It is highly probable that the serious syndrome sometimes resulting from coelenterate stings is actually anaphylactic shock in cases where the victim may have been stung on previous occasions by the same species or may be peculiarly sensitive to the proteins involved.

4. Digestion.—The main features of the digestive system were already considered. It is an epithelial sac, simple or more or less subdivided by septa in polyp types, consisting of a central stomach and radiating canals joining a marginal canal in medusoid types. In Scyphozoa the septa bear nematocyst-containing threads, the *gastric filaments*, and in Anthozoa the free edges of the septa are provided with a sinuous cord, the *septal filament*, beset with gland cells and nematocysts. The gastrovascular system is continuous throughout colonial forms.

The phylum is strictly carnivorous; the food consists of living animals or bodies of animals that on coming in contact with the tentacles are held and paralyzed by the nematocysts aided by adhesive secretions. If the prey is large or troublesome additional tentacles are brought into action. When the prey is subdued, the tentacles holding it shorten and bend toward the mouth, which opens widely to receive it; or in many cases the opened mouth also moves toward the food. The food grasped by the mouth rim is engulfed by ciliary or muscular action or both, aided by mucous secretion from the pharynx or from the gastrodermis of the manubrium.

Some anthozoans, however, employ a mucous-ciliary method in which small food objects are entangled in mucous strands and conveyed to the mouth by ciliary action. The bodies of coelenterates are highly distensible and surprisingly large objects can be swallowed. Coelenterates exercise considerable discrimination between food and other objects and even between different kinds of animal food; but some will accept nonnutritive bodies and most will take such when soaked in flesh juices. When satiated with food, coelenterates generally fail to react to additional food or drop it after capture and often remain in a contracted state until digestion is completed.

Digestion in the phylum is both extra- and intracellular. Extracellular digestion occurs in the main part of the gastrovascular cavity and is purely proteolytic. A protein-digesting enzyme of the nature of trypsin, acting in alkaline medium, is secreted into the cavity by the granular gland cells of the gastrodermis, in anthozoans primarily by those of the septal filaments. In some species it is stated that direct contact of the gastrodermis with the food is necessary for this preliminary digestion. By extracellular digestion the food is reduced to a sort of broth containing fragments and both fluid and fragments are then engulfed phagocytically into food vacuoles by the general gastrodermis. Intracellular digestion then proceeds in regular protozoan fashion; the contents of the vacuoles are first acid, then alkaline. In the vacuoles, the digestion of protein is completed by other types of proteolytic enzymes, fat is digested, and in some cases carbohydrates, but most coelenterates cannot digest starches.

Digestion is often rapid; the fleshy parts of prey may be broken down in a few hours and the resulting broth completely engulfed by the gastrodermis in 8 to 12 hours. Undigestible parts are then ejected through the mouth. Intracellular digestion within the gastrodermis requires a longer period, usually a few days. Excess food is stored in the gastrodermis chiefly as fat; glycogen may be stored without change.

5. The Muscular System.—The coelenterates are the simplest Metazoa possessing a muscular system, since in sponges muscles occur only as localized groups of cells. We may therefore seek in coelenterates the most primitive state of the muscular system. This we find in hydroid polyps, where the muscular system consists of two cylinders of muscle fibers, an outer one of longitudinal fibers located at the base of the epidermis and an inner one of circular fibers at the base of the gastrodermis. These must not be thought of as definite regular cylinders but as composed of short irregularly spaced strands, which anastomose to some extent (Fig. 112D). In hydroid polyps the fibers of both cylinders are parts of the epithelial cells. The transformation of the base of an epithelial cell into a contractile fibril is commonly regarded as the initial

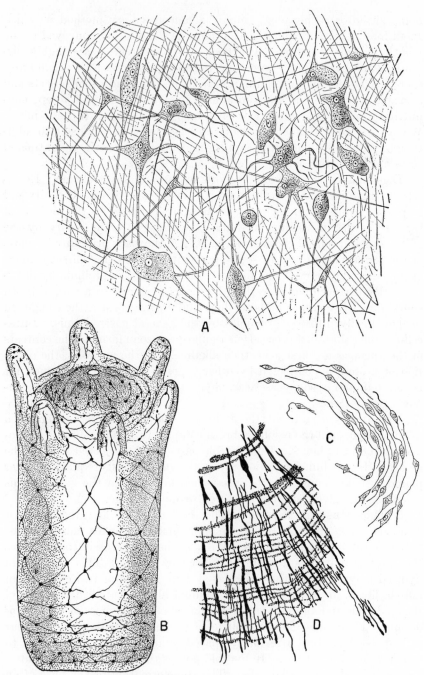

Fɪɢ. 112.— For descriptive legend see opposite page.

step in the differentiation of a muscle cell, but in sponges cells transform directly into muscle cells without any such preliminary epitheliomuscular stage.   The longitudinal fibers contract the animal as a whole or, through local contraction, can bend the body or its parts in any direction; the circular fibers on contraction extend the animal or its parts and bring about peristaltic waves aiding in locomotion, food swallowing, etc.   The system, simple as it is, suffices for the needs of sessile radial animals.

The presence of longitudinal and circular muscle cylinders can be recognized throughout the phylum.   In medusoid forms, the gastrodermal cylinder is nearly or quite absent, and the regular epidermal cylinder is also reduced, being limited to longitudinal fibers in tentacles and manubrium, and radial fibers in the subumbrella.   The principal musculature of medusae consists of extra epidermal muscle cells, which run in a circular direction in velum and subumbrella.   In the Anthozoa, on the other hand, the epidermal system is reduced in most cases to fibers in tentacles and oral disk, while the regular gastrodermal layer is widely present and strengthened by the addition of highly developed longitudinal bands.   As already noted (page 376) the muscle fibers in many Anthozoa and Scyphozoa have separated completely from the body epithelia as independent muscle cells.   In these two groups also the muscle cells or fibers often depart from the simple cylindrical arrangement and instead may be festooned (Fig. 109G) on plates of mesogloea penetrating the epithelia or may sink into the mesogloea as bundles (Fig. 109C).

In pedal and oral disks the epidermal fibers run in a radial direction, the gastrodermal fibers in a circular direction (Fig. 112D).

6. Respiration.—The coelenterates are devoid of any special respiratory mechanism.   The thin wall and tentacular extensions undoubtedly facilitate respiratory exchange.   Another assisting factor is the shifting of the gastrovascular contents by body movements and the flagellar beat of the gastrodermis.   In at least some medusae regular flagellar currents flow along the canal system, and in many Anthozoa the interior is bathed by a stream of water passed inside by the ciliated siphonoglyph.   In scyphozoans there are four deep pits indented into the subumbrella; it is generally supposed these serve a respiratory function, although the grounds for this belief are obscure.   So far as known the respiration of coelenterates is of the ordinary aerobic type, oxygen being taken up and carbon dioxide emitted.   The respiratory rate of medusae is very low,

---

Fig. 112.—Nervous and muscular systems.   A. Epidermal ganglion-cell layer from the oral disk of an anemone, seen from the inner surface of the epidermis (*after the Hertwigs*, 1879); note lack of continuity of the neurites.   B. Diagram of the nervous system of hydra (*after Hadzi*, 1909); the net-like connections are dubious.   C. Ring arrangement of epidermal nerve cells in the pedal disk of hydra.   (*After Hadzi*, 1909.)   D. Muscle fibers of a sector of the pedal disk of hydra (*after Gelei*, 1925), showing circular gastrodermal fibers and radial epidermal fibers.

but this results from their very small organic content. In anthozoans the rate is correlated with the degree of expansion, being low in the contracted state and increasing as the animal extends. Coelenterates in general require clean water of good oxygen content.

7. Excretion.—The phylum in general lacks any special structures for the voiding of nitrogenous wastes. In some hydro- and scyphomedusae each radial canal opens near the tentacles by a pore probably excretory, since the adjacent gastrodermal cells contain granules possibly nitrogenous. In *Aequorea* (Fig. 121*C*) that had been fed on flesh mixed with carmine particles, the author saw long strands of carmine exuded from these pores, so that they also serve for the ejection of nonnutritive materials. In certain Siphonophora (*Velella*, *Porpita*, Fig. 154*C*, *D*), there occurs beneath the float a so-called liver, a mass permeated with gastrodermal canals (Fig. 155*C*) whose walls are filled with guanine crystals and so thought to be excretory. In anthozoans, the septal filaments and adjacent parts of the septa seem to have excretory functions, since they contain xanthine crystals, and injected dyes and carmine grains are subsequently found in the sites mentioned. Yet in all these cases one is probably dealing merely with the limitation of the general secretory powers of the gastrodermis to certain locations. The transport of excretory matters to the exterior by granular amoeboid cells has been reported for *Alcyonium* and a number of hydroids.

The form in which the nitrogenous wastes are excreted in coelenterates has been little studied. Urea, uric acid, creatine, and creatinine are generally stated to be absent, although some investigators report traces of urea and uric acid in some anemones, and Myers (1920) found small amounts of urea, creatine, and creatinine in the fluid squeezed from the jelly of the scyphomedusa *Phacellophora*. The purine bases, xanthine and guanine, substances closely related to uric acid, seem to be of wide occurrence in the gastrodermis of coelenterates but are not necessarily waste matters. According to Pütter, anemones excrete 77 to 100 per cent of their nitrogenous wastes as ammonia, and ammonia was also found in the medusa just mentioned. In general the power of forming urea and uric acid as end products of nitrogen metabolism seems to be lacking in the lower Metazoa, and ammonia is the most common nitrogenous waste.

8. The Nervous System.—As the coelenterates are the lowest animals to possess a nervous system, the anatomy and physiology of this system have excited much interest. The nervous system consists of the sensory nerve cells located in the body epithelia and of a subepithelial nerve plexus (Fig. 112*A*, *B*) into which the fibrils from the sense cells run and from which (presumably) neurites pass to the muscles. The nerve plexus is made up of bipolar and multipolar nerve cells (ganglion cells) and their neurites (Fig. 112*A*, *B*, *C*), plus the neurites from the sensory cells.   The main nerve plexus is located in the inner part of the epidermis outside the muscle cylinder (Figs. 108*J* and 109*G*).   In most, possibly all, coelenterates a less developed plexus, similarly situated, exists in the gastrodermis.   Earlier workers denied any connections between the two plexuses, but neurite connections as well as nerve cells were later found in the mesgloea, and probably both plexuses should be regarded as one system.   In hydroid polyps the plexus is concentrated around the mouth, a fact suggesting the beginning of a centralized nervous system (Fig. 112*B*).   A similar ring containing larger and more numerous nerve cells than elsewhere was reported by the brothers Hertwig for the oral disk of anemones in their classical researches on these forms (1879); but later workers have failed to verify their finding.   In hydromedusae, the nerve plexus is limited to the subumbrellar surface and connects with two nerve rings in the bell margin (Fig. 125*A*), an upper ring with which the marginal sense organs communicate and a lower one that controls the ring muscle of the velum.   Scyphozoans lack the marginal nerve rings, but near each marginal sense body (rhopalium) there is a ganglion (acculumation of nerve cells) that connects with the subumbrellar plexus (Fig. 163*A*).   Morphologically the nervous system of coelenterates is characterized by its radial construction and the diffuse distribution of both neurones and neurites (Fig. 112*B*).

It has been believed for many years, chiefly from the work of Bethe (1903) that the nerve plexus of coelenterates is an actual network formed by the fusion of the neurites.   On this view there are no separate nerve cells in the plexus, and all the neurites are continuous.   Such a "nerve net" has been regarded as the primitive nervous system from which the synaptic nervous system of higher animals has evolved by the breaking up of the net into independent neurones.   However, the excellent studies of the Hertwigs fail to show any such net (Fig. 112*A*), and their figures have been recently completely confirmed by Bozler (1927) who, on some of the same forms studied by Bethe, has found that the nerve plexus consists of separate cells.   Their neurites terminate on the neurites of other cells by delicate, often varicose, endings.   Old and new studies therefore unite in indicating that the nervous system of coelenterates is *synaptic*, as in other animals, i.e., the impulse must pass across a break (*synapse*) between neurites.   However, the nervous system, although synaptic, differs from that of higher animals in that conduction occurs equally well in all directions, for the cells and neurites lack polarization. The system behaves as if it were actually a network with diffuse conduction.   Thus the stimulation of any small spot on the surface of anemones can bring the entire muscular system into action.   In medusae and anemones conduction occurs as usual through zigzag strips, provided

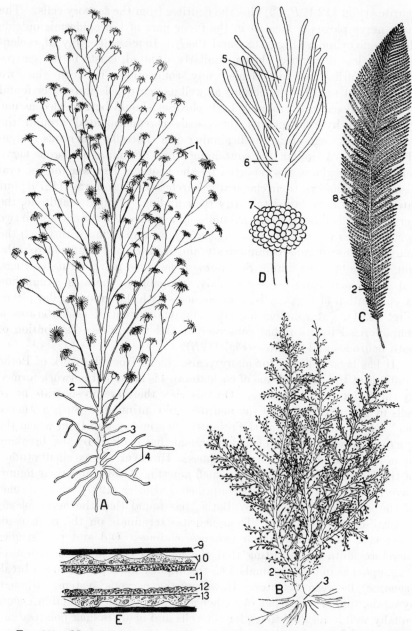

Fig. 113.—Main features of hydroid colonies. *A.* A gymnoblastic hydroid colony, *Eudendrium,* from life, illustrating also monopodial growth with terminal hydranths. *B.* A calyptoblastic hydroid colony, *Campanularia,* from life, illustrating also sympodial growth. *C.* A plumularian colony, *Aglaophenia,* showing feather-like form, illustrating monopodial growth with terminal growing points. *D.* Hydranth type with scattered

these remain in continuity. Localized responses do, however, obtain, and there is some indication of polarization, e.g., in anemones, where stimuli are conducted more readily in a longitudinal than in a transverse direction. Another feature of the coelenterate nervous system is the extreme autonomy or independence of parts; isolated portions of the body behave much as in the intact animal. Isolated tentacles and acontia execute their usual movements when stimulated, and isolated pedal disks of anemones creep about. There is little evidence of a central controlling mechanism around the mouth. Finally, the coelenterate nervous system is poor in reflexes, i.e., in specific responses to particular stimuli. In anemones, for instance, almost any stimulus of any region causes contraction of the column and withdrawal of the oral disk. Yet reflexes do occur in the phylum such as the righting reflex of medusae (page 533) and the opening of mouth and pharynx when the tentacles are stimulated by food. In general, however, the nerve plexus of coelenterates is characterized by diffuse unpolarized transmission, autonomy of parts, and paucity of reflexes.

The following sorts of mechanisms occur in the phylum. First, there are the *independent effectors* of G. H. Parker, comprising the nematocysts, gland cells, and cilia, all of which are said to react directly to stimuli without the intervention of any nervous elements. Parker also believes that certain muscles, e.g., the longitudinal muscle of the acontia of anemones, respond directly as do the muscle cells of sponges. Next, constituting the simplest neuromuscular mechanism, is the direct stimulation of a muscle by a sensory nerve cell. In such cases, the basal fibrils of a sensory nerve cell or the neurites of a subepithelial sensory ganglion cell having free nerve endings at the surface terminate on muscle cells. In the next stage the sensory fibrils make synapses with the neurites of a motor ganglion cell of the subepithelial nerve plexus, and such motor cells then have terminations on muscle fibers. Finally, two or more ganglion cells of the plexus may be interpolated in the nervous path.

The nerve plexus conducts without decrement and without fatigue, since circular strips cut from medusae will pulsate for days without alteration of rate. The rate of conduction has been measured for some forms and is given as 7 cm. per second in *Renilla*, 12 in *Physalia*, 12 to 15 in *Metridium*, 23 in *Aurelia*, 24 in *Pelagia*, and 15 to 120 in *Cassiopeia;* these rates may be compared with a speed of 12,500 cm. per second in the nerves of man.

---

filiform tentacles, *Clava*, and gonophores on the hydranth stem. *E*. A hydroid stem, from life, showing its structure. 1, hydranth; 2, hydrocaulus; 3, hydrorhiza; 4, stolon; 5, manubrium; 6, stomach region; 7, gonophores; 8, corbula; 9, periderm; 10, coenosarc; 11, gastrovascular cavity; 12, gastrodermis; 13, epidermis.

IV. CLASS HYDROZOA

1. Definition.—The Hydrozoa are polymorphic, or wholly polypoid, or wholly medusoid coelenterates, with tetramerous or polymerous radial symmetry, in which the gastrovascular system lacks stomodaeum, septa, or nematocyst-bearing structures, the mesogloea is noncellular, the gonads ripen in the ectoderm, the oral end of the polyp is elongated into a manubrium, and the medusae are craspedote and without rhopalia.

2. Morphology of the Hydroid Form.—A typical hydroid polyp is differentiated into three regions: the attached *base*, the *stalk* or *stem*, and the terminal *hydranth* (Fig. 106*A*). The base usually consists of a glandular area by whose secretion attachment is accomplished. From the base in colonial forms tubes known as *stolons* or *rhizomes* extend out over the substratum as a branching or anastomosing root-like tangle called the *hydrorhiza* (Fig. 113*A*, *B*). The stolons serve to fasten the colony firmly and also usually give off numerous upright buds that develop into new polyps or polypoid colonies. Solitary forms such as *Corymorpha* and some other Tubulariidae are anchored, generally to soft bottoms, by a number of short, unbranched, nonbudding, root-like holdfasts from the nonadhesive base (Fig. 119*A*). These at first consist of solid stolons that secrete a periderm and then die away leaving the empty skeletal tubes as anchorage. In the solitary fresh-water hydras, the attached end is a simple adhesive *pedal disk*, never forming stolons (Fig. 132). From the stolons arise the single stalks or *caulomes* of polyps or the main stalk, termed *hydrocaulus*, of a colony. Stolons, caulomes, and hydrocaulus consist of a living hollow tube (Fig. 113*E*) termed the *coenosarc*, usually covered over by a chitinous tube, the *periderm* (or perisarc), yellowish or brown in color, secreted by the epidermis. The coenosarc is composed of epidermis and gastrodermis with a mesolamella between them, and it and its enclosed gastrovascular cavity are continuous throughout the colony. In *Corymorpha* and related forms (see page 411) the stem contains a number of small canals instead of a single central gastrovascular canal (Fig. 119*E*).

The hydranth is an elongated, cylindrical, bottle-shaped or vase-like structure, having a terminal mouth and bearing tentacles (Figs. 113*D* and 114). It is often differentiated into an elongated distal part, called *proboscis*, *manubrium*, or (in hydras) *hypostome*, and an expanded basal stomach or gastral region. The proboscis is cylindrical, conical, or globular, and the mouth is capable of great expansion. The hydranth may join the stalk by way of a narrowed "neck" as in *Tubularia* (Fig. 114*C*). Primitively as in *Clava* (Fig. 113*D*) or *Syncoryne* (Fig. 114*A*) the tentacles are irregularly strewn over the hydranth. Then the basal tentacles arrange into a proximal circlet while the distal ones retain the

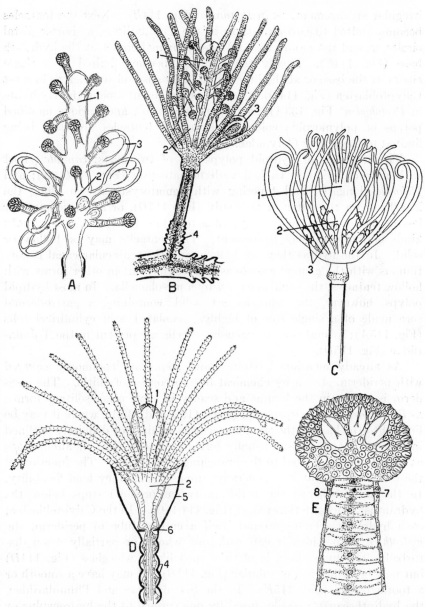

FIG. 114.—Types of hydranths and tentacles, all from life. *A. Syncoryne*, with scattered capitate tentacles. *B. Pennaria*, with distal scattered capitate tentacles, and a proximal circlet of filiform tentacles. *C. Tubularia*, with distal and proximal filiform circlets. *D. Obelia*, with a single filiform circlet. *E.* Capitate tentacle of *Pennaria*, enlarged, showing head of nematocysts and core of disk-like gastrodermal cells. 1, manubrium; 2, stomach region; 3, gonophore; 4, annuli of periderm; 5, hydrotheca; 6, shelf of hydrotheca; 7, gastrodermis; 8, epidermis.

irregular arrangement, as in *Pennaria* (Fig. 114*B*). Next the tentacles become limited to two circlets as in the Tubulariidae, a shorter distal circlet around the mouth and a longer proximal circlet at the hydranth base (Fig. 114*C*). Finally the tentacles become limited to a single circlet at the base or at the junction of proboscis and stomach as in most Calyptoblastea (Fig. 114*D*). Tentacles are absent among the Hydroida in *Protohydra* (Fig. 133*A*), some parasitic forms, and various modified polyps of polymorphic colonies. Branched tentacles are rare, being limited to the family Corynidae.

The tentacles of hydroid polyps are of two sorts: *capitate*, short with a terminal knob packed with nematocysts (Fig. 114*B, E*); and *filiform*, elongated and tapering with nematocysts strewn along the length, or on the outer surface only (Fig. 115*D*), or arranged more or less in circlets as in many Calyptoblastea (Fig. 115*A*). Either or both kinds of tentacles may be present. The tentacles may be hollow or solid. In the hydras they are hollow, and the tentacular canal is continuous with the general gastrovascular cavity, but in other forms with hollow tentacles, the canal is cut off by a mesolamella. In most hydroid polyps, however, the tentacles are solid, containing a gastrodermal core made of a single row of highly vacuolated, stiff cylindrical cells (Fig. 115*A*); several rows of vacuolated cells are present in the Tubulariidae (Fig. 115*D*).

As already mentioned, stolons and stems are commonly covered with periderm, shown by chemical test to consist of chitin. The periderm is absent in the hydras and scanty in some other solitary forms, as *Protohydra, Corymorpha*, etc. (Figs. 119*A* and 133*A*), where it may be limited to the base of the stem or occur as a thin, not definitely outlined investment. On stems it usually forms groups of rings or annulations at definite points related to the branching (Fig. 114*B*). The function of these is obscure, but it is generally supposed that they lend flexibility. In the Gymnoblastea the periderm (when present) stops below the hydranths, which are thus naked (Fig. 114*A–C*). In the Calyptoblastea, each hydranth secretes around itself a cup or tube of periderm, the *hydrotheca*, into which it can withdraw wholly or partially when disturbed. The hydrotheca is often shaped like a wineglass (Fig. 114*D*) but may be cylindrical or tubular (Fig. 115*B*) and may have a smooth or a toothed edge (Fig. 115*E*). In the Sertulariidae and Plumulariidae, the hydrothecae are sessile, fused by one surface to the hydrocaulus or branches and often bilaterally symmetrical and of bizarre shapes (Fig. 115*F*). Hydrothecae may be provided with a lid (*operculum*, families Sertulariidae and Campanulinidae) of one to several pieces (Figs. 115*B, C* and 134 *D*) which close over the contracted hydranth. In many forms a circular or one-sided chitinous shelf extends inward from the hydrotheca at the hydranth base (Fig. 114*D*) as a *diaphragm*, which narrows the opening into the stalk and prevents the passage of large food particles. The hydrotheca may be secondarily reduced to a small cup as in *Halecium* (Fig. 117*A*).

The stolons with their periderm encasement are usually distinct tubes running over the substratum (Fig. 116*C*). In *Hydractinia*, however, the stolons early fuse to a network, and their epidermis unites to form continuous upper and lower sheets enclosing gastrodermal tubes (Fig. 118*F*). Periderm is at first secreted above and below; but later the thin upper periderm disappears while continuous secretion below results in successive layers of periderm forming a mat applied to the snail shell on which *Hydractinia* colonies commonly grow (Fig. 118*C*). From this peridermal mat, there arise at frequent intervals spines of periderm that project among the polyp bases (Fig. 118*D*).

The formation of new hydranths by asexual budding is universal throughout hydroid polyps and commonly leads to colony formation. Such buds rarely form on the hydranths (only known case, *Heterosteph-anus*, Fig. 133*B*), nearly always on stems and stolons. In budding, both coenosarc layers project as a rounded outgrowth that as it elongates differentiates into a hydranth (Fig. 115*G–M*). The tentacles are formed by little gastrodermal cones (Fig. 115*L*), which push the epidermis before them and become the gastrodermal cores of the tentacles. In some cases prior to the appearance of a bud, interstitial cells accumulate at the spot and participate in the outgrowth, as is said to be the case in hydras. Periderm when present is dissolved by the advancing bud and later reformed.

Colony formation occurs in four different ways: *hydrorhizal* or *stolonal*, *monopodial* with *terminal* hydranths, *sympodial*, and *monopodial* with terminal *growing points*. In hydrorhizal budding, seen in *Clava*, *Coryne*, *Hydractinia*, etc., the polyps spring singly and irregularly from the basal stolonal tangle or mat, originating as erect buds directly from the stolons (Figs. 116*C* and 118*D*). Or a group of parallel stolons may erect themselves vertically as a bundle or rhizocaulome, which imitates a stem and from which also polyps spring directly and singly (*Clathrozoon*, Fig. 116*D*). Usually, however, a hydroid colony consists of one main erect stem or hydrocaulus, fastened at its base by spreading stolons and giving off branches bearing hydranths (Fig. 113*A*, *B*, *C*). The hydrocaulus may be straight; or it may be zigzag, with an angle at the origin of each branch. It is usually single (*monosiphonic*) but may be *fascicled* (*polysiphonic*), in which case the true hydrocaulus is covered over by stolons from the hydrorhiza or by branches from below (Fig. 116*A*, *B*).

Colonies with a hydrocaulus have a general plant-like aspect and form hydranths and branches in definite ways similar to those obtaining

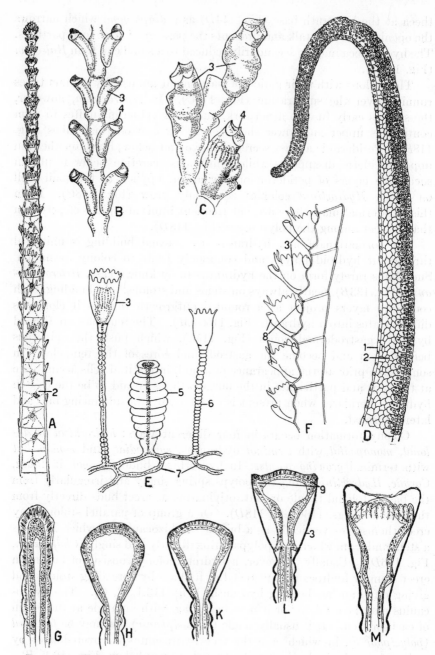

Fig. 115.—Hydroid structure (continued). *A.* Filiform type of tentacle, enlarged, from life. *B.* Tubular type of hydrothecae of a sertularian hydroid (*Diphasia*) with a lid of one flap. *C.* Hydrothecae of another sertularian, *Sertularella*, with lid of four flaps. (*B and C after Nutting, 1904.*) *D.* Filiform type of tentacle of *Tubularia*, with nemato-

in plant growth. Their mode of growth is either monopodial or sympodial. In the first kind of monopodial growth, which prevails among the gymnoblastic hydroids, the main stem and all branches are permanently topped by terminal hydranths and continue to elongate indefinitely by means of a growth zone just below each hydranth (Fig. 116E). Below the growth zone, lateral buds arise at intervals, and, since each bud has a growth zone, the stem elongates between successive buds, which thus come to be separated by a length (internode) of newly formed stem. Successive buds usually alternate. These buds differentiate into hydranths whose stems continue to grow and to bud in the same fashion, thus establishing new branches. A given spot buds but once. The original hydranth formed from the planula tops the hydrocaulus, the whole of whose length is really the stem of this hydranth. Similarly, each branch is the stem of its terminal hydranth, which is the oldest of that branch. Such branching is termed *racemose* and, because of the long, continuously growing hydranth stalks and their alternation on the branches, results usually in a loose bushy colony, as seen in *Tubularia*, *Eudendrium* (Fig. 113A), *Pennaria* (Fig. 116E), etc.

In sympodial growth, the hydranth stems have no growth zone and do not elongate after being formed. Below the temporary last hydranth of the hydrocaulus or branch is a budding zone from which a bud arises laterally. This grows, overtops its parent hydranth, and develops into the new temporary terminal hydranth, which repeats the process (Fig. 117A). The colony thus continues to grow only at the ends of the hydrocaulus or of the branches, and the terminal hydranths are such temporarily, also the youngest, the age increasing basipetally. Each internode is the stalk of a different hydranth, and the added stalks of all the polyps thereon compose the hydrocaulus or the main stem of each branch. Buds are usually given off alternately, and a colony may consist simply of a succession of alternate polyps. The budding zone of any hydranth may, however, continue to bud and so form branches. This type of branching is termed *cymose* and is characteristic of the lower families of calyptoblastic hydroids. The higher calyptoblastic forms, such as the plumularians, have, however, reverted to a second monopodial method, apparently by evolution from the sympodial type. The hydrocaulus and branches end in permanent growing points (instead of hydranths), which never differentiate into hydranths but continue to

cysts on the outer side and gastrodermis of many rows of cells, from life. *E.* A thecate hydroid, *Clytia*, with toothed hydrothecae and ringed gonothecae, illustrating also hydrorhizal type of growth. *F.* Part of a branch of a plumularian, *Aglaophenia*, showing bizarre hydrothecae fused on one side to the branch, and bearing nematothecae. *G–M.* Stages in the transformation of a growing point into a hydranth, from life. 1, epidermis; 2, gastrodermis; 3, hydrotheca; 4, lid; 5, gonotheca; 6, annuli; 7, stolons; 8, nematothecae; 9, gastrodermal cone pushing out to form tentacle.

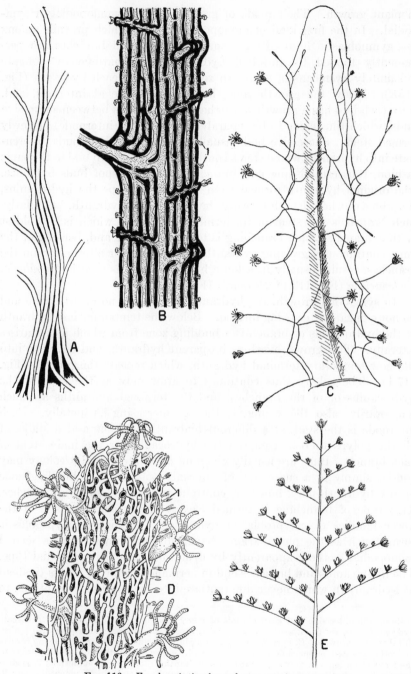

FIG. 116.—For descriptive legend see opposite page

elongate indefinitely, budding off branches and hydranths laterally (Fig. 117D). The hydrocaulus is the product of one continuously elongating, growing point originating from the planula; and each lateral branch (termed *hydrocladium*) is formed by a lateral growing point. This mode of growth seems to be the most successful, since the largest hydroid colonies originate in this way.

In either sympodial or monopodial growth, branching may occur in all planes, giving a bushy colony (Fig. 113A, B) or in one plane, producing a fan- or plume-like appearance (Fig. 113C). Hydranths and polyps generally arise alternately, but in many sertularians the budding zone or growing point gives rise to two buds simultaneously (Fig. 117B, C) instead of the usual one and dichotomously branched colonies result, having opposite instead of alternate polyps and branches. In the Sertulariidae and Plumulariidae with sessile hydrothecae fused along one surface to the stem, the branches are often rendered rigid and inflexible thereby and when arising in one plane form a characteristic feather shape, as in *Aglaophenia* (Fig. 113C). The plume form is particularly characteristic of the family Plumulariidae, where the regular alternate hydrocladi, bearing the sessile thecae on their upper surfaces only, spring from the hydrocaulus nearly at right angles and in one plane (Fig. 117D).

As already indicated, the hydroid polyps are divisible into the athecate and thecate forms. The athecate or gymnoblastic or tubularian hydroids include solitary forms without periderm or with a basal periderm but comprise chiefly hydrorhizal or monopodial colonies in which the periderm extends to the hydranth base (Fig. 114A–C). In the thecate or calyptoblastic or campanularian hydroids, the periderm continues as a hydrotheca around the hydranth and a gonotheca around the gonophores (Figs. 114D, 115E). This group includes colonies with stalked hydranths and sympodial growth and those with sessile thecae and terminal growing points.

Hydroid colonies are polymorphic, *i.e.*, consist of more than one kind of individual (called *zooid* or *person*). So far we have been describing the ordinary feeding polyp, also termed *nutritive polyp, gastrozooid*, and *trophozooid*, having mouth, tentacles, and gastric cavity, serving to capture and ingest food (Fig. 114). All colonies, however, are at least dimorphic including in addition to the gastrozooids, *medusoids* (Fig. 119A, F) in various stages of formation (or grades of degeneration when

---

Fig. 116.—Colony growth. A. Simple type of fascicled stem of parallel stolons, *Eudendrium*, from life. B. Complicated type of fascicled stem, true hydrocaulus in center encircled by stolons, *Plumularia*. (*After Spencer*, 1890.) C. Hydrorhizal type of colony, a campanularian hydroid, growing on a Sargassum "leaf," from life, Bermuda. D. Hydrorhizal colony forming an erect mass, or rhizocaulome, imitating a hydrocaulus, *Clathrozoon*. (*After Spencer*, 1890.) E. Monopodial type of colony, with terminal hydranths, *Pennaria*, from life. 1, Nematothecae.

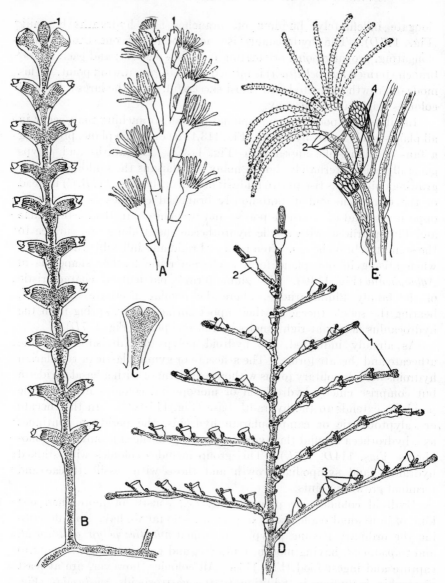

Fig. 117.—Colony growth (continued), all from life. *A*. Branch end of *Halecium*, showing sympodial growth. *B*. Branch of *Sertularia* showing dichotomous branching, and monopodial growth with terminal growing point. *C*. Growing point of *Sertularia* showing start of dichotomy. *D*. *Plumularia*, showing monopodial growth with terminal growing points. *E*. A hydranth of *Plumularia*, showing two of the three nematophores. 1, growing point; 2, hydrotheca; 3, nematothecae; 4, nematophores.

free medusae are not formed). Many colonies are trimorphic, having gastrozooids, medusoids, and *gonozooids;* the last are modified polyps that bud off medusoids or their morphological equivalents (Fig. 118*D*). Gonozooids and medusa formation are described later. Often a fourth type of zooid is present, the *protective polyp,* also termed *machozooid, dactylozooid,* and other names, which is derived from the gastrozooid by reduction or loss of mouth, tentacles, and gastric cavity, and which serves only for protection and food capture. Dactylozooids are elongated, highly extensile, nematocyst-bearing structures that may be provided with short capitate tentacles (Fig. 118*D*) but usually simply resemble long tentacles and are then termed *tentaculozooids* (Fig. 118*E*). They may be definitely arranged with respect to the gastrozooids. *Hydractinia* has two sorts of dactylozooids, the *spiral zooids* with capitate tentacles (Fig. 118*D*) found at the shell margin, and the *tentaculozooids* (Fig. 118*E*), found only at growing margins and often scarce. Very characteristic are the small dactylozooids of the Plumulariidae (Fig. 117*E*). They are called *nematophores* or *sarcostyles* and spring from tiny thecae, the *nematothecae,* located on stems and on the hydrothecae (usually three to each) of the gastrozooids. The nematophores (Figs. 117*E*, 118*G*) have club or capitate ends beset with nematocysts or adhesive cells or both. The adhesive cells contain droplets discharging into long sticky threads used to ensnare small prey while the nematocysts are employed against larger organisms. Small dactylozooids similar to those of plumularians occur in the curious hydroid *Clathrozoon* (Figs. 116*D* and 118*G*).

Some hydroid polyps are solitary, either because they never bud, or because the buds soon leave the parent. Most familiar of these are the fresh-water hydras (Fig. 132), which bud at a definite budding zone located at the junction of stomach and stalk. Each bud begins as a rounded protrusion involving both body epithelia; it rapidly elongates, sprouts tentacles at its free end, and differentiates completely into a small hydra before freeing itself from the parent by a basal constriction. The entire process occupies about 2 days under good conditions. Well-fed hydras may bear several buds, and these are found to be arranged in a spiral ascending from the oldest to the youngest. Under depressing conditions, buds may fail to detach and double-headed forms or colony-like aggregates result. Another solitary form is the minute tentacle-less *Protohydra* (Fig. 133*A*, page 440) multiplying by fission. Of a different type are the large solitary marine hydroids *Corymorpha* and *Branchiocerianthus,* which have no mode of asexual reproduction. The long stem is anchored in soft bottoms by a tuft of holdfasts and is topped apically by the large pink or rose hydranth having distal and proximal circlets of tentacles and grape-like bunches of gonophores (Fig. 119*A*, *C*).

Fig. 118.—Hydroid structure.   *A.* Longitudinal section (right half only) of ᴀ hydranth of *Tubularia*.   *B.* A hydroid of *Sertularia*, showing gastric pouch.   *C. Hydractinia*, growing on a snail shell occupied by a hermit crab, from life.   *D. Hydractinia*, showing polyp types, from life.   *E.* Tentaculozooid of *Hydractinia*.   *F.* Section through the basal mat of

Acaulus (Fig. 119*F*) and *Myriothela* (Fig. 133*C*), small solitary types also without asexual reproduction, have a short base and an elongated manubrium covered with capitate tentacles and bearing gonophores or gonozooids. Solitary forms with unusual modes of asexual multiplication are illustrated by *Heterostephanus* (Fig. 133*B*) and *Hypolytus* (Fig. 133*D*).

The gastrovascular cavity of hydroid polyps enlarges in the hydranth base into a stomach or gastric region (Fig. 114) in which extracellular digestion occurs. Only in the hydras are the tentacular cavities continuous with the main gastrovascular cavity. In the Sertulariidae (Fig. 118*B*), the stomach is outpouched into a blind sac that by periodic contractions forces the digesting broth into the stem. In *Corymorpha*, many species of *Tubularia*, and allied forms, the relatively large stem is more or less filled with vacuolated gastrodermal cells, probably serving for support through their turgescence, and in its periphery near the epidermis, is a circle of gastrodermal canals, opening distally into the stomach of the hydranth (Figs. 118*A* and 119*B*, *E*).

Histologically, hydrozoan polyps present nothing especial. Epidermal and gastrodermal epithelia vary from low to columnar form, and, in tentacles and hydranths, throughout the whole body in hydras and hydra-like types, are provided with muscular bases, longitudinal in the epidermis, circular in the gastrodermis. The circular fibers are often less developed than the longitudinal ones and apparently frequently absent. Stems and stolons appear to be devoid of muscle fibers. The epidermis is seldom ciliated or flagellated; it may be double, with a delicate outer layer next the periderm. Sensory cells occur abundantly in the epidermis of tentacles and manubrium. The gastrodermis is flagellated throughout, low in stems and stolons, often highly columnar and wavy in regions active in digestion. It extends to the mouth rim, a stomodaeum being absent, and is there supplied with many mucous gland cells (Figs. 108*A* and 107*E*) while in the gastric region it contains enzymatous gland cells. In the Tubulariidae, a gastrodermal cushion (Fig. 118*A*) of large vacuolated cells is present in the hydranth base and apparently serves to prevent large food particles from passing into the stalk. The nervous system is best known for the hydras, where an epidermal plexus of ganglion cells and neurites occurs throughout the body (Fig. 112*B*). The ganglion cells are slightly more concentrated in hypostome and pedal disk where the plexus also tends to a circular arrangement, suggesting nerve rings in these two locations (Fig. 112*B*, *C*).

Hydractinia, showing structure. (*After Collcutt*, 1897.) *G*. A dactylozooid of *Clathrozoon*. (*After Spencer*, 1897.) 1, distal tentacle; 2, gonophore cluster; 3, gastrodermal cushion of vacuolated cells; 4, proximal tentacle; 5, gastrodermal layer of same; 6, mesolamella; 7, gastrozooid; 8, spiral zooid; 9, gonozooid; 10, female gonozooid; 11, male gonozooid; 12, spine; 13, upper epidermis; 14, lower epidermis; 15, gastrodermal tubes; 16, spine; 17, periderm layers next the snail shell.

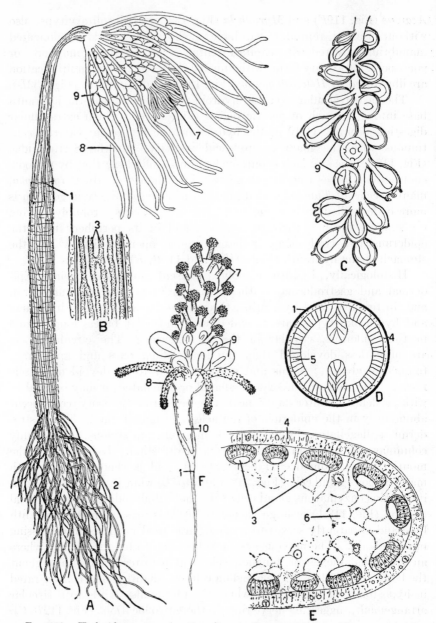

Fig. 119.—Hydroid structure (continued). *A. Corymorpha*, from life, actual height, 5 cm. *B.* Stem of the same, enlarged, showing gastrodermal canals. *C.* Gonophore cluster (*Tubularia*) enlarged, from life. *D.* Cross section of the stem of *Tubularia crocea*, showing partial division into two canals. *E.* Half of cross section of the stem of *Tubularia solitaria*, showing gastrodermal canals, as in *Corymorpha*. (*After Warren, 1906.*) *F. Acaulus primarius*, from life. 1, periderm; 2, holdfasts; 3, gastrodermal canals; 4, epidermis; 5, gastrodermis; 6, vacuolated gastrodermis of interior; 7, distal tentacles; 8, proximal tentacles; 9, gonophore; 10, basal stolon.

The neurites behave in various ways: they may connect with sensory nerve cells, or pass to the surface as free endings, or terminate by swollen tips on muscle fibers, or connect with the neurites of other cells.   There are also indications of a gastrodermal plexus in hydra, having much fewer and smaller cells than the epidermal plexus.   In the few cases investigated in the colonial hydroids, the nervous system resembles that of hydra; an epidermal plexus is present in hydranths and tentacles and tends to centralize to a ring in the manubrium.   Both epidermal and gastrodermal ganglion cells have been found in the coenosarc but whether a continuous nervous connection exists throughout hydroid colonies does not seem to be known.   Its occurrence is probable in at least some forms, since in *Clava*, for instance, the whole colony contracts when one polyp is touched (Föyn).

3. Morphology of the Medusoid Form.—A typical hydromedusa is a solitary, free-swimming animal, consisting of a gelatinous bell-, dome-, bowl-, or saucer-shaped bell or umbrella from whose rim and concave subumbrellar surface the principal parts depend (Fig. 106*E*).   The most striking general feature of the medusa is its perfect tetramerous radial symmetry.   From the center of the subumbrellar surface hangs the manubrium, a cylindrical or quadrangular tube of varying length, often provided with lobes, frills, or even tentacle-like projections (oral tentacles, (Fig. 120*A*, *B*), all heavily beset with nematocysts.   At the attachment of the manubrium to the bell there usually occurs a rounded or quadrangular gastric cavity or stomach.   Some forms, as *Sarsia* (Fig. 120*G*), have an extremely elongated extensile manubrium with the stomach near the tip; and in others, as *Eutima* (Fig. 120*F*), the manubrium is borne on a gelatinous extension, the *peduncle*, actually part of the umbrella, since the radial canals course in it.   From the gastric cavity, gastrodermal tubes, the radial canals, radiate to the bell margin.   They are nearly always four in number and 90 degrees apart, occupying the perradii (Fig. 120*F*, *G*); but other numbers, mostly six or eight (Fig. 121*A*) occur, and in some cases, as *Aequorea* (Fig. 121*C*), many radial canals are present, while in a few forms they branch (Fig. 135).   The radial canals open into a ring canal running in the bell margin; this is often a broad, irregular channel (Fig. 122).   Manubrium, stomach, radial canals, and ring canal constitute the gastrovascular system of the medusa A velum or craspedon is characteristic of hydromedusae but is occasionally rudimentary as in the medusae of *Obelia*.

The flat to tall bell is generally of simple contour but may be pointed at the summit (Fig. 121*B*, *D*) or provided with a constriction near the summit giving a turreted effect as in *Leuckartiara* (Fig. 120*E*).   The margin is circular and unscalloped in the medusae of the Hydroida and bears the most differentiated structures of the body, the tentacles and sense

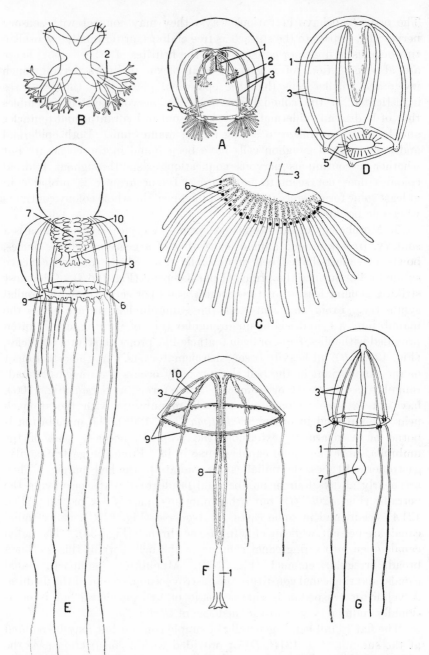

Fig. 120.—Types of hydroid medusae, all from life, except *D*.   *A*. Medusa of *Bougainvillia*, with four tentacle clusters and oral tentacles.   *B*. Oral tentacles of same, enlarged. *C*. Tentacle cluster of same, enlarged, showing eyespots.   *D*. Medusa of *Pennaria*, with

organs. The tentacles may be absent or mere bumps in some medusae, particularly short-lived species, as *Pennaria* (Fig. 120*D*). A single tentacle may be present as in *Steenstrupia* (Fig. 121*B*); or two as in *Stomotoca* (Fig. 121*D*); frequently the number is four as in *Sarsia, Eutima*, etc. (Fig. 120*F, G*); and often 8, 12, 16 (Fig. 120*E*), or an indefinite number occur (Fig. 121*C*). When indefinite the number often increases with age. When four or less in number, the tentacles are always perradial, i.e., each springs at the termination of a radial canal (Fig. 120*F, G*). When the number is greater than four, often one, two, three or more tentacles are symmetrically and regularly spaced between the perradial tentacles as in *Leuckartiara* (Fig. 120*E*). Frequently the perradial tentacles are much larger and longer than the interradial and adradial ones (Fig. 120*E*), and in many cases the last are small and rudimentary, apparently serving as sense organs or sites of nematocyst formation. In *Bougainvillia* (Fig. 120*A*) and related genera and *Margelopsis* the tentacles are grouped into four or eight clusters (Fig. 120*A*). The tentacles are generally unbranched, but in the family Cladonemidae they may bifurcate or branch, and some of the branches may end in suckers used for clinging to objects (Fig. 121*A*); or the tentacles may bear *cnidophores*, very contractile stalks having a terminal cavity filled with nematocysts as in *Zanclea* and *Gemmaria* (Figs. 121*E* and 111*G*). The tentacles are liberally strewn with sensory nerve cells and abundantly provided with nematocysts, usually grouped into warts, ridges, rings, spirals, and terminal swellings. They may be hollow containing an extension of the ring canal; or solid with a central core of gastrodermal disks as in the tentacles of many hydroid polyps. The base of each tentacle is commonly swollen into an enlargement, the *tentacular* or *ocellar* bulb, which may bear an ocellus and other sensory patches but functions primarily in digestion (page 449) and as a site of nematocyst formation, being packed with cnidoblasts in process of secreting nematocysts (Figs. 122 and 123*C*). Tentacles are often so reduced that they consist of nothing but the tentacular bulbs or perhaps more correctly have developed only as far as the tentacular bulb.

The bell margin is liberally provided with general sensory epithelium and usually bears special sense organs. These sense organs of medusae are the first organs encountered in the invertebrate series, and significantly they concern perception of the factors of the external world. In hydromedusae the chief sense organs are the *ocelli* ("eyes") and the *statocysts*, also called statoblasts, lithocysts, otocysts, and other names (Fig. 122). Each of these occurs in various grades of organization.

four abortive tentacles. (*After Mayer*, 1910.) *E. Leuckartiara*, with definite tentacle lengths related to the radii. *F. Eutima*, with umbrellar peduncle. *G. Sarsia*, with long manubrium. 1, manubrium; 2, oral tentacles; 3, radial canals; 4, circular canal; 5, velum: 6, ocellus; 7, stomach; 8, peduncle or pseudomanubrium; 9, tentacular bulbs: 10. gonad.

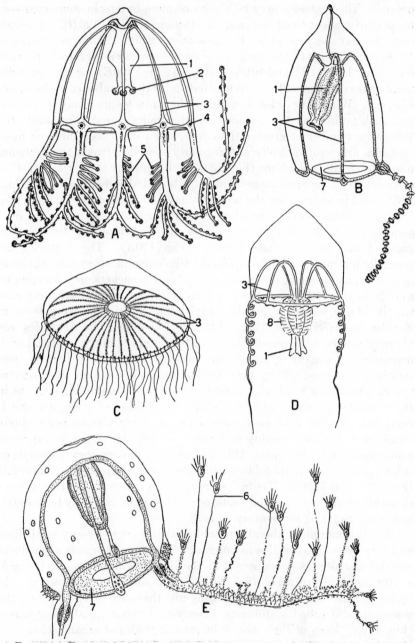

Fig. 121.—Types of hydroid medusae.   A. *Cladonema*, from life, with branched tentacles and suckers.   B. *Steenstrupia*, medusa of *Corymorpha*, with one tentacle.   (*After Mayer*, 1910.)   C. *Aequorea*, from life, with numerous radial canals.   D. *Stomotoca*, medusa of *Perigonimus* type of hydroids, from life, with two tentacles.   E. *Gemmaria*, with nematophores.   (*After Murbach*, 1899.)   1, manubrium; 2, oral tentacles; 3, radial canals; 4, ocellus; 5, suckers; 6, nematophores; 7, velum; 8, gonad.

The ocelli appear as red, brown, or black spots, usually one on each tentacular bulb (Fig. 122*A*), whether this continues as a tentacle or not, or

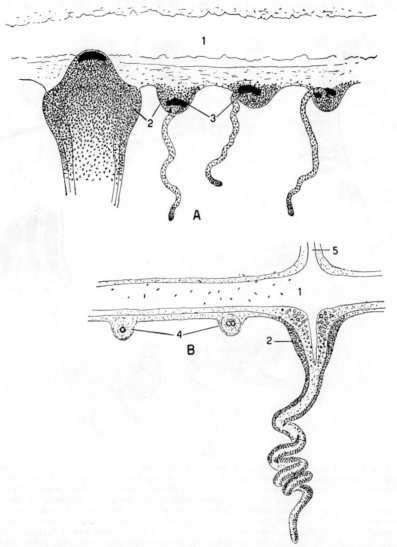

Fig. 122.—Marginal structure. *A*. Bell margin of an anthomedusan, *Leuckartiara* (Fig. 120*E*), showing nematocyst depots and ocelli in tentacular bulbs. *B*. Bell margin of a leptomedusan, *Phialidium*, showing statocysts between tentacle bases and lack of ocelli. Both from life, Puget Sound. 1, circular canal; 2, tentacular bulb; 3, ocellus; 4, statocyst; 5, radial canal.

sometimes on the bell margin itself. In *Bougainvillia* and other forms in which the tentacles occur in clusters, the single tentacular bulb of the cluster bears as many ocelli as there are tentacles (Fig. 120C).   In its simplest form an ocellus consists of a patch of pigment cells interspersed with sensory nerve cells as in *Turris* (Fig. 123A).   The pigment cells

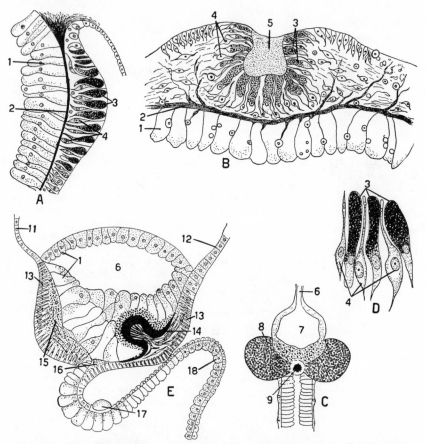

Fig. 123.—Histology of ocelli.   *A.* Section of the ocellus of *Turris*, simplest type, composed of pigment and sensory cells.   *B.* Section of the ocellus of *Sarsia*, more complex, with lens.   *C.* Tentacle base of *Sarsia*, from life, showing tentacular bulb with ocellus and nematocyst depots.   *D.* Sensory and pigment cells of *Sarsia* ocellus, enlarged.   *E.* Section of ocellus of *Tiaropsis* and adjacent parts, most complex type, with pigment cup and inverted retinal cells.   (*All after Linko*, 1900, *except C.*)   1, gastrodermis; 2, mesolamella; 3, pigment cells of ocellus; 4, sensory cells of ocellus; 5, lens; 6, radial canal; 7, ring canal; 8, tentacular bulb; 9, ocellus; 10, tentacle; 11, exumbrellar epidermis; 12, subumbrellar epidermis; 13, sensory epithelium; 14, pigment cup of ocellus; 15, upper nerve ring; 16, lower nerve ring; 17, statocyst; 18, velum.

appear to be epidermal cells filled with pigment, and the sensory cells resemble the general sensory cells of the epidermis (Fig. 123D).   At first such "eyespots" are flush with the surface as in *Turris* (Fig. 123A), but in the next stage of differentiation they bend into a cup shape; and then the cup comes to be occupied by a lens-like body formed of cuticle (*Sarsia*, Fig. 123*B*), while the pigment cells may be either epidermal or gastrodermal. The most complicated hydromedusan ocellus is that of *Tiaropsis* (Fig. 123*E*) with a gastrodermal pigment cup filled with sensory cells whose tips are directed toward the cup while their nerve fibers pass out of the opening of the cup; in short, the sensory cells are "inverted" as in the eyes of higher animals. The nerve fibers of the sensory cells of ocelli unite to strong strands joining the upper nerve ring. The ocelli presumably serve for the more exact perception of light (page 495).

The statocysts, absent in the Anthomedusae, are epidermal pits or vesicles (Fig. 122*B*) located in the velar base on its subumbrellar side and characterized by the presence of special cells (*lithocytes*), each of which contains a movable round concretion (*statolith*) composed of organic material and calcium carbonate. The *statocysts* are of two general types, *open* and *closed*. The simpler open type (*Mitrocoma*, Fig. 124*A*, *B*) consists of an epidermal pit facing the subumbrellar cavity and covered externally by a bulge of the outer epidermis of the velum modified over the pit into columnar palisade cells with thickened walls. In the bottom of the pit (Fig. 124*A*) are rows of lithocytes each containing a statolith, succeeded by a row of sensory cells, which send processes under the lithocytes and sensory hairs around the statoliths. The lithocytes in the open type vary from a few to 10 to 20 in number and may be arranged in one to several rows. Each lithocyte is supplied by three to five sensory cells. Various gradations occur between the open and closed type of statocyst; the latter is formed by the approximation and fusion of the margins of the pit. The closed vesicle so formed usually bulges toward the outer surface of the velum. Its wall (Fig. 124*C*, *D*) is composed of a double layer of flattened epidermis and bears a patch of lithocytes and sensory cells like those of the open type but reduced in number to less than ten of each kind of cell. The statocysts are usually located between the tentacle bases, although sometimes on them, and are often very numerous, numbering hundreds. Early workers regarded the statocysts as organs of hearing and termed them otocysts; but they are now considered to be organs of equilibrium (for evidence see page 533). The nerve fibers from their sensory cells run to the lower nerve ring, which also controls the velum.

Other marginal structures regarded as sense organs are the *sense clubs* or *cordyli* and the *tactile combs*. The former found in *Laodicea* and related Leptomedusae are small clubs mounted on sensory cushions situated between the tentacle bases; they are composed of large gastrodermal cells covered by a flat thin epidermis (Fig. 124*F*) and entirely resemble the lithostyles of the Trachylina (page 457) except that they

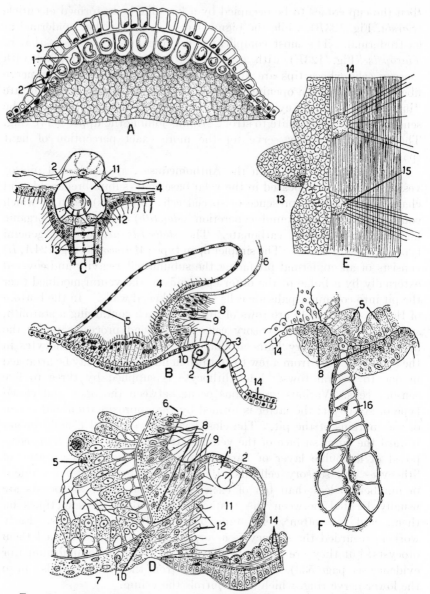

Fig. 124.—Sense organs of hydroid medusae. *A*. Open type of statocyst of *Mitrocoma*, optical section. *B*. Cross section through the same with adjacent parts. *C*. Closed type of statocyst, of *Obelia*. *D*. Section through the bell margin of *Aequorea*, showing closed statocyst, velum, and nerve rings. *E*. Bell margin and velum of *Aglaura* with two tactile combs. (*All after the Hertwigs*, 1878.) *F*. Cordylus or sensory club of *Laodicea*. (*After Brooks*, 1895.) 1, lithocytes; 2, statolith; 3, modified epidermis over lithocytes; 4, ring canal; 5, gastrodermis; 6, exumbrellar epidermis; 7, subumbrellar epidermis; 8, upper nerve ring; 9, sensory epithelium over same; 10, lower nerve ring; 11, closed statocyst; 12, sensory cells of same; 13, tentacle base; 14, velum; 15, tactile combs; 16, cordylus.

contain no statoliths.   The tactile combs (Fig. 124*E*) are patches bearing long stiff hairs.

In many medusae each radial canal opens near the ring canal onto the subumbrellar surface by a pore often set on a papilla formerly believed to be sensory.   These are now regarded as excretory pores for the ejection of wastes and undigestible material that have been seen passing through them (page 396).   The gastrodermis adjacent to the pore is filled with granules said to be nitrogenous.

The entire exumbrella and subumbrella, outer surface of the manubrium, and both sides of the velum are clothed with epidermis, mostly cuboidal but varying from flattened to columnar.   It is liberally supplied with nematocysts and sensory nerve cells.   Nematocysts are particularly abundant on the manubrium, especially around the mouth, on the bell margin, and on the exumbrella adjacent to the margin.   A thick welt of nematocysts, the *nettle ring*, may encircle the bell near the margin. Nematocysts may be scattered all over the exumbrella or may occur in meridional tracts, which accompanied by sensory and nerve cells ascend to the summit of the bell.   Sensory epithelium is particularly well developed on the bell margin, where it occurs as patches on the tentacular bulbs and other protuberances and as circular bands overlying each nerve ring.   Sensory epithelium is often provided with very long motile hairs resembling flagella (Fig. 124*B*, *D*).

The musculature is almost wholly epidermal.   The regular epidermal layer consists of longitudinal fibers in manubrium and tentacles and weakly developed radial fibers in the subumbrella.   These fibers are smooth and are basal extensions of epidermal cells.   In addition to this system there are highly developed striated circular muscles in subumbrella and velum.   In the subumbrella these are epitheliomuscular cells lying beneath the surface epidermis.   As a result the subumbrellar epidermis is double (Fig. 125*C*), consisting of the outer epitheliomuscular cells of the radial system, the inner ones of the circular system.   The velum (Fig. 125*B*) is composed of two epidermal epithelia with a mesolamella between.   It contains a wide band of striated circular muscles lying to the subumbrellar side of the mesolamella.   The velar muscle is separated at the bell margin from the circular layer of the subumbrella by a nonmuscular zone containing the nerve rings.   The exumbrellar epidermis is devoid of musculature except in the swimming bells of the Siphonophora.

The gastrodermis lies directly in contact with the subumbrellar and manubrial epidermis, from which it is separated by a thin mesolamella (Fig. 124*D*).   It lines the manubrium and forms the walls of the radial and ring canals.   It is histologically similar to the gastrodermis of hydranths wherever it is employed in digestive activities.   In the aboral walls of the canals (Fig. 124*B*) it is flattened, and this same flattened gastrodermis continues as a one-layered sheet, the gastrodermal lamella, between the radial canals. The gastrodermis appears to lack muscular extensions.

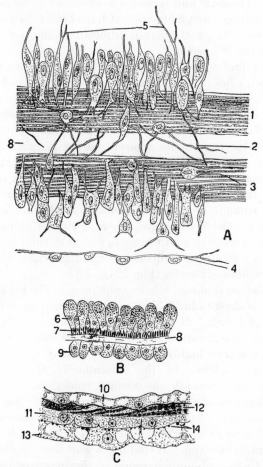

Fig. 125.—Histological structure of medusae. *A*. Nerve rings of *Gonionemus*, showing ganglion cells. (*After Hyde*, 1902.) *B*. Section through the velum. *C*. Subumbrellar epidermis of *Neoturris*, showing double layer. (*After Krasinska*, 1914.) 1, upper nerve ring; 2, fibers crossing mesolamella; 3, lower nerve ring; 4, marginal strand; 5, fibers to subumbrellar net; 6, subumbrellar epidermis of velum; 7, muscle fibers of same; 8, mesolamella; 9, exumbrellar epidermis of velum; 10, gastrodermis; 11, inner layer of subumbrellar epidermis; 12, muscle fibers of same; 13, outer layer of subumbrellar epidermis; 14, muscle fibers of same.

The mesogloea is a thick gelatinous noncellular mass lying wholly between the gastrodermis and the exumbrellar epidermis, from both of which layers it is separated by a mesolamella. It is crossed by fibers whose origin as well as that of the jelly is unknown.   Fibers and jelly are apparently secreted by both epidermis and gastrodermis.

The nervous system attains a much higher development than in the polyp.   It consists of a subepidermal plexus composed of neurites and several types of ganglion cells lying in the base of the epidermis of manubrium and tentacles and between the two epitheliomuscular layers of the subumbrella.   It is often more concentrated along the radial canals forming radial nerves.   At the bell margin the plexus connects with a thick nerve ring located at the attachment of velum to bell and composed of cables of neurites intermingled with ganglion cells.   This ring is divided into two parts, an upper and larger part above the velum attachment and a smaller, lower ring below this attachment (Figs. 124B, D and 125A).   Both are in the base of the outer epidermis next the mesolamella, and they connect with each other and the subumbrellar plexus by fibers penetrating the mesolamella.   The upper ring receives fibers from tentacles, sensory tracts and patches of the margin, tentacular bulbs, and ocelli.   The lower ring receives fibers from the statocysts and supplies the velar and subumbrellar musculature; the velum is said to be devoid of ganglion cells.   These rings may be regarded as a central nervous system.   As already mentioned, long-haired sensory tracts overlie each ring (Fig. 124B, D).

Medusae are the sexual individuals of the Hydrozoa.   The gonads consist of epidermal folds in which the sex cells ripen.   Medusae are nearly always dioecious.   An exception is the curious genus *Eleutheria* in which eggs and sperm develop together in the walls of an epidermal brood pouch situated above the stomach (Fig. 126A).

Although the medusa form can theoretically be derived from the polyp by oral-aboral shortening and radial expansion, medusae are not actually formed in this way except in the Trachylina (Fig. 143A–D). In the Hydroida they or their morphological equivalents develop on the polyp or polypoid colony as asexual buds termed *gonophores*.   The total assemblage of gonophores and associated parts in a species is called the *gonosome*, while the totality of the asexual structures is the *trophosome*.

In the Gymnoblastea, the gonophores are conspicuous oval or rounded stalked bodies without periderm covering.   They bud from the stolons (as *Perigonimus*, Fig. 126B), hydrocaulus, hydranth stalks (*Clava*, Fig. 113D; *Bougainvillia*, Fig. 126C), hydranths themselves (*Syncoryne*, Fig. 114A; *Pennaria*, Fig. 114B; *Tubularia*, Fig. 114C) or, less commonly, from modified hydranths known as gonozooids or blastostyles (*Eudendrium*, Fig. 126D, E; *Hydractinia*, Fig. 118D).   When borne upon the ordinary gastrozooids the gonophores may be strewn over the manubrium (Fig. 114A) but more often bud from a zone just above the proximal tentacles (Fig. 114B, C) or on the stalk just below the hydranth

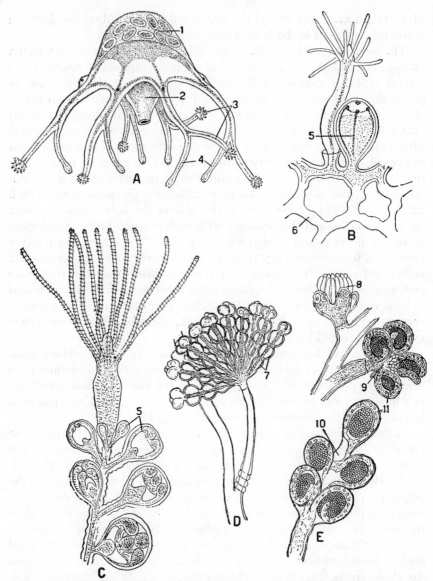

Fig. 126.—Brood chamber, types of gonophores. A. *Eleutheria*, showing suckers and brood chamber. (*After Hincks*, 1868.) B. *Perigonimus* with hydrorhizal gonophore. (*After Motz-Kossowska*, 1905.) C. Hydroid of *Bougainvillia* with gonophores, from life. D. Male gonophores of *Eudendrium*, from life. E. Three stages in the degeneration of the female gonozooid of *Eudendrium*, from life. 1, brood chamber with planulae; 2, manubrium; 3, nematocyst-bearing fork of tentacle; 4, sucker-bearing fork of tentacle; 5, gonophore; 6, hydrorhizal net; 7, male gonophores; 8, young female gonozooid with evident tentacles; 9, later stage, tentacles degenerating; 10, mature gonozooid with five gonophores; 11, spadix.

base (Fig. 113D). They frequently arise in a definite and orderly sequence with the oldest most basal and the age decreasing apically (Fig. 126C). Gonozooids in the Gymnoblastea present various degrees of modification from typical gastrozooids. Through reduction and eventual loss of tentacles, closure of the mouth, and reduction of the gastrovascular cavity, the gastrozooid alters into a *blastostyle*, a club-shaped projection bearing the gonophores upon its sides. In some hydroids, as *Eudendrium* (Fig. 126D, E), the transformation of a gastro-zooid into a blastostyle can be followed directly, for the gonophore-bearing hydranth starts out with mouth and tentacles and gradually reduces to a stump as the gonophores ripen (Fig. 126E). In this genus the male gonophores (Fig. 126D) occur as two or more successive swellings on stalks encircling the end of the stem that bore the gonozooid. In *Hydractinia* (Fig. 118D) the gonozooids retain short tentacles or nemato-cyst heads. In *Corymorpha* (Fig. 119A), *Tubularia* (Fig. 118A), and related forms, the numerous gonophores are borne on long branching stems (Fig. 119C) that spring in a circlet just above the proximal ten-tacles; it is debatable whether these stems represent blastostyles.

In the Calyptoblastea the gonophores are nearly always located on typical stalk-like blastostyles (Fig. 127A–F) and these are enclosed in a vase-like case of periderm termed the *gonotheca*, the opening of which is plugged by the blastostyle tip or sometimes closed by a lid. The gonotheca together with its enclosed blastostyle bearing one to many gonophores is often spoken of as a *gonangium*. In the gonangium the oldest gonophore bud is generally next to the top and the others decrease in age basally (Fig. 127D). Gonangia spring directly from the stolons in hydrorhizal colonies (*Clytia*, Fig. 115E; *Orthopyxis*, Fig. 128B); from the angles between branches or between hydranth stems and branches or on hydrocaulus or branches in other types of colonies (*Obelia*, Fig. 127D; *Plumularia*, Fig. 127E; *Sertularia*, Fig. 127A). The gonotheca is generally smooth but may be ribbed (*Clytia*, Fig. 115E) or spined. In *Halecium* (Fig. 127C) one or two hydranths often occur on the end of the gonangium.

Among some Hydroida the gonangia are limited to special regions of the colony modified for their protection. Thus in the Lafoeidae (*Lafoea*, *Filellum*, *Grammaria*) the gonangia are grouped into a mass interspersed with tentaculozooids (Fig. 127H, J). Such a mass was originally supposed to be a distinct kind of hydroid and was named *Coppinia*. Protective modifications for the gonangia are of common occurrence in the family Plumulariidae and are termed *phylactocarps*. A phylacto-carp is usually a modified hydrocladium or consists of accessory branchlets to a hydrocladium. Starting out as branches set aside for the bearing of gonangia and often characterized by an abundance of nematophores

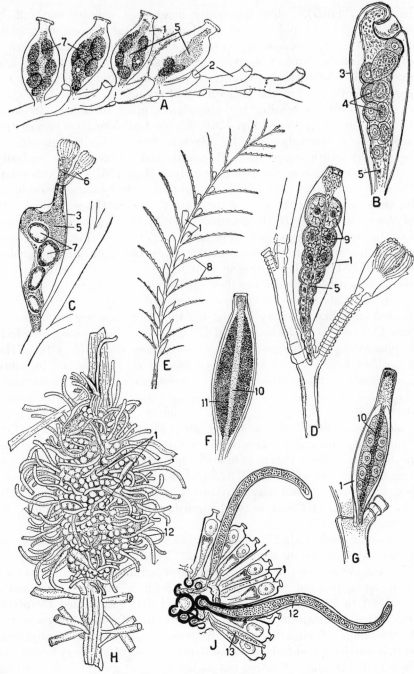

Fᴵɢ. 127.—For descriptive legend see opposite page.

and a lack or reduction of hydrothecae, phylactocarps reach a high degree of development in such genera as *Aglaophenia* (Fig. 113*C*) and *Theocarpus* where the modified hydrocladium bears leaf-like outgrowths that arch over the gonangia, forming a *basket* or *corbula*. This is termed *open* when the "leaves" are separate, as in *Theocarpus* (Fig. 128*C*), *closed* when they are fused sidewise into a pod-like case enclosing the gonangia as in *Aglaophenia* (Fig. 128*A*).

The Hydroida are commonly dioecious, and all the medusae, gonophores, and sex cells produced by one colony are of the same sex. Male and female gonophores may differ in appearance, as in *Eudendrium* (Fig. 126*D*, *E*). Some species are monoecious, and cases occur in which gonophores of both sexes bud on one hydranth or blastostyle or even in which eggs and sperm develop in the same gonophore. Sexual differentiation is well fixed in dioecious hydroids and is inherited in asexual reproduction. Föyn mingled the cells (obtained by squeezing stems through bolting cloth) from male and female colonies of the dioecious *Clava squamata* and obtained some hermaphroditic colonies among those regenerated from such masses.

When a gonophore bud transforms into a typical free medusa, its development proceeds as follows (Fig. 129). It begins as a protuberance composed of epidermis and gastrodermis. Very early in many forms, the epidermis splits off an outer layer that takes no part in further development but remains as a *sheath* or *mantle* enclosing the developing gonophore (Fig. 127*D*). The epidermis at the tip of the gonophore bud proliferates a group of cells that invaginate and roll up into a sphere; this is known as the *entocodon* ("Glockenkern" of German writers) and is the primordium of the subumbrella (Fig. 129*A–C*). The gastrodermis now pushes out around the entocodon into four tubes destined to become the radial canals; it also projects centrally carrying the entocodon before it to form the primordium of the manubrium (Fig. 129*D*, *E*). The surface epidermis of the gonophore then invaginates, forming with the adjacent epidermis of the entocodon a double epidermal plate, the *velar plate* (Fig. 129*F*). The gastrodermal lamella arises by outgrowth from the radial canals as a single plate of gastrodermis, being never double as often stated. The tips of the radial canals fuse sidewise to form the ring canal. The medusa is completed by the rupture of the center of the velar

---

Fig. 127.—Thecate gonangia. *A.* Branch of *Sertularia* with gonangia. *B.* Gonangium of *Campanularia* with sessile female gonophores. *C.* Gonangium of *Halecium* topped by two polyps. *D.* Gonangium of *Obelia*, with developing medusae. *E.* Sprig of *Plumularia*, with gonangia. *F.* Enlarged male gonangium of the same. *G.* Enlarged female gonangium of same. (*A–G*, from life.) *H.* Coppinia of *Lafoea*. (*After Pictet and Bedot*, 1900.) *J.* Part of a section through the coppinia. (*After Nutting*, 1899.) 1, gonangia; 2, ordinary hydrotheca; 3, gonotheca; 4, gonophore; 5, blastostyle; 6, polyps; 7, developing planulae; 8, hydrocladium; 9, gonophores developing into medusae covered by a mantle; 10, spadix; 11, testes; 12, special protective hydrothecae; 13, male gonangium.

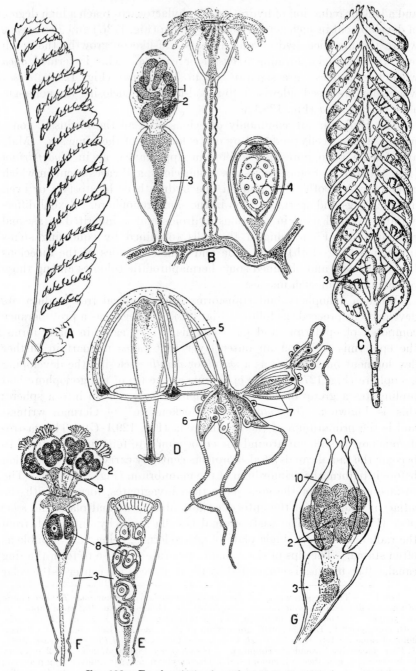

Fig. 128.—For descriptive legend see opposite page.

plate, freeing the velum, by outgrowth of tentacles and other marginal structures, and by narrowing of the stalk attaching it to the blastostyle. This stalk finally constricts through, the sheath if present ruptures, and the gonophore is freed as a complete medusa. Each gonophore becomes a single medusa. Often the medusa later increases in size and may develop additional tentacles, radial canals, and marginal structures.

In the majority of the Hydroida, however, the gonophores do not develop into free medusae but remain attached as *sessile* gonophores in which the sex cells ripen and the embryos develop. Some species constitute transitional cases in that the gonophores sometimes detach as free medusae and sometimes fail to do so. Examination of the structure of sessile gonophores reveals that they represent reduced medusae and that various stages in this reduction process can be recognized. The least modified or *eumedusoid* type of gonophore (Fig. 130A) may quite resemble a developing medusa but never puts forth tentacles and other marginal structures. Occasionally such eumedusoid gonophores detach as medusae but, lacking a mouth, cannot survive long. As a variant of the eumedusoid type, the manubrium may fail to develop, in which case the sex cells occur on the radial canals of the gonophore. The next or *cryptomedusoid* stage (Fig. 130B) lacks velar invagination and radial canals, having a simple gastrodermal layer in the gonophore wall. In the final stages of reduction, the gastrodermis remains inactive at the stage of the original simple evagination. These types are classified as *heteromedusoid* (Fig. 130E) when traces of the entocodon are present and *styloid* (Fig. 130C) where the gonophore has failed to develop beyond the original epidermal-gastrodermal protuberance. Finally in some cases all traces of gonophore evaginations have vanished, and the sex cells ripen directly on the sides of the blastostyle (Fig. 130D). These last three reduced types are often called *sporosacs*, and the central core on whose surface the sex cells ripen is termed the *spadix* (Fig. 130D). The type of gonophore formed by hydroids bears no relation to their systematic position; among closely related forms some may give off typical medusae while others produce sporosacs. Not infrequently the male and female gonophores of one species belong to different types.

This lack of relation of gonophore type to hydroid introduces many taxonomic difficulties. Often closely related hydroids produce very

Fig. 128.—Protective devices, budding medusa. *A.* A corbula of *Aglaophenia*, closed type. (*After Nutting*, 1900.) *B. Orthopyxis*, from life, with hydrorhizal gonangia which evert as acrocysts. *C.* Open type of corbula, *Theocarpus*. (*After Nutting*, 1900.) *D. Hybocodon*, budding medusae from the tentacular bulbs. (*After Mayer*, 1910.) *E* and *F.* Gonangia of *Gonothyraea*, from life: *E*, before and *F*, after, emission of the medusoid gonophores, acting as brood sacs. *G.* Gonangium of *Diphasia* with brood chamber of chitinous leaves, preserved. 1, acrocyst; 2, developing planulae; 3, gonangium; 4, acrocyst before emission; 5, nematocyst tracts; 6, tentacular bulb; 7, young medusae; 8, gonophores before discharge; 9, discharged gonophores (meconidia); 10, leaves of brood chamber.

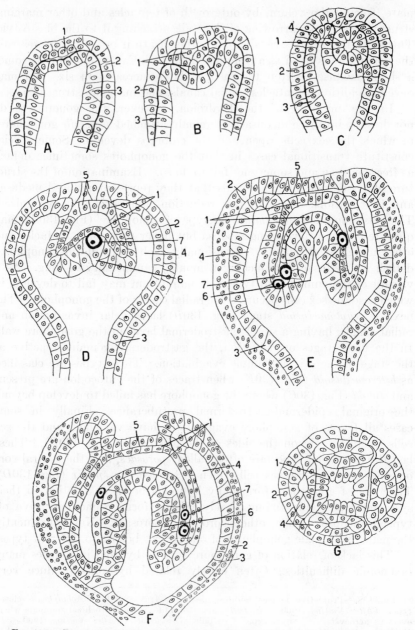

Fig. 129.—Development of a gonophore into a medusa. (*After Goette*, 1907.)   A. Early stage, epidermis proliferating the entocodon. B. Continued proliferation. C. Entocodon completed, cut off from epidermis, radial canals progressing. D. Velar plate and manubrium forming. E. Further growth of manubrium. F. Velar plate complete, invaginated. G. Cross section of D, showing entocodon surrounded by four radial canals. 1, entocodon; 2, epidermis; 3, gastrodermis; 4, radial canal; 5, velar plate; 6, manubrium; 7, sex cells.

different free medusae and vice versa, so that the medusae may be classified into a different family from the hydroids which bore them. In the case of many medusae, the hydroid stage has not been as yet identified, but since no hydroid medusa is known to develop directly from the egg, the existence of a polyp stage is always to be assumed. Because of these difficulties it is still necessary to classify the polyps and the medusae separately, and often the medusa bears a different generic name from its hydroid.

Medusae can arise not only by the transformation of gonophore buds but also by asexual budding from other medusae (Fig. 128D). This happens most commonly in the Anthomedusae, in such genera as *Rathkea* (includes *Lizzia*), *Sarsia*, *Corymorpha*, *Hybocodon*, *Bougainvillia*, and others; very rarely do the Leptomedusae bud. The buds form on manubrium, bell margin, tentacular bulbs, radial canals and other sites and appear in an orderly sequence. Medusae usually develop from such buds in the same way as they do from gonophore buds; but in some cases it appears that the buds are wholly ectodermal. In one species (*Phialidium mccradyi*), gonads may sprout out into blastostyles that give off medusae. One or two cases are known of longitudinal fission in hydroid medusae.

4. Sexual Reproduction.—The sex cells of the Hydrozoa are commonly stated in books to be of epidermal origin; but in fact they usually develop from interstitial cells located in either epidermis or gastrodermis. They may also descend from ordinary epidermal or gastrodermal cells, either directly or after a mitosis in which one daughter cell becomes a germ cell and the other remains a body cell. The sex cells often begin their differentiation at some distance from the gonads, into which they later wander by more or less definite routes. They complete their development in the base of the epidermis of the gonad, next to the mesolamella. The aggregation of young spermatogonia develops into spermatozoa of the ordinary flagellate type by a typical spermatogenesis. Of the many young ovocytes in an ovary, only a few (sometimes one) mature into ova; the others are engulfed by or fuse with the future ova or break down to serve as food for them. Adjacent body cells may also be utilized as food by the ova. The gonads can scarcely be designated organs, being merely accumulations of sex cells in definite sites. In the Anthomedusae the gonads are typically situated on the sides of the manubrium, and in the Leptomedusae on the under surface of the radial canals but exceptions occur. In a few hydroids in which all trace of a medusoid generation has been lost, the gonads develop directly in the epidermis (hydras) or the gastrodermis (*Protohydra*) of the polyp. Otherwise the gonads are confined to medusae or sessile gonophores.

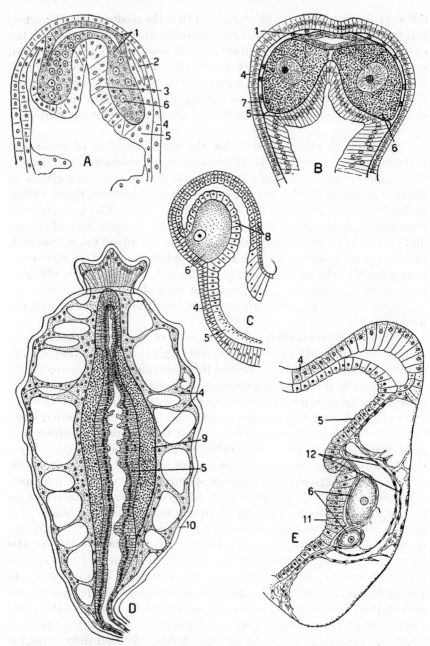

Fig. 130.—Types of sessile gonophores. *A*. Eumedusoid type, *Tubularia*. (*After Goette*, 1907.) *B*. Cryptomedusoid type, *Clava*. (*After Kühn*, 1910.) *C*. Styloid type, *Eudendrium*. (*After Weissmann*, 1883.) *D*. Section through gonangium of *Sertularella*, with no trace of gonophore evaginations. (*After Weissmann*, 1883.) *E*. Heteromedusoid

In many medusae the eggs are shed into the sea water, but in others they develop in situ to a late stage. In sessile gonophores the eggs develop to a planula or later stage inside the gonophores. In some medusae of the family Cladonemidae development occurs in the summit of the bell in a brood chamber formed by extension of the subumbrellar cavity (Fig. 126*A*). Special brooding arrangements also exist in some hydroids. Thus in the sertularian genus *Diphasia*, chitinous leaves sprout from the summit of the female gonotheca and arch over to form a brood chamber (Fig. 128*G*). A chitinous sac, the *acrocyst*, in which development is completed may protrude from the gonangium as in *Orthopyxis* (Fig. 128*B*). In *Gonothyraea* the very medusoid gonophores emerge one by one from the gonangium and act as external brood sacs, called *meconidia* (Fig. 128*E, F*).

Cleavage is indeterminate, holoblastic, adequal, and radial. The blastomeres are often very loosely associated and seemingly without definite arrangement. An adequal coeloblastula is usually formed, and this is a free ciliated larva in cases where the eggs are shed. The entoderm never arises by invagination. In blastular larvae, it forms by unipolar ingression at the posterior end; where the blastula stage is passed inside gonophores as in the vast majority of the Hydroida, the entoderm usually originates by multipolar ingression (Fig. 131*C*). Primary and secondary delamination also occur. In a few forms with very yolky eggs, the ectoderm arises by superficial cleavage and the entoderm is a central syncytial mass on whose surface an entodermal epithelium later differentiates. In any case, a stereogastrula results that is ordinarily set free as a ciliated mouthless larva termed a *planula*. The planula (Fig. 131*A*) is an elongated polarized organism with a broad anterior end, narrow posterior end, and a columnar ectoderm enclosing an entodermal mass. It possesses considerable cellular differentiation, having nerve, sensory, and gland cells, muscle extensions, and nematocysts (Fig. 131*H*). Sensory and nerve cells are more numerous at the anterior end.

After leading a free life for a few hours to several days, the planula fixes to some object (Fig. 131*D*) by its anterior end (sometimes the side). Meantime the entoderm mass has arranged into a regular epithelium lining the gastrovascular cavity. In the athecate and many of the thecate hydroids, the attached planula then develops directly into a hydranth by putting out tentacles, forming a mouth at its apical (originally posterior) end, and sending out stolons from its base (Fig. 131*E*–

type, *Plumularia echinata*, half of a gonangium, showing trace of entocodon. (*After Goette*, 1907.) Entocodon stippled in *A* and *B*. 1, entocodon; 2, radial canal; 3, manubrium; 4, epidermis; 5, gastrodermis; 6, eggs; 7, gastrodermal lamella; 8, spadix; 9, testis; 10, gonotheca; 11, gonophore evagination of gastrodermis; 12, trace of entocodon.

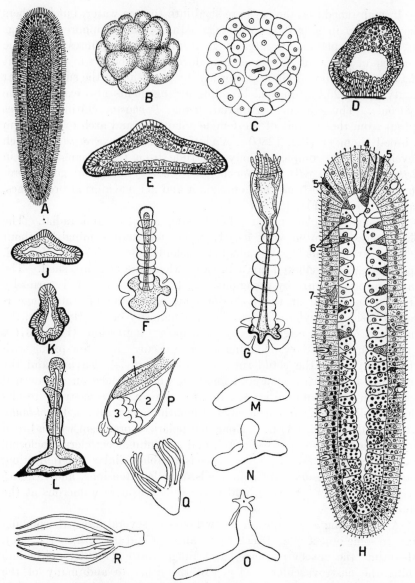

Fig. 131.—Development of hydroids.   *A.* A young planula, from life, with solid ento-dermal mass.   *B–H.* Development of *Gonothyraea* (*after Wulfert*, 1902): *B*, cleavage stage; *C*, entoderm formation by multipolar ingression; *D*, newly attached planula; *E*, later stage of attached planula; *F*, hydranth growing up from attached mass; *G*, hydranth completed; *H*, longitudinal section of mature planula of *Gonothyraea*, gastrovascular cavity formed.   *J–L*, *Sertularella polyzonias* (*after Müller-Cole and Krüger*, 1913): *J*, newly attached planula; *K*, upper surface of same developing a growing point; *L*, growing point elongated.   *M–O*, *Stomotoca* (*after Rittenhouse*, 1910): *M*, planula attaching on side; *N*, planula ends grow out to stolons and center buds a hydranth; *O*, later stage of stolons and hydranth.   *P–R*, Actinula development in *Tubularia*, from life: *P*, female gonophore with

G). From this single polyp the entire colony then originates by growth and budding. In the higher thecate forms such as the plumularians, the planula itself never changes into a polyp, but its free end becomes a continuous growing point leaving behind a stem from whose sides polyps and branches arise (Fig. 131*J–L*). In occasional cases, the planula transforms into a hydrorhiza, which buds off the colony (Fig. 131*M–O*).

In some hydroids, as many Tubulariidae and *Myriothela*, the planula remains in the gonophore and develops further into an *actinula,* a tentaculate larva resembling a short, stalkless polyp (Fig. 131*P–R*). This becomes free, creeps about, attaches, and develops directly into a polyp.

The rear end of the planula becomes the oral end of the polyp; but this reversal of polarity is only apparent, for the original polarity established by the attachment of the egg in the gonophore reasserts itself eventually. The free pole of the egg while in the gonophore is the animal pole, rear end of the planula, and oral end of the resulting polyp (Teissier). This polarity appears to constitute the only definite organization of the hydroid egg; for single blastomeres, groups of blastomeres, or portions of blastulae develop normally like whole eggs.

5. Order Hydroida.—The order Hydroida, to which the foregoing account of polyp and medusa chiefly applies, includes the majority of the Hydrozoa. The hydroid types are divisible into the athecate (Gymnoblastea) and thecate (Calyptoblastea) forms. The former are classified chiefly on the basis of tentacle type, the latter on the form of the hydrotheca and manubrium.

To the Athecata belongs the family Hydridae, comprising the hydras, with numerous species common in ponds and lakes throughout the world. Some species are cosmopolitan, as the green hydra (*Chlorohydra viridissima*) and the brown hydra (*Pelmatohydra oligactis*) but the majority are limited to continents or parts of continents; of the eight species known to occur in the United States, only the two just mentioned are also found in other countries.[1] The body or *column* is a few to 15 mm. or more long and is differentiated into a manubrium (or *hypostome*) bearing a circlet of tentacles, mostly five or six in number, a *stomach* or *gastric region*, the *stalk*, and the *pedal disk* (Fig. 132*D*). Each of these regions has special histological peculiarities. The gastrodermis of the manubrium is composed largely of mucous gland cells (Figs. 107*E* and 108*A*), which presumably play a role in the swallowing of food;

---

[1] For the taxonomy of American hydras consult the author's papers in the *Trans. Amer. Micros. Soc.*

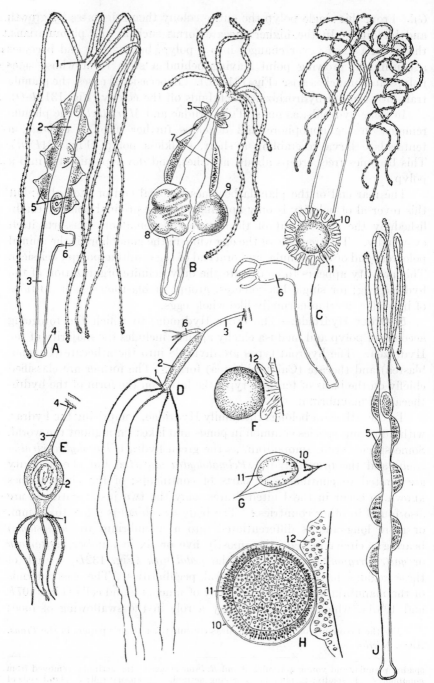

FIG. 132.—For descriptive legend see opposite page.

that of the gastric region, where digestion takes place, contains enzymatic gland cells, probably of two sorts (Fig. 107F); that of the stalk region lacks gland cells or digestive power and is highly vacuolated (Fig. 107G); and the pedal disk is distinguished by its secretory epidermis (Fig. 107H) producing an adhesive substance for attachment. The mouth on the summit of the manubrium has at rest a folded star-like shape (Fig. 108A) and is capable of great distension. The hollow, highly extensile tentacles are no longer than the column in some species, 1½ to 5 times its length in others. They are armed with batteries of nematocysts, each enclosed within a single epidermal cell (Fig. 111F). All hydras have four kinds of nematocysts (Fig. 110D–M, page 386). The stalk is very slender and obvious in some species, separated for that reason into the genus Pelmatohydra (Fig. 132D), less noticeable in others, retained in the genus Hydra, strict sense (Fig. 132A). The epidermis of the pedal disk not only secretes a substance enabling the disk to adhere to objects, but its central part is able to secrete gas (Kepner and Thomas, 1928). The gas bubble is held inside the adhesive secretion and enables the hydra to float to the surface and remain there suspended. The gastrodermis of the pedal disk also presents some peculiarities, containing many inclusions, probably of the nature of food, and having well-developed muscle extensions. In at least some species, there is a pore through the center of the pedal disk which may be completely closed during ordinary attachment (Kanajew, 1927).

Besides the regular asexual budding at the junction of gastric region and stalk (page 409), hydras sometimes undergo transverse and longitudinal fission but probably only as sequels to abnormal regenerations, persistence of buds, or other atypical conditions. A persistent bud will come to equal the parent in size, and the animal then appears to be a double-headed hydra. Such specimens then divide longitudinally to the base and eventually separate into two hydras. Abnormal specimens with double basal ends also split longitudinally toward the oral end. All longitudinal fissions are probably of this kind. Abnormalities that lead to fission probably in all cases result from a preceding period of depression (page 487). The author found that doubled parts and other abnormali-

---

Fig. 132.—American hydras, from life or slides. A. Male of the swift water hydra, Hydra littoralis. B. Hydra utahensis, a hermaphroditic species, with sex organs. C. Female of Hydra littoralis, with a developing egg enclosed in the spiny theca. D. The brown hydra, Pelmatohydra oligactis, extended. E. The same species after ingestion of a worm. F. Mature egg of hydra, just after extrusion, showing epidermal cup that holds egg. G. Developing egg of Hydra utahensis with smooth helmet-shaped theca. H. Embryo of Pelmatohydra oligactis, in stereogastrula stage, showing also smooth thin theca of this species. J. Male of Pelmatohydra oligactis, testes lack nipples. 1, hypostome with tentacles; 2, stomach region; 3, stalk; 4, pedal disk; 5, testes; 6, bud; 7, young ovary; 8, advanced ovary with egg in scalloped phase; 9, mature ovary, egg ready to be extruded; 10, embryonic theca; 11, embryo; 12, epidermal cup.

ties occur in nature in the ratio of about one per thousand (Hyman, 1928).

The food consists of a variety of small animals such as crustaceans (except ostracods), insect larvae, annelid worms, etc., and the larger species may even subdue and ingest newly hatched fish and tadpoles. The prey on striking the tentacles is held and quickly paralyzed. Animals much larger than the body diameter can be ingested, and the gastric region is capable of incredible distension. Extracellular digestion is completed in several hours, and indigestible portions of the prey are ejected through the mouth.

Sexual reproduction is seasonal, generally occurring in autumn or early winter as a consequence of lowered temperature; but in some species comes in spring or early summer, apparently in response to rising temperature. In some species gonads can be regularly induced within 2 or 3 weeks by experimentally altering the temperature. Whether feeding or starvation can induce the sexual condition is doubtful, since experiments on this point are indecisive. In laboratory cultures, hydras frequently become sexual without apparent cause. The gonads consist of accumulations of epidermal interstitial cells that cause the epidermis to bulge into elevations supported by the stretched epidermal cells. The testes are conical protrusions often provided with a nipple for the exit of the sperm (Fig. 132A); but such nipples are lacking in the brown hydra (*Pelmatohydra oligactis*, Fig. 132J). In the ovary the interstitial cells fuse with or engulf each other, and a single large food-filled ovum results (Fig. 132B). This is forced into a scalloped shape (Fig. 132B) usually but falsely considered to be an amoeboid phase, by the supporting columns of epidermal cells coursing through the ovary. The majority of hydra species are strictly dioecious, but some are hermaphroditic. In dioecious species the testes occur throughout the gastric region (Fig. 132A); in hermaphroditic species they are distal near the oral end (Fig. 132B). The ovaries are commonly proximal, near the budding zone, but in dioecious species may spread throughout the gastric region.[1] Each hydra produces a succession of eggs. In some species only one egg ripens at a time, and 2 or 3 days elapse between successive eggs; in other species a number of eggs ripen simultaneously. When the egg is ripe it bursts through the epidermis, which withdraws, forming a little cup or cushion in which the egg rests (Fig. 132F). The naked protruded egg must be fertilized within a short time or it perishes. When fertilized it cleaves into equal blastomeres; entoderm formation occurs by ingression and primary delamination (Fig. 74B, C) so that a stereogastrula results (Fig. 132H). During late cleavage the embryo

---

[1] Gonads never occur on the stalk region, as represented in some current textbook figures of hydra.

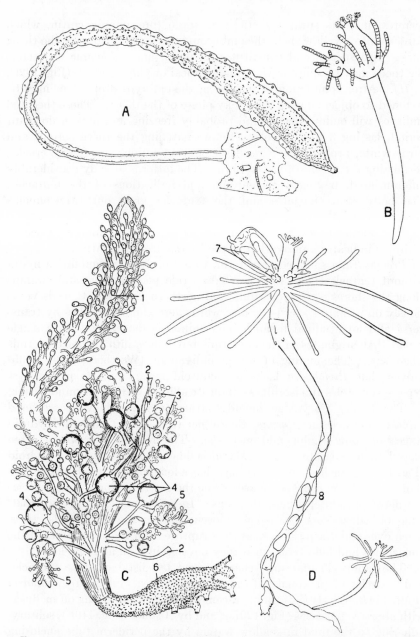

Fig. 133.—Various gymnoblastic hydroids. *A. Protohydra.* (*After Luther*, 1923.) *B. Heterostephanus*, budding from the hydranth. (*After Rees*, 1937.) *C. Myriothela*, with claspers. (*After Allman*, 1876.) *D. Hypolytus*, stolon breaking up into asexual reproductive bodies inside the periderm. (*After Miles*, 1937.) 1, manubrium with tentacles; 2, claspers; 3, gonozooids; 4, ripe egg held by claspers; 5, actinula larva discharging; 6, base with periderm covering; 7, gonophores; 8, reproductive bodies.

secretes upon its surface a sticky material, presumably chitin, which hardens into a yellow shell, the embryonic theca. The form of the theca varies with species and constitutes an important taxonomic character; the theca may be spiny or smooth, spherical or plano-convex (Fig. 132C, G, H). After completion of the theca, the embryos drop off or may be fastened to objects during the sticky phase of the theca. These thecated embryos will endure drying and probably freezing and have a dormant period, lasting 3 to 10 weeks. Before hatching the theca softens and turns white, probably as a result of enzyme action, and finally cracks, permitting the escape of the embryo. The latter is already considerably differentiated, having a coelenteron and indications of the tentacles. The body soon elongates and the tentacles grow out (McConnell's account, 1938).

The similarity of their nematocysts to those of marine athecate hydroids indicates a derivation of the hydras from the latter.

Protohydra, a small solitary form, to 3 mm. long, resembling a hydra without tentacles (Fig. 133A), inhabits tide pools and coastal swamps along the shores of Great Britain and northern Europe. It feeds voraciously on nematodes, crustaceans, worms, etc., and multiplies by transverse and longitudinal fission. The animal is dioecious, with a single gonad that originates in the epidermis but bulges into the gastrodermis when ripe. The finding of sexual individuals (Westblad, 1930, 1935) proves that *Protohydra* lacks a medusoid stage, and its nematocyst types—stenoteles and isorhizas—indicate affinity with the Gymnoblastea.

The family Corynidae includes athecate hydroids with scattered capitate tentacles as *Coryne*, *Syncoryne* (Fig. 114A) and the hydroid stages of some cladonemid medusae. The related *Myriothela*, often placed in a separate family, Myriothelidae, a small, solitary hydroid (Fig. 133C) attached by a short base, has a long manubrium covered with short tentacles and bears gonozooids on the gastric region. Some species are hermaphroditic, others dioecious. In some species as in Fig. 133C long-stalked suckers ("claspers") occur among the gonozooids; these reach over and grasp the eggs as they rupture from the gonophores of the gonozooids and hold them until they develop into an actinula larva.

The family Pennariidae, characterized by distal capitate tentacles and a circlet of proximal filiform tentacles, is exemplified by *Pennaria* (Figs. 114B and 116E), forming racemose colonies and giving off medusae with abortive tentacles (Fig. 120D); and by *Acaulus* (Fig. 119F), solitary, adhering to the mud in shallow waters by the periderm tube enclosing the pointed stem. *Heterostephanus*, also solitary, is notable in that the hydranth buds off other hydranths (Fig. 133B). Even more noteworthy is the fact that the oral end of the bud is attached to the parent, not the basal end, as is usual in hydroid budding.

The Tubulariidae are distinguished by oral and proximal circlets of filiform tentacles, the grape-like bunches of gonophores, and in many species, the stem structure (Fig. 119E). *Tubularia* (Fig. 114C) forms loose racemose colonies of long-stemmed pink hydranths. Here belong the largest hydroids, solitary forms with basal holdfasts: *Corymorpha* to 10 cm. in length (Fig. 119A) and the gigantic *Branchiocerianthus*, to 2 m. in height, with bilaterally arranged gonophore clusters and tentacles. The small solitary *Hypolytus*, living on mud bottoms along the New England coast, constricts off successive oval bodies from the basal end of the stem (Fig. 133D) and these regenerate into young polyps. *Ectopleura* and *Trichorhiza* are other solitary tubulariids, having a slender stem of which the lower end coils around objects. The pelagic hydranths, *Margelopsis* and *Pelagohydra*, may be considered here. The former, resembling a *Tubularia* head, breaks loose from the colony and leads a floating existence. The curious *Pelagohydra* (Fig. 134A), taken only once, on the New Zealand coast (Dendy, 1902), appears to be a true pelagic hydranth. Its basal region, bearing tentacles and blastostyles, and separated by a diaphragm from the distal digestive region, is greatly expanded into a float whose wall is provided with gastrodermal canals and whose cavity is crossed by radiating partitions.

Scattered filiform tentacles characterize the family Clavidae, exemplified by *Clava* (Fig. 113D). *Cordylophora*, the only fresh-water colonial hydroid, found in rivers and brackish inlets, forms typical branching colonies with sporosacs on the hydranth stems.

The Bougainvilliidae have an elongated manubrium with a single circlet of filiform tentacles. Typical forms are *Bougainvillia* (Fig. 126C), *Perigonimus* (Fig. 126B), and *Hydractinia* (Fig. 118C–F). In *Dicoryne*, the ciliated sporosacs become free and swim about (Ashworth and Ritchie, 1915). The curious *Clathrozoon* (Spencer, 1890) forms rhizocaulomic colonies (Fig. 116D) protected by numerous tiny dactylozooids (Fig. 118C).

The Eudendriidae include only *Eudendrium*, forming loose racemose colonies (Fig. 113A) with characteristic male and female gonophores (Fig. 126D, E). The pink hydranths have a globular manubrium and a single circlet of filiform tentacles.

The medusae of the athecate hydroids, termed Anthomedusae, have tall bells, manubrial gonads, usually ocelli on the tentacular bulbs, and no statocysts. The family Codonidae includes forms with mostly four simple radial canals, one, two, or four simple tentacles, and ring-like gonads. Typical examples are *Sarsia* (Fig. 120G) and the very similar *Slabberia*, *Corynitis*, etc., with four equal long tentacles, from the *Syncoryne* (Fig. 114A) type of hydroid; *Steenstrupia* (Fig. 121B) with one long and three abortive tentacles from *Corymorpha* (Fig. 119A, but

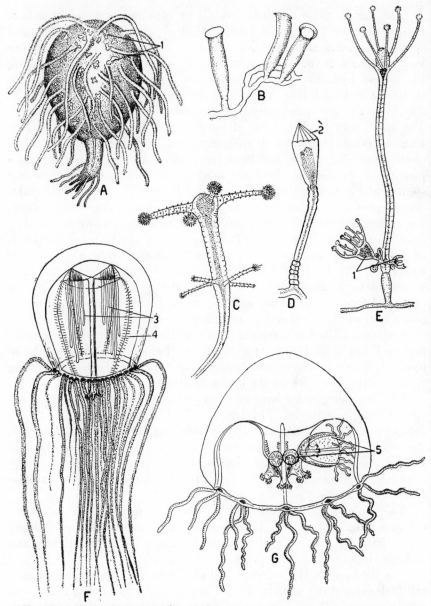

Fig. 134.—Hydroida (continued).   A. *Pelagohydra.*   (*After Dendy*, 1902.)   B. *Lafoea*, preserved.   C. *Stauridia*, hydroid of *Cladonema.*   (*After Hincks*, 1886.)   D. *Lovenella*, showing operculum.   (*After Fraser*, 1911.)   E. *Clavatella*, hydroid of *Eleutheria.*   (*After Hincks*, 1886.)   F. *Polyorchis*, from life, California.   G. *Rathkea* (= *Lizzia*) showing budding from manubrium.   (*After Fewkes*, 1881.)   1, gonophores developing into medusae; 2, operculum; 3, gonads; 4, branches of radial canals; 5, medusae budding from manubrium.

some species of *Corymorpha* do not give off medusae); the medusae of *Pennaria* (Fig. 120*D*) with four abortive tentacles; *Hybocodon*, from a *Corymorpha*-like hydranth; and *Hydrichthys* with a hydroid stage parasitic on fish (Fig. 136*B*). Some of these medusae reproduce asexually by budding off other medusae; thus several species of *Sarsia* bud medusae from the long manubrium or from the tentacular bulb; and *Hybocodon prolifer* (Fig. 128*D*) buds them from the tentacular bulbs. The medusae of the pelagic hydroids *Margelopsis* and *Pelagohydra* (Fig. 134*A*) belong here but differ from typical Codonidae in having clustered tentacles.

The anthomedusan family Cladonemidae presents several peculiarities. *Gemmaria* (Fig. 121*E*) has two and *Zanclea* four tentacles provided with nematophores; the hydroid stage is of the *Syncoryne* type. In *Cladonema* with branched tentacles (Fig. 121*A*) some of the branches may end in suckers; the hydroid is *Stauridia* (Fig. 134*C*). *Eleutheria* (Fig. 126*A*) from the hydroid *Clavatella* (Fig. 134*E*) has forked tentacles with one fork terminating in a sucker, the other in a nematocyst knob. This genus does not swim but walks about on the suckers. *Cladonema* and *Eleutheria* are both hermaphroditic, and the latter broods its young (page 423, Fig. 126*A*). The recently discovered *Oönautes* (Damas, 1933) has a gastrodermal float above the stomach. The minute *Mnestra* with abortive tentacles and gastrodermal canals replacing the manubrial cavity lives fastened to the throat of the snail *Phyllirhoe* on whose tissues it apparently feeds (Fig. 136*C*).

In the following anthomedusan families, the gonads form swollen corrugated masses on the stomach walls. The Tiaridae without oral tentacles are represented by *Stomotoca* (Fig. 121*D*) with two tentacles, and *Leuckartiara* (= *Tiara*, Fig. 120*E*) and *Neoturris* (= *Turris*) with four or more tentacles, all from *Perigonimus* (Fig. 126*B*). In the Margelidae there are oral tentacles and single or clustered marginal tentacles. *Turritopsis* with eight and *Oceania* with numerous single tentacles come from *Clava*-like hydroids. *Bougainvillia* (Fig. 120*A*) has four and *Rathkea* (includes *Lizzia*) eight tentacle clusters (Fig. 134*G*); the latter is noted for its habit of budding medusae from the manubrium (Fig. 134*G*) The Williidae are characterized by their branched radial canals, each branch terminating in a tentacle, and their *cnidothylacies*, clusters of nematocysts on the bell enclosed in gastrodermal canals; *Proboscidactyla* is representative (Fig. 135).

According to the studies of Weill on their nematocysts, the Gymnoblastea are a heterogeneous group. Desmonemes and stenoteles are characteristic, but both are lacking in *Eudendrium*, which together with *Clava*, *Hydractinia*, and some related forms, possesses microbasic euryteles. The combination of desmonemes, isorhizas, and stenoteles characteristic of the hydras also occurs in *Tubularia*.

The principal families of the calyptoblastean hydroids are: Campanulinidae, Lafoeidae, Campanulariidae, Bonneviellidae, Haleciidae, Sertulariidae, and Plumulariidae. In the first, exemplified by *Campanulina* and *Lovenella* (Fig. 134D), the hydranths have small manubria, and the hydrothecae are provided with a characteristic lid of several narrow pointed sectors. The Lafoeidae have elongated tubular hydrothecae without a lid (Fig. 134B) and gonangia in coppinia masses (page 426, Fig. 127H). To the Campanulariidae with globular manubria and goblet-shaped hydrothecae belong many of the most familiar hydroids, as *Obelia* (Fig. 127D), with free medusae; *Campanularia* (Fig. 127B) with sessile gonophores; *Clytia* (Fig. 115E) with hydrorhizal colonies and free medusae; *Orthophyxis* (Fig. 128B) with acrocysts; and *Gonothyraea*

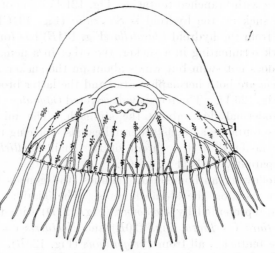

Fig. 135.—*Proboscidactyla*, from life, Puget Sound, showing branched radial canals and cnidothylacies. 1, cnidothylacies.

with external medusoid gonophores (Fig. 128F). The Bonneviellidae comprise the single genus *Bonneviella*, remarkable in the presence of a velum-like membrane above the mouth. The Haleciidae are known by the reduced hydrotheca (Fig. 117A), too small to receive the hydranth. The Sertulariidae have a stiff feathery type of growth (Fig. 136A) and curved tubular sessile hydrothecae with a lid of one to four pieces. Common genera are *Diphasia* (Fig. 128G) and *Abietinaria*, with one flap to the lid (Fig. 115B); *Sertularella* (Fig. 115C), with three or four flaps; *Sertularia* (Fig. 136A), with mostly two flaps and opposite hydrothecae; and *Thuiaria*, with one or two flaps and alternate hydrothecae. The gonothecae are vase-like (Fig. 127A). The Plumulariidae are known by the feathery form (Fig. 113C), type of colony growth (page 405, Fig 117D), sessile bell-like hydrothecae fastened along one surface

(Fig. 115*F*), and nematophores (Fig. 117*E*). Among the familiar genera are *Plumularia* and *Antennularia*, without special modifications for the gonothecae (Fig. 127*E*); *Schizotricha*, with gonothecae on special branchlets; and *Aglaophenia* (Fig. 128*A*) with closed, and *Theocarpus* (Fig. 128*C*) with open corbulae.

The majority of the Calyptoblastea lack free medusae. The medusae, known as Leptomedusae, typically have saucer- to bowl-shaped bells with gonads on the radial canals, statocysts, and mostly numerous tentacles. The families Laodiceidae and Thaumantiidae show affinities with the Anthomedusae in lacking statocysts and often possessing ocelli on the tentacular bulbs. The Laodiceidae, exemplified by *Laodicea*, *Staurophora*, and *Ptychogena*, are distinguishable from all other Leptomedusae by the cordyli or sense clubs (Fig. 124*F*) at the bases of some of the tentacles. The Thaumantiidae lack cordyli and statocysts but otherwise are a rather artificial assemblage; *Melicertum* with eight radial canals and *Polyorchis* (Fig. 134*F*), with long filamentous gonads and branched radial canals may be mentioned. The Mitrocomidae are characterized by the open type of statocyst (Fig. 124*A*, *B*) and include *Mitrocoma*, with large flat bell and four radial canals; *Halopsis*, with about 12 to 16 radial canals; and *Tiaropsis*, with four canals and eight remarkable ocelli (Fig. 123*E*). The Eucopidae with typical closed statocysts (Fig. 124*C*), no ocelli, and mostly four radial canals include some of the most common medusae, as *Obelia* (Fig. 136*D*), with eight, *Clytia*, with sixteen, and *Phialidium* (Fig. 136*E*), with many statocysts; and a group of forms exemplified by *Eutima* (Fig. 120*F*), in which the manubrium is at the end of a long *pseudomanubrium*, or peduncle. *Obelia* medusae (Fig. 136*D*) are peculiar in lacking a velum, which aborts during the growth of the gonophores. The hydroids of the Eucopidae belong to the families Campanulinidae and Campanulariidae. The Aequoridae with numerous radial canals include *Aequorea* (Fig. 121*C*) without, and *Zygodactyla* with, radial rows of warts on the subumbrellar surface.

As judged by their nematocysts, the Calyptoblastea are a homogeneous group. The characteristic nematocyst is the basitrichous isorhiza, and many forms have only this type. Atrichous isorhizas and microbasic mastigophores are common; stenoteles are lacking. *Halecium* differs from all other genera in possessing microbasic euryteles.

The Hydroida are almost exclusively marine and are among the most common animals encountered at the seashore. They are typically inhabitants of shore and shallow waters from low-tide level to depths of 50 to 100 m. The hydroid stage is with few exceptions immovably fastened to rocks, wharves, shells, seaweeds, other animals, or any firm object. On suitable bottom, hydroids may extend into deeper waters; the plumularians in particular, among the most common of hydroid forms, may go down to 1000 m. or more. *Corymorpha* and similar types, which can attach to soft bottoms, often occur in deeper waters; *Branchio-*

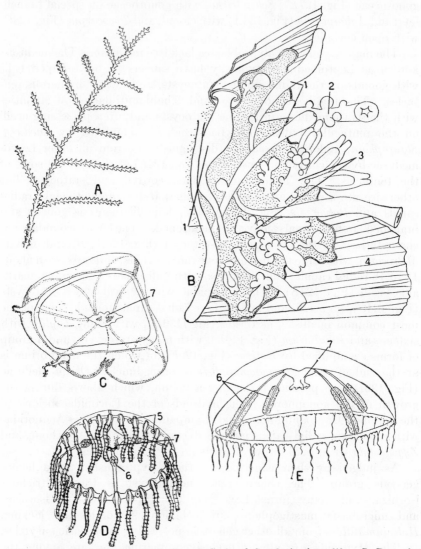

FIG. 136.—Hydroidea (continued). *A.* Sprig of *Sertularia*, from life. *B.* Part of a colony of *Hydrichthys*, growing on the tail fin of a fish. (*After Warren, 1916.*) *C. Mnestra.* (*After Günther, 1903.*) *D.* Medusa of *Obelia*, from life. *E. Phialidium*, from life, Puget Sound, a typical Leptomedusa. 1, gastrozooids; 2, gastrozooid with gonophores; 3, gonozooid with gonophores; 4, tail fin of fish; 5, statocysts; 6, gonad; 7, manubrium.

cerianthus inhabits ocean deeps 5000 m. down. Other ecological variants are brackish-water forms, as *Protohydra* (page 440) and *Cordylophora;*

fresh-water forms, as the hydras and *Cordylophora;* and pelagic types (page 441). The colony form can be much altered by environmental conditions, particularly currents and wave action. Some species and genera have a very wide distribution, while others are more or less zoned with relation to latitude, probably in response to temperature. The group reaches its greatest abundance in temperate and cold zones where single species may cover large areas of bottom.

Hydroid colonies are mostly of small to moderate size, varying from a few millimeters to 2 or 3 dm. in height. The largest colonies occur among the Plumulariidae, which may attain a length of 1 or even 2 m. The individual hydranths are generally small or microscopic but the solitary corymorphid types may attain a large size (page 441). Hydranths are usually white or of delicate coloration such as pink and violet; stems and stolons are brown from encasing periderm. Little is known of the length of life of marine hydroids, but probably the hydranths are short lived, while the coenosarc may survive for long periods, regenerating hydranths under favorable conditions. Hydras have been known to live for more than a year in laboratory conditions.

Because of their sessile habit, hydroids are apt to enter on definite relations with other organisms. Thus a number of hydroid species are found only on the floating alga *Sargassum* (Fig. 116C). Commensalism with other animals is of wide occurrence; one species is commensal with a gorgonian, and others seem to be constantly associated with particular sponges, mollusks, fish, etc. One of the most familiar associations is that of *Hydractinia* with snail shells (Fig. 118C). In temperate regions, *Hydractinia* colonies regularly grow on snail shells occupied by a hermit crab, while in the arctic the shells of live snails are utilized. The relation is not, however, obligatory as colonies are frequently found attached to inert objects. *Hydractinia* has two sorts of dactylozooids, the spiral zooids and the tentaculozooids (page 409, Fig. 118D, E). The spiral zooids occur only in colonies fixed to shells occupied by hermit crabs and are generally limited to the colony edge of the shell mouth. The tentaculozooids, of unproved function, occur in young, growing areas of the colony. Schijfsma's experiments (1935) indicate that crabs do not select shells bearing a *Hydractinia* colony, that *Hydractinia* planulae do not preferably settle on shells occupied by crabs, and that *Hydractinia* generally secures its own food, although sometimes partaking of the crab's food. The spiral zooids, surprisingly inert, were seen to lash out only to shell movement or sudden retreat of the crab into the shell. A certain degree of mutualism is indicated.

Ectocommensalism readily merges into ectoparasitism, and some of the associations of specific hydroids with specific other animals are probably of parasitic nature. The best established case is that of *Hydrichthys* on fish. The encrusting hydrorhizal mat sends stolons into the host tissues, and the tentacle-less polyps bend over and feed by applying their mouths to the injured parts (Fig. 136*B*), sucking in blood and tissues.

Symbiotic algae occur in several Hydroida, notably in the green hydra, which owes its green color to gastrodermal zoochlorellae. Its algae can be cultivated apart from the hydra and seem to be identical with free algae of the genus *Chlorella*. The relation is chiefly to the advantage of the algae, although the hydra probably uses dead and disintegrating algal cells as food. Yellow or brown zooxanthellae inhabit the gastrodermis of *Aglaophenia* and *Halecium*, and zoochlorellae occur in both epithelia of *Sertularella*.

The hydroid medusae are typical pelagic and plankton animals of shore and shallow waters. They swim by vigorous rhythmic contractions of subumbrella and velum and thus remain afloat but are powerless against currents and winds and are often carried in great numbers into bays and sounds. They may descend during the day or in rough weather and ascend at night. They are mostly of minute to moderate size, many being less than 10 mm. in diameter and few exceeding 50 mm. Among the largest forms is *Aequorea* (Fig. 121*C*), with numerous radial canals and a disk that may reach 150 mm. across. The bell is generally transparent or milky, but deeper tints often occur in manubrium, gonads, and tentacular bulbs. Many shed their eggs, apparently fertilized in advance, directly into the sea water, often at some definite hour of the day; while others retain their embryos to the planula stage, sometimes in a brood chamber (*Eleutheria*, page 423). Variants from the typical pelagic habit are seen in the creeping Cladonemidae (page 443) and the parasitic *Mnestra* (page 443).

A considerable number of Hydroida are luminescent; the light comes from granules that remain luminescent when rubbed off on the fingers. Among polyps, luminescence throughout hydranth and stalk has been noted in *Campanularia*, *Obelia*, *Sertularia*, *Plumularia*, and *Aglaophenia*. Many hydroid medusae are luminescent, such as *Lizzia*, *Oceania*, *Mitrocoma*, *Phialidium*, *Aequorea*, and *Turris*. The light comes in most cases from the tentacular bulbs and is emitted as a blue flash on mechanical or electrical stimulation.

Both hydroids and medusae are strictly or chiefly carnivorous, ingesting any small animals of appropriate size that happen to come in contact with the tentacles. Among the most common food animals are small crustaceans, nematode and annelid worms, eggs and larvae, and small fish; newly dead animals or portions thereof are also ingested. Exceptionally, the food consists of general bottom debris (*Corymorpha*, page 493). Digestion in hydras and hydroid polyps has been thoroughly studied by Beutler (1924, 1926). Hydras were made to ingest tiny bits of sponge soaked in animal juice and these were pulled out again by an attached hair. The digestive juice soaked into the sponges dissolved gelatin and fibrin and therefore contained a proteolytic enzyme active in alkaline medium (pH 8.0 to 8.2). Hydroids were induced to swallow bits of gelatin or fibrin soaked in crustacean juice, and such bits were observed to dissolve in a few minutes to an hour in the gastric cavity. After such extracellular digestion by a proteolytic enzyme, the food is reduced to a broth containing fragments. This broth is driven throughout the colony by intermittent convulsive peristaltic contractions of the hydranth and in the Sertulariidae by a pumping action of the blind sac of the gastric region of the polyp (Fig. 118*B*). The narrowed junction of hydranth and stalk prevents the passage of large particles. In the Tubulariidae, the narrowed "neck" below the hydranth was observed to be a contractile region forcing the broth into the stalk. The gastrodermal flagella are of some assistance in the circulation of the food. The broth is taken into the gastrodermis everywhere in food vacuoles and digestion completed in intracellular fashion. Fat droplets are ingested and digested by the gastrodermis, and the glycogen of the food may be taken in as such and stored; but starches, cellulose, and chitin are not digested by hydroids so far as known. In *Clava*, according to Rünnstrom, the gastrodermis spreads out as a syncytial network toward the food and digests by direct contact only.

In several genera of hydromedusae fed animal flesh coated with carmine paste, the author found that, within ½ hour after ingestion, carmine particles began to spread along the radial canals and in 1 or 2 hours the entire gastrovascular system was colored red, proof that food particles actually are distributed along this system. The carmine particles were ingested by the gastrodermal cells and retained for 2 or 3 days. The chief site of intracellular digestion (as judged by the distribution of the carmine particles) is the gastrodermis of the manubrium, stomach, and tentacular bulbs; radial and ring canals are of less importance, particularly the radial canals, which in some species took up very few carmine grains. Tentacular canals when present also ingest particles. The great importance of the tentacular bulbs in food digestion has not been hitherto realized; sections show them to be lined by a very thick gastrodermis filled with food vacuoles (Figs. 122*B* and 142*A*). The color often seen in the tentacular bulbs results from food remnants and hence is of no taxonomic importance. The beating of the numerous flagella could be readily seen throughout the gastrovascular system, but in none of the species studied were the flagellar currents definitely directed as claimed for *Melicertum*, where a peripheral current along the roof of stomach and radial canals and a central current along their floor were reported by Gemmill (1919). Stomach fluid obtained from *Aequorea* (Fig. 121*C*) was found to have considerable proteolytic and some lipolytic power but appeared to be devoid of amylase. The hydromedusae observed by the author (*Sarsia*, Fig. 120*G*; *Stomotoca*, Fig. 121*D*; *Phialidium*, Fig. 136*E*; *Aequorea*, Fig. 121*C*; and *Halistaura*) readily accepted bits of the flesh of freshly killed clams, barnacles, shrimps, crabs, and fish, when these were touched to the mouth. In nature they were seen with ingested crustaceans and crustacean larvae, polychaetous annelids, ctenophores, medusae, and refuse from adjacent salmon and pea canneries. Other medusae appeared to constitute the favorite food of *Stomotoca*, and the small *Phialidium* typically feeds on microscopic animals and larvae.

6. Order Milleporina, the Millepores.—This order together with the next, both characterized by a massive calcareous exoskeleton, are often united into the one order Hydrocorallina or even included under Hydroida. Recent students of these groups, except Broch who continues to maintain that they are Hydroida, agree, however, on the necessity of erecting separate orders for them.

The Milleporina, comprising the single genus *Millepora*, are common throughout tropical seas in shallow waters down to 30 m. They are regular components of the fauna of coral reefs, to whose formation they contribute no small share. They form upright leaf-like or branching calcareous growths (Fig. 137*A*), which may reach a height of 1 or 2 feet, or calcareous encrustations over corals or other objects, and are mostly white, flesh-like, or yellowish in color. The surface of the calcareous mass or *coenosteum* is pitted with pores of two sizes: the larger *gastropores*, through which the gastrozooids protrude, and the smaller *dactylopores*, which house the dactylozooids (Fig. 137*B*). These pores are usually irregularly scattered but may occur in *cyclosystems* with several dactylopores encircling a central gastropore. The pores lead into cavities crossed at intervals by horizontal calcareous plates or *tabulae* (Fig. 137*E*).

The minute polyps (Fig. 137*C*) have been seldom observed in the expanded state; probably like many corals they expand only at night. They are said to appear like a white felt on the coenosteum. The gastrozooid is short and plump with four to six tentacles reduced to nematocyst knobs. The dactylozooids are slender and mouthless, with a number of short, alternating, hollow capitate tentacles. Both can be completely withdrawn into the coenosteum. The latter is clothed in life with a coenosarc having a very tall epidermis and dipping down into the pores, where it becomes continuous with the zooid bases (Fig. 137*D*). Tubes of coenosarc ramify in a complicated network throughout the coenosteum and have numerous connections with the surface coenosarc and with the polyps (Fig. 137*D*). These tubes are, however, living only near the surface, and the polyps extend only to the top tabula of the tubes of the

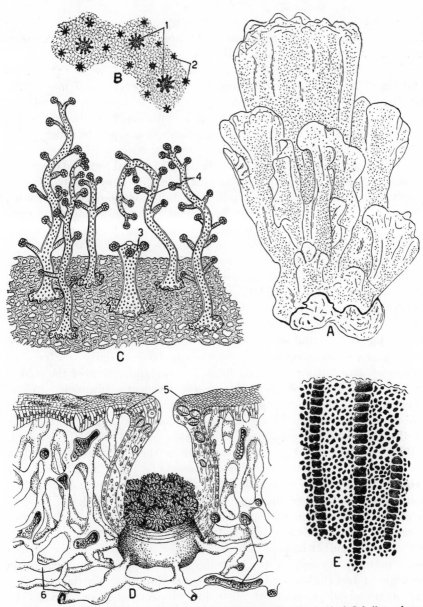

FIG. 137.—Milleporina. *A.* Piece of dry *Millepora*, showing typical flabellate shape. *B.* Same, magnified, showing pores. *C.* Polyps of *Millepora*. (*After Moseley*, 1876.) *D.* Section through *Millepora*, showing one dactylozooid, contracted; coenosteum removed by decalcification. (*After Moseley*, 1876.) *E.* Section through dry coenosteum at right angles to surface, showing polyp tubes crossed by tabulae. 1, gastropore; 2, dactylopore; 3, gastrozooid; 4, dactylozooids; 5, epidermis of surface; 6, network of coenosarc tubes throughout coenosteum; 7, coenosarc tubes cut open to show zooxanthellae.

coenosteum. The coenosarc tubes secrete the coenosteum, which in fact corresponds to the periderm of hydroid colonies. The coenosarc is thickly strewn with zooxanthellae.

The millepores have two or three kinds of nematocysts: stenoteles and (in at least some species) isorhizas on the polyps, and macrobasic mastigophores (Fig. 110*R*) at the polyp bases and in the general coenosarc. This last type of nematocyst is found only in the millepores and constitutes one reason for placing them in a separate order. The nematocysts are powerful, producing a burning sensation in man.

Gonophores bud from the coenosarc tubes in special rounded chambers of the coenosteum called ampullae (Fig. 138*A*). They become free as tiny medusae devoid of velum, tentacles, and radial canals (Fig. 138*B*). The edge of the bell bears four or five nematocyst knobs, and the gonads occur on the swollen manubrium. The medusae perish after a few hours of free life during which the sex cells are shed.

7. Order Stylasterina.—The Stylasterina superficially resemble the Milleporina, forming upright branching calcareous growths (Fig. 138*C*, *E*), often of a pink, red, violet, or purple hue; they live mostly in warm tropical and subtropical seas from shallow to deep waters, but some extend into temperate zones. An encrusting form, *Stylantheca* (Fig. 138*G*), has been found off California. The coenosteum as in *Millepora* bears gastro- and dactylopores, which may be irregularly scattered as in *Sporadipora* but are generally limited to certain regions of the colony and often occur in systems. Usually the coenosteum branches in one plane, giving a flabellate type of growth, and the systems are related to this plane, occurring only on one face of the colony or limited to the edges of the branches. Typically, as in *Stylaster* (Fig. 138*C*, *D*), *Allopora*, *Astylus*, *Cryptohelia* (Fig. 138*H*), and others the pores are arranged in cyclosystems. The gastropore is a deep cup (Fig. 139*B*), usually without tabulae and having in its bottom an upright pointed or rounded toothed spine, the *style* (whence the name of the order). The border of the cup is deeply grooved, and each groove bears a dactylopore. The dactylopores may also be provided with a style, while in some genera, as *Astylus*, styles are altogether lacking. In *Distichopora* (Fig. 138*E*, *F*) the gastropores occur on the edge of the branches in a row paralleled on each side by a row of dactylopores. In some genera as *Spinipora*, the dactylopores are mounted on tubular or spout-like projections (Fig. 138*J*). In *Cryptohelia* (Fig. 138*H*) the coenosteum forms a lid-like expansion over each cyclosystem.

The short stout gastrozooids (Fig. 139*A*) have a few to a number of short plump solid tentacles. The dactylozooids (Fig. 139*A*) are simple hollow finger-like projections without tentacles. The style occupies the center of the zooid pushing up the base of the latter into its body.

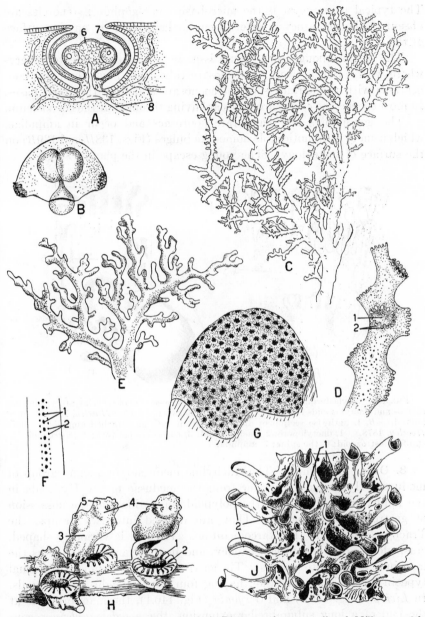

Fig. 138.—Milleporina, Stylasterina. A. Diagram of an ampulla of *Millepora* with contained gonophore. B. Medusa of *Millepora*, with three eggs. (*After Hickson, 1891.*) C. *Stylaster*, dry. D. Piece of same, magnified, showing zooid pores in cyclosystems. E. *Distichopora*, dry. F. Edge of branch of same, showing zooid pores. G. *Stylantheca*, incrusting stylasterine, California. H. *Cryptohelia*. (*After Hickson and England, 1905.*) J. *Spinipora*, with spouts for the dactylozooids. (*After Moseley, 1888.*) 1, gastropore; 2, dactylopore; 3, lid; 4, ampullae in lid; 5, nematocyst clusters; 6, manubrium; 7, umbrella; 8, coenosarc tubes.

The typical nematocyst is the microbasic mastigophore; stenoteles are absent. The nematocysts often occur in large clusters on the surface of the colony.

The porous spongy coenosteum is as in *Millepora* permeated everywhere with a rich network of coenosarc tubes that have abundant connections with the surface sheet of coenosarc and with the zooid bases. In most species the coenosarc tubes are living throughout the coenosteum.

The gonophores are degenerate sporosacs and occur in ampullae, which usually form noticeable dome-like bulges (Figs. 138*H* and 139*B*) on the surface of the colony. The young escape in the planula stage.

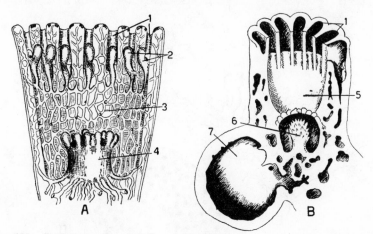

Fig. 139.—Stylasterina (concluded). *A.* Lengthwise section of a cyclosystem, showing gastro- and dactylozooids in place, and coenosarc network. (*After Moseley*, 1878, slightly altered.) *B.* Lengthwise section of dry cyclosystem with an attached ampulla. (*After Moseley*, 1878.) 1, dactylopore; 2, dactylozooid; 3, coenosarc network; 4, gastrozooid; 5, cup for gastrozooid; 6, the spine; 7, ampulla.

8. Order Trachylina.—The trachyline medusae are a small group of medusoid Hydrozoa that differ from the medusae of the Hydroida in the reduction or absence of the polypoid generation and the possession of gastrodermal lithocytes. They are divided into two groups, the Trachymedusae and the Narcomedusae. The bell is variously shaped, craspedote, often of stiff consistency, and in the Narcomedusae has the margin scalloped into lappets. The gastrovascular system is of the usual type in most Trachymedusae, having four, six, or eight radial canals. In *Liriope* (Fig. 146*B*) and *Geryonia* (Fig. 140*A*), the manubrium is at the end of a long subumbrellar extension, the *pseudomanubrium*, containing the radial canals. The Narcomedusae lack a manubrium, and the large round mouth opens directly into a capacious stomach (Fig. 140*B*), usually outpouched into 4, 8, or 16 broad gastric pockets; the ring canal is often reduced to a solid strand or absent; when present it follows the lappets in festoons and hence is often termed festoon canal (Fig. 141*A*). In both groups, numerous blind "centripetal" canals may extend from the ring canal toward the summit of the bell (Figs. 140*A*, and 145*A*).

The tentacles may correspond in number and position to the radial canals, or often numerous interradial tentacles of the same or less size are present in addition; frequently the young medusae have only four or eight tentacles (Fig. 142*D*) and the number increases with age (Fig. 142*E*). The tentacles often spring from the exumbrellar surface, not from the bell margin. When numerous they occur in sets attached at different levels of the exumbrella. They are hollow in some forms, as *Gonionemus* (Fig. 140*D*), but in the majority are solid and stand out stiffly from the bell. In the family Olindiidae, the tentacles bear near their tips a sucker or adhesive pad ("knee") devoid of nematocysts and employed in clinging to seaweeds (Fig. 140*C*); and tentacle-like out-growths terminating in a sucker may even be present (Fig. 141*B, C*). The gastrodermal core of the tentacles often continues into the jelly as the *tentacular roots* (Fig. 140*B*), and in many forms the epidermis of the inner face of the tentacle extends on the exumbrella to the bell margin as a thick epidermal tract, the *peronium*, containing nematocysts and muscle and nerve fibers (Fig. 141*A*). The peronia are limited to the Narcomedusae, where they divide up the jelly into scallops (Fig. 140*B*). The peronia terminate in the nettle ring, a thick welt of nemato-cysts encircling the bell margin. The peronia and the exumbrellar position of the tentacles result from developmental circumstances. The bell continues to grow after the larval tentacles have been formed, and, to retain connection with the bell margin, epidermis and gastrodermis of the tentacles lengthen, and the former becomes a peronium. In some species the larval tentacles later disappear, but their peronia persist.

Nematocysts are abundantly present on the tentacles, peronia, otoporpae, nettle ring when present, and in some forms in streaks ascend-ing the exumbrella. The *otoporpae* are tracts resembling reduced peronia, situated above the lithostyles (Fig. 141*A*). The Trachymedusae have but one kind of nematocyst, the heterotrichous microbasic eurytele (Fig. 141*D*). The Narcomedusae have likewise but one sort of nemato-cyst, the atrichous isorhiza (Fig. 141*E*). Each group is thus homo-geneous within itself, but the two groups are probably not closely related.

The Trachylina are histologically similar to the hydroid medusae. The muscle fibers are parts of the epidermal cells; they are often strongly developed in tentacles, subumbrella, and velum and may be borne on mesogloeal folds (*Geryonia*). Gastrodermal fibers are said to be present in *Geryonia*. Sensory cells with long hairs accompany all the nematocyst

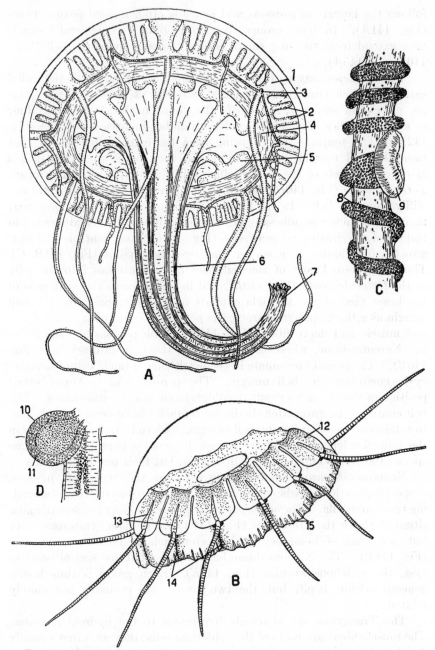

Fig. 140.—Trachylina. *A.* A trachymedusa, *Geryonia*, preserved. *B.* A narcomedusa, *Cunina.* (*After Bigelow*, 1909.) *C.* Tentacle of *Gonionemus*, showing adhesive pad, from life, Puget Sound. *D.* Tentacle base of *Gonionemus*, showing tentacular bulb, from life, Puget Sound. 1, radial canal; 2, blind centripetal canals; 3, statocyst; 4, velum; 5,

tracts mentioned above and form a ring external to each nerve ring; the sensory tract of the upper nerve ring lies in the nettle ring.

Ocelli are generally absent, but the group as a whole is provided with static organs, which probably represent reduced and modified tentacles. They are located between the tentacle bases and are of the same or greater number than the radial canals; the number may increase with age. The static organs are of two sorts, the *lithostyles* (also called *sense clubs* and *tentaculocysts*) and the statocysts. The former, common in the Narcomedusae, are little clubs hanging freely from the bell margin (Fig. 141*A*). Each club (Fig. 142*F*) springs from a basal cushion or eminence of long-haired epidermal sensory cells and consists of a low epidermis (usually also bearing sensory hairs) and a gastrodermal core of one or a row of lithocytes enclosing statoliths. In statocysts, the lithostyle is partly or completely enclosed in a vesicle derived by the folding of the sensory base over the club (Fig. 142*B*). The sensory hairs are lacking in the statocysts of *Gonionemus* (Fig. 142*B*), the statoliths in those of *Craspedacusta*. Statocysts are generally embedded in the bell margin. The development of lithostyles and statocysts has been followed in several Trachylina, and the lithocytes have been proved to be gastrodermal cells (Fig. 142*C*), whereas in the Leptomedusae they are epidermal, a difference that constitutes one of the chief distinctions between the groups.

The sexes are separate with one exception. The gonads are epidermal, occurring in Trachymedusae as folds (Fig. 141*B*) or pendant sacs (Fig. 145*B*) beneath the radial canals, in Narcomedusae in the floor of the gastric pockets. Early development and planula formation follow the same course as in the Hydroida. In most Trachymedusae, such as *Aglaura*, *Liriope*, *Geryonia*, *Rhopalonema*, a direct development ensues (Fig. 143*A*, *D*). The swimming planula develops mouth and tentacles and becomes an actinula (page 435, Fig. 143*C*). This metamorphoses directly into a medusa, expanding radially, forming the subumbrella by an invagination between mouth and tentacles, and developing velum and marginal structures. The larval tentacles may be retained or shed and replaced by new ones. A more complicated life history is seen in some Trachymedusae, notably *Gonionemus* and *Craspedacusta*. Here the planula attaches and develops into a minute polyp. The polyp stage of *Gonionemus* (Joseph, 1925) is the solitary tentacled *Haleremita* (Fig. 143*H*); that of *Craspedacusta* is the tentacle-less *Microhydra* (Fig. 143*E*), which by budding forms a small colony of a few polyps. Both reproduce asexually by constricting off laterally (Fig.

---

gonad; 6, pseudomanubrium; 7, manubrium; 8, nematocyst welts; 9, adhesive pad; 10, tentacular bulb; 11, nematocyst depot of same; 12, gastric pouches; 13, gastrodermal tentacle roots; 14, peronia; 15, otoporpae.

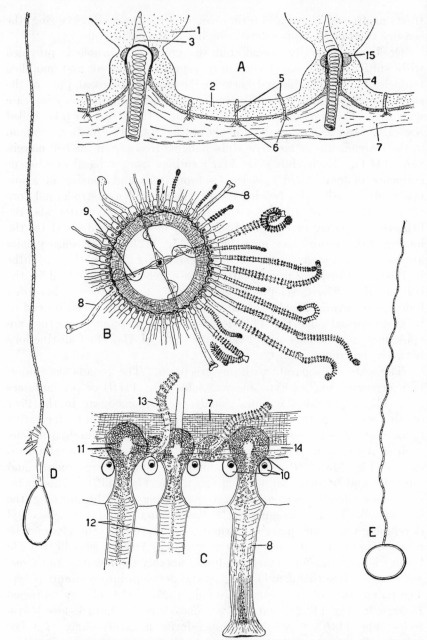

Fig. 141.—Trachylina (continued). *A.* Bell margin of *Cunoctantha (after Bigelow,*
1909), to show peronia and otoporpae. *B.* Olindiad similar to *Gonionemus,* having stalked
suckers, from life, Monterey Bay. *C.* Bell margin of same, showing nematocyst depots,
statocysts, two types of tentacles, and stalked sucker. *D.* Discharged nematocyst of
Gonionemus, from life. *E.* Discharged nematocyst of *Aegina,* narcomedusa, from life. 1,

143*F*, *G*) nonciliated planula-like buds (*frustules*), which creep or lie on the bottom and develop into polyps. Medusae arise as in the Gymnoblastea by typical naked gonophores budded from the sides of the polyps (Fig. 143*E*).

Some of the Narcomedusae have the direct planula-actinula-medusa type of life history, but in the majority the cycle is complicated by the parasitism of the actinula. The egg may develop parasitically in the mesogloea or gastric pockets of the mother, sometimes with the aid of a nurse cell (*phorocyte*), representing an enlarged blastomere (Fig. 144*A*, *B*). Development may proceed in the parent directly to an actinula, which often buds off other actinulae (Fig. 144*D*) at its aboral pole; all the actinulae transform eventually into medusae. Or the planula may escape and attach to the manubrium or subumbrella of other Trachylina or sometimes hydroid medusae, there budding and metamorphosing as in the previous case. In the most complicated life cycles, not yet clearly understood, as in *Cunina proboscidea*, the egg develops in the maternal tissues with the aid of a phorocyte and according to some accounts produces a reduced medusa that sheds its sex products and then degenerates. The planulae from this generation attach to *Geryonia* and develop parasitically into a flattened stolon (Fig. 144*E*), which buds off the definitive medusae (Fig. 144*F*). In the Narcomedusae, the body of the actinula represents only the aboral part of the future bell and the oral portion grows out later so that the tentacles are left behind on the exumbrella.

The Trachylina thus as a whole lack a polypoid generation. The direct mode of development (planula-actinula-medusa) may be taken as primitive and an indication that the trachyline medusae are the most primitive living coelenterates.

The Trachylina are of small to moderate size, ranging from a few to 100 mm. in diameter. Most of them inhabit the high seas, chiefly in warmer waters, occurring from the surface to depths as great as 3000 m. Some forms are confined to shallow waters and others live in brackish or fresh water.

The Trachymedusae are characterized by the simple bell margin and definite radial canals bearing gonads. The Olindiidae somewhat resemble the Leptomedusae; they have four to six radial canals, numerous hollow tentacles (some or all of which spring from the exumbrella), conspicuous tentacular bulbs, and an adhesive pad or sucker (Fig. 140*C*) ("knee") on some or all of the tentacles. The olindiads are typically shallow-

---

gastric pouch; 2, festoon canal; 3, tentacle root; 4, peronium; 5, otoporpa; 6, lithostyle; 7, velum; 8, stalked sucker; 9, gonad; 10, statocyst; 11, tentacular bulb with nematocyst depot; 12, large tentacles with bases embedded in bell; 13, small set of tentacles, coming directly from margin; 14, ring canal; 15, nematocyst cluster.

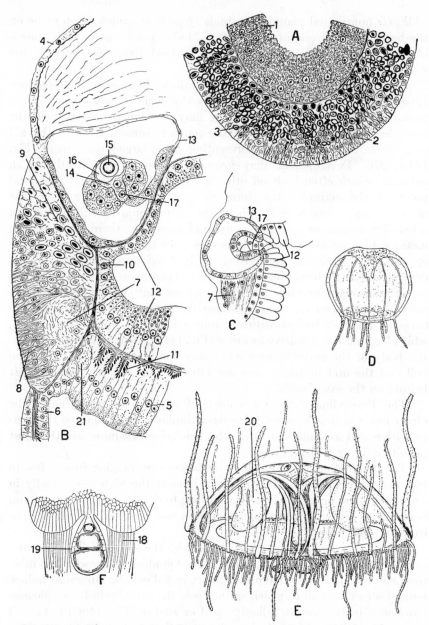

Fig. 142.—*A.* Tentacular bulb of *Gonionemus* enlarged, showing epidermis with sensory epithelium and developing nematocysts and gastrodermis filled with food vacuoles. *B.* Section of the bell margin of *Gonionemus*, showing statocyst and nerve rings. *C.* Developing statocyst of *Craspedacusta*, showing gastrodermal origin of lithocyte and stalk. (*After Payne*, 1924.) *D.* Newly released medusa of *Craspedacusta sowerbyi*, from life. *E.* Mature medusa of *Craspedacusta sowerbyi*. (*After Payne*, 1924.) *F.* Lithostyle of a narcomedusa, *Aegina*, from life, Puget Sound. 1, gastrodermis with food vacuoles; 2, sensory epithelium

water, bottom-living forms, clinging to seaweeds with their pads. The best-known genus, *Gonionemus*, has four radial canals with ruffled gonads; one set of tentacles whose bases pass through the jelly, so that the tentacles emerge slightly above the bell margin; large and conspicuous tentacular bulbs (often erroneously called "eyespots") that are partially separated from the tentacle bases (Fig. 140*D*), and numerous small closed statocysts embedded in the bell margin between the tentacle bases (Fig. 141*C*). The hollow tentacles bear conspicuous nematocyst ridges and a nematocyst-free adhesive pad a little distance back from the tip (Fig. 140*C*). The tentacular bulbs (Figs. 140*D* and 142*A*) have a thick epidermis bearing sensory epithelium and packed with developing nematocysts and a thick gastrodermis filled with food vacuoles. A *Gonionemus*-like olindiad from the California coast (Fig. 141*B*) differs in having stalked suckers among the tentacles (Fig. 141*C*) in addition to adhesive pads on the latter and small tentacles ("cirri") that spring directly from the bell margin (Fig. 141*C*). *Olindias*, from shallow tropical waters, has two sets of tentacles (Fig. 145*A*), and *Olindioides* from Japan bears tentacles irregularly all over the exumbrella; both have numerous centripetal canals from the ring canal (Fig. 145*A*).

The Petasidae, without adhesive pads, are exemplified by the freshwater medusa, *Craspedacusta sowerbyi*, discovered in 1880 in London in a botanical pond planted with an Amazonian water lily. Later findings in other European botanical ponds containing the same water lily support the supposition that the animal was brought from Brazil with the plant. The medusa now occurs in various natural habitats in Europe and has been found in the United States in many lakes, ponds, and streams as far west as Oklahoma. It may reach when mature a diameter of 15 to 20 mm. and then has numerous tentacles in three sets (Fig. 142*E*). Generally all the medusae in one habitat are of the same sex, presumably as a result of asexual propagation of the hydroid. The hydroid is the minute nontentacled *Microhydra ryderi*,[1] forming small colonies of a few polyps without definite periderm (Fig. 143*E*). This feeds voraciously on annelids, nematodes, etc., reproduces by frustules (page 487, Fig. 143*F*, *G*), and buds off tiny medusae that at first have only eight tentacles (Fig. 142*D*). The similar *Limnocnida*, found in lakes and streams of Africa, constitutes the family Limnocnidae, differing in that the gonads occur on the surface of the short wide stomach region, which may also bud

---

[1] So called before its relationship to the medusa was known; it should now of course bear the same name as the medusa, since this has priority.

of epidermis; 3, nematocyst depot of epidermis; 4, exumbrellar epidermis; 5, subumbrellar epidermis; 6, velum; 7, upper nerve ring; 8, sensory epithelium over same; 9, developing nematocysts; 10, mesolamella; 11, muscle fibers; 12, gastrodermis of ring canal; 13, statocyst; 14, lithocyte; 15, statolith; 16, cavity around same; 17, gastrodermal stalk of lithocyte; 18, sensory hairs; 19, lithostyle; 20, gonad; 21, lower nerve ring.

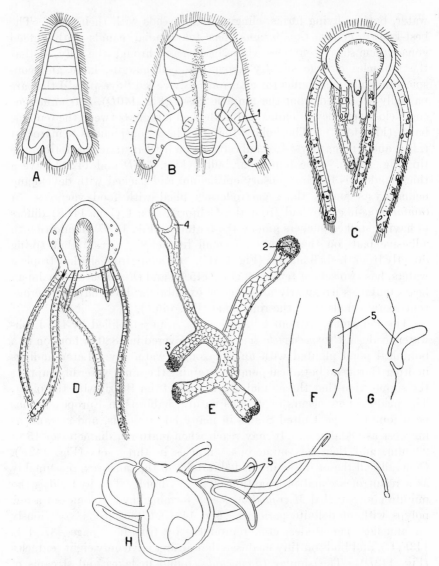

FIG. 143.—Reproduction of Trachylina.   *A–D.* Direct development of planula into a medusa, *Aglaura.*   (*After Metschnikoff,* 1886.)   *E. Microhydra,* hydroid stage of *Craspedacusta,* from life, showing four polyps and one medusa bud.   *F* and *G.* Formation of a frustule in *Microhydra.*   (*After Payne,* 1924.)   *H. Haleremita,* hydroid of *Gonionemus* (*after Joseph,* 1925); two frustules are being given off.   1, entodermal core of tentacles; 2, mouth; 3, nematocysts around mouth; 4, medusa bud; 5, frustule.

off medusae. A hydroid stage has not been discovered but presumably exists.

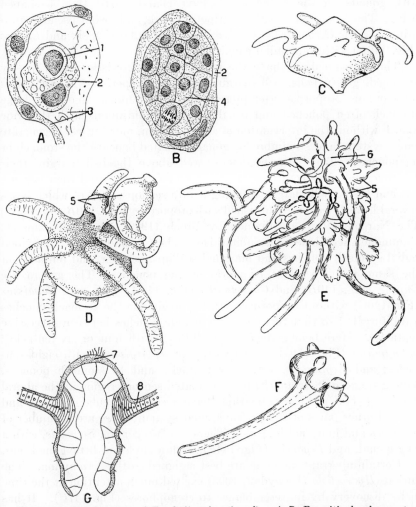

Fig. 144.—Development of Trachylina (continued). *A–D.* Parasitic development of *Pegantha* (*after Bigelow*, 1909): *A*, fertilized egg enclosed in the phorocyte, inside jelly of mother; *B*, stereoblastula, enclosed in phorocyte, still in maternal jelly; *C*, young actinula in gastric cavity of mother; *D*, later actinula budding other actinulae. *E.* Stolon of *Cunina* found attached to *Rhopalonema*, in process of budding medusae. *F*. One of the young medusae released from the stolon. (*E–F, after Bigelow*, 1909.) *G*. Larva of *Solmundella*, with aboral ciliated sense plate. (*After Woltereck*, 1905.) 1, fertilized egg; 2, phorocyte; 3, maternal tissue; 4, blastula; 5, buds; 6, stolon; 7, ciliated plate; 8, tentacle bases.

The family Trachynemidae, with usually eight simple radial canals and no centripetal canals, is exemplified by *Rhopalonema*, with alternating long and short tentacles, and by the aglaurine medusae with numerous tentacles, lithostyles, and a pseudomanubrium (Fig. 145*B*). *Aglaura* with gonads on the pseudomanubrium and *Aglantha* (Fig. 145*B*) with gonads on the radial canals have characteristic thimble-shaped bells. The Geryonidae with centripetal canals and also a pseudomanubrium include *Geryonia* (= *Carmarina*, Fig. 140*A*) with six and *Liriope* (Fig. 146*B*) with four radial canals.

The Narcomedusae have the following characteristics: firm, mostly flattened, glassy bells, bell margin scalloped by peronia, lithostyles as sense organs, otoporpae often present, stiff solid tentacles in one set, large stomach often pouched and usually directly continuous with the wide mouth without the intervention of a manubrium, more or less degenerate canal system, and subumbrellar gonads situated beneath the stomach or its pouches. The tentacles emerge well above the bell margin; their gastrodermal cores continue into the jelly as "roots," and their peronia descend to the bell margin, dividing it into scallops, each of which bears several lithostyles, often furnished with otoporpae (Figs. 140*B* and 141*A*). The Narcomedusae are divided by Broch (1929) into three families: Cuninidae, Aeginidae, and Solmaridae. The Cuninidae have undivided radial stomach pouches and marginal scallops, peronia, and tentacles of the same number (eight or more) as the pouches. The genera are *Cunina* (Fig. 140*B*) and *Cunoctantha* (Fig. 141*A*) with, and *Solmissus* (Fig. 146*C*) without otoporpae. In the Aeginidae the stomach pouches are bifurcated so that there are two or four pouches between successive tentacles. Here belong *Aegina* (Fig. 146*A*), with four or six tentacles; *Solmundella* (Fig. 144*G*), with two tentacles; *Aeginura*, with eight tentacles; and *Aeginopsis*, with four tentacles and 16 stomach pouches. Young stages of *Solmundella* have a ciliated sensory region at the aboral pole (Fig. 144*G*). The Solmaridae have a simple circular stomach and lack all other parts of the gastrovascular system; there are a number of tentacles and marginal lappets. There are two genera, *Solmaris*, with a ring gonad, and *Pegantha* (Fig. 144*F*), with a circlet of little gonad sacs.

Certain aberrant medusae are best assigned to the Trachylina. The curious *Hydroctena* (Dawydoff, 1903) excited much attention at the time of its discovery by its resemblance to ctenophores (Fig. 147*C*). It has two tentacles, each set in a deep pocket, and an apical sense organ in the form of a ciliated pouch containing two statocysts and encircled at its external pore by long-haired epidermal cells (Fig. 147*D*). The margin is devoid of tentacles or sense organs. It is probable that *Hydroctena* is a highly modified narcomedusa related to *Solmundella;* it is the only adult medusa with an apical sense organ, although one occurs in the larval *Solmundella* (Fig. 144*G*).

Another peculiar form is *Polypodium*, found in the Volga River basin and the Black and Caspian seas, a small solitary polyp that walks about on its eight distal and four shorter aboral tentacles (Fig. 147*F*). These polyps come from a budding stolon parasitic inside the ovarian eggs of the sturgeon. When the eggs are laid, the stolon escapes, matures its

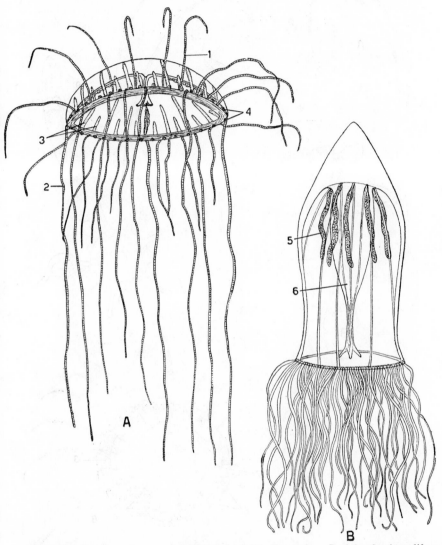

FIG. 145.—Trachymedusae. *A. Olindias*, from life, Bermuda. *B. Aglantha*, from life, Puget Sound. 1, upper set of tentacles; 2, lower set of tentacles; 3, centripetal canals; 4, tentacular bulbs; 5, gonads; 6, pseudomanubrium.

buds (Fig. 147*E*) by an evagination process, and then disintegrates, setting free the polyps. The remainder of the life history and the mode of infection of the sturgeon are unknown, but as the polyp forms gonads

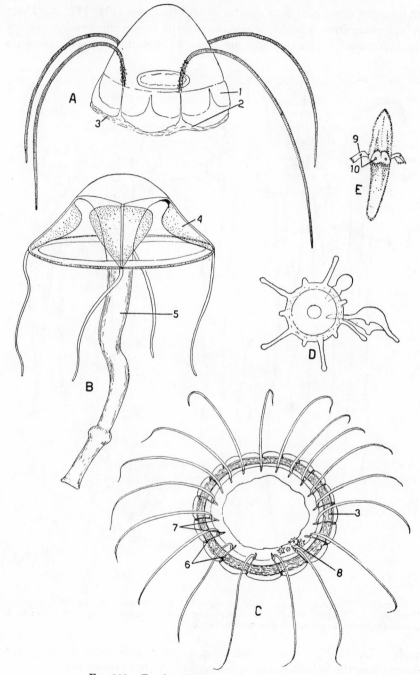

Fig. 146.—For descriptive legend see opposite page.

a medusoid stage is presumably lacking. *Polypodium* has but one kind of nematocyst, the atrichous isorhiza, and is therefore a narcomedusa; budding from a stolon is known for other members of this group (*Cunina*, page 459).

Another remarkable medusa is *Tetraplatia*, collected on several oceanic expeditions. It is a bipyramidal organism (Fig. 146*E*) with an equatorial groove from which project four swimming lobes, each bearing two statocysts (Fig. 147*A*). The aboral pyramid is the bell, the oral one the large manubrium with a mouth at its lower pole (Fig. 147*B*), and the swimming flaps apparently represent the velum. From a thorough study of its anatomy, Carlgren (1925) concluded that *Tetraplatia* is a trachyline medusa, a conclusion supported by the nematocysts, which are all atrichous isorhizas.

9. Order Siphonophora.—The Siphonophora are polymorphic swimming or floating hydrozoan colonies, consisting of modified medusoid and polypoid individuals of several sorts. The gonophores never develop into complete medusae and are seldom freed.

These colonies represent the highest degree of polymorphism found in the Cnidaria, as both polypoid and medusoid persons occur in several modifications, none of which, however, agree fully with typical hydroid forms. The polypoid zooids are of three sorts: gastrozooids, dactylozooids, and gonozooids. The gastrozooids, also called *siphons*, the only members of the colony capable of ingesting food, have the usual polyp form but lack the usually located tentacles; instead, one single hollow tentacle, very long and contractile, springs from or near the base of each gastrozooid (Fig. 148*O*). These tentacles bear lateral contractile branches, termed *tentilla*, each of which terminates in a large and complicated knob or coil of nematocysts (Fig. 150*D, E*). The dactylozooids, also called *palpons, feelers,* or *tasters,*[1] typically resemble the gastrozooids, except that they lack a mouth and their basal tentacle is unbranched (Fig. 152*C*). They may, however, consist simply of a hollow, tentacle-like body, as the fringing dactylozooids of *Velella* and *Porpita* (Fig. 155*C*). Such tentacle-like dactylozooids may be associated with the gonophores and are then termed *gonopalpons* (Fig. 148*K*). The gonozooids may resemble gastrozooids and even possess a mouth as in *Velella* and *Porpita* (Fig. 155*C*), but they lack a tentacle. Usually, however, they take the form of branched stalks, termed *gonodendra* (Fig. 148*K*),

[1] From the German word *tasten,* meaning to touch or feel.

FIG. 146.—Trachyline medusae. *A. Aegina,* from life, Puget Sound. *B. Liriope,* Japan, preserved. *C. Solmissus,* from life, Puget Sound. *D.* Budding medusae from gastric cavity of same, from life. *E. Tetraplatia,* swimming. (*After Viguier,* 1890.) 1, gastric pouches; 2, lithostyles; 3, velum; 4, gonad; 5, pseudomanubrium; 6, peronia; 7, tentacle roots; 8, budding medusae in floor of gastric cavity; 9, swimming flaps representing velum; 10, statocysts.

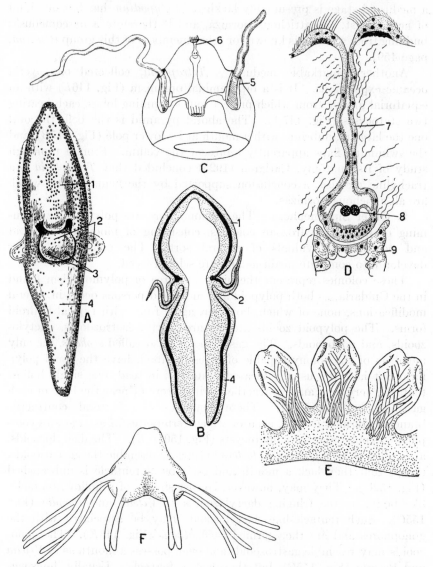

FIG. 147.—Aberrant Trachylina. *A. Tetraplatia*, enlarged. (*After Viguier*, 1890.) *B.* Vertical section of same. (*After Viguier*, 1890.) *C. Hydroctena*. (*After Dawydoff*, 1903.) *D.* Aboral sense organ of *Hydroctena*. (*After Dawydoff*, 1903.) *E.* Portion of the stolon of *Polypodium* with three polyp buds; these evert through the opposite side. (*After Lipin*, 1911.) *F. Polypodium* in walking position. (*After Lipin*, 1911.) 1, bell; 2, swimming flaps; 3, statocysts; 4, manubrium; 5, tentacle pouch; 6, sense organ; 7, canal of same; 8, statoliths; 9, gastrovascular canal.

which are probably blastostyles; these bear grape-like clusters of gonophores and are often provided with gonopalpons.

The medusoid forms include the swimming bells, the bracts, the gonophores, and the pneumatophore. The swimming bell, also termed *nectophore* and *nectocalyx*, is a medusa with a bell, velum, four radial canals, and a ring canal but devoid of mouth, manubrium, tentacles, and sense organs. It may have a typical medusa shape (Fig. 148A) but very often is of bizarre form, bilaterally flattened (Fig. 148B, D), or prismatic (Fig. 150B), or very elongated (Fig. 148C). In these bilateral types of nectophores, two of the radial canals often take a sinuous course (Fig. 148B). The nectophores are very muscular and hence have exceptionally good swimming powers, serving for the locomotion of the colony. The bracts (*hydrophyllia, phyllozooids*) are thick, gelatinous, prismatic (Fig. 148H) or leaf-like (Fig. 148F) or helmet-shaped (Fig. 148G) medusoids containing a simple or branched gastrovascular canal. They usually lack any resemblance to a medusa, but types occur that are transitional between medusae and bracts (Fig. 148E) and indicate the medusoid origin of the latter. The bracts apparently serve a protective function. The gonophores occur singly on separate stalks or in clusters on very polypoid gonozooids (*Velella*, Fig. 155C) or on simple or branched gonodendra. They may be very medusa-like (Fig. 148L, M) with bell, velum, radial canals, and a manubrium on which the gonads are borne; but mouth, tentacles, and sense organs are always lacking. In a few genera, as *Porpita* and *Velella*, such gonophores are set free but, since they cannot feed, perish after discharge of the sex cells. From the medusa-like gonophore various stages of reduction are seen (Fig. 148N) in which the bell closes to a rounded sac; but the gonophores never reach the extreme stages of reduction seen among the Hydroida. In many cases, the female gonophores are medusiform, while the male ones are saclike (Fig. 155B). The gonophores are dioecious, but the colonies are hermaphroditic, bearing both kinds of gonophores, in separate or in the same clusters.

The pneumatophore or float (Fig. 149) represents an inverted medusan bell, devoid of mesogloea and consisting simply of an external exumbrellar wall, termed the *pneumatocodon*, and an internal subumbrellar wall, the *pneumatosaccus* or *air sac*. Both walls have the usual two-layered structure (Fig. 149A) and are highly muscular. Between the two walls is a gastrovascular space that in the more complicated types of floats is divided into chambers by vertical septa (Fig. 149C). The original opening of the air sac or *pneumatopore*, directed upward, is quite closed or reduced to a pore guarded by a sphincter muscle. The air sac is usually lined by a chitinous layer secreted by the epidermis. At the bottom (original summit) of the air sac, there is commonly an expanded chamber,

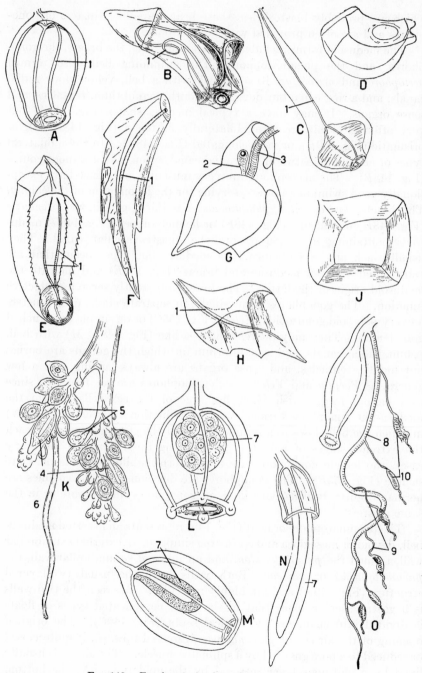

FIG. 148.—For descriptive legend see opposite page.

termed the *Trichter* or *funnel* (Fig. 149*A*) where the lining epidermis is modified into a glandular epithelium, the *gas gland*, which pushes up over the chitinous layer of the air sac so that the epidermis is here two-layered (Fig. 149*B*, *C*). A simple type of float, that of *Agalma*, is shown in Fig. 149*A*, where the outer and inner sacs, the chitinous lining, the funnel, and the simple gas gland are clearly evident. Often, however, the float is of a more complicated type. Thus in *Rhizophysa* (Fig. 149*B*), the gas gland is more complex, putting out branches into the gastrovascular cavity; these branches terminate in giant cells. In several genera, as *Anthophysa*, the gastrovascular cavity of the float is divided by vertical septa clothed with gastrodermis, and the gas gland contains branched giant cells that may be several millimeters long and send their branches into the septa and gas gland (Fig. 149*C*). The function of the giant cells is unknown. The gas gland secretes into the air sac gas of a composition similar to the air (in *Physalia* composed of 85 to 91 per cent nitrogen, 1.5 per cent argon, and 7.5 to 13.5 per cent oxygen). The float may open below by one to many so-called excretory pores.

The various medusoid types of the colony develop asexually by means of an invaginated epidermal mass, similar to an entocodon, which here continues to invaginate to form a sac, the subumbrellar epidermis.

All the persons of the colony are budded from the *stem* or *coenosarc*, usually an extensile tube of varying length but in some forms expanded radially into a disk. The tubular stem has the usual two-layered structure, but the mesogloea is thick and elastic and sends out radiating septa to which the muscle fibers are fastened (Fig. 151*A*). The gastrovascular canal of the stem is usually excentric; it is continuous with the canals of all the persons and begins at the summit of the colony as a rounded or branched canal, the *somatocyst* (Fig. 150*B*), which may contain an oil droplet; or when a float is present the stem canal starts from the gastrovascular cavity of the float. The stem buds the colony members either from one budding zone at its summit (Fig. 150*B*) or in addition from many budding zones along its length. All the persons are borne upon one surface of the stem, arbitrarily considered ventral, although they may appear to encircle the stem, through twisting of the latter. In disk-shaped types of siphonosome, the persons bud from the lower surface of the disk, which is usually inseparably incorporated into the wall of the float.

Fig. 148.—Types of persons of siphonophore colonies. *A–D*. Swimming bells or nectophores: *A*, unmodified type; *B*, *D*, flattened bilateral types; *C*, elongated type (*Forskalia*). *E–J*, Various shapes of bracts: *E*. type intermediate between bract and bell; *F*, *H*, leaf-like shapes; *G*, helmet shape; *J*, truncated pyramidal shape. *K–N*, Gonophore types: *K*, gonodendron with gonopalpon and male and female gonophores; *L*, medusoid female gonophore; *M*, medusoid male gonophore; *N*, reduced medusoid male gonophore. *O*. Gastrozooid with tentacle and tentilla. 1, gastrovascular canals; 2, somatocyst; 3, stem; 4, male gonophore; 5, female gonophore; 6, gonopalpon; 7, gonad; 8, tentacle; 9, tentilla; 10, nematocyst knob of tentilla.

Histologically, the medusoid and polypoid persons resemble the corresponding types of a hydroid colony, but in the medusoids in cor-

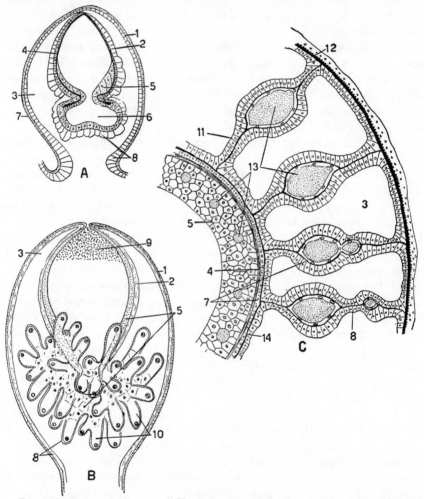

Fig. 149.—Pneumatophores.   *A*. Vertical section of simple type of pneumatophore of *Agalma*.   (*After Woltereck*, 1905.)   *B*. Vertical optical section of float of *Rhizophysa* show- ing branched gas gland, preserved specimen.   *C*. Part of cross section of complicated type of float with septa and branched giant cells, constructed from figures of Chun and Bigelow. 1, pneumatocodon (exumbrella); 2, pneumatosaccus (subumbrella); 3, gastrovascular cavity; 4, chitinous lining; 5, gas gland; 6, funnel; 7, epidermis; 8, gastrodermis; 9, pigment; 10, giant cells; 11, septa; 12, muscle fibers; 13, branches of giant cells in septa and gas gland; 14, mesolamella.

relation with the lack of sense organs the marginal nerve rings are reduced to a small ring or apparently may be altogether absent.   The nervous system is continuous throughout the colony.   The muscular system is highly developed; stem, tentacles, etc., are very contractile; and muscle fibers even occur in the exumbrella of the swimming bells. The floats are also contractile, having a layer of muscle fibers in the base of the external epidermis (Fig. 149*C*).

The nematocysts are often very large and are noted for their virulence. The complicated cnidoblasts have been much studied and may contain a fibrillar mechanism probably contractile (page 387, Fig. 111*C*). The nematocyst armature of the tentilla takes two general forms. In the Calycophora, each tentillum bears an oval body packed with parallel arched rows of elongate nematocysts, constituting the cnidoband; at the attached end of this there are on each side several very long nematocysts and at the other end a cluster of small round nematocysts; and from the cnidoband there hangs down an end filament also full of nematocysts (Fig. 150*D*). Chun has estimated one such nematocyst complex in *Stephanophyes* to consist of 1700 nematocysts of four different sorts. In many Physophorida, the cnidoband has the form of spiral coil (Fig. 150*E*) whose attached end is often covered by a little calyx, the *involucre*, and whose free end bears one or more end filaments and sometimes also a nematocyst-free sac or *ampulla*. In *Rhizophysa* (Fig. 154*A*) the tentilla are simply short filaments without a definite nematocyst knob or coil. Tentilla are absent in *Physalia* and *Velella*. The gastrozooids of siphonophores often have a basal region loaded with nematocysts (Fig. 152*B*).

The nematocysts may be of as many as five or six different sorts. (Fig. 150*F–K*). The types vary in the different groups of siphonophores. In the Calycophora and Physonectae there occur rhopalonemes, desmonemes, microbasic mastigophores, homotrichous anisorhizas, and atrichous isorhizas. Stenoteles are absent in the Calycophora but are found in all other groups of siphonophores. The Rhizophysaliae and Chondrophorae have only stenoteles and atrichous isorhizas. The greatest variety of nematocysts occurs among the Physonectae.

The arrangement of the various persons into colonies may now be described. In the suborder Calycophora, a float is absent and the summit of the colony consists of swimming bells. The family Monophyidae has a single unreplaceable bell at the summit, prismatic in *Muggiaea* (Fig. 150*B*), rounded in *Sphaeronectes*. This bell is not the primary bell formed by the larva, for this is cast off, but a secondary bell. In the Diphyidae, there are two superimposed bells, replaceable by reserve bells. The bells are mostly prismatic or polygonal, and in some genera, as *Abyla* (Fig. 151*C*), the upper bell is markedly smaller and of different shape than the lower bell, while in other genera, as *Diphyes* and *Galeolaria*, the two bells are similar. The Prayidae have opposite replaceable bells, two rounded bells in *Praya* (Fig. 151*B*), several in a circle in *Stephanophyes*. In the Hippopodiidae, exemplified by *Hippopodius*,

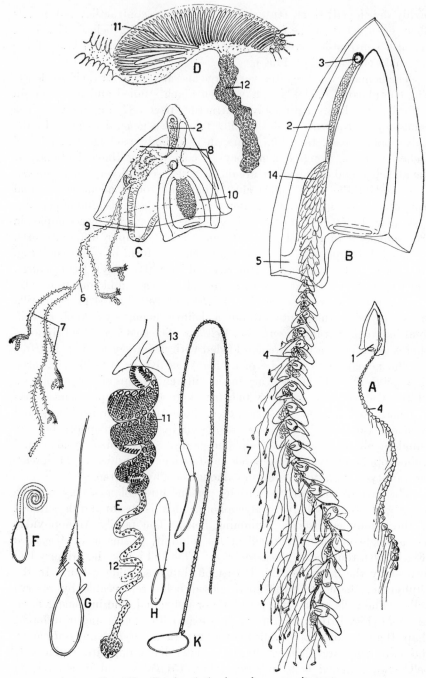

Fig. 150.—For descriptive legend see opposite page.

the summit of the colony is composed of a number of alternating closely appressed, rounded bells. In the Calycophora, the stem begins in one of the bells with a somatocyst, is generally protected, as it emerges from the zone of the bells, by a sheath-like extension, the *hydroecium*, from the adjacent bell, and trails below as a long extensile tube bearing one or more groups of persons (Fig. 150*A*, *B*). Each group, called a *cormidium*, consists typically of a helmet-shaped bract (Fig. 148*G*), a gastrozooid with a tentacle, and one or more gonophores of one sex, which commonly serve as swimming bells (Fig. 150*C*). Dactylozooids are lacking in the Calycophora. The stem grows and buds successive cormidia, all alike, from a growing zone near its summit, so that the lowermost cormidium is the oldest (Fig. 150*B*). When fully developed, the cormidia in most Calycophora break loose and lead a free existence for a time, being then termed *eudoxomes* or *eudoxids*. These were supposed to be distinct genera of Siphonophora until their relation to the colonies was discovered. The gonophores of Calycophora are mostly very medusiform but are never freed.

The remaining siphonophores, grouped as Physophorida, are charac- terized by an apical float, but otherwise vary considerably, being divisible into three groups; Physonectae, Rhizophysaliae, and Chondrophorae. In the Physonectae, the small apical float without a pore is succeeded by a length of stem bearing a column of swimming bells; this region of the colony is called the *nectosome* (Figs. 152*A*, 153*A*). The bells are replaceable from a budding zone beneath the float. Below the bells, the remaining portion of the stem, termed *siphonosome*, may be long and tubular, as in *Agalma* (Fig. 152*A*), *Forskalia*, *Stephanomia*, and *Halistemma*, bearing cormidia at intervals or closely crowded together. In *Forskalia*, the bells encircle the stem in many rows and are of elongated shape (Fig. 148*C*). In *Agalma*, *Stephanomia*, and *Halistemma*, the bells occur in two alternating rows and are closely pressed together, so that bizarre bilateral shapes result (Fig. 152*D*). The remaining Physonectae are characterized by progressive enlargement of the float; progressive shortening of the siphonosome, so that the cormidia become crowded together; and eventual loss of the nectosome. An early stage of this process is illustrated by *Nectalia* (Fig. 153*A*) with a slightly enlarged float, normal length of nectosome, and crown of bracts above the greatly

---

Fig 150.—Structure of siphonophores (continued). *A*. *Muggiaea*, example of a mono- phyid calycophoran, as seen by the naked eye. *B*. *Muggiaea*, enlarged, showing single swimming bell and long stem with cormidia. *C*. A cormidium enlarged. *D*. Nematocyst knob of tentilla, enlarged. *E*. Nematocyst coil of tentilla of *Halistemma* (Physonectae). *F–K*. Types of nematocysts of *Halistemma*: *F*, desmoneme; *G*, stenotele; *H*, rhopaloneme; *J*, microbasic mastigophore; *K*, atrichous isorhiza. (All from life, Puget Sound.) 1, swimming bell; 2, somatocyst; 3, oil drop; 4, stem with cormidia; 5, hydroecium; 6, ten- tacle; 7, tentilla; 8, bract; 9, gastrozooid; 10, gonophore; serving as swimming bell of the cormidium; 11, cnidoband; 12, end filament; 13, involucre; 14, growing region of stem.

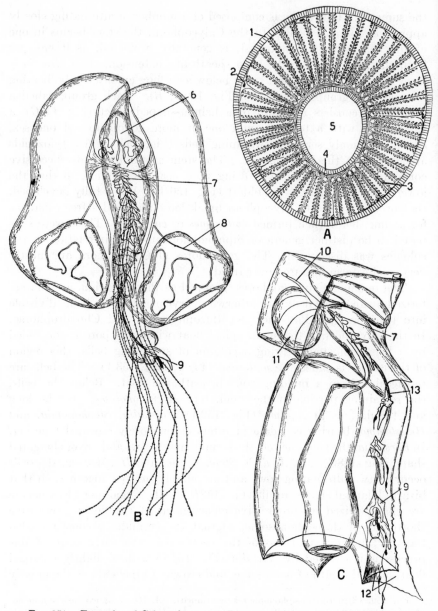

Fig. 151.—Examples of Calycophora.   A. Diagrammatic cross section of the siphonophore stem.   (*Based on figures of Korotneff and Schaeppi.*)   B. *Praya*, type with two
opposite like nectophores, stem with cormidia cut away.   C. *Abyla*, type with two superimposed unlike nectophores, stem cut off.   (*B–C, after Chun*, 1895.)   1, epidermis; 2,
nerve cells; 3, mesolamellar plates with muscle fibers; 4, gastrodermis; 5, gastrovascular
cavity, 6, growing region for new bells of which two are present; 7, upper end of stem with
cormidia; 8, gastrovascular canals of bells; 9, a cormidium; 10, somatocyst; 11, oil cavity;
12, hydroecium; 13, stem.

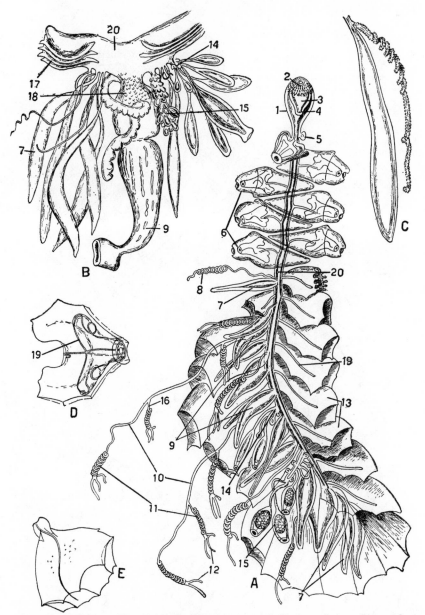

Fig. 152.—*Agalma,* illustrating the Physonectae. *A.* Entire colony. (*After Mayer,* 1900.) *B.* Cormidium, bracts cut away, leaving bases of mesolamellar plates bearing muscle fibers, and tentacle of gastrozooid cut off. *C.* Dactylozooid with tentacle. *D.* Swimming bell seen at right angles to view in *A.* *E.* Bract. (*B–E, after Bigelow,* 1909.) 1, float; 2, pigment of same; 3, air sac; 4, funnel; 5, budding zone of nectophores; 6, nectophores; 7, dactylozooids; 8, tentacles of dactylozooids; 9, gastrozooids; 10, tentacles of gastrozooids; 11, cnidoband; 12, end filaments; 13, bracts; 14, cluster of male gonophores; 15, cluster of female gonophores; 16, tentilla; 17, bases of removed bracts; 18, nematocyst-bearing base of gastrozooid; 19, gastrovascular canals; 20, stem.

FIG. 153.—Physonectae (continued).   *A. Nectalia*, type with shortened stem and crown of bracts below nectosome.   *B. Stephalia*, example of the Rhodaiiidae with an aurophore. (*A and B after Haeckel*, 1888.)   1, float; 2, aurophore; 3, nectophores; 4, growing zone for new nectophores; 5, main gastrozooid; 6, bracts; 7, gastrozooids; 8, tentilla.

shortened siphonosome. The similar *Physophora* has instead of the bracts a crown of dactylozooids. Finally accompanying great increase in the size of the float, the swimming bells are altogether lost and the cormidia are crowded beneath the float. Examples are *Anthophysa* and *Athorybia*, in which several crowns of muscular bracts protect the cormidia. The family Rhodaliidae (=Haeckel's group Auronectae) is peculiar in that a portion of the float is partially constricted off as a bell-like body, the *aurophore*, lying among the circle of swimming bells as in *Stephalia* (Fig. 153*B*).

The cormidia of the Physonectae (Fig. 152*B*) form larger groups and are more complicated than in the Calycophora, comprising one or more dactylozooids, each with an unbranched tentacle, one gastrozooid with a branched tentacle, one or more bracts, and clusters of gonophores often on gonodendra with gonopalpons. The cormidia are never set free as eudoxomes nor are their gonophores ever free-swimming.

In the remaining groups of the Physophorida there are a large float, no swimming bells or bracts, and simplified cormidia. The Rhizophysaliae have a large hollow float of typical construction with an apical pore (Fig. 154*A*). In *Rhizophysa* (Fig. 154*A*), the oval float containing a large branched gas gland (Fig. 149*B*) is followed by a long stout stem bearing a succession of simple cormidia, each consisting of a gastrozooid with a tentacle and a gonodendron bearing gonopalpons and clusters of gonophores (Fig. 154*A*). In *Physalia*, the Portuguese man-of-war, the stem is so shortened as to consist only of a budding coenosarc on the ventral surface of the large oval contractile crested float, from which there hang down several very large dactylozooids with long "fishing" tentacles, smaller dactylozooids with tentacles, bunches of gastrozooids without tentacles, and many-branched gonodendra, bearing gonopalpons, clusters of gonophores, and special "gelatinous" zooids of unknown function (Figs. 154*B* and 155*A*). The female gonophores are medusoid and may swim free; the male ones are reduced (Fig. 155*B*).

The Chondrophorae, exemplified by *Velella* (Fig. 154*C*) and *Porpita* (Fig. 154*D*) are the most modified of the Siphonophora. Here again the stem is shortened to a flat coenosarc, which together with the float forms a firm round or oval disk, containing many concentric air chambers and provided in *Velella* with an erect sail (Fig. 154*C*). On the underside of the disk is found a large central gastrozooid, encircled by gonozooids having a mouth and bearing directly the medusiform gonophores, while the margin is provided with tentacle-like dactylozooids (Fig. 155*C*). The coelentera of the zooids communicate with a system of gastrodermal canals above the main gastrozooid, constituting the so-called liver, believed to have an excretory function. The air chambers open above

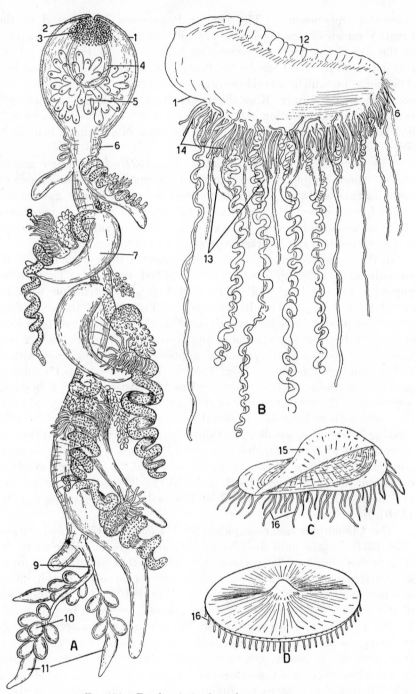

Fig. 154.—For descriptive legend see opposite page.

by pores and below between the zooids by chitinous canals. It is claimed that air is pumped through this system by contractions of the zooids and hence that it constitutes a respiratory apparatus. The gonophores of the Chondrophorae are freed as medusae named *Chrysomitra*, as they were originally supposed to be a separate genus (Fig. 155D).

The details of the development are complicated. The planula, formed chiefly by delamination, is broadly oval or rounded filled with large entoderm cells from which the definitive entoderm later separates. In the Calycophora (Fig. 156A), the planula buds from one side the primary bell (apparently always shed later and replaced by one or more secondary bells), and its lower or oral end becomes the primary gastrozooid. Between this and the bell the stem grows out and by budding gives rise to the other members of the colony. In the Physonectae, the lower or oral end of the planula also becomes the primary gastrozooid, but, preceding this change, the aboral end forms an umbrella-like expansion, the primary or larval bract, which serves to float the larva while the pneumatophore is developing, and is later shed (Fig. 156B, C). The pneumatophore arises beneath the primary bract as an ectodermal invagination (Fig. 156B, C); nearby are budded successively definitive bracts, dactylozooids, and eventually the swimming bells. The early development of the Chondrophorae and also probably of *Physalia* is passed in deep water and has not been observed. A section of a young stage of *Physalia* is shown in Fig. 156D and is seen to resemble a physonectid larva, having an invaginated air sac above, the main gastrozooid below, and the budding zone of the coenosarc to one side. The coelenteron of the pneumatophore, here widely continuous with that of the primary gastrozooid, later becomes separated from it by the formation of a septum. The earliest known larva of the Chondrophorae, termed a *conaria*, is a hollow sphere with an aboral thickening (Fig. 157A). The sphere represents the primary gastrozooid; the aboral thickening contains a small air sac, a system of eight entodermal canals, a ring-shaped nematocyst depot, and an entodermal plug that projects into the coelenteron of the primary zooid (Fig. 157C). In the later or *rataria* larva (Fig. 157B) the pneumatophore is greatly enlarged, the disk has begun to grow out like a ledge around it, and, at the junction of float and primary zooid, a ring-like budding zone is forming other zooids. A section of a stage intermediate between conaria and rataria is shown in Fig. 157C. The entodermal plug flattens out as the "liver," and the

---

Fig. 154.—Rhizophysaliae and Chondrophorae. *A, Rhizophysa; B, Physalia,* young, nonsexual specimen; *C, Velella; D, Porpita;* (All from preserved specimens.) 1, pneumatocodon; 2, pore; 3, pigment; 4, air sac; 5, branched gas gland; 6, growing region of stem; 7, gastrozooid; 8, tentilla of tentacle; 9, gonodendron; 10, gonophores; 11, gonopalpon; 12, crest of float; 13, large dactylozooids with fishing tentacles; 14, smaller dactylozooids and gastrozooids; 15, sail; 16, tentaculozooids.

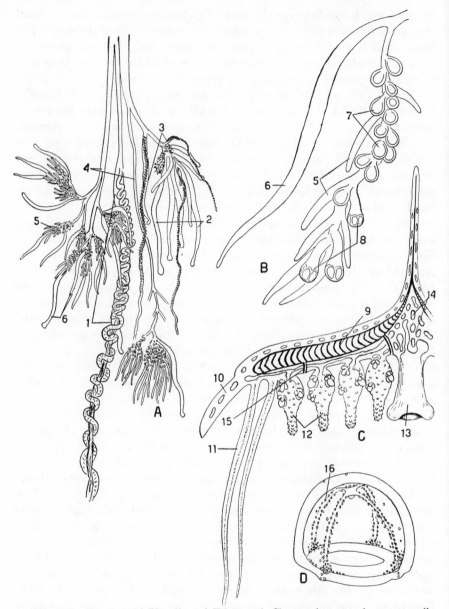

Fig. 155.—Structure of *Physalia* and *Velella*. *A*. Cluster of persons from a sexually mature *Physalia*. *B*. Small part of a gonodendron of *Physalia*, enlarged. *C*. Section across *Velella*. *D*. *Chrysomitra*, medusa of the Chondrophorae. (*After Delsman*, 1923.) (Others from preserved specimens.) 1, large dactylozooid with fishing tentacle (cut off); 2, gastrozooids; 3, smaller dactylozooids; 4, gonodendron; 5, gonopalpons; 6, gelatinous zooids; 7, male gonophores; 8, female gonophores; 9, concentric chitinous air chambers; 10, edge of disk; 11, tentaculozooids; 12, gonozooids; 13, main central gastrozooid; 14, "liver"; **15,** chitinous canals from air chambers to surface; 16, zooxanthellae.

chitinous lining of the pneumatophore cuts off at its periphery a succession
of air chambers that are thus concentric.

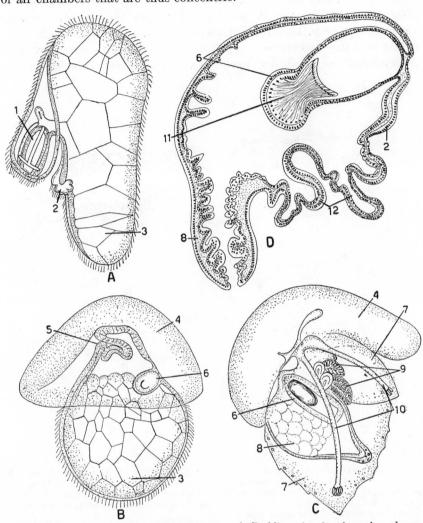

FIG. 156.—Development of Siphonophora. *A.* Budding planula of a calycophoran,
showing primary bell. *B. Agalma,* with primary larval bract and pneumatophore forming. *C.* Later stage of *Agalma* with two definitive bracts and planula becoming the first
gastrozooid. (*A–C, after Metschnikoff,* 1874.) *D.* Section of a young *Physalia,* showing
aboral end of larva becoming the float and the oral end becoming the first gastrozooid,
budding zone to the side. (*After Okada,* 1935.) 1, primary bell; 2, budding zone of stem;
3, part of planula to become first gastrozooid; 4, primary bract; 5, beginning of first definitive bract; 6, pneumatophore; 7, definitive bracts; 8, primary gastrozooid; 9, developing
tentilla; 10, gastrovascular canals of bracts; 11, gas gland; 12, secondary gastrozooids.

Little is known of the physiology or biology of the Siphonophora.
According to Jacobs (1937), the floating attitude depends on the distribu-

tion of lighter and heavier parts. *Agalma* and *Forskalia* float chiefly by means of their very large gelatinous bracts. Berrill (1930) observed that *Stephanomia* floats in a diagonal position with the tentacles trailing vertically. The author saw *Halistemma* dart about vigorously, often executing loop-the-loop curves. The Physonectae in general can probably descend and rise at will by altering the amount of gas in the float. Gas

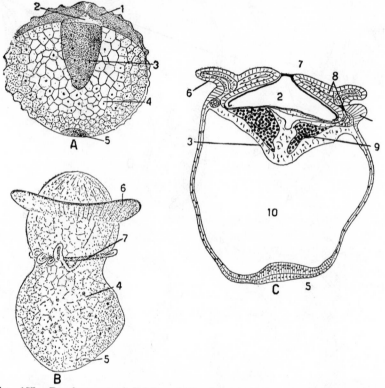

Fig. 157.—Development of *Velella*. (*After Leloup*, 1929.) A. Conaria larva. B. Rataria larva. C. Vertical section of a stage between A and B. 1, aboral thickening; 2, pneumatophore; 3, entodermal plug; 4, body of primary gastrozooid; 5, future mouth of same; 6, disk; 7, budding zone of other persons; 8, canal system of larva; 9, nematocyst depot; 10, coelenteron of primary gastrozooid.

can be emitted and quickly secreted again by the gas gland. *Physalia* and *Velella* cannot go below the surface but the crests of their floats are contractile. Bodansky and Rose (1922) extracted from *Physalia* proteolytic enzymes resembling pepsin, trypsin, and rennin, and also found lipase, maltase, and amylase. According to Chapeaux, digestion in siphonophores is wholly intracellular. The gastrodermis was observed to ingest particles of fibrin, starch grains, and fat droplets but the starch grains were not digested. *Velella* consists of 88 per cent water, 5.6 per cent salts, 3 per cent chitin, and 3+ per cent of other organic substances. No urea, uric acid, or creatinine, and very little carbohydrate were found, but considerable fat was present (Haurowitz and Waelsch, 1926). Zooxanthellae are abundant in the Chondrophorae, especially in the liver, and along the radial canals of the medusae (Fig. 155D).

The Siphonophora are typical pelagic animals, inhabiting the surface of the seas in all parts of the globe, but are somewhat more abundant in warmer waters. Although many are good swimmers, the delicate texture of the group leaves them at the mercy of winds and currents so that they often drift near shores and into bays and may accumulate in immense swarms, even in the open ocean. Many are able to alter the gas content of the float and so can sink in stormy weather. Most siphonophores because of their small size and transparency usually escape notice, but the larger forms such as *Velella*, the purple sail, and *Physalia*, the Portuguese man-of-war, attract attention through their bizarre shapes and exquisite coloring. *Velella* is tinted a delicate purple and the float of *Physalia* is often blue. *Physalia* may reach a large size with a float 10 to 30 cm. long and tentacles depending for many meters. The sting is highly dangerous to man (page 392). A remarkable case of commensalism occurs between Physalia and a small fish (*Nomeus*) that swims about among the deadly tentacles and is not known to live apart from *Physalia*. According to Kato (1933), *Nomeus* is not a real commensal but eats the tentacles and zooids of *Physalia;* this may account for its immunity to their sting. Many siphonophores are luminescent. The group is deficient in regenerative power, and portions of colonies are unable to replace missing parts.

The Siphonophora are commonly regarded as the most specialized of the Hydrozoa in that they attain the highest degree of polymorphism and present the greatest number of medusoid and polypoid types. Recently Moser[1] has revived an old idea that on the contrary the various persons are organs that have not yet attained the grade of polymorphic individuals and that therefore the siphonophores are the most primitive existing coelenterates. This poly-organ theory has not received any general acceptance, but it cannot be doubted that the siphonophores early diverged from the coelenterate stem.

10. Polymorphism and Alternation of Generations.—The class Hydrozoa provides some of the best examples of polymorphism in the animal kingdom. This phenomenon is essentially one of division of labor, i.e., different functions are assigned to different individuals rather than to the parts or organs of one individual. This splitting up of functions among diversified individuals in the coelenterates may result from their lowly organization and lack of organs, conditions that do not permit any

[1] *Kükenthal-Krumbach, Handbuch der Zoologie*, Vol. I.

great degree of specialization for different functions within the limits of the individual. Certain coelenterates lack polymorphism, but this is almost invariably a secondary condition. A dimorphic condition, in which the species consists of gastrozooids and gonophores, is common among the athecate Hydroida. Still more common is the trimorphic stage, in which in addition to gastrozooids and gonophores, special gonozooids are differentiated to bear the gonophores. In a limited number of Hydroida, a fourth type of person, the protective dactylozooid, is added. The greatest complication is exhibited by the Siphonophora, which may have three kinds of polypoids and four kinds of medusoids.

Polymorphism is intimately associated with the life history. The life cycle is simple in monomorphic forms, like the hydras, which even lack a larva,[1] and may be represented by the formula: polyp-egg-polyp. In such cases the polyp reproduces both asexually and sexually, and this condition applies to the entire class Anthozoa. With the advent of polymorphism, reproductive powers are divided: the polyp is capable only of asexual reproduction, while sexual reproduction is confined to the gonophores. Since, further, the egg in these cases never develops directly into the same type that produced it (gonophore) but always into a polypoid, the life cycle becomes: polyp-medusoid-egg-planula-polyp. There thus arises the so-called alternation of generations or metagenesis, in which the life cycle is conceived as consisting of an alternation of the asexual polypoid generation with the sexual medusoid generation.

The question arises whether metagenesis is a direct consequence of polymorphism or whether the life cycle of primitive coelenterates has led to polymorphism. On the first view, the original coelenterate was a polypoid type in which through specialization the sexual function was relegated to the secondarily developed medusoid form, and this process led to metagenesis. On the alternative view, the ancestral coelenterate was some sort of medusoid (further, see page 634), and the polypoid generation is a persistent larval form. This theory, advocated long ago by Brooks, finds support in the life history of the Trachymedusae where the egg develops directly into a medusa passing through a planula and an actinula stage, thus: medusa-egg-planula-actinula-medusa. In many cases, the actinula buds off other actinulae and in forms like *Gonionemus* and *Craspedacusta* produces a small colony that to all intents and purposes is a regular hydroid colony. Most of these trachyline hydroids bud off medusae in the same manner as hydroid colonies but in one species of *Microhydra* the medusa arises from the actinula-polyp by the transformation of its oral end. The facts indicate that the

---

[1] Fresh-water animals in general lack free larval stages, whereas marine animals usually possess them.

actinula, originally a larva stage, first developed the habit of asexual budding, and then took up a prolonged attached existence as a polypoid colony. It then ceased to transform directly into a medusoid, producing this rather by budding. Such a view accounts for the asexual nature of the polypoids. It may also be harmonized with the development of siphonophores where a portion of the planula goes to form a medusoid (primary bell, primary bract, float), the rest becoming a budding polypoid. On this view, metagenesis is a false conception; rather the medusa is the mature coelenterate, the polyp a persistent larva. It must also be concluded that the Trachylina are the most primitive living coelenterates, a view supported on other grounds, such as the simplicity of their nematocysts.

11. Asexual Reproduction and Regulative Processes.—As already noted, asexual reproduction is universal throughout the Hydrozoa. Polypoids may bud from stems or stolons or very rarely from other polypoids; medusoids bud from hydranths, stems, stolons, or other medusoids. Thus, a number of hydroid medusae and one or two trachylines bud medusae like themselves from manubrium (Fig. 134G) or tentacular bulbs (Fig. 128D); but medusae never bud off polypoids. Asexual budding may begin in larval stages as in the actinulae of the Trachylina (Fig. 144D) and the planula of siphonophores (Fig. 156). Fission regularly occurs in *Protohydra* and some similar forms and has been reported for one or two medusae. Propagation by frustules, planula-like nonciliated bodies (Fig. 143F–H) is widespread. In certain trachylines, they are constricted from the sides of the polyps (Fig. 143F, G); in many Hydroida they consist of the detached ends of stolons. They usually lie on the bottom or creep slowly for some time but eventually develop into polyps. Branches and portions of colonies containing coenosarc may be constricted off and develop into new colonies. Stolons often detach and set up independent colonies.

Under adverse conditions, such as raised temperature, lack of oxygen, transport from nature into the laboratory, and action of chemicals, the hydranths frequently detach from hydroid colonies and die while the coenosarc when conditions permit regenerates new hydranths. Often the coenosarc in such cases abandons one part of a colony and flows into other portions. In the hydras and some marine hydroids, under similar conditions, the hydranths instead of falling off undergo "depression." Tentacles and body shorten progressively, their cells detach and pass into the stem where they are digested, and the whole hydranth "melts" into the coenosarc. In hydras, this process continues until the entire animal is reduced to a rounded mass. Hydras may recover from early stages of depression if rapidly transferred to favorable conditions but generally die if the process is allowed to proceed to late stages. Upon

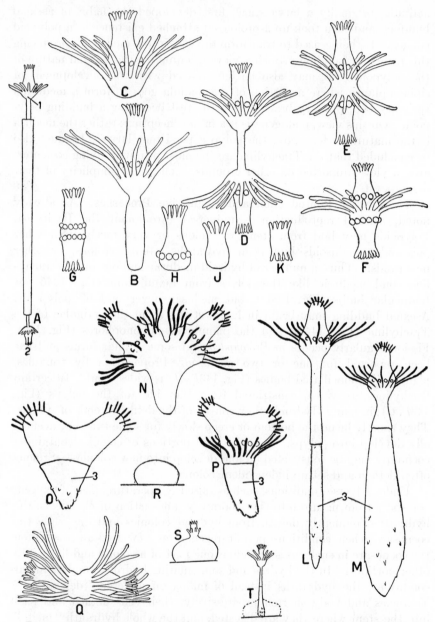

Fig. 158.—Regeneration of hydroids.   *A.* Usual mode of regeneration of longer pieces of *Tubularia* stems.   *B–K.* Types of regenerates of short pieces of *Tubularia* stems: *B*, hydranth with stem; *C*, hydranth without stem; *D–F*, bipolar hydranths with decreasing lengths of stem; *G*, bipolar hydranths without proximal tentacles; *H, J*, incomplete hydranths consisting of manubria; *K*, bipolar manubria.   *L–P.* Regeneration of *Corymorpha* pieces *(after Child,* 1926): *L*, regenerated distal piece; *M*, regenerated proximal piece; *N–P*,

recovery from depression, hydras often regenerate doubled parts or other abnormalities, and these lead to fission processes (page 437).

The Hydrozoa, having high regenerative powers, have often been employed by experimenters in the study of problems of regeneration, polarity, form regulation, etc.   Because of their long stems, *Tubularia* and *Corymorpha* have been most often used as material but studies have also been made on *Obelia, Campanularia, Pennaria, Eudendrium, Plumularia, Hydractinia*, and others.   Hydras, too, have been frequently utilized.   The regeneration of pieces of polyp stems is in general controlled by their polarity (orientation which they had in the whole), level from which cut, and length.   Pieces of hydras usually regenerate tentacles and hypostome at the apical end,[1] a pedal disk at the basal end; hydroid stems commonly regenerate a hydranth at each end, but exhibit their retention of the original polarity by the more rapid appearance and larger size of the apical hydranth (Fig. 158*A*).   Pieces may however produce a stolon at the basal end.   The more apical the level in the original stem or colony from which a piece is taken, the more rapid is the appearance, and the larger the size of the apical hydranth (Fig. 158*L–M*), and the greater is the tendency of such pieces to form hydranths rather than stolons; while basal pieces form smaller apical hydranths more slowly and show more tendency toward stolon or holdfast formation. Very short pieces, especially those from apical levels, usually form nothing but hydranths or portions of hydranths (manubria with tentacles), either bipolar (facing in opposite directions) or multipolar (Figs. 158*C–K, N–P* and 159*E*).   In *Pennaria*, however, short pieces grow out stolons, and in some forms all pieces produce stolons.   Contact plays a large role in stolon formation; whereas suspended pieces form hydranths at both ends, similar pieces lying on a substratum may form stolons at one or both ends.   Stolonization on contact is widespread throughout the hydroids; any cut surface or free end where hydranths have been removed or have fallen off may grow out into stolons (Fig. 159*A*) on contact.   In some cases darkness favors stolon formation as compared with hydranth formation.   Gravity is without action.

Hydranths replace removed portions of their manubria; but entire isolated hydranths usually die.   Manubria may regenerate a manubrium or entire hydranth from the cut surface.   In polymorphic forms like

---

[1] The end of the piece that in the whole was directed toward the hydranth is termed apical, distal, or oral; the end directed toward the colony base, basal, proximal, or aboral.

---

short pieces with doubled hydranths or manubria. *Q–T*, Alteration of polarity in *Corymorpha; Q*, bipolar regenerate lying on side; *R*, same, after treatment with alcohol, polarity obliterated; *S, T*, same regenerating at right angles to original polarity, on return to water. 1, oral hydranth; 2, aboral hydranth; 3, periderm.   (*Figs. A–K, and Q–T, from Child, Individuality in Organisms, courtesy The University of Chicago Press.*)

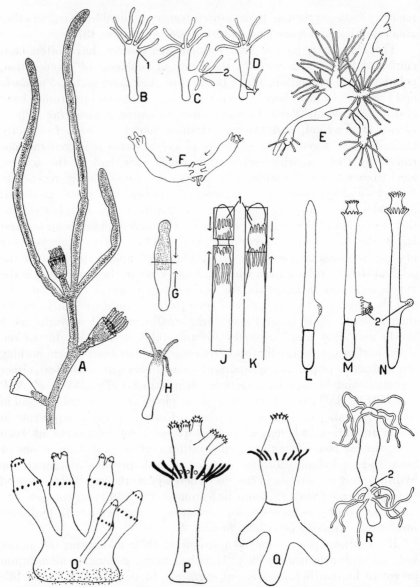

Fig. 159.—Grafting, alterations of polarity in hydroids.   *A.* End of *Obelia* branch giving off stolons.   (*After Billard*, 1904.)   *B–D.* Small grafts of tentacle base of hydra implanted near tentacles in *B*, in side of body in *C*, near pedal disk in *D*, showing effect of level. (*After Browne*, 1909.)   *E.* Piece of *Hydractinia* producing many hydranths.   (*After Billard*, 1904.)   *F.* Two pieces of *Hydractinia* stem grafted with the oral ends together (*after Peebles*, 1900); both pieces regenerate hydranths at both ends, no change of polarity. *G.* Two pieces of hydra grafted with oral ends together, then most of one (stippled) cut away.   *H.* The stippled bit remaining regenerates an oral end, polarity reversed.   (*After Browne*, 1909.)   *J* and *K.* Short distal pieces of *Tubularia* stem grafted in reverse on distal

Hydractinia, pieces of gastrozooids, dactylozooids, and gonozooids all regenerate their own kind of hydranth; nor can the result be altered by grafting small pieces of one type to large pieces of another. Isolated gonophores and gonangia can heal wounds but are incapable of regenerating; medusa or sex-cell formation continues if sufficiently advanced. Colonies do not regenerate gonophores or gonangia at points where these are removed; and if they are cut across, the stumps are absorbed into the colony. Isolated tentacles die.

Polarity may be reversed, i.e., the basal end of pieces may be caused to grow out a hydranth in advance of the apical end, by the electrical current, by burying the apical end, supplying more oxygen to the basal end, etc. The polarity of pieces may also be reversed or obliterated by treating the pieces with cyanides, anesthetics, and other depressing chemicals; upon return to normal conditions, such pieces may grow out one or more hydranths (Figs. 158*O–P* and 159*O–Q*) without regard to the original polarity (Fig. 158*Q–T*), usually from the surface most exposed to oxygen. A cut in the side of *Corymorpha* stems usually heals; but if stimulated by lacerating radiations, grows out a hydranth (Fig. 159*L*). Cell clumps obtained by squeezing hydroids through bolting cloth unite into masses from which a normal hydranth may grow up (*Clava, Eudendrium, Pennaria, Corymorpha*). In recent experiments of this type with *Cordylophora,* Beadle and Booth (1938) found that epidermis and gastrodermis retain their individuality and neither alone can regenerate a hydranth. Cell clumps from different genera will not fuse. Pieces of manubrium grafted into the reunition masses induce hydranths and overcome inhibiting factors.

Pieces of hydroid stems or of hydras may be readily grafted together in any orientation but retain their original polarity, so that apical ends regenerate hydranths whether free or united to other pieces (Fig. 159*F, J*). The curious forms thus obtained may pull apart or may regulate to approximately normal wholes. Polarity may be reversed in very small pieces grafted to large ones, and a single animal thus obtained (Fig. 159*G, H, K*). In *Corymorpha* and hydras small bits grafted into the side of stems may cause a hydranth, partly of host tissue, to grow out at the site of grafting (Fig. 159*B–D, R*); and grafted bits from apical levels are the most or alone effective (Fig. 159*M, N*).

ends of longer pieces: *J,* original polarity retained, double hydranths facing each other regenerated; *K,* polarity reversed in grafted piece, which makes one hydranth with the host. (*After Peebles,* 1900.) *L.* Wound in side of *Corymorpha* stem growing out to form a hydranth. *M.* Graft of distal bit. *N.* Graft of proximal bit of *Corymorpha* tissue in the side of stem pieces, after 48 hours; the graft of distal origin induces a much better hydranth than the proximal graft. *O* and *P.* Multiple manubria regenerated after treatment of *Corymorpha* pieces with ether (*O*) or alcohol (*P*). *Q.* Multiple stolons after treatment with acid. (*L–Q, after Child,* 1927.) *R.* Head of hydra grafted to cut aboral surface of another hydra induces a head there. (*After Mutz,* 1930.) 1, graft; 2, structure induced by graft. Arrows indicate direction of original polarity.

All the facts indicate that the polyp is a polarized system and that the polarization consists in some sort of condition that grades from the manubrium basally along hydranth and stem. In colonies having an orderly arrangement of hydranths and branches, a similar gradation exists throughout the colony as a whole, and, if all the hydranths are cut off, regeneration occurs first at the tips of the hydrocaulus and branches and proceeds basally (*Pennaria*, Gast and Godlewski, 1903). As no morphological differences exist along the stems and as the coenosarc can flow about and develop new hydranths at any point, the gradation must be of a physiological nature and readily susceptible to external conditions. Some aspect of metabolism is probably concerned. Many facts of grafting, regeneration, and asexual reproduction further indicate that hydranths and distal levels in general dominate over basal levels. Thus the presence of a hydranth inhibits or retards the regeneration and prevents the origin of other hydranths within certain distance limits; and grafts composed of distal tissue are more effective in inducing hydranth formation than those of proximal origin (Fig. 159*M*, *N*).

Medusae from which one or more quadrants have been cut out close together along the cut edges into a reduced bell without replacing the lost radial canals; or sometimes one radial canal will arise along the line of wound closure. When bells are cut in two transversely, the oral portion closes together at the summit to make a small bell while the aboral portion regenerates a new margin. The manubrium is always replaced. It appears that hydromedusae are capable of regenerating any of their parts, but the usual regulation into a bell shape inhibits further changes.

12. Reactions and Behavior.—The behavior of hydrozoan polyps has been studied chiefly in the hydras; among marine forms only in *Tubularia* and *Corymorpha*. Spontaneous movements are few. When undisturbed the body is extended and the tentacles spread; contractions and expansions occur at intervals without apparent cause, and the tentacles are often active, waving about or contracting and extending or executing the feeding reaction. Most forms orient or grow at right angles to the substratum without respect to gravity; but *Corymorpha* is negative to gravity, and whole animals or decapitated stems assume an erect position regardless of the plane of attachment of the base. Free forms like the hydras or *Corymorpha* can change location by basal gliding. The hydras usually move by looping and somersaulting, attaching oral end and pedal disk alternately, or in long-tentacled species also by attaching the tentacle ends and pulling themselves along. Most hydroids are indifferent to light, but *Eudendrium* is said to grow toward the light. Hydras, especially the green species, are positive to moderate light, quickly attaining by random movements the lighted side of an aquarium, but are negative to bright light. When the oxygen supply becomes deficient, hydras move to regions of higher oxygen content. Rise of temperature causes greater extension of body and tentacles. Hunger also provokes greater extension and activity of the tentacles and in hydras restless movements and changes of location. Unfavorable conditions in general cause hydra to detach and move about. When placed in an electric current, most hydroids direct tentacles and manubrium toward the cathode.

General stimulation such as jarring results in partial or complete contraction, followed by slow expansion. Jarrings repeated at sufficiently short intervals may finally fail to evoke any response. Light local mechanical or electrical stimulation elicits contraction of the spot or tentacle touched; moderate stimulation evokes contraction of a larger area or of all the tentacles; and strong local stimulation results in complete contraction. The stimulus is thus conducted and Parker's experiments on *Corymorpha* show that conduction occurs in the epidermis and chiefly in a longitudinal direction. In stems partly split, the impulse will pass from one half to the other through apical or basal ends but not through middle regions. Stimulation of the side of hydranth or body may cause a bending in the direction of the stimulus.

In tubularians the typical feeding reaction consists of the bending of the proximal tentacles bearing food toward the mouth while the manubrium in turn bends to meet them, the distal tentacles opening out. In hydras, the tentacles in which the food is entangled simply contract until the food touches the mouth. At or before contact with the food the mouth opens and grasps it by its rim, whereupon the tentacles detach. The food reaction may be given to mechanical or electrical stimulation or to meat juice, mechanical stimulation being the most effective. *Corymorpha* has a characteristic feeding behavior, repeated in quiet water about twenty times an hour. The stalk bends over, mouth and distal tentacles are touched to the mud, the stalk then straightens, and food material adhering to the tentacles is conveyed to the mouth. Decapitated stalks will carry on this rhythmic bowing.

In general the behavior is characterized by its mechanical nature, lack of exact responses, lack of integration, and great independence of parts. Isolated tentacles, hydranths, and stalks perform the same typical reactions as when they are parts of whole animals.

The behavior of hydrozoan medusae is known chiefly from the classical account of Romanes (1885), except for a few more recent studies on *Gonionemus*. Medusae swim by contracting the subumbrella and velum strongly, forcing water out of the opening in the velum. The animal thus progresses by jerks in the opposite direction. By contracting one side more strongly than the other, the animal can force the water out asymmetrically and so descend or change direction. Hydromedusae usually give a number of successive pulsations and then float for a time in almost any orientation. The degree of extension of the tentacles is not correlated with the periods of pulsation or quiescence. The rate of pulsation varies directly with temperature and indirectly with the size of the bell. Normally the entire bell contracts synchronously. Cuts through the bell do not disturb the pulsation, but cuts across the margin disorganize the reaction, and the parts between cuts then tend to beat at independent rates. If a single long radial cut is made through the margin, the contraction can be caused to begin at one side of the cut and to travel in a wave around the bell. The margin if cut off continues to contract as before, but the marginless bell ceases all spontaneous movement permanently. It can, however, be made to give single contractions on mechanical or electrical stimulation and will beat rhythmically in pure salt solution. These experiments show that the source of the pulsation lies in the bell margin and that this source has a discontinuous action. The marginal sense organs are the main initiators of the swimming contractions since in the four-tentacled *Sarsia* (Fig. 120*G*) removal of the four tentacular bulbs greatly diminishes the force of the pulsations.

The exumbrella is exceedingly insensitive to touch or to food and in some species even a strong blow elicits no perceptible response. Others, however, respond to a blow by ceasing swimming, and contracting the bell into the smallest possible shape. Some on being disturbed give a few quick pulsations, interpretable as an escape reaction. Any tentacle that is touched commonly contracts. Moderate mechanical stimulation of tentacles, bell margin, or subumbrella usually elicits the feeding reaction, described below. In a medusa of the eutimine group (Fig. 120*F*), having a long pseudomanubrium, Romanes found very exact responses to mechanical stimulation of the subumbrellar surface. Any spot that was touched contracted and bent inward while at the same time the manubrium curved and applied the mouth very precisely to the stimulated point. This is obviously also a feeding reaction. If a horizontal cut was made between the stimulated point and the base of the manubrium, the latter continued to execute the reaction but was no longer able to locate the affected spot and applied the mouth to the bell anywhere, a result indicating radial conduction of the stimulus. The author failed to find any such exact responses in several hydromedusae.

Romanes' experiments indicate that in medusae as in polyps, conduction is mainly radial (i.e., longitudinal). Conduction in a circular direction is very rapid at the margin but poor elsewhere in the bell, as shown by cutting a long horizontal strip having the manubrium at one end. Stimulation of such strips elicits little response from the manubrium except at very short distances.

Many medusae are indifferent to light, but some give definite responses, accelerating their swimming and exhibiting increased activity in the daylight, although avoiding direct sunlight. Others seek shaded places and some are said to descend during the daytime and ascend when the light diminishes. In *Sarsia*, which is strongly positive to light and will gather in a beam of light, extirpation of the four tentacular bulbs (bearing ocelli, Fig. 123*C*) completely abolishes all response to light; this is the main evidence that the ocelli are actually photoreceptors. In *Gonionemus*, which also reacts to light, the tentacular bulbs are not more sensitive to light than other body regions; but as these bulbs do not bear ocelli in the Trachylina, there is no reason to expect any other result.

Much experimentation on *Gonionemus* has failed to elucidate the function of the statocysts; but these experiments were of the extirpation type that also give no results in Scyphozoa. Properly designed experiments, such as those reported on page 533, would probably show an equilibratory function as in Scyphozoa.

When medusae are placed in a constant electric current, they direct manubrium and tentacles toward the cathode. This response is probably related to the higher activity of these regions.

In the presence of food, *Gonionemus* becomes more active and displays random "searching" movements, poorly directed. Many medusae, however, appear unable to detect the vicinity of food and give no reaction until actual contact with food occurs. When tentacles or bell margin come in contact with food, a typical feeding reaction ensues. The tentacles contract, the sector of the bell margin involved bends inward toward the manubrium, and the manubrium curves so as to bring the mouth in contact with the bent-in margin. In medusae with tall bells and long manubria, the manubrium plays the dominant role in this reaction, and the margin shows little activity; in species with broad flat bells and short manubria, the margin is of greater importance. Thus in *Phialidium* (Fig. 160*F*) and *Aequorea* (Fig. 121*C*) the part of the margin stimulated with food bends inward (after a definite delay) until it touches the manubrium. If two marginal regions are stimulated successively, only the first bends in if the time interval is too short; but if sufficient time elapses between the two stimulations, the second region also responds and bends in to touch the manubrium while the first region is still being held against the mouth frill (author's observations). The typical food reaction may be given to flesh juice in the water and to mechanical stimulation, particularly by an object moving across the tentacles or along the bell margin. Apparently, motility of an object rather than its chemical nature is of the most importance in eliciting the feeding reaction, but animal juice is undoubtedly perceived. This chemical sense is best developed on the mouth frill, which quickly grasps food brought in contact with it.

The majority of hydrozoan medusae exhibit no especial food-catching behavior beyond swimming or floating with the tentacles fully extended; and apparently depend for food entirely on chance contacts. *Gonionemus*,

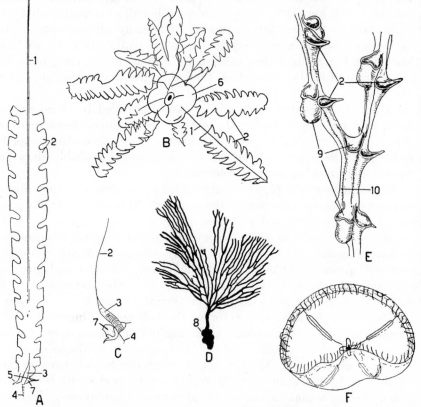

Fig. 160.—Feeding reaction, graptolites. *A*. A graptolite, *Climacograptus*, from a specimen. (*Some details added from figures by Ruedemann.*) *B. Glossograptus* with a number of rhabdosomes attached by their nemae to a float. *C*. Sicula of *Glossograptus*, with first theca. *D*. A dendroid graptolite. (*B–D, after Ruedemann*, 1908.) *E*. Detailed structure of a dendroid graptolite, *Dictyonema cervicorne* (*after Holm*, 1890), modified. *F. Phialidium* giving the feeding reaction, from life, Puget Sound. 1, nema; 2, thecae; 3, sicula; 4, terminal spine of sicula; 5, spines of first thecae; 6, float; 7, first theca; 8, holdfast; 9, bitheca; 10, budding person.

however, exhibits a characteristic food-getting behavior, swimming to the surface, then turning upside down, and floating downward with the tentacles widely spread. This "fishing" reaction may be carried on for hours but is inhibited by bright sunlight and by darkness.

As in polyps, the reactions are stereotyped, few in number, and not well directed. Isolated parts display the same reactions as in the whole;

tentacles will respond to food, and isolated manubria will grasp and swallow food.

13. Extinct Hydrozoa.—Of the groups with chitinous periderm only a few fossils have been found, but the skeletons of the calcareous hydro-corallines are not uncommon, some present genera going back to the Tertiary. The group known as the Stromatoporida, found in the Silurian and Devonian, has been doubtfully related to the hydrocorallines. These had rounded or encrusting skeletons composed of wavy parallel calcareous lamellae permeated with fine canals.   In some genera vertical tubes like those of *Millepora* are present.   Another fossil group of doubtful affinities but usually placed with the Hydrozoa is the *graptolites*, found abundantly from the Cambrian to the Devonian.   They occur mostly as flattened carbonized outlines in shales and similar rocks, but originally they had chitinous skeletons.   The typical graptolites consist of simple or branched stems (*rhabdosomes*) toothed along one or both edges (Fig. 160*A*); these teeth apparently represent sessile hydrothecae, presumably occupied in life by polyps.   The rhabdosome is hollow, and this central canal is directly continuous with the thecae.   A tube or rod, the *nema* or *virgula*, also runs up the interior of the rhabdosome and often projects for some distance beyond the uppermost thecae, not infrequently terminating in a holdfast or expansion that resembles a float.   In some genera (*Glossograptus*, Fig. 160*B*) a number of rhabdosomes occur attached by their nemas to an expanded object apparently representing a float.   The rhabdosome originates from a cornucopia-shaped young, the *sicula* (Fig. 160*C*), often spined, which remains as the base of the colony and which buds the first theca.   The first theca buds the second, that the third, etc.   The nema is a continuation of the pointed apex of the sicula.   In another group of graptolites, termed the Dendroidea, the colony is branched and bushy and suspended by its nema from a holdfast (Fig. 160*D*).   The dendroid colonies also begin with a sicula, but three types of individuals are budded simultaneously: the theca, a secondary theca termed the *bitheca* and compared by some authors to the nemato-thecae of the plumularians (page 409), and the *budding person*, which continues to elongate and which buds off the other types (Fig. 160*E*). It is believed that the graptolites in general had a pelagic habit of life, floating about or suspended from seaweeds.

V. CLASS SCYPHOZOA

1. Definition.—The Scyphozoa or Scyphomedusae are acraspedote tetramerous medusae or medusa-like polypoids in which the gastro-vascular cavity bears entodermal tentacles (*gastric filaments*) and gonads, and is divided in adult or larva by four interradial septa into a central space and four perradial pockets, in which the subumbrella is indented

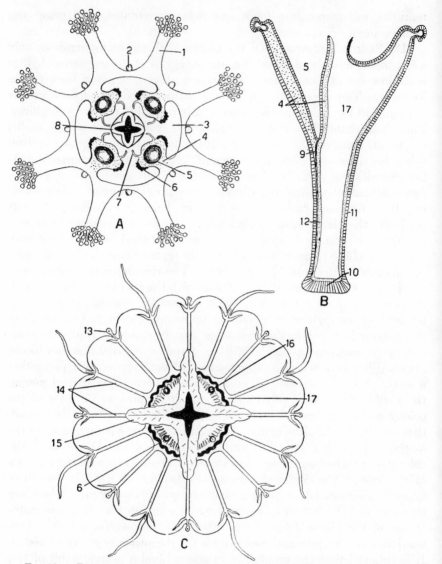

Fig. 161.—Diagrams of scyphozoan structure.   A. Diagrammatic view of the oral end of a stauromedusan.   B. Longitudinal section of a stauromedusan (Haliclystus), left side interradial, right side perradial.   (After Wietrzykowski, 1912.)   C. Diagrammatic view of a semaeostome medusa from the oral side.   1, arm with tentacles; 2, rhopalioid; 3, gastric pocket; 4, septum; 5, subumbrellar funnel; 6, gonad; 7, gastric filament; 8, oral lobe; 9, septal muscle; 10, pedal disk; 11, epidermis; 12, gastrodermis; 13, rhopalium; 14, radial canals; 15 oral arm; 16, subgenital pit; 17, stomach.

by four interradial pits (the *subumbrellar funnels* or *peristomial pits*), sunk into the septa when these are present, in which the mesogloea is cellular, and in which the marginal bodies consist of reduced tentacles or of tentaculocysts (*rhopalia*) having entodermal statoliths. The life history includes a polypoid larva (*scyphistoma*) which contrasts with hydroid polyps in its tetramerous symmetry and division of the gastrovascular cavity by four longitudinal septa and which either transforms into the adult or gives off medusae by transverse fission.

2. General Morphology.—The outstanding feature of the Scyphozoa is the strongly developed *tetramerous* radial symmetry of both polypoid and medusoid states. The main oral-aboral axis falls at the intersection of two principal planes of symmetry crossing at right angles (Fig. 161*A*, *C*). In conformity with the usage in hydromedusae, those planes on which lie the gastric pockets and mouth arms or angles are termed perradii. Halfway between them lie the interradii, on which occur the four septa and the subumbrellar funnels (Fig. 161*B*). The marginal bodies when four in number may be located on either the perradii (Cubomedusae) or interradii (Coronatae); when eight in number they occur at the ends of both per- and interradii (Fig. 161*C*). The adradii halfway between each per- and interradius bear additional marginal bodies, when the number exceeds eight. In nearly all scyphozoans, the parts are symmetrically repeated around the oral-aboral axis to the number of four or some multiple of four; but some species are constructed on the plan of six, and certain parts, as the tentacles, may be indefinite in number. Aside from such exceptions the body can be divided into four structurally identical quadrants. Tetramerous symmetry constitutes a step in the direction of bilateral symmetry, for its two principal planes correspond to the sagittal and transverse planes of bilateral animals.

The scyphozoan bell varies in shape in the different orders; it is goblet- or trumpet-shaped in the Stauromedusae, cuboidal or pyramidal in the Cubomedusae, and dome-, bowl-, or saucer-like in the other orders. In the Coronatae, the exumbrellar surface of the bell is subdivided by a horizontal circular groove, the *coronal groove* (Fig. 169). The bell is usually very gelatinous, whence the common name of jellyfish,[1] and is frequently of firm and even cartilage-like consistency. The jelly occurs not only on the exumbrellar but also on the subumbrellar side of the gastrovascular system and extends into the tentacles and oral arms. A true velum is absent, but an analogous structure, the *velarium*, a subumbrellar extension, occurs in the Cubomedusae (Fig. 167) and to a slight degree in the genus *Aurelia*. Both surfaces of the bell may bear everywhere or in definite areas clusters and warts of nematocysts (Fig.

[1] This name is, however, also applied to hydrozoan medusae and in fact has no exact connotation.

164B). The margin is usually scalloped into *lappets* (Fig. 161C) and is provided with tentacles and sensory bodies, usually to the number of four or some multiple thereof, symmetrically arranged with regard to the body radii and marginal lappets (Fig. 161C). The sensory bodies are borne in the niches between lappets, when these are present; the tentacles occur between the sensory bodies, in the niches, on the lappets, or on the subumbrellar surface and are usually definite in number. They are absent in the Rhizostomeae but are borne on gelatinous basal expansions, the *pedalia*, in the Cubomedusae and Coronatae (Figs. 167, 169). The tentacles are commonly hollow, but solid in the Coronatae, and generally very motile and contractile. In the Stauromedusae they are capitate with nematocyst-filled heads (Fig. 165C), in the other orders filiform with nematocysts strewn throughout, or on one surface only, or in rings, warts, etc.

Between manubrium and bell margin, there are seen on the subumbrellar surface in the orders Stauromedusae, Cubomedusae, and Coronatae, four deep funnel-like pits, interradially located, the *subumbrellar funnels* or *peristomial pits* (Fig. 161A, B). Their function is unknown, but it is possible that they aid in respiration, since water passes in and out of them with bell contractions. The subumbrellar funnels occur only in the larval stages of the orders Semaeostomeae and Rhizostomeae. In the adults of these orders there are found instead in the same locations, four shallow depressions, the *subgenital pits* (Fig. 161C).

The gastrovascular system shows in the different orders various grades of complexity derivable from the condition in the scyphistoma larva and the Stauromedusae. In the center of the subumbrellar surface depends the manubrium terminated by the four-cornered mouth, whose angles are commonly drawn out into four perradial lobes, mostly short, but extended into long frilly lobes, the *oral arms*, in the Semaeostomeae (Fig. 171B) and the Rhizostomeae. In the last, the edges of the branched, very gelatinous oral arms fuse so as to obliterate the mouth, forming instead hundreds or thousands of minute suctorial mouths (Fig. 172C). Throughout the Scyphozoa, the frilled edges of oral lobes and arms are liberally provided with batteries of nematocysts and may grow out into a fringe of tentacle-like projections beset with nematocysts.

The short quadrangular manubrium, often termed gullet or pharynx, is according to modern embryological studies lined by entoderm, not ectoderm, as stated in older works and most textbooks. A stomodaeum is therefore absent in the Scyphozoa. The manubrium leads into the general internal gastrovascular cavity, which in the lower orders is polypoid, i.e., orally-aborally elongated (Fig. 161B). The ground plan of the gastrovascular system for the class is as follows: From the wall of the exumbrella four partitions, the septa, composed of gastrodermis and mesogloea (plus certain epidermal enclosures), project along the inter-radii, part way into the interior (Fig. 161*A*). They divide the gastro-vascular cavity into an uninterrupted central part, the *central stomach*, and four perradial *gastric pouches* or pockets, which together are often spoken of as the *coronal* (or *coronary*) stomach. Peripherally each septum is pierced by a circular opening, the *septal ostium;* the four ostia put the gastric pockets into communication and constitute a *ring sinus*, somewhat corresponding to the ring canal of hydromedusae. From the subumbrellar surface, the four subumbrellar funnels penetrate deeply into the mesogloea of the septa, each of which is thus caused to bulge laterally, narrowing the passages between central and coronal stomach (Figs. 161*A* and 162*B*). Each septum contains a strong longitudinal muscle band, the *septal muscle*, which is of ectodermal origin (Fig. 162*B*). The free inner edge of each septum bears numerous tentacle-like gastric filaments (*digitelli*) arranged in a row (*phacella*) on each side (Fig. 162*B*). The filaments consist of a mesogloeal core covered with gastrodermis loaded with nematocysts and gland cells.

The division of the gastrovascular cavity into a central stomach and four gastric pouches by means of septa is characteristic of the Scyphozoa and distinguishes them from hydrozoan medusae. Although the gastric pockets may be regarded as very broad radial canals, their manner of formation is quite different. The radial canals of hydromedusae arise by active gastrodermal outpushings (page 427); the septa originate in scyphozoan larvae as ingrowing folds of the body wall, and the gastric pockets are merely the necessary consequence of this process. The occurrence of gastric filaments and the penetration of the septa by the subumbrellar funnels are also characteristic features of the Scyphozoa.

The condition of the gastrovascular system just described obtains for the adults of the orders Stauromedusae, Cubomedusae, and Coronatae but is limited to the larval stage (scyphistoma) of the other orders. In the process of medusa formation from the scyphistoma by transverse fission (page 522), the septa degenerate, and the larval funnels flatten out; in their place arise the subgenital pits, whose relation to the larval funnels is uncertain. There is a large central stomach whose margin is often slightly scalloped into four or more divisions, but these have no relation to the true gastric pockets of lower forms. Numerous gastric filaments spring from the stomach floor in interradial bands or groups, and from the periphery of the stomach simple, branched or anastomosed radial canals or wide channels run to the periphery where a ring canal may or may not be present (Fig. 162*A*). The gonads occur in the stomach floor as bands or sacs and may hang down into the subumbrellar cavity.

The Stauromedusae have two kinds of nematocysts, atrichous isorhizas and microbasic heterotrichous euryteles (Fig. 164*E*, *F*). The

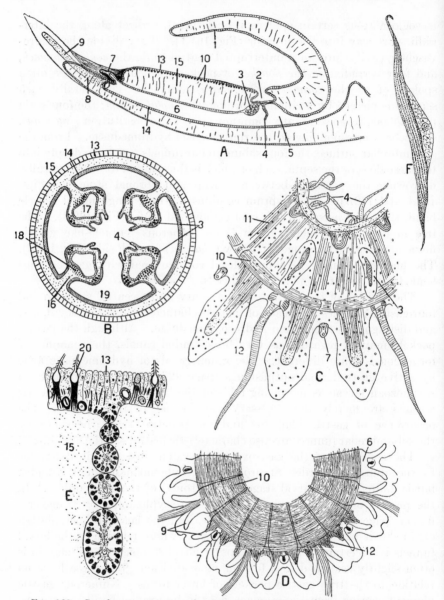

Fig. 162.—Scyphozoan structure (continued).   A. Diagrammatic section across the bell of a semaeostome (half only shown).   B. Diagrammatic section through a stauromedusa (*Haliclystus*).   C. Subumbrellar view of *Nausithoe* (Coronatae) to show musculature.   (*After Komai,* 1935.)   D. Subumbrellar view of *Pelagia* (Semaeostomeae) to show musculature and gastrovascular channels.   E. Muscle bundles of tentacle of *Pelagia* (cross section).   F. Single muscle cell of the same.   (*E and F after Krasinska,* 1914.)   1, oral arm; 2, subgenital pit; 3, gonad; 4, gastric filament; 5, stomach; 6, radial channel; 7, rhopalium; 8, hood of rhopalium; 9, gastrovascular channel in lappets; 10, coronal muscle; 11 delta muscles; 12, radial muscles of lappets; 13, epidermis; 14, gastrodermis; 15, col-

scyphistomae of the semaeostomes and rhizostomes have also these same two sorts, but the adults often possess in addition a third kind, holotrichous isorhizas. The nematocyst types of the other orders are not adequately known. The group is thus as a whole homogeneous as regards the nematocyst types.

The muscular system, as in the hydromedusae, is practically wholly epidermal and limited to marginal and subumbrellar structures. Its most conspicuous feature is the *coronal* muscle, the strong and broad circular muscle band of the subumbrella (Fig. 162C, D). This is commonly broken up into 4, 8, or 16 fields by radial mesogloeal partitions and hence has a polygonal shape. The coronal muscle constitutes the swimming mechanism and is therefore highly developed in all the orders except the sessile Stauromedusae, where it is represented by a narrow marginal band (Fig. 165A). The regular longitudinal epidermal system is developed to different degrees in the various orders. It occurs as the strong longitudinal fibers of tentacles (Fig. 162E, F) and pedalia, as a longitudinal layer in the manubrium and oral lobes, as strong fibers in the axes of the long oral arms of the Semaeostomeae, and as a radial sheet or radial bands, usually 4, 8, or 16 in number, extending on the subumbrella from the manubrial base to the inner edge of the coronal muscle or through this muscle along the mesogloeal partitions that divide the radial sheet into fields. In some forms the radial bands diverge into a fan shape as they proceed from the manubrium and so form triangular muscles known as *delta* muscles (Fig. 162C). The lappets may contain circular fibers of the same series as the coronal muscle, or short radial fibers may extend into them from the outer edge of the coronal muscle (Fig. 162C, D). The septa of the lower orders and the scyphistoma larva are provided with strong longitudinal bands, the septal muscles, best developed in the Stauromedusae and serving to contract the animal. Embryological study shows that they are of ectodermal origin. Circular gastrodermal muscles appear to be absent in the Scyphozoa.

The marginal sensory bodies consist of *rhopalioids* in the Stauromedusae (which see), *rhopalia* in the other orders. The rhopalia are borne on the sides of the bell in Cubomedusae, on pedalia in most Coronatae, and in the niches between the marginal lappets (Fig. 161C) in the other Coronatae, the Semaeostomeae, and the Rhizostomeae. Each rhopalium is set in a sensory niche whose roof is formed by a hood-like extension of the exumbrella (Fig. 163B, C). The marginal lappets between which the rhopalia occur in the Semaeostomeae and Rhizostomeae, often called *rhopalial lappets*, derive directly from the lappets

<hr>

lenchyme; 16, septum; 17, subumbrellar funnel; 18, septal muscle; 19, gastric pockets; 20, nematocysts.

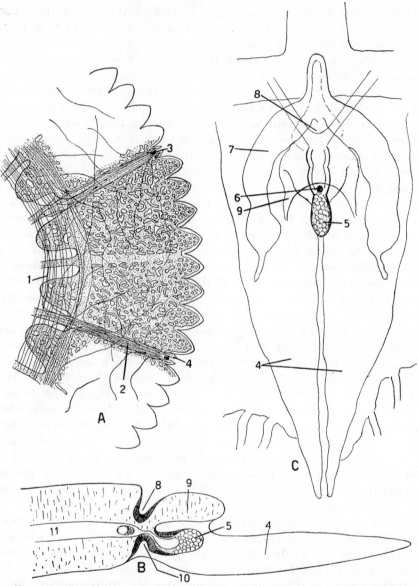

Fig. 163.—Scyphozoan structure.   *A*. Sector of bell of *Rhizostoma*, showing nerve plexus and gastrovascular network (stippled).   (*After Hesse*, 1896.)   *B*. Diagram of a radial section through a rhopalium of a semaeostome.   *C*. Rhopalium and surrounding parts of *Aurelia*, from life.   1, fibers of subumbrellar nerve net; 2, concentration of nervous tissue near rhopalium; 3, rhopalium; 4, rhopalial lappets; 5, statocyst; 6, ocellus; 7, special sensory lappets (peculiar to *Aurelia*); 8, outer sensory pit; 9, hood; 10, inner sensory pit; 11, gastrovascular canal.

of the ephyra larva, and may remain of small size as protective lappets for the rhopalium (Fig. 163C). The rhopalium itself develops at the base of the primary larval tentacles but is not, as often stated, a reduced or transformed tentacle. It is a small hollow club, essentially a tentaculocyst, very similar to the lithostyles of the Trachylina (Fig. 163B, C). The gastrodermal lining of the interior heaps up at the free end into a mass of polygonal cells each of which contains a statolith (Fig. 164A). This mass together with the overlying flat epidermis constitutes a statocyst or organ of equilibrium. The statoliths are composed of calcium sulphate (gypsum) with a small admixture of calcium phosphate. The epidermis of the sides and base of the rhopalium is mostly or in limited areas immensely thickened into a very tall sensory epithelium (Figs. 163B, 164A), provided with long sensory hairs, and underlain by a plexus of nerve fibers and ganglion cells. In addition, in most Semaeostomeae and Rhizostomeae, the exumbrellar side of the hood over the sensory niche bears a pit lined with sensory epithelium and often called the *outer olfactory pit;* a similar *inner olfactory pit* may occur in the floor of the sensory niche (Figs. 163B and 164A). The term olfactory is obviously gratuitous, since, so far as known, these pits serve the same general sensory functions as sensory epithelium elsewhere and hence will here be termed simply sensory pits. The rhopalia of some Scyphozoa, notably the Cubomedusae, are provided with ocelli (Fig. 168A) which may be pigment-spot ocelli, pigment-cup ocelli, or complicated eyes provided with a lens. Ocelli also occur on the rhopalia of some Coronatae, and in a few other forms, as *Aurelia* (Fig. 164A), but in general the rhopalia of semaeostomes and rhizostomes lack ocelli.

The nervous system differs from that of the Hydromedusae in the absence of a marginal nerve ring except in the Cubomedusae. It has been carefully described for only a few species. It consists of the rhopalial ganglia and of the usual subumbrellar plexus of ganglion cells and fibers, tending to concentrate into radial strands along the main radii. In *Rhizostoma* (Fig. 163A) there is also a more or less circular arrangement of the main part of the subumbrellar plexus. The rhopalial ganglia are concentrations of nerve cells near each rhopalium; they connect with the subumbrellar plexus and with the nervous plexus found in the rhopalium and sensory niche. The rhopalial ganglia have no direct connection with each other except in Cubomedusae. The subepidermal plexus also extends throughout the manubrium and oral lobes and into the tentacles. A subgastrodermal plexus in the walls of the gastrovascular system has been found in the Stauromedusae and is probably general throughout the class. The batteries of nematocysts so common on the bell of Scyphozoa seem also to be accompanied by special concentrations of nervous tissue.

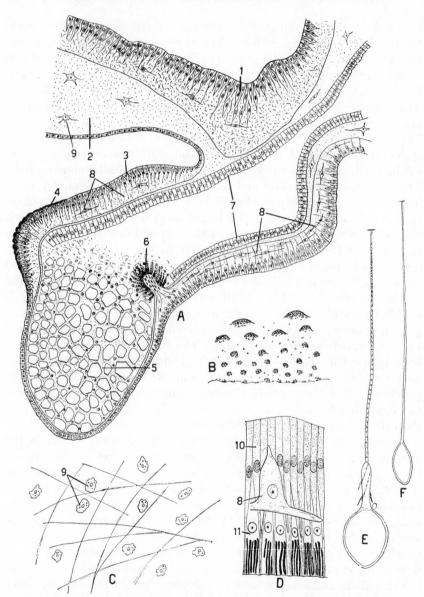

Fig. 164.—Microscopic structure of Scyphozoa. *A*. Section through the rhopalium of *Aurelia*. (*After Schewiakoff*, 1889.) *B*. Bit of bell edge of *Pelagia*, showing nematocyst warts. *C*. Collenchyme of *Aurelia*, from life. *D*. Section through the epidermis of subumbrella of *Rhizostoma* showing double layer of outer supporting cells and inner muscle cells. (*After Hesse*, 1895.) *E* and *F*. Nematocysts of *Aurelia*, from life. *E*. Microbasic eurytele. *F*. Atrichous isorhiza. 1, outer sensory pit; 2, collenchyme; 3, inner sensory pit; 4, pigment-spot ocellus; 5, statocyst; 6, pigment-cup ocellus; 7, gastrodermal lining of rhopalium; 8, nervous tissue; 9, amoebocytes of collenchyme; 10, supporting epidermal cells; 11, muscle cells of epidermis.

In some of the higher Scyphozoa, the radial canals open on the subumbrellar surface near the bell margin by the so-called excretory pores. It is stated that dissolved nitrogenous wastes and nitrogenous granules are emitted through these pores.

The Scyphozoa are dioecious, with the exception of a very few hermaphroditic forms, as *Chrysaora*. The sex cells originate and ripen in the base of the gastrodermis, which forms an epithelium over them. In those orders with septa, the gonads are borne on both sides of each septum, hence eight in number, as elongated or looped folded bodies projecting into the gastric pockets. There are accordingly two gonads in each pocket (Fig. 161*A*). In the Semaeostomeae and Rhizostomeae, which lack septa, the gonads occur in the floor of the gastric pockets, peripheral to the zone of the gastric filaments and above the subgenital pits to which, however, they have no functional relationship. They usually form four curved folded bodies (Fig. 171*A*) but may hang down as bags. In some rhizostomes the four subgenital pits fuse to a cavity, the *subgenital porticus*, situated beneath the central stomach and retaining the four original openings (Fig. 172*E*). The gonads in such species lie above this porticus and often hang down into it. It is believed the sex cells are discharged into the porticus, which may act as a brood chamber. In all other Scyphozoa the sex cells rupture into the gastrovascular cavity and escape by the mouth. The eggs develop in the sea water or in the folds of the oral arms into a coeloblastula and then a solid or hollow planula. This in most scyphozoans after attachment develops into a tentaculate polypoid larva, the *scyphistoma*, having a stalked trumpet-shaped body, fastened aborally by an adhesive disk and provided with four septa and four subumbrellar funnels (Fig. 171*D*). This is often followed by a young, free-swimming medusan stage, the *ephyra* (or *ephyrula*) (Fig. 172*B*) which undergoes extensive transformation into the adult medusa. Details of the development are given in connection with the account of each order.

Histologically, the chief difference from the Hydrozoa concerns the mesogloea. The jelly not only contains fibers, often so numerous as to make the bell stiff and rigid, but also loose amoeboid cells (Fig. 164*C*), of uncertain origin, but probably largely epidermal. The mesogloea is hence more accurately termed collenchyme. Although often similar to cartilage in consistency, it is not chemically related to cartilage (see page 382). The collenchyme occurs everywhere between epidermis and gastrodermis, from both of which it is always separated by a mesolamella. The epidermis consists of the usual flattened to columnar cells, may be flagellated on subumbrella and elsewhere, and contains abundant nematocysts, sensory, and gland cells. The latter secrete mucus, which in some species is given off in considerable quantities. Special types of gland cells are found in the anchors and pedal disk of the Stauromedusae and the pedal disk of the scyphistoma. Sensory epithelium is mostly limited to the rhopalia and their vicinity, as the marginal circular bands found in hydromedusae are absent. The sensory epithelium has the typical histology (Fig. 109A), consisting of elongated sensory nerve cells between regular epidermal cells The coronal muscle fibers and in some cases the longitudinal tentacle fibers are cross-striated; otherwise the muscle fibers are smooth. Muscle fibers are for the most part basal extensions of epidermal cells (Fig. 109G, H); but the epitheliomuscular cells may be internal to the regular epidermal cells so that the epidermis appears two-layered in muscular regions of the subumbrella (Fig. 164D). The coronal muscle fibers are borne on scallops or plates of hardened collenchyme, circularly arranged, and the delta muscles may be similarly fastened to radial plates. In Pelagia (Fig. 162E) the longitudinal tentacle fibers are independent of the epidermis and are attached to lengthwise folds of mesolamella that dip into the collenchyme between epidermis and gastrodermis. The gastrodermis often differs in different regions of the coelenteron and may be glandular, pigmented, or vacuolated; that lining the manubrium is commonly different from that of the interior. The gastrodermis is flagellated, and its flagella maintain definite currents through the gastrovascular system. In semaeostomes and rhizostomes a flat gastrodermal lamella runs through the jelly between the gastrovascular canals. The gastric filaments are interesting as an example of gastrodermis containing nematocysts.

The Scyphozoa differ then from the hydromedusae in the absence of a velum, the presence of subumbrellar funnels, the gastrodermal location of the gonads, and, in the orders Stauromedusae, Cubomedusae, and Coronatae, in the division of the gastrovascular cavity by the four septa combined with a lack of typical radial and circular canals. On the other hand, the gastrovascular system of the orders Semaeostomeae and Rhizostomeae resembles that of hydrozoan medusae, having radial and sometimes circular canals. In their scalloped margins and possession of tentaculocysts as marginal sense organs, the higher Scyphozoa recall the Narcomedusae, but differ from the medusae of the Hydroida. The septal division of the gastrovascular cavity and the presence of gastrodermal tentacles suggest an affinity with the Anthozoa.

3. Order Stauromedusae or Lucernariida.—The Stauromedusae are sessile scyphozoans with a polypoid, goblet- or trumpet-shaped body that flares at the oral end into a broad concave subumbrella and tapers aborally into a long or short stalk or peduncle, absent in a few cases (Fig. 165D, E). The end of the stalk or center of the exumbrella if the stalk is lacking bears an adhesive disk by which the animals attach to seaweeds, shells, rocks, etc., in polyp fashion. There are a four-cornered mouth with small oral lobes, and a short quadrangular manubrium. Between manubrium and margin four deep subumbrellar funnels sink into the interior (Fig. 165A, D). The margin may be circular, bearing tentacles, but typically is drawn out into eight (or four bifurcated) adradial arms or lobes, each tipped with a bunch of short capitate tentacles, numbering 20 or 30 to hundreds (Fig. 165D, E, F). On the exumbrellar side of the margin, halfway between the lobes, i.e., on the per- and interradii, are borne the eight rhopalioid marginal bodies, which are simply reduced tentacles, lacking any special sensory character. They are best developed in *Haliclystus* (Fig. 165E, B), in that genus termed *anchors* or *colletocystophores;* these are thick horseshoe-shaped or oval cushions made of elongated cells secreting adhesive material (Fig. 166A). The rhopalioids may also consist of simple tentacle-like projections; in *Lucernaria* and several other forms, rhopalioids are absent in the adult state.

The gastrovascular system closely resembles the ground plan already described. It is divided into central stomach and four perradial pouches by the four interradial septa, each of which encloses a subumbrellar funnel (Figs. 161A, B and 165A). The pouches communicate peripherally by way of the septal ostia, forming a ring sinus. The gastrovascular cavity continues into the eight arms, the tentacles, and the rhopalioids. The septa are provided with the usual gastric filaments and septal muscles and also contain at the sides of the funnels ectodermal masses, which are sites of nematocyst formation. The septa continue into the stalk to the pedal disk, as separate projections in some genera, in other genera, as *Haliclystus*, fusing in the center of the stalk and so forming four longitudinal canals in the stalk (Fig. 165H). In some Stauromedusae, longitudinal partitions, the *claustra*, are present between the septa, dividing the gastric pockets into inner and outer sets (Fig. 165J); the outer set is completely closed off, except below.

The coronal muscle is represented by a marginal band (Fig. 165A). There are radial epidermal muscle fibers and septal muscles. The nervous system differs in the presence of a well-developed exumbrellar plexus in addition to the usual subumbrellar plexus. The gonads are elongated bodies borne on the faces of the septa.

The Stauromedusae are inhabitants of bays, sounds, and coastal waters, mostly in the colder parts of the earth. They cannot swim and are fastened in a pendant attitude to seaweeds, and less often to other objects. Some can detach and reattach at will, moving about in hydra fashion, using the anchors or tentacles for adhesion. In other cases, it appears that reattachment is impossible, as the pedal disk is permanently fastened by a chitinous secretion. The Stauromedusae are of moderate size, usually several centimeters across the oral end, and mostly of

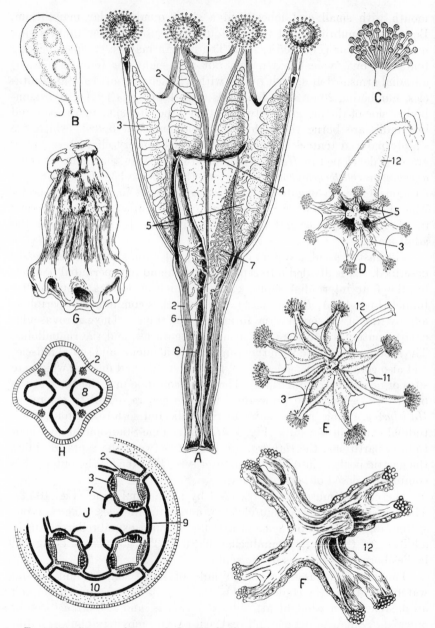

FIG. 165.—Stauromedusae. A. Longitudinal section of *Lucernaria*, manubrium cut away. (*After Antipa*, 1892.) B. Rhopalioid. C. Tentacle cluster of *Haliclystus*, from life. D. *Lucernaria*, preserved, New England Coast. E. *Haliclystus*, from life, Puget Sound. F. *Kishinouyea*, from aboral side. (*After Kishinouye*, 1902.) G. *Lipkea* (*Capria*). (*After Carlgren*, 1933.) H. Cross section of the foot of *Haliclystus*, showing the four canals, from life. J. Cross section through *Craterolophus*, showing claustra. (*After*

brownish or greenish coloration, although other colors as pink, orange, and blue or violet, also occur. Some can assume the color of the plant to which they are attached by absorption of its chromoplasts through the pedal disk. The Stauromedusae feed upon small animals. They apparently breed at all seasons and may live for several years. The principal and most common genera are *Haliclystus* (Fig. 165*E*), with eight anchors and four stalk canals (Fig. 165*H*), and *Lucernaria* (Fig. 165*D*), without rhopalioids and with a single stalk canal. Some other genera, seldom seen, are *Sasakiella* and *Kishinouyea* (Fig. 165*F*), with four bifurcated arms; *Lipkea* (Fig. 165*G*), without anchors and with short pointed tentacles devoid of terminal knobs; *Craterolophus*, similar to *Lucernaria* but with gastric pockets divided by claustra; *Halimocyathus*, similar to *Haliclystus* but also with claustra; and *Depastrum* without rhopalioids and with a simple margin bearing 16 tentacle clusters.

The sex cells are ejected by the mouth at night, and after fertilization in the sea water develop into coeloblastulae and then into solid unciliated vermiform planulae (Fig. 166*B*). The entoderm arises by multipolar ingression. The planulae creep for several days, attach at their anterior poles, develop a mouth as they begin to feed, and bud off other larvae by means of stolons (Fig. 174*F*). The larvae in the cases observed always attach in groups, since single ones seem unable to vanquish the animals used as food (rotifers, nematodes, copepods). Eventually the larvae elongate into stalked, trumpet-shaped polyps, which develop a manubrium, lined by entoderm, and put out first two, then four, eight, etc., tentacles (Fig. 166*C–F*). The first eight tentacles are per- and interradial and become the anchors through transformation of their basal ectoderm into adhesive cells and reduction of their distal ends into knobs (Fig. 166*E*). The later tentacles are adradial and are shifted into eight groups by the extension of the umbrella into eight lobes. The mesogloea appears at the four-tentacle stage and seems to be secreted by both germ layers. While the first tentacles are sprouting, the entoderm of the body wall thickens along four interradial lines and, accompanied by mesogloea, grows inward as the four longitudinal septa (Fig. 166*G*). Four ectodermal masses proliferate from the subumbrellar ectoderm into the septa, forming the septal muscles (Fig. 166*H*) and those parts of the funnel walls that become sites of nematocyst formation. The funnels are later ectodermal invaginations from the subumbrella into each septum (Fig. 166*H*). Near the margin, the outer part of each septum perforates as the septal ostium.

4. Order Cubomedusae or Carybdeida.—The members of this order have cuboidal bells with four flattened sides, simple margin, and square

Gross, 1900.) 1, marginal muscle; 2, septal muscle; 3, gonad; 4, cut edge of manubrium; 5, funnel; 6, septum; 7, gastric filaments; 8, gastrovascular canals of stalk; 9, claustrum; 10, gastric pockets; 11, rhopalioids; 12, stalk.

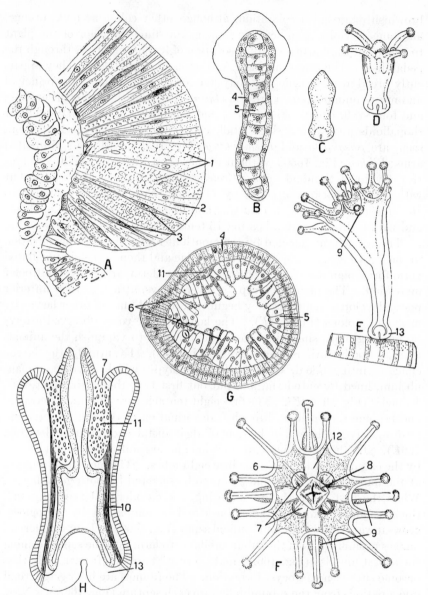

FIG. 166.—Stauromedusae (continued). A. Longitudinal section of the rhopalioid of *Haliclystus*, showing mucous glands. (*After Schlater*, 1891.) B–F. Development of *Haliclystus* (*after Wietrzykowski*, 1912): B, planula hatching; C, planula attached; D, four-tentacled larva; E, 16-tentacled larva; F, 16-tentacled larva seen from oral view. G. Cross section of four-tentacled stage, showing beginning of septa as entodermal bulges. H. Longitudinal section of eight-tentacled stage, to show ectodermal origin of septal muscles, funnels, and nematocyst tissue. 1, mucous glands; 2, supporting epidermal cells; 3, sensory cells; 4, ectoderm; 5, entoderm; 6, septum; 7, funnel; 8, manubrium; 9, beginning thickening of rhopalioid; 10, septal muscle; 11, nematocyst tissue; 12, gastric pockets; 13, pedal disk.

transverse section (Fig. 167). From the four interradial corners, slightly above the margin, springs a tentacle or group of tentacles. Each tentacle is differentiated into a basal flattened tough gelatinous blade, the *pedalium,* and a long, hollow, flexible, and contractile portion beyond the blade, armed with rings of nematocysts (Fig. 167*A, D*). Set in a niche above the margin in the center of each flat side, i.e., perradially, occurs a rhopalium (Fig. 167*A, C*). The subumbrella bends inward at the bell margin as a *velarium,* resembling and functioning as a velum, from which it differs anatomically in being a purely subumbrellar extension (Fig. 167*C*). The gastrodermal lamella of Cubomedusae reaches the bell margin in such a way as to cut off completely the exumbrellar from the subumbrellar epidermis. In consequence, tentacles, velarium, and rhopalia consist of subumbrellar epidermis plus gastrodermis. The velarium is supported by four perradial gelatinous folds (*frenula*) which extend to the subumbrella below the rhopalia (Fig. 167*C*).

In the center of the deep cuboidal subumbrellar cavity is found the short quadrangular manubrium, encircled at its base by the four subumbrellar funnels. The central stomach occupies the summit of the bell while the four gastric pockets, much flattened, are located in the four flat sides (Fig. 167*B*). The corners of the bell contain the four septa, extending completely across from ex- to subumbrella. Above, the septa project into the corners of the central stomach and as they here enclose the four subumbrellar funnels, they greatly narrow the openings from the central stomach into the gastric pockets (Fig. 167*B*). In the central stomach the free edge of each septum bears a bunch or U-shaped group of gastric filaments. In the genera *Chiropsalmus* and *Chirodropus* the upper parts of the gastric pockets are evaginated and hang down into the subumbrellar cavity as eight simple or branched *subumbrellar sacs* (Fig. 167*D*). The gastric pockets give off a canal into each rhopalium and below this point are divided in two by perradial folds continuous with the frenula of the velarium. At the bell margin the pockets communicate by way of openings in the septa and form a ring sinus, also giving off a canal into each tentacle and blind canals and pouches into the velarium.

The muscular system is wholly subumbrellar, as velarium and tentacles are subumbrellar extensions. The nervous system differs from that of other Scyphozoa in the presence of a marginal nerve ring that loops upward in each perradius to connect with the rhopalia (Fig. 167*A, C*). Each rhopalium is a stalked knob whose cavity is connected with the adjacent gastric pocket (Fig. 168*A*). The knob contains a large gastrodermal statolith and one or more ocelli, which, curiously enough, are located on the inner surface of the rhopalium and hence look into the subumbrellar cavity. The ocelli often comprise large complex eyes and smaller simple ones (Fig. 168*A, B*). The simple ocelli consist

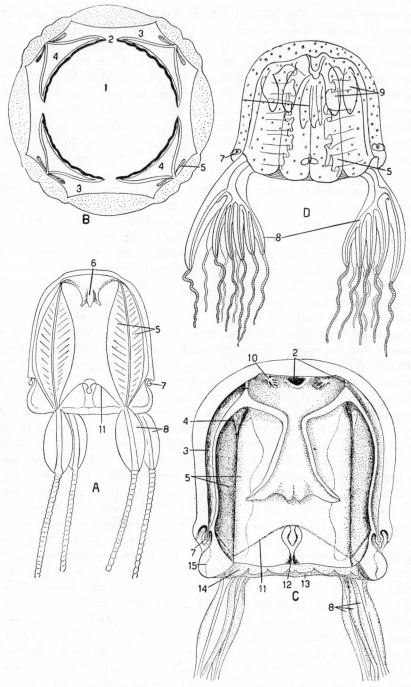

Fig. 167.—For descriptive legend see opposite page.

of a depression containing a lens-like body and lined by a tall pigmented epidermis. The complex eyes have a covering epidermis, a biconvex cellular lens, and a cup composed of two lengths of elongated retinal cells (Fig. 168B). The ends of the retinal cells next to the lens are clear and glassy forming a refractive "vitreous body," and their middle portions are pigmented, constituting a cup-like pigment zone. The gonads are eight thin flaps attached along one edge to a septum (Fig. 167A).

The Cubomedusae are characteristic of warm shallow waters of tropical and subtropical regions, inhabiting bays, harbors, and shore waters of continents and islands, but are also found in the open sea. They are strong and graceful swimmers and voracious feeders, subsisting mostly on fish. The rate of pulsation of the bell is said to exceed that of any other scyphozoans and may reach 120 to 150 contractions per minute. The group is noted for the virulence of its "sting," whence the common name of "sea wasps." The Cubomedusae may attain considerable size, reaching a height of 10 to 25 cm., but most range between 2 and 4 cm. They are colorless, with some color upon tentacles. The principal and best known genus is *Carybdea* (Fig. 167A), with four single pedalia and tentacles; each rhopalium has generally two large eyes and four small ones (Fig. 168A). *Tripedalia* (Fig. 167C) has three pedalia and tentacles on each bell corner. In *Chiropsalmus* (Fig. 167D), there springs from each bell corner a large thick pedalium that branches into a number of smaller pedalia with tentacles. This genus is one of the most dangerous coelenterates (page 392) and is greatly feared by Philippine and Japanese natives, who term it "fire medusa." Very little is known of the life cycle of the Cubomedusae. The egg of *Tripedalia* was observed (Conant, 1897) to develop into a planula that attached and became a polypoid larva with four tentacles.

5. Order Coronatae.—The medusae of this order present a more typical scyphozoan appearance than do the preceding orders, having conical, dome, or flattened scalloped bells, characterized by the coronal groove (page 499, Fig. 169A). Just below the coronal groove, the jelly of the bell is sculptured into a circlet of thick pedalia, separated from each other by radiating grooves that are in line with the center of the marginal lappets (Fig. 169A, C, E). Some or all of the pedalia bear a single solid tentacle. Below the zone of pedalia, the bell margin is scalloped into lappets that alternate with the pedalia. In the niches of some of the

---

Fig. 167.—Cubomedusae. *A. Carybdea*, Japan, preserved. *B.* Cross section through the upper part of the bell of *Carybdea*. (*After Conant*, 1898.) *C.* Perradial longitudinal section of *Tripedalia*. (*After Conant*, 1898.) *D. Chiropsalmus quadrumanni.* (*After Mayer*, 1910.) 1, central stomach; 2, gastric ostium; 3, gastric pocket; 4, funnel inside the septum; 5, gonad; 6, manubrium; 7, rhopalium; 8, pedalia; 9, subumbrellar sacs; 10, gastric filaments; 11, nerve ring; 12, frenulum; 13, gastrovascular branches in velarium; 14, velarium; 15, gastrodermal lamella.

lappets the rhopalia are borne, occurring at the ends of those pedalia which do not bear tentacles. The rhopalia and the tentacles hence

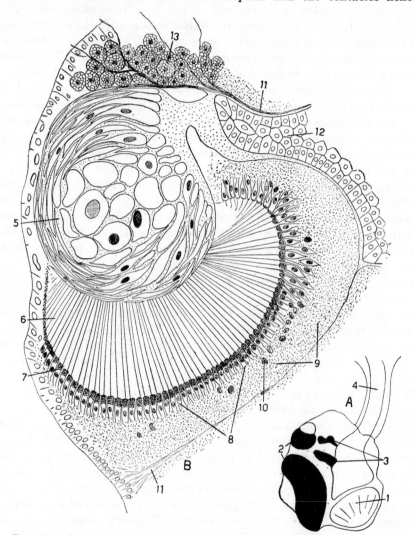

Fig. 168.—Cubomedusae. *A.* Rhopalium of *Carybdea.* (*After Conant*, 1898.) *B.* Section through the upper of the two larger eyes of *Carybdea.* (*After Berger*, 1900.) 1, statocyst; 2, large lens-bearing eyes; 3, smaller pigment-cup ocelli (two more on other side); 4, gastrovascular cavity of rhopalium; 5, lens; 6, vitreous body of retinal cells traversed by sensory fibers of the retinal cells; 7, pigment zone of retinal cells; 8, retinal cells; 9, nerve tissue; 10, ganglion cells; 11, fibers of the collenchyme; 12, gastrodermis; 13, network cells (unknown function).

always alternate but are not necessarily equal in number, as several tentacle-bearing pedalia may occur between rhopalium-bearing ones.

In the genus *Atolla* (Fig. 169*E*) the rhopalium-bearing pedalia form a circlet below the tentacle-bearing ones.   Rhopalia, pedalia, and tentacles occur to the number of four or some multiple thereof.

The large quadripartite mouth opening with a simple border leads into the short manubrium encircled at its base by the four subumbrellar funnels (Fig. 169*B*).   The upper part of the bell contains the central stomach, from whose periphery the four low triangular septa extend orally, widening as they do so.   Their edges, which project into the central stomach, bear a thick band of gastric filaments; as usual the septa enclose the subumbrellar funnels.   A membrane (claustrum) extending between the septa reduces the communication between central and coronal stomach to four slits, the gastric ostia (Fig. 169*B*).   The coronal stomach differs from that of all other Scyphozoa, consisting of a wide ring sinus occupying the lower half of the bell (Fig. 169*B*).   This sinus results from the reduction of the septa in this region to bulges (still containing the funnels) on the subumbrellar side; only at four limited interradial points (the *septal nodes* or *cathammata*) are the septa fused across with the exumbrellar side.   From the ring sinus, canals are given off into the pedalia and marginal lappets, uniting in the latter to a festoon canal.

The rhopalia of the Coronatae may bear ocelli (Fig. 170*C*).   There are often well-developed coronal, radial and delta muscles.   The eight crescentic or U-shaped gonads (Fig. 169*D*) occupy the usual position on the walls of the septa.

The Coronatae are typically inhabitants of the deeper waters of the ocean, and some species are known only from the collections of deep-sea dredging expeditions.   Others, however, as *Nausithoe* (Fig. 169*C*) and *Linuche* (Fig. 169*D*), are surface forms in warmer waters.   The Coronatae are of small to moderate size, reaching a diameter of 10 to 15 cm., although most are below 5 cm. in diameter.   The deep-water forms are often maroon or purple in color, the surface forms of lighter colors.   The principal genus, *Periphylla*, with a dome-like bell, has 16 lappets and 16 pedalia, four with rhopalia, and 12 bearing tentacles (Fig. 169*A*).   There is apparently but one species, *P. hyacinthina*, with a purple bell, common in the deep waters of all oceans and occasionally seen at the surface.   The similar *Periphyllopsis* differs in having 24 lappets and pedalia, and 20 tentacles.   The bowl-shaped *Nausithoe* (Fig. 169*C*) and thimble-like *Linuche* (Fig. 169*D*) both have eight rhopalia and tentacles and 16 pedalia and lappets.   These two genera are very common in shallow water in the Bahama-Florida region and in similar localities in various parts of the world.   *Atolla* (Fig. 169*E*) with two alternating sets of pedalia, 16 to 32 tentacles and rhopalia, and dark-red shallow bell, is another deep-sea form, usually not taken above 200 m.   *Atorella*,

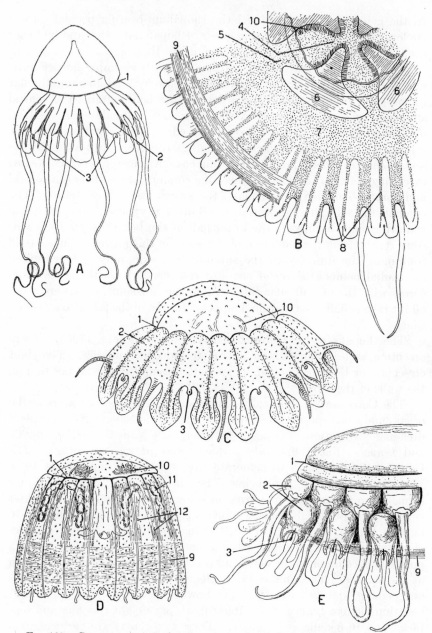

Fig. 169.—Coronatae. *A. Periphylla*, preserved. *B.* Sector of *Atolla*, showing gastro-vascular system. (*After Maas*, 1904.) *C. Nausithoe.* (*After Mayer*, 1910.) *D. Linuche*, preserved, Bahamas. *E. Atolla.* (*After Maas*, 1904.) 1, coronal groove; 2, pedalia; 3, rhopalia; 4, central stomach (exposed by cutting away manubrium); 5, gastric ostia; 6, septa; 7, ring sinus; 8, branches into lappets; 9, coronal muscle; 10, gastric filaments; 11, gonads; 12, delta muscles.

a surface form, varies from the tetramerous plan of other Coronatae, having six rhopalia and tentacles.

Knowledge of the development is scanty. In *Linuche*, the eggs shed into the sea water cleave to a coeloblastula, which becomes a planula by invagination of the entoderm. The typical ephyrae have been often seen and presumably come from a scyphistoma. In *Nausithoe* the scyphistoma stage occurs as a colony of trumpet-shaped polypoids (Fig. 170*A*) with an expanded oral end fringed with short tentacles and a stalk clothed with a ringed periderm. This colony, long known under the name *Stephanoscyphus* (earlier *Spongicola*), commonly permeates the interior spaces of sponges but may also occur in association with other animals or on inanimate objects. The polyps differ from typical scyphistomae in the absence of subumbrellar funnels and the presence of numerous longitudinal muscle bands in addition to the four septal muscles. They undergo typical polydisk strobilation (Fig. 170*B*) into ordinary ephyrae (Komai's account, 1935).

6. Order Semaeostomeae.—The semaeostome medusae are the most typical and familiar members of the class and the only ones usually seen in temperate regions. The flat, saucer-, or bowl-like bell is marginally scalloped into eight to many lappets (Fig. 161*C*). There are typically 8 or 16 rhopalia borne in some or all of the niches between lappets, but some species present irregular numbers. Between successive rhopalia occur one, three, five, seven, or many tentacles, set either in the niches, or on the lappets, or on the subumbrella. When numerous, the tentacles may be distributed along the margin as in *Aurelia* (Fig. 171*A*) or grouped into U- or V-shaped bunches as in *Cyanea* (Fig. 170*D*). The four angles of the mouth are drawn out into four long frilly pointed or rounded lobes, the oral arms, which are open troughs with thin sides and a thick stiff gelatinous axis (Fig. 170*D*). As already noted, septa, subumbrellar funnels, and gastric pockets are lacking in the adult semaeostomes. In some genera four shallow depressions, the subgenital pits, occur on the subumbrellar surface beneath the gonads but are often absent (Fig. 171*A*). The short manubrium leads into the capacious stomach, the periphery of which is often scalloped into pouches by projections of the jelly. Numerous gastric filaments spring in interradial bunches or bands from the floor of the periphery of the stomach (Fig. 171*A*). Numerous simple or branched radial canals or broad channels run to the bell margin where they branch to rhopalia and tentacles (Figs. 170*D* and 171*A*). A ring canal is generally absent. The coronal muscle and the radiating muscles of the marginal lappets are often conspicuous (Fig. 170*D*).

The semaeostome medusae in general inhabit the coastal waters of all oceans and of all zones and may occur in enormous numbers. They live mostly in warm and temperate latitudes, but some species, partic-

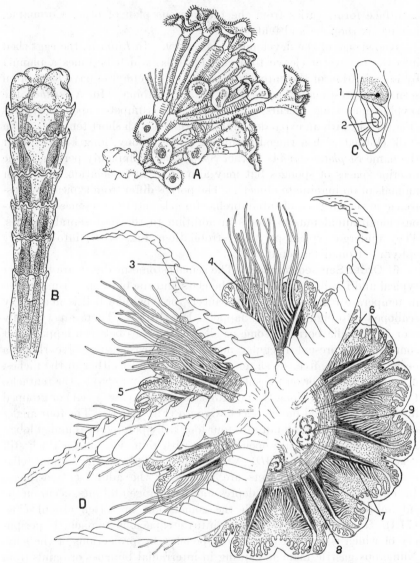

Fig. 170.—Coronatae (continued); Semaeostomeae. *A.* Scyphistoma colony of *Nausithoe* (*Stephanoscyphus*). *B.* Strobila of *Nausithoe*. *C.* Rhopalium of *Nausithoe*. (*A–C after Komai, 1935.*) *D. Cyanea*, aboral view, two of the oral arms pushed to one side. 1, ocellus; 2, statocyst; 3, oral arm; 4, V-shaped tentacle cluster; 5, rhopalium; 6, gastrovascular branches in lappets; 7, radial muscles; 8, coronal muscle; 9, gonads; gastrovascular channels stippled, tentacles partly cut away, in *D*.

ularly of the genus *Cyanea* (Fig. 170*D*), extend into polar regions.   Only the genus *Pelagia* (Fig. 171*B*), which lacks a fixed larval stage, inhabits the open ocean.   The group typically dwells at or near the surface but a few occur in deeper waters.   Most species have a rather wide distribution.   The semaeostomes are of moderate to large size, ranging mostly between 5 and 40 cm.; but *Cyanea arctica* may be over two meters (7 feet) across, the largest known coelenterate.   The group exhibits a variety of delicate and exquisite colorings, often in patterns of spots and streaks, and frequently certain structures, as the gonads, are of stronger coloration than the bell.

The order is divided by Mayer into the families Pelagidae, Cyaneidae, and Ulmaridae.   The Pelagidae have single tentacles borne in the niches between the lappets, simple radial channels from the stomach to the periphery, and no ring canal.   The chief genera are *Pelagia* (Fig. 171*B*), with 16 marginal lappets and 8 alternating tentacles and rhopalia; *Chrysaora*, with 32 lappets, 8 rhopalia, and 3 tentacles between successive rhopalia; *Dactylometra*, characteristic of warmer waters, with 48 lappets, 8 rhopalia, and 5 tentacles between successive rhopalia.   *Sonderia* with 16 rhopalia alternating with 16 tentacles is not common.   In the Cyaneidae the tentacles are clustered, and the wide radiating gastrovascular channels branch extensively in the lappets; a ring canal is absent.   The only common genus is *Cyanea* (Fig. 170*D*) with eight rhopalia and eight adradial V-shaped clusters of tentacles springing from the subumbrella.   The Ulmaridae have simple or branched radial canals, sometimes anastomosing, and a ring canal.   The chief genus is *Aurelia*[1] (Fig. 171*A*), with eight marginal lappets and numerous short tentacles borne on the edge of the lappets.   *Phacellophora*, from northern waters, is characterized by 16 rhopalia and tentacles in linear groups on the underside of the margin.

The developmental history has been studied in several genera, especially *Pelagia*, *Aurelia*, *Cyanea*, and *Chrysaora*.   Sexual maturity commonly occurs in spring or summer; the sexes are separate except in *Chrysaora*, which is somewhat hermaphroditic.   The eggs usually develop to the planula stage in pockets formed by the frills of the oral arms except in *Chrysaora*, where they develop inside the gonads.   Following a coeloblastula stage there are vestiges of multipolar ingression (Fig. 171*C*) but the cells so passed into the blastocoel later disappear, and the definitive entoderm arises by a more or less typical invagination (Fig. 171*C*).   The blastopore closes, and the hollow, two-layered planula escapes, swims about, fastens by the anterior end, and develops into a typical scyphistoma larva of trumpet form with basal stalk, adhesive

---

[1] According to Mayer, the original and hence correct spelling of this name is *Aurellia*.

pedal disk, and expanded oral end with mouth, manubrium, and tentacles (Fig. 171*D*). The mouth breaks through at the site of the closed blastopore. All recent accounts agree that the manubrial lining is entodermal, although given as ectodermal in older studies. Septa, septal muscles, septal ostia, and subumbrellar funnels develop as described for the Stauromedusae. The first tentacles are perradial, followed by interradial and then adradial ones, to the eventual number of 16 or 32. The scyphistoma (in species inhabiting temperate zones) remains without further change through fall and winter, feeding and producing other scyphistomae by various asexual processes (page 528, Fig. 171*D*, *E*). In winter and early spring, the process of strobilation, i.e., the production of young medusae (ephyrae) by transverse fission, sets in. In some genera, strobilation is *monodisk*, with but one ephyra forming at a time, while in others, the entire polyp undergoes a series of successive transverse constrictions (Fig. 172*A*) so that it resembles a pile of saucers diminishing in size aborally (*polydisk* strobilation). A large scyphistoma (*Chrysaora*) forms 13 to 15 ephyrae (Fig. 172*A*). A scyphistoma in process of polydisk strobilation is often called a *strobila*. In the transformation of the oral end of the scyphistoma into an ephyra, rhopalia develop at the bases of the primary tentacles, which then together with the other tentacles are cast off or absorbed. The septal ostia enlarge, or one may say that the gastrovascular cavity spreads peripheral to the septa. The septa are thus left stranded as columns that eventually rupture because of the disintegration of the septal muscles; the septal entoderm remains as the cores of the first gastric filaments. The subumbrellar funnels disappear in the expansion of the oral surface into the subumbrella of the ephyra. The subgenital pits appear to be later new formations having no relation to the larval funnels. The margin at the site of each rhopalium grows out into a bifurcated lobe with the rhopalium in the fork so that each rhopalium is flanked on either side by a lappet. These are the primary lappets and persist as the rhopalial lappets (Fig. 172*B*). The gastrovascular system sends into each octant a branch that bifurcates around the rhopalium. The ephyra when finished is constricted off by a muscular contraction and swims about as a tiny medusa (Fig. 172*B*). In monodisk strobilation, the scyphistoma usually regenerates its oral end before giving off another ephyra. In polydisk strobilation, the ephyrae are released at intervals; those below the original most oral one develop much as described above, except that tentacles are absent. Several workers attest that for each ephyra the manubrium lining is of entodermal origin.

The scyphistomae live for several years. After a period of strobilation in winter and spring they cease to form ephyrae and resume life as polyps, feeding and budding off other scyphistomae (Fig. 171*D*, *E*) until the

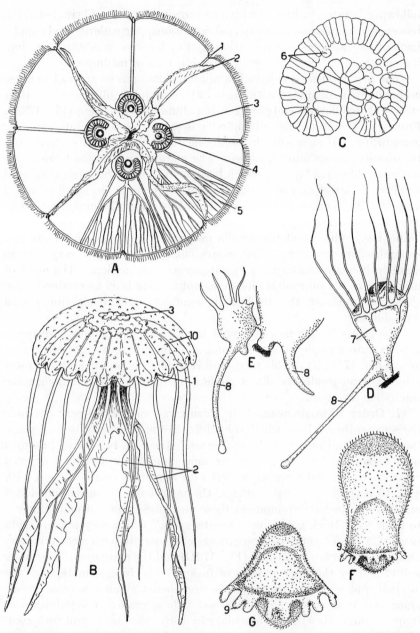

Fig. 171.—Semaeostomeae (continued). *A. Aurelia*, ventral view, from life. *B. Pelagia*, preserved. *C.* Entoderm formation in the embryo of *Cyanea*. (*After Okada*, 1927.) *D.* Scyphistoma with a stolon. *E.* Stolon budding another scyphistoma. (*D and E after Perez*, 1922.) *F* and *G.* Transformation of the planula of *Pelagia* directly into an ephyra. (*After Delap*, 1905.) 1 rhopalium; 2, oral arm; 3, gonad; 4, subgenital pit; 5, gastrovascular canals (filled in for only one quadrant in *A*); 6, ingressed entodermal cells; 7, septa; 8, stolon; 9, lappets of ephyra; 10, radial channels.

following winter, when strobilation again ensues. Their behavior, however, depends much on external conditions, particularly food supply. Lack of food suppresses strobilation, and under some conditions developing ephyrae may become scyphistomae instead of medusae.

The newly released ephyra is a minute gelatinous creature, 1 to a few millimeters in diameter with (usually) eight lobes bifurcated at their ends into two lappets embracing a rhopalium between them (Fig. 172B). From the center of the subumbrella depends the short quadrangular manubrium. If successful in obtaining food, the ephyra expands and transforms into an adult medusa. The margin between the lobes grows out into additional lappets, which become even with the original ephyral lappets; the latter may also enlarge or may remain as the small rhopalial lappets. The corners of the mouth grow into long frilly oral arms. The original gastrovascular branches are retained and additional ones form by branching. The entoderm lamella originates by the fusion of ex- and subumbrellar entoderm. The gastric filaments, at first very few in number, increase greatly later by entodermal evagination. The mode of formation of the subgenital pits seems not to have been ascertained. By spring or summer the medusa is complete and ready for sexual reproduction.

The genus *Pelagia* lacks a scyphistoma stage; the planula transforms directly into an ephyra by flattening and pushing out eight bifurcated lobes (Fig. 171F, G). This type of development is presumably the most primitive and recalls the direct mode of development seen among some trachyline medusae.

7. Order Rhizostomeae.—The rhizostome medusae closely resemble the semaeostomes, from which they differ in the absence of tentacles and the division and fusion of the oral arms. The firm bell, often provided with nematocyst warts, is bowl or saucer-shaped or flattened or even concave on top and marginally cleft into numerous small scallops, with 8 or 16 rhopalia. In early stages, the mouth has the usual four-lobed margin, but during development these oral lobes grow out and bifurcate to form eight thick gelatinous "mouth arms," which may branch again (Fig. 172C). The original arm grooves close over to form a canal in each arm, the *arm* or *brachial* canal (Fig. 172D) and the main mouth is usually obliterated by the same process of fusion. The fringed margins of the original oral lobes are brought close together, leaving a narrow groove along the inner surfaces of the arms. These grooves communicate at frequent intervals with the brachial canals by side canals, and such communications are the so-called *suctorial mouths*, of which very many may be present (Fig. 172D). In some genera, as *Rhizostoma* and *Stomolophus* (Fig. 173F, G), additional mouth-bearing fringed outgrowths, the *scapulets* or shoulder ruffles, occur on the outer surfaces of the arms near

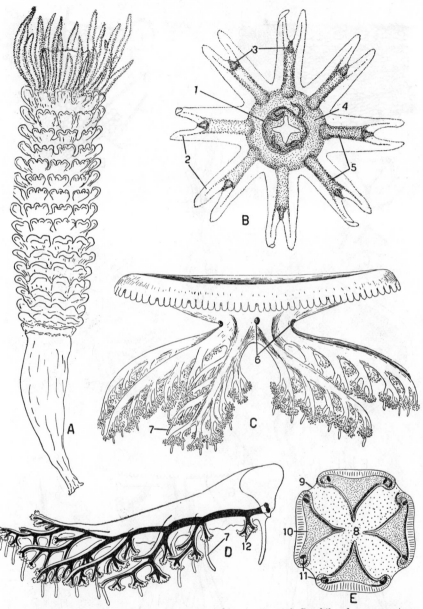

Fig. 172.—Development of semaeostomes; rhizostomes. *A.* Strobila of a semaeostome (probably *Chrysaora*). *B.* Complete ephyra of same. *A* and *B* from slides. (*Courtesy A. E. Galigher.*) *C. Cassiopeia*, preserved, Florida. *D.* Mouth arm of *Cassiopeia*, showing gastrovascular canals. *E.* Cross section of genital porticus of *Cotylorhiza.* (*D and E after Mayer,* 1910.) 1, manubrium; 2, lappets; 3, rhopalium; 4, stomach; 5, canals to lappets; 6, subgenital pits; 7, appendages; 8, genital porticus; 9, apertures of same; 10, stomach pillars; 11, brachial canals

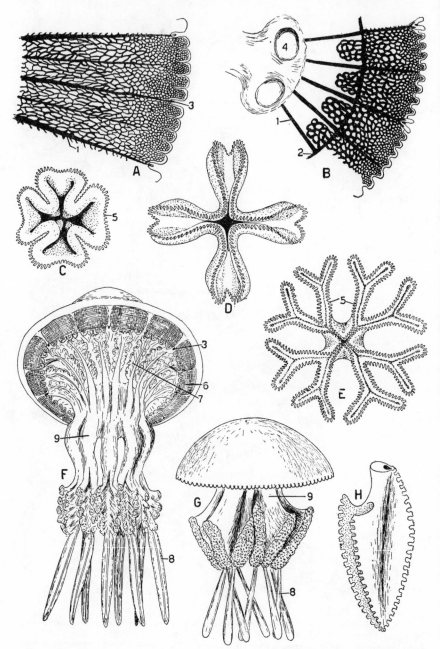

FIG. 173.—Rhizostomeae. *A.* Portion of bell of *Cassiopeia* to show gastrovascular network; no circular canal. *B.* Portion of bell of *Rhizostoma* with gastrovascular network; radial and circular canals present. *C–E.* Development of the mouth arms, *Mastigias* (*after Uchida,* 1926.) *C.* Early stage, showing ordinary four-lobed condition; *D,* lobes

the bell. The arms usually bear numerous vesicular or elongated or filamentous *appendages* (Fig. 172D), which are loaded with nematocysts and mucous cells and are of great assistance in the capture of food. In several genera a long club-shaped appendage of unknown function hangs down from each arm (Fig. 173F, G).

The eight single or four bifurcated brachial canals pass into the central stomach, beneath which they may be connected by cross canals. From the central stomach numerous radial canals or channels run through the bell to its periphery, usually anastomosing into a complicated network (Fig. 173A, B), in which a more or less definite circular canal may or may not be indicated. In one group of genera the original mouth persists (Fig. 174A).

The four subgenital pits are generally present in the base of the mass formed by the mouth arms and serve to divide this base into four gelatinous pillars. In most rhizostomes, the pits coalesce into a single cruciform space, the *subgenital porticus*, which lies below the stomach (Fig. 172E) and so separates the stomach from the general mass of the mouth arms, which hang from it by the four pillars just mentioned. The brachial canals reach the stomach by way of these pillars and their cross unions lie beneath the porticus. The porticus retains the original four apertures.

The rhizostomes have a well-developed subumbrellar musculature with a broad conspicuous coronal muscle and are vigorous swimmers as a rule, although *Cassiopeia* has sluggish habits (page 531).

The rhizostome medusae live in shallow waters in the tropical and subtropical zones of the globe, chiefly the Indo-Pacific region. The genus *Rhizostoma* (Fig. 173F) may extend into temperate waters. The group attains considerable size, ranging from 4 to 80 cm. in diameter. The order is subdivided on the basis of the mode of branching of the mouth arms. *Cassiopeia* (Fig. 172C) is typical of a group having eight laterally branching mouth arms bearing numerous vesicular appendages. This genus has four separate subgenital pits and many anastomosing radial canals (Fig. 173A). *Cassiopeia* is common around Florida and the West Indies and has been much used for experiment by American workers (see below). *Cephea*, from the Indo-Pacific, and *Cotylorhiza*, from the Mediterranean, exemplify a group of forms in which each mouth arm bifurcates into two short upturned wings; *Cotylorhiza* has a genital porticus (Fig. 172E). *Mastigias* (Fig. 173G) with several species in the Indo-Pacific, is representative of the *tripterous* rhizotomes with three-

bifurcated at tips, fringed edges closing together; E, bifurcation continued, fringed edges closed leaving a groove, mouth opening obliterated. F. *Rhizostoma*, preserved. G. *Mastigias*. (*After Uchida*, 1926.) H. Three-winged type of mouth arm. (*After Mayer*, 1910.) 1, radial canals; 2, circular canal; 3, rhopalium; 4, subgenital pit; 5, tentacular fringe; 6, coronal muscle; 7, scapulets; 8, terminal appendages; 9, mass of mouth arms.

winged mouth arms (Fig. 173*H*).   The loriferate rhizotomes, typified by *Lorifera*, have long slender mouth arms bearing three rows of frills.   The scapulate rhizotomes are characterized by the scapulets, two to each arm, hence 16 in number.   Well-known and widely distributed genera are *Rhizostoma*, with eight long terminal appendages (Fig. 173*F*) and *Stomolophus*, with a central persistent mouth (Fig. 174*A*).

The development is best known for *Mastigias* and *Cassiopeia*, although fragmentary observations are available for several other genera.   It is very similar to that of semaeostomes with the formation of typical scyphistomae and ephyrae.   The entoderm arises by invagination following vestiges of multipolar ingression (*Mastigias*).   The planula develops into a scyphistoma as described for semaeostomes.   Strobilation appears to have been observed only in *Cassiopeia*, where it is monodisk (Fig. 174*B*); rhopalia develop from the bases of certain tentacles and then all the tentacles disintegrate.   A typical ephyra with eight bifurcated arms and eight rhopalia is known for a number of genera, but in *Cassiopeia* the ephyra has an evenly scalloped edge with 16 or more rhopalia (Fig. 174*B*).   The young medusae possess a typical four-lobed mouth (Fig. 173*C*), but as these lobes expand they bifurcate, and the fringed edges approximate to form grooves with mouths (Fig. 173*D*, *E*).   The four genital pits are also always separate at first but in most genera expand and coalesce to become the porticus.

8. Asexual Reproduction and Regulatory Phenomena.—Asexual reproduction is limited to larval stages.   In the Stauromedusae, the larvae prior to tentacle formation put out one to four stolons (Fig. 174*F*) that detach, become vermiform creeping larvae, attach, and develop like larvae from planulae.   The scyphistomae of semaeostomes and rhizostomes produce other scyphistomae in various ways.   They may bud directly from the side of the stalk after the manner of hydra, but usually they send out hollow stolons from stalk or base (Fig. 171*D*, *E*), and these stolons bud off one or more scyphistomae and then detach (Fig. 171*E*). If cut off before they bud, such stolons develop directly into scyphistomae. Fragments left behind when scyphistomae move about regenerate into scyphistomae.   Some of the constrictions of strobilae may become scyphistomae instead of ephyrae.   In *Cassiopeia*, the upper part of the scyphistoma stalk constricts off ciliated buds (Fig. 174*B*) that resemble and develop like planulae (Fig. 174*C–E*).   In *Chrysaora*, under conditions not understood, the pedal disk secretes a chitinous cyst enclosing epidermal and mesenchymal cells.   These *pedal cysts* or *podocysts* have not been seen to hatch naturally, but if old ones are opened a ciliated larva escapes, which presumably becomes a scyphistoma.   When overfed, scyphistomae undergo depression similar to that described for hydroids (page 487) and cast off the tentacles (*Chrysaora*), which round up into

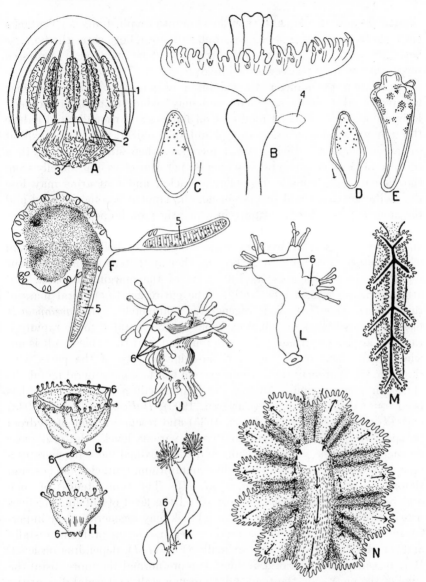

Fig. 174.—Scyphozoa, asexual reproduction, regeneration, feeding. *A. Stomolophus.* preserved. *B. Cassiopeia* in monodisk strobilation, with bud. *C–E.* Development of bud into a scyphistoma; arrow shows direction of locomotion. (*B–E, after Bigelow,* 1900.) *F. Haliclystus* larva giving of planula-like stolons. (*After Wietrzykowski,* 1912.) *G.* Regenerated distal crosspiece. *H.* Proximal crosspiece of *Thaumantoscyphus.* (*G and H after Hanaoka,* 1935.) *J.* Regenerated crosspiece of *Lucernaria,* with bipolar oral ends. *K.* Longitudinal quadrant of *Lucernaria,* beginning to regenerate new arms with tentacles. *L.* Proximal part of stalk of *Lucernaria,* regenerating a new oral end at the cut surface and an oral end laterally as a result of a cut made into the wall. (*J–L, after Carlgren,* 1909.) *M.* A mouth of *Cassiopeia* closed. *N.* The same expanded during feeding; arrows show flagellar currents. (*After Smith,* 1936.) 1, scapulet; 2, mass of mouth arms; 3, mouth; 4, bud; 5, stolons; 6, regenerated oral ends.

ciliated pseudoplanulae and then develop into scyphistomae. Tentacles cut from the scyphistoma behave similarly; but in both cases the tentacle base, actually a part of the oral surface, must be included. Depressed scyphistomae may recover or disintegrate.

Reduction phenomena are exhibited at all stages. Scyphistomae when starved cease to strobilate and may reduce to a clavate object. Ephyrae in the absence of food cast off lappets and rhopalia and reduce through a gastrula-like stage to a planula-like object, which may exhibit some tendency to attach. Adult medusae when starved reduce to a fraction of their volume and lose over 80 per cent of weight, chiefly from the collenchyme; gonads, rhopalia, tentacles, and oral arms may lose their differentiation and in *Cassiopeia*, the lappets become blunted and the mouth arms reduce to stumps in which the mouth openings fuse over.

Regeneration has been studied in a number of genera of scyphozoans and resembles that of hydromedusae. Halves of bells, or bells from which sectors have been cut, close together at the cut surfaces without replacing the missing parts. But parts of the margin, rhopalia, oral arms, etc., are replaced perfectly. The entire gelatinous oral mass of rhizostomes when cut off is regenerated completely. In *Cassiopeia* it has been shown that marginal excisions are regenerated more rapidly if rhopalia are present than if they are removed, and that this result is not wholly dependent on the greater muscular activity of the parts with rhopalia. Apparently the nervous system exerts some general metabolic effect on regeneration. Among the Stauromedusae, regeneration has been studied in *Lucernaria* (Carlgren, 1909), *Haliclystus* (Child, 1933) and *Thaumantoscyphus* (Hanaoka, 1935) and resembles that of hydroid polyps. If the animal is cut in two at various levels, the oral piece regenerates a stalk unless too short and the proximal piece regenerates a more or less perfect oral end, including manubrium, tentacle bunches, and rhopalioids, when present (Fig. 174*G*, *H*). The completeness of such oral regenerates is greater the more distal the level of cut and declines proximally so that levels near the pedal disk may regenerate very imperfectly (Fig. 174*G*, *H*). Cross sections regenerate an oral end distally and a pedal disk or oral end proximally (Fig. 174*J*), depending on level. Here again, the regenerated oral end is more normal the more distal the level of the piece, and the tendency to form a stalk and pedal disk at the proximal cut surface is greater the more proximal the level of the piece (*Lucernaria*). Cross sections of the arm bases or pieces from the exumbrellar or subumbrellar wall form tentacles and one or more manubria (*Lucernaria*). Longitudinal halves of *Lucernaria* when the plane of section is perradial close together and regenerate the missing half (Fig. 174*K*); but, if the plane is interradial, no replacement occurs. Structures cut out from the umbrellar margin, as tentacle clusters, rhopalioids, etc.

are replaced, sometimes in excess number. Small oral ends or sometimes a pedal disk grow out from cuts made into the side of *Lucernaria* (Fig. 174*L*), especially if the cut involves a septum. If the umbrella is cut across diagonally, replacement of the lost marginal structures is more rapid along the higher side of the oblique cut surface.

Variations in symmetry relations, number of septa, lappets, gonads, rhopalia, canals, tentacles, oral arms, etc., are of extremely common occurrence at all stages. They may be congenital or result from regeneration after injury.

9. Behavior and Physiology.—The Scyphozoa swim by rhythmic pulsations of the bell. These pulsations serve more to keep the animals near the surface than to effect progress through the water. Most medusae swim horizontally near the surface with the bell upright and pulsate at regular intervals, mostly 20 to 100 times per minute. Some species, however, swim upward until at or near the surface, then cease swimming and sink with the bell erect or inverted, repeating this behavior at intervals. This is presumably a food-catching reaction. Some may weave back and forth spreading their tentacles over the largest possible area. *Cassiopeia* habitually lies upside-down on the bottom of shallow lagoons, adhering by the sucker-like action of a raised circular zone on the bell, formed of especially tall epidermal cells. While so anchored, languid pulsations of the bell cause water currents to flow over the mouth arms bringing respiratory gases and food. The bell contractions are accelerated by rise of temperature (within limits) and are also more rapid the smaller (younger) the animal, although slowed in medusae reduced by starvation. The rate of pulsation is, however, very variable without apparent relation to external factors. Rough handling, injury, cutting away the oral arms, and other kinds of strong stimulation temporarily accelerate the pulsation rate, evidently an escape reaction. Touching the rhopalia, however, causes cessation of the pulsations and sinking, possibly another type of escape reaction. Flattening of the bell as when it touches the surface film or on inversion is also said to inhibit contractions.

As a velum is absent, the contractions reside solely in the coronal and radial fibers of the subumbrella. The coronal muscle has a lower threshold of stimulation but a longer latent period than the radial muscles; hence the latter contract first at each pulsation, causing the bell to shorten and bulge, followed immediately by the coronal muscle, which contracts the margin. Water is forced out beneath, and the animal is thus prevented from sinking. The contraction is synchronous over the bell. The coronal muscle resembles vertebrate muscle in its properties, exhibiting latent period, summation, all-or-none contraction, refractory period, and tetany. It also undergoes changes of tone that determine the curvature of the bell and the force of the contractions.

The effect of extirpation of the rhopalia has been studied by many investigators, but the results are variable, depending on the species used and the amount of tissue excised, often not clearly stated. The destruction of the statocysts (in the ends of the rhopalia) has no evident effect on behavior or locomotion. The removal of the rhopalia may have little result in some species or may decidedly slow or inhibit contractions, at least for a time, in others. Upon excision of the rhopalial centers (under which name are included the rhopalia, sensory niches, and rhopalial ganglia), spontaneous contractions cease; but in some species they are resumed in a short time, in others not for 2 or 3 days (*Cassiopeia*), while in others they are permanently abolished. In any event, in the absence of all rhopalial centers, the contractions are slower, often much slower, and more feeble than in the normal animal. The extirpation of the margin between rhopalia has no action, as might be anticipated from the absence of a marginal nerve ring in ordinary medusae. The presence of one rhopalial center is sufficient to maintain the pulsations in a nearly normal condition. The impulses to contraction are transmitted by way of the subumbrellar nerve net, since they are blocked if a strip of this is removed but will pass regions denuded of muscle tissue. All the evidence indicates that the bell pulsations are nervous in origin, coming from the subumbrellar nerve net but that the rhopalial centers play an important role in reinforcing and transmitting the impulses, to a degree varying in different species. If long radial cuts are made between rhopalia, each sector provided with a rhopalium beats at a rate independent of the others. This indicates that each rhopalial center discharges at its own rate and that the one with the fastest rate controls the rate of bell pulsation. The rhopalial centers are subject to change, however, so that now one, now another, may take the lead.

In bells that have ceased spontaneous pulsation following extirpation of the rhopalial centers, contractions can be elicited by mechanical, electrical, or chemical stimulation. Such contractions may be single; or rhythmical pulsations may be started by such means as, for instance, immersion in simple salt solutions. Contractions started by stimulating one point travel in both directions from that point and will pass along strips of bell cut into any imaginable bizarre zigzag shape, a fact showing once more the diffuse nature of transmission in the nerve net. In rings cut from the interior of the bell, by proper stimulation a contraction wave that will travel around the ring for days without diminution of rate can be initiated. Such rings have been much studied (notably by A. G. Mayer using *Cassiopeia*). Their rate of pulsation is more than twice that of the intact medusa and is more rapid the nearer to the margin the ring is cut and the shorter the circuit traversed, although a certain interval must elapse before any given point in the ring will again contract (refractory period). The wave will pass regions denuded of muscle tissue or in which the muscle has been paralyzed by submersion in a solution of magnesium salt. Salts of sodium, calcium, potassium, and magnesium in proper concentration (that of the sea water) are necessary for the maintenance of the wave over long periods, as the stimulating action of sodium is balanced by the inhibitory effect of the three other salts. According to Mayer, the rhythmic discharge from the rhopalial centers results from a chemical reaction involving calcium.

From the facts that medusae deprived of statocysts show no disturbances of behavior or orientation and automatically resume the usual position (bell horizontal) when displaced from it, many workers have denied any orienting or equilibratory function of the statocysts, considering that the position of the bell in the water results from the weight distribution of the parts of the medusa. The orienting function of the statocysts has, however, been recently demonstrated for several scyphozoans by Fränkel and Bozler. If a medusa is tilted out of the horizontal position, the musculature contracts more strongly on the upper than the lower side, fails to relax between pulsations, and so brings the bell back to the horizontal position. This "righting reflex" is given only when statocysts are present on the uptilted region of the bell; if they are extirpated no reaction whatever occurs to displacements. The righting reflex is also given if the bell is caused to list by attaching a small weight to one side; or if the rhopalium is appropriately bent without tilting the bell. The falling of the rhopalial end weighted with statoliths against the sensory epithelium of the sensory niche seems to constitute the stimulus for the reflex; in the hydromedusae where a similar function of the statocysts is scarcely to be doubted the stimulus would presumably arise from the rolling of the statocysts against sensory hairs or cells whenever the bell shifts position.

Many medusae indicate perception of light intensity by avoidance of bright sunlight, appearing at the surface in morning or late afternoon, and descending in midday or darkness. Clouding of the sky may bring them to the surface at any time. They are generally inactive in strong light and darkness and active in diffuse light, but some exhibit the contrary behavior and seem to prefer sunlight. Medusae descend in rough and stormy weather, although light conditions at such times would ordinarily attract them to the surface. A light-perceiving function of the eyespots has been demonstrated for *Aurelia* (Horstmann, 1934). Light accelerates the pulsation rate in normal specimens but has no such action after extirpation of the eyespots. Light had no effect on pulsation rate in *Cyanea*, a form devoid of ocelli. However, medusae not provided with ocelli may behave with reference to light, whence the perception of light intensity by the general sensory epithelium may be inferred.

The exumbrella appears to be devoid of any sensory perceptions whatever.

The reactions of the lower orders have been studied chiefly in the Cubomedusae. In this group the pedalia have a steering function, for, if they are cut away, the medusae are no longer able to swim in a directed manner. The purpose of the remarkable eyes has not been ascertained. In *Haliclystus*, the author was unable to observe any function for the anchors. They were never seen to be used for adhesion and were insensitive to food or touch. The tentacle clusters are extensively employed in adhering to objects and in locomotion after detachment. Detached *Haliclystus* individuals were observed to make strenuous efforts to reattach themselves by use of the tentacle clusters but never succeeded. Touching the tentacle clusters with or without food or touching the subumbrellar surface results in *Haliclystus* in a vigorous feeding reaction; the arm concerned is rapidly bent inward so that the tentacle cluster touches the manubrium.

Observations on food capture, ingestion, and digestion in Scyphozoa are limited. The group is carnivorous, feeding on almost any animal of appropriate size, eggs, larvae, pieces of animal flesh, etc. Fish are a favorite article of diet. Chuin (1930) has made an extensive study of digestion in the scyphistoma of *Chrysaora*. Small animals, marine eggs, etc., are caught by the tentacles and conveyed to the mouth, which opens to receive them. From the gastric filaments and gastrodermis of the septa, an acid digestive fluid capable of dissolving protein and chitin is extruded upon the food, which is reduced to a broth in about 6 hours. This broth is phagocytized by the vacuolated type of gastodermal cell, within which it undergoes intracellular digestion. These cells are said to lose their cell walls during digestion, and food vacuoles pass into the mesogloea where they are taken up by the amoebocytes and even by the epidermis. The gastrodermis of the gastric pouches serves chiefly for food storage, in the form of protein granules, fat droplets, and glycogen. The gastric filaments do not participate in either intracellular digestion or food storage but secrete only extracellular enzymes.

Ephyrae are voracious feeders, eating chiefly protozoans, although those of *Aurelia* were observed to stuff themselves with small hydromedusae and ctenophores. The food is caught by the lappets and entangled in mucus. The lappets curve to the mouth and wipe the food onto the widely opened manubrial edge. Flagellary currents on the exumbrella from center to periphery carry small food particles outward within reach of the lappets and subumbrellar currents run from the margin to the manubrium. In the gastrovascular system currents pass outward along the roof and inward along the floor.

Haliclystus (Stauromedusae), observed in Puget Sound, feeds chiefly on the amphipod *Caprella*, caught by the tentacle clusters, which then quickly bend inward depositing the food on the manubrium.   Adult semaeostomes capture their food with the tentacles or oral arms or both. Isolated oral arms or pieces thereof of *Aurelia* or *Cyanea* were found by Henschel (1935) to respond to mussel juice, proteins, peptones, and amino acids but not to sugars, starches, or glycogen.   *Aurelia* feeds primarily on small plankton organisms, such as mollusk, crustacean, and tunicate larvae, copepods, rotifers, nematodes, young polychaetes, protozoans, diatoms, and eggs.   These collect chiefly on the exumbrellar surface, where they become entangled in mucus, and are then passed by flagellar action to the margins, where they collect as eight masses in the center of the lappets.   These masses are licked off by the frilled edges of the oral arms and then transported by flagellary currents along the grooves of the oral arms and so into the stomach (Orton, 1922).   Definite flagellar currents exist in the gastrovascular system of semaeostomes. In *Aurelia*, they run outward along the eight straight adradial canals, and to the stomach along the branched canals, reaching these by way of the ring canal.   In *Cyanea*, which lacks a ring canal, the currents pass peripherally along the roof and centrally along the floor of the wide gastrovascular channels and are much assisted by bell contractions.

The details of digestion are best known for rhizostomes, mainly through the work of H. G. Smith (1937) on *Cassiopeia*, from whose account most of the following is drawn.   The food consists usually of small animals or bits of flesh, which are caught by the tentacular fringe aided by the vesicular appendages.   These last were observed to shoot out bags of nematocysts and mucus at small crustaceans.   The term suctorial mouths appears to be a misnomer, since there is no evidence of suctorial action, and the food entangled in mucus is swept inward by flagellary action.   The manner of ingestion of large prey, such as fish, by some rhizostomes is not understood although it is supposed that the prey is softened and macerated by digestive juices exuded upon it before it is taken into the mouths.   After the food has been caught, the mouths open widely (Fig. 174*N*) and the mucus food strings are carried by flagella into the brachial canals in which there are ingoing currents in the floor and outgoing currents in the roof.   The ingoing currents bring the mucous strands within reach of the gastric filaments, which grasp them and pull them into the stomach.   Rejected and waste particles are carried outward in the brachial canals to be emitted by the mouths.   In the stomach, extracellular digestion occurs by means of a protease accompanied by an acid secreted by the gastric filaments.   The acid brings the alkaline interior fluid almost to neutrality (pH 7.1), permitting good action of the protease, which breaks down proteins to polypeptides but not to amino acids. Following extracellular digestion, the partly digested material is phagocytized by the gastric filaments and four much folded areas in the stomach floor termed the *plaited membranes* (peculiar to *Cassiopeia*). Digestion to amino acids is completed in the cells of the filaments and membranes, which contain a protease acting best at pH 9.0 and capable of splitting proteins and polypeptides to amino acids, and also contain enzymes acting on fat and glycogen. The filaments are thus the chief source of enzymes; in *Stomolophus*, also, Bodansky and Rose (1922) extracted from them proteases resembling pepsin, trypsin, and rennin, as well as lipase, amylase, and maltase. In *Cassiopeia* the digested food is distributed throughout the body by the amoebocytes. Waste matters are excreted into the stomach by way of the gastric filaments and plaited membranes and carried out to the mouths.

The digestive process is therefore similar to that found in hydrozoans. Following extracellular digestion by a protease in an acidified medium, phagocytosis and intracellular digestion occur in the gastrodermis, in whole or in specialized areas. In Scyphozoa the gastric filaments are the chief sites of enzyme secretion and in some forms also of intracellular digestion. In food capture and ingestion mucus secretion and flagellary currents play an important role.

Almost nothing is known about the nature of the excretory products of Scyphozoa (see page 396).

Respiration is of the typical aerobic sort and was found by Thill (1937) in *Aurelia aurita* to range from 0.07 cc. of oxygen consumed per hour for a 27.5-g. specimen to 0.17 cc. for an 87-g. specimen. The respiratory rate is thus higher per gram of weight the smaller the animal, as is the case in animals in general. The respiratory rate is very low, no doubt in correlation with the low solid content. The respiratory rate declines with lowered oxygen content of the water. Increases or decreases in the salinity to which the animal is accustomed at first accelerate oxygen consumption, but further change decreases it.

Medusae can endure considerable range of temperature, from −0.6 to 31°C. in the case of *Aurelia*, with the optimum at 9 to 19°C. Rate of bell pulsation and oxygen consumption vary directly with temperature.

Despite their delicate and watery construction, medusae seem able to control the passage of the salts of sea water into or from their bodies since their salts, although about the same in total quantity as the salts of the surrounding sea water, differ from these in proportions. Thus Macallum (1903) found *Aurelia* and *Cyanea* to contain more potassium, and less magnesium and sodium than the sea water; he suggested that their salt content might represent that of some ancient sea. The water and salt content of medusae alter, although not proportionally, with salinity changes in the sea water. Medusae can endure considerable increase or decrease in the salt content of the sea. Thus Benazzi (1933) found that the rhizostomes *Rhizostoma* and *Cotylorhiza* can tolerate a medium of 30 parts sea water and 70 parts fresh water if the change is gradual, and *Aurelia* in particular is often seen living in very brackish water of as low as 0.6 per cent salt content (the open sea has around 3.0 per cent salt content); but most scyphozoans probably require higher salinities than these. In *Aurelia* (Thill, 1937), increased salinity augments and decreased salinity diminishes the bell curvature; both within limits accelerate bell pulsations, but too great extremes slow the contractions.

Scyphozoa can tolerate considerable changes in the reaction of the medium, normally quite alkaline (pH of sea water is around 8.0 to 8.2). Either increase or decrease of acidity may accelerate bell pulsations at first, but eventually pulsation is slowed and ceases. In *Aurelia*, Thill found slowing and damage below pH 7.2 and above 9.5.

A few Scyphozoa—*Pelagia*, *Chrysaora*, *Cyanea*, *Carybdea*—are luminescent and *Pelagia noctiluca* is particularly noted for this property. In this species the light comes from spots and streaks distributed over the body.

Many scyphozoans harbor symbiotic zoochlorellae and zooxanthellae, which abound chiefly in the collenchyme. They probably play no essential role in the life of jellyfish; they are ejected during starvation. The starch-splitting enzymes found in extracts of jellyfish probably come in all cases from these symbionts. Many curious associations between jellyfish and other animals have been observed. Thus the young of certain fish habitually accompany the larger semaeostomes and rhizostomes and when alarmed take refuge under the bell. How they escape being stung is unknown. They have been observed to eat the eggs, ovaries, oral frills, and tentacles of their protectors. Crabs, amphipods, and other crustaceans also regularly inhabit certain medusae, hiding among the arm frills; thus a spider crab (*Labinia*) apparently lives only on the manubrium of *Stomolophus*.

10. Fossil Scyphozoa.—Fossils believed to be medusae although very unlike existing forms occur in siliceous nodules set free by the decomposition of Cambrian shales in Sweden, Bohemia, and the United States. They are radial but not tetramerous; the bell consists of four to twelve lobes continued as raised areas to the center of the exumbrella. They had radial canals but no mouth or tentacles. In one species two to several such lobed bells are often found united by gastrovascular connections and may represent cases of fission. Certain striations in Cambrian rocks are thought to have originated by the trailing of the oral arms of medusae along the mud. The famous impressions of medusae in the

Jurassic lithographic slates of Bavaria were discovered by Leuckart in 1835. Although obviously medusae, they differ from present forms, having hexamerous as well as tetramerous symmetry and closing flaps for the subgenital pits. Some show tentacles and mouth opening and are therefore semaeostomes but most, being devoid of these structures, classify as rhizostomes. Besides marginal lappets, tentacles, and oral arms, the coronal muscle, gastric pouches, and general anatomy of the gastrovascular system are often indicated in the impressions. Through the presence of a coronal furrow and pedalia, some are recognizable as Coronatae, resembling *Atolla*.

VI. CLASS ANTHOZOA: SUBCLASS ALCYONARIA

1. Definition.—The Anthozoa are exclusively polypoid coelenterates, with hexamerous, octomerous, or polymerous biradial or radiobilateral symmetry, with the oral end expanded radially into an oral disk bearing hollow tentacles, with entodermal gonads and a cellular mesogloea, with a stomodaeum, usually provided with one or more siphonoglyphs, and with entodermal septa, some or all of which are fastened to the stomodaeum, projecting into the gastrovascular cavity from its wall and thickened on their free edges into the septal filaments. All traces of a medusoid stage are absent.

The anthozoan polyp is thus seen to differ from the hydrozoan polyp in several striking particulars. Whereas the latter is of long slender build with an elongated oral end, the former is relatively short and stout with the oral end flattened into a *disk*. The gastrovascular cavity in the Hydrozoa is a simple undivided canal, whereas in the Anthozoa it is a spacious cavity divided into chambers by longitudinal partitions, the *septa*, of which some or all cross from body wall to *stomodaeum*. This condition is already foreshadowed in the lower Scyphozoa and the scyphistoma larvae, whose septa are morphologically the same as the incomplete septa of the Anthozoa, those which do not reach the stomodaeum. The septal filaments, the thickened edges of the septa, recall the gastric filaments of Scyphozoa. The Anthozoa are the only coelenterates with a stomodaeum, i.e., a tube lined by invaginated ectoderm, which hangs down from the mouth into the gastrovascular cavity and serves chiefly in the ingestion of food. As stomodaeum is an embryological term, this structure in adult anthozoans is best termed pharynx. The ectodermal nature of the pharyngeal lining is somewhat disputed and has not been demonstrated for all groups of anthozoans. The pharynx commonly bears one or more siphonoglyphs, flagellated grooves by which water currents are directed into the interior. The Anthozoa exhibit externally a beautiful flower-like radial symmetry; but investigation of the internal structure, particularly of the disposition of the septa and their musculature reveals throughout the group a bilateral tendency shown by their embryology to be primary, not acquired. In the entodermal origin of their sex cells and the cellular nature of the mesogloea, which is always some form of connective tissue, the Anthozoa resemble the Scyphozoa.

The Anthozoa are exclusively marine, solitary or colonial, with or without skeleton, which may be either internal or external. The class includes a large number of common marine animals, such as sea anemones, corals, sea feathers, sea fans, sea pens, etc. It is divided into two large subclasses, best treated separately: the Alcyonaria or Octocorallia, with octomerous symmetry, and the Zoantharia or Hexacorallia in which the symmetry may be on the plan of six but is often otherwise.

2. General Morphology of the Alcyonaria.—The alcyonarian polyp is distinguished from all other coelenterate polyps by the possession of *eight pinnate tentacles* combined with *eight septa* attached to the *pharynx*. It has the form of a long or short cylinder terminating orally in a flat circular *oral disk* whose margin is drawn out into eight feathered tentacles (Fig. 175*B*). The tentacles, stout at base, tapering distally, bear short pointed projections, the *pinnules*, usually arranged in a row on each side, whence the *pinnate* (feathery) appearance. Tentacles and pinnules are motile, contractile, and hollow, their cavities being extensions of the gastrovascular chambers. When the polyp contracts, the tentacles fold over the oral disk and even may introvert, i.e., turn outside in, into the interior. In the center of the oral disk is situated the oval or elongated mouth which, unlike the mouth of Hydrozoa or Scyphozoa, does not open directly into the gastrovascular cavity but into a tube, the *pharynx*, also termed *gullet, esophagus,* and *actinopharynx*. The pharynx is lined by a very glandular epithelium, has a smooth or grooved interior, and is oval in section, and one of its narrowed ends forms a groove lined by a longitudinal tract of columnar cells bearing very long flagella (Fig. 175*H, J*) (often spoken of as cilia). This groove is called the *siphonoglyph* or *sulcus* and serves to drive a water current into the gastrovascular cavity for respiratory purposes. The side of the polyp that bears the siphonoglyph is commonly termed ventral, the opposite side dorsal; but there seems no real justification for this usage and the names *sulcal* and *asulcal* will be employed instead. The pharynx is relatively short and simply opens below into the gastrovascular cavity.

From the body wall, eight longitudinal partitions composed of gastrodermis and mesogloea and more or less evenly spaced around the circumference, project inward (Fig. 175*H*). They are known as *septa* or *mesenteries;* the former term will be employed because the word mesentery has a definite meaning in coelomate animals. The upper portions of the septa are fastened to the oral disk and pharynx so that in

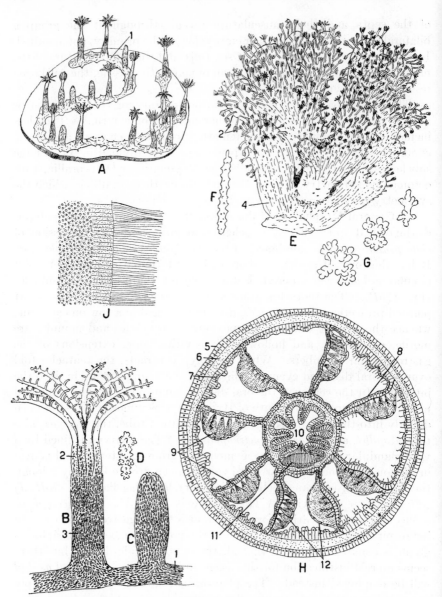

Fig. 175.—Alcyonaria. *A.* Colony of *Clavularia* growing on a stone, California. *B.* Polyp of the same enlarged, expanded. *C.* Contracted polyp of the same. *D.* Spicule. *E.* Fleshy type of alcyonacean, *Gersemia* (family Nephthyidae), Atlantic Coast. *F.* Spicule type of anthocodia. *G.* Spicule type of coenenchyme. *H.* Cross section through the pharynx region of *Alcyonium*, showing septal arrangement. *J.* Microscopic appearance of the siphonoglyph of *Alcyonium*. (*H and J after Hickson*, 1895.) 1, stolon; 2, anthocodium; 3, anthostele; 4, coenenchyme; 5, epidermis; 6, mesogloea; 7, gastrodermis; 8, septum; 9, septal retractor muscle; 10, pharynx; 11, siphonoglyph; 12, sulcal septa.

this region they cross from body wall to pharynx (Fig. 175*H*) dividing the gastrovascular cavity into eight compartments, each of which continues into a tentacle.   Below the pharynx, the inner edges of the septa are free (Fig. 176*A*) and the septa gradually decrease in breadth basally, finally being reduced to mere ridges (Fig. 176*E*).   Often only the two asulcal septa reach the base of the polyp.   The free edge of each septum below the pharynx is thickened into a cord, often sinuous, the *septal* (or *mesenterial*) *filament*.   The two asulcal filaments differ from the others, being heavily flagellated and serving to create an upward current; they are also long, extending to the polyp base (Fig. 177*A*).   The six other filaments, absent in some forms, are commonly short and have a digestive function, being loaded with gland cells.   The asulcal filaments are of ectodermal origin, formed by tongues of cells growing down from the stomodaeum; the six others are usually stated to be entodermal.   On its sulcal face, i.e., the side toward the siphonoglyph, each septum bears a strong longitudinal *retractor* muscle (Fig. 175*H*), serving to contract the polyp and draw the oral end down into the interior.   The arrangement of the retractors is such that those of the two sulcal septa face each other while those of the asulcal septa look away from each other (Fig. 175*H*).

The eight symmetrically arranged tentacles and septa confer upon the alcyonarian polyp a superficial octomerous radial symmetry.   But the elongation of the mouth and correlated flattening of the pharyngeal tube, the presence of only one siphonoglyph, the arrangement of the retractor muscles, and the specialization of the two asulcal septal filaments modify this radial symmetry in a bilateral direction.   Whereas in a perfect radial form, any plane passing through the oral-aboral axis divides the animal into like halves, in the Alcyonaria as in bilateral animals, there is but one plane of symmetry, that which bisects the siphonoglyph and passes between the two asulcal septa.

The Alcyonaria are all colonial, usually forming lobed or branching colonies, but the polyps do not connect directly with each other.   They communicate by means of gastrodermal tubes, termed *solenia*, which are continuations of the gastrovascular wall of the polyps and from which new polyps sprout.   In the simplest colonies, represented by such genera as *Cornularia* and *Clavularia* (Fig. 175*A*) of the order Stolonifera, the connecting solenia are limited to the base, where they are enclosed in flat stolons or a thin mat attached to the surface of a rock or other object. The polyps arise singly from the stolons or mat.   In the vast majority of Alcyonaria, however, the network of solenia embedded in mesogloea and covered with epidermis is erected from the substratum and encloses the basal portions of the polyps.   These upright growths vary from fleshy masses, variously shaped, often divided into fleshy lobes (Fig. 175*E*), to slender branched forms, of plume or fan shape (Figs. 180*C* and 181*D*).

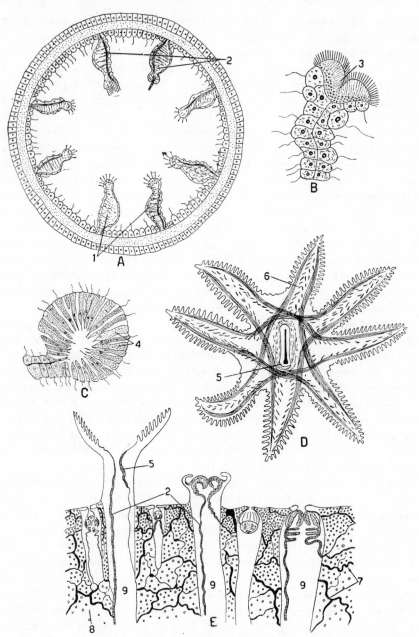

Fig. 176.—Alcyonacea. *A.* Cross section through *Alcyonium* below the pharynx, spicules not shown. *B.* Asulcal septal filament of *Alcyonium.* *C.* One of the other filaments. *D.* Oral disk of *Alcyonium,* showing muscle arrangement. *E.* Vertical section through the coenenchyme of *Alcyonium,* showing expanded and contracted polyps, and solenial network, spicules removed. (*All after Hickson,* 1895.) 1, sulcal septa; 2, asulcal septa; 3, flagellated tract; 4, gland cells; 5, siphonoglyph; 6, spicules; 7, solenial network; 8, coenenchyme; 9, gastrovascular tubes of polyps.

Only the oral ends, or *anthocodia,* of the polyps project from the surface; the greater part of their bodies is embedded in the common flesh or *coenenchyme,* through which they are connected by solenia (Fig. 176*E*). Only the anthocodia are clothed with epidermis, which is deflected to form the surface layer of the coenenchyme while the gastrovascular walls of the polyps continue into the coenenchyme as gastrodermal tubes (Fig. 177*A*). The coenenchyme beneath its surface epidermis then consists of a gelatinous mesogloea in which are embedded amoebocytes, singly or in strands and groups, skeletal elements, solenia, and the gastrodermal tubes of the polyps (Fig. 176*E*). The last can be distinguished from solenia by the presence of the septa.   In the order Alcyonacea, the long gastrovascular tubes of some or most of the polyps reach the base of the colony; in the Pennatulacea, one main axial polyp runs the length of the stem while the others arise laterally from it by way of solenia; and in the Gorgonacea, the coenenchyme is a shallow layer over an axial skeleton, and all the polyps are lateral with short bodies.   The arrangement of the solenia varies; in a common type of arrangement there is a set of interior longitudinal canals and a peripheral network.

The colonies are supported by skeleton that is generally a product of mesogloeal cells and is either calcareous or horny in nature.   It consists of separate calcareous spicules, or of such spicules fused by a calcareous cement, or of amorphous calcareous substance, or of calcareous spicules coated by horn or united by a horny network, or of strands and lamellae of horn.   Further details are given below in the consideration of the orders.

Some of the Alcyonaria, notably the Pennatulacea, are dimorphic, i.e., are composed of two kinds of polyps, the *autozooids* and the *siphonozooids.*   The former have the structure described above except that the siphonoglyph may be reduced or absent.   The siphonozooids are reduced in size and are further characterized by the absence or rudimentary nature of the tentacles (Fig. 178*B*), the reduction of the septa and septal filaments, of which often only the two asulcal filaments remain, and the strong development of the siphonoglyph (Fig. 178*C*).   The siphonozooids do not feed but serve to drive a water current through the colony and hence are characteristic of large, fleshy types of colonies.

The polyps of some of the simpler Alcyonacea are not retractile. In many forms, the basal part of the anthocodia is thickened and hardened into a *calyx,* usually armed with spicules, into which the apical part can withdraw, the tentacles folding over the oral disk, which is then pulled down.   In most alcyonarians, the anthocodia can be entirely drawn down into the coenenchyme so that in the contracted state of the colony nothing but small holes is seen upon the surface.

New polyps arise as follows except in the order Pennatulacea.   A solenium approaches the surface, enlarges to a chamber, and causes the epidermis to bulge above the surface. This bulge becomes the antho-codium, sprouts tentacles, and forms mouth and pharynx by an epidermal invagination. The solenial chamber becomes the gastrovascular cavity, from whose wall the septa grow inward. In the Pennatulacea, the polyps bud directly from the sides of older polyps.

The projecting portions of the polyps (anthocodia) are constructed of the usual three layers. The epidermis is either a syncytium or an epithelium, composed, in the latter case (Fig. 177*B*), of elongated cells, sometimes flagellated, of ordinary columnar form or with expanded outer ends, a type adapted to contraction. The regular epidermal cells are interspersed with mucous cells, sensory cells, and nematocysts, the last often in warts. On tentacles and oral disk the epidermis is underlain by muscle fibers, which may be independent or part of the epithelial cells. The base of the epidermis contains numerous interstitial cells (Fig. 177*B*). The epidermis covering the coenenchyme is similar to that of the anthocodia but is usually less columnar and sparse in sensory cells and nematocysts. On the basal parts of colonies the epidermis may secrete a horny covering. The pharyngeal lining is composed of tall flagellated cells, liberally interspersed with mucous cells of the goblet type; nemato-cysts and granular gland cells are also present. The siphonoglyph con-sists entirely of extremely elongated cells with very long flagella (Fig. 175*J*) and is usually confined to the lower part of the pharynx (Fig. 177*A*), although it may extend the entire length of the latter. The epidermis is not definitely bounded from the mesogloea, into which the interstitial cells pass freely (Fig. 177*B*).

The nematocysts of the Alcyonaria are all very small and are all, so far as known (Weill, 1934), varieties of one type, the atrichous isorhiza. The homogeneity of the subclass, shown by the anatomical similarity of their polyps, is thus confirmed by the identity of nematocyst type throughout the group.

The gastrodermis lines the inner surface of tentacles and oral disk, clothes the outer surface of the pharynx, forms both faces of the septa, and lines the gastrovascular cavity of the anthocodia. This lining con-tinues down into the coenenchyme as the gastrovascular tubes of the polyps, and these with the solenia form a system of gastrodermal canals permeating the coenenchyme. The gastrodermis may be a columnar or cuboidal epithelium (Fig. 177*B*) but is frequently a highly vacuolated syncytium and is usually flagellated in part. In many forms, the gastro-dermis is packed with symbiotic zoochlorellae and zooxanthellae (Fig. 177*B*). The base of the gastrodermis is often drawn out into circular muscle fibers fastened to the membrane that sharply separates the gastrodermis from the mesogloea (Fig. 177*B*). On the sulcal faces of the septa these fibers form a transverse layer (Fig. 177*A*). The retractor muscles on the sulcal faces are also gastrodermal but are sunk below the epithelium and fastened to longitudinal plates of mesolamella arranged in a fan-like manner (Fig. 175H).

The two asulcal septal filaments arise by downgrowth of the stomodaeal ectoderm, which they resemble histologically. Each is a broad band, usually with a central groove and thus bilobed in cross section, of tall flagellated cells (Fig. 176B), which cause a water current to flow toward the mouth. The six other filaments are usually said to be entodermal although stated by some to be ectodermal. They are narrower, ungrooved, and contain fewer flagellated cells with shorter flagella than the asulcal filaments, from which they differ chiefly by the presence of many gland cells serving to secrete digestive enzymes (Fig. 176C).

The mesogloea is really a mesenchyme, as it consists of a gelatinous matrix enclosing numerous stellate amoeboid cells (Fig. 177B), singly or in clusters and strands or arranged as canals. These cells often tend to aggregate near the epidermis and gastrodermis and may reach from one to the other by the contact of their delicate processes. Some become *scleroblasts* secreting calcareous spicules, others deposit horn, while still others function as *cnidoblasts*. The mesogloeal cells are epidermal interstitial cells that have wandered into the interior. The mesogloea is extensively developed in the coenenchyme but throughout the anthocodia it is little more than a mesolamella. As such it forms the interior layer of the septa, sending out, as noted above, longitudinal plates on the sulcal side for the support of the retractor muscles.

The muscular system is not particularly well developed. The epidermal system is represented by longitudinal fibers in pinnules and tentacles, chiefly or wholly on the oral (upper) side (Fig. 176D). These run onto the oral disk where some of them are fastened along the lines of fusion of the septa with the disk while others extend to the mouth rim, joining fibers encircling the mouth. The epidermal fibers of the disk may extend down the pharynx. Circular gastrodermal fibers occur in the tentacles in one or two cases (*Xenia, Veretillum*), in the oral disk, pharynx, throughout much of the gastrovascular wall, and as transverse fibers on the asulcal (in some forms both) faces of the septa. The retractors of the septa are longitudinal gastrodermal fibers in addition to the regular circular gastrodermal system. They are poorly developed in nonretractile polyps and in siphonozooids. The epidermis of the general coenenchyme appears to lack musculature except in the pennatulacean *Veretillum* where weak fibers occur.

The nervous system, known chiefly from the work of Kassionow on the alcyonacean *Alcyonium*, and of Niedermayer on the pennatulacean *Veretillum*, consists of a subepidermal plexus, best developed in the oral disk where it is concentrated around the mouth and upper end of the

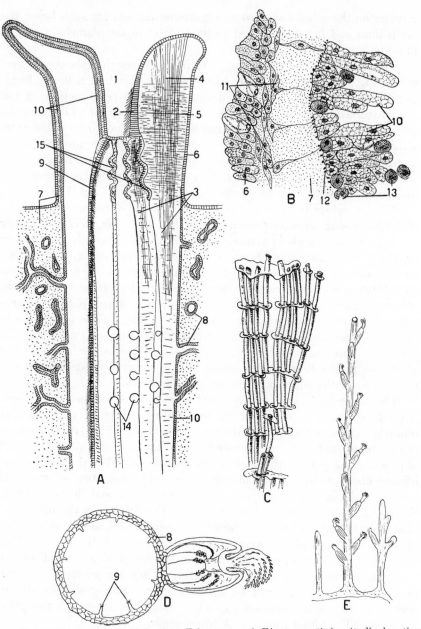

Fig. 177.—Alcyonacea, Stolonifera, Telestacea.   *A.* Diagrammatic longitudinal section of alcyonacean polyp, passing through a septum on the right, between septa on the left. *B.* Longitudinal section of polyp wall of *Xenia.*   (*After Ashworth,* 1899.)   *C.* Small piece of skeleton of *Tubipora. D.* Section of *Telesto* with one attached polyp.   *E. Telesto,* preserved.   1, pharynx; 2, siphonoglyph; 3, septa; 4, retractor septal muscle; 5, transverse fibers of septum; 6, epidermis; 7, mesogloea; 8, solenial tubes; 9, asulcal septum; 10, gastro-

pharynx, around the tentacle bases, and as eight radial strands along the lines of attachment of the septa to the oral disk. The plexus also extends along the oral surface of the tentacles (also weakly on the aboral surface in *Veretillum*) and down into the pharynx. In most alcyonarians a nervous plexus seems to be absent from the wall of the anthocodia and the general coenenchyme. In others the presence of a continuous nervous connection throughout the colony must be assumed, as stimuli applied to one polyp are transmitted to others; and the occurrence of such a plexus in the coenenchymal epidermis has been verified for *Veretillum* and may be expected in many Pennatulacea. A gastrodermal plexus also exists, particularly in the septa. In short, the development of the nervous system follows that of the musculature.

The gonads develop on the septa except the two asulcal ones, which are always sterile. In most dimorphic species, only the autozooids bear gonads, but in certain genera, as *Corallium* and *Paragorgia*, the reverse is the case, as the gonads are limited to the siphonozooids, apparently for better exposure to respiratory currents. The sex cells come from the interstitial cells of the entoderm. When ripe the gonads bulge from the septa, and in females such bulges consist of one large egg covered by a layer of gastrodermis (Fig. 177*A*). The Pennatulacea are strictly dioecious; the other orders may be dioecious or protogynous hermaphrodites. The sex cells are shed into the sea water or may be retained to the planula stage.

The Alcyonaria are divided by recent authors, notably Hickson (1930), into six orders: Stolonifera, Telestacea, Alcyonacea, Coenothecalia, Gorgonacea, and Pennatulacea. In some works, the first four are united and regarded as one order, Alcyonacea. The polyps of the orders are all very similar, and the differences consist in skeleton and mode of colony formation. All the Alcyonaria are exclusively marine and are most abundant in warm coastal waters.

3. Order Stolonifera.—In this order, which includes the simplest type of colony formation, there is no coenenchymal mass, but the polyps arise singly from a creeping base, which may consist of separate flat stolons or a more or less continuous thin crust or mat (Fig. 175*A*). The polyps may be thin-walled throughout and completely retractile into the base but more commonly present a thin-walled oral portion, corresponding to the anthocodium of forms with a coenenchyme, and a thicker walled aboral region, the *anthostele*, not itself retractile, into which the anthocodia can withdraw (Fig. 175*B*, *C*). In some forms, the basal part of the anthocodia is especially protected by spicules and is then termed *calyx*. The polyps are connected by one or more solenial tubes in the

dermis; 11, mesogloeal cells originating from epidermis; 12, transverse gastrodermal musculature; 13, zooxanthellae; 14, gonads; 15, septal filaments.

basal stolons or mat and sometimes also by short crossbars above the base or by transverse platforms as in *Tubipora* (Fig. 177*C*). The skeleton when present consists of separate warty calcareous spicules (Fig. 175*D*, *F*, *G*) like those of the Alcyonacea (see below), or of compact tubes and platforms (*Tubipora*).

The Stolonifera are shallow-water forms of both tropical and temperate waters. The genera are much confused and not well agreed upon. *Cornularia* lacks calcareous spicules but has a horny investment like the periderm of hydroids on stolons and polyp bases. *Clavularia*, the most common and representative genus (Fig. 175*A*, *C*), is well differentiated into anthocodium and anthostele and has numerous warty elongated spicules (Fig. 175*D*). The similar *Anthelia* is noncontractile without differentiated anthostele. *Sarcodictyon* differs from *Clavularia* in the tightly packed spicules of calyx and anthostele.

The genus *Tubipora*, or organ-pipe coral, occupies an isolated position. The colony consists of long parallel upright polyps springing from a basal plate and supported by skeletal tubes of fused spicules embracing the gastrovascular tubes of the polyps. The polyps are further united at definite levels by transverse stolons in which also the spicules fuse to solid platforms and from which new polyps may spring. The skeleton of *Tubipora*, often seen in museums, thus consists of a mass of closely set erect tubes united at spaced levels by transverse platforms (Fig. 177*C*). The dull red color of the skeleton results from iron salts. The organ-pipe coral is found on coral reefs in warm waters.

4. Order Telestacea.—In this group, typified by *Telesto* (Fig. 177*E*, *F*), the colonies consist of simple or branched stems bearing lateral polyps and arising from a creeping base. Each main stem or branch is the very elongated body of a single polyp, from which the lateral polyps arise by way of solenial networks as in the Pennatulacea. The spicules may be somewhat united by calcareous and horny secretions. *Coelogorgia* differs from *Telesto* in the much more branched colony, resembling a gorgonian.

5. Order Alcyonacea, the Soft Corals.—This order embraces the fleshy types of alcyonarians, known as soft corals. The polyp bodies are embedded in a gelatinous mass of coenenchyme from which only the anthocodia protrude. The colony may be massive or mushroom-shaped (Fig. 178*A*, *F*) or branched into stout blunt lobes (Fig. 175*E*) or into more plant-like forms (Fig. 178*G*). Usually the proximal part of the colony is devoid of anthocodia, hence termed sterile; the anthocodia may be strewn all over the distal regions as in *Alcyonium* but are more commonly limited to clusters on the ends of lobes or branches or on the top of the mushroom-like colony (Fig. 178*A*, *F*, *G*). The gastrodermal tubes of all or some of the polyps extend through the coenenchyme to the base

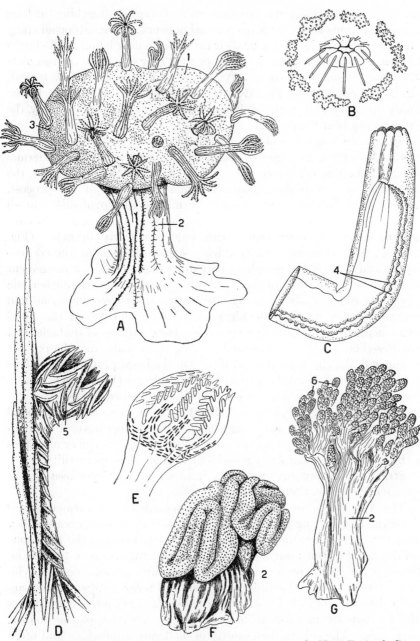

Fig. 178.—Order Alcyonacea. *A. Anthomastus*, preserved, New England Coast. *B.* A siphonozooid of the same. *C.* Siphonozooid of *Heteroxenia*. (*After Ashworth*, 1899.) *D.* Anthocodium of a nephthyid, showing spiculation. *E.* Anthocodium of *Gersemia*, showing spicule arrangement. *F. Sarcophyton.* (*After Schenk*, 1896.) *G.* A nephthyid. (*D and G, after Thomson and Dean*, 1931.) 1, mushroom top with anthocodia; 2, sterile stalk; 3, siphonozooids; 4, asulcal septa; 5, chevron spicules; 6, clusters of anthocodia.

and have many solenial cross connections. Polyps not reaching the base spring at various levels from the solenial network. The anthocodia may be nonretractile as in *Xenia*, or their distal parts may be retractile into a differentiated basal region, the *calyx*, or they may be capable of complete withdrawal into the coenenchyme. Several genera (*Anthomastus*, Fig. 178*A*, *Sarcophyton* Fig. 178*F*, *Lobophytum*) are dimorphic. In the family Xeniidae and in the siphonozooids of dimorphic forms, only the asulcal septa bear filaments.

The skeleton consists of isolated calcareous spicules, secreted by the scleroblasts of the mesogloea, which, it will be recalled, are epidermal cells. As in the calcareous sponges, each spicule is secreted in the interior of one scleroblast, which becomes binucleate in the process. In the family Xeniidae the spicules are minute thin oval disks; in all other Alcyonacea they are elongated spindles or rods or some derivative thereof, commonly ornamented with warts, or warty branches (Fig. 175*D*, *F*, *G*). They are usually thickly strewn throughout the coenenchyme, and those of the periphery may differ in size, shape, arrangement or abundance from those of the interior. The spicules of the anthocodia may be of different shape or size than those of the coenenchyme and commonly occur as eight double rows in the wall between the septal attachments and often also as rows on the aboral surfaces of tentacles and pinnules (Fig. 178*E*). In the double rows, the spicules may be parallel or diagonal like chevrons (Fig. 178*D*). On the basal parts of the polyps there is often a horizontal orientation of the spicules (Fig. 178*E*). Often the spicules project for defense over the openings when the polyps withdraw. In the family Nephthyidae (Fig. 178*G*), the stems and anthocodial bases are heavily armed with long spicules that project beyond the nonretractile polyp heads as a spiny defense (Fig. 178*D*). A heavy armature of the anthocodia is naturally associated with a loss of retractility.

Strands of horny material sometimes occur in Alcyonacea in the coenenchyme or between spicules.

The Alcyonacea are typically littoral animals of the warmer regions of the earth, centering in the Indo-Pacific Ocean. For this reason they are not very familiar animals. The majority live between the tidal zone and depths of 200 m.; but a few inhabit deeper waters down to 3000 m. Although the group prefers warmer temperatures, a number of species extend into temperate latitudes and even into polar waters. Many are fastened to hard objects by stolons or basal plates; others anchor in less solid bottoms by root-like tufts or simply by insertion of the pointed lower ends. The colonies are mostly of moderate dimensions and often of drab coloration, yellowish, brown, or olive, but dull red, purple, and various other hues are not uncommon. The shallow-water species, being subject to wave action, tend to be fleshy and flexible while the deeper forms incline toward a more arborescent type of growth with heavy spiculation.

The classification, after much confusion, has reached some stability through the work of Hickson and Roxas. In *Xenia* and *Heteroxenia* the nonretractile polyps are limited to the disk-like ends of the soft stout single or branched stalk. *Heteroxenia* is dimorphic. Of the principal family Alcyoniidae with about eight genera may be mentioned *Alcyonium*, forming a massive or lobed colony with scattered, completely retractile anthocodia; *Sarcophyton* (Fig. 178*F*) and *Lobophytum*, with polyps restricted to a folded or lobed top set on a sterile stalk; and *Anthomastus* (Fig. 178*A*), mushroom-like with polyps confined to the rounded top. The last three genera are dimorphic (Fig. 178*B*); in *Anthomastus* only the siphonozooids bear gonads, in the two others only the autozooids. The Nephthyidae (Fig. 178*G*) typically form branched bushy colonies, often heavily spiculated, with the anthocodia in clusters or tufts on the ends of the branches. The mesogloea is much reduced so that the gastrodermal tubes are close together in the coenenchyme. This family is represented on the New England coast by the somewhat atypical *Gersemia* (Fig. 175*E*) resembling *Alcyonium* in its lobed body and scattered anthocodia. The Siphonogorgiidae form branched colonies resembling gorgonians and having in the larger stems an axial core of long spicules, not bound together as in scleraxonian Gorgonacea.

6. Order Coenothecalia.—This order includes only the blue coral, *Heliopora*, found on coral reefs in the Indo-Pacific. It has a massive calcareous skeleton composed, not of spicules, but of crystalline fibers of aragonite fused into lamellae. This skeleton is perforated by numerous closely set erect cylindrical cavities, blind below, and of two sizes, larger ones occupied by the lower ends of polyps and much more abundant smaller ones occupied by erect solenial tubes (Fig. 179*A*). On the surface is a flat coenenchyme containing a network of solenia that connect with the middle regions of the polyps and also with the erect solenial tubes. The latter are thus blind downgrowths of the superficial solenial network. As the skeleton grows, the polyps and solenia are pushed upward by the formation of transverse calcareous partitions so that only the periphery of the mass is occupied by living tissue. The skeleton is a broad lobed mass of a blue color caused by iron salts, more or less concealed in life by the brown color of the polyps.

7. Order Gorgonacea, the gorgonians or horny corals.—This group includes the sea whips, sea feathers, and sea fans, whose graceful forms and soft coloration constitute one of the chief attractions of the "submarine gardens" along tropical and subtropical shores. The order is not sharply separable from the Alcyonacea from which it differs in the presence of an axial skeleton, usually containing a horn-like material, *gorgonin*.

Although the group includes some low encrusting forms and types composed of simple unbranched stems erected from a basal mat, in the great majority the colony is a plant-like growth of slender branching stems

Fig. 179.—Coenothecalia, Gorgonacea. *A. Heliopora*, skeleton removed, showing one polyp and many solenial tubes. (*After Bourne*, 1895.) *B.* Cross section through a plexaurid gorgonian. (*After Chester*, 1913.) 1, expanded polyp; 2, solenial tubes; 3, general coenenchyme; 4, solenial network; 5, axis; 6, longitudinal canals around axis; 7, contracted polyps; 8, spicules; 9, gonads. Spicules and solenial network are shown only in parts of Fig. *B*.

from a short main trunk fastened to the substratum by a basal plate or a tuft of stolons (Figs. 180*C* and 181*A*, *D*). The colony may branch in one plane in a feathery manner (Fig. 180*C*) or in all directions, giving a bushy shape. When the branches are in one plane they may be united by numerous cross connections, a type called sea fan (Fig. 180*C*). The small anthocodia, usually absent from the main trunk, may be strewed all over the stems and branches or limited to one surface or confined to the margins. The polyps are always so oriented that their sulcal surfaces face the substratum and their asulcal surfaces look upward. They are dimorphic in only a few cases, notably in the precious red coral, *Corallium* (Fig. 181*E*). The anthocodia may be retractile or not and provided or not with a calyx.

The gorgonian stem in general consists of a central axial rod covered by a shallow layer of coenenchyme (Figs. 179*B* and 181*B*). The coenenchyme contains the short gastrovascular tubes of the polyps, running at right angles to the surface, numerous solenia usually as longitudinal canals encircling the axial rod and a network at the surface, and loose calcareous spicules of various shapes—ovals, disks, scales, spindles, rods, needles, clubs, and dumbbells, usually warty or with warty lobes and branches (Fig. 179*B*). The spicules extend onto the anthocodia, which are frequently armed with needles in eight double rows or with imbricated scales. The uppermost scales or needles may form an operculum folding over the contracted oral disk.

The axial rod consists typically of a core, the *medulla*, covered over by a hardened cylinder, the *cortex*. In the typical gorgonians (suborder Holaxonia), the medulla is a loose spongy horny material often arranged to form a longitudinal row of chambers, and the cortex consists of bundles or cylindrical lamellae of gorgonin. Both may, however, be impregnated with calcareous matter, but spicules are absent in the axis. Around the cortex is an epithelium, the axial epithelium, which secretes the axial skeleton. The nature of this epithelium has been much disputed; some claim that it is ectoderm invaginated as a tube into the axis from the ectodermal base of the first polyp formed from the planula. Kükenthal, in his large monographs of the Gorgonacea, maintains that the axial epithelium is composed of mesogloeal cells.

The nature of the horny material gorgonin has been investigated by several biochemists. It is a protein, yielding typical amino acids on decomposition, but is lower in sulphur content than true horn (keratin, composing the hair, nails, scales, etc., of vertebrates). Its composition differs in different species of gorgonians, but it frequently contains bromine and iodine, united to the amino acid tyrosin.

In the less typical gorgonians (suborder Scleraxonia), the axial skeleton contains calcareous spicules, is variable in construction, and is often not clearly differentiated into medulla and cortex, nor sharply separated from the spicules of the coenenchyme. The axis may consist as in the primitive family Briareidae, with such genera as *Briareum*

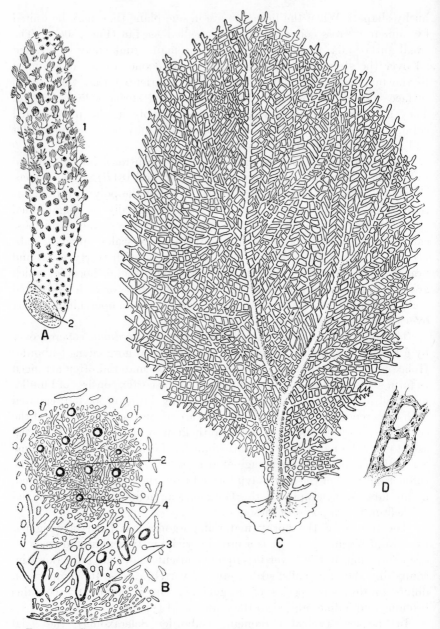

FIG. 180.—Gorgonacea. *A. Briareum.* *B.* Half cross section of same, showing axial spicules. *C.* Common sea fan, *Gorgonia*, from life, Bermuda. *D.* Magnified bit of same, showing holes for anthocodia. 1, anthocodia; 2, spicules of axis; 3, spicules of coenenchyme; 4, canals.

(Fig. 180*A*, *B*), *Paragorgia*, *Solenocaulon*, and *Spongioderma*, of thickly placed calcareous spicules connected by or embedded in strands of gorgonin.   In some of these forms one or many longitudinal canals occur in the axis (Fig. 180*B*).   In the family Suberogorgiidae, the axial spicules are united by calcareous cement into a latticework; in the genus *Subero-gorgia*, gorgonin and spicules are scattered throughout the axis; in *Keroeides*, spicules are limited to the cortex of the axis, while the medulla consists of gorgonin only.   Gorgonin is entirely absent from the red coral, *Corallium* (Fig. 181*E*), (family Coralliidae), which has a solid axis of calcareous spicules cemented together by calcium carbonate.   This pink or red axis, covered in life by a coenenchyme with polyps (Fig. 181*E*), forms the coral of jewelry.   Finally in the family Melitodidae (principal genus *Melitodes*), the axis is made up of alternating soft nodes, composed of spicules embedded in gorgonin, and hard internodes of cemented spicules with very little gorgonin.

In addition to the gorgonin of the axis, strands of gorgonin frequently occur in the coenenchyme, secreted by the clusters and strands of mesogloeal cells, and the basal plate is often strengthened by a lamella or network of gorgonin.

The gorgonians inhabit all seas through a range of depth from the tide mark to over 4000 m., but the vast majority are either littoral species or live in the deeper coastal waters above 1000 m.   They also prefer the warmer latitudes and are most abundant in the Indo-Pacific Ocean, especially the Malay Archipelago, but are also common in the subtropical Atlantic—Bermuda, the West Indies, the Bahamas, etc.   The littoral forms are mostly attached to hard objects by an expanded basal plate (Fig. 181*D*), while the deeper forms necessarily encounter soft bottoms to which they fasten by tufts of stolons.   Shallow-water species subject to a constant current tend to branch in the plane at right angles to the current and to assume a fan-form by cross unions.   Those inhabiting quiet or deep waters are apt to branch freely in all directions, although sometimes branching is suppressed.   Littoral forms are also stated to have small, retractile anthocodia and flexible stems with a large medulla. In those of deep waters, the anthocodia are larger, little or not retractile with a heavy spiculation of long needles or of scales, and the stems are rigid.   The red coral inhabits rocky bottoms chiefly in the Mediterranean and off Japan, at depths of 30 to 200 m.   Branches are broken off and entangled by dragging the bottom with a wooden cross provided with rope mops.   The gorgonians range from low forms to immense branching colonies 2 or 3 m. in height.   Yellow, orange, red, and purple are among the most common colors and add much to the beauty of coral reefs.

Because of their sessile habits and firmness, gorgonians frequently serve as a substratum for a variety of other sessile animals, such as

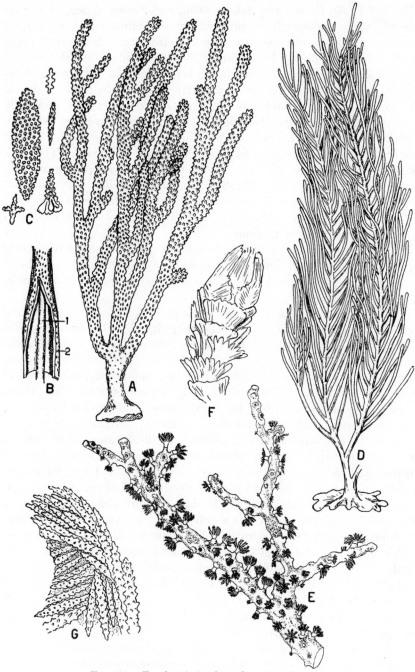

Fig. 181.—For descriptive legend see opposite page.

sponges, hydroids, bryozoans, brachiopods, etc., often to their own detriment. Some are regularly inhabited by small parasitic copepods that cause gall-like swellings of polyps or solenia. Certain polychaetous annelids stimulate gorgonians to make passageways for them formed of arched branches or pathologically enlarged polyps.

As already indicated the Gorgonacea are divided into two suborders: Scleraxonia with, and Holaxonia, without, axial spicules. The chief families and genera of the former were already considered. Among the Holaxonia, the family Isidae is distinguished from all the others by the alternating calcareous and horny stretches of the axis, a type of axis termed "segmented." The other families have a typical gorgonin axis of medulla and cortex, which may, however, be strengthened by calcareous substance. The principal families are: the Plexauridae with somewhat stout stems (Fig. 181*A*, *B*) having a thick coenenchyme and completely retractile anthocodia; the Gorgoniidae (Figs. 180*C*, 181*D*) with more slender graceful stems, thin coenenchyme, and partially retractile anthocodia; the Muriceidae, with a warty or prickly appearance caused by the spindle-shaped spicules (Fig. 181*G*) of the lids, calyces, and verrucae of the polyps; and the Primnoidae with stiff, heavily calcified axis, and prominent verrucae formed of imbricated scale-like spicules (Fig. 181*F*). Verrucae are spiculated nonretractile polyp bases corresponding to the anthosteles of the Stolonifera. The common sea fans (Fig. 180*C*) belong to the genus *Gorgonia*, family Gorgoniidae.

8. Order Pennatulacea, the sea pens.—The members of this order form more or less fleshy colonies composed of the very elongated body of a primary *axial polyp* and of numerous *secondary* polyps springing laterally from it (Figs. 182 and 183). The anthocodium of the primary polyp, which should occupy the summit of the colony, is usually degenerate. Its body is divided into a proximal stalk or *peduncle*, devoid of anthocodia, and a distal *rachis*, the region of the secondary polyps (Fig. 182*A*). The lower end of the peduncle lacks stolons or other means of attachment, being simply thrust into soft bottoms, usually by way of an enlarged end bulb (Figs. 182*A* and 183*A*, *E*, *F*). The rachis in the more primitive genera is a stout radially symmetrical cylinder or club over whose whole surface the anthocodia are strewed, as in the family Veretillidae, exemplified by *Veretillum* (Fig. 182*A*) and the similar *Cavernularia*. In all other families the rachis is bilaterally symmetrical with differentiated dorsal and ventral surfaces free from anthocodia, and

Fig. 181.—Gorgonacea (continued). *A*. A plexaurid gorgonian, from life, Bermuda. *B*. Stem of same, opened to show axis. *C*. Spicule types of same. *D*. Sea-whip type of gorgonian, preserved, family Gorgoniidae. *E*. Branch of the red coral, Mediterranean, preserved. *F*. An anthocodium of primnoid gorgonian, showing imbricated scale-like spicules. *G*. An anthocodium of a muriceid gorgonian, with warty fusiform spicules. 1, axis, 2, coenenchyme.

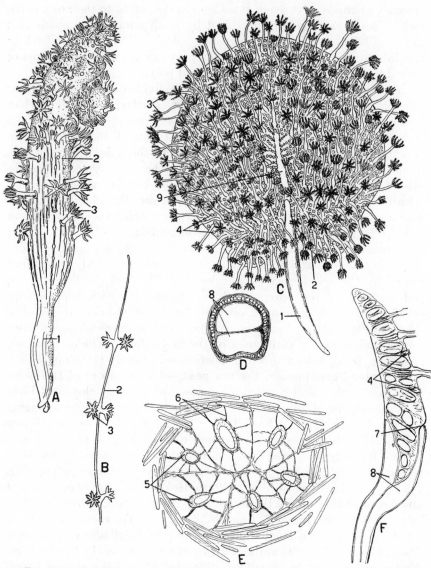

Fig. 182.—Pennatulacea. *A. Veretillum.* (*After Hickson*, 1916.) *B.* Distal end of *Chunella.* *C.* The sea pansy, *Renilla*, preserved, California; *D*, cross section of the peduncle, showing the two canals; *E*, cluster of siphonozooids with accompanying spicules; *F*, median lengthwise section of the rachis and peduncle, passing through the exhalant siphonozooid. 1, peduncle; 2, rachis; 3, anthocodia; 4, siphonozooids; 5, siphonoglyph; 6, sulcal septa; 7, special exhalant siphonozooid; 8, canals; 9, median dorsal track devoid of anthocodia.

laterally arranged secondary polyps. This bilateral condition presents several grades of structure. In the least modified forms, the rachis is still broad with irregularly strewed anthocodia as in the sea pansy, *Renilla*, sole genus of the family Renillidae. Here the leaf-shaped rachis (Fig. 182*C*) has a broad ventral surface devoid of polyps and a dorsal surface covered with auto- and siphonozooids except for a median bare "track" extending from the peduncle to about the middle of the rachis where it terminates at a special exhalant siphonozooid (see page 564). In the next stage, which includes a considerable number of families, the rachis is narrowed to a slender stem or axis with laterally borne anthocodia. The stem may be very long and whip-like as in *Chunella* (Fig. 182*B*) or shorter and less slender (Fig. 183*A*). The anthocodia may be arranged in a continuous row along each side of the stem as in the family Kophobelemnonidae and some species of *Anthoptilum* (Fig. 183*F*); or in spaced pairs or threes as in *Chunella* (Fig. 182*B*, family Chunellidae); or in a terminal tuft as in *Umbellula* (Fig. 183*E*, only genus of the Umbellulidae). The next development, illustrated by *Funiculina* (Fig. 183*D*, only genus of the Funiculinidae), or *Virgularia* (Fig. 183*C*) and *Stylatula*, family Virgulariidae, consists in the grouping and slight fusion of the anthocodia into transverse or oblique rows spaced at regular intervals along the stem. Finally in the most highly evolved families of pennatulids, the Pennatulidae and Pteroeididae, these rows are fused to form fleshy projections, termed leaves, each bearing anthocodia (Fig. 183*A*). Thus in these families, which form the typical *sea pens* seen in museum collections, the peduncle with end bulb continues distally into a moderately long and slender stem, free from autozooids, bearing on each side a succession of flattened fleshy leaves, provided with anthocodia. In the Pennatulidae (Fig. 183*A*, *B*), each leaf has a single row of anthocodia of which the outermost one is the oldest and nearest the dorsal side and the others are budded successively toward the ventral side of the stem. The leaves of the Pteroeididae bear numerous small anthocodia, and those of the genus *Pteroeides* are supported by a fan-like arrangement of spicules.

All the Pennatulacea are dimorphic. The autozooids may be retractile or not and may be differentiated basally into a calyx. As in gorgonians, the sulcal faces of all the anthocodia are directed toward the colony base. Autozooids are always absent from the dorsal and ventral surfaces ("tracks") of the rachis stem. The siphonozooids are warty protuberances (Fig. 182*E*) usually lacking tentacles, retractor muscles, and septal filaments except sometimes the two asulcal ones. They have a single tentacle in some species of the Umbellulidae and Chunellidae. They never develop gonads. Some species have two kinds of siphonozooids, the ordinary kind, and a second larger type

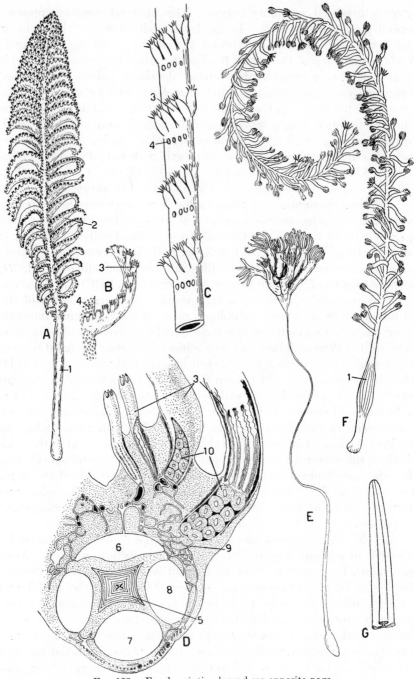

Fig. 183.—For descriptive legend see opposite page.

("mesozooids" of Hickson) with well-developed septa and retractors but weak siphonoglyphs. The mesozooids act as exhalant zooids while the typical siphonozooids are inhalant. The latter may be scattered among the autozooids or limited to portions of the rachis that lack autozooids, sometimes occurring even on the peduncle. In the Pennatulidae, the siphonozooids are confined to the rachis stem, usually the dorsal track and the sides between the leaf bases (Fig. 183*B*). In the Pteroeididae, siphonozooids occur only on the leaves. *Renilla* is peculiar in that the siphonozooids are arranged in clusters (Fig. 182*E*).

Some genera as, *Chunella* (Fig. 182*B*), have very few polyps while in others, the colony may comprise as many as 35,000 polyps.

The gastrovascular cavity of the primary polyp does not contain the usual septa but is divided by partitions into four longitudinal canals, dorsal, ventral, and lateral, which enclose between them a slender skeletal axis of calcified horn (Fig. 183*D*). In the peduncle and the distal end of the rachis, the lateral canals may be absent (Fig. 182*D*). Around the canals occurs a spongy tissue containing a network of solenia. In the periphery of the peduncle, less often of the rachis stem, there is usually a circlet of longitudinal solenia, separated by radial lamellae of mesogloea, and connected by transverse solenia. In some genera (*Virgularia, Anthoptilum,* and *Stylatula*) there are radially arranged solenia in the dorsal track. Although the secondary polyps arise in development as direct buds from the gastrovascular wall of the primary polyp, they later come to communicate with the longitudinal canals of the former only by way of solenia.

The peduncle and to a lesser extent the rachis stem are provided with a special gastrodermal musculature for executing peristaltic movements. This musculature consists of a strong circular layer around the four central canals, often thickened into a sphincter in the upper part of the peduncle; a longitudinal layer nearer the periphery; and diagonal muscles permitting lateral bendings, fastened to the skeletal axis.

The nervous system has been studied only in *Veretillum;* its arrangement in this genus was described above (page 545).

The skeleton of the coenenchyme and anthocodia consists of calcareous spicules, mostly ovals, rods, spindles, and needles, smooth, usually not warty as in the other orders (Fig. 182*E*). Characteristic is a rod type with ridges or three projecting flanges (Fig. 183*G*). In the

---

FIG. 183.—Pennatulacea (continued). *A. Pennatula. B.* A leaf of the same, showing siphonozooids. *C. Virgularia,* diagrammatic, with rudimentary leaves. (*After Hickson,* 1916.) *D.* Cross section through *Funiculina,* showing axis, canals, solenial net, and rudimentary leaf of four polyps. (*After Kölliker,* 1872.) *E. Umbellula,* preserved. *F. Anthoptilum,* preserved. *G.* Part of a three-flanged spicule of *Pennatula.* 1, peduncle; 2, leaf; 3, anthocodia; 4, siphonozooids; 5, axis; 6, dorsal canal; 7, ventral canal; 8, lateral canals; 9, solenial network; 10, gonads.

peduncle there is a peripheral layer of spicules, arranged perpendicular to the surface. The anthocodia may have a calyx armed with special spicules. In the genus *Echinoptilum*, the calyx has two projecting teeth stiffened by long rod spicules.

The Pennatulacea have much the same habitat and distribution as the other alcyonarian orders, preferring warmer coastal waters, but are limited to soft bottoms. The peduncle is thrust into the substratum by peristaltic contractions, and the rachis distended with water is held at an acute angle with the substratum, ventral surface down. The shorter more fleshy forms can withdraw into the mud by contraction and expulsion of water. The group varies from a few to 50 or 60 cm. in length, although some may be 80 cm. or even 1 m. long. The color is usually yellow, orange, red, or purple and results from a fixed lipochrome pigment in the spicules. There may also be brown or black pigment in the epidermal cells or diffuse soluble pigment.

The classification has been revised by Hickson (1916) who recognizes 13 families and 31 genera. Most of the families and their characteristics were mentioned above. Generic and specific distinctions are often based on spicule type and arrangement.

9. Development.—The development is best known for *Alcyonium* (order Alcyonacea) and *Renilla* (order Pennatulacea). Total equal cleavage results in a stereoblastula in which the central cells become entoderm by secondary delamination. A typical planula is formed, which swims about and attaches by the anterior end. The mouth and stomodaeum arise by the invagination of a plug of ectoderm from the oral end (Fig. 184*B*). The septa come from entodermal folds (Fig. 184*F*), which grow inward from the outer wall or in *Renilla* advance from the oral disk aborally. The asulcal septal filaments arise by downgrowth of ectodermal strands from the stomodaeum (Fig. 184*E*). The other filaments are said to be thickenings of the entodermal edges of the septa; but in *Alcyonium*, according to Matthews, they are ectodermal like the asulcal filaments. In the alcyoneans and gorgonians, the primary polyp puts out basal stolons from which new polyps erect themselves, and it soon loses its identity. In the gorgonians the axial skeleton is soon deposited, and as it is located outside the axes of the polyps it forces them into a lateral position as it is extended upward. New polyps in the alcyonaceans may bud from solenia anywhere on polyp-bearing regions; but the gorgonians grow chiefly at the ends of the branches.

In *Renilla* and other pennatulaceans so far as known, the primary polyp (Fig. 184*A*) does not attach, but its aboral end elongates into the peduncle whose cavity becomes divided into two canals (later four in some cases) by a longitudinal septum to which the septa of the anthocodium proper are fastened. At the region of junction of peduncle and anthocodial base, buds arise in symmetrical pairs directly from the primary anthocodium. Some of these are autozooids, others siphono-

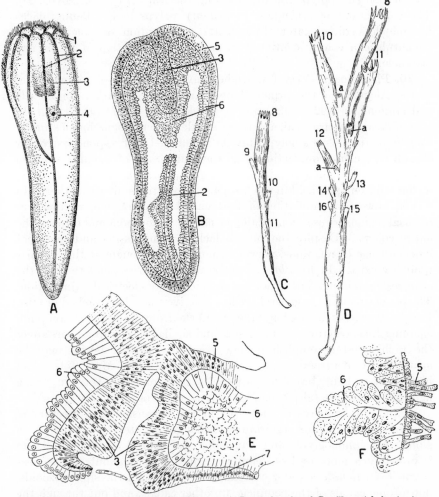

Fig. 184.—Development of Alcyonaria. *A*. Late planula of *Renilla*, with beginnings of septa and tentacles. *B*. Longitudinal section of *Renilla* larva, showing formation of the stomodaeum. *C* and *D*. Formation of anthocodia in young *Pennatula*. (*After Jungersen,* 1883.) *C*. Dorsal view; *D*, ventral view. *E*. Larva of *Alcyonium*, showing asulcal septal filament arising from the stomodaeal ectoderm. (*After Matthews,* 1917.) *F*. *Renilla*, method of origin of a septum. (*A. B, and F, after Wilson,* 1883.) 1, beginning tentacles; 2, septa; 3, stomodaeum; 4, polyp bud; 5, ectoderm; 6, entoderm; 7, beginning of septal filament; 8, first polyp; 9, axial polyp (special exhalant siphonozooid); 10–16, end polyps in order of their formation; *a*, second polyp of the respective leaves.

zooids, and the latter may bud other siphonozooids. As budding continues, the bases of the daughter polyps fuse to form the fleshy expansion characteristic of *Renilla*. In *Pennatula*, the first polyps budded become the end polyps of the "leaves"; by a succession of buds to the ventral side of this end polyp, the row forming the leaf arises (Fig. 184C, D). The connections of secondary to primary polyps in the Pennatulacea become less direct later through the intervention of solenia. The pennatulacean colony continues to grow at the junction of rachis and peduncle.

10. Physiology.—Very few studies have been made of the activities of the Alcyonaria; the principal ones are those of Parker on *Renilla* and gorgonians (1920, 1925) and of Krukenberg (1887) on *Xenia*. In general, reactions are local, and there is little or no transmission of stimuli. To a light stimulus of a polyp, only the stimulated spot responds; stronger stimuli may cause contraction of all the tentacles or of the anthocodium concerned. Touching or injuring a gorgonian branch causes contraction of the adjacent polyps, but the response is not transmitted farther. In *Xenia*, however, stimulation of the general coenenchyme, particularly in basal regions, causes contraction of nearby anthocodia and often of the entire colony. Despite the general lack of transmission and the great independence of reactions, nervous connections throughout the colonies probably exist. In *Renilla*, the anthocodia fail to respond to even the strongest prodding, but react to chemical and electrical stimulation. The pennatulaceans in general are less inactive than the attached groups. Peristaltic waves pass along the peduncle from upper to lower end, enabling this structure to bury itself, and similar waves may course over the rachis and accomplish a slow creeping. Partial burial may be achieved by contraction and expulsion of water. Most forms are indifferent to light, but some, especially gorgonians, contract in strong light and hence are fully expanded only at night or on cloudy days.

Water intake plays a large role in the expansion and erection of colonies as well as for respiratory exchange. Water currents pass in along the siphonoglyph and out along the asulcal filaments. There is probably a more or less definite circulation throughout the coenenchyme. In *Renilla* a water current flows in through the siphonozooids, down some canals of the peduncle, up other canals, and out through the special axial siphonozooid. Upon forceful contraction, water may exude from the mouths of any of the zooids and from various pores. The sphincter muscle of the peduncle, when present, also contracts, preventing water from backing down the peduncle.

The food consists of minute or small organisms and upon being swallowed is grasped by the six entodermal filaments, which secrete upon it a digestive fluid. After a certain amount of extracellular digestion, the food particles are phagocytized by the filaments and the general gastrodermis; many particles are passed to mesogloeal cells, which seem to distribute them throughout the colony. The asulcal filaments do not participate in digestion. It has been suggested that the symbiotic algae so abundant in the gastrodermis may be utilized as food.

Regeneration has been little studied. In gorgonians, coenenchyme may again cover denuded areas of stem and put out new anthocodia. When branches are broken off, the stumps grow out again so that the heavy damages often inflicted on gorgonian beds by severe storms are well repaired. In young colonies of *Renilla*, the terminal polyp readily regenerates the peduncle, but the latter usually fails to regenerate the polyp. Pieces including a budding zone may regenerate both primary polyp and peduncle; the larger buds continue to develop while the smaller ones are resorbed.

The Pennatulacea are noted for their phosphorescence, emanating from a slime that is exuded on stimulation. This slime, presumably secreted by the mucous gland cells of the epidermis, contains luminous granules and spherules. In some species the whole anthocodial surface of the colony, including the peduncle, is luminous; in others only the rachis, or only the anthocodia, not the peduncle. Again some are luminous at any time, others only at night or after being kept in the dark. The dried slime will luminesce when water is added but does not respond to stimulation. The intact animals luminesce only upon stimulation: mechanical, chemical, or electrical. A light localized stimulus may evoke only a localized flash of light; when stronger stimuli are applied, a wave of luminescence passes over the colony in concentric circles from the stimulated point. These waves will pass in any direction, are not interrupted by various kinds of superficial cuts, and may be transmitted by nonluminous parts, as the peduncle. Pieces of colonies also luminesce. In *Cavernularia*, Harvey (1917) found that oxygen is necessary for the luminescence. The color of the flash is blue or violet in most species, but may be yellowish or greenish. The explanation of bioluminescence generally accepted for mollusks and arthropods (light results from the interaction of an enzyme-like heat-labile substance *luciferase* with a heat-resistant substance *luciferin* in the presence of oxygen) was found by Harvey not to apply to the Pennatulacea.

11. Palaeontology.—Only forms with calcareous skeletons persist as fossils. Such fossils include calcareous spicules assigned to the Alcyonacea, the calcified axis of some Pennatulacea, and a few gorgonian axes containing calcareous matter. *Corallium*, *Heliopora*, and a number of forms related to *Heliopora* are found from the Cretaceous on; but curiously no fossils of *Tubipora* are known. A large fossil group, the *Tabulata*, which flourished from the Silurian into the Triassic and then died out completely, bore some resemblance to *Heliopora*. The colonies consisted of numerous cylindrical or prismatic tubes, divided into chambers by cross partitions (tabulae) and in one group (*favosites*) pierced by pores for the communication of the polyps.   It is now generally considered that the Tabulata were neither Alcyonaria nor Zoantharia but a separate subclass of the Anthozoa.

VII. CLASS ANTHOZOA: SUBCLASS ZOANTHARIA

1. General Characters.—The Zoantharia include all anthozoans in which the number and arrangement of the septa and location of the retractor muscles are otherwise than in the Alcyonaria, i.e., there are never just eight single complete septa with retractors all on the sulcal faces.   The negative character of this definition at once indicates that the group is heterogeneous and difficult to discuss in general terms.   In contrast to the uniformity of construction of alcyonarian polyps, zoantharian polyps present many anatomical variations.

The polyp (Fig. 185*A*) has the form of a short or tall cylinder, radially symmetrical in external features, with the oral end expanded into an *oral disk* bearing hollow tentacles arranged in a single marginal circlet, or in several circlets occupying most of the disk, or in radiating rows on the disk, or differentiated into oral and marginal circlets.   The tentacles are usually of simple elongated form but may be branched (Fig. 186*D*, *E*) or even feathery (if so, never eight in number, with one exception).   They vary from a few to hundreds or even a thousand or more in number.   The aboral end in solitary forms is commonly expanded into a *pedal disk* (Fig. 185*A*) but may be rounded (Fig. 188*A*) or pointed and inserted into a substratum.   The general body cylinder, termed the *column*, may be differentiated into several regions and bear various types of protuberances for adhesion or as sites of nematocyst batteries.

The oval or slit-like mouth, which may be raised on an eminence or have a protruding margin, leads into the pharynx, usually a long, stout and well-developed tube, flattened laterally and open below into the gastrovascular cavity.   The pharynx may lack siphonoglyphs but commonly bears one at one or both ends.   The single siphonoglyph appears in most cases to be homologous with that of the Alcyonaria, i.e., is "ventral"; but in the order Ceriantharia occupies the other or "dorsal" end of the pharynx.   When two siphonoglyphs are present they are often named *sulcus* and *sulculus* for convenience.

The gastrovascular cavity is divided into compartments by septa (Fig. 185*B*, *C*) all of which as in the Alcyonaria may extend from column wall to pharynx and are then termed *perfect* or *complete;* but in most zoantharians there are in addition *incomplete* or *imperfect* septa which project from the column wall into the interior and do not reach the pharynx.   In some cases the differences in size and structure between the complete and incomplete septa are so great that they are named

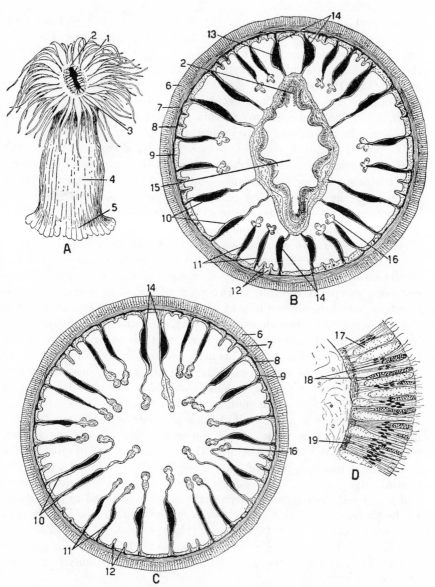

Fig. 185.—Zoantharia. *A.* An anemone (Sagartiidae) showing general features. *B.* Cross section of an ideal hexamerous actiniarian through the pharynx. *C.* Same, below the pharynx. *D.* Histological structure of the actinian pharynx. 1, oral disk; 2, siphonoglyph; 3, peristome; 4, column; 5, pedal disk; 6, epidermis; 7, mesogloea; 8, circular muscle layer; 9, gastrodermis; 10, primary septa; 11, secondary septa, 12, tertiary septa; 13, retractor muscle; 14, directives; 15, pharynx, 16, septal filament; 17, mucous cell; 18, gland cell; 19, supporting cell.

macro- and *microsepta,* respectively; in other cases the two kinds of septa are anatomically similar and exhibit all size gradations.   The septa are always *coupled,* i.e., are bilaterally symmetrical, corresponding on the two sides of the plane of symmetry that bisects the corners of the mouth (Fig. 190*B–E*).   In most forms, particularly sea anemones and corals, they are also *paired,* occurring in twos, close together (Fig. 185*B, C*).   The spaces between septa are termed *interseptal spaces* or *chambers.*   In the case of paired septa, the space between the members of a pair is named *endocoel,* between pairs, *exocoel.*   The cavities of the tentacles are necessarily extensions of the interseptal chambers, and tentacle number and arrangement are definitely related to these spaces.   In the region of the pharynx, the interseptal chambers may communicate by openings (*stomata*) through the septa (Fig. 187*A*). The septa usually bear upon one face a strongly developed longitudinal *retractor* muscle, also termed *muscle banner* and *muscle pennon* from the radiating plates of mesogloea upon which the fibers are borne.   The retractors of paired septa usually face each other, projecting into the endocoel, except in the case of two pairs of complete septa, known as *directives,* which occur one pair at each end of the pharynx, attached to the siphonoglyphs when these are present, and which are distinguished by the fact that their retractors are borne on their outer surfaces, facing the exocoels (Fig. 185*B, C*).   This arrangement differs from that of the Alcyonaria where the retractors of the two sulcar septa face each other. All the septa may be equal in length, reaching the aboral end; or of different lengths, some even confined to the oral end.

The free edges of some or all of the septa bear septal filaments, often much convoluted in part.   Their upper portions often have a very characteristic structure, consisting of three ridges, so that in cross section the filament has the shape of a trefoil or fleur-de-lis (Fig. 187*C*).   The central ridge, known as the *cnidoglandular band,* consists of nematocysts and gland cells secreting digestive enzymes; it is believed to correspond to the six nonasulcal filaments of the Alcyonaria and to be like them of entodermal origin.   The two lateral ridges consist of tall flagellated (usually called ciliated) cells and are known as the *flagellated* (or *ciliated*) *bands.*   They resemble the asulcal filaments of the Alcyonaria and are presumably ectodermal.

The number and disposition of the septa, the relative numbers and positions of complete and incomplete types, the placing of the retractor muscles, and the distribution of filaments and gonads among the septa are so variable among the different orders and within the same order of Zoantharia that no general rule can be formulated for the group.   In a common condition, often stated as characteristic of the subclass, the septa occur in pairs in cycles of six or some multiple of six (Fig. 185*A, B*).

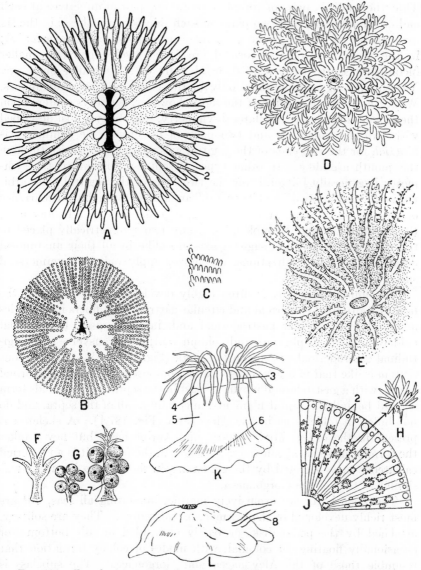

Fig. 186.—Zoantharia, external features. *A*. Diagram of tentacle arrangement of typical hexamerous anemone, five cycles shown. *B*. A stichodactyline anemone, *Stoichactis*, Bahamas, view of disk. *C*. Enlarged bit of same, showing radial endocoelic rows, single exocoelic tentacles. *D–G*. Anemones from the Great Barrier Reef, with branched tentacles. (*After Saville-Kent*, 1893.) *D*, *Rhodactis*; *E*, *Phymanthus*; *F*, branched tentacle and *G*, tentacles with sphaeromes of *Heterodactyla*. *H*, *J*. *Actinotryx*, Jamaica, with inner branched and outer simple tentacles. (*After Duerden*, 1900.) *K*. Young specimen of *Metridium*, from life expanded. *L*. The same specimen contracted with acontia protruded. 1, siphonoglyph; 2, lines of septal attachments; 3, capitulum; 4, parapet; 5, scapus; 6, pedal disk; 7, sphaerome; 8, acontia.

Thus there are six pairs of complete septa, one pair of directives at each end of the pharynx, and two pairs on each side between these; in the six exocoels between these occur six pairs of incomplete septa (*secondaries*); in the twelve exocoels so formed are found twelve pairs of smaller incomplete septa (*tertiaries*); then 24 pairs of still smaller ones, etc. Yet this arrangement obtains only in the corals and some anemones. Whatever is the disposition of the septa, however, it always confers upon the animal some degree of bilateral symmetry.   In the type just described with two siphonoglyphs and two pairs of directives, the symmetry is *biradial*, for the two ends of the sagittal axis passing lengthwise through the mouth are alike.   In other types of septal arrangement, the symmetry is generally bilateral, for the two ends of the sagittal axis, arbitrarily termed "dorsal" and "ventral," are unlike, through the occurrence of one siphonoglyph, retractor placing, or other factors.   In any case, the septa are always "coupled," i.e., any two symmetrically placed to the right and left of the sagittal axis are alike in all their anatomical details.   These generalizations, of course, apply only to symmetrical specimens.

The muscular system is often highly developed and consists of the usual longitudinal epidermal and circular gastrodermal fibers in tentacles and oral disk; circular gastrodermal and, in some cases, longitudinal epidermal fibers in pharynx and column wall; and transverse and longitudinal gastrodermal systems in the septa (Fig. 192*A*, *C*).   The nervous system is like that of other coelenterates, composed of a general epidermal plexus with a gastrodermal plexus at least in the septa.   The gonads form a band behind the septal filaments, in certain or all of the septa, and do not bulge in follicles as in the Alcyonaria (Fig. 187*A*).   A skeleton is present in the orders Madreporaria and Antipatharia but never takes the form of mesogloeal calcareous spicules; in the former it is an external calcareous mass secreted by the epidermis, in the latter a horn-like axis similar to that of the Gorgonacea.

The Zoantharia are exclusively marine, inhabiting all seas, but are most richly developed in the warmer coastal waters.   They are solitary, attached by the pedal disk, or partly embedded in soft bottoms, or occasionally floating; or colonial, with modes of colony formation that resemble those of the Alcyonacea and Gorgonacea.   The subclass is divided into five orders: Actiniaria, Madreporaria, Zoanthidea, Antipatharia, and Ceriantharia.

2. Order Actiniaria, the Sea Anemones.—The sea anemones, so-called from the flower-like appearance of the expanded oral disk, are among the most familiar animals of the seashore.   The solitary, cylindrical body is divided into *oral disk*, *column*, and *base*.   The oral disk is flat, with a circular, sometimes lobed or bilobed, margin, and is provided with tentacles except in the genus *Limnactinia*. The tentacles may be few in number, arranged in a single marginal circlet, or more numerous, covering much of the oral disk, disposed in two to many alternating circles (called *cycles*, Fig. 186A) or in radiating rows (Fig. 186B) or both; or the tentacles may be so numerous as to lack obvious arrangement (Fig. 187A). In some cases they are grouped into marginal and oral sets. The number when definite is often some multiple of six and doubles in each successive cycle after the innermost one, thus: 6, 6, 12, 24, 48, etc. The tentacles of one cycle are usually of the same size and form, but those of different cycles may differ in one or both regards. The innermost tentacles are the oldest and usually the largest, the size decreasing to the margin; but the opposite condition may obtain, and other patterns may occur. The tentacles are definitely related to the interseptal spaces. In most anemones there is one tentacle to each endocoel and each exocoel, and all the cycles except the outermost one are endocoelic. The outermost cycle is exocoelic but becomes endocoelic when new septa appear, whereupon a new set of exocoelic tentacles forms. The six innermost tentacles belong to the endocoels of the primary mesenteries; the next cycle, of six tentacles, to the endocoels of the secondaries; the third cycle, of 12 tentacles, to the endocoels of the tertiaries, etc. As the cycles of septa alternate, the successive tentacle cycles also necessarily alternate. In several families, known as stichodactyline anemones, each endocoel bears several tentacles in a radial row (Fig. 186B), and each exocoel has commonly one tentacle at the periphery but may have a radial row in some species. As the number of septa and consequently of endocoels commonly increases with age, the number of tentacles also increases and may eventually reach hundreds.

The tentacles are usually of simple conical form, tapering to a point; but the end may be swollen into an enlargement (nematosphere) bearing nematocysts, or the shape may be altered by a spiral band of nematocysts, or the tentacles may be laterally flattened, or short, or reduced to round or oval vesicles (sphaeromes, Fig. 186G) or papillae (Fig. 186B, C). In some tropical anemones simply or dendritically branched tentacles occur (Fig. 186D, E, J). All the tentacles may be branched, or the inner cycles simple and the outer branched or vice versa (Fig. 186J), or the outer ones elongated and the inner ones reduced to sphaeromes or papillae. The tentacles are often pierced by one or more pores, apically or elsewhere.

The junction of oral disk and column is termed the *margin* and may be marked by a groove (Fig. 187A). The column wall varies from a thin transparent to a thick leathery condition and is often marked by longitudinal lines representing the lines of attachment of the septa. The

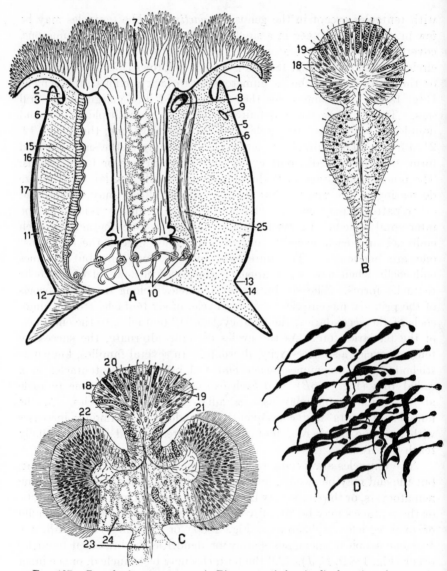

Fig. 187.—Zoantharia, structure. *A.* Diagrammatic longitudinal section of an anemone, based on *Metridium;* endocoelic face of a primary septum shown on the right; exocoelic face of a secondary septum on the left. *B.* Histological structure of a septal filament in levels below the pharynx. *C.* Histology of septal filament at levels through the pharynx. *D.* Sensory nerve cells of an anemone pharynx. (*After Groselj,* 1909.) 1, capitulum; 2, fosse; 3, sphincter; 4, parapet; 5, scapus; 6, septum; 7, siphonoglyph; 8, oral stoma; 9, marginal stoma; 10, acontia; 11, parietal muscle; 12, basilar muscle; 13, limbus; 14, pedal disk; 15, transverse musculature of septum; 16, gonad; 17, septal filament; 18, cnidoglandular tract; 19, gland cells; 20, nematocysts; 21, intermediate tract; 22, flagellated tract; 23, mesogloeal core of filament; 24, reticulated tract; 25, retractor muscle of septum.

column may be of the same texture throughout its length but in a number of common genera (as *Phellia, Peachia, Ilyanthus, Halcampa, Diadumene*) is differentiated into an upper short delicate, thin-walled region, the *capitulum*, and a lower thick-walled region, the *scapus* (Fig. 186K). In some genera with such column differentiation, as *Metridium, Tealia, Actinia, Anemonia*, the scapus just before joining the capitulum stands up as a prominent fold, the *collar* or *parapet*, and a shallow or deep groove, the *fosse*, results between collar and base of the capitulum (Figs. 187A, 188F). Regardless of the presence or absence of the capitulum, the upper part of the scapus may be differentiated into a short region, the *scapulus*, differing from the scapus not in thickness but in histological construction and general appearance. In the family Edwardsiidae, the column often exhibits all three regions, capitulum, scapulus, and scapus (Fig. 188A).

Shortly below the margin or at the lower boundary of the capitulum (when this is present) there commonly occurs a thickening of the circular muscle layer of the body wall forming the marginal *sphincter*. This functions to close the margin or upper end of the scapus over the retracted oral disk (and capitulum if present) when the animal contracts. In forms with a parapet, the sphincter is in the wall of the fosse (Fig. 187A).

The column wall often presents a variety of special structures or protuberances that classify as ornamental, adhesive, or protective. Some forms possess tubercles or ridges of thickened mesogloea that seem to have no special function and may be regarded as ornamental. A simple type of adhesive structure is seen in the genus *Sagartia* where the column is provided with adhesive spots consisting of a modified glandular epidermis. Adhesive papillae (which also bear nematocysts) occur in rows on *Haloclava* (Fig. 191A). More differentiated are the *warts* or *verrucae*, protuberances often in longitudinal rows between the septal attachments, as in *Bunodactis* (Fig. 188C), *Tealia, Anthopleura*, etc. They are hollow projections of the body wall provided with a special musculature and having a concavity lined by a glandular epidermis (Fig. 188D, E). *Tenaculi*, seen in *Halcampa*, differ in that the epidermis contains radiating supporting fibers as well as gland cells. By means of these various adhesive structures anemones can cover themselves with bits of shell, gravel, and other objects, presumably for protection. Special nematocyst-bearing structures are also of common occurrence in anemones. Most curious are the *nemathybomes* of the family Edwardsiidae, mesogloeal sacs containing a bundle of nematocysts (Fig. 188A, K, L); they occur in a single row or in a band (Fig. 190A) between the septal attachments. *Acrorhagi*, rounded or oval hollow bodies covered with nematocysts (Fig. 188G), occur in a circlet at the margin or on the parapet of such genera as *Actinia, Anemonia* (Fig. 188F), *Anthopleura*, and others. They may be in line with the

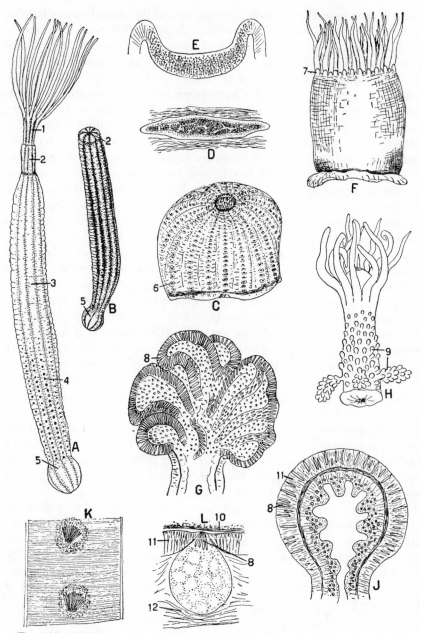

Fig. 188.—Actiniaria, external features. *A. Edwardsia*, preserved. *B. Edwardsia*, alive, contracted. *C. Bunodactis*, preserved, Cuba, showing verrucae. *D.* Verruca enlarged. *E.* Section through the same, showing secretion granules. *F. Anemonia*, Hawaii, with acrorhagi. *G.* One of the acrorhagi enlarged. *H. Bunodeopsis globulifera*, with vesicles, from life, Bermuda. *J.* Section through a vesicle. *K.* Surface view of two

rows of verrucae. In *Lebrunia*, West Indies, the margin bears four to eight branched *pseudotentacles* whose upper surfaces are provided with acrorhagi (Fig. 189*B–D*). In some members of the families Actiniidae and Phyllactidae, the acrorhagi may be compound and may enlarge into hollow, foliose expansions, termed *fronds* or *pseudoacrorhagi* (since they lack nematocysts), which may encircle the margin like a ruff (Fig. 189*A*). Finally may be mentioned the *vesicles*, simple or compound projections of the scapus, similar to acrorhagi, which occur in tropical anemones such as *Bunodeopsis* (Fig. 188*H*, *J*) and members of the families Aliciidae and Phyllactidae. In some anemones, the column wall is pierced by a few to many pores, the *cinclides*, which may open on papillae and may be arranged in rows. They seem to serve for the emission of water when the column contracts suddenly.

The base is separated from the column by a constriction, the *limbus*, and is usually expanded into a circular *pedal disk*, used to adhere to stones, shells, and other hard objects. In some deeper water forms, the disk curves around to grasp a ball of mud, and in other types, habitually commensal, may be drawn out into a lobe on each side used to wrap around stems or shells of other live animals (Fig. 195*A*). In forms inhabiting soft bottoms, the base may be simply rounded or pointed or often constricted by the limbus as an end bulb, the *physa* (Figs. 188*A* and 191*A*). In the tropical family Minyadidae (Fig. 189*E*), the pedal disk has become a float, being curved into a sac filled with a chitinous network. The base may be pierced by one or more pores (Fig. 191*A*).

The mouth is oval or slit-like (Fig. 185*A*), rarely round, often with a raised margin, and is usually separated from the nearest tentacles by a smooth space, the *peristome*. The pharynx is usually a long stout tube flattened laterally (Fig. 185*B*) to correspond with the mouth shape. The plane through the long axis of mouth and pharynx is termed the sagittal plane and establishes a condition of biradial or bilateral symmetry. The pharynx is short or reduced in a few forms. The siphonoglyphs may be absent or only slightly evidenced in the more primitive species, but most anemones have two well-developed siphonoglyphs, some only one. In monoglyphic forms, the single siphonoglyph or sulcus is considered from the arrangement of the retractors to be situated at the "ventral" end of the pharynx; such types are bilateral. In diglyphic forms, the second siphonoglyph, termed *sulculus* and sometimes smaller than the sulcus, is at the opposite or "dorsal" end of the pharynx. Diglyphic types are biradial and may offer no means of distinguishing "ventral" and "dorsal" surfaces in the adult. The terms sulcal and

nemathybomes of *Edwardsia*. *L*. Section of a nemathybome. 1, capitulum; 2, scapulus; 3, scapus; 4, rows of nemathybomes; 5, physa; 6, verrucae; 7, acrorhagi; 8, nematocysts; 9, vesicles; 10, cuticle; 11, epidermis; 12, mesogloea.

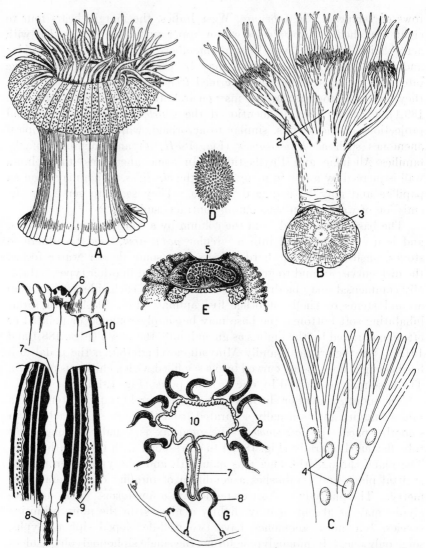

FIG. 189.—Features of Actiniaria (continued). A. *Asteractis expansa*, with ruff of fronds, Puerto Rico. (*After Duerden*, 1900.) B. *Lebrunia danae*, West Indies, with pseudotentacles. C. A pseudotentacle of the same, enlarged, to show acrorhagi. D. One of the acrorhagi, showing nematocysts. E. Aboral end of a minyad, showing float. (*After Carlgren*, 1924.) F. *Peachia*, opened out, to show long siphonoglyph and the conchula. G. Section through pharynx of *Peachia*, showing deep siphonoglyph. (*Both after Faurot*, 1895.) 1, fronds or pseudoacrorhagi; 2, pseudotentacles; 3, pedal disk; 4, acrorhagi; 5, float; 6, conchula; 7, siphonoglyph; 8, directives; 9, other septa; 10, pharynx.

asulcal in monoglyphic species and sulcal and sulculal for diglyphic ones seem preferable to ventral and dorsal. Both monoglyphic and diglyphic individuals occur in some species, as the common *Metridium*[1] of our Atlantic coast; and cases are recorded of anemones with three to ten or even more siphonoglyphs. It is probable that all such irregularities result from asexual modes of reproduction or regeneration after injury. In the genus *Peachia*, the single siphonoglyph is very deep (Fig. 189*F, G*) and is provided at its oral end with a sort of spout, the *conchula*. Otherwise the siphonoglyphs are deep, smooth-walled grooves, lined by flagellated cells, which beat a current of water into the interior. The rest of the pharynx lining is rough and usually strongly ridged along the insertions of the complete septa (Fig. 185*B*).

The septa may be all complete, but generally both complete and incomplete cycles are present. The two sorts may differ so much in size and other features that they are termed *macrosepta* or *macrocnemes* and *microsepta* or *microcnemes*. In adult anemones, the septa are always paired and never less than six pairs are present, although these 12 septa develop as couples rather than as pairs. The most primitive condition is found in such genera as *Gonactinia, Protanthea*, and *Edwardsia* (Fig. 190*A–D*). They have eight macrosepta, comprising a pair of directives at each end of the pharynx (whether this is monoglyphic, diglyphic, or without definite siphonoglyphs) and two single septa on each side. The retractors of the directives face away from each other while those of the four single septa face "ventrally" and thus alter the symmetry to a bilateral condition. This arrangement differs from that of the Alcyonaria only in that the sulcal retractors are on the exocoelic faces. In addition to the eight macrosepta there are always present at least four microsepta, which may be developed only near the oral disk and which pair with the four single macrosepta in such a way that their retractors face each other (Fig. 190*B–D*). Thus six pairs of septa are present at least distally. In the exocoels between these six pairs there are usually present additional pairs of microsepta, two pairs in *Gonactinia* (Fig. 190*B*), four in *Protanthea* (Fig. 190*C*) and none to several pairs in various members of the family Edwardsiidae (Fig. 190*D*). The statement often seen that the Edwardsiidae possess only eight septa is incorrect, as fully mature specimens always have four or more microsepta at least in the uppermost part of the column.

In the next stage, the four microsepta paired with the four lateral macrosepta complete themselves and become perfect septa. There results the condition very common in anemones, the presence of six pairs

[1] This anemone, very widely used for class study, is about the worst species that could be selected for this purpose, for it is always very irregular as regards siphonoglyphs and septa because of extensive multiplication by asexual methods.

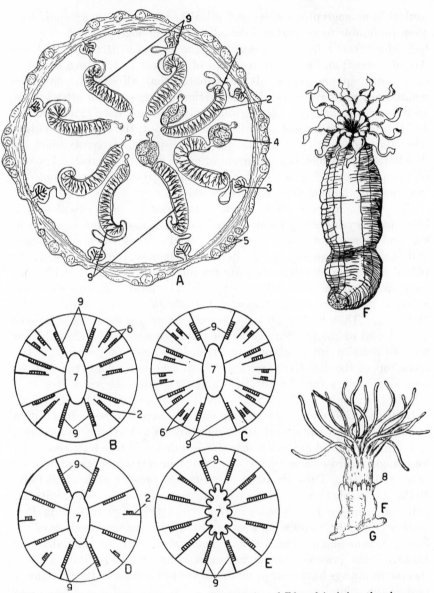

Fig. 190.—Actiniaria (continued).   *A*. Cross section of *Edwardsia*, below the pharynx, showing the eight macrosepta and their musculature.   *B–D*. Diagrams of the septal arrangement in four of the more primitive genera of anemones (*based in part on Carlgren*, 1891): *B, Gonactinia; C, Protanthea; D, Edwardsia. E. Halcampoides. F. Halcampoides.* (*After Pax*, 1926.)   *G. Gonactinia prolifera*, showing asexual reproduction.   (*After Blockman and Hilger*, 1880.)   1, macroseptum; 2, retractor muscle; 3, parietal muscle; 4, gonad (testis); 5, nemathybomes; 6, microseptum; 7, pharynx; 8, tentacles for daughter fission product; 9, directives.

of complete or primary septa, of which two pairs at the pharynx ends are directives with exocoelic retractors and the four other pairs, symmetrically placed two on each side, have endocoelic retractors. Some anemones remain permanently in this condition, as *Halcampoides* (Fig. 190*E, F*), with six pairs of macrosepta. Others may develop a cycle of six pairs of microsepta in the exocoels, as *Halcampa* (Fig. 191*B, C*) at least in the pharyngeal region; proximally, the septa of *Halcampa* may represent an earlier stage (Fig. 191*C*). Many anemones grow an indefinite number of cycles of incomplete septa, each cycle of smaller size than its predecessor so that the septa are not differentiated into macro- and microsepta (Fig. 185*C*). These incomplete septa usually arise in pairs which are usually alike in size and other features but not necessarily so. With few exceptions, the incomplete pairs appear only in the exocoels; those of the first cycle (secondaries) develop in the center of the exocoels between the primaries, those of the second cycle (tertiaries) in the exocoels between primaries and secondaries, etc. In typical hexamerous anemones, the number of pairs of septa in the various cycles is then: 6 (primaries), 6, 12, 24, 48, etc. Other arrangements, however, often occur, especially octomerous and decamerous (Fig. 191*H*) types in which there are 8 (or 16) and 10 pairs of complete septa, respectively, and corresponding numbers in the incomplete cycles. Thus the family Ilyanthidae, represented by *Haloclava* (Fig. 191*A, H*), is usually decamerous. Forms with five and seven pairs of complete septa also occur. In two or three genera (*Halcurias*), the incomplete septa develop in pairs in the endocoels only (except the endocoels of the directives), and their retractors face outward. With these exceptions, the retractors of all septa except the directives are endocoelic. There is usually a pair of directives at each end of the pharynx regardless of the presence or absence of siphonoglyphs; but in some monoglyphic species, there is but one pair of directives, at the siphonoglyph, and, in aberrant individuals with three or more siphonoglyphs, each is generally accompanied by a pair of directives. Many anemones evince great irregularity in septal number and arrangement in consequence of regeneration or asexual origin and to such specimens no generalizations apply.

The complete septa are usually pierced below the oral disk near the pharynx by an opening, the *oral* or *internal stoma;* and also often near the column by a *marginal* or *external stoma* (Fig. 187*A*), which may be present in the larger incomplete septa as well. These stomata permit water to flow between the interseptal chambers.

Below the pharynx the complete septa curve away (Fig. 187*A*), leaving a large central digestive space, often called coelenteron, and toward the base all the septa curve centrally so that their lower edges, which are fastened to the pedal disk, reach various points on the latter and mark

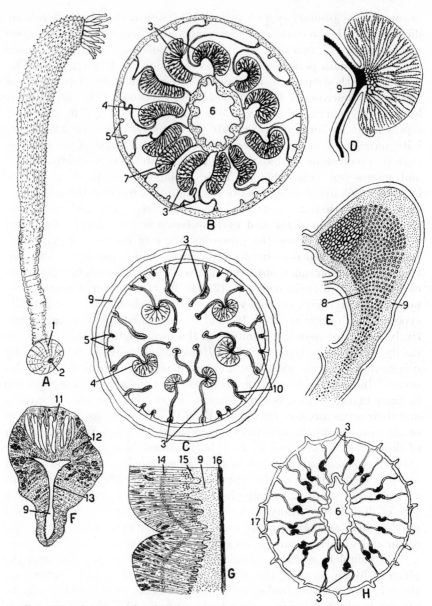

FIG. 191.—Actiniaria (continued). *A. Haloclava. B.* Cross section of *Halcampa* through the pharynx. *C.* Below the pharynx, showing persistence of primitive condition. (*After Faurot*, 1895.) *D.* Circumscript entodermal sphincter, *Bunodosoma*. (*After Duerden*, 1900.) *E.* Diffuse mesogloeal sphincter, *Calliactis*. (*After Duerden*, 1900.) *F.* Cross section of an acontium of *Sagartia*. (*After Carlgren*, 1892.) *G.* Cross section of the column wall of *Protanthea*. (*After Carlgren*, 1892.) *H.* Cross section through the pharynx of *Haloclava*, showing decamerous condition. 1, physa; 2, pore of physa; 3, directives; 4, macrosepta; 5, microsepta; 6, pharynx; 7, retractor muscle (circumscript type); 8, muscle bundles; 9, mesogloea; 10, small septa pairing with Edwardsian septa; 11, nemato-

it with radiating lines of varying lengths. The free edges of some or all the septa bear septal filaments that are trifid above, with a central cnidoglandular band and lateral flagellated bands (Fig. 187C), simple below, consisting only of the cnidoglandular band (Fig. 187B); and this latter condition prevails throughout the filaments of the more primitive anemones, which lack flagellated bands. Microsepta commonly are altogether devoid of filaments. In certain families of anemones, the lower ends of the septal filaments continue as free threads, the acontia, histologically similar to the cnidoglandular bands. These acontia fill up the lower part of the coelenteron with a mass of extended or coiled threads[1] springing from the septa (Fig. 187A). Their function is uncertain, but they seemingly serve for defense, since, when their owner contracts, they protrude through the mouth or the cinclides (Fig. 186L).

The muscular system is highly developed, particularly the gastrodermal musculature. The epidermal system is mostly limited to longitudinal fibers in the tentacles and radial fibers in the oral disk. In certain anemones, as *Protanthea*, there is also a complete cylinder of longitudinal epidermal muscles (Fig. 191G) in the column and pharynx; their presence is one reason for regarding such anemones as primitive. In most anemones, however, column and pharynx lack epidermal fibers (Fig. 192C). The gastrodermal system includes a well-developed circular layer in tentacles, oral disk, pharynx, column wall, and pedal disk. In certain genera (as *Bolocera, Boloceroides*) a gastrodermal sphincter is present in the bases of the tentacles, by whose contraction the tentacles can be cast off, apparently a defense reaction.

The circular layer of the column, as already noted (page 573), is thickened near the oral disk into a sphincter, which is commonly "entodermal," i.e., consists of fibers set on projecting mesoglocal plates that bulge the gastrodermis into a welt (Fig. 191D). Entodermal sphincters may be *diffuse*, i.e., low and broad, or *circumscript*, high and sharply delineated, attached to the wall by a narrowed base from which the mesogloeal plates radiate (Fig. 191D, B). Intermediate types, of course, occur. Sphincters may also be "mesogloeal" (Fig. 191E), composed of bundles of muscle fibers or cavities lined by muscle fibers embedded in a great thickness of mesogloea (Fig. 191E). The septa are extremely muscular, and the chief means of contraction of the animal. On one face, usually exocoelic, each septum has a transverse layer and near the column wall, especially basally, a narrow longitudinal band, the parietal muscle (Fig. 192A). The other, usually the endocoelic, face is covered with longitudinal fibers which near the inner edge of the septum

[1] Not infrequently mistaken for gonads.

cysts; 12, gland cells; 13, muscle fibers; 14, nerve net; 15, epidermal musculature; 16, gastrodermal musculature; 17, adhesive papillae.

form the retractor, near the outer edge, a parietal muscle (Fig. 192A).
The retractors may be diffuse (Fig. 192A) or circumscript (Fig. 191B) or
intermediate; they consist of fibers set on longitudinal projecting plates
of mesogloea which may run parallel (diffuse type) or have a radiating
pinnate or palmate arrangement.   Most illustrations of retractors show

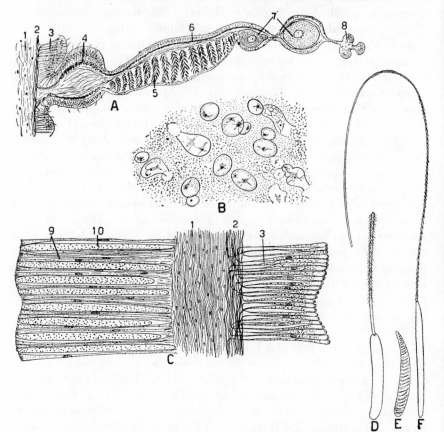

Fig. 192.—Histology of Anemones.   A. Cross section through a septum.   B. Chondroid
type of mesogloea, tentacle of *Bolocera*.   (*After Carlgren*, 1892.)   C. Cross section through
the body wall of an anemone.   D–F. Nematocysts of *Metridium*, from life: D, microbasic
amastigophore from the tentacles; E, spirocyst; F, basitrichous isorhiza, from the acontia.
1, mesogloea; 2, circular gastrodermal musculature; 3, gastrodermis; 4, parietal muscle;
5, retractor muscle; 6, transverse septal musculature; 7, gonad; 8, septal filament; 9,
supporting cells of epidermis; 10, mucous gland cells of epidermis.

only the mesogloeal plates, not the actual muscle fibers.   In forms with a
pedal disk, the parietal muscles, found on both faces of the septa, run out
onto the disk more or less parallel to it as the basilar muscles.   Sphincter
and basilar muscles are absent and the retractors but weakly indicated
in primitive anemones, such as *Protanthea;* and forms without a pedal disk

are also devoid of basilar muscles. Microsepta and the smaller cycles of incomplete septa usually lack retractors.

The nervous system consists of an epidermal plexus throughout the body and a gastrodermal plexus at least in the septa; the two are connected through the mesogloea. These plexi seem to consist primarily of the fibers from the numerous sensory nerve cells. The epidermal plexus contains ganglion cells in the tentacles, oral disk, and pharynx. According to the Hertwigs, the ganglion cells are most numerous in the oral disk at the tentacle bases, where they form a centralized oral ring. Later workers have failed to verify this statement, and Groselj (1909) locates the greatest concentration of the nerve plexus in the upper end of the pharynx. Experiments on behavior have failed to indicate the presence of any centralized nervous control. In primitive anemones (*Protanthea, Gonactinia*), the epidermal nerve plexus including ganglion cells is well-developed along the entire length of the column (Fig. 191G); but in most anemones it diminishes rapidly below the oral disk and appears to be altogether absent from most of the column except for mesogloeal fibers (Parker and Titus, 1916). The pedal disk contains a rich network of nerve fibers. In general the nerve fibers of anemones course in a longitudinal direction.

The gonads occur as thickened bands on the septa behind the septal filaments (Figs. 187A and 192A). All the septa may bear gonads or only the complete septa or only the incomplete septa, or the directives alone may be sterile. Where a sharp distinction between macrosepta and microsepta exists, the latter are commonly sterile. Anemones are either hermaphroditic or dioecious.

The epidermis consists of tall columnar supporting cells (Fig. 192C), commonly ciliated on tentacles and oral disk, also over the entire column in primitive genera. Between the supporting cells occur slender sensory nerve cells; gland cells, chiefly of the mucous type; and nematocysts. The sensory cells, of several different sorts, are very numerous in tentacles, oral disk, and pharynx (Fig. 187D), decrease in the column, and occur in fair abundance on the pedal disk. The pharyngeal lining is ciliated (flagellated?) throughout and contains besides the usual epithelial cells, numerous sensory nerve cells, mucous and granular types of gland cells, and nematocysts (Fig. 185D). The epidermal muscle fibers appear to be independent cells. The gastrodermis consists of columnar flagellated cells whose bases are drawn out into circular muscle fibers (Fig. 192C), sensory cells, nematocysts on the cnidoglandular bands and acontia, and numerous gland cells of the granular enzyme-secreting type. The gastrodermis is often crowded with zooxanthellae, especially in tentacles and septal filaments. The general structure of the septal filaments was already stated; in addition to the usual three tracts (Fig.

187*C*) they may present other histological regions, as the *intermediate* and *reticular* tracts. The former, between the cnidoglandular and flagellated tracts, may be packed with zooxanthellae, then forming the *zooxanthella* tracts, and seem to have excretory and phagocytic functions. The reticular tracts lie between the flagellated tracts and the septum proper. The acontia (Fig. 191*F*) are pyriform in cross section and consist of a mesogloeal core covered by a columnar epithelium that on the broad surface is packed with long nematocysts. Gland cells are also present as well as longitudinal muscle fibers and a nerve net.

The nematocysts of anemones are of two sorts: spirocysts (page 382 Fig. 192*E*), limited to tentacles and oral disk, and nematocysts proper, distributed everywhere. The nematocysts often occur on the tentacles in wart-like batteries and may also be mounted on the special nettle organs already mentioned—acrorhagi, pseudotentacles, nemathybomes, and vesicles (page 573). Anemone nematocysts are usually of elongated slightly curved form. The most widely distributed type is the basitrichous isorhiza (*spirula* of T. A. Stephenson, 1929); microbasic mastigophores and amastigophores ("bottle-brush" type or "*penicilli*" of Stephenson) are also of wide occurrence in anemones and very characteristic of the group (Fig. 192*D, F*). Atrichous isorhizas occur in the family Actiniidae on the acrorhagi and column, and the family Phyllactidae is notable for the possession of macrobasic amastigophores which are rare in other coelenterates.

Anemones are devoid of skeletal formations, although some species secrete a cuticle on the surface of column and pedal disk (Fig. 188*L*).

The mesogloea is always some form of connective tissue, gelatinous, fibrous, or chondroid. The first named is a mesenchyme composed of a gelatinous matrix in which amoeboid cells are scattered. The fibrous type (Fig. 192*C*), in which the matrix contains numerous fibers as well as amoebocytes, is the most common and often attains great thickness, consisting of several fibrous layers, running alternately in transverse and longitudinal directions. The chondroid type (Fig. 192*B*) somewhat resembles vertebrate hyaline cartilage in appearance but not chemically, having clusters of cells disposed in a firm colorless matrix. The mesogloeal cells are of ectodermal origin.

The anemones inhabit all seas but are larger and more abundant in warmer waters, gradually decreasing in size and numbers toward the poles. Some species are circumtropical, while many have a wide distribution. The stichodactyline anemones, which include the forms with branching tentacles and the floating family Minyadidae, are exclusively tropical. Although most abundant in shallow and coastal waters, the group descends to considerable depths. Typically, anemones inhabit rocky shores where dozens of specimens of one species may be crammed into a crevice (Fig. 193).   The anemones vary from quite small forms to the gigantic specimens of *Stoichactis* found on the Great Barrier Reef, which may measure up to 1 m. across the oral disk.   The prevailing colors are white, flesh, tan, brown, olive, and green, but bright colors, such as orange and red, are not uncommon, and some minyads are blue.   The tentacles and oral disk may display beautiful and complicated geometrical color patterns, and the column may be striped.   Some species regularly occur in several different color varieties.

The classification of anemones has always been a matter of great difficulty and much disagreement, but a general accord has at length

FIG. 193.—Anemones in a tide pool, Monterey Bay, Calif.   (*Courtesy Prof. W. K. Fisher.*)

been reached by two of the leading authorities on the group, Stephenson and Carlgren.   They divide the Actiniaria into two tribes, the Protantheae and the Nynantheae.   The former includes only the primitive family Gonactiniidae (genera *Gonactinia*, Fig. 190*G*, and *Protanthea*) characterized by the absence of flagellated tracts on the septal filaments, absence of siphonoglyphs, basilar muscles, and sphincter, presence of a complete epidermal muscle layer and nerve net throughout the column (Fig. 191*G*), weak development of the retractors, and presence of only eight complete septa (Fig. 190*B*, *C*).   The Nynantheae have flagellated tracts, and most of them have also siphonoglyphs, well-developed basilar and retractor muscles, and at least 12 complete septa.   The group is divided into five subtribes: Boloceroidaria, Athenaria, Endomyaria,

Acontiaria, and Mesomyaria. The Boloceroidaria, comprising only the primitive genera *Boloceroides* and *Bunodeopsis* (Fig. 188*H*), resemble the Protanthea in many ways, lacking basilar muscles, siphonoglyphs, and sphincter, and having weak retractors and a complete columnar epidermal muscle layer. Both genera possess tentacular sphincters, permitting the shedding of the tentacles. The septal arrangement is typical. The remaining subtribes of the Nynantheae lack epidermal column musculature. The Athenaria or Abasilaria are devoid of basilar muscles and hence of a typical pedal disk; the base is rounded or set off as a distinct physa but may sometimes spread out as a weak disk. The members of this group are typically burrowing anemones with elongated slender bodies, few tentacles and septa, and strong retractor muscles. Here belongs the family Edwardsiidae (*Edwardsia*, Fig. 188*A*, *B*, *Milne-Edwardsia*, etc.) with eight macrosepta and four or more microsepta (Fig. 190*D*). Other families are the Halcampidae (*Halcampa*, Fig. 191*B*, *C*), with typically six pairs of macrosepta and mesogloeal sphincter; the similar Halcampoididae, without a sphincter (*Halcampoides*, Fig. 190*F*, the tentacle-less *Limnactinia*); Ilyanthidae, with 12–40 macrosepta and one siphonoglyph (*Ilyanthus*, *Peachia*, Fig. 189*F*, *G*, *Eloactis*, *Halo-clava*, Fig. 191*A*, *Harenactis*). The remaining subtribes of the Nynantheae all have a distinct pedal disk provided with basilar muscles. The Endomyaria have an entodermal sphincter (whence the name of the group), sometimes lacking, and there are usually numerous complete septa and no differentiation of the septa into macro- and microsepta. The chief family seen in temperate regions is the Actiniidae, often with verrucae and acrorhagi but no vesicles (genera *Actinia*, *Anemonia*, Fig. 188*F*, *Bolocera*, *Tealia*, *Bunodactis*, Fig. 188*C*, *Anthopleura*, *Condylactis*, *Epiactis*, Fig. 194*K*). The closely related families Aliciidae (*Alicia*, *Phyllodiscus*) and Phyllactidae (*Phyllactis*, *Asteractis*, Fig. 189*A*, *Phymactis*, *Lebrunia*, Fig. 189*B*) are chiefly tropical or subtropical and usually have vesicles, fronds, pseudotentacles, etc. The Endomyaria include the stichodactyline anemones (now not regarded as a natural group) with radiating rows of tentacles, Fig. 186*B*, often branched, or reduced to sphaeromes (Fig. 186*G*) or papillae or sometimes borne on arm-like extensions of the oral disk (*Actinodendron*). Among the stichodactyline families may be mentioned the Minyadidae (Fig. 189*E*); the Aurelianidae, the Phymanthidae (*Phymanthus*, Fig. 186*E*), Actinodendridae, Thalassianthidae, Stoichactidae (*Stoichactis*, Fig. 186*B*), and the Discosomidae (*Discosoma*, *Ricordea*, *Rhodactis*, Fig. 186*D*, *Actinotryx*, Fig. 186*H*). The last-named family is not closely related to the others. The Acontiaria comprises those families with acontia; the sphincter is usually mesogloeal; and, in the families mentioned below, the septa are not differentiated into macro- and micro- types. Stephenson states that "the grouping of the Acontiaria into families has been one of the most thorny problems of Actinian systematics" (1935, page 182). He and Carlgren now classify this group chiefly on nematocyst types found in the acontia, but these are often imperfectly known. In the family Hormathiidae, the acontial nematocysts are chiefly isorhizas (*Hormathia, Actinauge, Paraphellia, Calliactis,* Fig. 191*E, Amphianthus, Adamsia,* Fig. 195*A*). The Metridiidae, sole genus *Metridium,* appear to have no very definite characteristics except that the primary septa usually lack gonads. *Metridium* (old name *Actinoloba*) has scapus, parapet, and capitulum (Figs. 186*K* and 187*A*), very numerous tentacles and ruffled oral disk in the larger specimens, and an irregular number of septa and siphonoglyphs. Both isorhizas and "penicilli" occur abundantly in the acontia of the families Diadumenidae without a sphincter, Aiptasiidae with a weak sphincter, and Sagartiidae (*Sagartia, Cereus, Actinothoe, Phellia*) with a well-developed mesogloeal sphincter, and 12 or more pairs of complete septa. The Mesomyaria lack acontia but have a mesogloeal sphincter like the Acontiaria. The principal family is the Actinostolidae (old name Paractidae) with genera *Actinostola, Stomphia*.

3. Sexual Reproduction in the Actiniaria.—The sex cells are gastrodermal interstitial cells that ripen in the mesogloea. In hermaphroditic species, testes and ovaries usually mature at different times, i.e., protandry is the rule. The sex cells may be expelled when ripe, and fertilization and development then occur in the sea water; but in some species fertilization is internal and the young develop to a tentaculate stage in the interseptal chambers. In some arctic and antarctic forms, the embryos develop in brood pouches formed on the external surface by saccular invaginations of the body wall (Fig. 194*A*). In *Epiactis prolifera,* the embryos settle on the lower column and pedal disk of the mother and there develop into young anemones (Fig. 194*K*). The tentaculate young of certain genera (notably *Peachia* and *Edwardsia*) are parasitic on the surface or in the gastrovascular system of medusae and ctenophores, adhering by means of the mouth margin and taking food particles from their hosts by means of the siphonoglyph current. The larvae of the minyads early adopt the floating habit. Some anemone larvae lead a long pelagic existence before attaching and developing tentacles, but most attach in the *Edwardsia* stage.

Cleavage is total, equal or subequal, and results in a coeloblastula. The entoderm arises usually by a typical invagination but in some cases by multipolar ingression. Both blastocoel and gastrocoel are commonly occupied by yolky material. The embryo now elongates into a ciliated planula (Fig. 194*C*), provided in some forms with an aboral tuft of sensory cilia (Fig. 194*B*). At the oral (posterior) pole the blastopore persists in cases of invagination or soon breaks through. The blastopore then

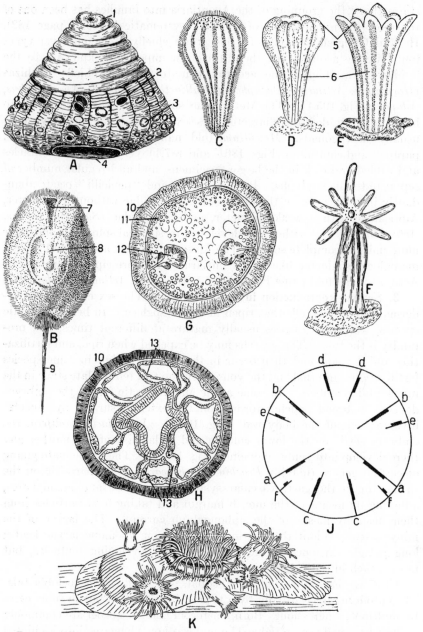

Fig. 194.—Development of anemones. *A.* An arctic anemone, *Epiactis marsupialis*, much contracted, with brood pouches in the lower part of the column. (*After Carlgren, 1893.*) *B.* Larva of *Sagartia*, with aboral sensory tufts. (*After Carlgren, 1906.*) *C–F.* Stages of *Lebrunia* (*after Duerden, 1899*): *C*, planula, without aboral tuft; *D*, planula settling, tentacles appearing; *E, F*, further development of first eight tentacles. *G.* Cross section

sinks inward and becomes the lower opening of the stomodaeum, which simultaneously arises by the rolling in of the ectoderm. The septa grow in from the outer wall in couples (Fig. 194G); four couples appear in rapid succession, first the ventrolateral couple, then usually the dorsolateral couple followed by the ventral and dorsal directives (Fig. 194J), but the order of appearance of these three couples may vary. A stage is thus attained called the *Edwardsia* stage (Fig. 194H) because of the identity of the eight coupled septa with the eight macrosepta of the Edwardsiidae. All anemones so far as known pass through this *Edwardsia* stage (Fig. 194F, H). The *Edwardsia* larva is considerably differentiated, having muscles, nematocysts, cnidoglandular bands, a nerve plexus best developed at the aboral pole, and other features. The gelatinous matrix of the mesogloea appears to be secreted by both germ layers, but the mesogloea cells are ectodermal. No agreement has been reached concerning the septal filaments, as some workers claim that they are wholly entodermal, while others assign an ectodermal origin to the cnidoglandular bands. In the next or *Halcampoides* stage, two couples of septa grow out to pair with the four lateral septa, so that six complete pairs result. These original twelve septa, which arise as couples, are termed *protocnemes*. Some anemones, as *Halcampoides* (Fig. 190E, F) remain in this stage throughout life but in most forms additional septa termed *metacnemes* arise in pairs (not couples) and the number of complete pairs may be increased beyond six by the extension of some of the later pairs to the pharynx.

Anemone larvae swim about in the plankton as tiny oval ciliated bodies, with or without an aboral tuft (Fig. 194B, C) and often grooved along the septal attachments. They have a mouth, stomodaeum, siphonoglyphs, and 8 to 24 septa, but tentacles are generally absent. They attach by the posterior pole (Fig. 194D) and push out eight tentacles simultaneously or nearly so (Fig. 194E); other tentacles then usually follow in a bilateral or radial order. Parasitic larvae or those retained in brood pockets or in the parental coelenteron develop many tentacles and septa before assuming an independent existence.

It will be seen that in the development bilateral symmetry (*Edwardsia* stage) precedes the biradial condition. This fact suggests that the Anthozoa may have been a bilateral group originally. The *Edwardsia* stage is reminiscent of the Alcyonaria, but there the eight septa arise simultaneously, while in the anemones they appear in successive couples.

of *Adamsia*, of about stage D showing precedence of ventrolateral septal couple over the others. H. Cross section of young *Adamsia*, *Edwardsia* stage. (G and H, after Faurot, 1895.) J. Diagram of usual order of appearance of the septa in the development of anemones. K. *Epiactis prolifera*, with growing young attached to column, from life, Puget Sound. 1, oral disk; 2, empty brood pouch; 3, embryo in pouch; 4, pedal disk; 5, tentacles; 6, lines of septal attachments; 7, stomodaeum; 8, septa; 9, sensory tuft; 10, ectoderm; 11, entoderm; 12, ventrolateral couple; 13, directives. a–f, order of appearance of septal couples.

4. Asexual Reproduction and Regeneration.—Some anemones reproduce regularly by asexual methods, including transverse and longitudinal fission, pedal laceration, and budding. Transverse fission is known only for the primitive *Gonactinia prolifera* (Fig. 190*G*) where it regularly occurs in young animals. A circlet of tentacles develops on the column, which then constricts in two above the tentacles. In several instances, anemones with partially or completely doubled oral ends have been seen in process of oral-aboral or aboral-oral constriction between the doubled structures. These have been interpreted as cases of longitudinal fission, but it is more probable that they are regulations following abnormal regenerations. Regular longitudinal fission or rather rupture does, however, occur in the genus *Sagartia* and probably other genera. The pedal disk elongates in the sagittal plane, stretching until it finally ruptures along the transverse plane, and the rupture then proceeds rapidly up through the oral disk. The tear may also begin in the side and proceed through to the other side, a more irregular method that may result in two to five pieces. In any case, the torn edges of a piece grow together and along this strip of wound closure new septa form, relating themselves to the old septa.

Pedal laceration, first seen in 1744, is a regular mode of multiplication in several genera, such as *Metridium, Sagartia, Aiptasia, Phellia, Bunodes,* and *Heliactis*. Either the pedal disk puts out lobes that are constricted off or pieces of the disk adhere and are torn off as the animal moves about. The torn edges unite, new tentacles and septa develop along the line of closure, the new septa relate themselves to the old septa left in such pieces, and soon complete little anemones arise, often in a trail marking the path of the mother. Naturally anemones regenerated from such pedal fragments or through rupture present many irregularities in septal arrangement and number of siphonoglyphs.

A few instances of budding from the column or pedal disk have been reported but may be misinterpretations, and certainly this type of asexual reproduction is rare in anemones. An astonishing mode of budding occurs in the genus *Boloceroides* (Okada and Komori, 1932), in which the tentacles have a basal sphincter and either in situ or when shed by a constriction below the sphincter bud a complete little anemone at the site of the sphincter (Fig. 195*D*). When the buds are formed in situ, their oral ends are toward the mother.

Regeneration has been considerably studied, chiefly in *Metridium* and *Sagartia* by Carlgren and others, and in *Harenactis* by Child. In these and similar forms, when the column is cut across, the aboral portion regenerates a new oral disk at any level; the oral piece usually fails to reform a pedal disk (except after long periods according to Kolodziejski, 1932) but may regenerate tentacles on the aboral surface, a case of "heteromorphosis" or reversed polarity. *Harenactis*, an elongated sand-dwelling anemone with a rounded base, reforms th's at any level. Cuts made into the column of anemones usually heal; but if they include the pharynx a crown of tentacles or an oral disk may grow out at the cut.

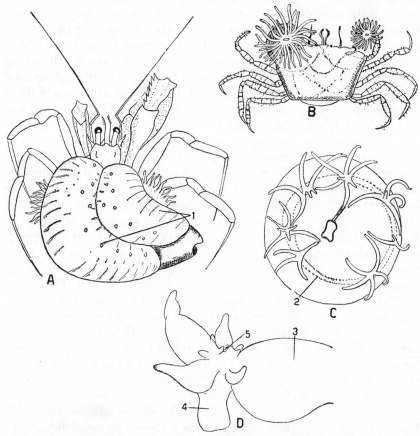

Fig. 195.—Mutualism, regeneration. *A.* The anemone *Adamsia palliata* with lobed pedal disk wrapped around a snail shell occupied by the hermit crab *Eupagurus prideauxi.* (*After Faurot*, 1910.) *B.* A crab holding a small anemone (*Bunodeopsis*) in each pincer for defense. (*After Duerden*, 1905.) *C.* A ring of *Harenactis* regenerating several imperfect oral disks with tentacles. (*After Child*, 1910.) *D.* A tentacle of *Boloceroides* regenerating an anemone at its proximal end. (*After Okada and Komori*, 1932.) 1, pedal disk of anemone; 2, line of union of oral and aboral cut ends to make the ring; 3, old tentacle; 4, column; 5, oral end of regenerated anemone.

Isolated tentacles (except in *Boloceroides* as noted above), pieces of septa, of the pharynx, and of the oral disk fail to undergo any regeneration. Pieces including column and the edge of the oral disk may form a pharynx, and pieces of the column wall may grow out tentacles on their orally directed edge. As could be inferred from the occurrence of pedal laceration, pieces of the pedal disk of any size regenerate into complete anemones, whether from the central part without roof or from the edge with two surfaces. The cut edges fuse, and, along the line of wound closure, new tentacles and pharynx appear, later moving to a symmetrical position, and new septa arise in couples usually in radial alignment with the old ones. If the piece contained no directives, the new septa may be all nondirective and radially arranged; or a monoglyphic anemone may result; if the piece had directives, the regenerated anemone is usually diglyphic. The new septa may follow a bilateral or a biradial plan and usually adjust themselves to the old septa. Many cases of double or multiple pharynges, directives, and oral ends occur in pedal disk regeneration, especially in elongated pieces. When cuts are made so that a piece of column and a piece of pedal disk are united by septa only, the two pieces fuse at the edges, and the resulting anemone has the polarity of the column piece. Various experiments show that the polarity of the column is strongly fixed. In *Harenactis* the level of crosspieces determines the rate of wound closure, amount of regeneration, number of tentacles formed, etc. Pieces through the pharynx usually regenerate an oral disk at each end. The regeneration of the basal end is greatest aborally and decreases the more oral the level of the section. In short crosspieces from which the septa have been removed the oral and aboral cut edges fuse so that a doughnut-like piece arises, and these rings regenerate irregular groups of tentacles along or near the line of fusion (Fig. 195*C*).

Primitive anemones in which the column wall has epidermal musculature and a nerve net may show much greater powers of regeneration than just stated. In *Boloceroides*, not only do cast-off tentacles regenerate into anemones but cross sections of the column regenerate into complete anemones at any level and pieces of the column wall also become perfect anemones. *Protanthea* has less regulative capacity.

5. Behavior and Physiology of Anemones.—The anemones are practically always solitary and chiefly sessile, although never immovably fixed. They fall into three ecological types: those with pedal disks, those without pedal disks, and the floating minyads. The majority possess pedal disks that adhere by mucous secretion and muscular action to any firm substratum, such as rocks, pilings, wharves, shells, plants, other animals, etc. Such forms move at will by a gliding motion of the pedal disk, which puts out a turgid lobe in the direction of advance while the opposite end contracts. Waves of muscular contraction, chiefly in the basilar muscles, then pass over the disk, from behind forward, so that the rear end advances first (Parker) or from before backward with the pushing out of a front lobe (Willem). The rate is slow, 8 to 10 cm. per hour at the most, usually much less. Some observers claim that anemones always move in the direction of the sagittal plane, but others find no evidence of this. Some species "walk" about on the tentacle tips; others may reach the surface film and float head downward; some release their foothold, inflate, and roll about in the waves; a few can climb by using adhesive column structures. *Aiptasia carnea* when "on the move" (only at night) lies on its side and progresses backward by a definite orderly sequence of events: attachment of pedal disk, peristaltic wave in circular column muscle from oral end to middle, strong septal contraction, resulting retraction of oral end, attachment of oral end in new position, release of pedal disk; continuation of circular wave to pedal disk so that latter takes a "step" backwards (Portmann, 1926). This process may be repeated for hours. Such movements as well as the ordinary creeping on the pedal disk are executed normally by decapitated anemones and are therefore independent of any central control, although they obviously involve a considerable degree of neuromuscular coordination. Some small species (*Gonactinia*, *Boloceroides*) considerably accelerate their progress by "swimming," erecting the tentacles and striking them downward. Anemones usually move about when disturbed or when conditions are unfavorable but may remain in approximately the same spot for very long periods. Some species are naturally much more restless than others. Deep-water forms probably seldom move.

Forms with pedal disks may inhabit soft or sandy bottoms by fastening to scattered objects; or in the case of some deep-water species by curving the disk around a ball of mud or a small object. The typical mud- or sand-dwelling anemones, however, have long slender bodies with rounded or pointed basal ends or a physa (Figs. 188*A* and 191*A*). These species live buried up to the capitulum and cannot maintain an erect posture or their normal shape when removed from their burrows. When so removed they again bury themselves with the aid of the physa. The animal at first distends with water but later ejects most of the water; the column contracts to a slender firm condition and curves into an arc, with the base directed almost vertically against the sand. With the oral end firmly closed to prevent escape of water, circular constrictions then pass rhythmically along the column from oral to aboral end driving water into the aboral end which is thus inflated and forced against the sand. Repetition of this process accomplishes the burrowing in about an hour (Faurot's account, 1895).

Most anemones are negative to light, moving away from bright illumination and in nature seeking dim corners, crevices, and the undersides of objects. They contract when suddenly illuminated by a bright light and in nature are contracted during the day, expanding fully only in dim light or darkness. Some littoral species, however, are either indifferent to light or may exhibit a positive reaction, moving toward a lighted region or turning the oral disk toward the light, and expanding in day and contracting at night.   Some anemones are negative to gravity, taking an erect position but most orient at right angles to the substratum. Shallow-water forms contract when the tide ebbs and expand again when the tide returns, apparently in response to the flow of water.   Certain workers claim that anemones removed to aquaria exhibit for several days contractions and expansions corresponding to day and night and the ebb and flow of the tide; but such statements have failed to obtain general verification.   Tide-zone species contract when exposed to the air by a falling tide and can endure several hours of such exposure with no injury.   The presence of food causes expansion of contracted specimens and hunger and cool temperatures also favor expansion.

Most anemones are capable of extreme contraction, drawing the oral disk into the coelenteron by means of the retractor muscles and closing the margin over the retracted disk by means of the sphincter (Fig. 186L). The pharynx is thrown into transverse folds in the process and water is ejected through mouth, cinclides, and other pores.   The acontia also usually protrude (Fig. 186L) as they are passively carried through any aperture by the outflow of water.   Contraction may occur very quickly, especially in burrowing types, which can draw down into their burrows with great rapidity.   Expansion is a slower process and is accomplished by intake of water along the siphonoglyphs.   In the normal extended condition, water currents pass inward along the siphonoglyphs, flow orally along the inner surface of the column and out through the pharynx, whose flagella (except those of the siphonoglyphs) beat predominantly toward the mouth.   In anemones with poorly differentiated retractor muscles, the oral disk cannot be retracted.

The tentacles and in some species the mouth are very sensitive to chemical stimulation (food juices), while other portions of the body lack such perception, except in primitive forms.   If food (giving off juices) is presented without touching the tentacles, these soon begin to wave about and the mouth may open.   The feeding behavior follows three main types.   In ordinary forms with elongated tentacles, the tentacles touched adhere to the food, partly by mucous secretions, partly by the nematocyst threads, then shorten, and bend toward the mouth, on or near which the food is held or deposited.   Other tentacles usually join in these reactions, and the oral disk also contracts.   The mouth either before or after being touched with food opens and grasps the food with its lips, and the tentacles then release their hold.   In other forms, especially those with short tentacles, the latter hold the food against the disk, the mouth opens, the pharynx protrudes as bladdery lobes, and, by contraction of the disk between food and mouth, these lobes reach the food and grasp it.   Ciliary action is often involved in the feeding of anemones and, in those species which feed on minute animals, plays the chief role.

In primitive anemones the whole surface is ciliated and has ciliary currents passing from aboral to oral end; but in most forms cilia are limited to the tentacles, beating from base to tip, and to the oral disk, beating toward the periphery. Ciliary currents on the column drive small organisms toward the oral disk where they may be caught in the tentacular currents, carried to the tentacle tips, and dropped on the mouth by the bending of the tentacles toward the mouth. The same ciliary mechanism helps deposit food on the mouth when the tentacles grasping food curve toward the mouth. Weakly ciliated anemones employ chiefly muscular movements of tentacles, disk, and mouth in food ingestion. After reaching the mouth, the food is carried inside mainly by the ciliary currents of the pharynx, which normally beat outward (except of course in the siphonoglyphs) but reverse their beat in the presence of food; or the cilia may regularly beat inward along the grooves of the pharynx, outward on the ridges; and peristaltic waves in the pharynx often assist the ingestion.

Many studies have been made on digestion in anemones, especially with regard to the occurrence of extracellular digestion in the coelenteron. Several workers have maintained that the food undergoes preliminary digestion only when in contact with the septal filaments but Jordan (1907) fed bags of filter paper containing fibrin and recovered the ejected bags intact and empty, and Ishida (1936) has demonstrated proteases and lipases in the coelenteric fluid of *Actinia*, 3 hours after feeding. In normal feeding, the food is grasped by the septal filaments and reduced to fragments under the action of a protease of the nature of trypsin, active in alkaline solution, secreted primarily by the granular gland cells of the cnidoglandular bands. Fats are also emulsified by this fluid; carbohydrates remain unattacked. After this preliminary digestion, there is the usual ingestion of the food broth by the general gastrodermis (except the cnidoglandular tracts), particularly of the septa, and digestion is completed in intracellular fashion by means of proteases of the type of pepsin and erepsin, and lipases. Traces of amylases have been found by some workers, but they may come from the zooxanthellae and in any case the ability of anemones to digest carbohydrates must be slight. The septal filaments and general gastrodermis of *Metridium* yield peptic and tryptic proteases, lipase, and maltase (Bodansky, 1924), and Ishida (1936) found trypsin, pepsin, erepsin, lipase, and esterase but no diastases of any kind in the coelenteric fluid and septal filaments of *Actinia*. Excess food is stored in the general gastrodermis chiefly as fat.

Anemones eat almost any live animals of suitable size, or pieces of animal flesh, living or dead, or some species feed wholly on minute organisms caught by ciliary currents. Some discriminate between food and inert bodies, rejecting the latter, while many, especially if hungry, will react to and swallow stones, filter paper, etc. They accept filter paper soaked in animal juices but may not swallow it or may soon disgorge it. When filter paper and flesh are both fed, the anemone may soon reject the paper while continuing to accept the flesh. After the ingestion of a number of pieces of food, the tentacles react more and more slowly and finally cease altogether to respond. However, tentacles not previously involved will respond to additional pieces of food but not to so many pieces as did the first tentacles. This fact seems to suggest that an internal condition of satiety affects the reactiveness of the tentacles, possibly through digestive products reaching the tentacular cavities. However, the same gradual loss of response in the tentacles to repeated feeding is seen if filter paper is fed or if the food is extracted with a forceps from the pharynx before it can be swallowed. A sensory fatigue in the tentacles after repeated stimulation seems to be indicated as part of the explanation. Anemones can exist for long periods without food and may diminish greatly in size during such times.

The disk is cleaned of objects falling on it or of ejected indigestible remains in various ways. Ciliary currents carry such matter to the disk edge; or the disk between the object and the edge may contract, forming a slope down which the object slides; or the disk under the object may stretch and elevate to form a smooth surface from which water currents will readily sweep the object away.

A feature of the behavior of anemones is the abundant secretion of mucus in response to almost any stimulus—touch, contact with food, or application of chemicals. Materials ejected from the digestive cavity are always coated with mucus. Mucus secreted during extracellular digestion prevents too great dilution of the enzymes with sea water.

The respiration of anemones is of the ordinary aerobic type, and its rate is directly dependent on the degree of expansion of the animal and to some extent on the oxygen content of the water. Some figures (Trendelenberg, 1909) are: 1.5 cc. of oxygen consumed per hour by a 120-g. specimen of *Anemonia sulcata* and 0.5 cc. by a 30-g. *Adamsia rondeletti*. The respiratory quotient (R.Q.) for the former species was 0.68. For the isolated tentacles of *Anemonia sulcata* a much higher respiratory rate (about four times) and R.Q. (0.9) were found by Kramer (1937). Anemones that harbor symbiotic algae of course give off oxygen when exposed to light, and consequently their true respiratory metabolism can be determined only in the dark.

For the excretory products of anemones see page 396.

As anemones are perhaps the commonest and largest forms with a simple nervous system, the characteristics of the latter have been much studied. In general the pedal disk (edge and upper surface) and the tentacles are very sensitive to touch, while the peristome and mouth are wholly or almost insensitive. The column varies in different species from a good sensibility to touch to almost complete insensitivity; in forms with a complete columnar nerve net, the column is everywhere highly sensitive to both mechanical and chemical stimuli. In general, column sensitivity decreases from the pedal disk orally. Repeated light stimulation of the column may cause contraction of the circular column muscle as a ring that slowly passes orally. Stronger stimulation brings about, first, column contraction by way of the parietal muscles, then lowering of the disk through the retractors. Very strong stimulation of pedal disk or column evokes rapid lowering of the oral disk and closure of the sphincter over it. The tentacles when lightly touched may bend toward the stimulated spot; usually or to stronger stimulation they shorten and bend toward the mouth (feeding reaction). A stimulus is more readily conducted proximally than distally in a tentacle. Light stimulation spreads to other tentacles only after continued repetition, and the oral disk may also react by elevating at the site of the stimulus (also a feeding reaction). Light contact on any sensitive region of an anemone causes movement of the tentacles, local contraction, and perhaps bending toward the stimulated region. Stronger stimulation is followed by varying degrees of column contraction, retraction of the oral disk, and closure of the sphincter. To slight stimuli repeated at short intervals, the animal may soon cease to respond. If a touch strong enough to cause contraction is repeated, the animal tries expanding in different directions to avoid the blow; but if this does not suffice eventually moves away. In burrowing forms, the whole animal is almost insensitive, except the oral end, which exhibits extreme sensitivity so that mechanical stimulation causes swift withdrawal into the substratum. The pedal disk in some species appears to distinguish between rough and smooth surfaces, and the anemone will move about restlessly until it finds a rough place to which to attach.

As in other coelenterates, the nervous system is characterized by great independence of parts, paucity of reflexes, lack of central control, diffuse conduction, variation of response according to the strength of the stimulus, and apparent decrement. According to Parker, the mucous gland cells, nematocysts, and acontia are "independent effectors," responding directly to stimuli without the intervention of any nervous mechanism; but doubt is cast upon this view by the intimate connections often seen between nematocysts and sensory nerve cells and fibrils and by the presence of a nerve net in the acontia. Isolated tentacles and acontia behave much like attached ones; and anemones deprived of an oral disk will execute normal creeping movements and will contract on stimulation. Various experiments have failed to indicate the presence of a controlling center in the oral disk or pharynx. The stimulus to contraction appears rather to be transmitted by way of the septa than the oral disk, for if a piece of column wall connected to the animal only by septa is stimulated, the animal contracts as usual. In longitudinally split anemones, stimulation of one half will cause contraction of the other half if the two halves are connected only by the pedal disk. Transmission in the column occurs much more readily in a longitudinal than in a transverse direction and in tentacles chiefly from tip to base. Coordinated neuromuscular action is shown, however, in the creeping movements and the feeding behavior where tentacles, oral disk, mouth, lips, and pharynx cooperate. Jennings has emphasized the ability of anemones to modify their behavior according to circumstances. Thus several different ways may be tried of freeing the disk from particles, and if contraction and expansion in new directions do not suffice to overcome unfavorable conditions, the animal moves away to more suitable neighborhoods.

In an analysis of the nerve net of *Calliactis*, Pantin (1935) has shown that the actinian nerve net is physiologically similar to vertebrate nerve, from which it differs chiefly in its diffuse conduction and extreme "facilitation." Facilitation means that the excitation wave from each stimulus leaves an aftereffect that facilitates the transmission of the next excitation wave. Because of this property, response in anemones occurs only to repeated stimuli, and its nature is dependent upon the number of stimuli and the time interval between them. Apparent relation between response and strength of stimulus results from the use of mechanical modes of stimulation that act on many sense organs thus sending out many impulses. Facilitation within the nerve net was found to explain apparent decrement in transmission on the oral disk. The nerve net of the column acts as a simple conductor between the sense organs and the various sets of muscles: circular column muscle, parietal muscles, septal retractors, sphincter. With increasing strength of stimulus, these muscles are called into action in the order named. The reason, however, is not one of stimulus strength but of frequency of impulse. The circular column muscle responds to very low frequency of stimulation, about 1 per 10 seconds, the sphincter to 1 stimulus per 0.6 second, the others to intermediate rates. Increasing frequency rates of stimulation evoke more rapid contraction of the muscles. In *Calliactis* there appeared to be a very direct conduction path between the septa and the sphincter, but elsewhere conduction is low and a high degree of facilitation obtains. On the other hand in *Anemonia sulcata*, a form with poor retractors and sphincter, Pantin found a high degree of autonomy and only local feeding-type responses of column, disk, or tentacles to even strong stimuli.

The anemones form some very remarkable relations with other animals, notably with hermit crabs. Certain anemones (almost always members of genera with acontia, as *Actinia, Adamsia,* and *Sagartia*) are habitually fastened either on top or below to snail shells inhabited by particular species of hermit crabs (Fig. 195*A*). The hermit crab is able to recognize its particular species of anemone, chiefly by touch, causes it to detach by massaging it with its claws, and then holds the anemone against the shell until attachment occurs. If deprived of its anemone, the crab seeks a new one, and, when moving to a larger shell because of growth, detaches the anemone and places it on the new shell. In the classical case of *Adamsia palliata* on *Eupagurus prideauxi* (Fig. 195*A*), the young ane-mone is placed below the mouth parts of the crab. At this time it has an ordinary circular pedal disk; but this grows upward in two lobes that embrace the snail shell and secrete a horny membrane to patch possible holes in the shell and to extend the opening so that the crab need not change shells so often. The anemone protects its host by its nemato-cysts and acontia, receives food particles dropped by the crab, and gets transported about. *Adamsia palliata* apparently cannot exist apart from the hermit crab, probably because of the modification of its pedal disk; but other anemones that have this same commensal habit appear to be less dependent upon the relationship. Certain crabs regularly clasp small anemones in their pincers and when annoyed hold them out in a defensive attitude (Fig. 195*B*). They also steal most of the food caught by the anemones, reaching up on the disk with their appendages, so that the advantage of the association seems to lie entirely with the crab. Anemones are also often commensal with fish that play among the tentacles or beneath the disk and when alarmed dive into the anem-one's interior. Gohar (1934) records observing a small fish commensal with *Actinia* driving a large fish near enough to be stung and eaten by the anemone. In most of these cases of commensalism with anemones, the immunity of the guest to the nematocysts has not been explained except in regard to the hermit crabs (page 391).

Many anemones are richly supplied with zooxanthellae, especially in the gastrodermis of tentacles and septa. They have not been shown to play any essential role in the life of anemones.

Anemones may live for several to many years, and specimens have been kept in aquaria for over 50 years.

6. Order Madreporaria, the True or Stony Corals.—The stony corals are the builders of coral reefs and islands and hence objects of great popular and scientific interest. They are mostly colonial, sometimes solitary, and are provided with a hard calcareous exoskeleton, secreted by the epidermis and lying wholly outside the polyp body (Fig. 196*A, E*).

The coral polyp itself may be regarded as a skeleton-forming anemone, for it closely resembles a typical hexamerous anemone. A pedal disk is absent, as the basal region occupies the skeletal cup (Fig. 196*A*). Above

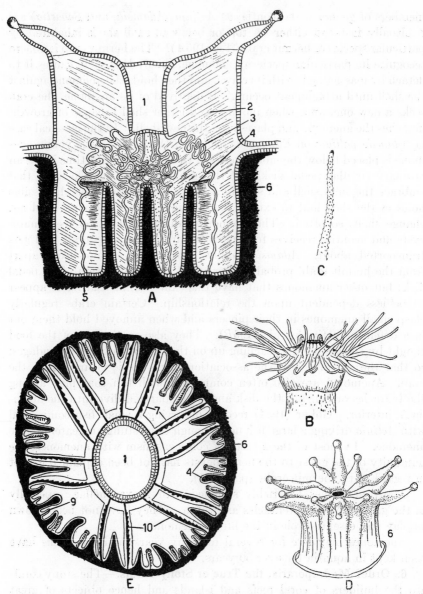

FIG. 196.—Corals. *A.* Diagram of a vertical section through a coral in its theca; three sclerosepta are shown. *B.* Solitary coral, *Balanophyllia*, from life, Calif. *C.* A single tentacle of the same. *D.* A single polyp of a colonial coral, *Siderastraea radians.* (*After Duerden*, 1904.) *E.* Section through the pharyngeal region of a coral. (*After Duerden*, 1902.) 1, pharynx; 2, septum; 3, septal filament; 4, scleroseptum; 5, basal plate; 6, theca; 7, primary septa; 8, secondary septa; 9, tertiaries; 10, septal muscles.

this the smooth or warty column lacks cinclides or special adhesive or nematocyst-bearing structures. There is a typical oral disk with tentacles in cycles of six, one tentacle over each interseptal space. There may be a single marginal circlet (Fig. 196D) of 6 or 12 tentacles; or severa alternating cycles, with numbers on the typical hexamerous plan: 6, 6, 12. 24, etc. Usually, however, the outer cycles are incomplete, as the tentacles increase coincidentally with the septa and these do not arise simultaneously around the circumference. All cyclical arrangement of the tentacles is lost after certain forms of asexual reproduction. The tentacles are of short to moderate length, simple except in *Siderastraea* where the endocoelic tentacles are bifurcated, and commonly end in a terminal knob of nematocysts (Fig. 196D), although they may be slender and tapering (Fig. 196B, C). There are also usually warts of nematocysts along the sides. In contraction, the tentacles may fold over the disk or may introvert or become incorporated into the disk so as almost to disappear.

The circular or oval mouth is surrounded by a flat, depressed, or conical peristome. The pharynx is short, circular or oval in section, ridged in some forms, and always devoid of siphonoglyphs. The septa follow the hexamerous plan. In some genera, as *Acropora* and *Porites*, the first 12 septa (protocnemes) remain in the Edwardsian stage, i.e., with two pairs of directives, four single complete septa and four incomplete septa paired with these. In other genera the protocnemes form six complete pairs. There are usually also in corals alternating cycles of incomplete septa that arise in pairs in the exocoels (Fig. 196E) to give the usual hexamerous arrangement: 6 (protocnemes), 6, 12, 24, etc., pairs. Because of the small size of the coral polyp, there are seldom more than three cycles of septa present, and the last cycle is usually incomplete, since the septa appear first on the "dorsal" side and only gradually complete the cycle ventrally. In some forms, septal pairs of the second cycle may reach the pharynx, increasing the number of complete pairs beyond six. In *Acropora* and *Porites*, the incomplete septa arise only in the endocoels of the dorsal or ventral directives or both; in other genera they are strictly exocoelic. After certain types of asexual reproduction, the septa lack any definite arrangement, and the offspring never form directives.

All the septa bear filaments that are often highly convoluted; they consist of the cnidoglandular band only and hence entirely resemble histologically the lower portions of the filaments of anemones (Fig. 187B). The filaments usually protrude through the mouth in feeding and may also be emitted through temporary ruptures in the column wall. The septal musculature is feebly developed as compared with anemones, but the retractors are usually in evidence although low and of the diffuse type (Fig. 196E). Stomata are lacking. The septa are more or less confined to the upper part of the coral polyp and are apparently continually absorbed below as more skeleton is secreted.

The lower part of the coelenteron is occupied by the folds into which the polyp base is forced by the skeletal ridges (Fig. 196A). These folds always occur between septa, and the depressions between the folds extend to the polyp base between the skeletal ridges as blind pockets termed *loculi* (Fig. 197A). Consequently if the skeleton is dissolved away with acid, the basal end of the polyp is seen to bear numerous deep radiating grooves, each of which was occupied by a skeletal ridge and which project into the interior as vertical folds.

Epidermis and gastrodermis are similar to those of anemones but are generally syncytial. The former is commonly ciliated on the free surface and contains numerous mucous gland cells. Basally the epidermis is modified to form the so-called calicoblastic layer, which secretes the skeleton. The pharyngeal epidermis is likewise ciliated and provided with both mucous and granular gland cells. The gastrodermis seems to lack the usual flagella; in the polyp base it is greatly thickened and highly vacuolated. As already noted, the septal filaments consist only of the cnidoglandular band, which contains large numbers of enzyme-secreting gland cells; and the convoluted portion, protruded through the mouth in feeding, bears in addition numerous nematocysts. The gastrodermis of the free part of the polyp is thickly packed with zooxanthellae, which are absent among shallow-water corals only in *Astrangia* and *Phyllangia*. The mesogloea of corals is very thin and composed of a matrix containing fibers and cells. In skeleton-covered regions it puts out desmoid processes, shaped like an inverted cone or wedge, covered with modified epidermis and apparently serving to anchor the polyp to the skeleton.

The nematocysts are very similar to those of anemones and very uniform throughout the Madreporaria so far as known (see Weill, 1934). They consist, besides the usual spirocysts, of holotrichous isorhizas and microbasic mastigophores.

The musculature is feebly developed. It comprises longitudinal epidermal fibers in the tentacles; radial epidermal fibers in the disk; a circular gastrodermal layer in tentacles, oral disk, pharynx and column wall; and transverse muscles on one side, longitudinal on the other side, of the septa. There may be some development of a sphincter muscle in the column by which the column can be closed over the retracted disk. The septal retractors are borne on slight longitudinal projections of mesogloea (Fig. 196E). The base inside the skeletal cup is devoid of musculature.

The nervous system is poorly known. A delicate epidermal plexus has been seen in tentacles and oral disk and, in *Coenopsammia*, also in the pharynx and column (Duerden and Ayres, 1905). In several colonial species tested, mechanical stimulation of one polyp was transmitted to others, so that the presence of a nerve net throughout the colony must be assumed.

As already indicated a considerable part of each coral polyp is inseparably fixed in a cup-like skeleton of calcium carbonate (aragonite), composed of masses made of calcareous fibers radiating from a central, probably organic, material. The manner of formation of the skeleton is not understood, but according to the most accepted view calcareous crystals are precipitated in a colloidal matrix secreted to the outer side of the epidermis.

The skeleton of the colony as a whole is termed *corallum*, of each polyp, *corallite*. The corallite consists of a cup containing vertical ridges radiating from the center to the periphery (Fig. 197*B*). The bottom of the cup beneath the polyp is called the *basal plate*, the wall of the cup that encloses the aboral portion of the polyp is termed the *theca*, and the ridges are known as skeletal septa or *sclerosepta*.[1] The theca can be an independent formation or can arise by the fusion of the outer ends of the sclerosepta, then called *pseudotheca*. The inner ends of the sclerosepta are fused to a central columnar skeletal mass termed the *columella*, which may be an independent upgrowth from the basal plate or formed by the union of the central ends of the sclerosepta, then named *pseudocolumella*. Outside the theca there may be secreted a second wall, or *epitheca*, which may be separated from the theca by a space crossed by continuations of the sclerosepta called *costae* (Fig. 197*C*). Small ridges between the columella and the main parts of the sclerosepta are known as *pali* (Fig. 197*B*). *Synapticula* are skeletal bars connecting adjacent sclerosepta. Horizontal plates between sclerosepta are called *dissepiments* when of small extent, *tabulae* if extending completely across the corallite. The sclerosepta are commonly spiny or thorny with jagged or toothed upper edges.

The sclerosepta are definitely related to the septa (Figs. 196*A*, *E*, 197*A*) and like the latter typically occur in hexamerous cycles of decreasing length: six primaries, six secondaries, 12 tertiaries, 24 quaternaries, etc.; but other numbers may obtain and of course much irregularity must be expected. The sclerosepta are commonly endocoelic, i.e., each skeletal ridge pushes up between the two septa of a pair (Fig. 196*A*, *E*). The original second cycle is, however, usually exocoelic, and by repeated bifurcations its outer ends always remain exocoelic (see further below).

---

[1] When the septa are called mesenteries, then the skeletal ridges are termed simply septa; but as the word mesentery has been avoided, it becomes necessary to distinguish the skeletal septa from the septa of the coelenteron, and hence the term sclerosepta will be employed whenever necessary to avoid confusion.

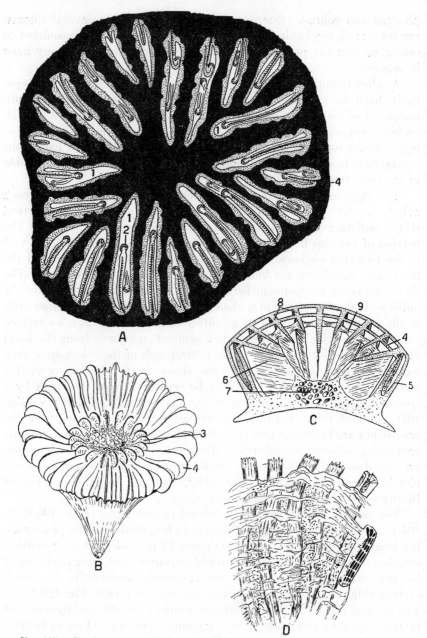

Fig. 197.—Coral structure (continued). *A.* Section through the base of a coral showing loculi with enclosed septa. (*After Duerden,* 1902.) *B.* Theca of the solitary coral *Caryophyllia,* showing pali. *C.* Diagram of half of a coral skeleton, showing particularly the epitheca. *D.* Section through a colonial coral, *Galaxea,* showing growth of thecae and horizontal depositions of lime. 1, loculus; 2, septa; 3, pali; 4, theca; 5, epitheca; 6, sclerosepta; 7, columella; 8, costae; 9, synapticula.

The formation of the sclerosepta usually precedes that of the corresponding septa (Fig. 199E–G), and hence there are commonly more sclerosepta than septal pairs (Fig. 196E). The first cycles of sclerosepta reach the columella, while the later ones fall short of it and may fuse with adjacent larger septa. It may again be emphasized that the corallite lies entirely outside the polyp body and that the polyp base is pushed up into ridges over the sclerosepta and descends into blind pockets (loculi) between sclerosepta and septa.

Some corals, as the genera *Fungia* (Fig. 200), *Flabellum, Caryophyllia* (Fig. 197B), *Balanophyllia* (Fig. 196B) are solitary, having disk-, cup-, or mushroom-shaped corallites, 5 mm. to 25 cm. across, often without a theca, lying loose on the bottom or fastened below by a stalk. They may reproduce by longitudinal fission or by budding from almost any part of the surface, in which process the sclerosepta of the buds build on from those of the parent. Most corals, however, are colonial and may form low flat plates or cushion-like or spherical masses or vases or cups or may be branched, with short stout or long slender or flattened plate-like or leaf-like branches (Fig. 201). Such colonies originate by asexual methods from a single sexually produced polyp and consist largely of calcareous secretion of which only the surface is occupied by living substance. The polyps may be widely spaced, each occupying a separate theca as in *Oculina* (Fig. 198A); or the thecae may be so close together as to have common walls as in *Favia* (Fig. 198D); or polyps and corallites may be confluent into rows that occupy valleys in the corallum separated by ridges. To this last type belong the familiar meandrine or "brain corals" (Fig. 201), large rounded masses whose surface is marked by long curved depressions occupied in life by a row of incomplete polyps having one common fringe of tentacles and many mouths and pharynges (Fig. 198E, F). In colonial corals, the polyps are small or even minute, varying from 1 mm. to 2 to 3 cm. in length; the colonies themselves reach a maximum of 2 to 3 m. in length or diameter.

The space between the thecae of coral colonies is occupied in life by a coenenchyme, an extension of the polyp walls, continuous with the latter above the upper edge of the theca (Fig. 196A) and containing a gastrovascular space continuous with the gastrovascular cavity of the polyps. The lower surface of this coenenchyme secretes the part of the corallum between the thecae, sometimes termed *coenosteum*.[1] In addition in many corals the polyps may be connected by canals coming from the polyp bases and passing through openings in the loosely con-

---

[1] Among coral specialists the living material between polyps is called coenosarc, and the skeleton that it secretes, coenenchyme. This is but one of innumerable examples of confusion in zoological terminology. The word coenenchyme will here be employed in the same sense as in the Alcyonaria.

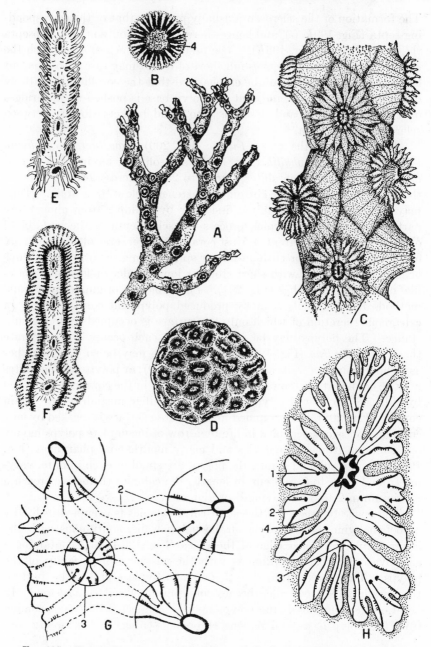

Fig. 198.—Types of corals, asexual budding. *A.* Ivory coral, *Oculina*, with separated thecae. *B.* A theca magnified. *C.* Ivory coral living, showing polyps and extension of coenenchyme between thecae. (*After Verrill*, 1901.) *D.* The coral *Favia*, with contiguous cups. *E.* One valley of the brain coral with confluent polyps, by night, expanded. *F.* The same, by day, contracted. From life. Bermuda. *G. Orbicella*, diagram of extratentacular

structed theca. Corals in which the corallite is thus perforated with many openings are termed *perforate*, and those in which the corallite is of solid texture and the polyps connect by coenenchyme only over the upper rim of the theca are called *imperforate;* but these distinctions are not now regarded of as much importance as formerly.

The manner in which colonial polyps increase asexually is not thoroughly understood. Contrary to former opinion, there is never any longitudinal fission through the pharynx. Matthai has distinguished two types of budding: extra- and intratentacular. In the former, occurring in colonies with well-separated polyps, new mouths and pharynges appear in the coenenchyme outside the oral disks already present and acquire septa continuous with those of adjacent polyps (Fig. 198G). Polyps so formed have usually typical hexamerous septa with two pairs of directives. In intratentacular budding, two or more new mouths and pharynges arise on the oral disks of old polyps inside the same circle of tentacles (Fig. 198H). One such new bud may arise at a time, or two, opposite each other or both on the same side, or the buds may spring in a circle or in a linear row. When two buds arise on the same side, branching results. The new pharynges may constrict off completely so that separate oral disks are formed; but in many species the process is incomplete, and huge polypharyngeal polyps result, which may be very elongated with many mouths in a row bordered by a single fringe of tentacles (Fig. 198E); or circular with many mouths in cycles inside one circle of tentacles. In intratentacular budding, the septa and sclerosepta are naturally totally irregular, and directives are absent.

Skeleton is continually secreted by the polyp bases so that the corallum grows in both length and diameter. By the formation of tabulae in the corallite the polyps are continually pushed up and so always remain on the surface of the mass (Fig. 197D).

The gonads are borne on the septa back of the septal filaments. Corals may be dioecious or hermaphroditic. Some species breed continuously for months, while others spawn at intervals throughout the year. The time of spawning may be related to phases of the moon. The embryos commonly develop to the planula stage (Fig. 199B) or later in the coelenteron of the mother. A typical *Edwardsia* stage is reached as in the anemones, with four couples of complete septa, usually appearing in the order: ventrolateral, dorsolateral, ventral directives, dorsal directives (Fig. 199C). Four incomplete septa then pair with the lateral couples and as already mentioned some corals remain permanently in this condition. Most pass on to the *Halcampoides* stage with six pairs

budding; one bud and three adult polyps. *H. Favia*, showing intratentacular budding; new pharynx forming. (*G and H after Matthai*, 1926.) 1, mouth; 2, septa; 3, bud; 4, sclerosepta.

of complete septa and later in any case incomplete pairs develop in cycles in the exocoels (endocoels in *Acropora* and *Porites,* page 601). The incomplete septa appear first in the dorsal exocoels, and the cycle only gradually completes itself ventrally; in fact before the secondary cycle is complete, septa of the tertiary cycle often appear in the dorsal exocoels;

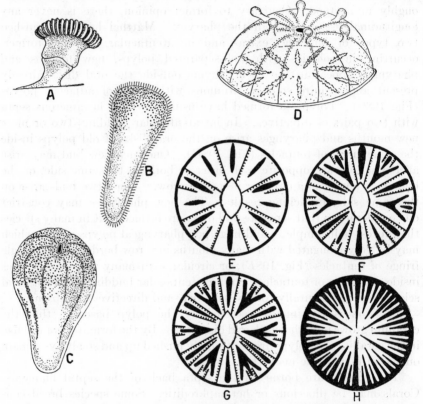

Fig. 199.—Reproduction of corals. *A.* Young *Fungia* in process of division. *B–H.* Development of *Siderastraea* (*after Duerden,* 1904): *B,* planula; *C,* later stage with three couples of septa; *D,* young polyp after attachment, with six tentacles, 12 septa, basal plate, and two cycles of sclerosepta beginning; *E,* diagram of stage similar to *D,* with two cycles of sclerosepta, septa in Edwardsian stage; *F,* next stage, secondary sclerosepta forked, tertiary sclerosepta appearing; *G,* next stage, tertiary sclerosepta fused with the secondary ones; *H,* final arrangement of the sclerosepta.

and not only that, but the tertiary septa arise earlier to the dorsal than to the ventral side of each pair of secondaries. There is thus expressed in the development of the septa a very strong bilaterality. After fixation the tentacles appear, either 12 simultaneously, or first the six exocoelic tentacles (Fig. 199*D*) and then the six endocoelic ones, for the primary cycle of septa. Later with increase in septa tentacles are added as in anemones. The skeleton begins to be secreted soon after fixation. Beneath the attached end a circular basal plate is formed and on this appear six sclerosepta under the six primary endocoels (Fig. 199D) followed by six more beneath the six primary exocoels (Fig. 199E); or all 12 may form simultaneously. The further development of the sclerosepta is best known for *Siderastraea*. In this genus, the first exocoelic septa bifurcate at their outer extremities, and the secondary endocoelic septa appear halfway between the two forks (Fig. 199F); the forks again bifurcate, and tertiary endocoelic septa arise between these bifurcations, etc. (Fig. 199G). As a result, the original exocoelic cycle (second embryologically) always remains exocoelic, and there are no new exocoelic cycles. The endocoelic cycles fuse with the unforked parts of the exocoelic cycle to make the adult endocoelic sclerosepta (Fig. 199G). In consequence, the adult secondary sclerosepta are not the embryologically second cycle but result from a fusion of the third embryonic cycle (second endocoelic cycle) with the original second cycle. Similarly the adult tertiary sclerosepta come chiefly from the fourth embryonic cycle, etc. In *Siderastraea*, the theca is an independent formation and the sclerosepta eventually extend peripherally and fuse with it (Fig. 199H). Theca and columella in other corals may be either independent formations or arise by the fusion of the ends of the sclerosepta. The sclerosepta like the septa appear first dorsally and later ventrally and often are secreted before the corresponding septa have developed.

A remarkable life history is known for the solitary coral *Fungia* (Fig. 200). The young coral developed from the planula is cup-shaped and buds off others like itself, often in fact becoming a little colony with several buds. In each of the young, the oral end finally expands into a disk (*anthocyathus*), which is eventually cut off by absorption of a ring of skeleton (Fig. 199A). The remaining stalk (*anthocaulus*) grows a new disk that is again cast off, and this process may be repeated several times. The disks heal below, expand greatly by growth, and live as solitary corals lying loose upon the bottom (Fig. 200). The whole process recalls monodisk strobilation in the Scyphozoa. *Fungia* as already noted (page 605) continues to give off ordinary buds throughout life.

The classification of corals, like that of many other invertebrate groups, is in an unsatisfactory state. The corals are usually divided into three groups: the imperforate or aporose corals, the fungids, and the perforate forms. The imperforate corals have compact thecae and sclerosepta and the loculi are usually partitioned off by dissepiments or synapticula. The families are: Flabellidae, Turbinolidae, Caryophyllidae, Seriatoporidae, Oculinidae, Astrangidae, Eusmiliidae, Orbicellidae,

Faviidae, and Mussidae. The Flabellidae are typified by the solitary *Flabellum*, having a large laterally flattened fan-like theca covered with an epitheca. The Caryophyllidae (*Caryophyllia*, Fig. 197*B*) are also solitary or nearly so with moderately sized goblet- or cornucopia-like theca provided with one or more cycles of pali. The Seriatoporidae (genera *Stylophora; Seriatopora; Pocillopora*, Fig. 201, lower right) form coarsely branched or lobed colonies with compact coenosteum and small crowded corallites and are important reef-builders. The Oculinidae or ivory corals (*Oculina*, Fig. 198*A, C*; *Lophohelia*, page 616) are slender

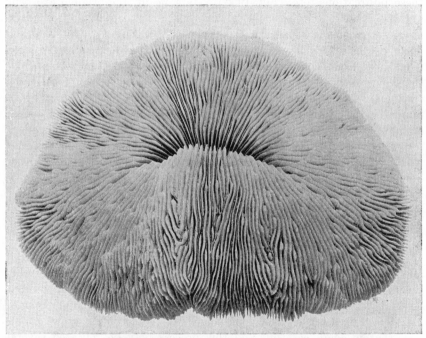

Fig. 200.—Fungia.   (*Photograph by American Museum of Natural History, New York City.*)

branching types with a smooth solid coenosteum and well-separated round elevated cups.

The Astrangidae (*Astrangia, Phyllangia, Oulangia*) form small encrusting or creeping colonies with closely placed thecae and protruding polyps. They occur along the coasts of the Americas and one species, *Astrangia danae*, is found on our Atlantic coast, from North Carolina north to Massachusetts. *Astrangia danae* consists of small encrusting colonies, usually not more than 2 or 3 inches across, growing on rocks and shells in sheltered places. The colonies proliferate along the margins, which are therefore thinner and flatter and with smaller cups than the median regions. The polyps cannot withdraw into the cups to any extent. The slender tentacles are covered with nematocyst warts and tipped with a nematocyst knob. The larger polyps have three cycles of tentacles (mostly 12 larger tentacles alternating with 12 smaller ones) and some fourth-cycle tentacles. Six pairs of primary septa, six pairs of secondary septa, and some tertiary pairs on one side are usually present. The sclerosepta also show the condition usual in coral polyps of being more advanced on one side than on the other, i.e., there are, in the larger cups, three complete cycles and a fourth incomplete cycle. In some regions of the theca, the alternation of the larger septa of the first and second cycles with the smaller septa of the third cycle is quite regular; but where the sclerosepta of the fourth cycle are appearing, the arrangement becomes irregular, and fusions of septa into groups are noticeable. *Astrangia danae* feeds on crustaceans, small fish, and bits of meat and will remain healthy for some time in aquaria.

The remaining four families of imperforate corals are known as the *astraeid* corals (old family Astraeidae) and furnish many of the most important genera of reef builders. They are typically of rounded massive form with contiguous or confluent thecae, but some are foliaceous. Important genera of the Orbicellidae are *Orbicella* (Fig. 201, second right), chief reef builder of the West Indian region and *Galaxea* (Fig. 197D) with protruding corallites. The Faviidae include a group of genera (*Favia*, Fig. 198D, *Favites, Goniastraea*) with closely placed polygonal cups and another group, exemplified by the brain coral *Meandra* (= *Meandrina*, Fig. 201, upper right) in which the thecae are confluent into winding valleys occupied by compound many-mouthed polyps bordered by a fringe of tentacles (Fig. 198E). The Mussidae (*Mussa; Symphyllia; Isophyllia*, Fig. 201, upper left) are similar to the brain corals but with deeper valleys and more protruding walls ("collines") between the valleys; in the genera mentioned the polyps are also compound as in *Meandra*.

The fungian corals have lamellate septa connected by synapticula and may be either perforate or imperforate. The Fungiidae comprise *Fungia* (Fig. 200) and several similar genera with a large flattened disk-like or elongated corallum solitary or compound, lying loose or attached. The interesting life history of *Fungia* has already been noted (page 609). The young are attached, but the adult disks bearing a single large polyp with many blunt tentacles lie loose upon the bottom and are particularly expert at freeing themselves from sand and silt. The Agariciidae (*Agaricia; Pavona; Siderastraea*, Fig. 201, center left, third right) are massive or foliaceous with numerous closely placed polyps as in the Faviidae, but there are no definite thecal walls, and the sclerosepta are more or less continuous between polyps. The indefinite bounding walls are well shown in the photographs of *Siderastraea* (Fig. 201).

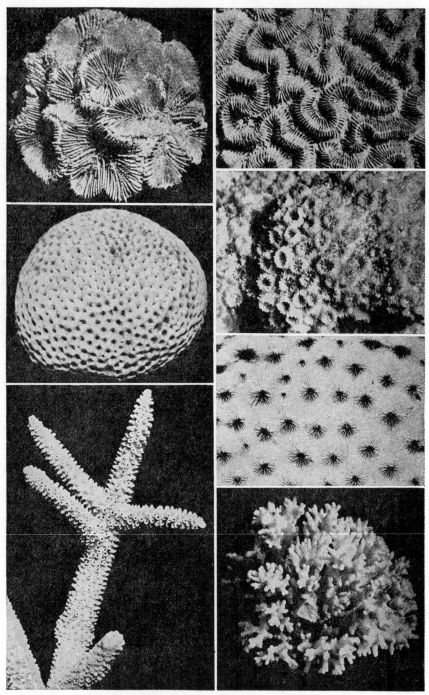

Fig. 201.—For descriptive legend see opposite page.

In the perforate corals, the corallum everywhere is extremely porous and of loose construction. There are three families: Eupsammidae, Acroporidae, and Poritidae. To the first family belongs the solitary *Balanophyllia*, of which a species occurs on the California coast (Fig. 196*B*). The Acroporidae, very porous, mostly branched corals with small polyps and cylindrical cups separated by perforate coenosteum, include some of the most important reef builders, notably the genera *Acropora* (= *Madrepora*, Fig. 201, left bottom, Fig. 202) and *Montipora*. The Poritidae (*Porites*, *Goniopora*) tend to be more massive or lobulate, with shallow contiguous cups, and are likewise common reef corals.

Activities are limited. In some the column can close over the retracted oral disk as in anemones, while in others on contraction the animal simply shortens into the corallite. The tentacles are often introverted into the interior. Ciliary currents and mucous secretion play a large role in behavior. On the column, the currents run upward in some species, downward in others; on the disk the cilia beat inward near the mouth, outward toward the margin elsewhere; on the tentacles the currents run from base to tip. These currents ordinarily serve to carry off sediment to which corals from the nature of their habitat are much exposed. Sediment mixed with mucus is wafted toward the edge of the disk or tips of the spread tentacles and so falls off. In some species great body distension, raising the disk above the corallum, assists in the removal of sediment. Some corals can clean themselves when completely covered with fine sand, but others perish under such conditions (Yonge, 1936).

Species with long tentacles feed much like anemones; the tentacles grasp the food and bend with it toward the mouth; or the widely opened mouth moves toward the food, aided by the contraction of the intervening region of the disk. Smaller types and those with reduced tentacles employ chiefly the ciliary-mucus method, in which the food entangled in mucous strands is wafted toward the mouth by ciliary currents. Food caught on the coenenchyme is conveyed to the nearest mouths by the same method. It appears that the usual outward beat on the oral disk is reversed in the ciliary-mucus method of feeding but not in the tentacular type. Near the mouth and in the pharynx the cilia always beat inward and the food as soon as it comes within the scope of these currents is carried down the pharynx. Usually the septal filaments protrude through the mouth, grasp the food, and may even start digestion outside.

FIG. 201.—Some common reef corals. Left-hand row: top, rose coral, *Isophyllia;* middle, *Siderastraea;* bottom, *Acropora* (= *Madrepora*). Right-hand row: top, enlarged view of a small part of a brain coral, *Meandrina* (= *Meandra*); second, *Orbicella annularis;* third, *Siderastraea*, small portion enlarged; bottom, *Pocillopora*. (*Acropora by American Museum of Natural History, New York City; other photographs by J. Steinberg and M. H. Nichols.*)

They secrete upon the food a powerful protease capable of splitting proteins to polypeptids in alkaline medium. The food particles are then phagocytized into the septal gastrodermis behind the filaments, where they are acted on by intracellular enzymes: another protease that completes protein digestion to amino acids, a lipase, and an enzyme splitting glycogen to glucose. Sensitivity to food objects is considerable; *Fungia* tentacles and mouth respond to mollusk coelomic fluid diluted $\frac{1}{160}$ to $\frac{1}{2500}$ times (Obe, 1938).

Coral polyps are usually more or less contracted in daytime (Fig. 198*F*), probably as a reaction to light, and expand and feed only at night (Fig. 198*E*) at which time the plankton, constituting their main food, rises to the surface. Digestion is very rapid so that by morning all traces of ingested food have usually disappeared. Interior currents are such as to cause undigested material to collect in the center of the coelenteron, whence it is ejected by convulsive contractions with the mouth held widely open. Excess food is stored in the gastrodermis, chiefly as fat, although glycogen was also found in *Fungia* by Hosoi (1938). (Foregoing data from the work of Yonge, and Yonge and Nicholls.)

On excretion the only data are those of Yonge (1931) who found that carmine grains injected into the body wall are passed (possibly by the mesogloeal cells) to the sides of the septal filaments (not into the cnidoglandular band) and then ejected into the coelenteron.

The oxygen consumption of corals is independent of the oxygen concentration of the medium at tensions above 2 cc. per liter and is dependent on the state of expansion of the polyps. In 30 species of reef corals, Kawaguti (1937) found an oxygen intake of about 0.03 cc. per gram wet weight per hour.

Broken ends are repaired by various methods in different species. One or more apical polyps may appear on the cut surface followed by other polyps; or the edges may close over the broken end through the proliferation of bounding polyps; or coenenchyme may cover the end and grow out before any polyps appear. Polyps will regenerate on the basal ends of branches held horizontally or upside down (Kawaguti, 1937).

Zooxanthellae occur abundantly in nearly all shallow-water corals, and their role has been much debated. Certain observers, failing to find any food in the coelenteron in the daytime (see above), concluded that the corals fed chiefly on their zooxanthellae. This idea has been conclusively disproved by Yonge and Nicholls (1931), who have shown that corals are wholly carnivorous and feed at night on plankton animals. The zooxanthellae are ejected if the corals are starved or kept in darkness and the corals undergo reduction from starvation when kept without animal food, whether in the dark or in the light. The zooxanthellae appear to be of use to the corals in that they remove the carbon dioxide given off by their hosts and the nitrogenous and phosphorous wastes resulting from protein metabolism. Near the surface the oxygen set free by the zooxanthellae in photosynthesis is sufficient during the daytime to supply the oxygen requirement of the corals (but not of planulae); below 4 m., because of the reduction of light, this is not the case. Corals with zooxanthellae are positive to light, and this reaction plays a role in the direction of their growth and regeneration.

Certain animals also live in close association with corals, particularly Crustacea, notably the coral-gall crabs *Harpalocarcinus* and *Cryptochirus*. The former is limited to the family Seriatoporidae, which branch dichotomously. The tiny immature female settles in a forming fork of the branches and by means of its respiratory current causes the young branches to broaden and curve around it so as to leave a chamber in which the crab is permanently imprisoned. The animal must necessarily feed on minute organisms brought by the respiratory current through the small apertures of the gall chamber, and its food-catching appendages and digestive system are much modified. The minute males form no galls and apparently creep into mature galls to fertilize the females. The related *Cryptochirus* is found only in massive corals, chiefly of the family Faviidae; both sexes live in cylindrical pits opening to the surface. The prawn *Paratyphon* lives in galls on *Acropora* and has been modified to a short stout shape with reduced sense organs (Borrodaile, 1921). Certain barnacles (*Creusia, Pyrgoma*) are epizoic on corals, eventually becoming embedded in the corallum, with whose growth they keep pace.

The reef-building corals require warm, shallow waters and consequently are limited to continental and island shores in tropical and subtropical zones. They cannot endure temperatures below 18°C. for any length of time and only above 22°C. do they exhibit a flourishing growth. They are almost absent from the western coast of South America and Africa because of the cold currents that course along those coasts from the antarctic. Consequently the reef corals inhabit two general regions: the Caribbean and related waters, including Florida, Bermuda, the Bahamas, and the West Indies; and the Indo-Pacific region from the east coast of Africa, including Madagascar, through the Indian Ocean, including the Maldive, Laccadive, Cocos, Chagos and other groups of islands, and throughout the western Pacific, embracing the Malay group of islands, the Philippines, the northeastern coast of Australia, and all those innumerable Pacific islands to the east of Australia as far as Hawaii. This second region is of course the major one for coral growth, and in fact the Pacific northeast of Australia is known as the

Coral Sea. The reef-building corals are also limited in vertical distribution by the decline in temperature of the ocean with depth; they do not grow below 50 m. at the most, and they flourish best above 30 m. The reef front exposed to the constant pounding of the waves is formed chiefly of massive types of corals, flat to rounded forms without branches or with short stout branches, with broad basal attachments. The more slender branching types and those with thin foliaceous expansions are characteristic of the quiet waters behind the reef front. The form of corals is, however, greatly altered by environment, and many species present a variety of ecological types, grading from resistant shapes with reduced branches when growing in the surf to tall forms with elongated branches in quiet water. Many of these ecological variants were formerly considered distinct species. Light and amount of sediment also limit the distribution of reef corals. They usually fail to grow in shaded areas otherwise suitable and according to Edmondson (1928) die if kept in total darkness (18 days). As inhabitants of shallow waters subject to strong wave action, corals must cope continually with sediment; and although provided as related above with a ciliary mechanism for freeing the disk from debris, they naturally cannot dispose of large amounts of sediment and may not grow fast enough to keep above bottom accumulation. Hawaiian reef corals were found by Edmondson to survive for several hours under 4 inches of sand and silt. On the other hand, the colonies on the reef surface are exposed to air and sun at the lowest tides, and, although they can endure such conditions for brief periods, the tops of colonies are often killed in this way. In Edmondson's experiments on Hawaiian reef corals (1928) the corals were killed by 1 hour exposure to 34°C. and died in 8 hours at 32°C. Corals therefore appear to flourish best at temperatures that are near their upper limit of survival. Exposure to the sun out of water killed the corals in less than an hour. Excessive rain and fresh water are also fatal to corals, but a 50 per cent dilution may be endured for many hours or even a few days.

Below depths of 50 m. occurs a coral fauna that does not build reefs. These grade from solitary forms between 50 and 75 m. related to the reef builders to deep sea corals going down to 8000 m., and living in very weak light or darkness at temperatures between 1 and 15°C. The deep-sea forms consist mostly of solitary cup corals and some delicate fragile branching types. In more northern latitudes they live in less deep waters. A sparse coral fauna extends even into very cold latitudes and may build deep-water reefs such as those formed by the branching coral *Lophohelia* at 200 to 600 m. depth in the North Sea.

Although the stony corals are the principal builders of coral reefs and islands, other organisms play a considerable role, notably the nullipores or coralline algae, encrusting or branching algae impregnated with lime and growing upon the coral colonies. Other important contributors to coral rock are the Foraminifera, *Millepora*, the much calcified alcyonarians *Tubipora* and *Heliopora*, some of the more fleshy alcyonaceans, and the gorgonians, which last form a conspicuous feature of coral beds in the Caribbean-West Indian region. Besides these, coral formations are inhabited by a vast throng of sponges, anemones, sea urchins, starfish, crabs, tubicolous annelids, holothurians, snails, and bivalves and are haunted by numbers of brightly hued fish. Coral beds composed of this multitude of organisms of varied shapes and colors, viewed through the deep blue waters of a lagoon, constitute one of the most beautiful sights in the world, rivaling the most gorgeous flower gardens. The coral polyps themselves are commonly some shade of yellow, brown, or green because of their zooxanthellae, but almost any hue may be found among them. The skeletons are white but are very often permeated with red and green boring algae whose colors they assume.

"A coral reef is a ridge or mound of limestone the upper surface of which is near the surface of the sea and which is formed of calcium carbonate by the action of organisms chiefly corals." (Vaughan, 1917.) Coral reefs are usually considered to be of three sorts: *fringing* reefs, *barrier* reefs, and *atolls*. A fringing reef extends from the shore a few feet to ¼ mile out and consists of the reef edge or *front* where the most active coral growth occurs and a slightly lower more or less flat surface, the reef *flat*, between the front and the shore, composed largely of coral sand and mud, dead coral, and other debris, and partly of living coral colonies and other animals. A barrier reef is the same as a fringing reef, with a reef front and a flat 20 to 1000 feet wide, but it is separated from the land by a lagoon 60 to 300 feet deep and ½ to 10 miles or more in width. The most noted barrier reef is the Great Barrier Reef off the northeast coast of Australia, which is over 1200 miles long and in some places 90 miles from the shore. An atoll is a more or less circular or horseshoe-shaped reef not enclosing any island but encircling a lagoon, which varies from less than a mile to 40 or 50 miles across. None of the reef types is to be thought of as constituting a continuous wall like a man-made breakwater; but is broken up into many reefs and islands by passages, the larger of which often represent "drowned" valleys, valleys sunk below the sea by land subsidence or rise in sea level. The lagoons usually contain inner islands, reefs, etc. The flats are more or less exposed at the lowest tides. The reef front is subject to continuous surf, the incessant booming of which is a characteristic feature of coral islands; the surf knocks off boulders and fragments of the reef and heaves them up on the flat behind the reef edge. The reef front usually siopes at first but after a couple of hundred feet may descend steeply to great depths, although this is not necessarily the case. The lagoon floor is composed largely of coral sand, mud, skeletons of corals and other organisms, and various debris; but in places, especially near the passages, it supports a rich growth of the more fragile, slender, branching types of corals, which together with other animals make up the coral beds so admired by naturalists.

Since the present reef-building corals do not grow below 150 feet at the outside and since geological evidence indicates that those of past ages were also littoral in their habits, it becomes necessary to explain the great

Fig. 202.—Scene in the Great Barrier Reef, Australia, at low tide, showing exposed corals. (*Rephotographed by American Museum of Natural History from Saville-Kent, The Great Barrier Reef of Australia,* 1893.) The conspicuous corals are a species of *Acropora* (= *Madrepora*).

vertical thickness often attained by coral reefs. Many theories have been propounded, of which the following are the chief ones:

1. *Darwin-Dana Subsidence Theory.*—Reefs begin as fringing reefs on a sloping shore; by subsidence of the shore they become barrier reefs with water between them and the land; and if the land is an island and sinks completely out of sight, the barrier reef becomes an atoll. This theory grew out of Darwin's observations on coral formations when as a young man in his twenties he spent 5 years as a naturalist aboard the ship "Beagle."

2. *Semper-Murray Solution Theory.*—Sir John Murray was the chief biologist on the "Challenger," the British ship that from 1874 to 1876 cruised the oceans in an extensive exploration of the conditions and

life in the sea. Murray proposed that corals grow on high summits of the ocean bottom when these have been built up to the right level by sediments and that barrier reefs and atolls result from the better growth of corals at the edge and through solution of the inner coral rock. This theory is now completely discarded.

3. *Submerged Bank Theory.*—On this theory, supported by many recent students of the problem, coral formations grow on flat preexisting surfaces, during or after the submergence of such surfaces.

4. *Daly Glacial-control Theory.*—During the last glacial period, the abstraction of water from the ocean to form the great ice caps is believed to have lowered the ocean level 60 to 70 m. below the present surface. Wave action cut out on shores and below the surface flat platforms suitable for coral growth, then inhibited by the low temperatures. As the ice melted and temperatures rose, corals began to grow upon these platforms and kept pace with the rising ocean level. This theory accounts for the very uniform depth of coral lagoons, whose bottoms, below the debris since deposited, would consist of the platforms cut when the ocean stood at its low level.

Theories 3 and 4, which supplement each other, are at present most favored by students of the problem, although Darwin's idea still finds much support. Several lines of evidence attest that most coral reefs today are growing on submerged land: the drowned valleys already mentioned, submersed cliffs that could have been cut only on land, and the eroded surface of the substratum on which many recent and fossil reefs can be observed to rest. The submergence theory agrees with Darwin's subsidence theory in that both consider the reef foundations to be now at greater depths than they were when the coral growth began; but the submergence theory does not admit any relationship between the various kinds of reefs, postulating that both barrier reefs and atolls have grown up on preexisting flattish platforms. Atolls are considered to have been shaped by prevailing winds and currents.

The rate of coral growth is of much interest in connection with these theories. Observation of living corals shows the rate to be extremely variable from unknown causes. The rate varies from 5 mm. per year for slow-growing massive types, which increase in all diameters simultaneously, to 10 to 20 cm. or more per year for the faster growing branching sorts, which increase in length mainly at the tips. At these rates Vaughan estimates that a reef 50 m. deep could be formed in 1000 to 7600 years and that all the reefs now known could have been built in 10,000 to 30,000 years.

Attempts have been made to solve the problem of reef formation by borings, of which the deepest one was made in 1904 on Funafuti Atoll in the South Pacific north of Fiji by a special expedition sent by the Royal Society of London. The boring, 3 to 5 inches in diameter, was carried to a depth of 1114 feet (without reaching the reef base), and in the bore were identified 28 genera of well-known reef-building corals, 22 of which are now living on the reef above 60 m.; but it contained none of the deep water corals living in that locality at the depth to which the boring went. This result supports the subsidence theory. Cary (1931) made three borings at different distances from the shore into a reef in Samoa and concluded that the reef rested on a level wave-cut platform, a result in accord with theory 4. Two borings were made into the Great Barrier Reef by the Great Barrier Reef Committee, one in 1928 and one in 1938. Both borings yielded the same result—that the coral material extended only to 400 to 450 feet and that below this there was nothing but shore sand containing shells of various animals. There was no evidence of any underlying platform. This finding also supports Darwin's subsidence theory, which thus applies to at least many reefs, but some reefs were apparently laid down on preexisting platforms.

7. Fossil Corals.—There are about 2500 living species of corals and over 5000 extinct ones; hence these animals reached their height in past ages and are now on the decline. Reports of diminishing coral growth have come from various localities, and many coral colonies described by Saville-Kent in his book are no longer living. | The extinct corals belong to two orders, the Tetracoralla or Rugosa, wholly vanished, and the Madreporaria. | The Tetracoralla appeared in the Ordovician of Europe and North America in company with the Tabulata (page 565) and alcyonarians resembling *Heliopora*, reached their height in the Silurian and Devonian, and died away in the Permian. The Tetracoralla are so called because their sclerosepta (their soft parts are of course quite unknown) are grouped about four main septa, the *main, counter,* and *lateral* septa (Fig. 203*B, H*), equally spaced around the circumference of the theca. The septa between the main and lateral septa run obliquely, meeting the main septum at an angle, giving a pinnate appearance (Fig. 203*A*), whence the name *feather corals* often applied to these fossils. The septa between the counter and lateral septa are more nearly vertical. Although at first the tetramerous scleroseptal arrangement in the Tetracoralla was considered to differ widely from the hexamerous plan of the Madreporaria, several workers, especially Carruthers and Duerden, have shown that the Tetracoralla pass through a hexamerous stage. In the development of the sclerosepta, there first appears in the sagittal plane one single septum (Fig. 203*C*) whose opposite ends later become the main and counter septa by the disappearance of the middle part (Fig. 203*G*). Then a lateral or *alar* couple appears, one to each side of the main septum (Fig. 203*D*), and later a similar couple forms in relation to the counter septum (Fig. 203*E*). This produces a hexamerous stage, which however certainly differs from anything seen in the development of present Zoantharia. The later septa (metasepta) develop in four places: to each side of the main septum and to each side of the counter septum (Fig. 203*G*, *H*). At first the metasepta take a very oblique position but later tend to become more radial, and all of them shift toward the counter septum. A depression medial to the much shortened main septum may indicate the presence of a siphonoglyph.

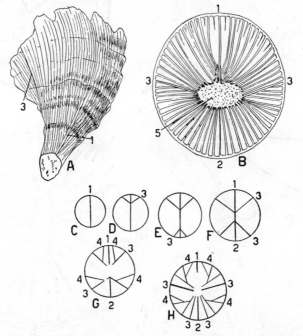

Fig. 203.—The extinct Rugosa. *A*. A rugose coral, *Zaphrentis*, from the outside, showing the main and one of the lateral septa. *B*. Diagrammatic view of the arrangement of the septa of the same specimen shown in *A*. *C–H*. Diagrams of the order of appearance of the septa in the Rugosa (*after Carruthers*, 1906): *C*, appearance of the primary septum; *D*, formation of the second or lateral septa; *E*, appearance of septa alongside the counter septum; *F*, later stage of *E*; *G*, primary septum has separated into the main and counter septa; new septa are arising in four regions; *H*, additional septa have formed in the four regions; all the septa move toward the counter septum. 1, main septum; 2, counter septum; 3, lateral septum; 4, regions of formation of new septa; 5, columella.

Most of the Tetracoralla were solitary, shaped like a curved cornucopia (Fig. 203*A*), with a ridged surface (hence the name Rugosa or rugose corals often applied to the group); important genera of this type are *Zaphrentis* (Fig. 203*A*, *B*), *Cyathaxonia*, *Streptelasma*, and *Omphyma*. Others such as *Cyathophyllum* and *Lonsdaleia* were colonial, massive with contiguous thecae or bushy and branched with separate cups. The Tetracoralla formed great coral reefs in the upper Silurian and the Devonian strata of Europe, North America, and elsewhere. The falls

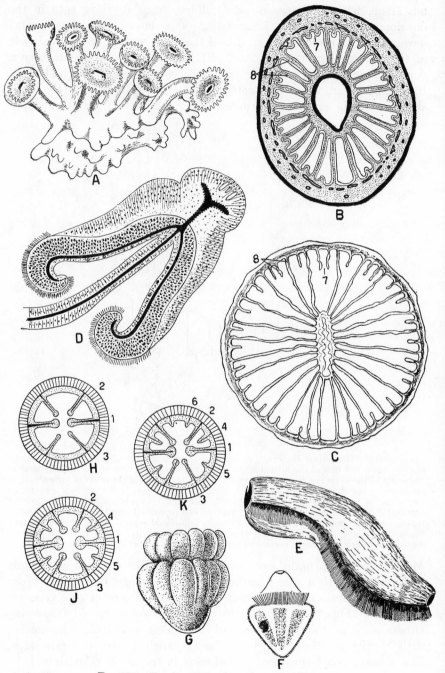

Fig. 204.—For descriptive legend see opposite page.

of the Ohio River at Louisville, Ky., are caused by a Devonian tetracoralline reef.

The order Madreporaria began in the Triassic and became very rich in species in the Upper Jurassic, Cretaceous, and Lower Tertiary. Many well-known living genera have a long fossil history, as *Orbicella* and *Favia*, which began in the Jurassic, *Caryophyllia* and *Flabellum*, dating back to the Cretaceous, and *Acropora*, *Fungia*, *Seriatopora*, *Pocillopora*, and *Galaxea*, originating in the Tertiary. These madrepores formed fringing and barrier reefs, but no atolls, under much the same conditions as they do today, in littoral waters on preexisting substrata, but apparently did not require such warm temperatures.

8. Order Zoanthidea.—The zoanthids are a small group of mostly colonial, sometimes solitary, forms, without skeleton, resembling small anemones (Fig. 204*A*). A pedal disk is absent, and the aboral end of solitary species is stalked or wedge-shaped. In colonial types the polyps are united, as in the Alcyonaria, by basal stolons containing solenia, or by a thin basal coenenchyme (Fig. 204*A*) or by a thick coenenchyme from which only the oral ends protrude. The column wall is divided into scapus and capitulum, is usually without special structures except tubercles of thickened mesogloea in *Isaurus*, and is often encrusted with sand grains, sponge spicules, foraminiferal shells, etc., embedded in the surface. The oral disk bears a marginal circlet of unbranched tentacles consisting of an exocoelic and an endocoelic cycle. The mouth is oval or slit-like and the pharynx laterally flattened with a single ventral siphonoglyph.

The septal arrangement differs from that of any other living Anthozoa but somewhat resembles that of the extinct Tetracoralla. The septa are paired and coupled and occur in a single cycle, composed of macrosepta and microsepta (Fig. 204*B*, *C*). There are two pairs of directives with external retractors, but the dorsal directives are microsepta (Fig. 204*B*, *C*), i.e., do not reach the pharynx. In most of the zoanthids, the other septa show the *brachycnemous* arrangement, i.e., they all form pairs composed of one macroseptum and one microseptum, with retractors facing the endocoels (Fig. 204*C*). Such forms possess only one pair of complete septa, the ventral directives. Some genera of zoanthids are, however, *macrocnemous*, i.e., the fourth and fifth septa on each side

Fig. 204.—Zoanthidea. *A*. A zoanthid growing on a piece of coral, from life, Bermuda. *B*. Cross section of *Epizoanthus*, to show macrocnemous type of septal arrangement. (*After Lwowsky*, 1913.) *C*. Cross section of *A*, to show brachycnemous type of septal arrangement, from life. *D*. Septal filament of a zoanthid. (*After Duerden*, 1900.) *E*. Zoanthella larva. (*After Carlgren*, 1906.) *F*. Zoanthina larva. (*After Menon*, 1902.) *G*. Later stage of zoanthina larva, with 12 septa, as in *K*. (*After Carlgren*, 1906.) *H–K*. Septal development of zoanthid larva (*after Menon*, 1902): *H*, with three primary couples; *J*, microsepta forming; *K*, dorsal directives formed. 1-6, order of formation of the septal couples; 7, dorsal directives; 8, fourth and fifth septa.

counting from the dorsal directives down are both macrosepta and form a pair of macrosepta on each side (Fig. 204*B*) so that such genera have three pairs of macrosepta. New septa in zoanthids arise exclusively in the exocoels to either side of the ventral directives, whereas in anemones and corals they form anywhere around the circumference. It should be recalled that in the Tetracoralla also these two places were regions of septal formation. Altogether the septal conditions in the zoanthids are highly bilateral.

The column epidermis is usually covered with a thick cuticle and in many zoanthids is divided up into polygonal areas or groups of cells by cuticular or mesogloeal strands, which run to the cuticle and may spread out between cuticle and epidermis as a subcuticular layer. The thick gelatinous mesogloea contains some fibers and cells and usually also a complicated network of canals, apparently of epidermal origin, which course mostly in a radial direction from epidermis to gastrodermis. A space, the ring sinus, extending throughout the column next to the gastrodermis and connected with this canal system may also be present. The function of these spaces is unknown. The septal filaments occur only on the macrosepta and as in anemones are provided in their upper portions with flagellated bands; these project out like wings (Fig. 204*D*) and may be very broad. Zooxanthellae are present not only in the gastrodermis but in the mesogloeal canals and epidermis. The muscular system is poorly developed, especially in the basal region, with diffuse retractors. A column sphincter is generally present, diffuse and entodermal or of the mesogloeal type. Little is known of the nervous system. The nematocysts of the zoanthids are similar to those of other zoantharians, consisting of spirocysts on tentacles and oral disk, and holotrichous isorhizas and microbasic mastigophores.

The zoanthids are chiefly dioecious, but some genera are also hermaphroditic. Gonads are limited to the macrosepta except in *Palaeozoanthus*. The complete development has not been described for any zoanthid, but the pelagic larvae, known from their discoverer as *Semper's larvae*, have often been taken in the plankton. They are of two types: the *Zoanthina* larva (Fig. 204*F*, *G*), oval with a girdle of particularly long cilia near the oral pole, and the *Zoanthella* larva (Fig. 204*E*), elongated with a ventral band of very long cilia. The septa apparently develop in the following order: a lateral couple, the ventral directives, then a dorsolateral couple, making six macrosepta (Fig. 204*H*). Four microsepta then appear, completing the lateral pairs (Fig. 204*J*), followed by the two microsepta that form the dorsal directives (Fig. 204*K*). Thereafter all septa develop in the exocoels lateral to the ventral directives. This development is obviously similar to that of anemones and corals up to the 12-septal condition. In some, a ciliated larval stage is omitted and the young develop inside the parent to a stage with 16 septa.

The Zoanthidea inhabit both littoral and deeper ocean waters and range from the tropics to quite cold latitudes but are more abundant in warm shallow waters. They include solitary forms, whose lower ends are thrust into the substratum, colonies of a few polyps, and large colonies with many polyps. Some colonial types, like *Palythoa*, grow upon inert objects as flat, concave, convex, or mushroom-shaped membranous expansions, their form following the shape of the substratum. Most genera, however, such as *Epizoanthus, Parazoanthus, Zoanthus, Isozoanthus*, are *epizoic*, i.e., habitually grow on other animals, such as sponges, hydroids, corals, gorgonians, bryozoans, worm tubes, and shells inhabited by hermit crabs. Some of these associations are very specific; thus, certain species of *Epizoanthus* occur only on particular hexactinellid sponges, and other species of this genus are addicted to shells occupied by hermit crabs. The coenenchyme enwraps the shell, dissolves it away, and comes eventually to enclose the crab directly, being then termed *carcinoecium* (Fig. 205*A*). Zoanthid polyps are generally small, a few millimeters to a few centimeters in height, but the solitary *Isozoanthus giganteus* may reach a length of 19 cm.

9. Order Antipatharia, the black or thorny corals. The Antipatharia (or Antipathidea) form slender branching, plant-like colonies (Fig. 205*B*) which, like the gorgonians, consist of a skeletal axis covered by a thin coenenchyme bearing polyps. The lower end of the colony usually consists of a flattened basal plate adherent to some firm object but is sometimes simply thrust into the substratum. From this arises a main stem that may give off a number of slender unbranched stems (*Stichopathes*) but more commonly breaks up into branches in a plant-like manner. Some have a "bottle-brush" appearance, consisting of a main stem with numerous short lateral branches (*Parantipathes*). The polyps may be close or distant, strewn over the colony or limited to one surface of the branches (Fig. 205*G, H*), and are oriented at right angles to the length of the branch. They are of short cylindrical form, projecting but little above the general coenenchyme and have a circlet of six simple nonretractile tentacles (Fig. 205*G*), except in *Dendrobrachia* (Fig. 205*E*), which possesses eight retractile pinnate tentacles. In some genera as *Schizopathes* and *Bathypathes* (Fig. 205*H*), the polyps are drawn out along the branches so as to appear divided into three projections each with two tentacles. The tentacles are covered with numerous warts of nematocysts. The nematocysts (Tischbierek, 1936) resemble those of anemones, consisting of basitrichous isorhizas and microbasic mastigophores, besides the usual spirocysts.

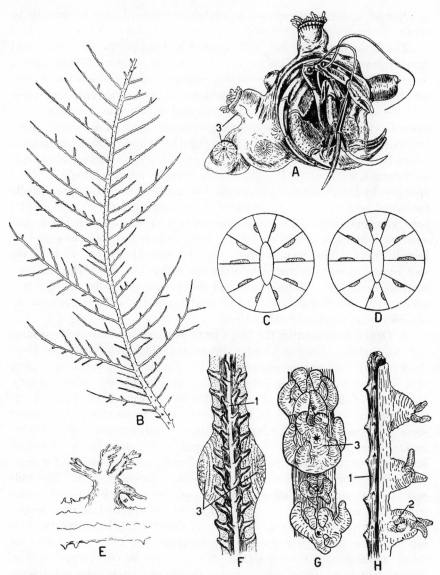

Fig. 205.—Zoanthidea, Antipatharia. *A.* A carcinoecium, *Epizoanthus* colony, enclosing a hermit crab that originally occupied a snail shell. (*After Carlgren*, 1923.) *B. Antipathes*, preserved. *C, D.* Two main types of septal arrangement and retractor muscles in Antipatharia. (*According to Pesch*, 1914.) *E, Dendrobrachia.* (*After Brook*, 1889.) *F.* Piece of *B* cleared and magnified showing thorny axis and two contracted polyps. *G. Stichopathes*, showing polyps. *H. Bathypathes*, one polyp constricted into three parts. (*G and H, after Cooper*, 1909.) 1, thorny axis; 2, eggs; 3, polyps.

The skeletal axis is brown or black in color and is provided with thorns (Fig. 205F, H), whence the common name of black or thorny corals; the thorns are usually simple elevations but are sometimes branched or beset with papillae. The axis is composed of concentric cylinders of a horn-like material and may or may not have a central spongy canal. The thorns are formed by an outward bulge of the concentric layers. The axis is too poor in sulphur to classify as true horn (keratin) but closely resembles gorgonin chemically and like this substance often contains iodine and bromine.

The elongated mouth, situated on a conical elevation, leads into a pharynx provided with two slightly differentiated siphonoglyphs. There are 6, 10, or 12 complete single septa, usually 10, (Fig. 205C, D), arranged in couples, six of which are considered to be primary, the rest (when present) secondary. The primary six consist of a pair attached to each siphonoglyph and a couple in the transverse plane; the latter are the largest septa in the body and ordinarily the only ones bearing filaments and gonads. To these six septa may be added one or two short couples close to the couples at the siphonoglyphs. The six tentacles are extensions of the interseptal spaces between the six primary septa. The septal musculature is weakly developed, and in most species definite retractors are lacking so that comparison with other anthozoans is difficult; but in a few cases von Pesch claims to have determined the retractor arrangement and describes two types (Fig. 205C, D). The septal filaments, well-developed only on the transverse couple, consist only of the cnidoglandular band, thickly strewn with both types of gland cells. The "dorsal" siphonoglyph continues below the pharynx along the septal edges as the *hyposulculus*. The gastrovascular cavities of the polyps are connected by passages near the skeleton, but such connections are often much narrowed by interzooidal septa between the polyps.

The histology resembles that of anemones except that the mesogloea is reduced to a thin homogeneous layer without or but scantily provided with cells. The musculature is greatly reduced; longitudinal epidermal fibers occur in the tentacles and to a less extent in the body wall and pharynx; circular gastrodermal fibers are mostly absent. The general body surface is ciliated, the beat directed toward the mouth.

The polyps are dioecious, but colonies may be hermaphroditic. Nothing is known of the development.

The Antipatharia are typically animals of the deeper and abyssal waters of the ocean, from 100 m. down, and are most abundant in tropical and subtropical zones. They are known chiefly as preserved specimens obtained on dredging expeditions, and therefore our ignorance of their embryology and biology is not surprising. The colonies vary in height from a few centimeters to 2 or 3 m. Like other sessile animals, they often provide homes for a variety of other organisms, to some of which they respond by structural modifications such as the gall-like skeletal encasements they form around certain barnacles and the maze of short branches they put out to serve as "worm-runs" for certain polychaetes.

10. Order Ceriantharia.—The cerianthids, best known by the genus *Cerianthus*, are anemone-like anthozoans, with smooth, muscular, elongated, cylindrical bodies, thrust into sand up to the oral disk (Fig. 206*A*). The aboral end is simply rounded and provided with a terminal pore. The oral disk bears simple slender tentacles arranged in two sets, an outer *marginal* set and an inner smaller *oral* or *labial* set encircling the mouth; each tentacle group may be arranged in one to four circles. There is one marginal and one oral tentacle to each interseptal chamber, and consequently all the tentacles are coupled except for the single dorsal marginal tentacle that overlies the endocoel of the directives. There may be a corresponding single dorsal oral tentacle. The pharynx is laterally flattened and bears one siphonoglyph, which is commonly accepted as dorsal, corresponding to the sulculus of anemones but not to the single siphonoglyph of the Alcyonaria. The siphonoglyph continues along the edge of the directives below the pharynx as a groove termed the *hyposulculus.*

The septal arrangement differs (Fig. 206*B*) from that of all other anthozoans, consisting of one cycle of complete single septa, which are coupled, not paired, and which increase in number by addition of new couples in the ventral interseptal space only. The septal musculature is weakly developed and retractors are absent but that face on which longitudinal fibers occur presumably corresponds to the retractor face of other anthozoans: and this surface in all the septa is directed ventrally as in the Alcyonaria. The number of septa is indefinite, since new ones are continually formed ventrally. The three most dorsal couples, namely, the directives attached to the siphonoglyph and the two couples to either side of them, are termed *protosepta*, since they are the first to develop embryologically, and the other septa are called *metasepta*. The directives and couple 3 are sterile; couple 2 may or may not be provided with gonads. The fourth couple, i.e., the first metaseptal couple, is long and fertile; counting ventrally from them every other metaseptal couple is fertile while the ones between are sterile. The metasepta are also arranged in quartettes as regards length; the first and third septa in each quartette, i.e., the fertile septa, are longer than the second and fourth or sterile septa (Fig. 207*B*, *E*). Furthermore, superimposed on this alternation of long and short septa, there is in many species a gradual decrease in the septal length from dorsal to ventral sides. Most of the septa thus fail to reach the aboral end, and the most recently formed ones extend but a short distance below the pharynx.

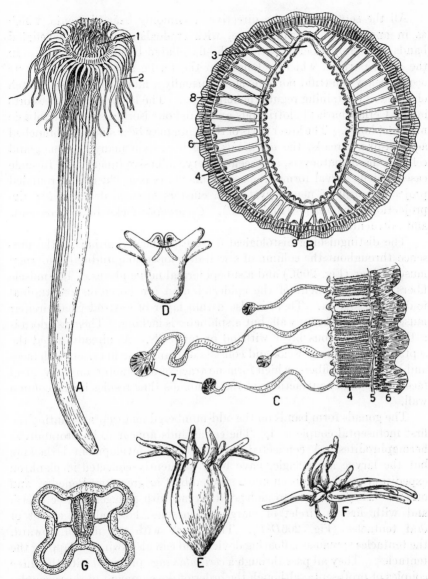

FIG. 206.—Ceriantharia.   A. *Cerianthus*, preserved.   B. Section through the same, showing pharynx and septa.   C. Piece of body wall of *A*, below the pharynx, showing one quartette of septa.   D. Young cerianthid larva, *Arachnactis*.   (*After van Beneden*, 1891.) E. *Cerianthula* larva.   F. Later stage of *Arachnactis* larva.   (*E and F, after Carlgren*, 1924.) G. Cross section of larva like *D*, showing first couple and four tentacle buds.   (*After van Beneden*, 1891.)   1, oral tentacles; 2, marginal tentacles; 3, siphonoglyph; 4, longitudinal muscle layer; 5, nerve net, 6, epidermis; 7, septal filament; 8, gastrodermis; 9, youngest septa.

All the septa except the directives commonly bear filaments, which as in anemones are trifid above, with cnidoglandular and flagellated bands, and simple below without the flagellated bands (Fig. 206C). In the trifid portion, which is longer on the fertile septa, only spirocysts occur; below the trifid portion there is usually a much convoluted stretch of filament containing regular nematocysts. The latter are of three sorts in the Ceriantharia: holotrichous and atrichous isorhizas and microbasic mastigophores. The lower parts of the septa may bear simple or branched acontia-like threads, the *acontioids*, which contain many mucous gland cells but no nematocysts, and seem to serve adhesive functions. In some cases, chiefly larval forms, the septal filaments bear clusters of rounded projections full of nematocysts; the clusters are called *botrucnids*, the projections *cnidorhagi* (Fig. 207C). *Cerianthus* lacks both acontioids and botrucnids.

The distinguishing histological feature of the cerianthids is the presence throughout the column of a well-developed longitudinal epidermal muscle layer (Fig. 206C) and a subepidermal nerve plexus. The muscle fibers are independent of the epidermis and are borne on longitudinal folds of mesogloea. There is also a thin layer of gastrodermal circular muscles in the column wall, but a sphincter is lacking. The mesogloea is a thin homogeneous layer with no or few cells. As already noted the septal musculature is weak and consists of transverse fibers on both faces and longitudinal fibers, which form no trace of a retractor, on the ventral face. The high contractility of these animals thus resides in the column wall.

The gonads form bands on the odd-numbered metasepta, counting the first metaseptal couple as 1. The cerianthids appear to be protandrous hermaphrodites. A connected account of the development is lacking but the larvae are pelagic, have been frequently collected in plankton expeditions, and have been much studied by Carlgren, van Beneden, and others. They are oval to elongated larvae with a flagellated ectoderm and with first a circlet of marginal tentacles, later also a circlet of oral tentacles (Fig. 206D–F). They float with the mouth upward, the tentacles spread as a floating device, and can also swim by flapping the tentacles. They all pass through a *cerinula* stage provided with the three couples of protosepta, although the order of development of these couples is not certainly known (Figs. 206G, 207A). Thereafter metaseptal couples appear, each successive couple being formed between the two septa of the preceding couple. After having developed many septa and tentacles, the larvae gradually sink toward the bottom, and eventually take up life as bottom-dwelling animals.

The cerianthids live in vertical cylindrical cavities in the sea bottom inside a case formed of hardened slimy secretion in which are embedded shed nematocysts, sand grains, and other foreign objects. Because of the lack of a sphincter, the anterior end cannot be retracted into the

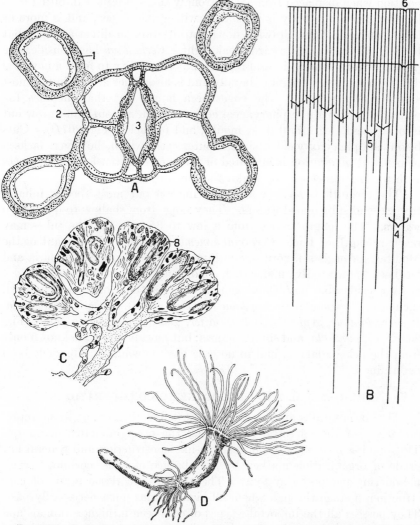

Fig. 207.—Ceriantharia (continued). *A.* Cross section of later larval stage with three couples of protosepta formed. (*After van Beneden*, 1891.) *B.* Diagram of septa of a cerianthid, only one side shown (*after McMurrich*, 1910); the three couples of protosepta and the quartettes of metasepta are indicated by brackets. *C.* A botrucnid with four cnidorhagi, from a *Cerianthula* larva. (*After Carlgren*, 1924.) *D.* Cerianthus regenerating an oral end from a cut in the side. (*After Loeb*, 1905.) 1, ectoderm; 2, entoderm; 3, pharynx; 4, the three pairs of protosepta; 5, quartette of metasepta; 6, siphonoglyph; 7, nematocysts; 8, cnidorhagi.

column, but, when disturbed, the oral end is swiftly drawn down into the tube by contraction of the column musculature. Extension as in other anthozoans depends upon water intake by way of the siphonoglyph. *Cerianthus* is markedly negative to gravity, soon resuming an upright position when displaced from it; is strongly thigmotactic, exhibiting restlessness unless the body is in contact with some object; and is more or less negative to light, drawing down into its tube in direct sunlight but turning the oral end toward weak light. *Cerianthus* has considerable powers of regeneration in oral regions, but the ability to form a new oral disk with tentacles declines aborally and is altogether absent in the most aboral pieces (Child). The edges of a lateral cut that includes the pharynx fuse with the pharyngeal edges to form a mouth and grow out into a "head" with oral disk, mouth, and tentacles (Fig. 207*D*). Cuts below the pharynx yield a similar outgrowth, which, however, lacks a mouth. Regeneration is inhibited or retarded if distension of the pieces with water is prevented by making an opening in them.

The cerianthids have a wide distribution but most species inhabit tropical and subtropical waters. They range from shallow to quite deep waters. The length varies from a few to 35 cm., but the tubes may reach a length of 1 m. *Cerianthus membranaceus*, an inhabitant of the Mediterranean, is a favorite aquarium animal in European aquaria and has been known to live under such conditions for 10 to 40 years.

A considerable number of genera of cerianthids have been named, such as *Arachnanthus*, *Arachnactis* (Fig. 206*F*), *Ovactis*, *Anactinia*, *Pachycerianthus*, *Apiactis*, *Botrucnidifer*, *Botruanthus*, *Cerianthula* (Fig. 206*E*), *Calpanthula*, and similar names; but most of these are known only from the pelagic larvae, and in no case has the complete life cycle been determined.

VIII. GENERAL AND PHYLOGENETIC CONSIDERATIONS

The coelenterates are commonly regarded as the nearest living representatives of the ancestral stock of all the other eumetozoan groups. This opinion rests upon their gastrula-like construction and general low grade of organization marked by the absence of anus, coelom, "true" mesoderm, and organ systems. They are at the tissue grade of construction, a stage through which all higher forms must necessarily pass. They possess all the important types of cells seen in higher animals and increase in complexity becomes primarily a matter of the aggregation of these various sorts of cells into organs and systems. The ectoderm and entoderm of the Cnidaria already display that differentiation for surface-protective-sensory and digestive-absorptive functions, respectively, which characterize them throughout the animal kingdom. The differentiation has not proceeded very far, since these two layers are amazingly similar in general appearance and cell types present. Nevertheless the functional divergence appears to be fixed, since, as shown by experiments in turning hydras inside out, the two layers are not interchangeable. If the hydras remain turned, epidermal and gastrodermal cells wander past each other through the mesogloea and resume their original relations (old experiments recently verified by Roudabush). Nor is either epidermis or gastrodermis alone capable of regenerating a hydra (Pappenfuss and Bodenham, 1939).

The question of the diploblastic nature of the radiate phyla (Cnidaria, Ctenophora) was discussed in Chap. IV. The author considers that the radiate and bilateral phyla should no longer be distinguished on the basis of the alleged absence of a mesoderm in the former and should not be offset against each other as diploblastic and triploblastic groups, respectively. From a morphological point of view, shorn of phylogenetic theory, no actual difference exists between the construction of a sea anemone and a planarian, as regards general body layers. The difference, if one must be set up, appears to lie in the pure mesenchymal nature of the "mesoderm" of the radiate phyla and its indefinite mode of formation by inwandering of ectoderm cells (also entoderm cells in some coelenterates). Nor is it correct to say that the mesenchyme of the Radiata appears late in ontogeny, since in many cases we know that it begins immediately after entoderm differentiation; but apparently it may continue to arise throughout life. In the coelenterates the mesenchyme never forms anything but various types of connective tissue, as this phylum is characterized by the ectodermal and entodermal origin of its muscles.

The muscular system of the Cnidaria, composed of longitudinal and circular muscle cylinders, is the most generalized to be found among the Eumetazoa and constitutes the type plan from which the higher muscular systems are derivable. That the muscle fibers begin in coelenterates as parts of epithelial cells is also commonly regarded as a primitive character, but this interpretation seems rather doubtful since the muscle cells of sponges and of higher forms do not pass through such a stage; and the condition may be merely the consequence of the fact that in coelenterates, in the absence of a typical mesoderm, the muscles necessarily develop from differentiated epithelia. In all Eumetazoa above Cnidaria, muscle cells arise by the direct transformation of mesoderm cells.

The nervous system is also in a primitive stage of organization, consisting of a diffuse, unpolarized plexus with ganglion cells strewed throughout and without true nerves (i.e., bundles composed only of neurites). The process of concentration of the ganglion cells into a central nervous system with the neurites passing outside as nerves has barely begun in the coelenterates. The nervous system of coelenterates also differs from that of all other Eumetazoa in that it apparently originates from interstitial cells, which classify as a kind of mesenchyme, and not from the ectoderm, the usual source in Eumetazoa. The high degree of development of sense organs in medusae is worthy of note.

Concerning the origin of the Cnidaria, nothing definite can be said. It seems unavoidable to assume that they come from a gastraea type of organism, a ciliated (or flagellated?), polarized, free-swimming animal with an outer ectoderm and inner entoderm. Such an ancestry is strongly indicated by the occurrence throughout the phylum of the planula larva, i.e., a stereogastrula. The fact that the entoderm of the planula is seldom formed by invagination and mostly by some sort of delamination has been puzzling to phylogeneticists who adhere to the Haeckelian invaginate gastrula as the prototype of all the Metazoa. It has already been argued (page 250) that a mouthless stereogastrula might well have been the next stage after the blastula and may be represented in the coelenterate planula. Such an organism fed on minute prey that was passed to the interior mesenchymal cells for digestion, a method seen in sponges and not entirely abandoned by coelenterates (page 534). A mouth and archenteron might next have developed by rearrangement of entoderm cells if the stereogastrula took to feeding on the bottom, a habit generally assumed by phylogeneticists. The presence of a sensory center at the aboral pole may also be postulated, since many planulae show a greater development of nervous tissue at this pole than elsewhere, and some trachyline and anemone larvae bear an aboral tuft of sensory cilia. We thus picture as the remote eumetazoan ancestor a small rounded bottom-feeding organism with a ciliated surface, mouth, archenteron, and aboral sense organ. There were probably some mesenchyme cells of ectodermal origin between ectoderm and entoderm, and the archenteron may have had lateral pockets in which the sex cells ripened. Such a hypothetical organism has been named by Naef a *metagastraea*.

It is generally surmised that the coelenterate stock arose from the gastraea by the attachment of the latter at the aboral pole and its development into a hydra-like polyp (archhydra of Haeckel). This by asexual budding gave rise to hydroid colonies, which through division of labor became polymorphic; and some polyps were modified into medusae specialized for sexual reproduction and a pelagic life, to which mode of existence they owe their higher organization. This phylogenetic scheme places the Hydroida nearest the ancestral stock. This point of view raises many difficulties. It presents the curious spectacle of a lower type evolving into a higher type and continuing to exist simultaneously with it as part of its life cycle. Furthermore, no stages in this process are known, since all specialists on the Hydroida agree that the stem form of the Hydroida had already a fully developed alternation of generations. As remarked by Brooks, sessile animals are usually hermaphroditic, and the separation of the sexes in the Hydroida suggests their origin from a free-swimming type.

The contrary theory, that the ancestral coelenterate was a primitive medusa, therefore seems more acceptable. This could readily have developed from the metagastraea by putting forth tentacles and when thus armed for food capture would not have been limited to a bottom habitat. This primitive medusa seems still to be represented in the actinula larva of the Trachylina and, as long ago suggested by Brooks, the ontogeny of this group appears to repeat more nearly than that of other coelenterates the phylogenetic history. The trachyline medusae are thus the nearest of the hydrozoan groups to the stem line, although the present representatives must be regarded as somewhat specialized. At first in the Trachylina, the actinula larva develops directly into the adult medusa; then it gets the habit of budding off other actinulae larvae before completing its development; and finally as in *Microhydra* attaches and gives rise to small colonies, which bud off the adult medusae. All that is needed to produce a typical hydroid colony with alternation of generations is further development of the polypoid stage. The hydroid colony thus represents a persistent larval state. The occurrence in the Trachylina of but one kind of nematocyst is a primitive character; while the scalloped margin, gastric pockets, and tentaculocysts suggest the Scyphozoa.

According to Kühn, the stem form of the Hydroida must have had a small, unspecialized hydroid stage and a fully developed medusa stage. The life cycle of many Trachylina fits these requirements. From such a type, the athecate and thecate hydroids are believed to have diverged independently, and in the former group evolution proceeded in the direction from indefinite to definite tentacle arrangement. Thus in the athecate hydroids, Kühn recognizes two lines of evolution: first, from *Coryne* with strewn capitate tentacles through *Pennaria* with the proximal tentacles arranged in a circlet to the tubularians with the tentacles, now all filiform, limited to distal and proximal circlets; and, second, from *Clava* with strewn filiform tentacles through *Bougainvillia* to *Eudendrium* with a single circle. The thecate hydroids, arising independently of the Athecata, start with forms like *Campanulina*, with sympodial growth and vase-like thecae on stalks and lead to the sertularians and plumularians with sessile bilateral thecae and derived types of colony growth.

Once established, the hydroid and medusan stages, owing to their different modes of life, could evolve along independent lines, with the result that similar hydroids may have quite dissimilar medusae and vice versa. The different types of sessile gonophores found among the Hydroida are now universally regarded as degenerated medusae. The affinities of the fresh-water hydras are fairly evident. The hydras were formerly regarded as primitive coelenterates, but their high degree of histological differentiation and possession of four kinds of nematocysts belie this view. They are rather to be regarded as offshoots from the athecate hydroids which through adaptation to fresh-water life have lost all trace of a medusan stage.

According to Moser, the Siphonophora arose very early from the primitive medusa, soon became polymorphic, although the various persons never fully differentiated as they did in the Hydroida, and end blindly. The fact that the planula soon develops a swimming bell points to a medusan ancestry. The monophyids, small colonies with one swimming bell, are regarded as the most primitive types from which those with many bells and those with floats have been derived. The considerable differences between the persons of a siphonophore colony and those of a hydroid colony would seem to indicate that polymorphism had arisen independently in these two groups after each had diverged from the ancestral medusa, although Moser regards the Siphonophora as ancestral to the Hydrozoa. She believes that the poly-organs of the former by further differentiation became the poly-persons of the latter and that the medusoid gonophores evolved into an anthomedusa, foreshadowed in the free medusoids of *Porpita*. This view is not very convincing.

The Hydrozoa may thus have come from a primitive medusa, a tentaculate metagastraea, something like the present actinula larva, which early gave off a blind shoot, the Siphonophora, remaining wholly pelagic and developing its own type of polymorphism, and then evolved further into a medusa, whose polypoid larva adopted a sessile life and reproduced asexually into a small colony. The present Trachylina stand the closest to such a stem form and show stages in the establishment of a polypoid colony. Further development of the polypoid colony with retention of a fully developed medusa leads directly from the trachyline stem to the Hydroida.

The relationship of the Scyphozoa to the Hydrozoa is obscure, but it is not unreasonable to derive them from the trachyline stem since the scalloped margin, gastric pockets, and tentaculocysts already appear in the Narcomedusae. The general life history of the Scyphozoa and the modes of asexual propagation of the scyphistoma resemble those of the Trachylina. *Nausithoe* (Coronatae) has a branching larval stage resembling a hydroid colony (page 519), and one species of *Microhydra* (Trachylina) forms medusae from the polyp heads. The principal changes undergone by the Scyphozoa are the formation of septa, gastric filaments, and subumbrellar funnels, and these structures appear to have been initiated in the larval polyp stage and to have been carried over into the adult. The significance of the funnels remains enigmatical, but the other innovations seem to be correlated with a tendency to increase the digestive surface of the coelenteron. Small size must be a disadvantageous character, since increase in size from the more generalized to the more specialized members of a group is a common phenomenon. In forms like coelenterates with intracellular digestion, and no circulatory or respiratory systems, increase in size entails the invention of devices for insuring proper distribution of food and respiratory gases. Increase in size of the polyp stage interferes with proper contact of the food with the entoderm for intracellular digestion, and the projecting septa may be a device to meet this difficulty. The food cannot escape contact with the septal edges, which are known to specialize in extracellular digestion, aided by devices, such as the gastric filaments, for increasing the number of gland cells. In adult Scyphozoa, compensation for increased size is seen in the greater complexity of the gastrovascular system, which is the seat of currents for distributing food and respiratory gases, and in the substitution of the strong coronal muscle (derived from the subumbrellar fibers of hydromedusae) for the velum, a swimming organ suitable only for small forms.

The Stauromedusae were long regarded as ancestral to the other scyphozoan orders because of their polypoid characters; but these characters lose significance if the coelenterate stem form was a medusa. It seems more probable that the Stauromedusae represent a state of arrested development, a permanent post-larval stage, in which the oral end begins the process of alteration into a medusa but fails to complete the differentiation or to constrict off a free adult form. This accounts for the lack of rhopalia also. The very typical construction of the scyphistoma larva of the Stauromedusae indicates that this group, although not in the direct line of evolution of the higher scyphozoan orders, must be close to that line. The Cubomedusae are apparently the most primitive existing adult scyphozoans, as shown by their tetramerous symmetry and possession of fully developed septa, gastric pockets, subumbrellar funnels, rhopalia, and a marginal nerve ring. But it is difficult to relate them to the higher orders, and lack of knowledge of their development hinders their evaluation. The same may be said of the Coronatae, which seem, however, to be more nearly in the direct line of scyphozoan ascent. The Semaeostomeae and Rhizostomeae are clearly derived forms which in the adult have lost the septa, gastric pockets, and funnels and have specialized in the elongation of the mouth frills. The rhizostomes have obviously come from the semaeostomes by fusion of the mouth frills and loss of tentacles.

The tendency seen in various coelenterate groups toward emphasis of the polypoid stage, originally a larval stage, reaches its climax in the Anthozoa, where all trace of the medusa is lacking. The resemblance of the scyphistoma larva to the anthozoan polyp was early noted and led many to postulate a common stem for the Scyphozoa and the

Anthozoa. The septa are certainly entirely homologous in the two groups; the gastric and septal filaments probably correspond; in both, the gonads are borne on the septa, and the septa have retractor muscles, although these originate differently in the two groups; but one resemblance formerly postulated must now be withdrawn, since we know the scyphistoma has no stomodaeum. In addition, the gap between the tetramerous radial symmetry of the scyphistoma and the octomerous bilateral symmetry of the Anthozoa is difficult to bridge. Perhaps we may conclude that the scyphistoma and ancestral anthozoan have evolved along similar lines but are only remotely related. The significance of the septa may be explained on the same basis as above, as devices for increasing the amount of surface available for the secretion of digestive enzymes and for intracellular digestion. The Anthozoa have also met the necessity for a respiratory mechanism, when size increases, by means of the siphonoglyphs, whose formation may explain the elongation of the mouth and thereby the appearance of bilateral symmetry in the group.

As regards relationships within the Anthozoa, three lines of evolution are usually recognized: the antipatharian-cerianthid line, the alcyonarian line, and the zooanthid-anemone-coral group. Colony formation and skeleton production apparently arose independently many times within the Anthozoa, and their occurrence cannot be regarded as indicative of relationship. Formerly considered as degenerate anthozoans, the Antipatharia are now regarded as the most primitive living Anthozoa, and the remains of a very old group related to the cerianthids. Among their primitive characters are the simple arrangement of the septa and tentacles, the lack of special musculature, the lack of differentiation of the mesogloea, the slight development of the siphonoglyphs, which differ but little from the rest of the pharynx, and the absence of flagellated bands on the septal filaments. The relationship of the cerianthids to the Antipatharia is indicated by the strong resemblance of the cerinula larva to the latter; both have six septa in couples, of which the central tranverse couple is the largest, apparently the first formed, and the only fertile one of the three couples. Later the cerianthids diverge from the Antipatharia by the development of additional couples in the ventral interseptal space. Arguing from the primitive nature of the Antipatharia, some authors postulate as the ancestral anthozoan a small, solitary, skeletonless, weakly muscular polyp with six septa in couples and six simple tentacles. How this would be related to the tetramerous scyphistoma or the octomerous groups of Anthozoa is obscure; but it seems that the six septa represent the lateral couples and one pair of directives and would become eight by the addition of the other directives.

At any rate, it seems clear that the ancestor of the alcyonarian and zoanthid-anemone-coral lines was a small skeletonless polyp, with weak musculature, eight single septa in couples, and eight tentacles. Such a form leads directly to the Alcyonacea in which group evolution proceeds from forms with polyps connected only by basal stolons to those with a coenenchyme. The Gorgonacea come from the Alcyonacea by way of forms in which the skeletal spicules aggregate into an axial skeleton; and the Pennatulacea also derive from the Alcyonacea.

The position of the zoanthids in the zoanthid-anemone-coral line is not at all clear, but the history of the anemone-coral group can be stated with some plausibility. The universal occurrence in this group of an *Edwardsia* stage indicates as ancestor a *Gonactinia*-like form, a small weak anthozoan, without basilar muscles, retractors, sphincters, or flagellated bands on the filaments, with a complete ectodermal muscle layer and nerve plexus, with weakly developed siphonoglyphs, and eight complete septa arising in successive couples. In the next stage four incomplete microsepta pair with the four complete lateral septa to give a 12-septal stage. The *Edwardsias* remain permanently in this condition, and some workers derive the zoanthids at this point, since in them also the non-directive septal pairs consist of one macroseptum and one microseptum. The microseptal state of the dorsal directives in zoanthids would then be considered a degenerative change. In the anemone-coral line, the *Halcampoides* stage follows, in which four incomplete septa become complete, making a total of six complete pairs and changing the symmetry from a bilateral to a biradial condition. Somewhere about this time, the line split into the anemones, specializing in strong musculature and siphonoglyph differentiation, and the stony corals, weak, sedentary skeleton builders. Stephenson considers the madrepores readily derivable from two families of stichodactyline anemones, the Corallimorphidae and the Discosomidae. These may form sheet-like colonies by means of a basal coenenchyme, may reproduce by fission, are weak in musculature, with feeble or no retractors and sphincters, and no basilar muscles, have capitate or reduced tentacles, and lack siphonoglyphs and flagellated bands.

Opinions differ as to the relation of the extinct Tetracoralla to the existing anthozoan groups. Some workers consider them directly ancestral to the Madreporaria, but it is more probable that the latter arose from the anemones, as stated above, and that skeleton production originated independently in the two groups of corals. The Tetracoralla pass through a stage with six sclerosepta, and this may relate them to the antipatharian-cerianthid line and place them far back on the anthozoan stem. After the six-septal stage, new septa are added in the Tetracoralla in four locations (see page 621), two of which are the same as those to which septal formation is restricted in the zoanthids. This fact suggests an affinity of the zoanthids to the Tetracoralla and probably justifies the placing of the zoanthids at the bottom of the zoanthid-anemone-coral line rather than as an offshoot of anemones.

These phylogenetic speculations may be summarized by the diagram of Fig. 208, which is to be taken as conjectural.

Many suggestions have been offered as to the origin of bilaterality in the anthozoan stem. Some consider the condition correlated with colonial life, in that the surface facing the substratum might come to differ from the surface facing upward. Such an orientation of zooids is still seen in the Gorgonacea and the Pennatulacea. Others believe the

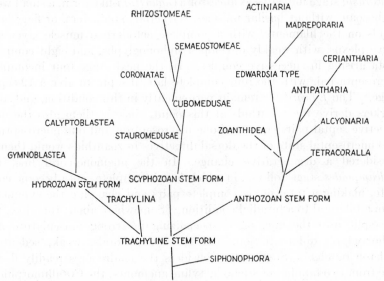

Fig. 208.—Diagram of coelenterate relationships; to be regarded as highly speculative.

bilateral symmetry could have resulted only from a creeping habit and therefore derive the Anthozoa from a creeping type. A third suggestion refers the bilaterality to the possible habit of primitive solitary anthozoans of lying upon or being attached by one side, as we know to have been the case with many Tetracoralla. The most probable cause, however, of bilaterality is the elongation of the mouth, which in turn seems to have happened because of the necessity of providing an ingoing respiratory current when the size of the gastrovascular cavity increased. A round mouth is obviously ill adapted for the maintenance of definite currents. If there was primitively but one siphonoglyph, as was almost certainly the case, a condition of bilateral symmetry is already established. It also seems probable that the stem form had three couples of septa, one at each end of the elongated mouth, and a transverse couple. Why the retractor muscles should face outward on the septal couple attached to the siphonoglyph has not been answered but may result from the necessity of providing space in the endocoel for the folding up of the siphonoglyph on contraction. This retractor arrangement then augments the bilaterality of the organism. The six-septal state is retained in many Antipatharia and is seen in young tetracorals, larval cerianthids, and probably larval zoanthids. A fourth couple was then added, giving the eight-septal stage retained in the Alcyonaria and passed through as the *Edwardsia* stage by all anemones and stony corals. The later history is clear from the ontogeny of the anemone-coral group and consists in the change of the septal arrangement from a coupled to a paired condition. The original number of pairs was six (*Halcampa* stage); but almost any number of additional pairs may be formed in various anemone groups. The pairing of the septa imposes a biradial symmetry upon the ancient bilateral symmetry.

Bibliography

General

Allman, G. J. 1872. Monograph of the Gymnoblastic or Tubularian hydroids. Ray Society. **Bodansky, M.** 1924. Digestion in coelenterates. Amer. Jour. Physiol. 67. **Bodansky, M.,** and **W. C. Rose.** 1922. Digestive enzymes of coelenterates. Amer. Jour. Physiol. 62. **Bozler, E.** 1927. Nervensystem der Coelenteraten: Kontinuität oder Kontact. Ztschr. Zellforsch. Mikros. Anat. 5. **Brooks, W. K.** 1886. Origin of medusae and significance of metagenesis. Boston Soc. Nat. Hist. Mem. 3. **Cantacuzène, J.** 1925, 1934. Action toxique des poisons d'Adamsia palliata. Soc. Biol. [Paris], Compt. Rend. 92, 117. **Chapeaux, M.** 1893. Digestion des Coelentérés. Arch. Zool. Expt. Gén. Ser. 3, Vol. 1. **Cosmovici, N. L.** 1925. Action convulsivante des poisons d'Adamsia. Soc. Biol. [Paris], Compt. Rend. 92. **Crutchfield, E. O.** 1925. Dermatitis from Portuguese man-of-war. Arch. Dermat. Syph. 12. **Dawydoff, C.** 1904. Hydroctena. Acad. Imp. Sci. St. Pétersbourg, Mém., Ser. 8, Vol. 14. **Ehrenberg, C.** 1833. Beiträge zur Kenntnis der Korallenthiere des Rothen Meeres. Abhandl. König. Akad. Wiss. Berlin. **Eschscholtz, F.** 1829. System der Acalephen. **Ewald, A.** 1915. Nesselkapseln von Hydra und Porpita. Naturh. Med. Ver. Heidelberg, Verhandl. 13. **Gelei, J. von.** 1927. Das Rätsel der Nesselzellen. Biol. Zentbl. 47. **Glaser, O. C.,** and **C. M. Sparrow.** 1909. Physiology of nematocysts. Jour. Expt. Zool. 6. **Groselji, P.** 1909. Nervensystem der Aktinien. Arb. Zool. Inst., Univ. Wien. 17. **Hargitt, C. W.** 1904. Medusae of the Woods Hole region. U. S. Bur. Fisheries, Bul. 24. **Harvey, E. N.** 1921. Luminescence in the coelenterates. Biol. Bul. 41. **Havet, J.** 1901. Système nerveux chez des Actinies. La Cellule 18. **Hertwig, O.,** and **R. Hertwig.** 1877. Nervensystem und Sinnesorgane der Medusen. Jenaische Ztschr. Naturw. 11. 1878. Das Nervensystem und die Sinnesorgane der Medusen. Leipzig. 1880. Die Organismus der Medusen und seine Stellung zur Keimblättertheorie. Jenaische Med. Naturw. Denkschr. Gesell. 2. **Huxley, T. H.** 1856. Lectures on general natural history. Med. Times Gaz. 12, 13. **Hyde, I.** 1902. Nervous system in Gonionema. Biol. Bul. 4. **Iwanzoff, N.** 1896. Nesselkapseln der Coelenteraten. Soc. Imp. Nat. Moskau, Bul. 10. **Krasinska. S.** 1914. Zur Histologie der Medusen. Ztschr. Wiss. Zool. 109. **Loeb, J.** 1891. Untersuchungen zur physiologischen Morphologie der Tiere. **Martin, C. H.** 1914. Occurrence of nematocysts and similar structures in the various groups of the animal kingdom. Biol. Zentbl. 34. **Mayer, A. G.** 1900. Some medusae from the Tortugas. Harvard Univ., Mus. Compar. Zool. Bul. 37. 1910. Medusae of the World. 3 vols. Carnegie Inst. Wash. **McConnell, C. H.** 1932. Development of the ectodermal nerve net in the buds of Hydra. Quart. Jour. Micros. Sci. 75. **Okado, Yo K.** 1932. Regeneration of Coelenterata. Kyoto Univ., Col. Sci. Mem. Ser. B, 7. **Pappenfuss, E. J.,** and **N. Bokenham.** 1939. Fate of the ectoderm and entoderm of Hydra when cultured independently. Biol. Bul. 76. **Parker, G. H.** 1919. The elementary nervous system. **Pawlowsky, E. N.** 1927. Gifttiere und ihre Giftigkeit. Jena. **Peyssonel, J. A.** 1856. Coral insects. Roy. Soc. London, Phil. Trans. 47. **Poche, E.** 1914. Das System der Coelenterata. Arch. Naturgesch. 80, Abt. A, Heft 5. **Portier, Richet,** and others. Articles on nematocyst poisons in Acad. Sci. Paris, Compt. Rend. 134, and Soc. Biol. [Paris], Compt. Rend. 54. **Reisinger, E.** 1937. Der Entladungsvorgang der Nesselkapseln. Zool. Anz. Sup. 10. **Romanes, G. J.** 1885. Jelly-fish, starfish, and sea-urchins. **Schulze, P.** 1922. Penetranten von Hydra. Arch. Zellforsch. 16. **Thiel, M. E.** 1935. Wirkung des Nesselgiftes der Quallen auf den Menschen. Ergeb. Fortsch. Zool. 8. **Toppe, O.** 1910. Bau- und Nesselzellen der Cnidarien. Zool. Jahrb., Abt. Anat. Ontog. Tiere 29. **Vernon, H. M.** 1899. Respiratory exchange of the lower marine invertebrates. Jour. Physiol. 19. **Wade, H. W.** 1928. Post-mortem findings in acute jelly-fish poisoning. Amer. Jour. Trop. Med. 8. **Weill, R.** 1923. Numerous articles on nematocysts in Soc. Biol. [Paris], Compt. Rend. 89, 92, 94; Acad. Sci. Paris, Compt. Rend. 180, 182. 1929. New results from the study of coelenterate nematocysts. Nation. Acad. Sci. Wash., Proc. 15. 1930. Classification des nematocystes. Bul. Biol. France Belg. 64. 1934. Contribution a l'étude des Cnidaires et de leurs nematocystes. Trav. Stat. Zool. Wimereux. 10, 11. 1935. Protistes commensaux ou parasites des Cnidaires. Arch. Zool. Expt. Gén. 77. **Weismann, R.** 1915. Accidents graves consecutifs aux piqures des Meduses. Soc. Biol. [Paris], Compt. Rend. 78. **Will, L.** 1909. Kontraktile Elemente in den Nesselzellen. Naturf. Gesell. Rostock, Sitzber. Abhandl., 1909. Die Klebkapseln der Aktinien. Naturf. Gesell. Rostock, Sitzber. Abhandl. **Wolff, M.** 1904. Das Nervensystem der polypoiden Hydrozoen. Ztschr. Allg. Physiol. 3. **Zervos, S.** 1903. La Maladie des pécheurs d'éponges. Semaine Medicale 23. **Zick, C.** 1929, 1932. Wirkung der Nesselkapseln auf Protozoen. Zool. Anz. 83, 98.

HYDROIDA

Abonyi, A. 1929. Protohydra. Internatl. Cong. Zool. Budapest. **Agassiz, A.** 1865. North American Acalephae. **Allen, C. M.** 1900. Development of Parypha (Tubularia). Biol. Bul. 1. **Allman, G. J.** 1875. Myriothela. Roy. Soc. London, Phil. Trans. 165, Pt. 2. **Ashworth, J. H.,** and **J. Ritchie.** 1915. Free-swimming sporosacs of Dicoryne. Roy. Soc. Edinb. Trans. 51. **Beadle, L. C.,** and **F. A. Booth.** 1938. Reorganization of tissue masses of Cordylophora. Jour. Expt. Biol. 15. **Berninger, J.** 1910. Einwirkung des Hungers auf Hydra. Zool. Anz. 36. **Beutler, R.** 1924. Verdauung bei Hydra. Ztschr. Vergleich. Physiol. 1. 1926. Beobachtungen an gefütterten Hydroidpolypen. Ztschr. Vergleich. Physiol. 3. 1927. Die Wasserstoffionkonzentration im Magen der Hydra. Ztschr. Vergleich. Physiol. 6. **Bigelow, H.** 1909. Albatross Medusae. Harvard Univ., Mus. Compar. Zool. Mem. 37. **Billard, A.** 1903. Excrétion chez les Hydroides. Acad. Sci.

Paris, Compt. Rend. 137. 1904. Contribution a l'étude des Hydroides. Ann. Sci. Nat. Zool. Ser. 8, Vol. 20. **Blackburn, W.** 1898. Myriothela. Manchester Micros. Soc. Trans. **Boecker, E.** 1914. Depression und Missbildung bei Hydra. Zool. Anz. 44. **Boulenger, C.** 1910. Origin and migration of the stinging cells in craspedote medusae. Quart. Jour. Micros. Sci. 55. **Braem, F.** 1908. Die Knospen der Margeliden. Biol. Zentbl. 28. **Brauer, A.** 1891. Entwicklung von Hydra. Ztschr. Wiss. Zool. 52. **Briggs, E. A.** 1927. Myriothela. Austral. Mus. Rec. 16. **Broch, H.** 1916. Hydroida I, II. Dan. Ingolf Exped. V. 1917. Craspedote Medusen. Nord. Plankton Lief. 21. **Brooks, W. K.** 1887. Life history of Epenthesis McCradyi. Johns Hopkins Univ., Studies Biol. Lab. 4. 1895. Cordyli of Laodice. Jour. Morph. 10. **Browne, E.** 1909. Lateral grafts in hydra. Jour. Expt. Zool. 7. **Browne, E. T.** 1896. On British hydroids and medusae. Zool. Soc. London. Proc. **Burch, P. R.** 1928. Endodermal flagella of Hydra. Biol. Bul. 54. **Bulman, O. M. B.** 1927. Monograph of British dendroid graptolites. Palaeontol. Soc. London. 1938. Graptolithina. Handbuch der Paläozoologie. Lief. 2. **Buntung, M.** 1894. Origin of the sex cells in Hydractinia and Podocoryne. Jour. Morph. 9. **Child, C. M.** 1907–1909. Form-regulation in Tubularia. Arch. Entwickl. Mech. Organ. 23, 24. 1914–1921. Axial gradients of Hydrozoa. Biol. Bul. 36, 37, 41. 1923. Axial transformations in hydroids. Biol. Bul. 45. 1925. Modification of development. Biol. Bul. 48. 1926. Axial gradients of Corymorpha. Biol. Gen. 2. 1927. Modification of polarity and symmetry in Corymorpha. Jour. Expt. Zool. 47, 48. 1928. Axial development in aggregations of dissociated cells from Corymorpha. Physiol. Zool 1. 1929. Lateral grafts and incisions as organizers in Corymorpha. Physiol. Zool. 2. 1932. Determinations of new axes by lateral grafts and incisions in Corymorpha. Physiol. Zool. 5. 1935. Dominance of hydranths induced by grafts in Corymorpha. Jour. Expt. Zool. 71. **Child, C. M.** and **O. Rulon.** 1937. Developmental pattern in Pelmatohydra oligactis. Physiol. Zool. 10. **Chun, C.** 1896. Die Knospungsgesetze der proliferiernden Medusen. Biblioth. Zool. 7, Heft 19. **Citron, E.** 1902. Beiträge zur Kenntnis der feineren Baues von Syncoryne. Arch. Naturgesch. 68. **Collcutt, M. C.** 1898. Structure of Hydractinia. Quart. Jour. Micros. Sci. 40. **Congdon, E.** 1906. Morphology and development of Eudendrium. Biol. Bul. 11. **Damas, H.** 1934. Hydrichthys. Soc. Roy. Hist. Nat. Belg. Bul. 10. 1936. Oönautes. Soc. Roy. Liège, Mém. Ser. 4, Vol. 1. **De Morgan, W.** and **Drew, G. H.** 1914. Restitution masses formed by the dissociated cells of Antennularia. Jour. Mar. Biol. Assoc. 10. **Dendy, A.** 1902. Pelagohydra mirabilis. Quart. Jour. Micros. Sci. 46. **Driesch, H.** 1897, 1899. Studien über das Regulationsvermögen der Organismen (Tubularia). Arch. Entwickl. Mech. Organ. 5, 9. **Fewkes, J. W.** 1881. Jelly-fish of Narragansett Bay. Harvard Univ., Mus. Compar. Zool. Bul. 8. **Föyn, B.** 1927. Geschlecht und Geschlechtszellen bei Hydroiden. Arch. Entwickl. Mech. Organ. 109, 110. **Franz, V.** 1937. Füssoffnung an Hydra. Biol. Zentbl. 57. **Fraser, C. M.** 1910. Some hydroids of Beaufort, N. C. U. S. Bur. Fisheries, Bul. 30. 1911. Hydroids of the west coast of N. A. Iowa State Univ., Lab. Nat. Hist. Bul. 6. 1914. Some hydroids of the Vancouver Island region. Roy. Soc. Canada, Proc. Trans. Ser. 3, Vol. 8. 1916. Development of Aequorea. Roy. Soc. Canada, Proc. Trans. Vol. 10. **Frischholz, E.** 1909. Biologie von Hydra. Biol. Zentbl. 29. **Gast, R.,** and **E. Godlewski.** 1903. Regulationserscheinungen bei Pennaria. Arch. Entwickl. Mech. Organ. 16. **Gelei, J. von.** 1924. Cytologie der Hydra. Ztschr. Zellforsch. Mikros. Anat. 1. 1925. Morphologische und physiologische Gliederung des Körpers unsere Süsswasser. polypen. Zool. Anz. 64. **Gemmill, J. F.** 1919. Ciliation of Melicertidium. Zool. Soc. London, Proc. 1921. Life history of Melicertidium. Quart. Jour. Micros. Sci. 65. **Gilchrist, F.** 1937. Corymorpha as Gestalt and as history.

Amer. Nat. 71. **Gilchrist, J.** 1919. On Eleutheria. Quart. Jour. Micros. Sci. 63.
Goette, A. 1907. Vergleichende Entwicklungsgeschichte der Geschlechtsindividuen der Hydropolypen. Ztschr. Wiss. Zool. 87. 1916. Podocoryne, Stylactis, und Hydractinia. Zool. Jahrb., Abt. System. Geog. Ökol. Tiere 39. **Goetsch, W.** 1919–1920. Neue Beobachtungen und Versuche an Hydra. Biol. Zentbl. 39, 40. 1921. Nahrungsaufnahme, Regeneration, und Fortpflanzung bei Hydren. Naturwissenschaften 9. 1921, 1922. Unsterblichkeit, Lebensdauer und geschlechtliche Fortpflanzung bei Hydren. Biol. Zentbl. 41, 42. 1926. Geschlechtsbestimmung bei Hydra. Biol. Zentbl. 46. 1927. Geschlechtsverhältnisse der Süsswasserhydroiden. Arch. Entwickl. Mech. Organ. 111. **Goldfarb, A. J.** 1907. Regeneration of Eudendrium. Jour. Expt. Zool. 4. **Greenwood, M.** 1888. Digestion in Hydra. Jour. Physiol. 9. **Gross, J.** 1925. Biologie der Hydriden. Biol. Zentbl. 45. **Gudger, E. W.** 1925. Association between sessile colonial hydroids and fishes. Ann. Mag. Nat. Hist. Ser. 10, Vol. 1. 1927. Hydras as enemies of young fishes. Nat. Hist. 27. **Günther, O.** 1903. Structures and affinities of Mnestra. Mitt. Zool. Stat. Neapel 16. **Haase-Eichler, R.** 1931. Reizphysiologie von Hydra. Zool. Jahrb., Abt. Allg. Zool. Physiol. Tiere 50. **Hadzi, J.** 1906. Biologie von Hydra. Arch. Entwickl. Mech. Organ. 22. 1909. Nervensystem von Hydra. Univ. Wien., Arb. Zool. Inst. 17. Die Entstehung der Knospen bei Hydra. Univ. Wien., Arb. Zool. Inst. 18. **Hargitt, C. W.** 1900. Development of Pennaria. Amer. Nat. 34; Arch. Entwickl. Mech. Organ. 18. 1904. Development of Eudendrium. Zool. Jahrb., Abt. Anat. Ontog. Tiere 20. 1906. Organization and early development of the egg of Clava. Biol. Bul. 10. 1915. Regeneration potencies of dissociated cells of Hydromedusae. Biol. Bul. 28. **Hargitt, G. T.** 1902. Regeneration of Gonionemus. Biol. Bul. 4. 1918, 1919. Germ cells of coelenterates. Jour. Morph. 31, 33. **Harm, K.** 1903. Entwicklungsgeschichte von Clava. Ztschr. Wiss. Zool. 73. **Hartlaub, C.** 1897. Hydromedusae Helgolands. Helgoland Wiss. Meeresuntersuch. Biol. Anstalt, New Ser. 2. 1907–1917. Craspedote Medusen. Nord. Plankton, Lief. 6, 12, 16, 19. **Hazen, A.** 1902. Regeneration in Hydractinia and Podocoryne. Amer. Nat. 36. **Hertwig, R.** 1906. Über Knospung und Geschlechtsentwicklung von Hydra. Biol. Zentbl. 26. **Hickson, S. J.** 1920. Protohydra in England. Quart. Jour. Micros. Sci. 64. 1925. Hydra and the tadpoles. Nature 115. **Hincks, T.** 1868. A history of the British hydroid zoophytes. **Holm, G.** 1890. Graptoliter. Bihang til K. Svenska Vetensk. Akad. Handl. 16. **Huxley, J. S., and G. De Beer.** 1923. Resorption and differential inhibition in Obelia and Campanularia. Quart. Jour. Micros. Sci. 67. **Hyman, L. H.** 1928. Observations on Hydra. Biol. Bul. 54. 1929. Taxonomic Studies on the hydras of North America. Amer. Micros. Soc. Trans. 48, 49, 50. Amer. Mus. Novitates No. 1003. **Ishiwaka, C.** 1890. Trembley's Umkehrungsversuche an Hydra nach neuen Versuchen erklärt. Ztschr. Wiss. Zool. 49. **Issajew, V.** 1926. Untersuchungen an Hydren. Arch. Entwickl. Mech. Organ. 108. **Jickeli, C. F.** 1882. Die Bau der Hydroidpolypen. Morph. Jahrb. 8. **Kanajew, J.** 1926. Histologische Vorgänge bei der Regeneration von Pelmatohydra. Zool. Anz. 65. Bau des Entoderm im Mundkegel von Pelmatohydra. Zool. Anz. 67. 1927. Porus aboralis bei Pelmatohydra. Zool. Anz. 76. Wiederbildung der Fussscheibe bei Hydra. Zool. Anz. 81. 1930. Bedeutung der interstitiellen Zellen bei Hydra. Arch. Entwickl. Mech. Organ. 122. 1935. Regeneration von complantierten Stücken der Pelmatohydra. Acad. Sci. U. S. S. R., Compt. Rend. 3. **Kepner, W. A.,** et al. 1926. Nutrition of the ovum of Hydra viridis. Biol. Bul. 50. 1928. A new histological region in Hydra. Biol. Bul. 54. Histological features correlated with gas secretion in Hydra. Biol. Bul. 54. 1938. The place of origin and the manipulation of cnidoblasts in Chlorohydra. Zool. Anz. 121. **King, H. D.** 1901, 1903. Regeneration in Hydra. Arch. Entwickl. Mech. Organ. 13, 16. 1904.

Regeneration in Tubularia. Biol. Bul. 6. **Kleinenberg, N.** 1872. Hydra. Leipzig. **Koch, W.** 1911. Geschlechtsbildung und Gonochorismus von Hydra. Biol. Zentbl. 31. **Koelitz, W.** 1908. Querteilung bei Hydra. Zool. Anz. 33. 1909. Längsteilung und Doppelbildungen bei Hydra. Zool. Anz. 35. 1910. Untersuchungen an Hydra. Arch. Entwickl. Mech. Organ. 31. **Koller, G.** 1927. Geschlechtliche Fortpflanzung der Protohydra. Zool. Anz. 73. **Kühn, A.** 1909. Sprosswachstum und Polypenknospung bei den Thecaphoren. Zool. Jahrb., Abt. Anat. Ontog. Tiere. 28. 1910. Die Entwicklung der Geschlechtsindividuen der Hydromedusen. Zool. Jahrb., Abt. Anat. Ontog. Tiere 30. 1913. Entwicklungsgeschichte und Verwandtschaftsbeziehungen der Hydrozoen. Ergeb. Fortschr. Zool. 4. **Kramp, P. L.** 1933. Craspedote Medusen. Part 3. Leptomedusen. Nord. Plankton, Lief. 22. **Leiber, A.** 1909. Längsteilung bei Hydra. Zool. Anz. 34. **Lebour, M. L.** 1930. Protohydra, a very simple animal. Sci. Prog. 25. **Lendenfeld, R.** 1883. Über Wehrpolypen und Nesselzellen. Ztschr. Wiss. Zool. 38. **Linko, O.** 1899. Observations sur les Méduses. Soc. Imp. Nat., St. Pétersbourg, Trav. 29. 1900. Bau der Augen bei den Hydromedusen. Acad. Imp. Sci. St. Pétersbourg, Mém. Ser. 8. Vol. 10. **Lloyd, R.** 1908. Nudiclava, type of a new hydroid parasitic on fish. Indian Museum, Rec. 1. **Lowe, E.** 1926. Embryology of Tubularia. Quart. Jour. Micros. Sci. 70. **Lund, E. J.** 1921. Experimental control of organic polarity by the electric current. Jour. Expt. Zool. 34. **Luther, A.** 1923. Protohydra. Acta Soc. Fauna Flora Fenn. 52. **Marshall, S.** 1923. Behavior and structure of Hydra. Quart. Jour. Micros. Sci. 67. **May, A. J.** 1903. Morphology of Corymorpha. Amer. Nat. 37. **McConnell, C. H.** 1935. Formation of the shell around the embryo of Hydra. Arch. Entwickl. Mech. Organ. 132. 1936. Mitosis in Hydra. Arch. Entwickl. Mech. Organ. 135. 1938. Discharge of the peristomal glands of Hydra. Zool. Anz. 121. 1938. The hatching of Pelmatohydra eggs. Zool. Anz. 123. **Merejkowsky, C.** 1883. Histoire du développement de la méduse Obelia. Soc. Zool. France, Bul. 8. **Metschnikoff, C.** 1886. Embryological Studien an Medusen. Vienna. **Miles, S. S.** 1936. New tubularian hydroid. Bul. Mt. Desert Island Biol. Lab. 1937. New genus of hydroid and its asexual reproduction. Biol. Bul. 72. **Miller, D. E.** 1936. Limnological study of Pelmatohydra. Amer. Micros. Soc. Trans. 55. **Miyajima, M.,** 1900. Specimen of a gigantic hydroid Branchiocerianthus imperatur. Tokyo Imp. Univ., Col. Sci. Jour. 13. **Morgan, T. H.** 1900–1906. Regeneration in Tubularia. Arch. Entwickl. Mech. Organ. 11, 13, 16. Jour. Expt. Zool. 1, 3. **Morgenstern, P.** 1901. Entwicklung von Cordylophora. Ztschr. Wiss. Zool. 70. **Moser, J.** 1930. Microhydra. Gesell. Naturf. Freunde Berlin Sitzber. 1929. **Motz-Kossowska, S.** 1905. Hydraires gymnoblastiques de la Méditerranée. Arch. Zool. Expt. Gén. Ser. 4, Vol. 3. **Müller, H. C.** 1913. Regeneration der Gonophore bei den Hydroiden. Arch. Entwickl. Mech. Organ. 37, 38. **Müller-Calé, K.,** and **E. Kruger.** 1913. Entwicklung von Aglaophenia, und Sertularella. Mitt. Zool. Stat. Neapel 21. Symbiotische Algen bei Aglaophenia und Sertularella. Mitt. Zool. Stat. Neapel 21. **Murbach, L.** 1899. Hydroids from Woods Hole. Quart. Jour. Micros. Sci. 42. **Mutz, E.** 1930. Transplantationsversuche an Hydra. Arch. Entwickl. Mech. Organ. 121. **Nussbaum, M.** 1909. Über Geschlechtsvildung bei Polypen. Arch. gesam. Physiol. Mensch. Tiere 130. **Nutting, C. C.** 1899. Hydroida from Alaska and Puget Sound. U. S. Nat. Mus., Proc. 21. The hydroids of the Woods Hole region. U. S. Comm. Fish. Bul. 1900, 1904, 1915. American hydroids. Part I. Plumulariidae. Part II. Sertularidae. Part III. Campanularidae and Bonneviellidae. Smithsn. Inst. Spec. Bul. **Okada, Yo K.** 1927. Régénération chez les Coelentérés. Arch. Zool. Expt. Gén. 66. **Papenfuss, E.** 1934. Reunition of pieces in hydra. Biol. Bul. 67. **Parke, H. H.** 1900. Variation and regulation of abnormalities in hydra. Arch. Entwickl. Mech. Organ. 10. **Parker, G. H.** 1917. Activities of Corymorpha. Jour. Expt. Zool. 24. **Parker, T. J.** 1879. Histology of hydra. Roy. Soc. London, Proc. 30. **Pauly, R.** 1900. Bau und Lebensweise von Cordylophora. Zool. Anz. 23. Jenaische Ztschr. Naturw. 36. **Pearse, A. S.** 1906. Reactions of Tubularia. Amer. Nat. 40. **Peebles, F.** 1897–1905. Regeneration and grafting in Hydrozoa. Arch. Entwickl. Mech. Organ. 5, 10, 14. Jour. Expt. Zool. 5. **Perkins, H. F.** 1904. Hybocodon. Amer. Nat. 38. **Philbert, M.** 1934. Gonothèques femelles de Diphasia. Bul. Inst. Oceanogr. Monaco 647. **Pictet, C.,** and **M. Dedot.** 1900. Hydraires. Result. Campagnes Sci. Albert I. Monaco. fasc. 18. **Place, J. A.** 1917. Morphology, structure, and development of Hydractinia. Amer. Micros. Soc. Trans. 36. **Rand, H. W.** 1899. Regeneration and regulation in hydra. Arch. Entwickl. Mech. Organ. 8, 9. 1911. Problem of form in hydra. Science 33. **Rand, H. W., J. F. Bovard,** and **D. E. Minnich.** 1926. Location of formative agencies in hydra. Nation. Acad. Sci. Wash., Proc. 12. **Ranson, G.** 1937. Cnidactines et cnidothylacies chez les Anthomédusae. Soc. Zool. France, Bul. 62. **Rees, W. J.** 1937. Remarkable process of bud formation (Heterostephanus). Jour. Mar. Biol. Assoc. 21. 1938. British and Norwegian hydroids. Jour. Mar. Biol. Assoc. 23. **Reisinger, E.** 1937. Entladungsvorgang der Nesselkapsel. Zool. Anz. Sup. 10. **Roch, F.** 1924. Cordylophora. Ztschr. Morph. Ökol. Tiere 2. **Roskin, G.** 1922. Bau der Epithel-Muskelzellen von Hydra. Anat. Anz. 56. **Roudabush, R. L.** 1933. Phenomenon of regeneration in everted hydra. Biol Bul. 64. **Rulon, O.,** and **C. M. Child.** 1937. Developmental pattern in Pelmatohydra. Physiol. Zool. 10. **Ruedemann, R.** 1895. Development of the graptolite Diplograptus. Amer. Jour. Sci., Ser. 3, Vol. 49. 1904. Graptolites of N. Y. N. Y. State Mus., Mem. 7. **Runnström, J.** 1929. Histophysiologie von Clava. Acta Zool. 10. **Rittenhouse, S.** 1910. Embryology of Stomotoca. Jour. Expt. Zool. 9. **Russell, E. S.** 1906. Trichorhiza. Zool. Soc. London, Proc. pt. 1. 1938. Nematocysts of hydromedusae. Jour. Mar. Biol. Assoc. 23. **Ryder, T. A.** 1885. Microhydra. Amer. Nat. 19. **Saint-Hilaire, K.** 1930. Periderm der Hydroiden. Zool. Jahrb., Abt. Allg. Zool. Physiol. Tiere 47. **Schijfsma, K.** 1935. Hydractinia und Eupagurus. Arch. Néerland. Zool. 1. **Schneider, G.** 1926. Protohydra. Zool. Anz. 68. **Schuberg, A.** 1905. Süsswasserpolypen als Forellenfeinde. Allg. Fischerei Zeit. 11. **Schulze, P.** 1917. Monographie der Gattung Hydra. Arch. Biontologie 4. **Smallwood, M.** 1899. Pennaria. Amer. Nat. 33. 1909. Cytology of Hydractinia and Pennaria. Biol. Bul. 17. **Spencer, W. B.** 1890. Clathrozoon. Roy. Soc. Victoria, Trans. 2. **Splettstösser, W.** 1929. Zur Kenntnis der Sertulariden. Zool. Jahrb., Abt. System. Geog. Biol. Tiere 58. **Stechow, E.** 1909. Hydroidpolypen der Japanischen Ostküste. Akad. Wiss. München, Abhandl. Sup. 1. 1929. Symbiosen von Hydrozoen mit Polychaeten. Zool. Anz. 86. **Stevens, N. M.** 1906. Regeneration in Antennularia. Arch. Entwickl. Mech. Organ. 15, 30. **Strelin, G.** 1936. Physiologische Gradient Pelmatohydra. Arch. Russ. Anat. Histol. Embryol. 15. **Tannreuther, G. W.** 1908. Development of Hydra. Biol. Bul. 14. 1909. Green cells of hydra. Biol. Bul. 16. Budding in hydra. Biol. Bul. 16. **Teissier, L.,** and **G. Teissier,** 1928. Développement d'Hydractinia. Soc. Zool. France, Bul. 52. 1930. Polarité et localizations germinales de l'oeuf des Hydraires. Soc. Biol. [Paris], Compt. Rend. 105. **Thacher, H. F.** 1903. Absorption of hydranths of hydroid polyps. Biol. Bul. 4. **Torrey, H. B.** 1902. Hydroida of the Pacific Coast. Calif. Univ., Pubs. Zool. 1. 1904. Studies on Corymorpha. Jour. Expt. Zool. 1; Calif. Univ., Pubs. Zool. 3, 6; Biol. Bul. 19. 1905. Behavior of Corymorpha. Calif. Univ., Pubs. Zool. 2. 1905. Differentiation in hydroid colonies and senescence. Calif. Univ., Pubs. Zool. 2. 1909. Leptomedusae of the San Diego region. Calif. Univ., Pubs. Zool. 6. 1910. Differentiation in hydroid colonies. Biol.

Bul. 18. 1912. Oxygen and polarity in Tubularia. Calif. Univ., Pubs. Zool. 9. **Trembley, A.** 1744. Mémoires pour servir a l'histoire d'un genre de polypes d'eau douce. Leiden. **Tripp, K.** 1928. Die Regenerationsfähigkeit von Hydra. Ztschr. Wiss. Zool. 132. **Uchida, T.** 1927. Japanese Hydromedusae. Tokyo Univ. Facult. Sci. Jour. Sect. 4, Pt. 1; Jap. Jour. Zool. 2. **Wager, R. E.** 1909. Oögenesis and early development of hydra. Biol. Bul. 18. **Wagner, G.** 1905. Movements and reactions of hydra. Quart. Jour. Micros. Sci. 48. **Warren, E.** 1906. Tubularia solitaria. Natal Mus. Ann. 1. 1909. Lafoea dispolians, parasitic on Sertularia. Natal Mus. Ann. 2. 1916. On Hydrichthys boycei. Durban Mus. Ann. 1. **Weill, R.** 1926. Cnidome specifique caractéristique de l'état larvaire. Soc. Zool. France, Bul. 51. 1936. Cnidome des Cladonémides. Acad. Sci. Paris, Compt. Rend. 203. 1937. Cladonema. Bull. Biol. France et Belg. 71. **Weismann, A.** 1883. Die Entstehung der Sexualzellen bei den Hydromedusen. Jena. **Weese, A. S., and M. T. Townsend.** 1921. Reactions of the jellyfish Aequorea. Puget Sound Biol. Sta. Pub. 3. **Welch, P. S., and H. A. Loomis.** 1924. Limnological study of Hydra in Douglas Lake, Mich. Amer. Micros. Soc. Trans. 43. **Wermel, E.** 1926. Cytologische Studien an Hydra. Ztschr. Zellforsch. Mikros. Anat. 4. **Westblad, E.** 1930. Geschlechtsorgane von Protohydra. Arkiv Zool. 21.A. 1935. Protohydra. Zool. Anz. 111. **Whitney, D. D.** 1907. Influence of external factors in causing the development of sex organs in Hydra viridis. Arch. Entwickl. Mech. Organ. 24. Artificial removal of the green bodies in Hydra viridis. Biol. Bul. 13, 15. **Wilson, H. V.** 1911. Behavior of the dissociated cells of hydroids. Jour. Expt. Zool. 11. **Wulfert, J.** 1902. Die Embryonalentwicklung von Gonothyrea. Ztschr. Wiss. Zool. 71. **Zoja, R.** 1895. Sullo sviluppo dei blastomeri isolate delle uove di alcune Meduse. Arch. Entwickl. Mech. Organ. 1.

MILLEPORINA

Hickson, S. J. 1888. Sexual cells and early development of Millepora. Roy. Soc. London, Phil. Trans. 179 B. 1891. Medusae of Millepora. Quart. Jour. Micros. Sci. 32. 1898. Genus Millepora. Zool. Soc. London, Proc. 1900. Medusae of Millepora. Roy. Soc. London, Proc. 66. 1902. Report on the genus Millepora. Zool. Results from New Britain, New Guinea, etc. Collect. by A. Willey. **Moseley, H. N.** 1877. On the structure of Millepora. Roy. Soc. London, Phil. Trans. 167. **Rice, W. N.** 1878. Animal of Millepora. Amer. Jour. Sci. 16.

STYLASTERINA

Broch, H. 1936. Untersuchungen an Stylasteridae. Norske Vedensk. Akad. Oslo. Math. Nat. Kl. Skr. 2, art. 8. **England, H.** 1926. Development of gonophores of the Stylasteridae. Zool. Soc. London, Proc. **Fisher, W. K.** 1931. California hydrocorals. Ann. Mag. Nat. Hist., Ser. 10, Vol. 8. 1938. Hydrocorals of the North Pacific Ocean. U. S. Natl. Mus. Proc. 84. **Hickson, S. J., and H. England.** 1904. Stylasterina of the Siboga Expedition. Siboga Exped. 8. **Hickson, S. J.** 1909. Stylasterina. Cambridge Nat. Hist. 1. **Moseley, H. N.** 1878. Structure of the Stylasteridae. Roy. Soc. London, Phil. Trans. 169, pt. 2.

TRACHYLINA

Bennitt, R. 1930. Craspedacusta in Missouri with a summary of the American records to date. Amer. Nat. 66. **Bigelow, H. B.** 1909. Albatross Medusae. Harvard Univ., Mus. Compar. Zool. Mem. 37. **Boulenger, C. L., and W. K. Flower.** 1928. Regent's Park medusa Craspedacusta sowerbyi and its identity with C. (Microhydra) ryderi. Zool. Soc. London, Proc. **Breder, C. M. Jr.** 1937. Freshwater jellyfish at the Aquarium (N. Y.). N. Y. Zool. Soc. Bul. 40. **Broch, H.** 1929.

Trachy- und Narcomedusae. Nord. Plankton, Lief. 21 (12). **Carlgren, O.** 1925. Die Tetraplatien. Wiss. Ergeb. Deut. Tiefsee Exped. Valdivia 19. **Dantan, J. L.** 1925. Tetraplatia. Ann. Instit. Oceanogr. Monaco, N. S. 2 (5). **Dejdar, E.** 1934. Die Süsswassermeduse Craspedacusta in monographische Darstellung. Ztschr. Morph. Ökol. Tiere 28. **Douglas, R.** 1912. Systematische Stellung von Limnocodium sowerbyi. Ztschr. Wiss. Zool. 102. **Fantham, H. B.,** and **A. Porter.** 1933. Limnocnida rhodesiae and its distribution. Nature [London] 132. **Goette, A.** 1920. Ungeschlechtliche Fortpflanzung von Microhydra. Zool. Anz. 51. **Goto, S.** 1903. Olindias and some of its allies. Mark Anniversary Vol. 1. **Hargitt, C. W.** 1899. Experimental studies on hydromedusae. Biol. Bul. 1. **Hargitt, G. T.** 1902. Regeneration of Gonionema. Biol. Bul. 4. **Hanitzsch, O.** 1912. Entwicklung der Narcomedusen. Deut. Zool. Gesell. Verhandl. 22. 1921. Über die Eigenart und Entstehung der Vermehrungsweise durch aborale und orale Proliferation bei Narco- polypen. Zool. Jahrb., Abt. Anat. Ontog. Tiere 42. **Joseph, H.** 1925. Morph- ologie und Entwicklungsgeschichte von Haleremita und Gonionemus. Ztschr. Wiss. Zool. 125. **Lipin, A.** 1911. Morphologie und Biologie von Polypodium. Zool. Jahrb., Abt. Anat. Ontog. Tiere 31. 1926. Polypodium. Zool. Jahrb., Abt. Anat. Ontog. Tiere 47. **Maas, O.** 1892. Bau und Entwicklung der Cuninen- knospen. Zool. Jahrb., Abt. Anat. Ontog. Tiere 5. **Metschnikoff, E.** 1881. Vergleichende embryologische Studien. Ztschr. Wiss. Zool. 36. **Milne, L. J.** 1938. Behavior of the fresh-water jellyfish. Amer. Nat. 72. **Morgan, T. H.** 1899. Regeneration in Gonionemus. Amer. Nat. 33. **Murbach, L.** 1895. Life history of Gonionemus. Jour. Morph. 11. 1903. Static function in Gonionemus. Amer. Jour. Physiol. 10. Egg laying in Gonionemus. Science 17. 1907. Light percep- tion function of the marginal papillae of Gonionemus. Biol. Bul. 14. 1909. Light reactions of Gonionemus. Biol. Bul. 17. **Payne, F.** 1926. Life history of Cras- pedacusta. Biol. Bul. 50. 1924. Study of the fresh-water medusa. Jour. Morph. 38. **Schmitt, W. L.** 1938. Fresh-water jellyfish records since 1932. Amer. Nat. 73. **Perkins, H. F.** 1902. Degeneration phenomena in the larvae of Gonionema. Biol. Bul. 3. 1903. Development of Gonionema. Acad. Nat. Sci. Phila. Proc., 54. **Persch, H.** 1933. Microhydra germanica. Ztschr. Wiss. Zool. 144. **Potts, E.** 1906. Medusa of Microhydra. Quart. Jour. Micros. Sci. 50. **Salensky, W.** 1911. Solmundella und actinula. Acad. Imp. Sci. St. Pétersbourg, Mém., Ser. 8, Cl. Physico- math. 30. **Stschelkanowzew, J.** 1906. Entwicklung von Cunina proboscidea. Mitt. Zool. Stat. Neapel 17. **Thiel, M. E.** 1936. Systematische Studien zu dem Trachylinae der Mitra Exped. Zool. Jahrb., Abt. System. Geog. Biol. Tiere 69. **Thomas, L. J.** 1921. Morphology and orientation of the otocysts of Gonionemus. Biol. Bul. 40. **Vanhöffen, E.** 1909. Narcomedusae. Wiss. Ergeb. Deut. Tiefsee Exped. Valdivia 19. **Vigiuer, C.** 1899. Tetraplatia. Arch. Zool. Expt. Gén. 8. **Weill, R.** 1938. Gonionemus suvaensis. Soc. Zool. France, Bul. 63. 1936. Larves polypoides de Olindias. Acad. Sci. Paris, Compt. Rend. 203. **Uchida, T.** 1929. Olindiidae. Annot. Zool. Jap. 12. **Wilson, H. V.** 1887. Structure of Cunoctantha. Johns Hopkins Univ., Studies Biol. Lab. 4. **Woltereck, R.** 1905. Entwicklung der Narcomedusen. Deut. Zool. Gesell. Verhandl. 15. **Yerkes, R. M.** 1903. Reactions and reaction time of Gonionema. Amer. Jour. Physiol. 9. 1904. Reaction time of Gonionema to electric and photic stimuli. Biol. Bul. 6.

SIPHONOPHORA

Barrois, J. 1927. Stade médusoide des Vélelles. Acad. Sci. Paris, Compt. Rend. 184. **Berrill, M. J.** 1930. Occurrence and habits of Stephanonomia. Jour. Mar. Biol. Assoc. 16. **Bigelow, H. B.** 1911. Albatross Siphonophorae. Harvard Univ., Mus. Comp. Zool. Mem. 38. **Chun, C.** 1881. Nervensystem der

Siphonophoren. Zool. Anz. 4. 1882. Die Gewebe der Siphonophoren. Zool. Anz. 5. 1886. Bau und Entwicklung der Siphonophoren. Akad. Wiss. Berlin, Sitzber. 1887. Postembryonale Entwicklung von Physalia. Zool. Anz. 10. 1892. Die Canarischen Siphonophoren. Senckenb. Naturf. Gesell. Frankfurt. Abhandl., 16, 18. 1897. Über den Bau und die morphologische Auffassung der Siphonophoren. Deut. Zool. Gesell. Verhandl. 7. 1897. Die Siphonophoren der Plankton-Exped. Ergeb. Plankton. Exped. 2 K. **Delsman, H. C.** Entwicklungsgeschichte von Porpita. Treubia 3. **Fewkes, J. W.** 1880. Anatomy and development of Agalma. Amer. Nat. 14. 1881. Jellyfishes of Narragansett Bay. Harvard Univ., Mus. Compar. Zool., Bul. 8. 1881. Report on the Acalephae. Blake Rpts. XI. Harvard Univ., Mus. Compar. Zool., Bul. 8. 1885. Development of Agalma. Harvard Univ., Mus. Compar. Zool., Bul. 11. **Haeckel, E.** 1889. Siphonophora. Challenger Rpts. Zool. 28. **Iwantzoff, N. A.** 1928. Histologie der Siphonophoren. Soc. Nat. Moskau. Bul. Sect. Biol. 37. **Haurowitz, F.,** and **H. Waelsch.** 1926. Chemische Zusammensetzung der Velella. Ztschr. Physiol. Chem. 161. **Henze, M.** 1908. Chemische Zusammensetzung der Gerüstsubstanz von Velella. Ztschr. Physiol. Chem. 55. **Iwantzoff, N. A.** 1928. Histologie der Siphonophoren. Soc. Nat. Moskau. Bul. Sect. Biol. 37. **Jacobs, W.** 1937. Über das Schweben der Siphonophoren. Ztschr. Vergleich. Physiol. 24. **Kato, K.** 1933. Is Nomeus a harmless inquiline of Physalia? Tokyo Imp. Acad. Proc. 9. **Kuskup, M.** 1921. Symbiose von Siphonophoren und Zooxanthellen. Zool. Anz. 52. **Leloup, E.** 1929. Anatomie und développement de Velella. Arch. Biol. 39. **Lens, A. D.,** and **T. von Riemsdijk.** 1908. Siphonophora of the Siboga Expedition. Siboga Exped. 9. **Lochmann, L.** 1914. Entwicklungsgeschichte der Siphonophoren. Ztschr. Wiss. Zool. 108. **Metschnikoff, E.** 1874. Studien über die Entwicklung der Medusen und Siphonophoren. Ztschr. Wiss. Zool. 24. **Moser, F.** 1921. Ursprung und Verwandtschaftsbeziehungen der Siphonophoren. Preuss. Akad. Wiss., Berlin, Sitzber. 1924. Die larval Verhältnisse der Siphonophoren. Zoologica 28. 1925. Die Siphonophoren der deutschen Südpolar Expedition. Deut. Südpolar Exped. 17 (Zool. 9). **Okado, Yo K.** 1932. Développement post-embryonale de la Physalie. Kyoto Univ. Coll. Sci. Mem. Ser B, 8. 1935. Les jeunes Physalies. Kyoto Univ., Col. Sci., Mem. 10. **Russell, F. S.** 1938. Development of Muggiaea. Jour. Marine Biol. Assoc. 22. **Schaeppi, T.** 1898. Nervensystem der Siphonophoren. Jenaische Ztschr. Naturw. 32. **Schloessing, T.,** and **J. Richard,** 1896. Recherche de l'argon dans les gaz de la vessie natatoire des Physalies. Acad. Sci. Compt. Rend. 122. **Schneider, K. C.** 1896, 1898. Mittheilungen über Siphonophoren. Zool. Jahrb., Abt. Ontog. Tiere 9; Zool. Anz. 21; Univ. Wien., Arb. Zool. Inst. 11, 12. **Stecke, O.** 1907. Die Genitalanlagen der Rhizophysalien. Ztschr. Wiss. Zool. 86. **Vanhöffen, E.** 1906. Siphonophoren. Nord. Plankton, 11, Lief. 5. **Wallich, G. C.** 1863. Structure and habits of Physalia. Intell. Observer 2. **Woltereck, R.** 1905. Ontogenie und Ableitung der Siphonophoren. Ztschr. Wiss. Zool. 82.

SCYPHOZOA

General

Bauer, V. 1927. Schwimmbewegungen der Quallen. Ztschr. Vergleich. Physiol. 5. **Bozler, E.** 1926. Sinnes- und Nervenphysiologische Untersuchungen an Scyphomedusen. Ztschr. Vergleich. Physiol. 4. **Corrington, J.** 1927. Association of a spider crab and a medusa. Biol. Bul. 53. **Fränkel, G.** 1925. Der statische Sinn der Medusen. Ztschr. Vergleich. Physiol. 2. **Goetsch, W.** 1923. Unsterblichkeitsprobleme der Metazoen. IV. Scyphozoen. Biol. Zentrbl. 43. **Gudger, E. W.** 1937. Jellyfishes as fish eaters. N. Y. Zool. Soc. Bul. 37. **Gutsell, J. S.**

1928. Spider crab and jellyfish. Ecology 9. **Hadzi, J.** 1909. Rückgängig-gemachte Entwicklung einer Scyphomedusa. Zool. Anz. 34. 1911. Haben die Scyphomedusen einen ectodermalen Schlund? Zool. Anz. 37. **Haeckel, E.** 1879. Das System der Medusen. **Hamann, O.** 1883. Beiträge zur Kenntnis der Medusen. Ztschr. Wiss. Zool. 38. **Hatai, S.** 1917. Composition of Cassiopea and changes during starvation. Carnegie Inst. Wash., Pub. 251. **Henschel, J.** 1935. Über den chemischen Sinn der Scyphomedusen. Wiss. Meeresuntersuch. Abt. Kiel. N.F. 22. **Heymans, C.,** and **A. R. Moore.** 1924. Luminescence in Pelagia. Jour. Gen. Physiol. 6. **Jordan, H.** 1912. Über reflexarme Tiere. III. Die acraspen Medusen. Ztschr. Wiss. Zool. 101. **Kieslinger, A.** 1926. Fossile Medusen. Zool. Bot. Gesell. Wien. Verhandl. 74. **Krukenberg, C.** 1880. Über den Wassergehalt der Medusen. Zool. Anz. 3. **Lehmann, C.** 1923. Sinnesograne der Medusen. Zool. Jahrb., Abt. Allg. Zool. Ontog. Tiere 39. **Maas, O.** 1907. Die Scyphomedusen. Ergeb. Fortschr. Zool. 1. **MacCallum, A. B.** 1903. Inorganic composition of Aurelia and Cyanea. Jour. Physiol. 29. **Mayer, A. G.** 1912. Temperature reactions of medusae. Science, N.S. 35. **Mohr, M.** 1937. Über Stickstoffhaltige Bestandteile der Qualle Cyanea. Ztschr. Biol. 98. **Myers, R. G.** 1920. Blood of several invertebrates. Jour. Biol. Chem. 41. **Okada, Y. K.** 1927. Sur l'origine de l'endoderme des Discoméduses. Bull. Biol. France Belg. 61. **Scheuring, L.** 1915. Parasitismus pelagischer Jungfische. Biol. Zentbl. 35. **Schewiakoff, W.** 1889. Zur Kenntnis des Acalephenauges. Morph. Jahrb. 15. **Spek, J.** 1914. Chemische Natur der Statoconien in den Rhopalien von Rhizostoma. Zool. Anz. 44. **Tretyakoff, D. K.** 1937. Mesogloea of Black Sea Scyphomedusae. Arch. Russ. Anat. Hist. Embryol. 17. **Walcott, C. O.** 1900. Fossil medusae. U. S. Geol. Survey, Monog. 30.

STAUROMEDUSAE

Antipa, E. 1892. Die Lucernariden der Bremer Expedition. Zool. Jahrb., Abt. System. Geog. Biol. Tiere 6. 1893. Eine neue Stauromeduse. Mitt. Zool. Stat. Neapel 10. **Carlgren, O.** 1909. Studien über Regeneration. III. Versuche an Lucernaria. Kungl. Sven. Vetensk. Handl. new ser. 44. 1933. Zur Kenntnis der Lucernariiden Lipkea, Capria, und Brochiella. Lunds Univ. Arsskrift, n.f. 29. 1935. Ueber eine neue südafrikanische Lucernariide Depastromorpha. Kungl. Svenska. Vetensk. Handl. Ser. 3, Vol. 14. **Child, C. M.** 1933. Reconstitution in Haliclystus. Tohoku Imp. Univ. Sci. Rpts. Ser. 4 Biol. VIII. **Clark, H. J.** 1878. Lucernariae and their allies. Smithsn. Inst. Contrib. 23, Art. 242. **Gross, J.** 1900. Zur Anatomie der Lucernariden. Jenaische Ztschr. Naturw. 33. **Hanoaka, H.** 1934. Early development of a stalked medusa. Tokyo Imp. Acad. Proc. 10. 1936. Polarity of a stalked medusa Thaumatoscyphus. Hokkaido Imp. Univ. Faculty Sci. Jour. Ser. 5; Zoology 4. **Kassianow, N.** 1901. Nervensystem der Lucernariden. Ztschr. Wiss. Zool. 69. **Kishinouye, K.** 1902. Some new Scyphomedusae of Japan. Tokyo Imp. Univ. Col. Sci. Jour. 17. **Leuschel, H.** 1932. Histologie und Physiologie der Lucernariden. Zool. Jahrb., Abt. Allg. Zool. Physiol. Tiere 52. **Migot, A.** 1922. Sur le mode de fixation des Lucernaires a leur support. Soc. Biol. [Paris], Compt. Rend. 86. **Schlater, G.** 1891. Die Sinneskolben von Haliclystus. Ztschr. Wiss. Zool. 52. **Uchida, T.** 1929. Studies on the Stauromedusae and Cubomedusae. Jour. Zool. Tokyo, 2. **Uchida, T.,** and **K. Hanoaka.** 1934. Anatomy of two stalked medusae. Hokkaido Imp. Univ. Faculty. Sci. Jour. Zool. 2. **Weill, R.** 1925. Foyers de formation et voies de migration des nématocystes de Haliclystus. Acad. Sci. Paris, Compt. Rend. 180. **Wietrzykowski, W.** 1910. Développement des Lucernaires. Arch. Zool. Expt. Gén. Ser. 5, Vol. 10.

CUBOMEDUSAE

Berger, E. L.   1898.   Histological structure of the eyes of Cubomedusae.   Jour.
Compar. Neurol. 8.   1900.   Physiology and histology of the Cubomedusae.   Johns
Hopkins Univ. Memoirs Biol. Lab. 4.   **Conant, F. S.**   1898.   The Cubomedusae.
Johns Hopkins Univ. Memoirs Biol. Lab. 4.   **Ishida, J.**   1936.   Note on the digestion
of Charybdea.   Annot. Zool. Jap. 15.   **Okada, Yo K.**   Note sur l'ontogenie de
Charybdea.   Bul. Biol. France Belg. 61.   **Uchida, T.**   1929.   (See under Stauro-
medusae.)   **Yatsu, N.**   1917.   Notes on the physiology of Charybdea.   Tokyo Imp.
Univ. Col. Sci. Jour. 40.

CORONATAE

Komai, T.   1935.   On Stephanoscyphus and Nausithoe.   Kyoto Univ. Col. Sci.
Mem. Ser. B 10, 5.   **Lo Bianco, S.**, and **P. Mayer.**   1890.   Spongicola und Nausithoe.
Zool. Anz. 13.   **Maas, O.**   1897.   Die Medusae.   Albatross Expedition 1891.
Harvard Univ., Mus. Compar. Zool. Mem. 23.   1903.   Die Scyphozoen der Siboga
Expedition.   Siboga Monog. 11.   1904.   Méduses provenant des campagnes.   Result
Camp. Sci. Prince de Monaco, fasc. 28.   **Vanhöffen, E.**   1900.   Tiefseemedusen und
ihre Sinnesorgane.   Zool. Anz. 23.   1903.   Die acraspeden Medusen der deutschen
Tiefsee Expedition.   Wiss. Ergeb. Deut. Tiefsee Exped. Valdivia 3.

SEMAEOSTOMEAE

Agassiz, A., and **A. G. Mayer.**   1898.   Dactylometra.   Harvard Univ., Mus.
Compar. Zool. Bul. 32.   **Agassiz, L.**   1862.   Contributions to the natural history of
the U. S.   Vol. 4, Pts. 1 and 3.   **Bigelow, R. P.**   1910.   Comparison of sense organs
in Pelagidae.   Jour. Expt. Zool. 9.   **Chuin, T. T.**   1928.   Absence de strobilisation
et persistence du bourgeonnement pendant l'hiver chez les scyphistomes.   Acad.
Sci. Paris, Compt. Rend. 186.   1929.   Les phénomènes cytologiques au cours de
la digestion intracellulaire chez le scyphistome de Chrysaora.   Soc. Biol. [Paris]
Compt. Rend. 102.   1930.   Le cycle évolutif du scyphistome de Chrysaora.   Trav.
Stat. Biol. Roscoff. 8.   **De Beer, G. R.**, and **J. Huxley.**   1924.   Dedifferentiation and
reduction in Aurelia.   Quart. Jour. Micros. Sci. 68.   **Delap, M. J.**   1902.   Rearing
of Cyanea.   Sci. Invest. Fisheries Ireland.   1905.   Rearing of Aurelia and Pelagia.
Sci. Invest. Fisheries Ireland.   **Friedemann, O.**   1902.   Postembryonale Ent-
wicklung von Aurelia.   Ztschr. Wiss. Zool. 71.   **Galigher, A. E.**   1925.   Occurrence
of larval stages of Scyphozoa in Monterey Bay, Calif.   Amer. Nat. 59.   **Gemmill,
J. F.**   1921.   Food capture and ciliation in the ephyrae of Aurelia.   Roy. Phys. Soc.
Edinb., Proc. 20.   **Gilchrist, F. G.**   1937.   Budding and locomotion in the scy-
phistomas of Aurelia.   Biol. Bul. 72.   **Halisch, W.**   1933.   Beobachtungen an
Scyphopolypen.   Zool. Anz. 104.   **Hargitt, C. W.**, and **G. T. Hargitt.**   1910.   Devel-
opment of Scyphomedusae.   Jour. Morph. 21.   **Hein, W.**   1900.   Entwicklung
von Aurelia.   Ztschr. Wiss. Zool. 67.   **Henschel, J.**   1935.   Chemischer Sinn der
Scyphomedusen Aurelia und Cyanea und der Hydromeduse Sarsia.   Wiss. Meeres
Untersuch. Kiel, N.F. 22.   **Heric, M.**   1907.   Zur Kenntnis der polydisken Stro-
bilation von Chrysaora.   Arb. Zool. Inst., Univ. Wien 17.   **Hérouard, E.**   1907.
Existence de statoblastes chez le scyphistome.   Acad. Sci. Paris, Compt. Rend.
145.   1913.   Relation entre la dépression et la formation de pseudoplanula chez
le scyphistome.   Acad. Sci. Paris, Compt. Rend. 156.   **Horstmann, F.**   1934.
Zur Physiologie der Schwimmbewegungen der Scyphomedusen.   Arch. Gesam.
Physiol. Mensch. Tiere 234.   1934.   Nerven- und muskelphysiologische Studien zur
Schwimmbewegung der Scyphomedusen.   Arch. Gesam. Physiol. Mensch. Tiere 234.
Lendenfeld, E.   1882.   Cyanea.   Ztschr. Wiss. Zool. 37.   **McMurrich, J. P.**   1891.

Development of Cyanea. Amer. Nat. 25. **Orton, J. H.** 1922. Feeding of Aurelia. Nature [London] 110. **Papenfuss-Johnstone, W.** 1936. Utility of nematocysts in the classification of certain scyphomedusae. Lunds Univ. Arsskr. N.F. Avd. 2, 31. **Percival, E.** 1923. Strobilization of Aurelia. Quart. Jour. Micros. Sci. 67. **Perez, C.** 1920. Élevage de scyphistomes. Bul. Biol. France Belg. 54. 1922. Multiplication gemmipare d'un scyphistome. Bul. Biol. France Belg. 56. **Renton, R.** 1930. Budding of a scyphistome. Zool. Soc. London Proc. **Schäfer, E. A.** 1878. Nervous system of Aurelia. Roy. Soc. London, Phil. Trans. 169, pt. 2. **Steiner, G.** 1934. Die Verlust der Glockenautomatie bei randorganlos aufgezogenen Ohrenquallen. Biol. Zentbl. 54. **Teissier, G.** and **L. Teissier.** 1925. Jeunes scyphistomes de Chrysaora. Soc. Zool. France Bul. 50. **Teissier, G.** 1929. La croissance embryonnaire de Chrysaora. Arch. Zool. Expt. Gén. 69. 1932. Composition chemique de Chrysaora. Soc. Zool. France Bul. 57. **Thill, H.** 1937. Zur Kenntnis der Aurelia. Ztschr. Wiss. Zool. 150. **Widmark, E. M. P.** 1911. Gastrovascularströmungen bei Aurelia und Cyanea. Zool. Anz. 38.

RHIZOSTOMEAE

Bigelow, R. P. 1900. Anatomy and development of Cassiopea. Boston Soc. Nat. Hist. Mem. 5, also Johns Hopkins Univ. Memoirs Biol. Lab. 4. **Cary, L. R.** 1916. Influence of the marginal sense organs on the rate of regeneration in Cassiopea. Jour. Expt. Zool. 21. 1917. Physiology of the nervous system of Cassiopea. Carnegie Inst. Wash., Pub. no. 251. **Hargitt, C. W.** 1904. Regeneration in Rhizostoma. Jour. Expt. Zool. 1; Amer. Nat. 38. **Hatai, S.** 1917. Composition of Cassiopea and changes after starvation. Carnegie Inst. Wash. Dept. Mar. Biol. Papers 11. **Hein, W.** 1902. Entwicklung von Cotylorhiza. Ztschr. Wiss. Zool. 73. **Hesse, R.** 1895. Nervensystem und Sinnesorgane von Rhizostoma. Ztschr. Wiss. Zool. 60. **Mayer, A. G.** 1906. Rhythmical pulsation in scyphomedusae. Carnegie Inst. Wash., Pub. No. 47; No. 102. 1916. Nerve conduction and other reactions in Cassiopea. Amer. Jour. Physiol. 39, 42; Carnegie Inst. Wash., Pub. No. 251. **Okada, Yo K.** 1927. Régénération chez les coelentérés. Arch. Zool. Expt. Gén. 66. **Stiasny, G.** 1920. Gefässsystem der Rhizostomeen. Tijdschr. Nederl. Dierkund. Vereen. Ser. 2, Vol. 18. 1923. Das Gastrovascularsystem als Grundlage für ein neues System der Rhizostomeen. Zool. Anz. 57. **Uchida, M.** 1926. Anatomy and development of Mastigias. Tokyo Univ. Faculty Sci. Jour. Sect. 4, Zool. 1. **Zeleny, C.** 1907. Effect of degree of injury, successive injury, and functional activity upon regeneration in Cassiopea. Jour. Expt. Zool. 5. **Zeynek, R.** 1912. Chemische Studien über Rhizostoma. Akad. Wiss. Wien, Math. Naturw. Kl. Sitzber. 121, Abt. IIb.

ANTHOZOA

General

Boschma, H. 1925. Studies on anthozoan polyps. Carnegie Inst. Wash., Tortugas Lab. Yearbook, Ann. Rpt. 24. **Carlgren, O.** 1905. Über die Bedeutung der Flimmerbewegung für den Nahrungstransport bei den Actiniarien und Madreporarien. Biol. Zentbl. 25. 1906. Die Aktinienlarven. Nord. Plankton 11, Lief. 5. 1923. Ceriantharia und Zoantharia. Wiss. Ergeb. Deut. Tiefsee Exped. Valdivia 19. 1924. Die Larven der Ceriantharia, Zoantharia, und Actiniaria. Wiss. Ergeb. Deut. Tiefsee Exped. Valdivia 19. 1934. Ceriantharia, Zoantharia, und Aktiniaria. Sci. Results N. Atlantic Deep Sea Exped. Michael Sars 5. **Clarke, F. W.**, and **W. C. Wheeler.** 1915. Inorganic constituents of Alcyonaria. Proc. Nation. Acad. Sci., Wash. 1. **Hargitt, C. W.** 1912. Anthozoa of the Woods Hole region. U. S. Bur. Fisheries Bul. 32. **Hickson, S. J.** 1883. Ciliated groove (siphonoglyph) in the stomodaeum of Alcyonarians. Roy. Soc. London Phil. Trans. 174, Pt. 3. 1930. Classification of the Alcyonaria. Zool. Soc. London, Proc. **Kassianow, N.** 1908. Vergleich des Nervensystems der Octocorallia mit dem der Hexacorallia. Ztschr. Wiss. Zool. 90. **Kükenthal, W.** 1921. System der Oktocorallen. Akad. Wiss., Berlin, Sitzber. **McMurrich, J. P.** 1891. Phylogeny of the Actinozoa. Jour. Morph. 5. **Parker, G. H.** 1925. Interrelations of zooids in soft corals. Nation. Acad. Sci. Wash., Proc. 11. **Pax, F.** 1924. Lebensdauer der Korallentier. Monatsschr. Seeaquar. Meereskunde 1. **Pratt, E. M.** 1906. Digestive organs of the Alcyonaria and their relation to the mesogloeal cell plexus. Quart. Jour. Micros. Sci. 49. **Van Beneden, E.** 1898. Anthozoa. Ergeb. Plankton Exped. II, K, e. **Wilson, E. B.** 1884. The mesenterial filaments of the Alcyonaria. Mitt. Zool. Stat. Neapel 5. **Wright, E. P.,** and **T. H. Studer.** 1889. Alcyonaria. Challenger Rpts., Zool. 31.

ALCYONACEA AND SMALLER GROUPS

Ashworth, J. 1899. Structure of Xenia. Quart. Jour. Micros. Sci. 42. **Bock, S.** 1938. Bathyalcyon. Kungl. Svenska Vetensk. Handl. Tredje Ser. Vol. 16. **Bourne, G. C.** 1895. Structure and affinities of Heliopora. Roy. Soc. London, Phil. Trans. 186. 1900. Genus Lemnalia. Trans. Linn. Soc. London, Zool. Ser. 2, Vol. 7. Structure and formation of the calcareous skeleton of the Anthozoa. Quart. Jour. Micros. Sci. 41. **Brown, W. L.** 1895. Chemical constitution of the mesogloea of Alcyonium. Quart. Jour. Micros. Sci. 37. **Cary, L. R.** 1931. Studies on coral reefs with special reference to the Alcyonaria. Carnegie Inst. Wash., Pub. 413. **Deichmann, E.** 1936. Alcyonaria of the western part of the Atlantic Ocean. Harvard Univ., Mus. Compar. Zool. Mem. 53. **Hickson, S. J.** 1894. Revision of the Stolonifera. Zool. Soc. London, Trans. 13. 1895. Anatomy of Alcyonium digitatum. Quart. Jour. Micros. Sci. 37. 1901. Alcyonium. Mem. Liverpool Mar. Biol. Comm. 5. 1930. Classification of the Alcyonaria. Zool. Soc. London, Proc. Pt. 1. 1931. Family Xeniidae. Great Barrier Reef Exped. Sci. Rpt. 5. **Hiro, F.** 1937. Observations on Heteroxenia. Annot. Zool. Jap. 16. **Holm, O.** 1895. Alcyonidgattung Spongodes. Zool. Jahrb., Abt. System. Geog. Biol. Tiere 8. **Jungersen, H. F. E.** 1927. Anthomastus. Danish Ingolf Exped. 5, Pt. 11. **Kassianow, N.** 1908. Das Nervensystem der Alcyonaria. Ztschr. Wiss. Zool. 90. **Krukenberg, C. F.** 1887. Die nervösen Leitungsbahnen in den Polypen der Alcyoniden. Vergleich. Physiol. Studien, Reihe 2, Abt. 4, Teil 1. **Kükenthal, W.** 1902. Die Familie der Xeniiden. Zool. Jahrb., Abt. System. Geog. Biol. Tiere 15. 1903–1907. Die Familie der Nephthyiden. Zool. Jahrb., Abt. System. Geog. Biol. Tiere 19, 24. 1906. Alcyonacea. Ergeb. Deut. Tiefsee Exped. 13, I. 1906. Die Stammgeschichte und die geographische Verbreitung der Alcyonaceen. Deut. Zool. Gesell. Verhandl. 16. **Laackmann, H.** 1916. Zur Kenntnis der Telesto. Zool. Jahrb. Sup. 11. **Macfayden, L. M. S.** 1935. Alcyonaria. Great Barrier Reef Exped. Sci. Rpt. 5. **Matthews, Annie.** 1916. Development of Alcyonium. Quart. Jour. Micros. Sci. 62. **Molander, A. R.** 1918. Der Kelch als systematischer Charakter bei den Alcyonaceen. Arkiv Zool. 11. **Moseley, H. N.** 1876. Structure and relations of Heliopora. Roy. Soc. London, Phil. Trans. 166, pt. 1. **Moser, J.** 1919. Eireifung, Spermatogenese, und erste Entwicklung der Alcyonarien. Zool. Anz. 50. **Nutting, C. C.** 1909. Alcyonaria of the California coast. U. S. Natl. Mus. Proc. 35. **Ranson, G.,** and **A. Durivault.** 1937. Le pigment d'Heliopora et de quelques autres Alcyonaires. Soc. Biol. [Paris], Compt. Rend. 126. **Roxas, H. A.** 1933. Philippine Alcyonaria. Philippine Jour. Sci. 50. **Schenk, I.** 1896. Clavulariiden, Xeniiden, und Alcyoniiden von Ternate. Senckenb. Naturf.

Gesell. Abhandl. 23. **Sherriffs, W. R.** 1922. Evolution within the genus Dendronephthys. Zool. Soc. London, Proc. **Thomson, J. A.,** and **W. D. Henderson.** 1906. Lebendiggebärende Arten von Alcyonaceen. Zool. Anz. 30. **Thomson, A. J.,** and **L. M. I. Dean.** 1931. Alcyonacea of the Siboga Expedition. Siboga Exped. Monog. 13 d. **Woodland, W.** 1905. Spicule formation in Alcyonium. Quart. Jour. Micros. Sci. 49.

GORGONACEA

Cary, L. R. 1914. Growth rate and ecology of gorgonians. Carnegie Inst. Wash., Pub. No. 182. **Chalmers, D.** 1928. Alcyonarian genus Siphonogorgia. Roy. Phys. Soc. Edinb. Proc. 21, Pt. 4. **Chester, W. M.** 1913. Structure of the gorgonian Pseudoplexaura. Amer. Acad. Arts Sci. Proc. 48. **Cook, F. C.** 1905. Chemical composition of some gorgonian corals. Amer. Jour. Physiol. 12. **Dantan, J. L.** 1928. La croissance du corail rouge. Soc. Zool. France, Bul. 53. **Hickson, S. J.** 1905. Precious corals. Manchester Micros. Soc., Trans. 26th Ann. Rpt. 1932. Gorgonacea. Great Barrier Reef Exped. Sci. Rpt. 4. **Kinoshita, K.** 1910. Postembryonale Entwicklung von Anthoplexaura. Tokyo Imp. Univ. Col. Sci. Jour. 27. 1913. Morphologie und Stammesgeschichte der Gorgoniden. Tokyo Imp. Univ. Col. Sci. Jour. 32. **Koch, G. v.** 1889. Die Gorgoniden. Fauna Flora Golf. Neapel 15. **Kükenthal, W.** 1916. System und Stammesgeschichte der Scleraxonier und der Ursprung der Holaxonier. Zool. Anz. 47. 1919. Gorgonaria. Ergeb. Deut. Tiefsee Exped. 13, II. 1919. Eireifung und Spermatogenese bei den Gorgonarien. Zool. Anz. 50. 1924. Gorgonaria. Tierreich 47. **McIntosh, D.** 1910. Red or precious coral. Zoologist (4) 14. **Morner, C. T.** 1907. Über die organische Gerüstsubstanz des Anthozoenskeletts. Ztschr. Physiol. Chem. 51. 1913. Isolierung und Identifizierung der Bromgorgosäure. Ztschr. Physiol. Chem. 88. **Müller, R.** 1910. Bildung des Achsenskelets von Corallium. Mitt. Zool. Stat. Neapel 20. **Neumann, H.** 1911. Bildung der Achsenskelettes einiger Gorgonaceen. Jenaische Ztschr. Naturw. 47. **Nutting, C. C.** 1914. Parasites, commensals, etc. found on Alcyonaria. Science 39. **Parker, G. H.** 1925. Interrelations of zooids in soft corals. Nation. Acad. Sci. Wash., Proc. 11. **Schimbke, G. O.** 1914. Anatomie der Gorgonaceen. Arch. Naturgesch. 8, Abt. A, Heft 11. **Schneider, A.** 1905. Das Achsenskelet der Gorgoniden. Arch. Naturgesch., Jahrg. 71, Vol. 1. **Stiasny, G.** 1935. Revision der Plexauridae. Siboga Exped. Monog. 13, b 7, Sup. 1938. Genus Eunicella. Verhandl. kun. Nederl. Akad. Wetensch. Afd. Natur. Sect. 2, Deel 37.

PENNATULACEA

Fowler, G. H. 1894. Sea-pens of the family Veretillidae. Zool. Soc. London, Proc. **Harvey, E. N.** 1917. Light production by a Japanese pennatulid, Cavernularia. Amer. Jour. Physiol. 42. **Hickson, J. S.** 1916. Pennatulacea. Siboga Exped. Monog. 14. **Jurgensen, H.** 1888. Bau und Entwicklung der Kolonie von Pennatula. Ztschr. Wiss. Zool. 47. **Kölliker, A.** 1872. Die Pennatuliden. Senckenb. Naturf. Gesell. Abhandl. 7, 8. 1880. Report on the Pennatulida. Challenger Rpts. Zool. 1. **Kükenthal, W.** 1915. Pennatularia. Tierreich 43. **Kükenthal, W.,** and **H. Broch.** 1910. System und Stammesgeschichte der Seefedern. Zool. Anz. 36, also 45. 1911. Pennatulacea. Ergeb. Deut. Tiefsee Exped. 13. **Lacaze-Duthiers, H. de.** 1887. Sur le développement des Pennatulés. Acad. Sci. Paris, Compt. Rend. 104. **Musgrave, E.** 1909. Organs of assimilation and power of locomotion of pennatulids. Quart. Jour. Micros. Sci. 54. **Niedermayer, A.** 1911. Pteroides. Arb. Zool. Inst. Univ. Wien. 19. 1914. Beiträge zur Kenntnis des histologisches Baues von Veretillum. Ztschr. Wiss. Zool. 109.

Parker, G. H.   1920.   Circulation of water in Renilla.   Neuromuscular movements and phosphorescence of Renilla.   Jour. Expt. Zool. 31.   **Torrey, H. B.**   1901. Regeneration and regulation in Renilla.   Biol. Bul. 2.   **Wilson, E. B.**   1883.   Development of Renilla.   Roy. Soc. London, Phil. Trans. 174.   1903.   Merogeny and regeneration in Renilla.   Biol. Bul. 4.

ACTINIARIA

Ackermann, D., F. Holtz, and H. Reinwein.   1924.   Extraktstoffe von Actinia. Ztschr. Biol. 79, 80, 81.   **Allabach, L.**   1905.   Behavior of Metridium.   Biol. Bul. 10. **Andres, A.**   1884.   Die Actinien.   Fauna Flora Golf. Neapel 9.   **Annandale, N.** 1912.   Aged sea anemones.   Nature [London] 89.   **Appellöf, A.**   1900.   Über Aktinienentwicklung.   Bergens Mus. Aarbok.   **Arndt, W.**   1913.   Fett bei Actinien. Zool. Jahrb., Abt. Allg. Zool. Physiol. Tiere 34.   **Badham, C.**   1917.   Larval actinian parasitic in a rhizostome.   Quart. Jour. Micros. Sci. 62.   **Balss, H.**   1924.   Über Anpassungen und Symbiose der Paguriden.   Zeitschr. Morph. Ökol. Tiere 1.   **Bamford, E.**   1912.   Pelagic actiniarian larvae.   Trans. Linn. Soc. London, Zool. (2) 15. **Blochmann, F. and C. Hilger.**   1888.   Gonactinia prolifera.   Morph. Jahrb. 13. **Bohn, G.**   1907.   Les états physiologiques des Actinies.   Inst. Gén. Psychol. Bul. 7. 1908.   Les facteurs de la rétraction et de l'épanouissement des Actinies.   Soc. Biol. [Paris], Compt. Rend. 64.   **Bourne, G. C.**   1910.   Edwardsiidae.   Jour. Linn. Soc. London, Zool. 32.   **Cardot, H.**   1937.   De la spécificité dans les phénomènes de capture chez les Actinies.   Soc. Biol. [Paris], C. R. 97.   **Carlgren, O.**   1891.   Protanthea simplex.   Öfvers Kungl. Vetens. Akad. Förhand. 48.   1892.   Zur Kenntnis der Edwardsien.   Öfvers Kungl. Vetens. Akad. Förhand. 49.   1893.   Über das Vorkommen von Brutraumen bei Actinien.   Öfvers Kungl. Vetens. Akad. Förhand. 50.   1893. Studien über nordische Actinien.   Kungl. Svenska Vetensk. Akad. Handl. 25, pt. 2. 1894.   Zur Kenntnis der Minyaden.   Öfvers Kungl. Vetensk. Akad. Förhand. 51. 1897.   Zur Mesenterienentwicklung der Actinien.   Öfvers Kungl. Vetensk. Akad. Förhand. 54.   1899.   Über abschnurbare Tentakel bei den Actiniarien.   Zool. Anz. 22. 1899.   Ostafrikanische Actinien.   Mitt. Naturh. Museum Hamburg 17.   1900.   Zur Kenntnis der stychodactylinen Actiniarien.   Öfvers Kungl. Vetensk. Akad. Förhand. 57.   1901.   Die Brutpflege der Actiniarien.   Biol. Zentbl. 21.   1904.   Studien über Regenerations- und Regulationsverscheinungen.   Kungl. Svenska Vetensk. Akad. Handl. 37.   1905.   Zur Mesenterienmuskulatur der Actiniarien.   Zool. Anz. 28. 1906.   Die Actinien-Larven.   Nord. Plankton. 6, Lief. 11.   1909.   Studien über Regenerations- und Regulationserscheinungen II.   Kungl. Svenska Vetensk. Akad. Handl. 43.   1918.   Die Mesenterienanordung der Halcuriden.   Lunds Univ. Årsskr., n.f. 14.   1921.   Actiniaria.   Danish Ingolf Exped. 5, No. 9.   1923.   Die Larven der Ceriantharien, Zoantharien, und Actiniarien.   Wiss. Ergeb. Deut. Tiefsee Exped. 19.   1924.   On Boloceroides, Bunodeopsis and their supposed allied genera.   Arkiv Zool. 17.   1928.   Zur Symbiose zwischen Actinien und Paguriden.   Ztschr. Morph. Ökol. Tiere 12.   1929.   Zur Biologie und Regeneration der niederen Actiniarien. Ztschr. Morph. Ökol. Tiere 14.   1934.   Revision der Actiniarien.   Arkiv Zool. 26. **Carlgren, O. and T. E. Stephenson.**   1928.   British Edwardsidae.   Jour. Mar. Biol. Assoc. 15.   **Cary, L. R.**   1910.   Formation of germ layers in Actinia.   Biol. Bul. 19. 1911.   Pedal laceration in actinians.   Biol. Bul. 20.   **Child, C. M.**   1908–1909. Regulation of Harenactis.   Biol. Bul. 16, 20; Jour. Expt. Zool. 6, 7.   **Cotté, J.**   1922. Sur le comportement et les réactions des actinies.   Bul. Inst. Oceanogr. Monaco 410. **Cowles, R. P.**   1920.   Transplanting of sea-anemones by hermit crabs.   Nat. Acad. Sci. Wash., Proc. 6.   **Crespigny, C. C. de.**   1869.   Friendship between the malacopterygian fish Premnas and Actinia.   Zool. Soc. London, Proc.   **Davis, D. W.** 1919.   Asexual multiplication and regeneration in Sagartia.   Jour. Expt. Zool. 28.

Duerden, J. E. 1897. Family Aliciidae. Ann. Mag. Nat. Hist. Ser. 6, Vol. 20. 1899. Edwardsian stage of Lebrunia. Jour. Linn. Soc. London, Zool. 27. 1899. Actinians of Porto Rico. U. S. Fish Comm. Bul. 20, pt. 2. 1900. Jamaican Actiniaria. Roy. Dublin Soc. Sci. Trans. Ser. 2, Vol. 7. 1902. On Bunodeopsis. Linn. Soc. London, Trans. Ser. 2, Vol. 8. 1905. Habits and reactions of crabs bearing actinians in their claws. Zool. Soc. London, Proc. **Elmhirst, R.** 1925. Feeding habits of the sea-anemone Actinoloba. Scot. Nat. **Faurot, L.** 1895. L'anatomie, l'histologie, et le développement les Actinies. Arch. Zool. Expt. Gén. Ser. 3, Vol. 3. 1907. Développement du pharynx et des cloisons chez les Hexactinies. Arch. Zool. Expt. Gén. Ser. 4, Vol. 1. 1910. Associations entre les Pagures et les Actinies. Arch. Zool. Expt. Gén. Ser. 5, Vol. 5. **Fleure, H. J.,** and **C. L. Walton.** 1907. Habits of some sea-anemones. Zool. Anz. 31. **Fosse, R.** 1913. Presence de l'urée chez les invertébrés. Acad. Sci. Paris, Compt. Rend. 157. **Fox, D. L.** and **C. R. Moe.** 1938. An astacene-like carotenoid from a Pacific coast anemone. Nat. Acad. Sci. Wash., Proc. 24. **Gee, W.** 1913. Modifiability in the behavior of the California shore anemone. Jour. Anim. Behavior 3. **Gemmill, J. F.** 1920. Development of Metridium, and Adamsia. Roy. Soc. London, Phil. Trans. 209 B. **Gohar, H. A. F.** 1934. Partnership between fish and anemone. Nature [London]. 134. **Groselj, P.** 1909. Über das Nervensystem der Aktinien. Arb. Zool. Inst. Univ. Wien 17. **Gravier, C. J.** 1919. Sur le role des cinclides chez les Actinies. Paris, Mus. Hist. Nat. Bul. 25. **Haddon, A. C.** 1885. On Halcampa. Roy. Dublin Soc. Sci. Proc. 4, 5. 1887. Arrangement of mesenteries in the parasitic larva of Halcampa. Roy. Dublin Soc. Sci. Proc. 5. **Haddon, A. C.,** and **G. G. Dixon.** 1885. Structure and habits of Peachia. Roy. Dublin Soc. Sci. Proc. 4. **Haddon, A. C.** 1885. On Halcampa. Roy. Dublin Soc. Sci. Proc. 4, 5. 1887. Arrangement of mesenteries in the parasitic larva of Halcampa. Roy. Dublin Soc. Sci. Proc. 5. **Haddon, A. C.,** and **G. G. Dixon.** 1885. Structure and habits of Peachia. Roy. Dublin Soc., Sci. Proc. 4. **Hahn, C. W.** 1905. Dimorphism and degeneration in Metridium. Jour. Expt. Zool. 2. **Hargitt, C. W.** 1907. Behavior of sea-anemones. Biol. Bul. 12. **Harnisch, O.** 1932. Die Sauerstoffaufnahme (anemones). Ztschr. Vergleich. Physiol. 16. **Hausding, B.** 1913. Über Actinoloba. Arch. Entwickl. Mech. Organ. 38. **Hausman, L. A.** 1919. Sagartia. Biol. Bul. 37. **Haurowitz, F.,** and **H. Waelsch.** 1926. Vergleichende chemische Untersuchungen an Aktinien. Ztschr. Physiol. Chem. 161. **Havet, J.** 1901. Étude du système nerveux des actines. La Cellule 18. 1922. La structure du système nerveux des actinies. Libro en honor Ramon j Cajal, Madrid 1. **Hazen, A. P.** 1903. Regeneration in Sagartia. Arch. Entwickl. Mech. Organ. 16. **Heilbron, I. M., H. Jackson,** and **R. N. Jones.** 1935. Lipochromes of sea-anemones. Biochem. Jour. 29. **Henze, M.** 1910. Einfluss der Sauerstoffsdrucks auf den Gaswechsel einiger Meerestiere. Biochem. Ztschr. 26. **Hertwig, O.,** and **R. Hertwig.** 1879. Die Aktinien. Jenaische Ztschr. Naturw. 13. **Hertwig, R.** 1882, 1888. Actiniaria. Challenger Rpts. Zool. 6, 26. **Horst, R.** 1902. Case of commensalism of a fish and a large sea-anemone. Leyden Mus. Notes 23. **Hosoi, K.** 1935. Exchange of calcium ion and water between sea-anemone and the surrounding medium. Tohoku Imp. Univ. Sci. Rpts. (4) 10. **Ishida, J.** 1936. Digestive enzymes of Actinia. Annot. Zool. Jap. 15. **Jennings, H. S.** 1905. Behavior of sea-anemones. Jour. Expt. Zool. 2. **Jordan, H.** 1907. Die Verdauung bei den Aktinien. Arch. Gesam. Physiol. Mensch. Tiere 116. 1908. Die Physiologie des Nervenmuskelsystems von Actinoloba. Ztschr. Allg. Physiol. 8. 1934. Die Muskulatur der Aktinie Metridium. Arch. Néerland. Zool. 1. **Klenk, E.,** and **W. Diebold.** 1935. Actiniasterin, ein neues Sterin des Tierreiches. Ztschr. Physiol. Chem. 236. **Klemzinger, K. L.** 1877. Die Korallthiere des Rothen Meeres. **Kolodziejski, Z.** 1932. Régénération du disque pédal chez l'Actinie. C. R. Polon. Acad. Sci. Lettres, Cl. Sci. Math. 6, Bull. Internatl. Acad. Pol. (B). **Komori, S.** 1931. Biologie der Aktinie Boloceroides. Kyoto Univ., Col. Sci. Ser. B. 7. **Kramer, G.** 1937. Stoffwechsel der Seeanemone. Zool. Jahrb., Abt. Allg. Zool. Physiol. Tiere 58. **Landauer, W.** 1924. Laceration, Knospung, und Heteromorphose bei Actinia. Ztschr. Morph. Ökol. Tiere 3. **Malo-witschko, E.** 1931. Über entzündliche Entstehung des Bindegewebes bei Actinien. Arch. Pathol. Anat. Physiol. 280. **McClendon, J. F.** 1906. Locomotion of a sea-anemone. Biol. Bul. 10. **McMurrich, J. P.** 1890. Development of the Hexactiniae. Jour. Morph. 4. 1891. Phylogeny of the Actinozoa. Jour. Morph. 5. 1893. Report on the Actiniae collected by the Albatross. U. S. Natl. Mus. Proc. 16. 1899. Actiniaria of the Bahama Islands. Jour. Morph. 3. 1899. Actinology of the Bermudas. Acad. Nat. Sci. Phila., Proc. 1901. Halcurias and Endocoelactis. Biol. Bul. 2. **Mesnil, F.** 1901. Digestion intracellulaire et les diastases des Actinies. Instit. Pasteur [Paris], Ann. 15. **Moseley, H. N.** 1877. Two new forms of Actiniaria dredged in the deep sea with a description of certain pelagic species. Trans. Linn. Soc. London, Zool. 1. **Mouchet, S.** 1929. Sort de la xanthine au cours de jeûne chez les Actinies. Soc. Biol. [Paris], Compt. Rend. 102. 1930. Excrétion chez les Actinies. Notes Stat. Oceanogr. Salammbo 15. **Nagel, W.** 1892. Das Geschmacksinn der Aktinien. Zool. Anz. 15. **Okada, Yo K.** 1926. Actinienregeneration aus abgeworfenen Tentakeln. Arch. Entwickl. Mech. Organ. 108. **Okada, Yo K.** and **S. Komori.** 1932. Reproduction asexuelle d'un Actinie Boloceroides. Bul. Biol. France Belg. 66. **Panikkar, N. K.** 1938. Studies on Peachia. Indian Acad. Sci. Proc. Sec. B. 7. **Pantin, C. F. A.** 1935. The nerve net of the actinians. Jour. Expt. Biol. 12. **Parker, G. H.** 1896. Reactions of Metridium. Harvard Univ., Mus. Compar. Zool. Bul. 29. 1897. Mesenteries and siphonoglyphs in Metridium. Harvard Univ., Mus. Compar. Zool. Bul. 30. 1899. Longitudinal fission in Metridium. Harvard Univ., Mus. Compar. Zool. Bul. 35. 1900. Synopsis of North American Invertebrates. XII. Actiniaria. Amer. Nat. 34. 1905. Reversal of the effective stroke of the labial cilia of sea-anemones. Amer. Jour. Physiol. 14. 1916. Effector systems in Actinians. Jour. Expt. Zool. 21. 1917. Actinian behavior. Jour. Expt. Zool. 22. 1917. Pedal locomotion in actinians. Jour. Expt. Zool. 22. Movements of the tentacles in actinians. Jour. Expt. Zool. 22. Nervous transmission in actinians. Jour. Expt. Zool. 22. 1918. Rate of transmission in the nerve net of the coelenterates. Jour. Gen. Physiol. 1. 1928. Feeding habits of Metridium. Scot. Nat. **Parker, G. H.,** and **A. P. Marks.** 1928. Ciliary reversal in Metridium. Jour. Expt. Zool. 52. **Parker, G. H.,** and **E. G. Titus.** 1916. Structure of Metridium. Jour. Expt. Zool. 21. **Pax, F.** 1910. Studien an westindischen Actinien. Zool. Jahrb. Sup. 11. 1911. Die Psychologie der Aktinien. Ztschr. angew. Psychol. 4. 1914. Die Aktinien. Ergeb. Fortschr. Zool. 4. 1926. Die Aktinien. Deut. Südpolar Exped. 18. **Philips, C. E. S.** 1927. Fluorescence of sea-anemones. Nature [London]. 119. **Pieron, H.** 1909. La rythmicité chez Actinia. Soc. Biol. [Paris] Compt. Rend. 65; Inst. Gen. Psychol. Bul. 6. **Portmann, A.** 1926. Die Kriechbewegung von Aiptasia. Ztschr. Vergleich. Physiol. 4. **Portielje, A. F.** 1933. On a remarkable purposive feeding behavior in the sea-anemone Diadumene. Tijdschr. Nederl. Dierk. Vereen. 3. **Poulton, E.** 1912. Experimental evidence that commensalism may be beneficial to Crustacea. Zool. Soc. London, Proc. **Pütter, A.** 1911. Das Stoffwechsel der Actinien. Ztschr. Allg. Physiol. 12. **Rand, H. W.** 1915. Wound closure in actinian tentacles. Arch. Entwickl. Mech. Organ. 41. **Raubaud, E.** 1937. Les rapports des Pagures avec les Actinies. Soc. Zool. France, Bul. 62. **Rees, O. M.** 1915. Comparative anatomy of some British actiniae. Jour. Mar. Biol. Assoc. 10. **Sonderhoff, R.** 1936. Das Gift der Seeanemonen. Liebigs Annalen 525. **Sawano, E.** 1932. Digestive enzymes of some coelenterata. Ann. Rpt. Saito Grat. Found. Sendai 8. **Shoup, C. S.** 1932. Salinity in the medium and its effect on respiration in the sea anemone. Ecology 13. **Stephenson, T. A.** 1920. Classification of the Actiniaria. Quart. Jour. Micros. Sci. 64, 65. 1922. Ilyanthus. Jour. Mar. Biol. Assoc. 12. 1928. The British Sea-Anemones. Ray Society. 1929. Nematocysts of sea anemones. Jour. Mar. Biol. Assoc. 16. 1929. Genera Phellia and Sagartia. Roy. Soc. Edinb., Trans. 56. **Sulina, A.** 1914. Zur Kenntnis des Harnsäurestoffwechsels niederer Tiere. Ztschr. Biol. 63. **Takemura, S.** 1938. Proteolytic enzymes in a sea anemone. Tohoku Imp. Univ. Sci. Rpts. Ser. 4, Biol., 12. **Torrey, H. B.** 1898. Monogenesis in Metridium. Calif. Acad. Sci. Proc. Zool. 1. 1902. Variation in Metridium. Wash. Acad. Sci. Proc. 4. 1904. Habits and reactions of Sagartia. Biol. Bul. 6. 1906. California shore anemone Bunodactis. Calif. Univ., Pubs. Zool. 3. **Torrey, H. B.,** and **J. R. Mery.** 1904. Regeneration and asexual reproduction in Sagartia. Calif. Univ., Pubs. Zool. 1. **Trendelenburg, W.** 1909. Gaswechsel bei Symbiose zwischen Alge und Tier. Arch. Anat. Physiol., Physiol. Abt. **Uchida, T.** 1928. Actinian larva parasitic on a Leptomedusa. Proc. Imp. Acad. Tokyo 4. 1934. A brood-caring actinian. Hokkaido Imp. Univ., Faculty Sci. Jour. Zool. 3. **Uexküll, J. von.** 1909. Recherches sur les tentacules de l'Anemonia. Bul. Inst. Oceanogr. Monaco. No. 148. **Verrill, A. E.** 1869. Radiata in the museum of Yale. Conn. Acad. Arts Sci. Trans. 1. 1883. Anthozoa dredged by the Blake. Harvard Univ., Mus. Compar. Zool. Bul. 11. 1898–1899. New American actinians. Amer. Jour. Sci., Ser. 4, Vol. 6. **Walton, A. C.** 1918. Longitudinal fission in Actinia. Jour. Morph. 31. **Walton, A. C.,** and **O. M. Rees.** 1913. Rare and interesting anemones from Plymouth. Jour. Mar. Biol. Assoc. 8, 9, 10. **Willem, V.** 1927. Sur le locomotion des Actinies. Brussels Acad. Roy. Belg. Bul. Cl. Sci. 13.

MADREPORARIA

Agassiz, A. 1903. Coral reefs of the tropical Pacific. Harvard Univ., Mus. Compar. Zool. Bul. 33. **Agassiz, E. C.** and **A. Agassiz.** 1865. Seaside studies in natural history (Astrangia). **Agassiz, L.** 1850. Structure of coral animals. Amer. Assoc. Adv. Sci. Proc. 2. **Atoll of Funafuti.** 1904. Roy. Soc. London, Rpt. Coral Reef Comm. **Borrodaile, L. A.** 1921. Coral-gall prawn Paratypton. Manchester Lit. Philos. Soc. Mem. Proc. 65. **Boschma, H.** 1923. Knospung und verwandte Erscheinungen bei Fungia. Treubia 3. 1925. Feeding reactions and digestion in Astrangia. Biol. Bul. 49. 1929. Food of reef corals. Internatl. Cong. Zool. Budapest, Proc. 1929. Postlarval development of the coral Meandra. Carnegie Inst. Wash. Pub. No. 391. **Bourne, G. C.** 1887. Anatomy of Mussa and Euphyllia. Quart. Jour. Micros. Sci. 28. 1887. Anatomy of Fungia. Quart. Jour. Micros. Sci. 27. 1893. Postembryonic development of Fungia. Roy. Dublin Soc. Trans. 5. **Broch, H.** 1922. Riffkorallen im Nordmeer einst und jetzt. Naturwissenschaften 10. **Carpenter, F. W.** 1910. Feeding mechanism in the rose coral Isophyllia. Amer. Acad. Arts Sci. Proc. 46. **Carruthers, R. G.** 1906. Primary septal plan of the Rugosa. Ann. Mag. Nat. Hist. Ser. 7, Vol. 18. **Cary, L. R.** 1931. Coral reefs of Tutila. Carnegie Inst. Wash. Pub. No. 413. **Crossland, C.** 1928. Ecology of the reef-builders of Tahiti. Zool. Soc. London, Proc. 1935. Coral faunas of the Red Sea and Tahiti. Zool. Soc. London, Proc. **Daly, R. A.** 1915. Glacial-control theory of coral reefs. Amer. Acad. Arts Sci. Proc. 51. **Dana, J. D.** 1890. Corals and coral islands. **Darwin, C.** 1842. Structure and distribution of coral reefs. **Davis, W. M.** 1928. The coral reef problem. Amer. Geogr. Soc. Spec. Publ. 9. **Duerden, J. E.** 1900. Order of appearance of the mesenteries and septa in the Madreporaria. Johns Hopkins Univ. Cir. 19. 1902. West Indian madreporarian polyps. Nat. Acad. Sci. Mem. 8. 1902. Morphology of the Madreporaria.

Ann. Mag. Nat. Hist. Ser. 7, vol. 10. 1904. Recent results on the morphology and development of coral polyps. Smithsn. Misc. Collect. 47. 1904. Morphology of the Madreporaria. V. Septal sequence. Biol. Bul. 7. 1904. Coral Siderastraea and its postlarval development. Carnegie Inst. Wash. Pub. 20. 1906. Primary septa of the Rugosa. Ann. Mag. Nat. Hist. Ser. 7, Vol. 18. 1906. Role of mucus in corals. Quart. Jour. Micros. Sci. 49. **Duerden, J. E.,** and **S. A. Ayres.** 1905 Nerve net in the coral Coenopsammia. Mich. Acad. Sci. Arts Letters 7th Ann. Rpt. **Edmondson, C. H.** 1928. Ecology of an Hawaiian coral reef. Bul. Bernice Bishop Mus. 45. **Eguchi, M.** 1938. Reef-building corals of the Palao Islands. Palao Trop. Biol. Sta. Studies 3. **Faustino, L. A.** 1927. Madreporaria of the Philippine Islands. Manila Bur. Sci., Monog. 22. **Fewkes, J. W.** 1889. Anatomy of Astrangia danae. **Fowler, G. H.** 1885–1889. Anatomy of the Madreporaria. Quart. Jour. Micros. Sci. 25, 27, 28, 30. **Gardiner, J. S.** 1901. Rate of growth of some corals from Fiji. Cambridge Phil. Soc. Proc. 11. 1902. South African corals of the genus Flabellum. Mar. Invest. So. Africa. 2. 1931. Coral reefs and atolls. **Great Barrier Reef Comn.** Brisbane, Rpts. Vol. 2, 1928, Vol. 4, 1938. **Horst, C. J.** 1923. Arrangement of the septa in eupsammid corals. Bijdragen tot de Dierk. 22. **Hosoi, K.** 1938. Occurrence of glycogen and its content in Fungia. Palao Trop. Biol. Sta. Stud. 3. **Kawaguti, S.** 1937. Physiology of reef corals. Palao Trop. Biol. Sta. Stud. 2. **Koch, G. v.** 1897. Entwicklung von Caryophyllia. Mitt. Zool. Stat. Neapel. 12. **Lister, J. J.** 1888. Natural history of Fungia. Quart. Jour. Micros. Sci. 29. **Manton, S. M.** 1932. Growth of the adult colony of Pocillopora. Great Barrier Reef Exped., Sci. Rpts. 3. **Marshall, S. M.** 1932. Oxygen production of coral planulae. Great Barrier Reef Exped., Sci. Rpts. 1. **Marshall, S. M.,** and **T. A. Stephenson.** 1933. Breeding of corals. Great Barrier Reef Exped. Sci. Rpts. 3. **Matthai, G.** 1918. Reactions to stimuli in corals. Cambridge Phil. Soc. Proc. 19. 1918. Is the madreporarian skeleton an extraprotoplasmic secretion of the polyps? Cambridge Phil. Soc., Proc. 19. 1923. Histology of the soft parts of astraeid corals. Quart. Jour. Micros. Sci. 67. 1926. Colony formation in astraeid corals. Roy. Soc. London, Philos. Trans. 214 B. 1928. Monograph of the recent meandroid Astraeidae. Brit. Mus. Cat. Madrepor. Corals 7. **Mavor, J. W.** 1915. Development of the coral Agaricia. Amer. Acad. Arts Sci. Proc. 51. **Murray, John.** 1880. Structure and origin of coral reefs. Roy. Soc. Edinb. Proc. 10. **Obe, J.** 1938. Feeding behavior and nematocysts of Fungia and 15 other species of reef corals. Palao Trop. Biol. Sta. Studies 3. **Ogilvie, M. M.** 1896. Microscopic and systematic study of madreporarian types of corals. Roy. Soc. London, Phil. Trans. 187 B. **Potts, F. A.** 1915. Harpalocarcinus, the gall-forming crab. Carnegie Inst. Wash. Dept. Marine Biol. Papers 8. **Richards, H. C.** 1938. Work of the Great Barrier Reef Comm. Austral. Jour. Expt. Biol. Med. Sci. 1. **Robinson, W. I.** 1917. Relationship of the Tetracoralla to the Hexacoralla. Conn. Acad. Arts Sci. Trans. 21. **Roughley, T. C.** 1936. Wonders of the Great Barrier Reef. **Saville-Kent, W.** 1893. The Great Barrier Reef of Australia. **Stephenson, T. A.** 1931. Development and formation of colonies in Pocillopora and Porites. Great Barrier Reef Exped., Sci. Rpts. 3. 1933. Growth and asexual reproduction in corals. Great Barrier Reef Exped., Sci. Rpts. 4. **Tamura, T.,** and **L. Hada.** 1932. Growth rate of reef-building corals. Tohoku Imp. Univ. Sci. Rpts. Ser. 4. Biol. Vol. 7. **Thiel, M. E.** 1929. Zur Frage der Ernährung der Steinkorallen. Zool. Anz. 81. **Vaughan, T. W.** 1907. Recent Madreporaria of the Hawaiian Islands. U. S. Natl. Mus. Bul. 59. 1916. Ecology of the Floridian and Bahaman shoal-water corals. Nation. Acad. Sci. Wash., Proc. 2. 1917. Corals and the formation of coral reefs. Smithsn. Inst. Ann. Rpt. 1918. Some shoal-water corals from Murray Island, Cocos-Keeling Island, and Fanning Islands. Carnegie Inst. Wash., Pub. 213

Wilson, H. V. 1888. Development of Manicina. Jour. Morph. 2. **Wood-Jones, F.** 1908. Rate of growth of the reef-building corals. Zool. Anz. 33. 1912. Corals and atolls. **Yonge, C. M.** 1930. A year on the Great Barrier Reef. 1930. Studies on the physiology of corals. I, III. Great Barrier Reef Exped., Sci. Rpts. 1. 1936. Studies on the biology of Tortugas corals. Papers Tortugas Lab. 29, 31. **Yonge, C. M., and A. G. Nicholls.** 1930-1932. Studies on the physiology of corals, II, III-VI. Great Barrier Reef Exped., Sci. Rpts. 1.

ZOANTHIDEA

Carlgren, O. 1906. Actinienlarven. Zoanthidea. Nord. Plankton XI, Lief. 5. **Duerden, J. E.** 1900. Jamaican Actiniaria. II. Roy. Soc. Dublin Sci. Trans. 7. 1900. Report on the actinians of Porto Rico. U. S. Fish Comn. Bul. 20, Pt. 2. 1914. The antiquity of the zoanthid actinians. Mich. Acad. Sci., Arts, Letters, Ann. Rpt. 6. **Lwowsky, F.** 1913. Revision der Gattung Sidisia (Epizoanthus). Zool. Jahrb., Abt. System. Geog. Biol. Tiere 34. **McMurrich, J. P.** 1889. Actiniaria of the Bahama Islands. Jour. Morph. 3. 1899. Mesenterial filaments in Zoanthus. Zool. Bul. 2. **Menon, K. R.** 1902. Notes on Semper's larvae. Cambridge Phil. Soc. Proc. 11. **Pax, F.** 1937. Krustenanemone. Deutsch. Ital. Instit. Meeresbiol. Rovigno. Thalassia 2. **Pax, F., and H. Lochter.** 1935. Epizoanthus, eine neue Carcinoecien bildende Krustenanemone. Not. Instit. Biol. Rovigno 17. **Seifert, R.** 1928. Die Nesselkapseln der Zoantharien. Zool. Jahrb., Abt. System. Geog. Biol. Tiere 55. **Semper, C.** 1867. Über einige tropische Larvenformen. Ztschr. Wiss. Zool. 17.

ANTIPATHARIA

Broch, H. 1920. Antipatharia. Michaelsen, Meeresfauna W. Afrika 2. **Brook, G.** 1889. Report on the Antipatharia. Challenger Rpts. Zool. 32. **Cooper, C.** 1909. Antipatharia of the Percy Sladen Trust Exped. Linn. Soc. London, Trans. Zool. 7. **Dantan, J. L.** 1921. Recherches sur les Antipathaires. Arch. Anat. Micros. 17. **Koch, G. von.** 1878. Zur Phylogenie der Antipatharia. Morph. Jahrb. 9. 1889. Die Antipatharien des Golfes von Neapel. Mitt. Zool. Stat. Neapel 9. **Pax, F.** 1918. Die Antipatharien. Zool. Jahrb., Abt. System. Geog. Biol. Tiere 41. 1914. Beiträge zur Histologie des Antipatharienkörpers. Zool. Jahrb., Abt. Anat. Ontog. Tiere 38. 1918. Die Antipatharien. Zool. Jahrb., Abt. System. Geog. Biol. Tiere 41. 1925. Die Antipatharien. Deut. Tiefsee Exped. 19. **Pesch, U. J. van.** 1914. Die Antipatharia. Siboga Exped. Monog. 17. **Roule, L.** 1904. La place des Antipathaires dans le systématique. Bull. Mus. Oceanogr. Monaco 16. **Schultze, L. S.** 1903. Die Antipatharien. Deut. Tiefsee Exped. 3. **Tischbierek, H.** 1936. Die Nesselkapseln der Antipatharien. Thesis, Breslau. Abstract Zool. Ber. 43, No. 504. **Totten, A. K.** 1923. Antipatharia and their cirripede commensals. Brit. Antarct. Exped. Nat. Hist. Rpt. Zool. 5. **Van Beneden, E.** 1897. Les Anthozoaires de la Plankton Expedition. Ergeb. Plankton Exped. 2 K e.

CERIANTHARIA

Bourne, G. C. 1920. Arachnactis. Quart. Jour. Micros. Sci. 64. **Carlgren, O.** 1893. Septenmuskulature bei Ceriantheen. Öfvers Kungl. Svenska Vetensk. Akad. Forhandl. 50. 1912. Ceriantharia. Danish Ingolf Exped. 5. 1924. Die Larven von Ceriantharien, Zoantharien, und Actiniarien. Deut. Tiefsee Exped. 19. **Child, C. M.** 1903-1908. Form regulation in Cerianthus. Biol. Bul. 5, 6, 7, 8, 15. **Faurot, L.** 1891. Cerianthus membranaceus. Soc. Zool. France Mém. 4. 1892.

Développement du Cerianthus. Soc. Zool. France, Bul. 17. **Heider, A. V.** 1879. Cerianthus membranaceus. Akad. Wiss. Wien, Math. Nat. Kl. Sitzb. 79, Pt. 1. **Kingsley, J. S.** 1904. Cerianthus borealis. Tufts Col. Studies 1. **Loeb, J.** 1905. Studies in general physiology. **McMurrich, J. P.** 1890. Structure of Cerianthus americanus. Jour. Morph. 4. 1910. Ceriantharia. Siboga Exped. Monog. 15a. 1910. Genus Arachnactis. Jour. Expt. Zool. 9. **Moore, Mary.** 1927. Reactions of Cerianthus to light. Jour. Gen. Physiol. 8. **Torelli, B.** 1939. Istologia e senescenza in Cerianthus. Pubbl. Staz. Zool. Napoli 17. **Van Beneden, E.** 1891. Recherches sur le développement des Arachnactis. Arch. Biol. 11. **Vanhöffen, E.** 1895. Anatomie und Entwicklungsgeschichte von Arachnactis. Biblioth. Zool. 20.

CHAPTER VIII

THE RADIATE PHYLA—PHYLUM CTENOPHORA

I. CHARACTERS OF THE PHYLUM

1. Introduction.—Although *Beroë* was probably known to the ancients, the first definite account with recognizable figures of ctenophores is that of a ship's doctor Martens who saw *Mertensia* and *Bolinopsis* in the vicinity of Spitzbergen in 1671. Linnaeus placed two species of ctenophores in his group Zoophyta under the name *Volvox*, included among a mixture of lower invertebrates. In Cuvier's early system, *Beroë* was classified under Zoophytes along with medusae and anthozoans, and, in the first edition (1817) of his Règne animal, several genera of ctenophores were mentioned under Zoophyta, class Acalephes. Following much collecting of coelenterates on oceanic voyages, Eschscholtz was able in 1829–1833 to make the first rational arrangement of pelagic coelenterates, creating the orders Ctenophorae, Discophorae (all medusae), and Siphonophorae, understanding the first and last groups in their present sense. These orders were made subdivisions of the class Acalepha, regarded as intermediate between zoophytes and echinoderms. As already mentioned, Leuckart in 1847–1848 first achieved the separation of the coelenterates from the echinoderms, but his phylum Coelenterata also included sponges and ctenophores. Vosmaer (1877) was responsible for the separation of the sponges from the coelenterates, and Hatschek (1889) removed the ctenophores as a separate group. Although many zoologists still retain the ctenophores in the phylum Coelenterata we here follow Hatschek in regarding them as a distinct phylum.

2. Definition.—The Ctenophora are biradially symmetrical Radiata without nematocysts, with a gelatinous ectomesoderm containing mesenchymal muscle fibers, and with eight meridional rows of ciliary plates present throughout life or (in two genera) in the larva only.

3. General Characters of the Phylum.—The Ctenophora constitute the second and last of the radiate phyla. They resemble the coelenterates in their general symmetry relations, with parts arranged with reference to an oral-aboral axis, in the general structure of the digestive system, in the gelatinous nature of the mesenchyme, in the absence of internal spaces other than the digestive cavity, and in the general lack of organ systems. But the presence of mesenchymal muscles, the more definite organization of the digestive system, and the occurrence of an aboral sensory region indicate a higher structural grade than that of the coelenterates.

The ctenophores are monomorphic, without any trace of polymorphism or of attached stages. The primitive shape is spheroidal, but modifications to laterally or dorsoventrally compressed shapes occur. The general construction is similar to that of scyphomedusae—there is an external and an internal epithelium with a collenchyme between, containing amoebocytes, connective-tissue fibers, and muscle cells differentiated directly from mesenchyme cells. The symmetry is always very definitely of the biradial type. The most distinguishing external feature is the presence on the surface of eight meridional rows of ciliary plates. Nematocysts are wholly absent. Tentacles are often present in a biradial arrangement, provided in place of nematocysts with adhesive cells. All the systems remain at the tissue grade of construction except for indications of genital ducts in some forms. The digestive system as in coelenterates is essentially an epithelial sac but is provided with a large stomodaeum and branches extensively through the collenchyme. Muscles as already noted are independent fibers often showing some aggregation into bundles. The nervous system is similar to that of coelenterates, consisting of a subepidermal plexus concentrated into eight strands beneath the plate rows. Skeleton and excretory systems are absent. The gonads arise in the walls of the digestive canals. Development is of the mosaic type, very different from that of coelenterates, a planula larva is lacking (one possible exception), and a very distinctive larval type, the cydippid larva, resembling the primitive genera of ctenophores, is of general occurrence.

The ctenophores are exclusively marine, of planktonic habit, although some have become modified for a creeping existence.

II. CLASSIFICATION OF THE PHYLUM

The ctenophores are usually subdivided as follows. 80 species.

Class I. Tentaculata. With tentacles.

Order 1. Cydippida (Cydippidea or Cydippea). Of simple rounded or oval form; gastrovascular branches ending blindly; with two branched tentacles retractile into sheaths.

Order 2. Lobata. With two large oral lobes and four auricles; tentacles various, without sheaths; oral ends of gastrovascular canals anastomosed.

Order 3. Cestida (Cestidea or Cestoidea). Compressed in the tentacular plane to a band-like form; four of the plate rows rudimentary; two main tentacles reduced, sheaths present; two rows of small tentacles along the oral edge.

Order 4. Platyctenea. Aberrant ctenophores, compressed in the oral-aboral plane to a flattened form, creeping: with two tentacles and sheaths; comb rows may be present in the larva only.

Class II. Nuda. Without tentacles.

Order 5. Beroida. Of conical form, with very wide mouth and pharynx; meridional gastrovascular canals with numerous side branches.

III. GENERAL MORPHOLOGY AND PHYSIOLOGY

1. General Morphology.—The ctenophores, commonly called comb jellies or sea walnuts, are typically transparent gelatinous forms of

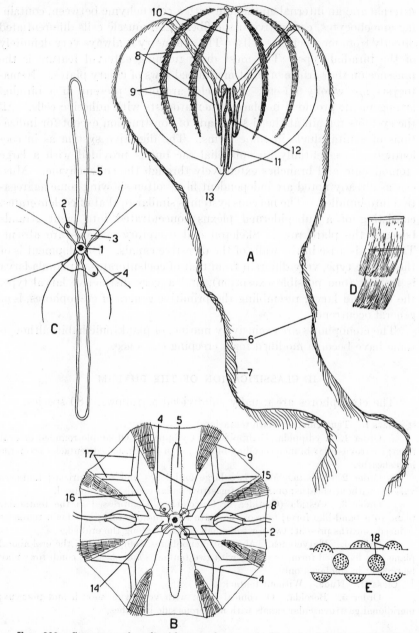

Fig. 209.—Structure of cydippid ctenophores. *A. Pleurobrachia*, from life, Puget Sound. *B.* View of same from aboral pole. *C.* Aboral sense organ and polar fields of same. *D.* Ciliated plates of same, enlarged. *E.* Magnified view of lateral filament of tentacle. 1, statocyst; 2, anal pores; 3, blind ends of anal canals; 4, ciliated furrows; 5, polar fields; 6, tentacle; 7, lateral filaments of tentacle; 8, tentacle sheath; 9, comb row; 10, aboral canal; 11, pharyngeal canal; 12, pharynx; 13 mouth; 14, transverse canal; 15, tentacular canal; 16, interradial canal; 17, meridional canal; 18, colloblasts.

moderate size and radiate construction. The ground plan of the group is best described with reference to its simpler, more generalized members, those belonging to the order Cydippida, including such genera as *Pleurobrachia* (Fig. 209*A*) and *Hormiphora*. The cydippids have a rounded, oval, egg-shaped, or pyriform gelatinous body, usually somewhat flattened in one plane so that the cross section is oval. One pole, the oral, bears in its center the mouth opening, while the opposite pole, the aboral or sensory pole, is occupied by a complicated sense organ of the nature of a statocyst (Fig. 210*B*). On the surface occur eight equally spaced meridional rows of little plates, which begin near the aboral pole and terminate before reaching the oral pole. Each plate is composed of a transverse band of long fused cilia (Fig. 209*D*) and hence from its appearance is termed a *comb* or *ctene* (whence the name Ctenophora, or comb bearers). The rows of combs are known as *plate rows, comb rows, ribs,* or *costae*. At opposite points on the surface between two comb rows is found a deep pouch, the *tentacle sheath,* to whose inner wall is fastened the tentacle base. The two tentacles are very long, very extensile, solid filaments bearing a row of lateral branches, and they can be completely retracted into the sheath.

With these main external features in mind, the symmetry relations may now be defined. The parts are arranged with reference to the oral-aboral axis extending from mouth to statocyst. Some parts, such as the comb rows, appear radially disposed, but the presence of only two tentacles and tentacle sheaths at opposite points on the surface changes the symmetry to the biradial type, and as will appear shortly the branches of the gastrovascular system also follow the biradial plan (Figs. 209*B* and 210*A*). In biradial symmetry, as explained in connection with anemones, the parts are arranged with reference to two vertical planes, a *sagittal* and a *transverse.* There has been no agreement as to which plane shall be called sagittal and which transverse in ctenophores; but on the whole it seems best to adhere to the terminology adopted for Anthozoa and term that plane *sagittal* (also called *median* and *stomodaeal* plane) in which the long axis of the flattened stomodaeum lies. The plane at right angles to the sagittal plane bisects the tentacle sheaths symmetrically and is called the *tentacular, transverse,* or *lateral* plane. Two identical halves can be obtained by bisecting the animal along either the sagittal or the tentacular plane; but a sagittal half is not identical with a tentacular half. The plane across the body may be termed *equatorial.* None of the comb rows lies along the principal planes, but two occur in each of the quadrants formed by the intersection of the two principal planes. These quadrants may be considered *interradial* and the comb rows *adradial,* borrowing the terminology used for medusae. The four comb rows situated near the two ends of the sagittal plane are conveniently

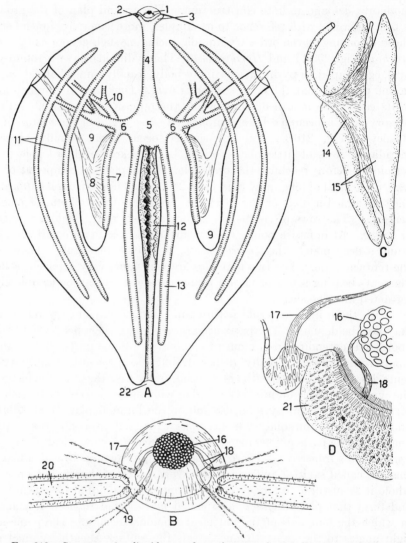

Fig. 210.—Structure of cydippid ctenophores (continued). *A*. Diagram of the digestive system of a cydippid. *B*. Statocyst enlarged. (*Based on figures of Chun, 1880.*) *C*. Tentacle base. *D*. Histological structure of statocyst, half shown. (*C and D after R. Hertwig, 1880.*) 1, statocyst; 2, anal pore; 3, anal canal; 4, aboral canal; 5, stomach; 6, transverse canal; 7, tentacular canal; 8, tentacle base; 9, tentacle sheath; 10, interradial canal; 11, meridional canal; 12, pharynx; 13, pharyngeal canal; 14, central muscular part of tentacle base; 15, lateral swellings of tentacle base, containing the tentacular canals; 16, statoliths; 17, dome; 18, balancers; 19, ciliated furrows; 20, polar fields; 21, epidermis of floor of statocyst; 22, mouth.

termed the *subsagittal* rows and the other four, near the ends of the tentacular plane, the *subtentacular* rows.

The gastrovascular system ramifies throughout the thick mass of jelly (Fig. 210*A*). The mouth, often elongated in the sagittal plane, leads into a tube, also much elongated sagittally, hence flattened in the tentacular plane, which was formerly called stomach but is known from embryology to be a *stomodaeum* or *pharynx*. Its much folded walls appear to perform most of the work of digestion. It extends about two-thirds of the distance to the aboral pole and then opens by way of a short constricted portion, sometimes called *esophagus*, into a chamber, the true *stomach*, formerly termed *infundibulum* or *funnel*. The stomach is entodermal and is flattened in the sagittal plane, i.e., at right angles to the plane of flattening of the pharynx. From the stomach arise the canals of the gastrovascular system, which course in a very definite arrangement through the jelly. From the roof of the stomach an *aboral* or *infundibular* canal runs to the underside of the statocyst where it gives off four so-called *excretory* canals, which extend to the aboral surface terminating in little sacs or ampullae (Fig. 209*C*). Two of these, diagonally opposite, open on the surface by the so-called *excretory pores;* the other two are blind. Since it is definitely known that these canals and pores serve for the ejection of indigestible matter, they will here be termed the *anal canals* and *pores*. They lie in the interradii. From its oral surface the stomach gives off a pair of *pharyngeal* or *paragastric* canals, which run orally, one along each flattened surface of the pharynx, and terminate blindly near the mouth (Fig. 210*A*). From each side of the stomach in the tentacular plane, a large *transverse* canal arises and proceeds horizontally as the *tentacular* canal, terminating blindly in the tentacular sheath; but before reaching the sheath each gives off on each side an *interradial canal*, which again bifurcates so that there are four branches in each tentacular half of the body (Fig. 209*B*). Each of these eight canals proceeds to the inner side of a comb row, where it elongates orally and aborally into a curved *meridional* canal underlying the length of each comb row (Fig. 210*A*). The biradial arrangement of the gastrovascular canals is a prominent feature of ctenophore morphology.

The sensory region at the aboral pole presents a number of details (Fig. 210*B, D*). Its center is occupied by the statocyst, which has a concave floor of tall ciliated epidermal cells. From four points, interradially located in this sensory floor, four very long S-shaped tufts of cilia, termed *balancers*, project upward and meet to support a rounded mass of calcareous spherules which constitute the *statolith*. The whole is enclosed as in a bell jar by a transparent dome, the *cupule* or *bell*, which seems to be composed of modified fused cilia springing from the edge of the sensory floor. The statolith spherules are said to be formed in the epidermal

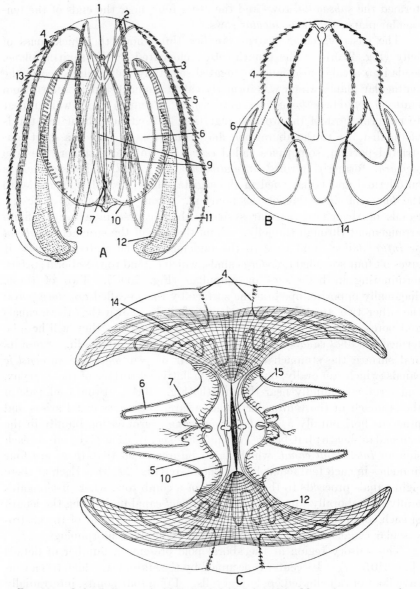

Fig. 211.—Order Lobata.   *A. Mnemiopsis leidyi*, from life, Massachusetts, seen from the tentacular side.   *B.* Young *Mnemiopsis*, seen from the sagittal surface, to show the oral lobe.   *C.* Oral view of *Mnemiopsis.* (*After Mayer,* 1912.)   1, statocyst; 2, meridional canals; 3, subtentacular comb rows; 4, subsagittal comb rows; 5, row of tentacles in auricular groove; 6, auricles; 7, main tentacle; 8, pharynx; 9, pharyngeal canals; 10, their continuations along the labial ridge; 11, oral lobe; 12, muscle fibers of oral lobe; 13, muscle bundles; 14, loop from subsagittal canals; 15, mouth.

cells of the floor and then to be ejected together with the remnants of these cells. The whole structure presumably serves as an organ of equilibrium, since changes in the position of the animal with respect to gravity would alter the pressure of the statolith on the balancers. Around the statocyst in the interradii are seen the four ampullae of the anal canals, two blind and two opening by pores (Fig. 209B). From each balancer two *ciliated furrows* run out along the four interradii to the beginning of the two comb rows of each quadrant. The sensory floor of the statocyst continues on each side in the sagittal plane as a long ciliated depression termed the *polar plates* or *polar fields,* presumably sensory (Fig. 209C).

The variations in general structure seen among the ctenophore orders may now be briefly considered. The cydippids conform to the described plan. In the Lobata (Figs. 211, and 218) the oval body is somewhat compressed in the tentacular plane and is expanded in the sagittal plane on either side of the mouth as a rounded muscular *oral lobe,* very large in some forms. As a result, the four subsagittal comb rows are longer than for the four subtentacular ones; and from the lower ends of the latter, short or long, sometimes spirally coiled, processes, the *auricles,* with a ciliated edge, project above the mouth, two on each side (Fig. 211). Typical cydippid tentacles and sheaths are present in the cydippid larva of the Lobata, but the tentacle sheaths disappear during metamorphosis, and the tentacles move orally until they lie practically alongside the mouth. There is also a row of short tentacles lying in the ciliated *auricular grooves* (Fig. 211A). In the lobate digestive system the two transverse canals are lacking so that the four interradial canals spring directly from the stomach. The shift in the position of the main tentacles brings about an elongation of the tentacular canals that underlie the auricular grooves. The four subtentacular meridional canals loop around the edges of the auricles and then anastomose with the oral ends of the two pharyngeal canals to form a ring around the mouth, which is drawn out into a loop in each oral lobe (Fig. 211B, C). The two subsagittal meridional canals of each side also unite by way of sinuous loops inside each oral lobe.

The cestids, represented chiefly by the Venus's girdle, *Cestum veneris,* exaggerate the peculiarities of the Lobata. The process of transverse compression begun in that order is carried in the cestids to such an extent that the body is elongated in the sagittal plane to a flattened gelatinous band, which may be $1\frac{1}{2}$ m. long (Fig. 212A). As a result the four subtentacular comb rows are reduced to very short lengths (Fig. 212B) while the four subsagittal rows are elongated to run along the entire aboral edge of the band-like body (Fig. 212A). The tentacle sheaths and tentacles have shifted orally to a position alongside the mouth, and the tentacles are reduced to a tuft of filaments. As in the

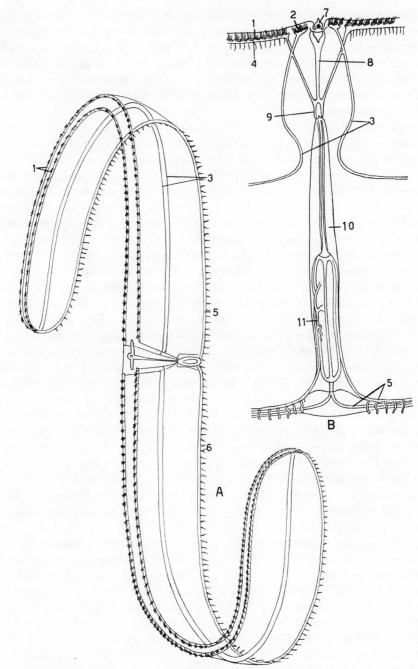

Fig. 212.—Order Cestida. *A. Velamen.* *B.* Central region of *Cestum veneris.* (*A and B after Mayer,* 1912.) 1, subsagittal comb rows; 2, subtentacular comb rows; 3, subtentacular meridional canals; 4, subsagittal meridional canals; 5, pharyngeal canals; 6, tentacles; 7, statocyst; 8, aboral canal; 9, stomach; 10, pharynx; 11, main tentacle.

Lobata there are also two rows of short tentacles running in grooves along the entire oral edge of the band. The four interradial meridional canals arise directly from the stomach. The subsagittal canals accompany the corresponding comb rows along the whole aboral edge. The four subtentacular ones descend to an equatorial position and then run, two on each side, along the middle of the band to its ends (Fig. 212B). The two pharyngeal canals on reaching the mouth level fork and proceed along the oral edge. Thus each half of the band contains two subsagittal meridional canals along its aboral edge, two subtentacular ones in its middle, and two pharyngeal ones along its oral edge, all running horizontally. The six anastomose at the ends of the band.

The beroids are conical or thimble-shaped, compressed in the tentacular plane, with a very large mouth opening and pharynx (Fig. 213A). All traces of tentacles and tentacle sheaths are absent even in the larva. The rounded polar fields are edged with branched papillae (Fig. 213B). The small stomach lies very near the statocyst and from it the four interradial canals spring directly (Fig. 213B). Because of the great expansion of the pharynx the pharyngeal canals run close to the surface, in the center of each broad side of the animal. Meridional and pharyngeal canals give off along their lengths numerous branched lateral diverticula (Fig. 213A), which may anastomose into a network. At their oral ends the meridional and pharyngeal canals of each half unite by a canal running along the mouth rim; and in some species those of the two halves are also united to form a ring canal around the mouth. The comb rows are of equal length and extend from over half to nearly the entire length of the animal in different species.

The Platyctenea are highly modified ctenophores that through great oral-aboral flattening have assumed a creeping mode of life. They will be described in connection with the order.

The epidermis is either syncytial or a cuboidal to columnar epithelium, ciliated in certain regions, and often very granular and apparently has a general glandular function. In many forms, however, the epidermal cells are interspersed with numerous gland cells, of both the mucous and granular types, often filled with large spheres (Fig. 214A, B). The epidermis may also contain pigment granules, or special branched pigment cells (melanophores) may be present. Two sorts of sensory cells have been described: some with several stiff bristles (Fig. 214F) and others with a single stout projection (Fig. 214E). The ciliated cells of the polar fields are also considered sensory, although evidence for this view is lacking. In some lobate and cestid ctenophores, the surface bears contractile sensory papillae (Fig. 218A) whose tips are loaded with gland and sensory cells and are very sensitive to contact. The combs as already remarked consist of a horizontal row of very long cilia (Fig. 209D) that spring from a basal cushion of tall epidermal cells (Fig. 215E). The ciliated furrows that run from the statocyst to the beginnings of the comb rows are formed of epidermal cells bearing two or three cilia. In

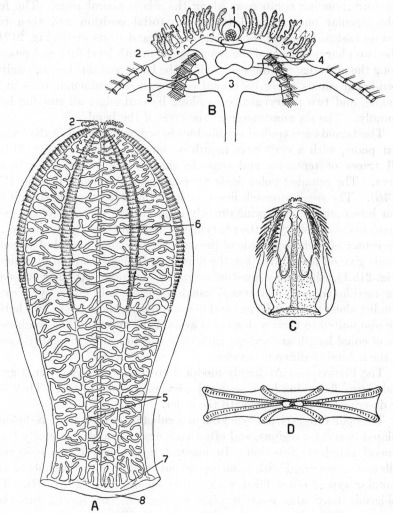

Fig. 213.—*Beroë*. *A.* Adult *Beroë*, preserved. *B.* Aboral region of *Beroë*, enlarged. *C.* Cydippid larva of *Beroë*. *D.* View of *Beroë* from the aboral end, showing great flattening. (*B–D after Mayer, 1912.*) 1, statocyst; 2, branched papillae of polar fields; 3, stomach; 4, aboral canals; 5, meridional canals; 6, pharyngeal canal; 7, canal along mouth rim; 8, mouth.

most ctenophores the area between successive combs in the row is covered by ordinary epithelium, but in many Lobata the combs of a row are connected by a ciliated band. It seems probable that the combs differentiated from such bands.

The tentacles are of complicated structure. They are solid, composed of a core covered by an epidermis that consists largely or entirely of the characteristic adhesive or "lasso" cells, better termed *colloblasts* (Fig. 214*C*, *D*, *G*). Each colloblast has a hemispherical head containing granules that discharge as a sticky secretion, utilized in the capture of prey. The head is fastened to the tentacle core by way of a contractile *spiral filament*, which encircles a *straight filament* (Fig. 214*G*). The colloblast develops from a single cell whose nucleus becomes the straight filament (Fig. 214*H–L*). The tentacle core varies in construction in different parts of the tentacle and in different species. There is usually a small central strand, probably nervous, and the rest of the core may consist entirely of muscle fibers, or the muscles may be arranged in bundles with mesogloea between (Fig. 214*C*, *D*). The tentacle grows at its base inside the tentacle sheath and there is continuous with the body layers. The tentacle sheath is an invaginated epidermal pouch lined by a flattened ciliated epithelium. The tentacle base consists of three parts (Fig. 210*C*), a median region where the muscle bundles of the core originate and paired lateral elongated swellings, each containing the blind end of a tentacular canal and covered with a thickened epidermis continuous with the epidermal layer of the tentacle (Fig. 215*A*). This thickened epidermis is composed of numerous small darkly staining cells that are the mother cells of the colloblasts.

The lining of the pharynx is similar to the surface epidermis, consisting of gland cells and supporting cells bearing a thick tuft of cilia (Fig. 214*B*). In *Beroë* the pharyngeal lining just inside the mouth rim is highly specialized into three bands composed, respectively, from the edge inward, of ciliated cells, gland cells, and sensory cells having a single thick projection.

The stomach and gastrovascular canals are lined by a simple epithelium of entodermal origin, thicker and highly vacuolated on the outer side of the canals (i.e., the side in contact with the comb rows, tentacle roots, and other organs), low and ciliated on the inner side (Fig. 215*B*). The thick epithelium probably serves for intracellular digestion while the flat portion functions to produce a current. Peculiar to the canals are the "cell rosettes," consisting of two circles of ciliated gastrodermal cells surrounding a small opening into the collenchyme (Fig. 215*C*). The cilia of one circle beat toward the collenchyme, those of the other toward the canal lumen. The function of these rosettes is unknown, but they are probably excretory or act as regulators of the fluid content of the collenchyme.

The collenchyme is interpretable as an ectomesoderm; it consists of a gelatinous substratum containing scattered cells, connective-tissue fibers, probably nervous tissue, and above all numerous muscle fibers (Fig. 214*M*). All the cells of the collenchyme including the muscle fibers

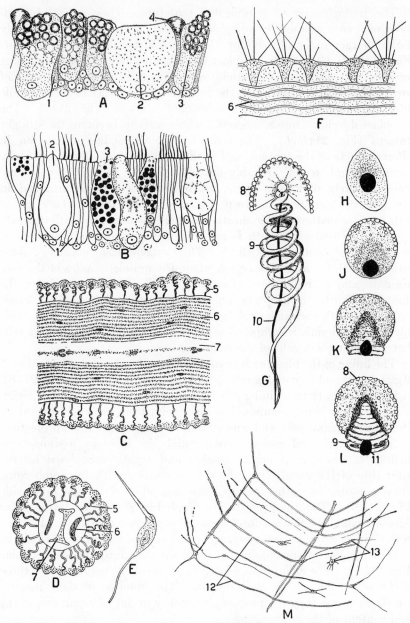

Fig. 214.—Histology of ctenophores. *A.* Epidermis of *Coeloplana.* *B.* Pharyngeal lining, *Coeloplana.* *C.* Longitudinal section of tentacle. *D.* Cross section of lateral filament of tentacle. *E.* Sensory cell with single bristle. *F.* Sensory cells of tentacle with several hairs. *G.* Colloblast. *H–L.* Stages of development of a colloblast from an epidermal cell. *M.* Collenchyme of *Pleurobrachia,* from life, showing amoebocytes and

are of ectodermal origin, according to Hatschek's account of the embryology (see page 679).

The muscle fibers are independent cells not related to either the epidermis or the gastrodermis but arising by the direct transformation of amoeboid mesenchyme cells. They are elongated fibers of the smooth type, sometimes anastomosed, often with branching ends (Fig. 214M). Their disposition varies in different species. Usually there are longitudinal and circular fibers at the surface just beneath the epidermis, similar fibers along the pharynx, often sphincters around the mouth and the statocyst, and radial fibers extending between pharynx and body surface. The oral lobes of the Lobata have on their inner surfaces a crisscross arrangement of muscle fibers (Fig. 211C), making them very contractile. The muscle bundles of the tentacles were already noted; they are chiefly longitudinal.

Whether or not the ctenophores possess a differentiated nervous system and whether the beating of the combs is nervously controlled or not are questions that have been agitated for decades. Fortunately the matter has now been definitely settled by the work of Heider (1927), who completely verifies the findings of R. Hertwig in 1880. The ctenophores possess a distinct nervous system of the same type as that of the Cnidaria. There is a general subepidermal plexus throughout the surface, composed of multipolar ganglion cells and neurites (Fig. 215D). Whether the neurites actually anastomose or only make contact as found by Bozler for coelenterates (page 397) was not determined with certainty by Heider, but Hertwig's figures indicate a system of the synaptic type (Fig. 215D). Beneath the ciliated furrows and the comb rows the meshes of the plexus are elongated so that the neurites are brought close together to form a strand imitating a nerve; but these eight strands are not nerves, merely compressed parts of the plexus. The basal cushions of the combs are permeated with a rich plexus of nerve tissue, containing cells and neurites and continuous with the nerve strand of the comb row. The plexus forms a ring around the mouth. The nervous system is thus diffuse as in the Cnidaria with no concentration of ganglion cells into ganglia and no region of central control. R. Hertwig described nerve fibers passing into the collenchyme to supply the muscles, and although Heider did not succeed in seeing them their existence is scarcely to be doubted.

Whether the ctenophores possess an excretory system cannot be stated. The cell rosettes may have an excretory function. The anal

---

muscle cells. (*A, B, G–L, after Komai,* 1922; *others, except M, after R. Hertwig,* 1880.) 1, ordinary epidermal cell; 2, clear type of gland cell; 3, granular type of gland cell; 4, degenerate gland cell; 5, colloblasts; 6, muscle fibers; 7, tentacle core; 8, adhesive spherules; 9, spiral filament; 10, straight filament; 11, nucleus; 12, muscle fibers; 13, amoebocytes.

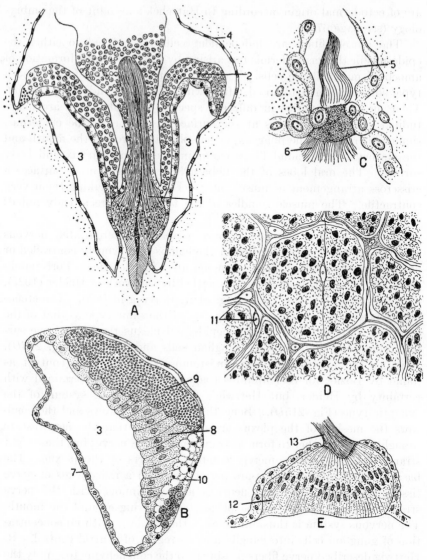

FIG. 215.—Histology of ctenophores (continued). *A.* Section of tentacle base. *B.* Section through a meridional canal showing gonads. *C.* Rosette of *Coeloplana.* *D.* Surface of *Beroë,* showing the nerve net. *E.* Section through comb base. (*C. After Komai,* 1922; *others after R. Hertwig,* 1880.) 1, muscular center of tentacle base; 2, epidermis of lateral thickenings; 3, tentacular canal; 4, lining of tentacle sheath; 5, ciliary tuft on side leading into collenchyme; 6, cilia of side facing gastrovascular canal; 7, inner thin wall of meridional canal; 8, outer thick wall of same; 9, testis; 10, ovary; 11, ganglion cells; 12, thickened epidermis of comb base; 13, base of cilia of comb.

canals and pores of the gastrovascular system are not known to perform any excretory function but serve rather for the voiding of indigestible particles. Certain ciliated epidermal sacs found in the peculiar ctenophore *Tjalfiella* (see below) have been regarded by some as modified invaginated combs forming a primitive excretory system, but this interpretation is purely conjectural.

All the ctenophores are hermaphroditic, and many have two periods of sexual maturity, one in the larva and a final one in the adult, with a degeneration of the gonads between the two phases. This peculiar phenomenon has been termed *dissogeny;* whether the larva actually produces normal offspring does not seem to be known. The gonads nearly always occur in the walls of the meridional canals as continuous or discontinuous bands, the ovary on one side and the testis on the other (Fig. 215*B*), so arranged that, in adjacent canals, like gonads face each other and the ovaries are always next to the principal planes. The ripe sex cells are discharged through the mouth except in the curious genera *Coeloplana* and *Ctenoplana* (see below), in which the testes open on the aboral surface by ducts, an arrangement that apparently foreshadows the reproductive system of the Bilateria. The sex cells appear to be of entodermal origin.

2. Development.—Usually the sex cells are shed into the sea water, where fertilization occurs; but *Coeloplana* and *Tjalfiella* brood their young. Development is best known for *Beroë*, but other genera agree so far as studied. Four blastomeres arise by the usual two meridional cleavages, but the third cleavage is also nearly vertical and results in a curved plate of eight cells, arranged in two rows of four each with the central cells larger than the end ones (Fig. 216*A*). The long axis of this eight-celled embryo becomes the tentacular plane of the adult, so that a condition of biradial symmetry is already established at this early stage. This type of symmetry persists throughout development, and ctenophores in fact furnish the only cases of biradial cleavage. The eight blastomeres now divide twice, giving off each time eight small cells, termed micromeres, on the concave surface of the embryo, which is the future aboral pole (Fig. 216*B*). The 16 micromeres undergo rapid divisions to form a wreath of small cells on the aboral surface of the eight large macromeres (Fig. 216*C, D*), which eventually divide to 16. The micromeres are the source of the entire epidermis; the macromeres become the entoderm. Thus we see that the ctenophore egg belongs to the type with determinate cleavage and mosaic development, in which the parts of the adult are mapped out in cleavage stages. The micromeres continue to multiply, finally spread over the aboral pole, and grow down as a one-layered sheet over the macromeres (Fig. 216*E*). The latter also invaginate into the interior so that the gastrula arises by the combined

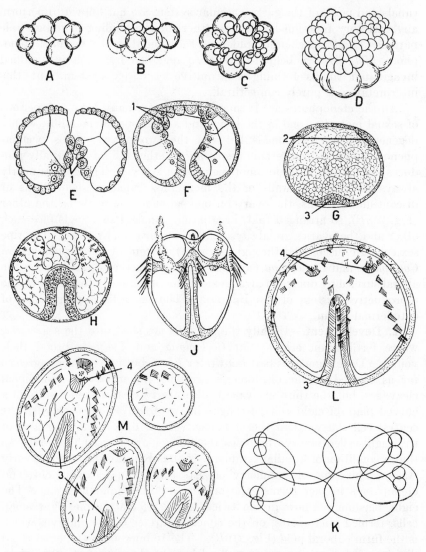

Fig. 216.—Embryology of ctenophores. *A.* Eight-cell stage, from above. *B.* First set of micromeres given off, seen from side. *C.* Wreath of micromeres, viewed from above. *D.* Micromeres numerous, beginning to cover macromeres. *E.* Section through gastrulating embryo, showing so-called mesoderm cells given off from oral ends of macromeres. *F.* Invagination complete, "mesoderm" in roof of archenteron. *G.* Later stage, showing thickenings for comb rows and stomodaeum. *H.* Stomodaeum invaginated, comb rows differentiated. *J.* Young cydippid larva. (*A–C, G, H after Agassiz,* 1874; *D after Chun,* 1880; *E, F after Metschnikoff,* 1885; *J after Mayer,* 1912.) *K.* 16-cell stage of *Beroë,* each half experimentally rotated outward. *L.* Resulting embryo, with two statocysts, each with four comb rows around it. *M.* Four embryos produced from cutting a gastrula of *Beroë* into four pieces. (*K–M. after Fischel,* 1897, 1898.) 1, mesoderm cells; 2, thickenings for comb rows: 3, stomodaem; 4, statocyst.

processes of epiboly and emboly (invagination). Just before invagination the macromeres give off at their oral poles a circle of 16 small cells (Fig. 216E) whose fate has been much disputed. According to the careful work of Metschnikoff (1885) these cells are carried inward in the gastrulation process, proliferate to form a cross-shaped mass of cells topping the aboral pole of the entoderm (Fig. 216F), and become the cells of the collenchyme, including the muscle cells. Hatschek (1911), however, claims they are entodermal cells, becoming incorporated into the gastrovascular system, and supports the findings of Kowalevsky (1866) and Chun (1880) that the collenchymatous cells arise by inwandering of ectodermal cells, especially from the region of the mouth. Unfortunately, Hatschek has never published his evidence although Korschelt and Heider (1900, page 265) testify that they saw his drawings and found them convincing. The matter is extremely important on theoretical grounds. If Metschnikoff is correct, then the ctenophores have a "true" mesoderm of entodermal origin and are thus allied to the protostomous Bilateria (page 31). If on the other hand, the muscle and other cells of the collenchyme come from the ectoderm, they constitute an ectomesoderm and indicate close affinity of the ctenophores with sponges and coelenterates. It appears impossible to decide the matter on available evidence, but the ectomesodermal interpretation is the more appealing and is here adopted.

As the micromeres cover the embryo to become the epidermis, four interradial bands of particularly small, rapidly dividing cells become noticeable (Fig. 216G), and these differentiate into the comb rows, of which two arise from each ectodermal band. The aboral ectoderm differentiates into the statocyst and related parts. The ectoderm at the oral pole invaginates extensively to form the stomodaeum (Fig. 216G), which pushes against the entoderm in such a way as to constrict it into four pockets, two on each side of the tentacular plane (Fig. 221B). These have been compared to the four gastric pockets of the scyphistoma. From them the gastrovascular canals arise by active entodermal outgrowth. The tentacle sheaths in forms that possess them originate as ectodermal invaginations from whose base the tentacle sprouts. The muscle cells of tentacle core and of the general body come from collenchymatous cells. Each muscle cell results from the differentiation of a mesenchymal cell.

The embryo now escapes as a free-swimming *cydippid larva* (Figs. 216J and 217C), which closely resembles adult ctenophores of the order Cydippida and in that order assumes the adult morphology through slight changes. The Lobata and Cestida also have a typical cydippid larva suggesting in its lateral compression the genus *Mertensia;* it undergoes a marked transformation or metamorphosis to the adult condition.

The tentacles migrate orally and become much reduced and altered, losing their sheaths in the Lobata. The oral end expands on each side into the oral lobes in the Lobata, and in the Cestida the lateral compression becomes more and more pronounced and the body elongates in the sagittal plane. The larva of the beroids (Fig. 213C) is similar to a cydippid larva but lacks all trace of tentacles or tentacle sheaths. The chief change to the adult consists in the enormous expansion of the stomodaeum.

The development of ctenophores is seen to differ widely from that of the Cnidaria. Whereas in the latter, cleavage results in an irregular mass of cells having no relation to adult structure, there is in the ctenophores a very exact cleavage pattern on which the ultimate morphology is definitely mapped. The ctenophores further lack a planula larva (except *Gastrodes*, see below) so characteristic of the coelenterates and instead produce an invaginate gastrula and a larval type having no counterpart in the Cnidaria.

Experiments on the developing ctenophore embryo (chiefly *Beroë*) confirm the fact of mosaic development (Fischel, Yatsu, Ziegler). Isolated blastomeres of two- or four-cell stages cleave fractionally as they would if remaining part of the whole, and become reduced larvae with four or two comb rows, respectively. Isolated cells of later stages do not survive, but portions of such stages develop in the same fractional manner (Fig. 216M). If the micromeres are displaced into two equal masses, the resulting larva has two statocysts with four comb rows radiating from each (Fig. 216K, L). Irregular displacements of the micromeres result in two or even three statocysts with disordered combs. Thus the combs and the statocyst are fixed in the micromeres and incapable of regulation. On the other hand, the formation of the stomodaeum depends on external factors, since each reduced larva develops a stomodaeum at its oral pole, although it is somewhat excentric in position.

3. Order Cydippida.—The members of this order are the least modified ctenophores of simple globular, oval, or pyriform shape with blindly ending gastrovascular canals and two long tentacles springing from pouch-like sheaths and generally provided with a fringe of lateral filaments covered with colloblasts. The chief genera are *Mertensia*, much flattened laterally; *Pleurobrachia* (Fig. 209A), globular to egg-shaped with no or little flattening; *Hormiphora* similar in shape to *Pleurobrachia* but with two sorts of tentacle filaments; *Callianira*, wth two aboral crests (Fig. 217A); and *Lampetia*. of elongate cylindrical form with shallow tentacle sheaths and a very expansible oral end, permitting the eversion of the pharynx as a creeping sole (Fig. 217B). Of these genera, species of *Pleurobrachia* are the only ones commonly seen along the coasts of the United States.

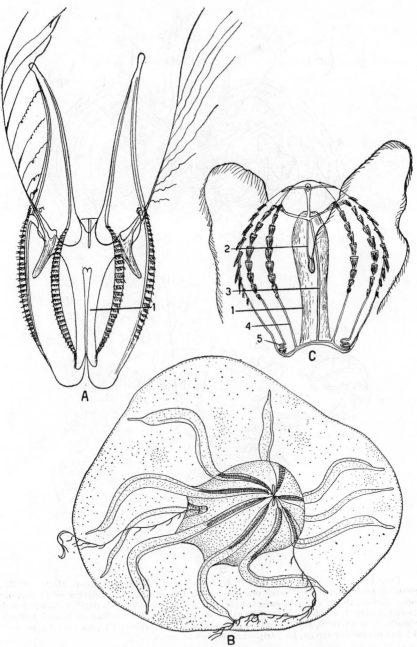

Fig. 217.—Cydippida and Lobata.   A. *Callianira*, after Chun, 1880; only bases of long tentacles shown.   B. *Lampetia* crawling with pharynx everted.   (*After Komai*, 1934.)   C. Late cydippid stage of *Mnemiopsis leidyi*, from life; note fusion of pharyngeal and subtentacular canals along mouth.   1, pharynx; 2, tentacular canal; 3, pharyngeal canal; 4, subtentacular canal; 5, beginning of loop in oral lobe.

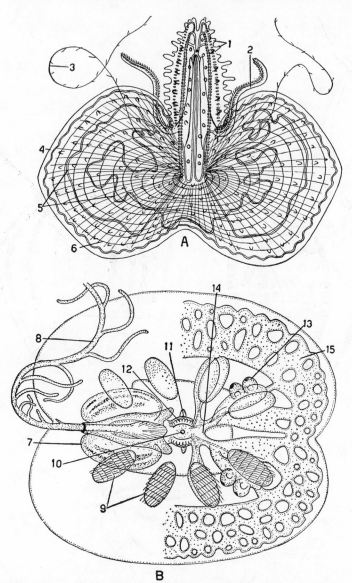

Fig. 218.—Lobata, Platyctenea. A. Leucothea (=Eucharis) (after Mayer, 1912), showing papillae and very large oral lobes. B. Diagram of the structure of Ctenoplana (after Komai, 1934); left side, external parts; right side, internal. 1, papillae; 2, auricles; 3, main tentacle; 4, oral lobe; 5, winding canals of oral lobe; 6, muscle fibers of lobe; 7, tentacle sheath, 8, tentacle; 9, comb rows; 10, statocyst; 11, anal pores; 12, pharynx; 13, gonads; 14, gastrovascular canals; 15, peripheral network of same.

4. Order Lobata.—In this order the body is always laterally compressed, and the oral end is expanded on each side into a rounded contractile lobe, provided with a latticework of muscle fibers on its inner surface (Fig. 211). The tentacles lack a sheath, are situated to either side of the mouth, and are usually reduced to a short filament with lateral branches. From either side of each tentacle base a ciliated *auricular groove* extends to the base of the auricles and bears a row of short tentacles. The auricular apparatus is important in the capture of food. The modifications of the lobate canal system were explained above (page 669); most noticeable are the sinuous loops in the oral lobes. *Bolinopsis* (= *Bolina*) with short auricular grooves and *Mnemiopsis* with very deep grooves that extend to the level of the statocyst are common in summer and fall along the Atlantic coast. *Bolinopsis infundibulum* ranges from Maine north into arctic waters and *Mnemiopsis leidyi* (Fig. 211) occurs from Cape Cod south to the Carolinas, often in immense swarms. *Leucothea* (= *Eucharis*) has very large oral lobes, long slender auricles, long main tentacles with or without lateral filaments, a papillate surface, and two deep narrow pits extending aborally from near the tentacle bases (Fig. 218*A*). The papillae on the surface of this genus are very motile and extensile with tips loaded with large gland cells interspersed with the projecting bristles of tactile sensory cells. They probably aid in the capture of food organisms. *Eurhamphaea* has two pointed aboral crests over which the subtentacular comb rows run and which terminate in a slender filament. *Ocyropsis* (= *Ocyroë*) is distinguished by the large muscular oral lobes, whose flapping serves as the chief swimming mechanism. The last three genera are limited to warmer waters, and species of them occur in the tropical Atlantic.

5. Order Cestida.—The elongated ribbon form (Fig. 212*A*) renders the members of this order recognizable at once. The modifications in structure accompanying this alteration of shape were explained above. The main tentacles are reduced and shifted alongside the mouth, as in the Lobata, but the sheaths are retained. There are two genera, *Cestum* (erroneously spelled *Cestus*) and *Velamen* (= *Vexillum, Folia*) limited to the Mediterranean and to tropical waters. Practically the only difference between these genera is that in *Cestum* the four subtentacular canals first arch upward to supply their very short comb rows, then curve down, and then extend straight out to the body ends (Fig. 212*B*); while in *Velamen* there is no such arch but these canals proceed directly outward in the equatorial plane (Fig. 212*A*). Species of both genera may be seen around Florida. The famous Venus's girdle, *Cestum veneris*, may reach a length of 1½ m. but is generally under 80 cm. in length (really the width). *Velamen* is smaller, to 15 cm. The cestids swim not only by their combs but by graceful undulations of the body.

6. Order Beroida.—The beroids (Fig. 213) are conical or thimble-shaped, compressed in the lateral plane (Fig. 213D), with no trace of tentacles or tentacle sheaths. The interior is occupied chiefly by the immensely enlarged pharynx. Other noticeable features are the papillae edging the polar fields (Fig. 213B) and the numerous fine branches springing from the gastrovascular canals (for other details see page 671). The principal genus is *Beroë*, found in all seas, to 20 cm. in height and often of a pink color, especially in colder waters (Fig. 213A).

7. Order Platyctenea.—The construction of the curious genera *Coeloplana*, *Ctenoplana*, *Tjalfiella*, and *Gastrodes* will now be described. Our present understanding of these aberrant ctenophores is based upon the work of Komai, Mortensen, and Dawydoff.

A single specimen of *Ctenoplana* was discovered off Sumatra by Korotneff in 1886, but his imperfect description was supplemented by the fortunate finding by Willey in 1896 of four more specimens floating on a cuttlebone off New Guinea. The animal was not seen again until recently, when a number of specimens were taken on the coasts of Indo-China and Japan by Dawydoff (1929) and Komai (1934). The latter has given the best description of the anatomy. The various species are 5 to 8 mm. long in the tentacular plane and colored dorsally, mostly olive green, brown, or reddish, some with patterns. The flattened oval body has a central thick portion and two rounded thin lobes in the sagittal plane (Figs. 218B, 219A). At each end in the notch between the lobes there are a large tentacle sheath and a long retractile tentacle edged with lateral filaments as in the cydippids. In the center of the dorsal surface occurs a typical statocyst with polar plates; the latter are encircled by eight prominent ciliated papillae (Fig. 219A), believed by some to be respiratory. They are characteristic of the genus. Eight short comb rows, of several plates each, radiate from the aboral region and are connected to the statocyst by the usual ciliated furrows. The shortened gastrovascular system consists of a low broad pharynx with folded walls, a long esophagus, and a rounded stomach directly beneath the statocyst. Comparison with other ctenophores shows that the apparent oral surface is actually everted pharynx so that only a small part of the pharynx is situated in the interior, and the so-called mouth is a connection between the internal and external portions of the pharynx. The stomach gives off to the aboral surface two anal canals, each opening by a pore, and laterally six canals branch off, four for the comb rows and two for the tentacle sheaths (Fig. 218B). The six canals of each side proceed to the periphery where they anastomose to a network (Fig. 218B). The gonads occur as four bilobed masses in the walls of the subtentacular canals; so far only testes have been found, and these are remarkable in that each mass opens to the surface by a duct and pore. *Ctenoplana* is a plankton animal; it swims by folding the lobes together (thus restoring the typical ctenophore condition) and then using its combs or more often flapping the lobes in and out (Fig. 219A).   Opened out to its flat form it

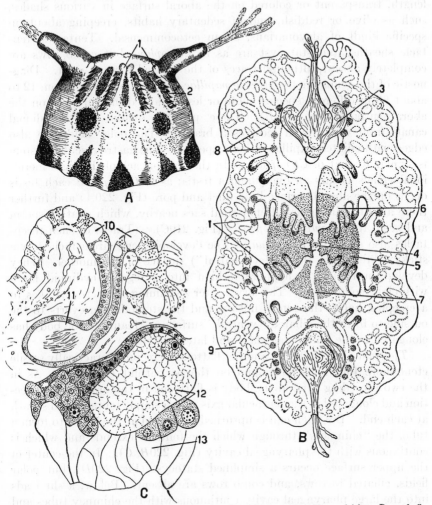

Fig. 219.--Platyctenea (continued). A. Ctenoplana swimming. (After Dawydoff, 1933.) B. Coeloplana mesnili. (After Dawydoff, 1933.) C. Section through an ovary of Coeloplana, showing seminal receptacle. (After Komai, 1922.) 1, papillae; 2, comb rows; 3, tentacle sheath; 4, statocyst; 5, pharynx; 6, meridional canals; 7, tentacular canals; 8, gonads; 9, peripheral network of digestive system; 10, epidermis; 11, seminal receptacle; 12, ovary; 13, wall of meridional canal.

may rest upon the bottom, not creeping very much, or travel upside down on the surface film by ciliary action.

Coeloplana, discovered in the Red Sea in 1880 by Kowalevsky, has since been found in abundance on the coasts of Japan and thoroughly studied by Komai (1922), and several species have been described by Dawydoff (1938) from Indo-China. It is similar to *Ctenoplana*, a flat, oval animal (Fig. 219*B*), elongated in the tentacular plane, to 60 mm. in length, transparent or colored on the aboral surface in various shades, such as olive or reddish, and of sedentary habits, creeping about on specific kinds of alcyonarians, as an ectocommensal. Tentacles, tentacle sheaths, and statocyst are as in *Ctenoplana* but comb rows are completely absent, although traces of the ciliated furrows exist. Diagnostic of the genus are the erectile *papillae*, varying in number from 12 to about 60 in different species, more or less arranged in four rows on the aboral surface (Fig. 219*B*). These papillae overlie the meridional canals from which each receives a branch. The polar fields are also edged with ciliated papillae in most species. The gastrovascular system is similar to that of *Ctenoplana*. In the wall of each of the eight meridional canals occurs an ovary and a testis; as in *Ctenoplana* each testis opens on the aboral surface by a duct and pore (Fig. 220*A*) and further there are little invaginated epidermal sacs nearby, which contain sperm and seem to be *seminal receptacles* (Fig. 219*C*). (Traces of such receptacles also exist in *Ctenoplana*.) The developing eggs are attached by a sticky secretion to the oral ("ventral") surface of the mother. They develop in typical ctenophore fashion into a regular cydippid larva with eight comb rows. The larva, after swimming for a time, takes to a creeping habit, the combs fall off, and the stomodaeum everts to the outside to form the ciliated "ventral" surface. Meantime the body has elongated in the tentacular plane and later flattens.

Tjalfiella (Fig. 220*B*) is another flattened, creeping, practically sessile ctenophore found off Greenland on the pennatulid *Umbellula*. As in the two preceding genera, the body is flattened in the oral-aboral direction and elongated in the tentacular axis with a simple tentacle and sheath at each end. But each end is upturned and fused at the edges to form a tube, the "chimney," through which the tentacle extends and which is continuous with the pharyngeal cavity (Fig. 220*B*, *C*). In the center of the upper surface occurs a simplified statocyst (Fig. 220*D*), but polar fields, ciliated furrows, and comb rows are absent. Below, a slit leads into the large pharyngeal cavity continuous with the chimney tubes and having a much folded roof in the center of which a small aperture connects with the stomach. From each side of the latter a large transverse canal proceeds to the tentacle base giving off en route two pairs of blind sacs, which appear to represent the meridional canals, and one pair of canals branching to the periphery and around the chimney (Fig. 220*C*). An ovary and a testis occur in each of the eight blind sacs and form eight bulges on the upper surface (Fig. 220*C*). Over the gonads lie ciliated epidermal sacs opening on the aboral surface. These have been interpreted by some as the sunken and modified comb rows, possibly representing the beginning of an excretory system (nephridial tubes). It is

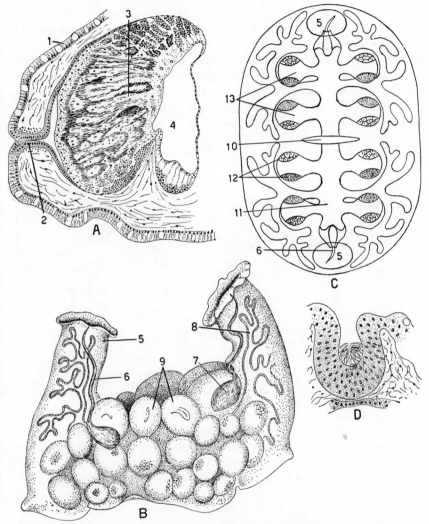

Fig. 220.—Platyctenea (continued). *A.* Section through a testis of *Coeloplana* (*after Komai*, 1922), showing vas deferens. *B. Tjalfiella* with embryos. *C.* Diagram of the structure of *Tjalfiella*. *D.* Reduced statocyst of *Tjalfiella*. (*B–D After Mortensen*, 1922.) 1, epidermis; 2, vas deferens; 3, testis; 4, meridional canal; 5, chimney; 6, tentacle; 7, tentacle base; 8, gastrovascular branches in chimney; 9, embryos; 10, mouth; 11, gastro-vascular canals; 12, gonads; 13, sacs containing gonads, representing meridional canals.

more probable that they are seminal receptacles as in *Coeloplana*. The eggs of *Tjalfiella* develop in brood pouches in the aboral surface into typical cydippid larvae[1] of rounded form with statocyst, polar fields, ciliated furrows, tentacles and tentacle sheaths, eight comb rows set in deep indentations, and a four-pouched gastrovasular system. A long furrow in the tentacular plane on the oral surface separates this surface into two oral lobes (as in the Lobata), which can be opened and closed as in *Ctenoplana*. The cydippid larva leaves the brood pouch and after a short free life settles on the pennatulid, opening out the two lobes and the stomodaeal wall to form the "ventral" surface. The animal thus permanently adopts the form that can be assumed by *Lampetia* (Fig. 217B) in creeping. The tentacular ends of the two lobes unite at their adjacent edges to form the chimneys.

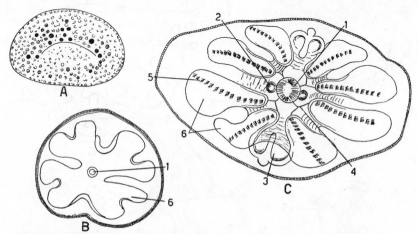

Fig. 221.—*Gastrodes*. A. Bowl-shaped stage in *Salpa*. B. Later stage, with four-lobed canal system. C. Comb-bearing stage. (*All after Komai*, 1922.) 1, statocyst; 2, anal pores; 3, tentacle sheaths; 4, ciliated furrows; 5, comb rows; 6, meridional canals.

At the time of their discovery *Ctenoplana* and *Coeloplana* were hailed by certain zoologists as the missing links between the coelenterates and the flatworms, and much phylogenetic speculation was based upon them. More thorough study of their anatomy shows, however, that they as well as *Tjalfiella* are simply highly modified ctenophores that have adopted a creeping or even sessile mode of life and thereby in two cases lost the combs. The flattened form is not primarily derived as might be thought by a mere shortening of the oral-aboral axis but is brought about by the opening out of the stomodaeum so that the ciliated "ventral" surface is actually in large part the pharyngeal lining and the so-called mouth is the aperture between the pharynx and the stomach or a connection between everted and internal parts of the pharynx. *Ctenoplana* and

[1] It was the finding of these cydippid larvae in the brood pouches that enabled Mortensen to recognize *Tjalfiella* as a ctenophore, one of the many striking examples of the validity of the principle of ancestral reminiscence during development.

Tjalfiella seem to be related to the Lobata in that they are provided with oral lobes having the same morphological relations as in the Lobata. None of these forms has real bilateral symmetry nor any indication of anterior and posterior ends; and it is highly doubtful if the way in which they have become "dorsoventrally" flattened has any relation to the way in which this happened in the evolution of the Bilateria.

The true nature of *Gastrodes*, a parasite in the tunicate *Salpa*, was elucidated by Komai. It was known as a minute bowl-shaped organism embedded in the mantle of *Salpa* (Fig. 221*A*). Komai and Dawydoff have found that these grow into a cydippid type with statocyst, tentacles, eight comb rows, and typical gastrovascular system (Fig. 221*B*, *C*). These leave *Salpa*, settle to the bottom, casting off the comb rows, and flatten out by everting the pharynx as in other Platyctenea. This is probably the adult form. The eggs occur in the pharyngeal epithelium and seem to be of ectodermal origin. A typical planula larva with solid entoderm is formed, and this bores into new hosts.

8. Biology and Physiology.—The ctenophores are among the most characteristic plankton organisms of the ocean and inhabit all seas, although most species probably have a limited range of latitude. Although predominantly pelagic organisms, they also occur in deep waters, down to 3000 m. They are feeble swimmers and through tides and currents may often be aggregated into immense swarms that work havoc among small pelagic organisms. The beroids are often pink, and most Platyctenea variously colored above; otherwise most ctenophores are colorless and transparent with a bronze iridescence along the comb rows. Apart from the very elongated cestids, the size ranges between a few millimeters and 20 cm.

The Ctenophora are exclusively carnivorous, and this statement applies even to the flattened sedentary Platyctenea. The food consists of any small animals and in the cydippids is caught by the tentacles, which are spread out in fishing positions by a variety of maneuvers including "loop-the-loop" turns. Any food caught is held by the sticky colloblasts, and the tentacle then shortens, wiping the food upon the mouth rim. *Pleurobrachia* is known to eat small plankton organisms, such as crab and oyster larvae, copepods, fish eggs, and arrowworms (*Sagitta*). The Lobata (and presumably also the cestids), lacking extensile tentacles, can capture only small and weak organisms. The process has been described in detail for *Mnemiopsis leidyi* (Fig. 211*A*) by Main (1928) and Coonfield (1936). Ciliary action brings the prey into the auricular grooves, where they become entangled by the row of short tentacles that passes them across the adjacent labial ridge into another groove, the labial trough. The four labial troughs lead directly to the mouth. Food touching the surface of the animal in oral regions becomes entangled in a sheet of mucus and is passed by ciliary action into the labial troughs. The chief food of *Mnemiopsis leidyi* is mollusk larvae; copepods, other minute plankton forms, and general debris are also eaten. One specimen had eaten 126 oyster larvae (Nelson, 1925). It is probable that ctenophores may be of economic importance through the enormous numbers of oyster larvae that swarms of them can devour. *Beroë* uses the large and extensile mouth rim in the capture of prey and can devour relatively large animals, such as other ctenophores and small crustaceans. The Platyctenea appear to feed on the same types of animals as do the pelagic ctenophores; in *Tjalfiella*, which is practically sessile so that the mouth is functionless, food is ingested by way of the chimneys, which open directly into the pharyngeal cavity. In tentaculate forms, prey is held by the sticky colloblasts, and probably poisons also play a role. Thus a toxin can be extracted from *Beroë* which kills small invertebrates and when injected into frogs, toads, rabbits, and dogs elicits excessive skin secretion, muscular weakness, paralysis, and death.

Extracellular digestion takes place in the pharynx and is very rapid so that the pharynx may empty itself in 20 to 30 minutes. The partially digested material passes throughout the canals of the gastrovascular system and is phagocytized by the cells of the outer walls of the canals. Indigestible material is ejected through the mouth or through the anal pores, which in cases observed erect above the surface in a definite act of defecation.

The epidermis of ctenophores as mentioned above is liberally provided with the projecting bristles of sensory cells, and therefore it is not surprising that the entire surface is found to be sensitive to chemicals, temperature, and mechanical stimuli; the mouth rim is particularly sensitive to chemicals, especially in the beroids. On testing the surface of *Mnemiopsis* with clam juice, Coonfield (1936) noted a response only from the lips, auricles, region around the main tentacles, and parts of the oral lobes adjacent to the mouth. The response consists in a brief stoppage; then a reversal of the beat of the combs, followed by the secretion of a sheet of mucus to entangle the food particles. The comb rows are very sensitive to contact and in many ctenophores are retracted into the jelly when touched.

Many ctenophores tend to assume a resting position, possibly really a feeding position, hanging vertically from the surface film, usually with the mouth up, but sometimes in the reverse position, and with the combs quiescent. If lightly disturbed from this position the animal resumes it by appropriate comb beats. If too much disturbed, the animal rotates and swims rapidly downward with the mouth in advance. Ctenophores are said to go below in rough weather or bright sunlight but the reaction to light is not very definite.

The Ctenophora are noted for their luminescence, which in adults comes from beneath the comb rows, apparently from the outer walls of the meridional canals. Pieces containing at least four combs will luminesce as long as they remain alive. The ability to luminesce begins in cleavage stages and continues throughout life but the animals luminesce only after being in the dark for some time. Oxygen is not necessary for the luminescence but is necessary for the preliminary building up of the luminescent substance (Harvey and Korr, 1938).

The beating of the combs has been much studied both as an example of ciliary movement and as a possible case of nervous control of cilia. Isolated combs or groups of combs or even fractions of a comb will continue to beat as long as the basal cushion is included; in the absence of the cushion, movement ceases. Ordinarily the beat in each row begins in the most aboral comb and proceeds successively along the combs of the row to the oral end like a wave. The combs in the two rows of each quadrant (which come in development from one ectodermal band) beat synchronously. The beat consists of a strong flap of the comb toward the aboral pole so that the animal is driven forward with the mouth in advance, the normal swimming position. Stimulation of the oral end as by the striking of an object or immersion in certain chemicals causes not only a reversal of the direction of the wave, which now passes from the oral to the aboral ends of the comb rows, but a reversal in the direction of the effective stroke of each comb, so that the animal temporarily swims backward with the aboral pole in advance. According to Fedele, this ability to reverse the direction of the effective stroke is best developed in the cydippids and the cydippid larvae of other groups, all of which can swim equally well with either pole foremost, but is somewhat lost in adult Lobata and is absent in the beroids. In any ctenophore the direction of the wave is reversible. If sections of a comb row are cut out and replaced in the reverse orientation, they continue to beat according to their original orientation.

That the beat of the combs is nervously controlled has been proved in many ways. Stimulation of the oral end causes stoppage and reversal in the comb rows; stimulation of the aboral end accelerates the normal beat; displacement from a resting vertical position results in a stronger beat on one side and return to the vertical. All these responses are reflexes by way of nervous connections; they are not abolished by extirpation of the statocyst; and they continue to be exhibited by comb rows so cut as to be attached at only one end, but they do not continue if the cut passes to the inner side of the row. Such experiments show a diffuse nervous connection not mediated by the statocyst. The transmission along a comb row is not stopped by loss of a comb or by inhibiting the beat of some combs through cooling or stretching. If a comb row is cut across, the combs of the two parts beat independently.   If a ciliated furrow is cut across, the two comb rows of that quadrant are no longer synchronous. Removal of the statocyst also results in lack of coordination of the comb rows, irregularity in swimming, and inability to maintain the resting vertical position.   The statocyst is thus concerned in maintaining coordination between the comb rows and in orientation with regard to gravity.

In the ctenophores, therefore, it is definitely proved that ciliary movement can be controlled by the nervous system.   The existence of nervous transmission is also proved by the foregoing observations even if no anatomical evidence of the presence of a nervous system were available.   During the many years that the occurrence of nervous tissue along the comb row remained undemonstrated, the observed transmission was called "neuroid"; but this term need no longer be employed, since Heider's finding of the nerve connections shows the transmission to be of the ordinary nervous type.

The ctenophores have high powers of regeneration, and the many injuries to which their fragility and watery construction subject them are quickly repaired.   Any parts removed, including the statocyst, are replaced.   If quadrants are extirpated, the missing comb rows and other parts are regenerated.   Longitudinal or equatorial halves regenerate the missing half, but the part containing the statocyst is more viable and regenerates more quickly.   In general, regeneration of pieces containing the original statocyst is more rapid than that of pieces without a statocyst. The latter regenerate the statocyst first, and plate rows and other parts then arise in relation to it.   These facts indicate the dominance of the statocyst.   Portions of ctenophores may also close together without regenerating the lost comb rows and may continue a normal existence. In *Lampetia*, if the body is cut transversely into three or more pieces the viability and regenerative power are greatest in the most aboral piece and decline orally (Zirpolo, 1924); but in *Mnemiopsis* all crosspieces appear to regenerate equally well (Coonfield and Goldin, 1937).   Pieces of ctenophores will fuse together, and if they are similarly oriented with regard to polarity will regulate to a single animal; but if grafted so that their polarities are opposite, each piece retains its original polarity.   Grafted statocysts are absorbed the more rapidly the nearer they are placed to the host's own statocyst, but if the latter was extirpated no difference in graft absorption in different locations is seen.   A grafted statocyst can inhibit the regeneration of the host's statocyst.

It is suspected that ctenophores may reproduce asexually by fission. In *Ctenoplana* and *Coeloplana* a form of asexual multiplication occurs that resembles pedal laceration in anemones.   Small portions fragment off as the animal creeps, and these regenerate into complete animals.   As described for *Coeloplana* (Tanaka, 1932), the epidermis at the site of wound closure forms one tentacle and sheath and gives off a bud from which the other tentacle and sheath arise. Polarity is thus established with reference to the wound. The statocyst differentiates halfway between the two sheaths, the mouth and pharynx arise by epidermal invagination, and the gastrovascular canals form from the gastrodermal spaces left in the piece.

The water and solid content of ctenophores is similar to that of medusae. Some ctenophores can endure great changes of salinity and may flourish in bays having a salinity not more than one-third that of the ocean.

The Ctenophora are devoid of any respiratory mechanism, although undoubtedly the circulation in the digestive system is of some respiratory value. The oxygen consumption is very low, being about 0.007 cc. per gram per hour for *Beroë* and half that for *Cestum* (Vernon, 1899); but when calculated per gram of dry weight is similar to that of other animals. The oxygen consumption increases greatly with rise of temperature, is inversely proportional to size, and is also increased by starvation involving much loss of weight.

9. Phylogenetic Considerations.—Although the Ctenophora are obviously of about the same grade of structure as the Cnidaria, it is not possible to derive them from any existing groups of the latter. Characters common to the two phyla are: tetramerous symmetry, absence of coelom, gelatinous mesogloea, branching gastrovascular canals, diffuse nerve plexus, statocyst, and general lack of organ systems. There have been repeated attempts to relate the ctenophores directly to Hydrozoa by way of medusae having an aboral statocyst and two opposite tentacles in sheaths such as *Hydroctena* (page 464). It is now accepted that *Hydroctena* is a trachyline medusa; the aboral shoving of the tentacles is characteristic of this group, and there are other trachyline forms with an aboral sense organ. Nevertheless, relationship to the trachyline stem form, which is here considered ancestral to the Cnidaria, is probably indicated by such resemblances. The ctenophores also have certain scyphozoan-anthozoan characteristics: the stomodaeum, the cellular mesogloea, the four-lobed condition of the gastrovascular cavity of the larva (Fig. 221*B*), and the general tetramerous symmetry. Finally in certain features the ctenophores diverge widely from any known coelenterates: in the direct development of muscle cells from mesenchyme, the lack of nematocysts and presence of colloblasts, the comb rows, and the determinate type of development. Altogether it seems that the ctenophores must have diverged very early from the trachyline stem form about the time this gave off the three coelenterate stocks: trachyline-hydrozoan, scyphozoan, and anthozoan lines. The ancestral ctenophore appears to have been a rounded organism with an aboral nerve center from which eight nerves radiated as concentrated parts of a general nerve plexus. It had a mouth at the oral pole leading into a large stomodaeum from which extended a branched digestive system. An anus was absent. (The anal pores of present ctenophores cannot be regarded as a definite morphological anus, since similar pores from the radial canals to the exterior also occur in many medusae, page 421.) Between epidermis and gastrodermis was a considerable quantity of mesenchymal ectomesoderm, part of which had differentiated into muscle fibers. The entire surface was ciliated, with the ciliation concentrated or better developed along eight meridional rows, since the combs have probably been derived by the differentiation of an originally completely ciliated surface. Such a primitive ctenophore has been termed by some writers a *protrochula* since they regard it as a forerunner of the trochophore larva of several of the bilateral phyla. But this view implies that the ctenophores are intermediate between radiates and Bilateria.

The view that the ctenophores lead directly to certain lower Bilateria (the polyclad flatworms) has been advocated and adopted by several prominent German zoologists, notably Lang. The flattened Platyctenea, which superficially suggest a polyclad, have been considered the missing links between the coelenterates and flatworms. As already indicated, this theory must now be considered without foundation, since the careful study of Platyctenea reveals that they are typical ctenophores, simply highly modified for a creeping or sessile existence. Further, it is now clear that not the polyclads but the Acoela are the most primitive flatworms, and the Platyctenea bear less resemblance to these than they do to the polyclads. In view of these considerations, the suggested line of ascent—ctenophores-Platyctenea-polyclads—becomes untenable. Although both ctenophores and polyclads have determinate cleavage, the details of the development are not strikingly similar. The assumption, therefore, that a ctenophore-like organism was ancestral to the Bilateria does not appear very convincing to the author. The view here adopted is that the planula larva leads directly to the most primitive Bilateria, the acoel flatworms. The ctenophores are then regarded as a blind early offshoot from the trachyline stem form that reached a considerable grade of differentiation without leading to any higher forms.

It cannot be denied, however, that the ctenophores present certain advanced structural features that appear to look forward to the Bilateria. Chief of these are the prominence of an apical nervous region, the mode of origin of the musculature, the presence of gonoducts (sexual ducts), and the determinate type of cleavage. In explanation it may be suggested that the evolutionary possibilities of animals of the radiate grade are limited and that structural advances can take place only along certain lines. Probably the most important next line of advance is the development of a mesoderm, and tendencies in this direction are seen among all the higher groups of Radiata. In short, the ctenophores appear to indicate along what lines structural complication will proceed in the next grade (organ-system grade of construction) without themselves being directly in the line of ancestry of this grade. They are the most differentiated radiates, and the stock from which they came, differentiating along the same paths but in another direction (that of bilaterality, and anteroposterior axiation), gave rise to the Bilateria.

Bibliography

Abbott, J. F. 1907. Morphology of Coeloplana. Zool. Jahrb., Abt. Anat. Ontog. Tiere 24. **Agassiz, A.** 1874. Embryology of ctenophores. Amer. Acad. Arts Sci. Mem. 10, Pt. II, Sup. **Bauer, V.** 1910. Über den anscheinend nervöse Regulation der Flimmerbewegung bei den Rippenquallen. Ztschr. Vergleich. Physiol. 10. **Chun, C.** 1880. Die Ctenophoren. Fauna Flora Golfes Neapel 1. 1898. Die Ctenophoren der Plankton-Expedition. Ergeb. Plank. Exped. 2 K a. **Coonfield, B. R.** 1934. Coordination and movement of the swimming plates of Mnemiopsis. Biol. Bul. 66. 1936. Regeneration in Mnemiopsis. Biol. Bul. 71. Apical dominance and polarity in Mnemiopsis. Biol. Bul. 70. 1937. Symmetry and regulation in Mnemiopsis. Biol. Bul. 72. **Coonfield, B. R., and A. Goldin.** 1937. Physiological gradient in Mnemiopsis during regeneration. Biol. Bul. 73. **Dawydoff, C.** 1933. Morphologie et biologie des Ctenoplana. Arch. Zool. Expt. Gén. 75. 1936. Les Ctenoplanides des eaux de l'Indochine. Bul. Biol. France Belg. 70. 1937. Les Gastrodes. Acad. Sci. Paris, Compt. Rend. 204. 1938. Multiplication asexuée chez les Ctenoplana. Acad. Sci. Paris, Compt. Rend. 206. 1938. Les Coeloplanides indochinoises. Arch. Zool. Expt. Gén. 80. **Fedele, M.** 1924. Regolazione nervosa del movimento ciliare. Staz. Zool. Napoli Pub. 5. 1925. Sulle inversioni del movimento vibratile nei Ctenofori. Soc. Natural. Napoli Bol. 37. **Fischel, A.** 1897–1898. Experimentelle Untersuchungen am Ctenophorenei. Arch. Entwickl. Mech. Organ. 6, 7. **Göthlin, F. G.** 1920. Inhibition of the ciliary movement in Beroe. Jour. Expt. Zool. 31. **Harvey, E. N., and I. M. Korr.** 1938. Luminescence in absence of oxygen in the ctenophore Mnemiopsis. Jour. Cell. Compar. Physiol. 12. **Heider, K.** 1927. Vom Nervensystem der Ctenophoren. Ztschr. Morph. Ökol. Tiere 9. **Hertwig, R.** 1880. Über den Bau der Ctenophoren. Jenaische Ztschr. Naturw. 14. **Komai, T.** 1922. Studies on two aberrant ctenophores—Coeloplana and Gastrodes. Kyoto. Published by author. 1934. On the structure of Ctenoplana. Kyoto Univ. Col. Sci. Mem. Ser. B. 9. 1936. Nervous system, Coeloplana. Kyoto Univ. Col. Sci. Mem. Ser. B. 11. **Korotneff, A.** 1886. Ctenoplana. Ztschr. Wiss. Zool. 43. **Kowalevsky, A.** 1866. Entwickelungsgeschichte der Rippenquallen. Acad. Imp. Sci. St. Pétersbourg. Mém. Ser. 7, Vol. 10. 1880. Coeloplana. Zool. Anz. 3. **Krumbach, T.** 1927. Ctenophora. Tierwelt Nord- und Ostsee, Teil. 3 f (Lief. VII). **Kuhl, W.** 1932. Rippenquallen beim Beutefang. Natur und Museum 62. **Lojacono, M.** 1908. Sur le poison de la Beroe. Jour. Physiol. Path. Gén. 10. **Main, R. J.** 1928. Feeding mechanism of Mnemiopsis. Biol. Bul. 55. **Mayer, A. G.** 1912. Ctenophores of the Atlantic coast of N. A. Carnegie Inst. Wash. Pub. 162. **Metschnikoff, E.** 1885. Gastrulation und Mesodermbildung der Ctenophoren. Ztschr. Wiss. Zool. 42. **Mortensen, T.** 1912. Tjalfiella. Danish Ingolf Exped. 5, Pt. 2. 1913. Regeneration in ctenophores. Vidensk. Meddel. Dansk. Naturhist. For. Kopenhavn, 66. **Nagel, W.** 1893. Sinnesphysiologie von Beroe. Arch. Gesam. Physiol. Mensch.

Tiere 54. **Nelson, T. C.** 1925. Occurrence and food habits of Ctenophores in New Jersey inland coastal waters. Biol. Bul. 48. **Okada, Y. K.** 1926. Light localization in ctenophores. Science 63. **Parker, G. H.** 1905. Swimming plates in ctenophores with reference to theories of ciliary metachronism. Jour. Expt. Zool. 2. **Peters, A. W.** 1905. Phosphorescence in ctenophores. Jour. Expt. Zool. 2. **Tanaka, H.** 1932. Reorganization in regenerating pieces of Coeloplana. Kyoto Univ. Col. Sci. Mem. Ser. B. 7, Pt. 5. **Verworn, M.** 1890–1891. Physiologie der Flimmerbewegung, Gleichgewicht und Otolithenorgan. Arch. Gesam. Physiol. Mensch. Tiere 48, 50. **Willey, A.** 1896. Ctenoplana. Quart. Jour. Micros. Sci. 39. **Yatsu, N.** 1911. Experiments on the ctenophore egg. Annot. Zool. Jap. 7, 8. **Ziegler, H. E.** 1898. Furchungszellen von Beroe. Arch. Entwickl. Mech. Organ. 7. **Zirpolo, G.** 1924. Rigenerazione degli Ctenofori. Bol. Soc. Natural. Napoli 36.

INDEX

Pages bearing illustrations are given in boldface when not included in text references.

A

Abasilaria, 586
Abbreviation, 275
Abietinaria, 444
Abyla, 473, **476**
Abyssal, 80
Acalepha, 28, 365
Acalephes, 662
Acantharia, **140**, 141, 143
Acanthocystis, **72**, **137**, 138
Acanthometra, **140**, 143
Acanthostyle, 297, **298**, **340**
Acaulus, 411, **412**, 440
Acceleration, 275
Acellular animals, 5, 32, 44
Acephaline gregarines, **146**, 147
Achromatic figure, **10**, 12, 13
Achromatin, 8
Acid, food vacuoles, 61
Acineta, 48, 202–205
Acontia, **569**, **572**, **580**, 581
Acontiaria, 586–587
Acontioids, 630
Acraspedote medusae, 375, 497
(*See also* Scyphozoa)
Acrocyst, **428**, 433
Acropora, 601, 608, **612**, 613, 615, **618**, 623
Acrorhagi, 573, **574**, 575, **576**
Actinauge, 587
Actinia, 573, 586, 595, 599
Actiniaria, 371, 570–599
asexual reproduction, 590
behavior, 592–599
bibliography, 655–658
development, 588–589
ecology, 584–585, 592–599
excretion, 396
histology, **374**, **375**, **378**, **380**, **394**, **580**, 581–584
morphology, **567**, **569**, 570–587
muscular system, 568, 581–583
nematocysts, **384**, 386, 391, **582**, 584

Actiniaria, nervous system, **378**, **380**, **394**, 583, 596–599
regeneration, 590–592
sexual reproduction, 587–589
systematic account, 585–587
Actiniidae, 584, 586
Actinobolina, 205
Actinobolus, 205
Actinodendridae, 586
Actinodendron, 586
Actinoloba, 587
Actinomyxidia, 47, 162, **163**
bibliography, 224
Actinophilus, **146**
Actinophrys, **72**, 76, **137**, 138
Actinosphaerium, 54, 61, 62, **137**, 138
Actinostola, 587
Actinostolidae, 587
Actinothoe, 587
Actinotryx, 386, **569**, 586
Actinula, **434**, 435, **439**, 457, **463**, 486–487, 635
Adamsia, 587, 588, 596, 599
symbiosis with hermit crab, 391, **591**, 599
Adaptation, 4
Addition, 274
Adelea, **150**, 151
Adeleidea, **150**, 151
Adhesive pad, medusae, 455, **456**, 459
Adineda, 46, 93
Adoral zone, 167, **190**, 191, **192**, 193, 194, 196, 197, **198**
Adradius, 373, 499
Aegina, **458**, 460, **464**, **466**
Aeginidae, 464
Aeginina, 464
Aeginopsis, 464
Aequorea, 382, 396, 413, **416**, **420**, 445, 448, 450, 495
Aequoreidae, 445
Agalma, 471, **472**, 475, **477**, 483, 484
Agamete, 75
Agamogony, 75, 144

697

Thecate hydroids, 407
(*See also* Calyptoblastea)
Theileria, 158, 159
Theileriosis, 159
Thelohania, 162
Theocarpus, 427, **428**, 445
Thermotaxis, 68
Thesocytes, 295, 304
Thorny corals, 625
Thuiaria, 444
Tiara, 443
Tiaridae, 443
Tiaropsis, **418**, 419, 445
Ticks, in piroplasmosis, 158
Tillina, 73, **74**, 185
Tintinnidae, 164, 193, **194**
Tissues, of invertebrates, 276–282
Tjalfiella, 677, 684, 686–690
Tonofibrils, **6**, 8
Topotaxes, 67, 69
Tornote, 297, **298**
Trachelius, **184**, 185
Trachelomonas, 99, **100**
Trachylina, 370, 454–467, **468**
 bibliography, 647–648
 development, 457–459, **462**, **463**
 phylogeny, 635, 636
 systematic account, 459–464
Trachymedusae, 370, 386, 454–464
Trachynemidae, 463
Transverse axis, **19**, 20, 372
Treptoplax, 243
Triactinomyxon, 162, **163**
Triaene, **298**, 299, 337, **338**, 339
Trial-and-error behavior, 67
Tribrachion, 336, **338**
Trichites, **50**, 51, **60**, 83, 169–170, **184**, 185
Trichocysts, 49, **50**
 Ciliata, 165–167, **168**
 Dinoflagellata, 93, **96**
Trichodina, 82, 199, **200**
Trichomastix, 113
Trichomitis, **114**, 115
Trichomonas, **84**, **89**, **114**, 115, 117
Trichonympha, **116**, 117
Trichoplax, 243
Trichorhiza, 441
Trichosphaerium, 130–131
Trichostomata, 48, **184**, 185
Tripedalia, **514**, 515

Triploblastic structure, 254, 264
Tripylea, **142**, 143
Triradiate spicules, 299
Trochophore, 31, 694
Trophosome, 423
Trophozoite, 144–146
Tropism, 69
Trypanoplasma, **108**, 109
Trypanosomes, **108**, 109–113
Tsetse flies, in trypanosomiasis, 111
Tubipora, **546**, 548, 617
Tubularia, **384**, 385, 386, 400, **401**, **404**, 405, **410**, 411, **412**, 423, 425, **432**, **434**, 443, 488, **490**, 492
Tubularian hydroids (*see* Gymnoblastea)
Tubulariidae, 400, 402, 411, **434**, 435, 441, 449, 635
Turbinolidae, 609
Turris, **418**, 443, 448
Turritopsis, 443
Tylostyle, 297, **298**, 343, **344**, 349
Tylote, 297, **298**

U

Ulmaridae, 521
Umbellula, 559, **560**, 686
Umbellulidae, 559
Umbrella, 373
Undulating membrane, 167, **184**
Undulipods, 58
Unipolar ingression, **261**, 262, 433
Urceolaria, 199
Urocentrum, 171, **184**, 185, 188
Uroleptus, 77, 176, 178, 196
Uronychia, 77, 196
Urostyla, **194**, 196
Ute, 317

V

Vacuolar apparatus, 52, 63–64, **97**, **98**, 171
Vacuome, 9
Vaginicola, 201
Vaginicolidae, 199
Valkampfia, **72**, 127
Vampyrella, 127, **128**
Variety, 23
Velamen, **670**, 683
Velar plate, 427, **430**
Velarium, 499, 513, **514**